RESEARCH IN PHOTOSYNTHESIS

Research in Photosynthesis

Volume IV

Proceedings of the IXth International Congress on Photosynthesis, Nagoya, Japan, August 30–September 4, 1992

edited by

NORIO MURATA
National Institute for Basic Biology, Okazaki, Japan

KLUWER ACADEMIC PUBLISHERS
DORDRECHT / BOSTON / LONDON

Library of Congress Cataloging-in-Publication Data

International Congress on Photosynthesis (9th : 1992 : Nagoya-shi, Japan)
Research in photosynthesis : proceedings of the IXth International Congress on Photosynthesis, Nagoya, Japan, August 30-September 4, 1992 / edited by Norio Murata.
p. cm.
Includes index.
ISBN 0-7923-2073-5 (HB : acid free)
1. Photosynthesis--Congresses. 2. Photosynthesis--Research--Congresses. I. Murata, Norio. II. Title.
QK882.I55 1992
581.1'3342--dc20 92-39162

ISBN 0-7923-2090-5 (Vol. I)
ISBN 0-7923-2091-3 (Vol. II)
ISBN 0-7923-2092-1 (Vol. III)
ISBN 0-7923-2093-X (Vol. IV)
ISBN 0-7923-2073-5 (Set)

Published by Kluwer Academic Publishers,
P.O. Box 17, 3300 AA Dordrecht, The Netherlands.

Kluwer Academic Publishers incorporates
the publishing programmes of
D. Reidel, Martinus Nijhoff, Dr W. Junk and MTP Press.

Sold and distributed in the U.S.A. and Canada
by Kluwer Academic Publishers,
101 Philip Drive, Norwell, MA 02061, U.S.A.

In all other countries, sold and distributed
by Kluwer Academic Publishers Group,
P.O. Box 322, 3300 AH Dordrecht, The Netherlands.

Printed on acid-free paper

Printed in the Netherlands

GENERAL CONTENTS

Volume I

1. Antenna Systems in Photosynthetic Procaryotes 1
2. Antenna Systems in Algae and Higher Plants 169
3. Bacterial Reaction Center 339
4. Photosystem I 485

Volume II

5. Photosystem II 1
6. Oxygen Evolution 255
7. Electron Transport System 445
8. Energy Transduction 643
9. Chemical Models and Artificial Photosynthesis 785

Volume III

10. Synthesis and Function of Pigments and Lipids 1
11. Protein Import and Processing 131
12. Expression of Plastidic Genes 217
13. Genetic Approaches in Photosynthesis Research 347
14. Evolution of Photosynthesis 473
15. Design and Action of Herbicides 535
16. Rubisco 583
17. Metabolic Interaction between Chloroplasts and Cytosol 657
18. Specialization in Carbon Assimilation 745

Volume IV

19. Nitrogen and Sulfur Metabolism 1
20. Temperature Stress 111
21. Water and Salt Stresses 193
22. Light Acclimation 299
23. Photoinhibition 393
24. Photosynthesis in Intact Leaf 585
25. Photosynthesis Control by Sink 727
26. Photosynthesis and Global Climate Change 793

CONTENTS TO VOLUME IV

19. NITROGEN AND SULFUR METABOLISM

The response of *Synechococcus* sp. strain PCC7942 to sulfur- limited growth.
A.R. Grossman, J.L. Collier, D.E. Laudenbach 3

Coupling of the nitrate assimilatory pathway with photosynthetic processes.
M. Vincentz, T. Moureaux, T. Becker, Y. Kraepiel, M. Caboche 11

Regulation of gene expression of photosynthetic proteins by nitrogen.
T. Sugiyama, B. Sugiharto, I. Suzuki 19

The role of nitrogen metabolism in photorespiration.
P.J. Lea, R.D. Blackwell, R.E. Hausler, R.C. Leegood 27

Glutamate synthesis in non-photosynthetic plastids.
C.G. Bowsher, M.A. Cooper, M.J. Emes 35

Glutamine induces expression of phospho*enol*pyruvate carboxylase and carbonic anhydrase genes in maize plants.
B. Sugiharto, T. Sugiyama 39

Engineering and analysis of ferredoxin and related genes in *Rhodobacter capsulatus*.
K. Saeki, K. Tokuda, H. Matsubara 43

Application of the flux control theory to the GS/GOGAT cycle in isolated barley chloroplasts.
A.C. Baron, R.M. Wallsgrove, A.K. Tobin 47

A different role for redox regulation of enzymes: Response of PRK and G6PDH in N-limited *Chlamydomonas* to nitrogen resupply.
H.C. Huppe, T.J. Farr, D.H. Turpin 51

Regulation of asparate-family amino acid biosynthesis: Studies using isolated pea chloroplasts.
W.R. Mills, B.W. Stephens, M. Reeves 55

Properties of nitrate reductase from a marine red alga *Porphyra yezoensis*.
Y. Nakamura, T. Ikawa 59

Autophosphorylation of maize leaf NADH: Nitrate reductase.
W.H. Campbell, B. Ingemarsson 63

Characterization of glutamine synthetase purified from *Chlorobium limicola f. thiosulfatophilum* NCIB 8327.
J.-U. Na, J.-Y. Kim, H. Youn, S.-O. Kang, Y.-C. Hah 67

Effects of light and nitrate on expression of genes for glutamine synthetases and ferredoxin-dependent glutamate synthase in maize.
H. Sakakibara, T. Sugiyama 71

Gene expression and regulation of nitrate assimilating enzymes in *Synechococcus* PCC7942.
I. Suzuki, T. Omata, T. Sugiyama 75

"Air-pollutant-philic plants" from nature.
H. Morikawa, A. Higaki, M. Nohno, M. Kamada, M. Nakata, G. Toyohara, K. Fujita, K. Irifune 79

Transgenic "Air-pollutant-philic plants" produced by particle bombardment.
M. Kamada, A. Higaki, Y. Jin, M. Seki, T. Sawasaki, S. Ida, G. Toyohara, K. Irifune, H. Morikawa 83

Lysine and threonine sensitive isozymes of aspartate kinase in rice and pea.
S. Kiyota, K. Sakano 87

Purification and properties of ATP-phosphoribosyl-transferase from wheat germ.
S. Münzer, R. Hashimoto-Kumpaisal, A. Scheidegger, D. Ohta 91

Histidinol dehydrogenase in higher plants. Purification, cloning, and expression.
A. Nagai, K. Suzuki, E. Ward, M. Moyer, J. Mano, J. Beck, S. Tada, M. Hashimoto, J.-Y. Chang, J. Ryals, A. Scheidegger, D. Ohta 95

Kinetic analysis of cabbage histidinol dehydrogenase.
J. Mano, A. Nagai, N. Uodome, A. Kosaka, G. Iwasaki, A. Kheilrolomoon, A. Scheidegger, D. Ohta 99

Light-dependent maintenance of active nitrogenase in the non- heterocystous cyanophyte *Trichodesmium* sp. NIBB1067.
K. Ohki, Y. Fujita 103

The effects of abscisic acid and indole acetic acid on nitrogen fixation and anthocyanin formation in *Azolla pinnata*.
N.M. Cadiz, A.A. Alejar 107

20. TEMPERATURE STRESS

The molecular basis for the acclimation of photosynthesis toward temperature.
N. Murata, H. Wada, I. Nishida, Z. Gombos, Y. Nishiyama, H. Hayashi, T. Sakamoto, O. Ishizaki-Nishizawa, S. Higashi 113

Molecular and cellular acclimation of plants to cold.
H. Ougham, P. Schünmann, A. Quigley, C. Howarth 121

Genetic approaches to the function of the chloroplast low molecular weight heat shock protein.
K.W. Osteryoung, E. Vierling 129

The adaptation of photosynthesis to high temperature in *Synechococcus* PCC7002.
Y. Nishiyama, E. Kovàcs, H. Hayashi, T. Watanabe, N. Murata 137

Heat stability of photosynthetic electron transport in thylakoid membranes from the cyanobacterium.
M.D. Mamedov, H. Hayashi, N. Murata 141

Daytime expression of a 35 kDa chloroplast protein is delayed in tomato by chilling.
T.L. Jones, D.R. Ort 145

Plasticity of the stress tolerance of photosystem II *in vivo*.
M. Havaux, R.J. Strasser 149

D1 protein metabolism in maize at low temperatures.
G.J. Bredenkamp, N.R. Baker 153

Heat shock proteins and thermal resistance of photosystem II.
N. Miller, R. Carpentier 157

Chilling damage of dark stored cucumbers (*Cucumis sativus* L.) affects the maximum quantum yield of photosystem 2.
O. van Kooten, M.G.J. Mensink, E.C. Otma, A.C.R. van Schaik, S.P. Schouten 161

Freezing damage and protection of photosystem II particles by sucrose and trehalose.
E. Apostolova, M. Busheva, B. Tenchov 165

Effects of light and high temperature on the leaves of a rice mutant sensitive to solar radiation.
T. Fuse, K. Iba, H. Satoh, M. Nishimura 169

Characteristics of the photosynthesis in alpine plants on Qinghai plateau.
G. Ben, C. Lu, F. Han, S. Shi 173

The chlorophyll fluorescence temperature curve as a plant damage and light acclimation diagnostic tool.
R. Kuropatwa, J. Naus, T. Klinkovsky, P. Illk, J. Kalina, M. Maslàn, D. Zàk, J. Lattovà, Z. Pavlovà 177

The effect of leafstalk chilling on photosynthesis of intact leaf in plants with different type of phloem loading.
N.I. Filatova, N.S. Mamyshina 181

Temperature behavior of photosystem II in chilling-resistant and chilling-susceptible plant species, studied by fluorescence and luminescence methods.
A. Glèmin, T. Miranda, J.-M. Ducruet 185

A new kind of induction response found in two rainforest species.
J. Watling, I. Woodrow 189

21. WATER AND SALT STRESSES

Diverse genetic responses to environmental stress in a salt- tolerant plant: Classes of transcripts.
J.C. Cushman, E.J. DeRocher, D.M. Vernon, J.C. Thomas, C.B. Michalowski, H.J. Bohnert 195

Mechanisms of the acid resistance of *Dunaliella acidophila*.
H. Gimmler 203

The effect of temperature on leaf photosynthesis of dehydrated C3 plants.
G. Cornic 211

Salt tolerance in higher plants: The identification of the vacuolar Na^+/H^+ antiport.
B.J. Barkla, E. Blumwald 219

Characterization of genes responsive to desiccation and their expression in *Arabidopsis thaliana*.
K. Shinozaki, K. Yamaguchi-Shinozaki, T. Kiyosue, T. Iwasaki, S. Urao 227

Selection and characterization of stress-tolerant cultured green cells of tobacco.
F. Sato, K. Murota, S. Takeda, Y. Yamada 231

Two isoforms of NADP-malic enzyme in the facultative CAM plant *Mesembryanthemum crystallium*.
K. Saitou, W. Agata, Y. Masui, M. Asakura, F. Kubota 235

cDNA cloning of betaine aldehyde dehydrogenase from barley and regulation of its expression by osmotic stress.
M. Ishitani, T. Takabe 239

Immunological studies of betaine aldehyde dehydrogenase in barley.
K. Arakawa, K. Mizuno, T. Takabe 243

Betaine aldehyde dehydrogenase protein is present in leaves of both betaine accumulators and nonaccumulators in various cereal plants.
K. Arakawa, K. Mizuno, S. Kishitani, T. Takabe 247

Facultative halophytes accumulate proline as the early response to salt stress.
Y. Sanada, K. Kuribayashi, T. Andoh, M. Takeda, N. Tamai, K. Wada 251

Salt stress-induced cell injury and H^+- gradient between the cytoplasm and the vacuole in suspension- cultured plant cells.
K. Kuchitsu, K. Kasamo, N. Shibuya 255

Salt stress responses in cultured green tobacco cells.
F. Sato, K. Murota, S. Aso, Y. Yamada 259

Changes of protein phosphorylation in *Dunaliella tertiolecta* cells in osmotic shock.
T. Yuasa, S. Muto 263

Photofixation of $^{14}CO^2$ and photosynthetic electron transports in a desiccation tolerant cyanobacterium *Scytonema geitleri*.
S.N. Tripathi, B.S. Tiwari 267

The effects of drought and UV-radiation upon chlorophyll fluorescence and CO^2 assimilation.
H. Nonami, M. Kohchi, T. Fukuyama, Y. Hashimoto 271

Aspects of photosynthetic carbon metabolism on soybean under water stress.
A. Battistelli, M. Guiducci, T. Schiappa 275

Some aspects of carbohydrate metabolism in bean plants under water deficit.
M. Castrillo, A. Kazandjian 279

The relationship between resistance to water transport and the midday depression of photosynthetic rate in rice plants.
T. Hirasawa, K. Ishihara 283

Effects of drought on water relations of field-grown Douglas fir.
E. Steingröver, W. van Orden, G. van Roekel, R. Blikman, J. van der Beek, W. Jans 287

Analysis of the photosynthesis/transpiration ratio of plant canopy by computer simulation.
T.-D. Wang, D.-X. He, J.-Z. Shi, W. Fu 291

Gas exchange and water use efficiency in water stressed *Setaria sphacelata*.
J.M. da Silva, M.C. Arrabaça 295

22. LIGHT ACCLIMATION

Light acclimation of thylakoid system in cyanophytes: Regulation of PSI formation in response to light regime.
Y. Fujita, A. Murakami, K. Aizawa 301

Degradation products of the D1 protein are located in the non- appressed regions of the thylakoid membrane *in vivo*.
R. Kettunen, E. Lehtonen, E. Tyystjärvi, E.-M. Aro 309

Mechanisms of chloroplast acclimation to suboptimal and adverse irradiance.
J.H. Kim, A. Melis 317

Blue and red light irradiance effects on chloroplast gene expression in Arabidopsis and Sorghum.
K. Eskins, N. Alexander 325

Regulation of PS I formation induced by light quality observed with *Synechocystis* PCC6714.
K. Aizawa, Y. Fujita 329

Variation of chlorophyll-protein complexes of *Oryza punctata* and *Oryza eichingeri*: Its consequence for adaptation in high and low light environments.
N. Watanabe, Ch. Fujii, M. Shirota, Y. Furuta 333

Light-induced D1 protein degradation and photosynthesis in sun and shade leaves.
A.J. Syme, H.R. Bolhár-Nordenkampf, C. Critchley 337

Effects of light on degradation of chlorophyll and chloroplast proteins during senescence of rice leaves.
K. Okada, S. Katoh 341

Purification of the 15 kDa phosphoprotein of *Synechococcus* 6301.
B.F. Nore, M.A. Harrison, J.F. Allen 345

Role of light-harvesting chlorophyll *a/b* protein complexes in photosynthesis under low light and heat stress.
Y. Kobayashi, T. Yoshihira, K. Yamamoto, E. Nishimoto, T. Oku 349

Effects of dark adaptation on parameters of prompt and delayed fluorescence of chlorophyll in *Chlorella*.
I.R. Vasil´ev, L.V. Shenderova, Y.N. Konev, Y.V. Kazimirko, P.S. Venediktov 353

Responses to light in the green alga *Mesotaenium caldariorum* : A possible role for photosynthetic activity in the regulation of phytochrome.
L.Z. Morand, J.C. Lagarias 357

Short-term treatment of pea plants with supplementary ultraviolet-B radiation: Recovery time-courses of some photosynthetic functions and components.
W.S. Chow, Å. Strid, J.M. Anderson 361

Protein turnover of light-harvesting chlorophyll *a/b* protein of photosystem II in rice *(Oryza sativa* L.) leaves aged under different irradiances from full expansion through senescence.
J. Hidema, A. Makino, Y. Kurita, T. Mae, K. Ojima 365

The light response curve of the CO^2 gas exchange of separated for the abaxial and adaxial leaf surface under different light environments and CO^2 concentrations.
W.F. Postl, H.R. Bolhàr-Nordenkampf 369

Sunfleck acclimation in relation to photosynthetic CO^2 assimilation in *Quercus serrata* seedlings.
Y. Tang, H. Koizumi, I. Washitani, H. Iwaki 373

Photosynthetic characteristics of rice leaves aged under different irradiances from full expansion through senescence.
J. Hidema, A. Makino, T. Mae, K. Ojima 377

Effects of light, nutrient and age on nitrogen content and photosynthesis of leaves.
K. Hikosaka, I. Terashima, S. Katoh 381

Time course responses of photosynthetic adaptation of two freshwater diatoms to temperature changes and its ecological interpretation.
Y. Suzuki, M. Takahashi 385

Adaptation of the photosynthetic apparatus of green algae to intensities and wavelengths of light.
H. Senger, K. Humbeck, N.I. Bishop 389

23. PHOTOINHIBITION

On the molecular mechanisms of light-induced D1 protein degradation.
A.H. Salter, J. De Las Rivas, J. Barber, B. Andersson 395

The light-stress syndrome: Protein turnover and possible protective mechanisms.
I. Adamska, A. Gal, Y. Soroka, S. Tal, H. Zer, N. Ohad, J. Hirschberg, K. Kloppstech, I. Ohad 403

Sequential reduction and protonation of the first quinone acceptor promotes chlorophyll triplet formation in photosystem II during photoinhibition.
I. Vass, S. Styring 411

Light-dependent turnover rate of the D1 polypeptide in new site- specific *Synechocystis* PCC 6803 mutants.
T. Kallio, E.-M. Aro, C. Jansson, P. Mäenpää 419

Light-induced turnover of the D1 protein of the photosystem II reaction centre and photoinhibition *in vivo*.
B. Schnettger, U.J. Santore, C. Critchley, J. Leitsch, G.H. Krause 423

Revealing the mechanisms of D1 protein degradation using isolated photosystem two complexes.
J. De Las Rivas, C.A. Shipton, M. Ponticos, J. Barber 427

Turnover of D1 protein during photoinhibition and recovery in a moss *Ceratodon purpureus*.
E. Rintamäki, R. Salo, E.-M. Aro 431

Studies on D1 protein degradation in isolated photosystem II membranes from *Synechocystis* 6803.
Å. Hagman, F. Nilsson, B. Andersson 435

Multi-step reaction of the photodamage to photosystem II reaction center D1/D2/cyt *b*-559 complex.
C.-Q. Tang, T.-Y. Kuang, Z.-B. Yu, Y.-H. Lu, D.-C. Peng, P.-S. Tang 439

Photosystem II function, photoinhibition and turnover of D1 protein at different irradiances in normal and atrazine-resistant plants with an altered Q^B-binding site.
C. Sundby, S. McCaffery, W.S. Chow, J.M. Anderson 443

Photoinhibition of photosystem II *in vivo* : Does photoinhibition take place in the centres down-regulated by acidification of the lumen?
K.J. van Wijk, P.R. van Hasselt 447

Photoinactivation of PS2 secondary donors by PS2 cation radicals and superoxide radicals.
G.-X. Chen, D.J. Blubaugh, J.H Golbeck, G.M. Cheniae 451

On the susceptibility of photosynthesis to photoinhibition at low temperatures.
C. Ottander, T. Hundal, B. Andersson, N.P.A. Huner, G. Öquist 455

Simultaneous determination of *in vivo* activities of PSI and PSII following high-light stress.
M. Charland, K. Veeranjaneyulu, R.M. Leblanc 459

Investigation of the role of the accessory chromophores of isolated photosystem two reaction centres.
A. Telfer, J. De Las Rivas, J. Barber 463

Effects of mineral deficiencies on PS II activity and on the turnover of the D1 reaction center protein.
D. Godde, M. Hefer 467

The influence of photoinhibition on α- and β-centres of photosystem II.
A. Wild, M. Richter, B. Böthin 471

Analysis of the induction kinetics of chlorophyll fluorescence and oxygen evolution obtained by simultaneous measurement of the fluorescence and photoacoustic signal: Effect of a photoinhibitory treatment.
G. Schansker, J.F.H. Snel, J.J.S. van Rensen 475

Biochemical evidence for loss of Q^A form photosystem II reaction centres during photoinhibition.
A. Koivuniemi, E. Swiezewska, S. Styring, E.-M. Aro, B. Andersson 479

Response of site-specific *psbA* mutants of *Synechocystis* 6803 to photoinhibitory illumination.
P. Mäenpää, T. Kallio, P. Mulo, G. Salih, E.-M. Aro, E. Tyystjärvi, C. Jansson 483

Characterization of paraquat resistant mutants of *Chlamydomonas reinhardtii*.
K. Kitayama, R.K. Togasaki 487

Photoinhibition studied in a mutant of *Chlamydomonas reinhardtii* lacking the 23 kDa extrinsic subunit of photosystem II.
P.-O. Fredriksson, L.-G. Franzèn, S. Styring 491

Defence mechanisms against photooxidative damage in paraquat- atrazine co-resistant *Conyza (Erigeron) canadensis*.
Gy. Vàradi, E. Pölös 495

Role of the PSII acceptor site in the light induced degradation of D1.
O. Prasil, H. Zer, D. Godde, I. Ohad 501

Photosystem II degradation pathways after photoinhibition of isolated thylakoids.
G.M. Giacometti, R. Barbato, G. Friso, A. Frizzo, F. Rigoni 505

Assay of protease activity in isolated reaction center complex of photosystem II.
M. Miyao-Tokutomi 509

Degradation of CP43 and CP47 by Tris-treatment of PS II membrane in weak light.
H. Mori, Y. Yamamoto 513

Studies on the photoprotective function of zeaxanthin at high-light conditions.
H.K. Lichtenthaler, C. Schindler 517

Rapid loss of the proton gradient across the thylakoid membrane during photoinhibitory illumination.
S.E. Tjus, B. Andersson 521

Measurements of photosynthetic efficiency and photoinhibition of phytoplankton by fluorescence measurements using the saturating pulse method.
C. Geel, J.F.H. Snel, J.W. Hofstraat, J.C.H. Peeters 525

Separate assays of ascorbate peroxidase and guaiacol peroxidase and of chloroplastic and cytosolic isozymes of ascorbate peroxidase.
K. Amako, K. Asada 529

Molecular properties of monodehydroascorbate reductase.
S. Sano, K. Asada 533

Peroxide removal in cyanobacteria.
A. Rozen, S. Lechno, R. Mittler, E. Tel-Or 537

Interactive effects of strong light and heat stress on photosynthetic apparatus of wheat.
G.S. Singhal, R.K. Mishra 541

Gene regulation of a rice superoxide dismutase in response to oxidative stress.
A. Sakamoto, K. Tanaka 545

Photodamage involves multiple sites and is distinguishable from photoinactivation.
H. Gong, S. Nilsen, J.F. Allen 549

Shock protein synthesis by near-UV irradiation in *Anacystis nidulans* R-2.
H. Shibata, K. Baba 553

Photoinhibition in transgenic sulphur tobacco containing sense and antisense superoxide-dismutase genes from tomato, assayed by the photoacoustic method.
D. Aviv, A.R.J. Driesenaar, S. Malkin, E. Galun 557

Photoinhibition in field grown kiwifruit vines.
D.H. Greer, W.A. Laing 561

Photoinhibition of indica and japonica rice and their reciprocal F^1 hybrids.
D. Jiao, B. Ji, C. Li, H. Tong 565

Photosynthetic activity and transpiration rate of Azolla under declining photosynthetic photon flux density.
J.S. Lales, M.A. Lapitan 569

The gradients of carbon fixation, ribulose-bisphosphate carboxylase/oxygenase content, and photosynthetic pigments across "sun" and "shade" leaves of spinach (*Spinacia oleracea*).
J.N. Nishio, J. Sun 573

Phosphorylation and disassembly of PSII core during photoinhibition.
M.T. Giardi 577

Photoinhibition and zeaxanthin formation in the brown algae *Laminaria saccharina* and *Pelvetia canaliculata*.
J.C. Duval, M. Harker, B. Rousseau, A.J. Young, G. Britton, Y. Lemoine 581

24. PHOTOSYNTHESIS IN INTACT LEAF

From leaf photosynthesis to crop productivity.
L.T. Evans 587

Photosynthesis in transgenic tobacco plants with reduced Rubisco contents.
S. von Caemmerer, J.R. Evans, G.S. Hudson, Y.B.C. Arvidsson, B.A. Setchell, T.J. Andrews 595

Modulation of efficiency of primary conversion in leaves, mechanisms involved at PS2.
B. Genty, Y.Goulas, B. Dimon, G. Peltier, J.M. Briantais, I. Moya 603

Screening a biotope by fluorescence techniques: Two wavelengths fluorescence amplitude analysis and O-J-I-P fluorescence rise analysis.
P. Eggenberg, B. Schwarz, R.J. Strasser 611

Formation of inactive PS2 centers in spinach leaves during light adaptation.
J.F.H. Snel, H. Boumans, W.J. Vredenberg 615

Differing patterns of enhancement by O^2 of photochemical efficiency in photosystem 2 among C^3, C^3- C^4, and C^4 species of *Panicum*.
R.B. Peterson 619

Mercury-induced light-dependent alterations of chlorophyll fluorescence kinetics in barley leaf slices.
C.-H. Lee, H. Chang, S.-B. Ha, B.Y. Moon, C.B. Lee 623

Effect of O_2 content in gas mixture on the millisecond delayed light emission in wheat leaves.
J.-Y. Ye 627

Pleiotropy in triazine resistant *Brassica napus* : Differential stomatal and leaf responses to the environment.
J. Dekker 631

Relation between photosynthetic activities and contents of chloroplast pigments in green and red leaves of *Perilla* grown under different grades of shading.
K. Ida, H. Koyama, S. Takeda 635

Changes in leaf fluorescence spectral shape during the Kautsky kinetics.
G. Agati, I. Ambrosini, F. Fusi, P. Mazzinghi 639

The turnover of photosystem II reaction centre proteins as a function of light.
B. Geiken, C. Critchley, G. Renger 643

Difference in photosynthetic rates among leaves at equivalent positions on the main stem and its tillers in rice plants.
T. Ookawa, E. Kuroda, K. Ishihara 647

Comparative studies on the photosynthetic traits and chloroplast ultrastructure in different genome wheat species.
R. Zhang, G. Ma, Y. Wu 651

Differences in the relationships between Rubisco, carbonic anhydrase, and photosynthesis in wheat and several other C_3 plants in response to nitrogen nutrition.
A. Makino, H. Sakashita, J. Hidema, T. Mae, K. Ojima, B. Osmond 655

The effect of low temperatures on the operation of photosynthesis in *Saintpaulia ionantha* (African Violet) leaves.
J. Harbinson, P. van Vliet 659

Photosynthetic response to CO_2 concentration and light intensity in mungbean (*Vigna radiata* (L.) Wilczek) leaves with and without epidermis.
M.T. Islam, F. Kubota, W. Agata, A. Hamid 663

Effects of intermittent illuminations on photosynthesis in sweet potato (*Ipomoea batatas* Lam.) leaf.
K. Nada, F. Kubota, W. Agata 667

Study on the photosynthetic characteristics of crop in shelterbelt network.
J. Chen, W. Wang, B. Zhang, Y. Wang, Y. Feng 671

Study on the photosynthetic characteristics and the primary productivity of *Larix olgensis*.
W. Wang, J. Chen, B. Zhang, Y. Feng, Y. Wang 675

How to improve CO_2 balance in obligate CAM, pineapple, *Ananas comosus* (L.) Merr.
A. Nose 679

Changes of CO_2 transfer and carboxylation resistances in the senescing process of rice leaves (*Oryza sativa* L.).
H. Sasaki, M. Samejima, R. Ishii 683

The effects of fire and tree-fell on photosynthesis in *Quercus ilex* resprouts.
I. Fleck, M. Sanjose, D. Grau, D. Vidal 687

Water stress effects on photosynthesis in subterranean clover leaves.
X. Socias, F. Aguilò, A. Pol, J. Vadell, H. Medrano 691

Evidence for ^{18}O labeling of photorespiratory CO^2 in photoautotrophic cell cultures of higher plants illuminated in the presence of $^{18}O^2$.
L. Cournac, B. Dimon, G. Peltier 695

Phosphate-deficiency reduces the photosystem II efficiency of chinese cabbage leaves.
Y.-I. Park, Y.-N. Hong 699

Senescence and the photosynthetic performance of individual leaves of deciduous broadleaved trees as related to forest dynamics.
T. Koike, M. Sanada, T.T. Lei, M. Kitao, M.J. Lechowicz 703

Flag leaf photosynthesis and senescence of the upper three leaves during spikelet filling in rive (*Oryza sativa* L.).
T.S. Park, A.A. Alejar, B.S. Vergara 707

[^{14}C] Sucrose uptake of individual spikelets in rice
J.P. Kim, A.A. Alejar, B.S. Vergara 709

Translocation of photoassimilates form leaves to fruits in grape shoots.
Y. Motomura 711

Signal transduction in blue light response of stomatal guard cells.
K. Shimazaki 715

Dephosphorylation of the LHC II protein by light in guard cell protoplasts from *Vicia faba* L.
T. Kinoshita, K. Shimazaki, M. Nishimura 719

Light-induced changes in membrane potential and cytoplasmic pH in aquatic plants, *egeria* and *chara*.
M. Tazawa, N. Iwasaki, Y. Okazaki 723

25. PHOTOSYNTHESIS CONTROL BY SINK

The possible effects of sink demand for assimilate on photosynthesis.
L.C. Ho 729

The role of sucrose phosphate synthase in determining assimilate partitioning and photosynthesis capacity in tomato leaves.
C.H. Foyer, N. Galtier, S.C. Huber, P. Quick 737

Molecular biology and biochemistry of the 62 kD sucrose binding protein and its possible role in sucrose transport.
H.D. Grimes 745

Sugars, fatty acids, and photosynthetic gene expression.
J. Sheen, H. Huang, A.R. Schäffner, P. Leon, J.-C. Jang 753

Changes in activity of ADPglucose pyrophosphorylase from maize leaf during day/night cycle.
E. Jeannette, J.-L. Prioul 761

Expression of yeast derived invertase in the apoplast of potato plants: Effect on metabolism.
D. Heineke, U. Sonnewald, G. Günter, K. Leidreiter, D. Büssis, I. Wilke, K. Raschke, L. Willmitzer, H.W. Heldt 765

The role of inorganic phosphate in activation of RuBPcase activity in response to changes in source/sink balance.
S. Sawada, H. Usuda 769

Concentrations of amino acids and sucrose in various subcellular compartments and in the phloem sap of barley leaves.
G. Lohaus, H. Winter, D.G. Robinson, H.W. Heldt 773

Polar transport of photoassimilates in *Chara corallina*.
D.-Q. Ding, S.-I. Amino, T. Mimura, M. Tazawa, T. Nagata 777

Effect of ear removal on dry matter production, its partitioning and photosynthesis in rice.
H. Nakatani, K. Koide, K. Ishihara 781

Ear removal effect on diurnal change of the flag leaf photosynthesis in wheat.
K. Koide, K. Ishihara 785

Nitrogen effects on relationships between leaf growth and leaf photosynthesis.
C.J. Nelson, S.Y. Choi, F. Gastal, J.H. Coutts 789

26. PHOTOSYNTHESIS AND GLOBAL CLIMATE CHANGE

Modelling photosynthesis and transpiration in plants growing in an atmosphere enriched in CO^2.
I. Woodrow 795

Phytoplankton photosynthesis in the ocean in relation to the global carbon cycle.
P.G. Falkowski 803

The implications of concurrent increases in temperature and CO^2 concentration for terrestrial C^3 photosynthesis.
S.P. Long, G.Y. Nie, B.G. Drake, G. Hendrey, K. Lewin 811

Effects of climatic change on the photosynthesis, biomass production and yield of field-sown wheat (*Triticum aestivum* L.) and meadow fescue (*Festuca pratensis* Hudson) during Finnish growing season.
K. Hakala, E.-M. Tuhkanen, T. Mela 819

Field photosynthesis study in arctic plants: Implications for climate change.
T.V. Gerasimenko, E.L. Kaipianen 823

The effect of elevated CO^2 on photosynthesis biomass production and chloroplast thylakoid structure of crop plants.
A. Pennanen, V. Kemppi, D. Lawlor, E. Pehu 827

Predicting canopy assimilation of rice in response to carbon dioxide concentration and temperature.
K.J. Boote, N. Pickering, J.T. Baker, L.H. Allen 831

Climate change and wheat photosynthesis: Interactive effects of CO^2, temperature and nitrogen nutrition.
E. Delgado, S.P. Driscoll, R.A.C. Mitchell, V.J. Mitchell, M.A. Parry, D.W. Lawlor 835

Changes of the enzyme activities and glutathione level in the leaves of C^3 and C^4 plants grown under high O^2 atmosphere.
H. Ohno, T. Tsuru, R. Kanai 839

On the relationship between isoprene emission and photosynthetic metabolites under different environmental conditions.
F. Loreto, T.D. Sharkey 843

Algal photosynthesis: Inhibition by UV-B radiation, recovery and UV-absorbing pigments.
A. Post, S. Gentle, A.W.S. Larkum 847

An analysis of ozone inhibition of photosynthesis following short- and long-term exposure in three contrasting species.
P.K. Farage, S.P. Long 851

The effect of prolonged growth in elevated CO^2 concentrations in the field on the amounts of different leaf proteins.
G.Y. Nie, S.P. Long 855

Index of Names 859

19. Nitrogen and Sulfur Metabolism

THE RESPONSE OF *SYNECHOCOCCUS* SP. STRAIN PCC 7942 TO SULFUR-LIMITED GROWTH

A.R. GROSSMAN[1], J.L. COLLIER[1] AND D.E. LAUDENBACH[2]
[1]Carnegie Institution of Washington, Department of Plant Biology, 290 Panama Street, Stanford, CA 94305
[2]University of Western Ontario, Department of Plant Sciences, 1151 Richmond St. N., London, Ontario, Canada N6A 5B7

INTRODUCTION

Cyanobacteria exhibit a suite of responses during nutrient-limited growth. Some of these are specific, and are triggered by the depletion of only one specific nutrient. Others are general and are manifest in medium that is lacking in any of a number of different nutrients. Information is beginning to accumulate about both types of responses in cyanobacterial cells grown under conditions in which macronutrients such as nitrogen, sulfur, phosphorus and carbon are limiting.

During sulfur-limited growth *Synechococcus* sp. Strain PCC 7942[1] exhibits elevated transport of sulfate into the cell. Sulfate uptake is dependent upon light and varies with both temperature and pH (1, 2). Metabolic poisons such as DCCD and CCCP, sulfate analogues such as selenate and chromate and the sulfur compounds thiosulfate and sulfite all inhibit the transport of sulfate into the cell. Utkilen and coworkers reported a $K_{1/2}$ of 0.75×10^{-6} M and a V_{max} of 0.7 pmol/(10^6 cells x min) for sulfate transport at 42°C in sulfur-starved *Synechococcus*. Periplasmic components were implicated in the transport process since osmotic shock treatment was inhibitory.

Once sulfate is transported into *Synechococcus* cells it is reduced via the PAPS sulfotransferase pathway (3). Other cyanobacteria can reduce sulfate via the APS sulfotransferase pathway (4). Sources of sulfur other than sulfate that can satisfy the cells' requirement (5, 6) for this nutrient include thiocyanate, cysteine, cystine, thiosulfate and reduced glutathione. Methionine cannot serve as a sole sulfur source. A combination of classical genetics aided by molecular technology has been valuable for dissecting the responses of *Synechococcus* sp. Strain PCC 7942 to growth in medium lacking sulfur. In this report we will describe both general and specific responses that *Synechococcus* sp. Strain PCC 7942 exhibits when challenged with sulfur limitation.

---

[1]In this text the genus *Synechococcus* is used when referring to *Synechococcus* sp. Strain PCC 7942, *Synechococcus* sp. Strain PCC 6301 and *Synechococcus leopoliensis*, all of which are very similar.

N. Murata (ed.), Research in Photosynthesis, Vol. IV, 3–10.

MATERIALS AND METHODS

All materials used were of reagent grade. Culturing of the cells and the molecular and biochemical methods used have all been previously described (7, 8).

RESULTS AND DISCUSSION

Initial physiological studies (9) demonstrated that while the V_{max} for sulfate transport increased between 10- and 20-fold during sulfur-limited growth, the $K_{1/2}$ was approximately 1 μM in both sulfur-sufficient and sulfur-deficient medium. This suggested that sulfur deficiency caused elevated accumulation of a single sulfate transport system. A region of the *Salmonella typhimurium* genome that was genetically defined to contain genes important for growth of the bacterium on sulfate was used to isolate an analogous region of the cyanobacterial genome (10). This region of cyanobacterial DNA, shown in the map of Figure 1, contains a number of genes (see below) that appear to be activated when the cells are starved for sulfur. Transcripts from many of the genes in this region could either not be detected or were detected at very low levels when the cells were grown in nutrient replete medium. A marked increase in the accumulation of the mRNA transcribed from these genes was apparent when the cells were deprived of sulfur.

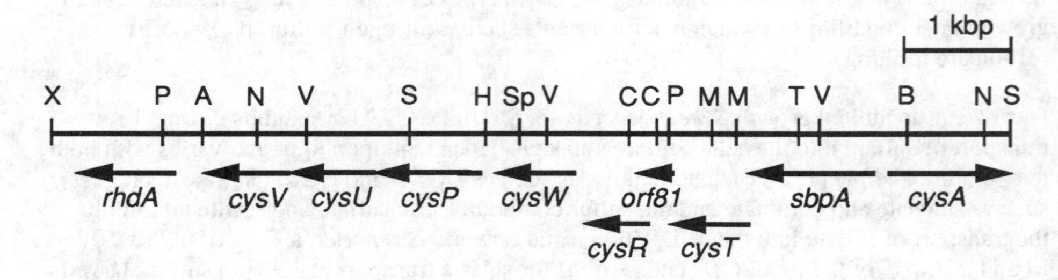

Figure 1. Restriction map of a region of the *Synechococcus* sp. strain PCC 7942 genome that is regulated by sulfur availability. The restriction sites shown on the map are abbreviated as follows: X, *XbaI*; P, *PstI*; A, *ScaI*; N, *NaeI*; V, *EcoRV*; S, *SalI*; H, *HindIII*; Sp, *SphI*; C, *ClaI*; M, *SmaI*; T, *StuI*; B, *BglII*. The extent of each gene and the gene designation are given below the map.

Complete sequence characterization of the region of the cyanobacterial genome selected with the *Salmonella typhimurium* DNA probe demonstrated the presence of genes encoding all of the components of a periplasmic transport system (*cysA*, nucleotide binding protein; *sbpA*, periplasmic substrate binding protein; *cysT* and *cysW*, two cytoplasmic membrane proteins that probably form a pore in the membrane) (7, 12). In periplasmic transport systems (reviewed in 11), the periplasmic binding protein forms a complex with the substrate to be transported, and transfers the substrate to the two membrane-spanning proteins. The substrate is then brought into the cell against a concentration gradient via the hydrolysis of ATP by the nucletide binding protein. To prove that the system sequenced from the cyanobacterium was involved in the transport of sulfate, each of these genes was inactivated by interposon mutagenesis. The results of these experiments confirmed that we had isolated the sulfate permease genes, although some of our findings suggested that not all of the components of the system were absolutely required for the transport of sulfate. If the genes encoding either of the integral membrane components (*cysT* or *cysW*), or the nucleotide binding protein (*cysA*) were inactivated, the cells could no longer transport sulfate and required an alternate sulfur source for growth. In contrast, if the gene encoding the periplasmic sulfate binding protein (*sbpA*) was inactivated, the cells could still grow if sulfate were supplied as the sole sulfur source. These results suggested that the sulfate binding protein was not absolutely required for growth on sulfate, or that a second gene encoding a sulfate binding protein was present in another location on the cyanobacterial genome. Using the *sbpA* gene as a hybridization probe, we could not detect another gene encoding the sulfate binding protein, supporting the former hypothesis. The situation may be similar in *E. coli* since, although there have been extensive searches for mutants unable to grow when sulfate was supplied as the sole sulfur source, none harbored lesions in the gene encoding the binding protein (the gene encoding the binding protein was fortuitously isolated, 13). It is thought that the hydrophobic membrane components of the transport system do contain binding sites for the substrate that are only exposed during interaction with the substrate binding protein. These binding sites may also become exposed by mutagenesis, as has been suggested in studies of the maltose permease system (14). In the case of the sulfate permease, the binding sites of the integral membrane proteins may normally be exposed, and therefore the binding protein is not absolutely required for sulfate transport.

Other genes from this region have been characterized by sequence analysis, transcript accumulation studies and insertional inactivation. While the sulfate permease may also function in the uptake of thiosulfate, thiosulfate transport may be augmented by a specific periplasmic thiosulfate binding protein in *E. coli* (15). Based on homology to the *E. coli* gene, the binding protein gene immediately downstream of *cysW* may encode a thiosulfate binding protein, CysP. The two genes downstream of *cysP* encode integral membrane proteins of a permease system (see Figure 1). These two proteins (CysU and CysV) may be part of a permease specific for the transport of thiosulfate. Mutational analysis of this region is being performed to confirm the proposed gene functions. There does not appear to be a gene analogous to *cysA* associated with this system. However, preliminary results suggest that CysA of the sulfate transport system may also function with the thiosulfate 'enhancer' system.

Another gene depicted on the map, located in the middle of the sulfate permease operon, has been designated *cysR*. The *cysR* gene product resembles transcriptional regulators such as those encoded by *fixK*, *crp,* and *fnr,* which bind DNA (7). When the *cysR* gene is interrupted the cyanobacterial cells can no longer grow on the sulfur source thiocyanate. Thusfar this has been the only sulfur molecule that is no longer effective as a sole sulfur source in supporting growth of the $cysR^-$ strain. These results suggest that during sulfur-limited growth of *Synechococcus* sp. Strain PCC 7942 other systems involved in the acquisition of diverse sulfur-containing compounds are activated. A number of these compounds may be found in the natural habitats of this cyanobacterium.

Finally, positioned downstream of the putative thiosulfate transport genes is a gene designated *rhd*, which encodes a protein with some similarity to the enzyme rhodanese (16).

Rhodanese is a thiosulfate-sulfur transferase that can cleave a sulfane bond and transfer the thiol group released to a thiophilic acceptor molecule (17). This protein is located in the periplasmic space and becomes very abundant in *Synechococcus* sp. Strain PCC 7942 during sulfur-limited growth. It is still uncertain whether this *Synechococcus* protein displays rhodanese activity or just functions in binding certain sulfur-containing molecules. Hence, the protein may have a catalytic role in the acclimation process, or may simply deliver specific sulfur-containing compounds from the environment to cytoplasmic membrane-localized permeases. This latter function would also help prevent leakage of sulfur-containing molecules from the cell. Further studies on the function of the *rhd* gene product should help elucidate physiological processes that are important for optimizing survival of the cyanobacterium during sulfur starvation.

General responses to nutrient-limited growth have been sporadically examined over the last 25 years. Dramatic alterations in the ultrastructure of cyanobacterial cells grown under adverse nutrient conditions have been observed via electron microscopy. Sherman and Sherman (18) and Wanner et. al. (19) demonstrated that iron-, nitrogen-, and sulfur-deficient *Synechococcus* cells had less than half of the normal complement of thylakoid membranes. The remaining membranes were disorganized and interspersed with large deposits of glycogen. There was also a decrease in the number of carboxysomes and increased formation of polyphosphate granules. Temporal studies of nitrogen deficient *Synechococcus* sp. Strain PCC 7002 demonstrated that removal of the nutrient caused a loss of phycobilisomes (PBS) followed by a reduction in ribosomes and thylakoid membranes (20).

A visually dramatic response of cyanobacteria to nutrient-limited conditions is the reduction of pigment molecules in the cell, a general response occurring upon deprivation of sulfur, nitrogen, phosphorous, carbon, or iron. The first quantitation of pigment levels during nutrient deprivation was performed by Allen and Smith (21). They showed that levels of carotenoids and chlorophyll in nitrogen-deprived cultures did not change, but that phycocyanin (PC) was undetectable after 30 hours. Other studies have shown that sulfur-deprived cultures behave in a similar manner, and have also revealed that cellular chlorophyll content declines in both cases because cell division continues after pigment accumulation ceases (8, 19). In contrast, the pigment content of phosphate-deprived cells declines only because cell division continues after pigment biosynthesis stops; there is little or no PC degradation (8).

Although total carotenoid content appears stable, the relative amounts of various carotenoids change after *Synechococcus* is deprived of a macronutrient, as shown in Figure 2. Nutrient deprivation causes little change in the ratio of β-carotene to chlorophyll (Figure 2B), except perhaps for phosphate-deprived cells (closed squares). However, nutrient-deprived cells show an increase in the ratio of zeaxanthin to chlorophyll (Figure 2A). The increase is 3-fold for sulfur-deprived cells (closed circles), 2-fold for phosphate-deprived cells (closed squares), and slight for nitrogen-deprived cells (open triangles). These changes may reflect an increased need for the photoprotective function of carotenoids, particularly of zeaxanthin, during the acclimation process.

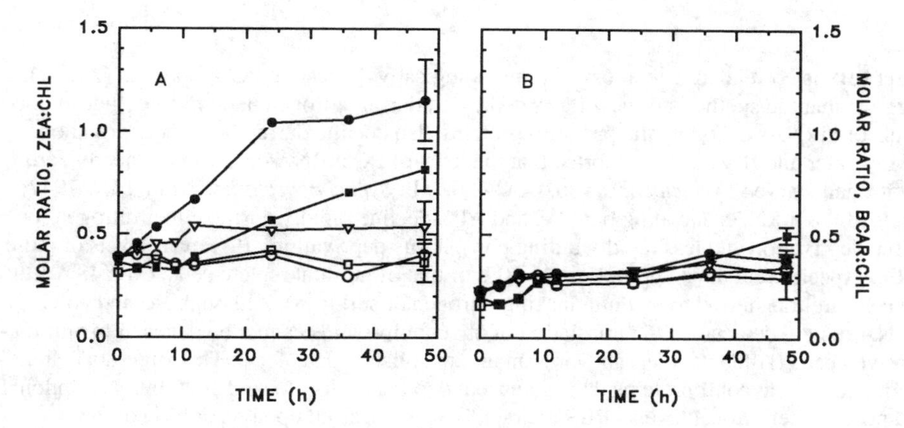

Figure 2. Molar ratio of zeaxanthin to chlorophyll (A) and β-carotene to chlorophyll (B) for nutrient-replete and nutrient-deprived cells, as determined by HPLC. Values are the average of 3 independent experiments. The standard deviation is shown only at 48h, for clarity; the error is generally the same percentage of the average value at other points. Exponentially growing cells were washed in medium lacking nitrogen, sulfur, and phosphate, then innoculated at time 0 into sulfur-free (●), nitrogen free (∇), phosphate free (■), or nutrient replete (control) (O, □) media. See (8) for an explanation of the experimental protocol.

The loss of PC in both nitrogen- and sulfur-deprived cells is due to the rapid and near complete degradation of the PBS (8, 23). Degradation of this abundant complex, the major light harvesting apparatus in the cell, could provide amino acids or carbon skeletons for the production of other cellular constituents (such as nutrient uptake systems) during nutrient deprivation. The use of phycobiliproteins as amino acid storage molecules may be especially important for marine cyanobacteria, since nitrogen may frequently be limiting in marine environments (22). Phycobiliprotiens are a poor source of sulfur amino acids, although their degradation in sulfur-deprived cells suggests that the sulfur is recycled. PBS contain no phosphorus at all, and cells limited for phosphorus do not degrade the PBS. Hence, the 'general' losses of pigmentation in response to macronutrient limitations are not all the same.

The degradation of the PBS during nitrogen- and sulfur-deprivation is an ordered process, and is very similar in both cases. The sequence of events that results in PBS degradation is shown in Figure 3. Elimination of nitrogen or sulfur from the growth medium provokes a rapid loss of the terminal PC hexamer of the PBS rods and its associated 30 kDa linker polypeptide (8, 23). This is followed by some loss of the second PC hexamer and its associated 33 kDa linker polypeptide, along with a decrease in the number of rods per PBS. The loss of these components results in a decrease in the PBS sedimentation coefficient and a reduction in the ratio of PC to allophycocyanin (APC). The smaller PBS can still function in harvesting light energy. The generation of a smaller PBS is followed by the destruction of the remainder of the complex. The loss of spectrophotometrically detectable PC and of intact PBS is correlated with a loss of immunologically detectable PC apoprotein (24). This suggests that the synthesis of new PC is depressed during nitrogen deprivation. Indeed, the levels of mRNAs encoding the phycobiliproteins also decline during nutrient deprivation. De Lorimier and Bryant (25) reported that the level of PC mRNA decreased to nearly zero in nitrogen-starved *Synechococcus* sp. PCC 7002. In *Synechococcus* sp. Strain PCC 7942, levels of the mRNAs encoding both PC and APC decline rapidly during either nitrogen- or sulfur-deprivation and less rapidly during phosphorus-deprivation. However, levels of these mRNA species remain at approximately 10% of that of nutrient replete cells, even 48 h after the cells are transferred to medium lacking nitrogen or sulfur (8). Although PC and APC mRNA remain detectable, the translation of phycobiliproteins cannot be detected in nutrient-deprived cells (Allen, Collier, and Grossman, unpublished data; 24). This suggests that the production of phycobiliproteins during nutrient deprivation is blocked at both transcriptional and post-transcriptional levels. PBS are rapidly resynthesized upon readdition of the limiting nutrient to starved cultures.

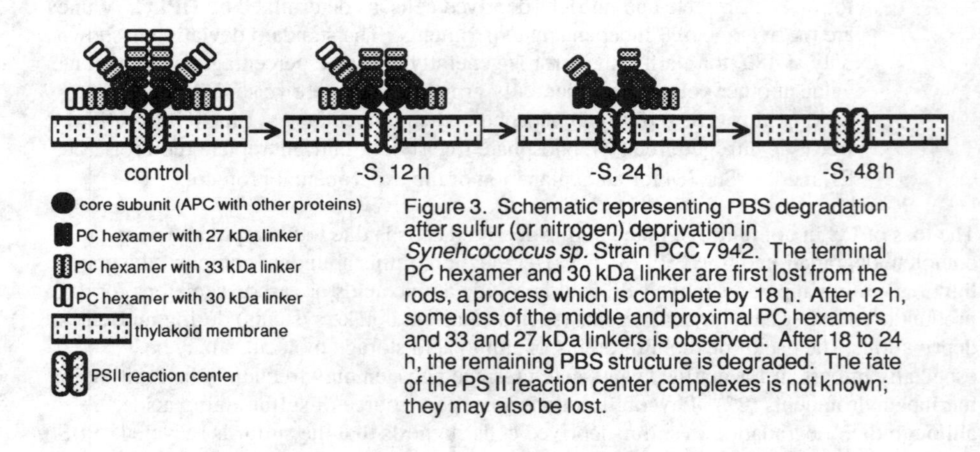

Figure 3. Schematic representing PBS degradation after sulfur (or nitrogen) deprivation in *Synehcococcus sp.* Strain PCC 7942. The terminal PC hexamer and 30 kDa linker are first lost from the rods, a process which is complete by 18 h. After 12 h, some loss of the middle and proximal PC hexamers and 33 and 27 kDa linkers is observed. After 18 to 24 h, the remaining PBS structure is degraded. The fate of the PS II reaction center complexes is not known; they may also be lost.

The analysis of PBS biosynthesis and degradation during changes in the nutrient status of the cells provides us with the opportunity to examine events important for the production of this abundant macromolecular complex. In early studies of PBS degradation it was suggested that a specific protease increased four-fold in nitrogen-limited *Anabaena* and that this increase was responsible for the degradation of the complex (26). Since the PBS is stable in nutrient-sufficient medium and extremely unstable in medium lacking either nitrogen or sulfur, it seemed unlikely that a four-fold increase in a specific protease alone could account for the rapid degradation initiated by exposure to nutrient limitation. To examine this process from a different perspective, we mutated *Synechococcus* sp. Strain PCC 7942 and screened for cells unable to degrade their PBS. Colonies of such cells appeared blue-green when grown on agar substantially free of sulfur, while wild-type colonies bleached. Some mutants obtained exhibited no PBS degradation during either sulfur- or nitrogen-deprivation, although no new PBS were synthesized during the stress treatment. Surprisingly, these cells grew at a similar rate, and exhibited a similar susceptibility to high light during the acclimation process, as wild type cells. Hence, even though the mutant cells had a considerable number of PBS, they appeared to be no more photosensitive than normally acclimating wild-type cells. Additional experiments suggested that the PBS present in the mutant organisms were not able to efficiently transfer harvested light energy to the photosynthetic reaction centers. This uncoupling of the light harvesting complex from the primary photochemical reactions may explain the lack of increased photosensitivity in these strains. To define the lesion responsible for the nonbleaching phenotype, mutant strains were complemented back to the bleaching, wild-type phenotype and the DNA responsible for complementation was characterized. Three genes, designated *orf2, nbl,* and *txl,* were located on a 2.0 kbp fragment of genomic DNA shown to be effective in complementation. *orf2* is constitutively expressed and does not appear to be involved in acclimation to nutrient deprivation. The expression of both *nbl* and *txl* is regulated by the nitrogen or sulfur status of the cells. The *txl* gene product resembles both a thioredoxin and a protein disulfide isomerase. Its role in the response of cells to nitrogen and sulfur limitations is unclear at this juncture, and will not be further discussed. The *nbl* gene contains an open reading frame of 59 amino acids. A small transcript covering this gene only accumulates at high levels in cells starved for nitrogen or sulfur, although very low levels of the transcript can be detected in cells maintained in phophorous-free or in complete medium. Insertional inactivation of this gene results in a nonbleaching phenotype. Inactivation of *orf2* or *txl* does not prevent bleaching during nutrient-deprivation. The strain initially isolated as a nonbleaching mutant contained a single base change in *nbl* which would result in a single amino acid substitution. When the wild type *nbl* gene is placed on a plasmid in *Synechococcus* sp. Strain PCC 7942, the cells bleach in nutrient replete medium, suggesting that expression of *nbl* may be controlled by a repressor. The cells will degrade the PBS during phosphate stress if *nbl* is placed under the control of the alkaline phosphatase promoter (which is only active during phosphate-limited growth). Hence, any condition that allows for the expression of *nbl* triggers the degradation of PBS. No homology was observed between the amino acid sequence encoded by *nbl* and any sequence in the Genbank databases. A number of interesting ideas can be gleaned from these studies. First, since multiple copies or aberrant expression of this gene can induce PBS degradation, it is likely to be the only gene whose activity needs to be increased during sulfur or nitrogen stress to provoke bleaching. Second, the small size of this protein and the lack of similarity to any known protease suggests that it is not a protease itself. There are a number of possible functions that this polypeptide may have which would explain its absolute requirement for bleaching. The *nbl* gene product may function to activate a protease, such as the one studied by Wood and Haselkorn (26), that subsequently breaks down the PBS. The small protein may trigger PBS degradation by interacting with the constituents of the complex and altering their susceptability to proteolysis. This targetted degradation may involve covalent attachment, similar to the binding of ubiquitin to proteins in eukaryotes, or the disruption of hydrophobic and\or ionic interactions among various constituents of the PBS.

There are many questions to be explored that will help us understand how a photosynthetic microbe senses its environment and responds to changing levels of a specific nutrient. By using a combination of physiological, biochemical, genetic and molecular approaches, we have made some progress in unraveling acclimation processes in cyanobacteria. Insightful analyses of exciting biological problems, such as those involving acclimation processes, using cyanobacteria has become simplified with the expanding set of technical tools that have been developed.

Acknowledgement: This work was supported by the NSF grant DCB-8916301 awarded to ARG. This is CIW publication no. 1154.

REFERENCES

1 Jeanjean, R. and Broda, E. (1977) Arch. Microbiol. 114, 19-23
2 Utkilen, H.C., Heldal, M. and Knutsen, G. (1976) Physiol. Plant. 38, 217-220
3 Schmidt, A. and Christen, U. (1978) Planta 140, 239-244
4 Tsang, M. and Schiff, J.A. (1975) Plant Sci. Lett. 4, 301-307
5 Schmidt, A., Erdle, I. and Kost, H.-P. (1982) Z. Naturforsch. 37c, 870-876
6 Lawry, N.H. and Jensen, T.E. (1986) Arch. Microbiol. 144, 317-323
7 Laudenbach, D.E. and Grossman, A.R. (1991) J. Bact. 173, 2739-2750
8 Collier, J. and Grossman, A.R. (1992) J. Bact. 174, 4718-4726
9 Green, L.S. and Grossman, A.R. (1988) J. Bact. 170, 583-587
10 Green, L.S., Laudenbach, D.E. and Grossman, A.R. (1989) Proc. Natl. Acad. Sci. U.S.A. 86, 1949-1953
11 Ames, G. F.-L. (1986) Annu Rev. Biochem. 55, 397-425
12 Sirko, A., Hryniewicz, M., Hulanicha, D and Bock, A. (1990) J. Bact. 172, 3351-3357
13 Helliga, H.W. and Evans P.R. (1985) Eur. J. Biochem. 149, 363-373
14 Shuman, H.A. (1982) J. Biol. Chem. 257, 5455-5461
15 Hryniewicz, M., Sirko, A., Palucha, A., Bock, and Hulanicka, D. (1990) J. Bact. 17, 3358-3366
16 Laudenbach D.E., Ehrhardt, E., Green, L. and Grossman, A.R. (1991) J. Bact. 173, 2751-2760
17 Westley, J. (1973) Adv. Enzymol. 39, 327-368
18 Sherman, D.M. and Sherman, L.A. (1983) J. Bact. 156, 393-401
19 Wanner, G., Henkelmann, A., Schmidt, A. and Kost, H.-P. (1986) Z. Naturforsch. 41c, 741-750
20 Stevens, S.E., Jr., Balkwill, D.L. and Poane, D.A.M. (1981) Arch. Microbiol. 140, 204-212
21 Allen, M.M. and Smith, A.J. (1969) J. Phycol. 4, 1-3
22 Wyman, M., Gregory R.P.F. and Carr, N.G. (1985) Sci. 230, 818-820
23 Yamanaka, G. and Glazer, A.N. (1980) Arch. Microbiol. 124, 39-47
24 Lau, R.H., Mackenzie, M.M. and Doolittle, W.F. (1977) J. Bact. 132, 771-778
25 De Lorimier, R., Bryant, D.A., Porter, R.D., Liu, W.-Y., Jay, E. and Stevens, S.E. (1984) Proc. Natl. Acad. Sci. U.S.A. 81, 7946-7950
26 Wood, N.B. and Haselkorn, R. (1980) J. Bact. 141, 1375-1385

COUPLING OF THE NITRATE ASSIMILATORY PATHWAY WITH PHOTOSYNTHETIC PROCESSES.

Michel Vincentz, Thérèse Moureaux, Thomas Becker, Yvan Kraepiel and Michel Caboche, Laboratoire de Biologie Cellulaire et Moléculaire, INRA 78026 Versailles Cedex, France.

1. INTRODUCTION

Nitrate assimilation has been shown by a number of physiological studies to be linked to photosynthesis. For instance in many species there is a positive correlation between photosynthetic activity and the flow of the pathway. In photosynthetic organisms, the incorporation of nitrate-derived N into glutamate and glutamine requires reductants, ATP and a carbon skeleton (a-ketoglutarate) generated from photosynthesis (1). The availability of reducing power provided as NADH and reduced ferredoxin is an obvious metabolic basis for this synergy. Light also controls the expression of nitrate reductase (NR) and nitrite reductase (NiR). A signal originating from chloroplasts is required for the control of NR expression by light (2). In darkness, which results in decreased NR levels, an exogenous supply of glucose can maintain or induce NR activity (3) (4). This observation suggests that light might indirectly affect NR expression, or more generally nitrate assimilation, by carbohydrates synthesized through photosynthesis. We have explored with molecular techniques the possibility that a coupling between the providing of light and nitrate assimilation might take place at the transcription level.

2. MATERIALS and METHODS

2.1 N. tabacum, N. plumbaginifolia and L. esculentum seeds were germinated and grown on peat in the green house. A nutrient solution containing nitrate and ammonium was applied daily as previously described (5). At the five-leaves stage, the plants were transferred to a controlled culture room for a week under the following conditions: 85% relative humidity, 16-h photoperiod (130 mmol photons/ m2/ s, fluorescent lamps; 7/8 cool white, Philips, Trappes, France; 1/8 true lite, Durolux, Paris, France). Experiments utilizing detached leaves were made with leaves of the same size sampled at random (average fresh weight of 1 g). Leaves were harvested and surface-sterilized. Their petioles were cut again before dipping them into a 5-ml solution in a Petri dish of 9-cm diameter containing a Whatman 3 mm filter paper soaked with different nutrient solutions. Solutions used were 40mM KCl, 10mM CaCl2 with or without 0.15 M to 0.25 M sugar, 0.1M glutamine, 0.1M asparagine or 0.1M glutamate, depending on the experiment. Four to five detached leaves were used for each harvest. At the end of the treatment leaves were collected, cut into fragments, mixed, weighed, divided into 1g samples, transferred rapidly to liquid N2 and stored at -80°C until analysis. A green safety lamp was used when necessary.

N. Murata (ed.), Research in Photosynthesis, Vol. IV, 11–17.

2.2. Total RNAs from leaves were extracted and analyzed as described previously (6). The probes were gel purified and labelled by random priming. The NR probe was the complete cDNA from pCSL16 (6); the NiR probe was a 1.7kb tobacco cDNA (7). Extraction and measurement of NR activity and immunological quantification were performed as reported previously (5). Soluble proteins were measured on crude extracts by the Bradford method.

3. RESULTS and DISCUSSION

3.1. Nitrate reductase, nitrite reductase and chloroplastic glutamine synthetase (GSc) transcript levels are under phytochrome control.

Etiolated tobacco and tomato plantlets grown in the dark express very low levels of NR, NiR (8) and GSc transcripts (9). Upon standard white light treatment, these plantlets rapidly accumulate these transcripts. This accumulation is also observed if a 5 min red light treatment is provided, but a red light treatment followed by a far red light treatment of the same intensity prevents transcript accumulation (8). This observation suggests that the different steps of the pathway leading to ammonium and glutamine production are all under phytochrome control, at least in etiolated growth conditions.

3.2. Steady state levels of NR and NiR transcripts are under the control of a circadian rythm in green tissues.

In the green tissues of plants grown under light, the steady state levels of NR and NiR transcripts were found to be modulated by light in several ways. It was first found that plants grown under a 16h-8h day-night cycle expressed cycling levels of NR and NiR transcripts (10)(5). A similar fluctuation of the steady state level of the chlorophyll a,b binding protein (Cab) transcript was also previously observed with a maximum taking place at the middle of the light period (11) However, unexpectedly the highest levels of the NR and NiR transcripts were reached at the end of the dark period, and declined during the light period. When cycled plants were transferred to permanent light, the same cycling of the transcript levels was observed, suggesting that light was not directly controlling this fluctuation, but might only contribute to the setting of an internal clock, responsible for this cycling of the transcripts (5). To explore further the mechanism controlling this cycle we studied the consequences of impairments of NR or NiR activities on its characteristics. Different situations were compared: poisening of NR whith tungstate, an analog of molybdate (12); mutations preventing the biosynthesis of the molybdenum cofactor (13); mutations affecting the structure of the NR apoenzyme, resulting in loss of NR activity (13); antisense inhibition of NiR expression (14). It was systematically observed that all these situations resulting in the impairment of nitrate assimilation also resulted in the suppression of the circadian rythm of NR and NiR transcript accumulation, the level of the transcripts remaining constitutively high. This suggests that a metabolite derived from nitrate assimilation contributes as a signal for the regulation of the circadian rythm. However, since such plants in which the circadian expression of NR and NiR transcripts is lost, still cycle the Cab transcript (13), this circadian rythm affecting NR and NiR expression as specific features of control which are not shared by other genes displaying a circadian rythm of expression.

3.3. NR and NiR transcript levels are under light control in green tissues.
When cycled plants expressing fluctuating levels of NR and NiR transcripts are transferred in the dark, the timing of the cycle remains basically unchanged but the amplitude fades away rapidly. After 72 h in the dark this amplitude has decreased to less than 1% of the levels observed in control plants. Plants kept in the dark for 96h and then illuminated for two or four hours rapidly re-accumulate NR and NiR transcripts in their leaves, in parallel with light-regulated genes such as the small subunit of ribulose-bis-phosphate carboxylase (RbcS) (5).

3.4. Overimposed to the light regulation of NR steady-state transcript levels, light also controls the level of NR protein in gree tissues.
We obtained Nicotiana plumbaginifolia mutant plants in which the resident NR genes has been disrupted by the insertion of a transposon in the first exon of the gene (Meyer, to be published). As a consequence of this, these plants do not express any detectable NR transcript when a cDNA probe 3' to the site of insertion of the transposon is used, and they are unable to utilize nitrate as a nitrogen source. The mutant was transformed with a gene consisting of the 35S promoter derived from CaMV, linked appropriately to a full lenght cDNA sequence derived from a functional tobacco NR gene, and to 3' non-transcribed sequences also derived from this NR gene, allowing the proper termination of transcription (6). Transformants able to grow on nitrate were recovered and a transformant expressing approximately twice the level of NR activity found in the wild type was further characterized. In this transformant the steady state level of the NR transcript, detected with the 3' NR cDNA probe was found to be basically unchanged under different light regimes suggesting that the circadian rythm and the light inducibility were under transcriptional control. However when such plants were kept in the dark for 96h a 80-90% decrease in NR activity and NR protein levels, althoug the level of the transcript remained high (6). This suggests that NR protein level is somewhat regulated by light at a postranscriptional level. Recently it was found in other laboratories that NR produced in the dark is sensitive to magnesium, due presumably to a phosphorylation event. We hypothesize that this phosphorylated form of NR may be more labile and result in a decreased steady state level of the enzyme in the dark. Conversely, the translation of the NR transcript may require a light-dependant signal, and be therfore preferentially reduced in the dark.

3.5. The requirement of light for the transcription of the NR and NiR genes can be alleviated by the providing of hexoses.
Nicotiana plumbaginifolia plants grown aseptically still express high levels of NR transcript in their leaves when in kept in the dark for 65h. This discrepancy with data obtained on plants grown in the soil and kept in the dark led us to find out that the sucrose present in the culture medium was stimulating the expression of NR in dark-adapted plantlets grown in vitro. Further experiments were performed on greenhouse-grown plants from which leaves were collected either on plants kept under light or preincubated for 65h in the dark. Petioles of detached leaves were then provided with a saline solution containing various nutrients, and leaves further incubated in the dark. It was found that glucose, fructose, and sucrose were able to restaure high NR transcript levels, whereas mannitol or ribose were not (Fig. 1).

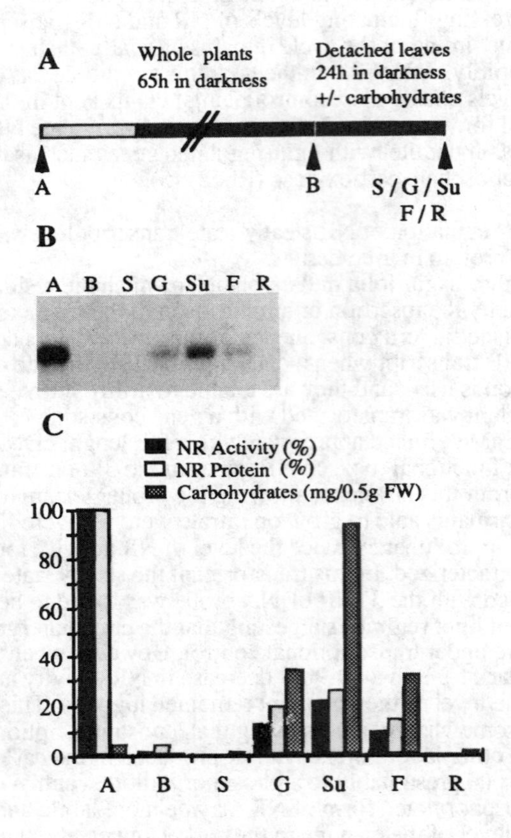

Figure 1. Effect of different sugars on the expression of NR in the dark. Plants grown under a 16-h light / 8-h dark cycle were transferred into darkness for 65 h. Leaves were detached from these plants in the dark, their petioles were dipped in 5ml of salt solution (S) or the same solution adjusted to 0.2M glucose (G), sucrose (Su), fructose (F) or ribose (R) and they were then further incubated for 24 h in the dark. A Scheme of the experiment with time points of harvest. Leaves from whole plants at the beginning of the ligth period of a normal day -night cycle (A); leaves from whole plants after 65 h of darkness (B). B Northern blot analysis of NR mRNA level. Each lane was loaded with 5mg of total RNA. C Nitrate reductase activity (100% = 85 nmol NO2- / min / g FW), NR Protein (100% = 222 ng / g FW) and sugar (fructose + glucose + sucrose) accumulation in detached leaves.

In parallel the level of NR transcript found in plants expressing a 35S-NR construct was unaffected by these different physiological conditions. When NR NiR and RbcS transcript levels were compared in this series of experiments, RbcS transcript remained strictly light-dependant for proper expression as expected, whereas NiR expression had features intermediate between NR and RbcS (data not shown). We hypothesize that this characteristic of NiR expression, a chloroplast -located enzyme, may be related to the requirements of an enzyme activity depending on the presence of ferredoxin derived from photosynthesis and required to be active whenever NR is also active and generating nitrite.

3.6. The stimulation of NR transcription by sugars can alleviate the needs for red light stimulation in etiolated plants.

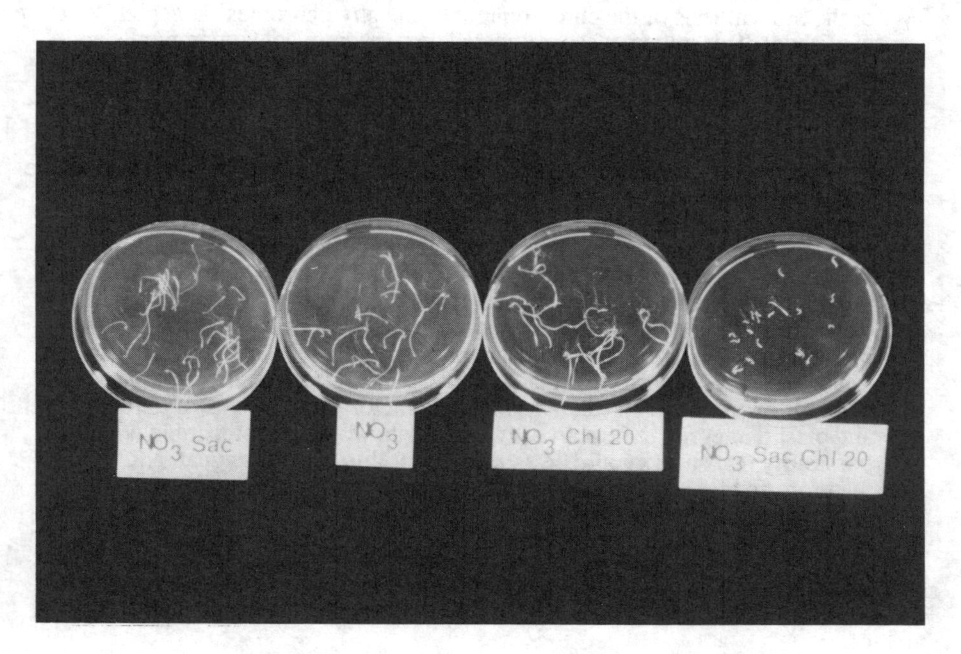

Figure 2. Growth characteristics of etiolated plantlets of the phytochrome -deficient mutant EMS 28 grown on a nitrate-containing medium (NO3) supplemented or not with 20 mM chlorate (Chl20) or with 3% sucrose (Sac) as indicated. Note the deleterious effect of chlorate on plantlets grown on a medium containing sucrose.

NR is not expressed in etiolated tissues. We have shown that a red light stimulation of etiolated plantlets induces the accumulation of the NR transcript. However such red light-stimulated plants kept in the dark will not express high levels of the NR protein, due to a post-transcriptional control of the expression of the enzyme involving a light signal. We have tested the possibility that NR expression could be restaured by the providing of sucrose. Because light interferes with NR expression in several ways, we used phytochrome mutants grown in the light to do these experiments. Etiolated mutants of N. plumbaginifolia were isolated on the basis of their phenotype among M2 seeds. Several mutants were obtained and further characterized. One of them, EMS 28 was found to be homozygote for a recessive mutation involved in the phenotype (etiolated growth, chlorotic leaves, low germination potential). Partial restauration of the germination potential, greening of cotyledon leaves and shortening of the hypocotyl of germinating plantlets was observed when seeds from this mutant were grown on a medium containing 100uM biliverdin, a precursor of the phytochrome chromophore. A spectrophotometric assay of the phytochrome accumulatyed in etiolated mutant plantlets revealed that less than 1% of functionally active phytochrome was present when compared to wild type plantlets. We conclude from this that the target of the mutation is one of the steps of the biosynthesis of the chromophore of the phytochromes (Kraepiel, Y., to be published). This mutant was germinated on a medium containing nitrate and chlorate underlight and found to be chlorate resistant under these conditions. As opposed to this the supply of sucrose in the culture medium restaured chlorate sensitivity (Fig. 2).

We conclude from this experiment that the providing of the carbohydrate source was able to restaure the expression of a functional NR, even in a genetic background preventing the proper stimulation of NR transcription due to a phytochrome defect. These observations are complementary to transcription studies performed on etiolated Arabidopsis plantlets showing that light requirements can be alleviated by the providing of a carbohydrate. From this experiment we conclude also that phytochrome is probably not stringently involved in the post-transcriptional control by light of NR activity. It has been established several years ago that a plastidic factor was required for proper NR and NiR expression (2)(15). This plastidic factor was also shown to require light and plastid integrity to be active (16). Our data would be compatible with the possibility that sugars could be an element of this plastidic signal. NR would therefore be regulated primarily by the respective availability of N and C assimilates, for the needs of further biosynthesis of the aminoacids and purines required for the building of macromolecules. Experiments are under way to further characterize the DNA motives and regulatory proteins involved in this regulation at the transcription level.

REFERENCES

1. House, C. M., Anderson, J. W. (1980) Phytochemistry 19, 1925-1930.
2. Oelmüller, R., Schuster, C., Mohr, H. (1988) Planta 174, 75-83.
3. Nicholas, J. C., Harper, J. E., Hageman, C. H. (1976) Plant Physiology 58, 731-735.
4. Diez, J., Lopez-Ruiz, A. (1989) Archives of Biochemistry and Biophysics 268, 707-715.
5. Deng, M., Moureaux, T., Leydecker, M. T., Caboche, M. (1990) Planta 180, 257-261.
6. Vincentz, M., Caboche, M. (1991) EMBO Journal 10, 1027-1035.
7. Faure, J. D., Vincentz, M., Kronenberger, J., Caboche, M. (1991) Plant Journal 1, 107-113.
8. Becker, T. W., Foyer, C., Caboche, M. (1992) Planta 188, In press.
9. Becker, T. W., Caboche, M., Carravol, E., Hirel, B. (1992) Plant Molecular Biology 19, 367-379.
10. Galangau, F., et al. (1988) Plant Physiology 88, 383-388.
11. Giuliano, G., Hoffman, N. E., Kenton, K., Scolnik, P. A., Cashmore, A. R. (1988) EMBO Journal 7, 3635-3642.
12. Deng, M., Moureaux, T., Caboche, M. (1989) Plant Physiology 91, 304-309.
13. Pouteau, S., Chérel, I., Vaucheret, H., Caboche, M. (1989) Plant Cell 1, 1110-1120.
14. Vaucheret, H., Kronenberger, J., Caboche, M. (1992) Plant Journal 2, 559-569.
15. Seith, B., Schuster, C., Mohr, H. (1991) Planta 184, 74-80.
16. Schuster, C., Mohr, H. (1990) Planta 181, 125-128.

REGULATION OF GENE EXPRESSION OF PHOTOSYNTHETIC PROTEINS BY NITROGEN

Tatsuo Sugiyama[1], Bambang Sugiharto[2], and Iwane Suzuki[1]
Department of Agricultural Chemistry[1], School of Agriculture, Nagoya University, Nagoya 464-01, Japan and Faculty of Agriculture[2], Jember University, Jember 68121, Indonesia.

Many of photosynthetic proteins are developmentally regulated by light. However, nitrogen (N)-availability can also selectively regulates the level of some of photosynthetic proteins by modulating the gene expression and thereby causes a differential partitioning of N into proteins altering cellular function. These proteins include light-harvesting chlorophyll *a/b* apoprotein (1) and thylakoid-bound NADH-PQ oxidoreductase (2) in *Chlamydomonas reinhardtii* and some C_4-enzymes such as phospho*enol*pyruvaye carboxylase (PEPC), pyruvate,Pi dikinase (PPDK), and carbonic anhydrase (CA) in *Zea mays* (3, 4, 5, 6) and alanine aminotransferase (AlaAT) in *Panicum miliaceum*, a NAD-malic enzyme type C_4 plant (7). These C_4-enzymes preferentially accumulate in N-recovering leaf as a consequence of increases in level of their mRNAs. By contrast, the fractions in leaf proteins of Rubisco and cytosolic glutamine synthetase (GS1) in maize, for example, remain unchanged or even reduce during recovery from N-starvation. Regulation of gene expression for photosynthetic proteins by N particularly in higher plants must require a complex network of intercellular and intracellular communication because this element is mobile. Furthermore, N assimilation, photosynthetic electron transport, and CO_2 fixation are interwoven processes. In this article, we will describe the mode of regulation and the possible metabolic signal and intracellular messenger for the N-dependent expression of photosynthetic genes focussing on C_4-photosynthetic genes in maize leaf.

Regulatory Mode of the N-Dependent Gene Expression of PEPC and PPDK

The levels of C_4-enzymes, most prominently, PEPC in the photosynthetic maturing cells of maize leaf are selectively regulated by N-availability primarily at the level of synthesis of protein with a concomitant change in level of their mRNAs (3, 5). To establish whether or not the enhanced synthesis of these proteins in N-recovering plants is a result of control of gene expression at the level of transcription we used *in vitro* transcription in leaf nuclei isolated from plants during recovery from N-starvation (Fig. 1).

N. Murata (ed.), Research in Photosynthesis, Vol. IV, 19–26.

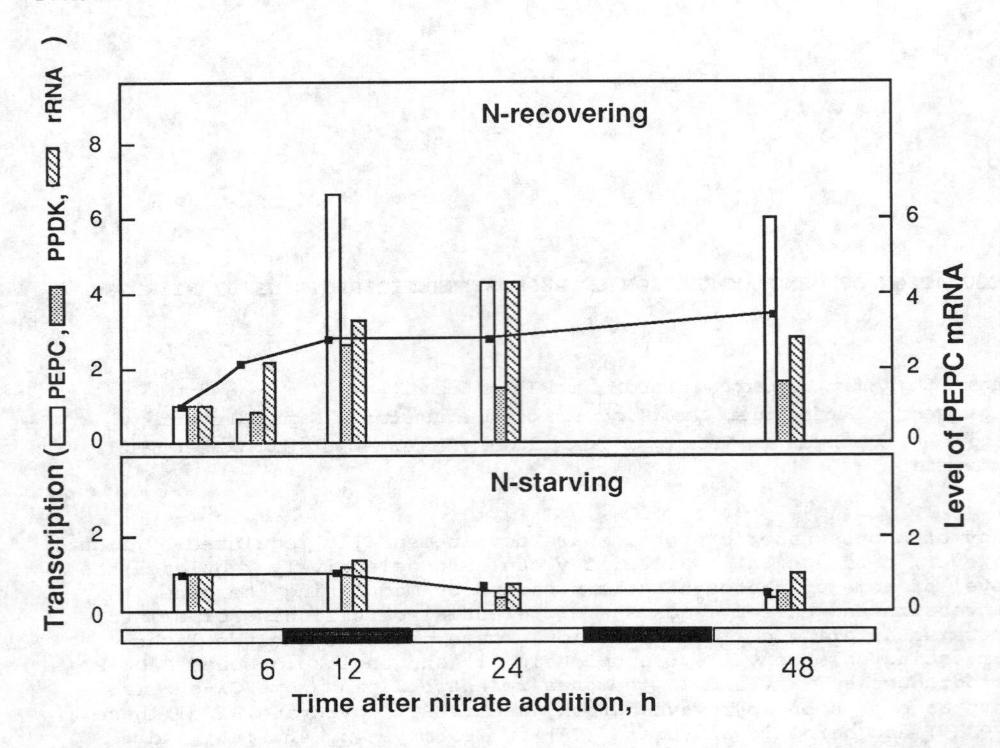

FIGURE 1. *Changes in transcription activity of genes for rRNA, PEPC, and PPDK during recovery from N-starvation* Nuclei were isolated from maize leaf tissue (8) and the RNA-synthesizing activity was assayed in the following standard mixture; 20 mM Tris-HCl, pH 7.9, 5 mM HEPES-KOH, pH 7.0, 75 mM KCl, 12.5 mM $MgCl_2$, 0.5 M hexyl glycol, 12.5% (v/v) glycerol, 0.5 mM each of ATP, CTP, and GTP, 5 mM DTT, 5 mM 2-mercaptoethanol, 0.5 U/ml RNasin, 100 µCi α^{32}P-UTP, and isolated nuclei (2-5 µg DNA) in 0.2 ml. Same amount of radioactivity incorporated was used in hybridization. The results are expressed as relative values of the control at 0 h (=1.0). Photo period in a growth chamber is shown at the bottom.

Enhancement of ribosomal RNA transcription began 6 h after nitrate supply preceding a substantial increase in transcription of PEPC and PPDK genes, while the transcription of these genes in N-starved plants changed less. This indicates that the N-dependent regulation of PEPC and PPDK gene expression in maize leaf is primarily regulated by transcription. However, contribution of the post-transcriptional processes such as the processing and stability of transcript and its translation can not be ruled out because there was a discrepancy in extent of between transcription activity and accumulation of mRNA during recovery as exemplified by PEPC gene.

In the leaves of maize two distinct isoforms of PEPC have been described (9, 10). Reflecting the multiplicity, it has been suggested based upon Southern and Northern analyses that maize PEPC is encoded by a small gene family (11). We measured mRNA for C_3-PEPC in poly(A)$^+$-RNA extracts of maize leaves using a probe of sorghum C_3-PEPC cDNA (12). However, the level of C_3-type of PEPC mRNA unchanged at least over 48 h of recovery from N-starvation. The result indicates that the N-dependent expression of PEPC gene is specific for C_4-type PEPC in maize leaf. Collectively, the results will lead to the concept that N functions as a modulator of expression of C4-photosynthetic genes at least for PEPC and PPDK by altering their transcription. Understanding of the underlying clue in this control might provide a molecular strategy for manipulation of gene expression enabling to modify or design cellular function in plants by altering N-partitioning into proteins.

Specificity of N-Source for the N-dependent Expression of PEPC Gene

Nitrate and ammonium are effective as an inorganic N-source to induce the N-dependent PEPC gene expression although ammonium salt is more effective, producing a 2-fold higher rate and extent than nitrate (5). Essential lack of the specificity among the inorganic N-source for the accumulation of PEPC mRNA excludes the possibility that these inorganic compounds exert positive control as a primary signal on its gene expression. If a metabolite(s) is involved as a signal to modulate the positive control of N-dependent PEPC gene expression, a likely candidate should be sought among the down-stream product(s) of ammonium assimilation. It has been shown that Gln is the most influenced metabolite during recovery from N-starvation and its level increases in parallel with the steady-state levels of mRNA as well as protein for PEPC, reflecting the differences in both rate and extent of the mRNA and protein accumulations due to the different sources of inorganic N (5). In this study it has also been shown that ammonium supply to N-starved plants causes a parallel increase in activity of ferredoxin-glutamate synthase (Fd-GOGAT) and GS, whereas nitrate supply to the plants causes a relative increase in activity of Fd-GOGAT versus GS. The differential changes in GS/Fd-GOGAT may be the biochemical basis for the preferentially accumulation of Gln in ammonium-supplemented plants. Certainly, Gln can increase the accumulation of PEPC mRNA when administered through roots to the N-starved maize plants accompanying an increase in the endogenous level(5). In contrast, administration of Glu decreases the level of PEPC mRNA to some extent, with a slight decrease in the level of endogenous Gln. The results suggest that Gln and/or its metabolite(s) may exert a positive control on the expression of PEPC gene altering its gene expression.

Cytokinin Requirement for the N-Dependent Expression of C_4-Photosynthetic Genes

Regulation of gene expression in particular by N must require a complex network of intercellular and intercellular communication because N is mobile. To identify possible messenger(s) in the N-dependent gene expression of maize C_4-enzymes, which mediates the communication between leaf and root tissues, we have chosen detached maize leaves as the experimental material. Leaves were detached from N-starved plants and incubated in either low or high nitrate culture solution. mRNAs for PEPC and CA were chosen as targets since we previously demonstrated evidence to show that the mechanism controlling these enzymes in the

C_4-pathway, are closely related (4). Both mRNAs decreased dramatically in a similar manner over 8 h of incubation regardless of the N-concentration in culture solution although the rate of decrease in the levels of mRNAs were much extensive in low-N plants compared to high-N plants (Fig. 2).

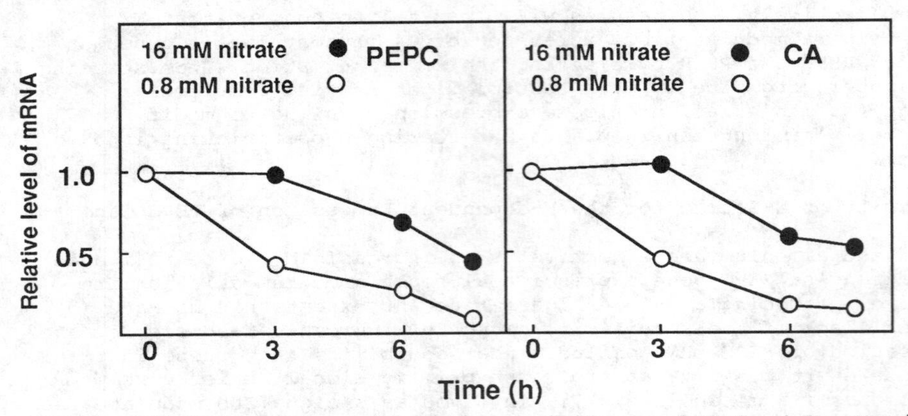

FIGURE 2. *Effect of nitrate administration on the levels of PEPC and CA mRNAs in detached leaves of N-starved maize plants* (6) The detached leaves of plants grown at 0.8 mM nitrate were used for the experiment. The leaves were incubated with 0.8 mM or 16 mM nitrate medium for up to 8 h. The results are expressed as relative values of the control at 0 h (=1.0).

Administration of 5 mM Gln or its combination with 2% (w/v) sucrose, did not effect the levels of their mRNAs. The decrease in level of mRNAs, however, was totally blocked by administration of zeatin and the levels of both PEPC and CA mRNAs increased in parallel over 3 h when nitrate (16 mM) plus zeatin (5 µM) was administered (Fig. 3). The effect of zeatin was dose-dependent and the levels of both mRNAs 3 h after incubation reached saturation at 1 µM zeatin. Benzyladenine, a synthetic cytokinin, was also effective. However, IAA was ineffective even when administered together with zeatin. ABA decreased the levels of mRNAs compared to those of the control incubated with high-nitrate alone. The fact that both a synthetic and naturally occurring cytokinins gave similar results suggests that the effect of these compounds is due to their function as cytokinins. Although the exact role of cytokins in gene expression in maize leaves is still unknown, cytokins did not affect the production and/or transport of Gln (Sugiyama et al, unpublished observation). The results imply that cytokinins which are thought to be synthesized in roots (13) are essential for the N-dependent expression of PEPC and CA genes in leaves by stimulating transcription and/or by stabilizing the transcript. It is interesting to note that cytokins affect similarly the expression of genes for Rubisco-small subunit (14, 15), light-harvesting chlorophyll *a/b* apoprotein (14, 16, 17, 18, 19), and nitrate reductase (NR) (20). Extremely saying, these proteins could be considered functionally as appendage. It is worthwhile to note that PEPC and CA mRNAs were effected by N and cytokinin in an identical manner throughout the experiments. These observations draw attention to the possibility that the gene expression of PEPC and CA, cytosolic enzymes in mesophyll cells, in the C_4-pathway is coordinately controlled by the same or a very similar mechanism.

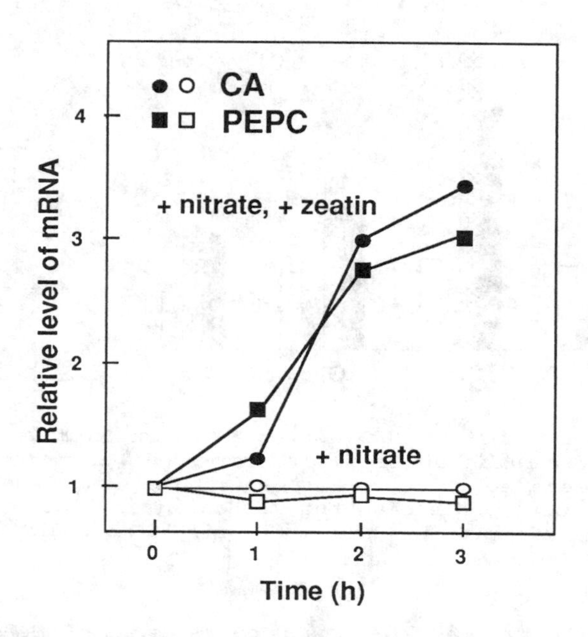

FIGURE 3. *Effect of co-administration of nitrate and zeatin on the levels of PEPC and CA mRNAs in the detached leaves of N-starved plantss* (6) The detached leaves of plant grown at 0.8 mM nitrate were used for the experiment. The leaves were incubated for 3 h with 5 µM zeatin. The results are expressed as relative values of the controls at 0 h.

Possible Metabolic Signal for the N-Dependent Expression of C_4-Photosynthetic Genes

We have used detached leaves to study the N-dependent control of expression of PEPC and CA genes in maize using Gln, Glu, and Ala as N-source (21). Among these Gln was the most effective amino acid. As shown in Fig. 4, following supplementation with Gln (20 mM) as a N-source and zeatin (5 µM) PEPC and CA mRNA levels increased in detached leaves to an extent comparable with nitrate plus zeatin. Glu and Ala were less effective but significantly increased the levels of both mRNAs compared to the control. The effects of these two amino acids may be due to an increase in endogenous levels of Gln formed, presumably, through their transamination by glutamate transaminase and/or alanine-transaminase and GS/GOGAT cycle. This N-dependent induction appears to be gene-specific since the levels of mRNAs for GS1 and α-tublin remained unchanged under the conditions. Bearing these considerations in mind we further studied the possible role of Gln in the N-dependent gene expression by analyzing the expression of genes for PEPC and CA, and GS1 in the presence of methionin sulfoximine (MSX), a specific inhibitor of GS activity (21). Addition of MSX totally inhibited the N-dependent increase of PEPC and CA mRNA but did not effect the Gln-

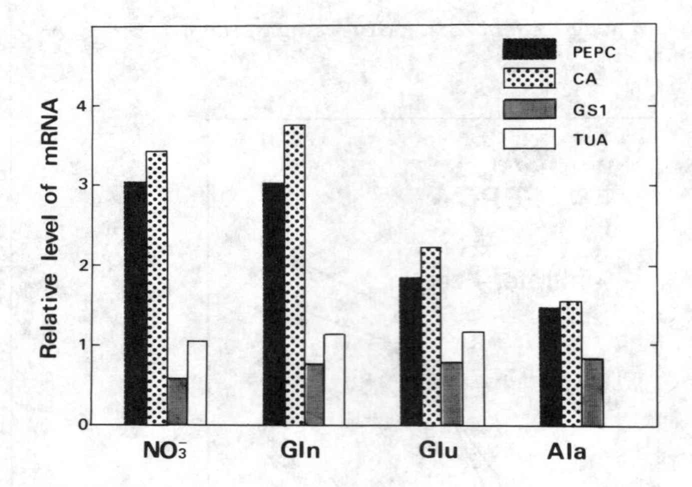

FIGURE 4. *Effects of administration of Gln, Glu, or Ala on the accumulation of mRNAs for PEPC, CA, GS1, and α-tublin in the detached leaves of N-starved maize plants* (6).The results are expressed as relative values of the control at 0 h. TUA represents α-tublin.studies addressing the mechanism of N-dependent gene regulation of C_4-enzymes may also help to clarify a molecular basis for the high N-use efficiency of C_4 plants.

Table 1. *Effects of administration of N-compounds on the levels of mRNAs for PEPC, CA, and GS1 in MSX-pretreated detached leaves of N-starved maize plants* (6) The results are expressed as relative values of the controls at 30 min preincubation with MSX.

	75 min-incubation			150 min-incubation		
Treatment	PEPC	CA	GS1	PEPC	CA	GS1
- MSX, + nitrate	1.79	1.61	1.37	4.20	5.50	1.20
+ MSX, + nitrate	0.69	0.95	1.15	0.12	0.50	0.99
+ MSX, + Gln	2.00	1.89	0.83	2.96	4.73	0.90
+ MSX, + Glu	0.39	0.81	0.95	0.15	0.40	1.49
+ MSX, + Gly	-	-	-	0.20	0.23	1.08
+ MSX, + Ser	-	-	-	0.21	0.20	1.20

dependent increase of PEPC and CA mRNA levels (Table 1). Most strikingly, among amino acids, nitrate, and ammonia Gln was found to be the only compound which levels changed with a positive correlation with the changes in levels of PEPC and CA mRNAs. Collectively, we conclude that Gln and/or its metabolite(s) is the most likely effector for controlling the N-dependent expression of PEPC and CA genes in maize plants. Furthermore, the failure of Glu, Gly, and Ser to act as a N-source for the induction in MSX-pretreated leaves indicates that if there is a positive signal other than Gln, it may be a metabolite(s) in the pathway(s) other than in protein synthesis.

Gln and/or its metabolite(s) has been suggested as a negative signal for NR gene expression in tobacco by Deng et al.(22) who demonstrated that an inhibitor of GS caused a drop in Gln level and abolished the day-time decrease of NR mRNA levels. A similar effect of Gln on the accumulation of NR mRNA has been reported in squash cotyledons (23). In maize leaves NR levels increase preceding an increase in the the accumulation of PEPC when nitrate is supplied to N-starved plants (5). These results predict that the level of NR mRNA would accumulate earlier than a rise in Gln levels which, in turn, would cause an inhibition of NR gene expression in detached maize leaves after supplying nitrate to N-starved plants. This will be one of aspects of N-dependent gene regulation which still demand attention and may prove as fruitful in its resolution as one leading to the characterization of N and C assimilations interwoven.

In addition to PEPC, PPDK, and CA, the gene for AlaAT in *Panicum miliaceum*, a NAD-malic enzyme type C_4 plant, is regulated by N-availability in an identical manner (7). We believe that further studies addressing the mechanism of N-dependent gene regulation of C_4-enzymes also help to clarify a molecular basis for the high efficiency in N-use by C_4-plants.

ACKNOWLEDGEMENTS: This work was supported in part by Grant-in-Aid for Scientific Research on Priority Areas (No.04273103) and Grant-in-Aid fo Scientific Research (B) from the Ministry of Education, Science, and Culture, Japan to T.S.

REFERENCES

1 Plumley, F.G. and Schmidt, G.W. (1989) Proc. Natl. Acad. Sci. USA 86, 2678-2682
2 Peltier, G. and Schmidt, G.W. (1991) Proc. Natl. Acad. Sci. USA. 88, 4791-4795
3 Sugiharto, B., Miyata, H., Nakamoto, H., Sasakawa, H. and Sugiyama, T. (1990) Plant Physiol. 92, 963-969
4 Burnell, J.N., Suzuki, I., and Sugiyama, T. (1990) Plant Physiol. 94, 384-387
5 Sugiharto, B. and Sugiyama, T. (1992) Plant Physiol. 98, 1403-1408
6 Sugiharto, B., Burnell, J., and Sugiyama, T. Plant Physiol. in press

7 Son,D., Kobe, A., and Sugiyama, T. (1992) Plant Cell Physiol. 33, 507-509
8 Luthe, D.S. and Quatrano, R.S. (1980) Plant Physiol. 65, 305-308
9 Ting, I.P., and Osmond, C.B. (1973) Plant Physiol. 51, 439-447
10 Hayakawa,S., K. Matsunaga, and Sugiyama, T. (1981) Plant Physiol. 67, 133-138
11 Taylor, W.C. (1989) Plant Cell, 1, 259-264
12 Cretin, C., Santi, S., Keryer, E., Lepiniec, L., Tagu, D., Vidal, J., and Gadal, P. (1991) Gene. 99, 87-94
13 Feldman, L.J. (1975) In Torrey, J.G., and Clarkson, D.T. (Eds.) The Development and Function of Roots.pp 55-72, Academic Press, London
14 Fuckes-Shippy, C.L., and Levine, A.D. (1985) In Steinback, K.E., Bonizt, S., Arntzen, C.J., and Bogorad, L.(Eds.) Molecular Biology of the Photosynthetic Apparatus. Cold Spring Harbor Laboratory, pp 407-411
15 Lerbs, S., Lerbs, W., Klyachko, N.L., Romanko, E.G., Kulaeva,O.N., Wollgiehn, R., and Parthier, B. (1984) Planta, 162, 289-298
16 Flores, S., and Tobin, E.M. (1986) Planta 163, 340-349
17 Flores, S., and Tobin, E.M. (1989) Plant Mol. Biol. 11, 409-415
18 Longo, G.P.M., Bracale, M., Rossi, G., and Longo, C.P. (1990) Plant Mol. Biol. 14, 585-594
19 Teyssendier de la Serve, B., Axelos, M., and Peaud-Lenoel, C.(1985) Plant Mol. Biol. 5, 155-163
20 Lu, J.-L., Ertl, J.R., and Chen, C.-M. (1990) Plant Mol. Biol.14, 585-594
21 Sugiharto, B., Burnell, J.N., and Sugiyama, T. Plant Physiol. in press
22 Deng, M.-D., Moureaux, T., Cherel, I., Boutin, J.-P., and Caboche, M. (1991) Plant Physiol. Biochem. 29, 239-247
23 Martino, S.J. and Smarreli Jr, J. (1989) Plant Sci. 61, 61-67

THE ROLE OF NITROGEN METABOLISM IN PHOTORESPIRATION

Peter J. Lea, Ray D. Blackwell

DIVISION OF BIOLOGICAL SCIENCES, UNIVERSITY OF LANCASTER, LANCASTER, LA1 4YQ, U.K.

Rainer E. Hausler and Richard C. Leegood

ROBERT HILL INSTITUTE, DEPARTMENT OF ANIMAL AND PLANT SCIENCES, UNIVERSITY OF SHEFFIELD, SHEFFIELD, S10 2UQ, U.K.

1. INTRODUCTION

The enzyme RuBP carboxylase/oxygenase (Rubisco) is able to catalyse both the carboxylation of RuBP to yield two molecules of phosphoglycerate and the oxygenation of RuBP to yield one molecule of phosphoglycerate and one of phosphoglycollate (1). The phosphoglycollate formed in the oxygenation reaction is metabolised through the photorespiratory carbon and nitrogen cycle shown in Fig. 1. Initially the cycle was proposed on evidence derived from ^{14}C, ^{18}O and ^{15}N-labelling data (2). However, the cycle was confirmed by the isolation of mutants that lacked key enzymes involved in phosphoglycollate metabolism. Such mutants initially described by Somerville and Ogren (3) using *Arabidopsis thaliana* grow normally at elevated levels of CO_2 when the oxygenation reaction is depressed. However, when the mutants are exposed to air, the metabolism of phosphoglycollate via the cycle in Fig. 1 is blocked at a position dependent upon the enzyme lesion. Phosphoglycerate is not returned to the chloroplast and ultimately the rate of photosynthetic CO_2 assimilation falls and the plants exhibit severe symptoms of stress. A similar extended range of mutants of barley (*Hordeum vulgare*) have been isolated both at Rothamsted and at the University of Lancaster (4).

In the following sections a brief summary of the current status of mutant plants lacking enzymes involved in photorespiratory nitrogen metabolism will be provided. In addition studies attempting to establish the minimum level of enzyme activities required to maintain the normal flux throughout the photorespiratory pathway will be described.

2. SERINE:GLYOXYLATE AMINOTRANSFERASE

The first steps of the photorespiratory nitrogen cycle are the two aminotransferase reactions in the peroxisome that convert glyoxylate to glycine. Although initially it was thought that glutamate and serine formed a closed cycle within the photo-respiratory pathway, there is also good evidence that asparagine and alanine may also act as aminodonors in the synthesis of glycine (5). Mutants lacking serine:glyoxylate aminotransferase have been isolated in *Arabidopsis* (6), barley (7) and *Nicotiana* (8). It has been shown that the serine:glyoxylate aminotransferase enzyme also catalyses asparagine:glyoxylate and serine:pyruvate aminotransferase activities (5). The barley mutants LaPr 85/84 lacked all these enzyme activities (7).

Following exposure to air the rate of photosynthetic CO_2 assimilation in the serine:glyoxylate aminotransferase deficient mutant fell to 20-30% of the wild type rate

N. Murata (ed.), Research in Photosynthesis, Vol. IV, 27–34.

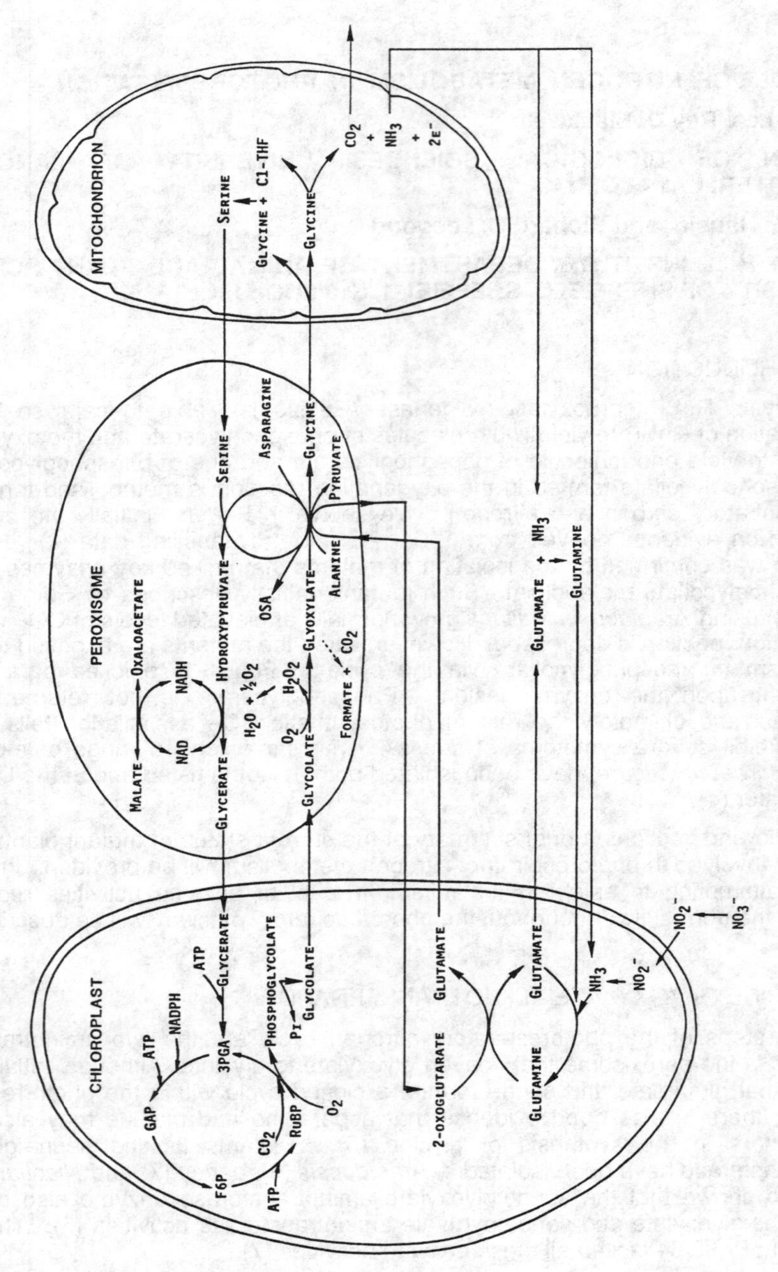

FIGURE 1. THE PHOTORESPIRATORY NITROGEN CYCLE

and there was a large accumulation of serine in the leaves. The presence of glutamate:glyoxylate aminotransferase allowed half the flow of carbon through to glycine. There was also evidence in the absence of serine as an aminodonor that glyoxylate was oxidised to yield formate and CO_2.

Serine:glyoxylate aminotransferase has been extensively studied by Becker and his colleagues in cucumber cotyledons and a cDNA clone isolated (9). The barley mutant LaPr85/84 was shown to lack two peaks of enzyme activity following ion exchange chromatography. However, SDS PAGE and Western blot analysis using antisera raised to the cucumber enzyme demonstrated that the mutant contained normal levels of the enzyme protein.

3. GLYCINE TO SERINE CONVERSION

Glycine is metabolised in the mitochondria of the leaves of C_3 plants in the following reaction:-

Glycine + H_2O + NAD^+ ----> Serine + CO_2 + NH_3 + NADH + H^+

The reaction is catalysed by the multi-enzyme complex glycine decarboxylase and serine hydroxymethyltransferase. Rates of glycine metabolism are frequently higher than 1mmol min^{-1} mg^{-1} protein and the amino acid is oxidised in preference to all other mitochondrial substrates (10).

The glycine decarboxylase complex is composed of four different component proteins and is present in leaf mitochondria at concentrations above 100 mg ml^{-1}. The complex comprises 2 P-protein dimers (2 x 97 kDa), 27 H-protein monomers (13.9 kDa), 9 T-protein monomers (45 kDa) and 1 L-protein dimer (2 x 60 kDa) with a total molecular weight of 1300 kDa. At concentrations below 10 mg ml^{-1}, the complex dissociates into the respective proteins (11).

Changes in the levels of the four subunits have been examined during the development of wheat leaves (12). Three of the sub-units (P, T and H) showed a steady increase in concentration from 1.5cm distance from he leaf base. The L-protein however, was readily detectable at the leaf base and was present in etiolated leaves in a higher proportion than the other three proteins. The L-protein (lipoamide dehydrogenase) is known to be a component of other mitochondrial dehydrogenases, which would account for the presence of the protein in non-photosynthetic tissue (12, 13). Genes for the P (14, 15), H (16, 17) and L (13, 18) protein have now been cloned from pea leaves and the regulation of mRNA transcription studied.

Mutant lines deficient in glycine decarboxylase have been isolated in both *Arabidopsis* (19) and barley (20). As might be expected, the mutants accumulated glycine following exposure to air and photosynthetic CO_2 assimilation was reduced to 30% of the wild type rate. This inhibition could be removed by the addition of serine, which presumably allowed carbon to return to the Calvin cycle in the chloroplast and provided nitrogen donors to convert glyoxylate to glycine.

A mutant of barley (LaPr 87/30) was unable to metabolize [^{14}C]-glycine fed to the detached leaves. LaPr 87/30 also showed a considerable reduction in the rate of glycine-bicarbonate exchange reaction and the liberation of ammonia in the presence of the glutamine synthetase inhibitor methionine sulphoximine. Western blot analysis using monospecific antisera raised by Dr. S. Rawsthorne revealed that the leaves of LaPr 87/30 lacked both the P and H proteins of the glycine decarboxylase complex (20).

Serine hydroxymethyltransferase catalyses the combination of the 5,10-methylene tetrahydrofolate formed in the glycine decarboxylation reaction with a second molecule of glycine to form serine. Experiments using *A. thaliana* mutants lacking either glycine decarboxylase or serine hydroxymethyltransferase activities showed that they were functionally equivalent (19, 21). In a particularly elegant series of experiments Somerville and Somerville (22) were able to show that the mutant lacking serine hydroxymethyltransferase was able to continue to accumulate glycine in air, provided it was supplied with a suitable nitrogen source. In this way they were able to demonstrate that the rate of glycine accumulation was equal to 40% of the rate of photosynthetic CO_2 assimilation. This method allowed a novel method of determining the rate of photorespiration, a procedure fraught with difficulties (23).

4. THE RE-ASSIMILATION OF AMMONIA LIBERATED DURING PHOTORESPIRATION

As shown in the previous section, during the conversion of glycine to serine, ammonia is released at the same rate as CO_2. As this rate of ammonia production is approximately ten times the rate of nitrate reduction, it is imperative that the ammonia is re-assimilated into amino acids as rapidly as possible. The pathway of re-assimilation is via the combined action of the two enzymes glutamine synthetase (GS) and glutamate synthase (GOGAT). The pathway has been the subject of a number of reviews over the last few years (24, 25).

There is now good evidence from mutant and inhibitor experiments that the ammonia is not re-assimilated in the mitochondria, but that the majority passes through the cytoplasm into the chloroplast. The leaves of C_3 plants contain both cytoplasmic and chloroplastic GS, but the latter is normally present in higher concentrations. The isoenzymes differ in the immunological characteristics and are coded for by different genes (26, 27). The chloroplast enzyme is coded by a single nuclear gene and the protein is transported into the chloroplast and subject to the cleavage of a transport peptide. The enzyme is subject to regulation by light and may under some (but not all) circumstances be repressed under conditions of elevated CO_2 that prevent photorespiration (26, 28).

Although they have not been isolated in *A. thaliana*, barley mutants deficient in chloroplastic GS have been isolated by two laboratories (29, 30). The mutants exhibit remarkably similar properties to plants treated with the inhibitors methionine sulphoximine and phosphinothricin. These are characterised by a massive accumulation of ammonia and a reduction in the rate of photosynthetic CO_2 assimilation following exposure to air. The maximum rate of ammonia evolution has been calculated to be 40% of the rate of CO_2 assimilation and again can be taken as a direct measurement of the rate of photorespiration (29).

Western blot analysis using *Phaseolus vulgaris* GS (28) has shown that the mutants analysed so far, contain variable amount of of enzyme protein (24, 30). Freeman *et al.* (31) have extended the analysis of the Rothamsted GS deficient mutants by employing the pcHvGS6 clone to detect mRNA levels in the leaves. Four mutant lines (designated Class I) contain low levels of chloroplastic GS enzyme protein and low or undetectable levels of mRNA. Class II was unusual in that it contained normal levels of mRNA but no cross reacting protein. It was suggested that the aberrant protein was not able to form the normal octameric structure or was not transported into the chloroplast, and was therefore susceptible to rapid proteolysis. Mutants in Class III contained variable amounts of protein and mRNA.

GOGAT is present in higher plants in two forms, ferredoxin and NADH-dependent. The ferredoxin-dependent form predominates in green leaves, whilst the NADH-dependent form is found in roots and is particularly active in nitrogen fixing nodules (24, 25). The enzymes have been purified to homogeneity from a number of sources (24, 25) and more recently a cDNA clone isolated for the ferredoxin dependent enzyme from maize leaves (32, 33).

Photorespiratory mutants lacking the chloroplastic ferredoxin dependent enzyme have been isolated from *A. thaliana* (34), barley (35, 36) and pea (24). Following exposure to air the leaves of the deficient mutants accumulate large quantities of glutamine and small amounts of ammonia, the levels of all other amino acids are greatly reduced. Ten minutes after the transfer to air, the rate of photosynthetic CO_2 assimilation had fallen to 10% of the rate of the wild type plant. This loss of photosynthetic capacity is much faster than that seen in the GS deficient mutants and could be reversed by the pre-feeding of alanine or asparagine. Mutants deficient in both enzymes of ammonia assimilation have been obtained by normal genetic crossing. Such mutants lacking both chloroplastic GS and ferredoxin dependent GOGAT are still capable of growing in elevated CO_2. The double mutants contain low levels of amino acids and are very sensitive to exposure to air (36).

The use of mutants of the photorespiratory carbon and nitrogen cycle has confirmed the pathway as shown in Fig. 1. The lack of individual enzymes causes a severe disruption of amino acid metabolism, when the mutant plants are exposed to air and ultimately the plants die. However, if the plants are grown in elevated CO_2, enzyme levels of less than 10% of the wild type are capable of maintaining near normal growth. Recent studies with ^{15}N-labelling have confirmed this suggestion (37). In an extension of these earlier findings, back crossed plants have been selected that contain GS levels in the range of 48-96% of the wild type and 70 and 80% of the ferredoxin dependent GOGAT wild type level of activity.

A reduction in the total amino acid content of the leaves and an increase in the ammonia concentration was correlated with the lowering of GS activity. At high light intensities and/or reduced external CO_2, ammonia accumulation was more pronounced as would be predicted. No alteration in Rubisco activity was detected in any of the barley plants with reduced GS activity.

A reduction of GS activity by 50% had no effects on the rates of CO_2 assimilation (A) over a wide range of internal CO_2 partial pressures (C_i) when determined at a PFD of 570mmol m^{-2} s^{-1} in 21% O_2. However the assimilation rates in the mutant containing

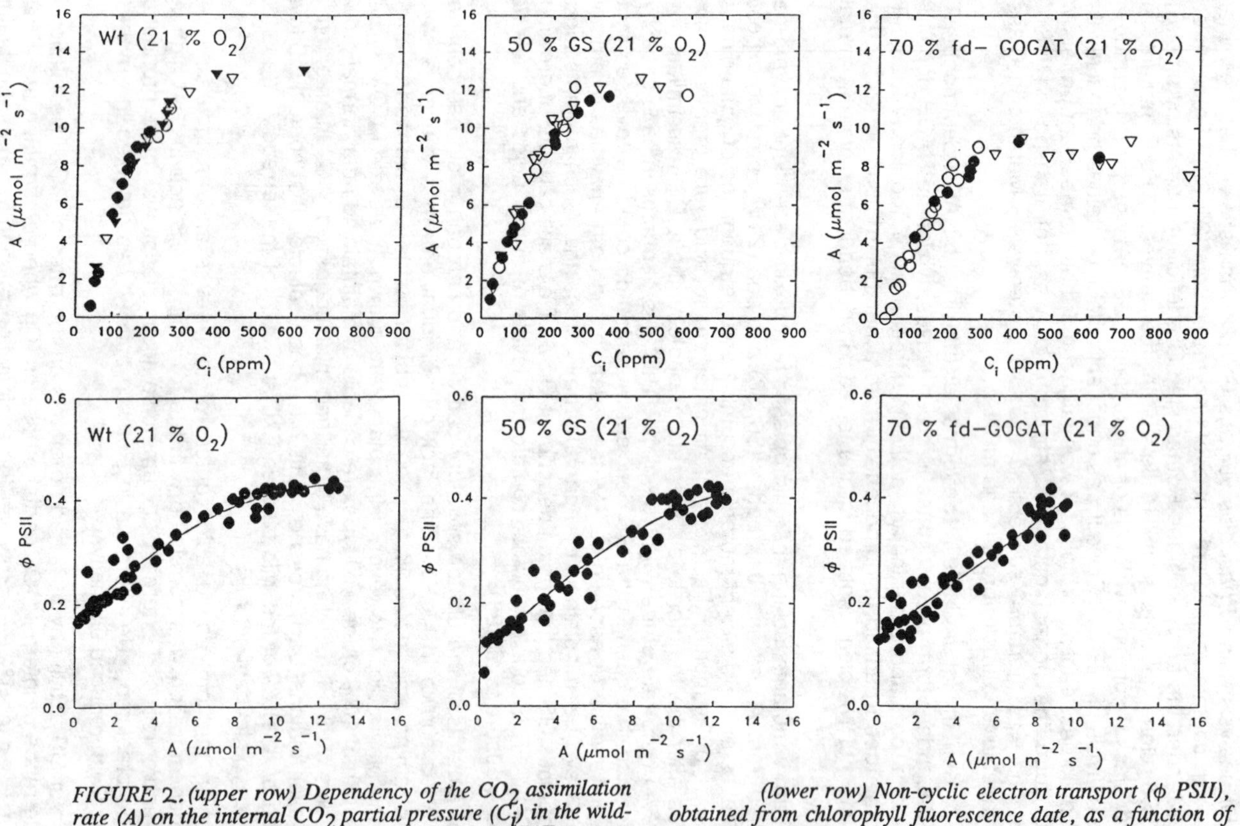

FIGURE 2. (upper row) Dependency of the CO_2 assimilation rate (A) on the internal CO_2 partial pressure (C_i) in the wild-type, a 50% GS mutant and a 70% Fd-GOGAT mutant. Experiments were performed in the presence of 21 % oxygen. (lower row) Non-cyclic electron transport (φ PSII), obtained from chlorophyll fluorescence date, as a function of the assimilation rates shown in the upper row.

70% GOGAT remained constant at a C_i above 300ppm and decreased above 700ppm (Fig. 2 upper row). Under non-photorespiratory conditions (e.g. 2% O_2) the relationship between A and C_i was not affected by a lowering of either the GS or GOGAT activity.

The re-assimilation of ammonia via the GS/GOGAT cycle requires ATP as well as reducing equivalents. Hence, the determination of non-cyclic electron transport (Φ PSII) can give an indication of the relative electron requirement for primary carbon assimilation as well as for photorespiration (38).

In the absence of photorespiration, in 2% O_2, Φ PSII was directly proportional to the CO_2 assimilation rate in the wild type and mutants (data not shown). A plot of Φ PSII versus A obtained with the wild type and mutant plants is shown in Fig. 2 (lower row). Electron transport in the 50% GS mutant was decreased when compared to the wild type. The difference was most pronounced at low assimilation rates (e.g. low C_i) but disappeared at high assimilation rates. At high PFD (1300mmol $m^{-2}s^{-1}$) and reduced C_i (100ppm), the rate of electron transport required to support the given CO_2 assimilation rate in the 50% GS mutant was much lower than would be expected theoretically. One possibility is that CO_2 fixation by ammonia stimulated PEP carboxylase is responsible for the observed discrepancy.

The relationship between Φ and the CO_2 assimilation rate (A) for the mutant containing 70% GOGAT activity is more complex. Similarities with the wild type were detected at low and high C_i. Interpretation of the curve is not possible at the present time.

It is hoped that studies of this nature utilising mutants containing intermediate levels of GS and GOGAT activity will establish the extent to which the two enzymes contribute to the control of photorespiratory carbon and nitrogen metabolism.

REFERENCES

1 Keys, A.J. (1990) Perspectives in Biochemical and Genetic regulation of photosynthesis (Zelitch, I., ed.) pp.207-224. Wiley-Liss, New York.
2 Husic, D.W., Husic, H.D. and Tolbert, N.E. (1987) CRC. Crit. Rev. Plant Sci. 5, 455-500.
3 Somerville, C.R. and Ogren, W.L. (1979) Nature 280, 833-836.
4 Blackwell, R.D., Murray, A.J.S., Lea, P.J., Kendall, A.C., Hall, N.P., Turner, J.C. and Wallsgrove, R.M. (1988) Photosynthesis Research 16, 155-176.
5 Joy, K.W. (1988) Can. J. Bot. 66, 2103-2109.
6 Somerville, C.R. and Ogren, W.L. (1980) Proc. Natl. Acad. Sci. USA, 77, 2684-2687.
7 Murray, A.J.S., Blackwell, R.D., Joy, K.W. and Lea, P.J. (1987) Planta 172, 106-113.
8 McHale, N.A., Havir, E.A. and Zelitch, I. (1989) Theoretical and Applied Genetics 76, 71-75.
9 Hondred, D., Wadle, D.M., Titus, D.E. and Becker, W.M. (1987) Plant Mol. Biol. 9, 259-275.
10 Oliver, D.J., Neuburger, M., Bourguignon, J and Douce, R. (1990) Physiol. Plant 80, 487-491.

11 Oliver, D.J., Neuburger, M. and Bourguignon, J. (1990) Plant Physiol. 94, 833-839.
12 Rogers, W.J., Jordan, B.R., Rawsthorne, S. and Tobin, A.K. (1991) Plant Physiol. 96, 952-956.
13 Bourguignon, J., Macherel, D., Neuburger, M. and Douce, R. (1992) Eur. J. Biochem. 204, 865-873.
14 Kim, Y., Shah, K. and Oliver, D.J. (1991) Physiol. Plant. 81, 501-506.
15 Turner, S.R., Ireland, R and Rawsthorne, S. (1992) J. Biol. Chem. 267, 5355-5360.
16 Kim, Y. and Oliver, D.J. (1990) J. Biol. Chem. 265, 848-853.
17 Macherel, D., Lebrun, M., Gagnon, J., Neuburger, M. and Douce, R. (1990) Biochem. J. 268, 783-789.
18 Turner, S.R., Ireland, R. and Rawsthorne, S. (1992) J. Biol. Chem. 267, 7745-7750.
19 Somerville, C.R. and Ogren, W.L. (1982) Biochem. J. 202, 373-380.
20 Blackwell, R.D., Murray, A.J.S. and Lea, P.J. (1990) Plant Physiol. 94, 1316-1322.
21 Somerville, C.R. and Ogren, W.L. (1981) Plant Physiol. 67, 666-671.
22 Somerville, S.C. and Somerville, C.R. (1983) J. Exp. Bot. 34, 415-424.
23 Gerbaud, A. and Andre, M (1987) Plant Physiol. 83, 933-937.
24 Lea, P.J., Blackwell, R.D. and Joy, K.W. (1991) in Nitrogen metabolism in plants (Pilbeam, D.J. and Mengel, K. eds.) pp.173-186. Oxford University Press, Oxford.
25 Lea, P.J., Robinson, S.A. and Stewart, G.R. (1990) in The Biochemistry of Plants (Miflin, B.J. and Lea, P.J., eds.) Vol. 16, pp.257-276. Acadmic Press, San Diego.
26 Coruzzi, G.M. (1991) Plant Science, 74, 145-155.
27 Forde, B.G. and Cullimore, J.V. (1989) in Oxford Surveys of Plant Molecular and Cell Biology (Miflin, B.J. ed.) Vol. 6, pp.247-296. Oxford University Press, Oxford.
28 Cock, M.J., Brock, I.W., Watson, A.T., Swarup, R., Moreby, A.P. and Cullimore, J.V. (1991) Plant Mol. Biol. 17, 761-771.
29 Blackwell, R.D., Murray, A.J.S. and Lea, P.J. (1982) J. Exp. Bot. 38, 1799-1809.
30 Wallsgrove, R.M., Turner, J.C., Hall, N.P., Kendall, A.C. and Bright, S.W.J. (1987) Plant Physiol. 83, 155-158.
31 Freeman, J., Marquez, A.J., Wallsgrove, R.M., Saarelainen, R. and Forde, B.G. (1990) Plant Mol. Biol. 14, 297-311.
32 Sakakibara, H., Kawabata, S., Takahashi, H., Hase, T. and Sugiyama, T. (1992) Plant Cell Physiol. 33, 49-58.
33 Sakakibara, H., Watanabe, M., Hase, T. and Sugiyama, T. (1991) J. Biol. Chem. 266, 2028-2035.
34 Somerville, C.R. and Ogren, W.L. (1980) Nature, 186, 257-259.
35 Kendall, A.C., Wallsgrove, R.M., Hall, N.P., Turner, J.C. and Lea, P.J. (1986) Planta. 168, 316-323.
36 Blackwell, R.D., Murray, A.J.S., Lea, P.J. and Joy, K.W. (1988) J. Exp. Bot. 39, 845-858.
37 Joy, K.W., Blackwell, R.D. and Lea, P.J. (1992) J. Exp. Bot. 43, 139-145.
38 Genty, B., Briantais, J.M. and Baker, N.R. (1989) Biochem. Biophys. Acta. 990, 87-92.

GLUTAMATE SYNTHESIS IN NON-PHOTOSYNTHETIC PLASTIDS.

C.G. Bowsher, M.A. Cooper and M.J. Emes; Plant Metabolism Research Unit, School of Biological Sciences, Williamson Building, University of Manchester, Manchester, M13-9PL, U.K.

INTRODUCTION

In higher plants the assimilation of ammonia is catalysed by the glutamine synthetase/glutamate synthase pathway (1). In leaves both enzymes are located in the chloroplast and, in light, the ATP and reductant necessary for the respective reactions are generated photochemically (2). There is little reported evidence concerning the source of these substrates in roots. In the case of glutamate synthase two forms are present in both roots and leaves, one of which is NADH dependent and the other ferredoxin dependent (3). In most species both forms are located in non-photosynthetic root plastids (3, 4) The specific activity of the ferredoxin dependent enzyme increases markedly during root development, eventually accounting for 95% of the total activity in roots. A number of groups have now demonstrated that a redox protein with ferredoxin-like properties is present in roots (5). Obviously there is no photosynthesis occuring, which raises the question as to how reductant for glutamate synthase is initially generated. The oxidative pentose phosphate pathway (OPPP) enzymes are located in root plastids (6) and we have previously demonstrated that this pathway supports nitrite reduction in purified preparations of these organelles (7). Like glutamate synthase, nitrite reductase is a ferredoxin-dependent enzyme in roots and leaves (8) and we have therefore investigated whether the root plastid OPPP also functions to provide reductant for glutamate synthesis.

Using purified, intact pea root plastids, we have examined (i) the ability of intermediary metabolites to support glutamate synthesis in these organelles (ii) the evolution of CO_2 from [1-^{14}C]-glucose 6-phosphate (G6P) during glutamate synthesis (iii) the effect of azaserine, a potent inhibitor of glutamate synthesis on carbohydrate fluxes in plastids (iv) the effect of competition for reductant by nitrite reductase and glutamate synthase on the OPPP flux.

MATERIALS AND METHODS

Plastids were prepared from 150-300 g of pea (*Pisum sativum* L., cv. Early Onward) roots, as described previously (7). When required 'broken' plastids were

N. Murata (ed.), Research in Photosynthesis, Vol. IV, 35–38.

ruptured osmotically, by first resuspending in distilled water and then adding an equal volume of double strength resuspension buffer to standardise the salt concentrations.
Hexose-phosphate-dependent glutamate synthesis was assayed in 150 mM Tris-HCl, pH 8.0, 330 mM Sorbitol, 5 mM glutamine, 5 mM 2-oxoglutarate, hexose-phosphate and intact or broken plastids. The reaction was stopped by the addition of 40 mM 5-sulfosalicylic acid, centrifuged at 11000 g for 10 min and neutralised with 80 mM NaOH.
Glutamate was estimated using a modification of the standard glutamate purification method (9). G6P-dependent nitrite reduction was assayed as in (7). For radiochemical experiments [1-^{14}C]-glucose 6-phosphate (37 kBq) was used at a specific activity of approximately 3.7 kBQ μmol^{-1}. Assays were carried out in a final volume of 1 ml containing 330 mM sorbitol in the main compartment of a Warburg flask, the centre well containing 0.2 ml 10% (w/v) KOH. Glutamine (5 mM) and 2-oxoglutarate (5 mM) in 150 mM Tris-HCl buffer (pH 8.0) and 600 μg plastid protein were added to the main compartment, the flasks stoppered and agitated in a water bath at 25°C. The reaction was stopped by the addition of 5-sulfosalicylic acid, and radioactivity in the KOH determined as described previously (11). All assays were corrected for $^{14}CO_2$ release from broken plastids by subtracting the values obtained with osmotically lysed organelles.

RESULTS AND DISCUSSION

Purified pea root plastids were supplied with glutamine, oxoglutarate and a number of phosphorylated sugars. Formation of glutamate was linear for 75 minutes and was dependent upon the intactness of the organelles.

Table 1: The ability of phosphorylated sugars to support glutamate synthesis in pea root plastids (mean of at least 3 values ± S.E.).

Phosphorylated sugar substrate (10mM)	nmoles glutamate formed.min^{-1}. mg pro.$^{-1}$
G6P	10 ± 2
R5P	12.3 ± 1.9
F6P	7.7 ± 4.3
G1P	5.9 ± 1.1
6PG	0
Glucose	2.7 ± 0.3
Glucose + 5mM ATP	4.4 ± 1.1

The substrates best able to support glutamate formation were G6P and ribose 5-phosphate (R5P) (Table 1). Glucose-1-phosphate (G1P), fructose -6-phosphate (F6P), glucose and glucose+ATP supported lower rates of glutamate synthesis, whilst 6-phosphogluconate was ineffective (Table 1). The Km for G6P-dependent glutamate synthesis was found to be 0.20 mM, whilst the Km for R5P-dependent synthesis was 0.77 mM. G6P is taken up into the plastids by a phosphate translocator, but we do not know how these other substrates enter the organelles. The ability of R5P and F6P to support glutamate synthesis suggests that the OPPP may be operating in a cyclic manner.

Monitoring the release of $^{14}CO_2$ from [1-^{14}C]-G6P is diagnostic of the flux through the OPPP in these purified organelles (7,10). $^{14}CO_2$ evolution was dependent upon the presence of both glutamine (Km=0.44 mM) and 2-oxoglutarate (Km=1.1 mM) and could be inhibited by the application of 0.1mM azaserine, a known inhibitor of glutamate synthase. The data imply that G6P is oxidised in root plastids to support glutamate formation. The NADPH generated by the OPPP is probably used to reduce root ferredoxin via a plastidial ferredoxin $NADP^+$ oxidoreductase (5). Since glutamate synthase uses ferredoxin, as does nitrite reductase, we have carried out preliminary experiments to look at the competition between nitrite reduction and glutamate synthesis for the reductant generated. The rates of G6P dependent nitrite reduction were lower at all concentrations of G6P used when carried out in the presence of 5mM glutamine and 5mM 2-oxoglutarate (Gln,OG; Figure 1).

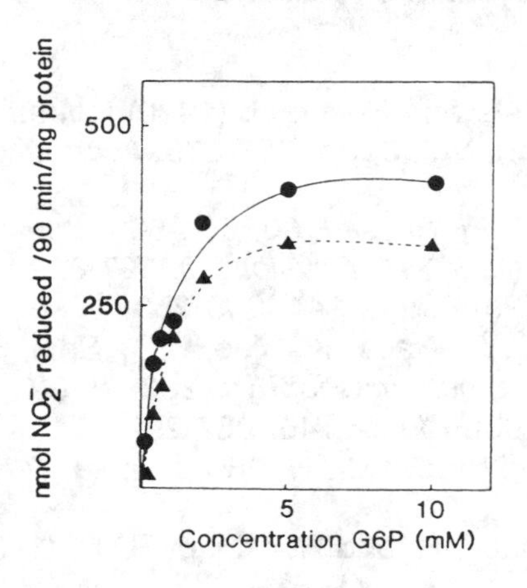

Figure 1: G6P-dependent nitrite reduction with 1mM NO_2^- only (●) or 1mM NO_2^- and Gln,OG (▲).

The rates of $^{14}CO_2$ evolution from 1-^{14}C-glucose-6-phosphate in the presence of the substrates for nitrite reductase and glutamate synthase were not as great as calculated theoretically from the simple addition of the rates obtained separately for each (Figure 2).

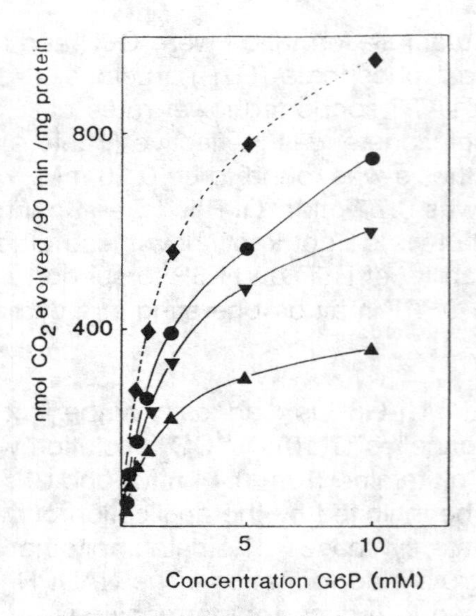

Figure 2: $^{14}CO_2$ evolution from [1-^{14}C]-G6P supplied to plastids in assays containing 1mM NO_2^- (▼), Gln,OG (▲), NO_2^- + Gln,OG (●). Theoretical values representing simple addition of the rates obtained separately with NO_2^- + Gln,OG (◆).

It would therefore appear that this flux through the OPPP saturates at levels which are sub-optimal for nitrite reductase and glutamate synthesis when these reactions are operating simultaneously. Work is currently underway to examine how these reactions compete and how the stoichiometric balance is maintained *in vivo* between nitrite reduction which requires 6 electrons and glutamate synthesis which requires 2 electrons per reaction.

REFERENCES

1. Lea, P.J., Blackwell, R.D., Chen, F.-L. and Hecht, U. (1990) in *Methods in Plant Biochemistry* (Lea, P.J., ed.), Vol. 3, pp. 257-276, Academic Press, New York
2. Anderson, J.W. and Done, J. (1977) *Pl. Physiol.* 60, 504-508
3. Suzuki, A., Vidal, J. and Gadal, P. (1982) *Pl. Physiol.* 70, 827-832
4. Emes, M.J. and Fowler, M.W. (1979a) *Planta* 144, 249-253
5. Morigasaki, S., Takata, K., Sanada, Y., Wada, K., Yee, B.C., Shin, S. and Buchanan, B.B. (1990b) *Arch. Biochem. Biophys.* 283, 75-80
6. Emes, M.J. and Fowler, M.W. (1979b). *Planta* 145, 287-292
7. Bowsher, C.G., Hucklesby, D.P. and Emes, M.J. (1989). *Planta* 177, 359-366
8. Bowsher, C.G., Emes, M.J., Cammack, R. and Hucklesby, D.P. (1988). *Planta* 175, 334-340
9. Matoh, T. and Takahashi, E. (1982). *Planta* 154, 289-294
10. Bowsher, C.G., Boulton, E.L., Rose, J., Nayagam, S. and Emes, M.J. (1992) *Plant Journal* (in Press)
11. Emes, M.J. and Fowler, M.W. (1983). *Planta* 158, 97-102

GLUTAMINE INDUCES EXPRESSION OF PHOSPHO*ENOL*PYRUVATE CARBOXYLASE AND CARBONIC ANHYDRASE GENES IN MAIZE PLANTS.

BAMBANG SUGIHARTO[1], AND TATSUO SUGIYAMA[2], FACULTY OF AGRICULTURE, JEMBER UNIVERSITY[1], JEMBER 68121, INDONESIA AND SCHOOL OF AGRICULTURE, NAGOYA UNIVERSITY[2], NAGOYA 464-01, JAPAN

1. INTRODUCTION

Maize leaves selectively accumulate phospho*enol*pyruvate carboxylase (PEPC) in response to N-availability presumably at the transcriptional level (1, 2). The expression of carbonic anhydrase (CA) has also been reported to be regulated by N-availability in maize leaf tissue (3). Based on the correlation analysis of the levels of mRNA and intermediates of N-assimilation, glutamine (Gln) and/or its metabolite(s), have been implicated in the control of expression of the PEPC gene (2). However, no conclusion can be drawn from this study regarding the cause and effect of parameters involved.

It is well documented that ammonia assimilation occurs in higher plants through the combined operation of GS and GOGAT cycle, and that methionine sulfoximine (MSX) inhibits the production of Gln via GS (4). In maize, this cycle is known to operate in both roots and shoots (5, 6). To simplify the interpretation of experiments designed to determine the role of Gln in the regulation of PEPC and CA gene expression, we developed a detached leaf system which allows administration of N-containing or related compounds directly to the leaf tissue (7).

The aim of the present work is to study the effect of MSX on the N-dependent expression of PEPC and CA gene using the detached leaf system of maize plants. The results indicate that Gln and/or its down-stream metabolite(s) is a positive signal of N-availability for the induction of these photosynthetic genes.

2. MATERIAL AND METHODS

Maize (*Zea mays* L. cv. Golden Cross Bantam T51) plants were grown hydroponically in low nitrate as described previously (2, 7) and youngest, fully developed leaves (third leaves) were used as detached leaf materials. Fifteen of detached leaves were placed vertically in a beaker containing 5 μM trans-zeatin in the presence or absence of various compounds and incubated at indicated times as reported previously (7).

Glutamine synthetase (GS) activity and contents of nitrate, ammonium, and amino acids were determined as described previously (2). Levels of mRNA for PEPC, CA and GS1 were measured by dot-blot and Northern hybridization using their specific probes (5, 2, 7) and level of mRNA for α-tubulin was determined in the same way using a probe which was kindly provided by Dr. D.P. Snustad (8). Relative accumulation of mRNA was determined after densitometer scans of the resulting autoradiographs.

3. RESULTS AND DISCUSSION

When detached leaves of plants grown at low nitrate are incubated with high nitrate and cytokinin, the levels of mRNA encoding PEPC and CA increase relative to total RNA (7). To identify the inorganic N-source effective for the induction of PEPC and CA genes in detached maize leaves, Gln, Glu, and Ala were selected and examined their effects on

N. Murata (ed.), Research in Photosynthesis, Vol. IV, 39–42.

the level of expression of PEPC and CA genes in detached leaves. Nitrate and amino acids in the presence of cytokinin were administered to the detached leaves of N-starved plants and the steady state levels of mRNAs for PEPC, CA, GS1 (a cytosolic form of GS) and α-tubulin (TUA) were measured in the leaves (Fig. 1). Gln increased the levels of PEPC and CA mRNA to an extent comparable with nitrate. Glu and Ala were less effective but significantly increased the levels of both mRNAs compared to the control at 0 h. The effect of these amino acids may be due to an increase in endogenous levels of Gln formed, presumably, through their trans-amination by Glu transaminase and/or Ala-Glu transaminase and GS/GOGAT cycle. By contrast, the levels of mRNA for GS1 and α-tubulin remained unchanged regardless of the N-sources. The results suggest that Gln is a primary signal for the induction of N-dependent expression of genes for PEPC and CA in maize leaves. Furthermore, the results indicated that this induction is gene-specific.

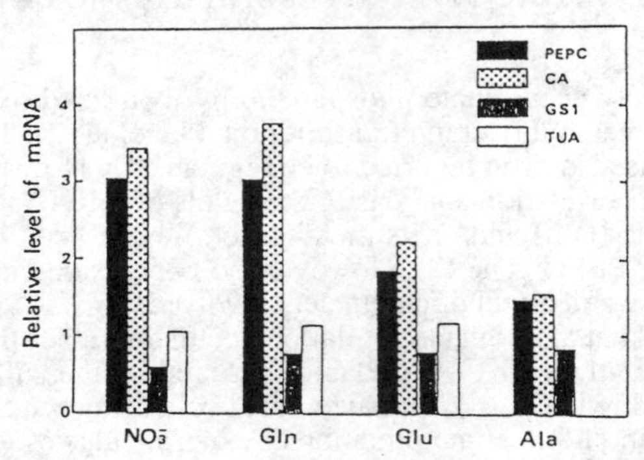

Figure 1. Effects of administration of Gln, Glu or Ala on the accumulation of mRNA for PEPC, CA, GS1 and α-tubulin in detached maize leaves.
Detached leaves of N-starved plants were incubated in medium containing 16 mM nitrate or 20 mM of amino acids in the presence of 5 μM of zeatin for 3 h. The levels of PEPC, CA, GS1, and a-tubulin (TUA) mRNA were measured by dot-blot hybridization with total RNA 1-2, 2-4, 5-10, and 10-20 μg, respectively. The results are expressed as relative values of the control at 0 h.

To confirm the above results, we examined the expression of genes for PEPC and CA, and GS1 as a control in the presence of MSX, a specific inhibitor of GS activity. Initial experiments were conducted to determine the concentration of MSX and incubation time required to inactivate the activity of GS. GS activity was inhibited by 88 %, 30 min after incubation with 2 mM MSX and inhibited completely after 45 min. Thus detached leaves were pre-incubated for 30 min with or without 2 mM MSX, then incubated with N-sources for 150 min addition time, and levels of mRNA for PEPC, CA and GS1 were measured (Table 1). In the leaves pre-treated with an MSX-minus solution, administration of nitrate increased the levels of mRNA for PEPC and CA by 4.2- and 5.5-fold, respectively. In contrast, in the leaves pre-treated with MSX the levels of both mRNAs decreased dramatically in spite of the presence of nitrate. However, administration of Gln to the MSX-pretreated leaves resulted in an increase in the level of both mRNAs to an extent comparable with that of the minus MSX control. Administration of either Glu, Gly, or Ser, which are considered to be N-compounds on the down-stream side of Gln synthesis (4), did not restore the decreased levels of either PEPC or CA mRNA. In respect to GS1, the levels of mRNA remained unchanged regardless of the treatment.

Table 1. Levels of mRNA for PEPC, CA and GS1 in detached maize leaves after administration of N-sources in the presence or absence of MSX
Detached leaves of N-starved plants were pre-incubated for 30 min with or without 2 mM MSX, and then 16 mM nitrate or 20 mM of amino acids were added and incubated for 150 min additional times. The levels of mRNA for PEPC and CA were measured by Northern hybridization. The level of GS1 mRNA was measured in the same way, except that GS1 probe was hybridized with the membrane after removal of CA probe.The results are expressed as relative values of the control at 30 min pre-incubation.

Treatment	75 min-incubation			150 min-incubation		
	PEPC	CA	GS1	PEPC	CA	GS1
-MSX, +nitrate	1.79	1.61	1.37	4.20	5.50	1.20
+MSX, +nitrate	0.69	0.95	1.15	0.12	0.50	0.99
+MSX, +Gln	2.00	1.89	0.83	2.96	4.73	0.90
+MSX, +Glu	0.39	0.81	0.95	0.15	0.40	1.49
+MSX, +Gly	-	-	-	0.20	0.23	1.08
+MSX, +Ser	-	-	-	0.21	0.20	1.20

To determine the relationship of N metabolism to the expression of PEPC and CA genes, we examined the levels of nitrate, ammonia, Gln, Glu, Ser, and Gly in detached leaves (Fig. 2). In the leaves treated with MSX, there was an increase in the level of ammonia 5.5- to 8.7-fold higher than that in MSX-minus, and a decrease in the level of Gln to an undetectable level, except in the case of where Gln was administered. This change in the levels of ammonia and Gln is a result of inactivation of GS. Most strikingly, of the N-containing compounds examined Gln was the only compound which levels changed with a positive correlation with the changes in the levels of PEPC and CA mRNAs.

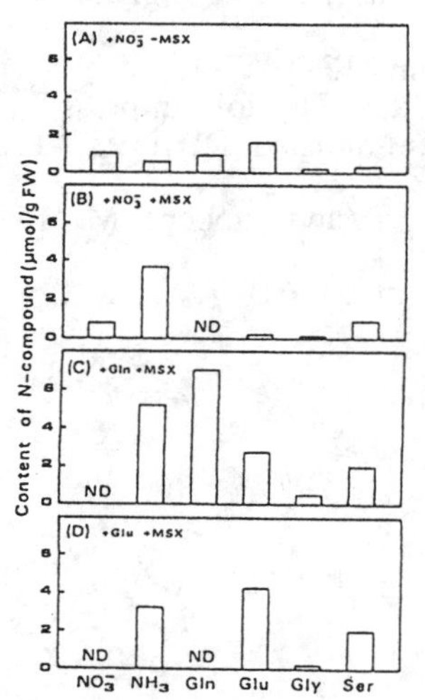

Figure 2. Levels of nitrate, ammonia, Gln, Glu, Gly and Ser in the MSX-treated detached maize leaves after administration of N-sources.
Detached leaves of N-starved plants were pre-incubated and incubated as described in the legend to table 4, and levels of metabolites were measured at 150 min incubation time. (A) nitrate-administered leaves without treatment with MSX as a control, (B) nitrate-administered leaves after treatment with MSX, (C) Gln-administered leaves after treatment with MSX, and (D) Glu-administered leaves after treatment with MSX. ND: not detectable.

Collectively, the results imply that Gln and/or its metabolite(s) may be a positive signal for the induction of N-dependent gene expression of PEPC and CA in maize leaves. Furthermore, the failure of Glu, Gly, and Ser to act as a N-source for the induction in MSX-treated leaves indicates that if there is a positive signal other than Gln, it will probably a metabolite(S) in the pathway(s) other than in protein synthesis.

Gln and/or its metabolite(s) has been suggested as a negative signal for nitrate reductase (NR) gene expression in tobacco (9) and squash cotyledons (10). In maize leaves NR levels increase preceding an increase in the accumulation of PEPC when nitrate is supplied to N-starved plants (2). These results predict that the level of NR mRNA would accumulate earlier than a rise in Gln levels which, in turn, would cause an inhibition of NR gene expression in detached maize leaves after supplying nitrate to N-starved plants.

4. CONCLUSION

We have used detached leaves to study the N-dependent control of expression of PEPC and CA genes in maize. Following supplementation with a N-sources and zeatin levels of mRNA for PEPC and CA increased in the leaves detached from N-deficient maize plants. Addition of MSX, a specific inhibitor of GS inhibited the nitrate-dependent increase of PEPC and CA mRNAs, but did not effect the Gln-dependent increase of PEPC and CA mRNA levels. Gln level in detached maize leaves treated with various N-sources in the presence or absence of MSX correlated with the levels of PEPC and CA mRNA. We conclude that Gln is the most likely effector for controlling the N-dependent expression of PEPC and CA in maize plants.

REFERENCES

1. Sugiharto, B., Miyata, K., Nakamoto, H., Sasakawa, H. and Sugiyama, T. (1990) Plant Physiol. 92, 963-969
2. Sugiharto, B. and Sugiyama, T. (1992) Plant Physiol. 98, 1403-1408
3. Burnell, JN., Suzuki, I. and Sugiyama, T. (1990) Plant Physiol. 94, 384-387
4. Miflin, BJ. and Lea, PJ. (1980) in The Biochemistry of Plants. Amino Acids and Derivatives (Miflin, BJ., Ed), Vol. 5, pp. 169-202, Academic Press, New York
5. Sakakibara, H., Kawabata, S., Takahashi, H., Hase, T. and Sugiyama, T. (1992) Plant Cell Physiol. 33, 49-58
6. Suzuki, A., Gadal, P. and Oaks, A. (1981) Planta 151, 457-461
7. Sugiharto, B., Burnell, JN. and Sugiyama, T. Plant Physiol. (in press)
8. Ludwig, SR., Oppenheimer, DG., Silflow, CD., Snustad, DP. (1987) Proc. Natl. Acad. Sci. USA. 84, 5833-5837
9. Deng, MD., Moureaux, T., Cherel, I., Boutin, J-P. and Caboche, M. (1991) Plant Physiol. Biochem. 29, 239-247
10. Martino, SJ. and Smarrelli, Jr.J. (1989) Plant Sci. 61, 61-67

ENGINEERING AND ANALYSIS OF FERREDOXIN AND RELATED GENES IN *RHODOBACTER CAPSULATUS*

KAZUHIKO SAEKI, KEN-ICHIRO TOKUDA and HIROSHI MATSUBARA
Dept. Biol., Fac. Sci., Osaka Univ., Toyonaka 560, JAPAN

1. INTRODUCTION

Ferredoxins are small iron-sulfur proteins which function as electron carriers in diverse metabolic pathways (1). The purple non-sulfur photosynthetic bacterium *Rhodobacter capsulatus* has ferredoxins of distinct structural and biochemical properties (2-5). The *fdxN* and *fdxA* genes encoding 2[4Fe-4S] ferredoxin I (6-8) and[4Fe-4S][3Fe-4S] ferredoxin II (8-10), respectively, have been cloned. During cloning work on *fdxN*, the *fdxC* gene which encodes a [2Fe-2S] ferredoxin similar to chloroplast ferredoxins has been identified (7,8,11). Another potential ferredoxin gene locates just upstream of the *nifQ* gene (12). The *fdxA* gene can not be disrupted (7) and its expression is constant under various growth conditions (11,13). The remaining three ferredoxin genes express under the conditions to derepress known *nif* genes (6,12-14). Klipp has reported that the disruption of *fdxN* causes reduced growth on nitrogen gas (15) and we have shown recently by interposon mutagenesis and complementation that both *fdxC* and *fdxN* are required for nitrogen fixing growth (7). In this paper we present refined characterization of such mutants using increased light intensity during nitrogen fixing growth, nitrogenase activity assay by intact cells, complementation of the *fdxN* polar mutant and effect of over-expression of *fdxA* in the *fdxN* non-polar mutant.

2. MATERIALS and METHODS

R. capsulatus and *Escherichia coli* strains, their media and growth conditions used were as described previously (7). Growth by fixing nitrogen gas was tested on ammonium-free malate minimal medium (RCV-NF medium) plates incubated in a GasPak anaerobic jar (BBL Microbiology System) under illumination at approximately 3 mW/cm^2. Mating between *E. coli* and *R. capsulatus* was performed as described by Young *et al.* (16). Other genetic and recombinant DNA techniques were by standard procedures (17). Plasmids pCP-BH2, pKTS1 and pKTS2 are reported previously (7). Plasmid pCPB1 was constructed by inserting the 5.7 kbp *Bam*HI fragment with *fdxC* and *fdxN* from cosmid A75 (7) into a shuttle vector pKSV12 (Saeki *et al.* submitted to *Plant Cell Physiol.*). Plasmid pYSA1 was constructed by ligating the *Xho*I-*Eco*RI fragment which contains *R. capsulatus puf*-promoter region (16) in front of *fdxA* using the *Hin*dIII site created for the construction of pFBL22 (13). Nitrogenase activity was measured by acetylene reduction method using *R. capsulatus* cells grown for over night in malate-glutamate medium (RCV-E medium) to derepress *nif* genes. Cells (OD_{660}=2)in 8.5-ml serum tube under acetylene:argon (1:9) atmosphere were incubated under illumination of 5 mW/cm^2 and produced ethylene was determined by a Shimadzu GC-14APF gas chromatograph.

N. Murata (ed.), Research in Photosynthesis, Vol. IV, 43–46.

3. RESULTS AND DISCUSSION

3.1 Growth on nitrogen gas and nitrogenase activity of *fdxN* and/or *fdxC* mutants: The restriction map of the two ferredoxin genes in *R. capsulatus* mutants is presented in Fig. 1.a. Each mutant was created by replacing a portion of target ferredoxin gene(s) with the kanamycin resistance gene (*neo*) cartridge originally from transposon Tn5 (7). First we examined the ability to grow on nitrogen gas by increasing the light intensity approximately twice to that in our previous experiments (7). The growth rates of wild type strain SB1003 was essentially equal to that under the previous conditions with lower light intensity. The *fdxN* mutant MSA1 which had the *neo* cartridge in the same orientation to *fdxCN* but not the other *fdxN* mutant MSA2 which had it in the reverse orientation showed slight growth. These are consistent with their nitrogenase activities: the acetylene reduction activity by the former strain was nearly 5% of that by SB1003 but that by the latter strain was less than 2%. The *fdxC* mutant MSB1 which had *neo* in the same direction to *fdxCN* exhibited very slow but evident growth which was probably supported by the nitrogenase activity nearly 10% of that of wild type. The mutant MSC1 whose *fdxC* and *fdxN* were doubly disrupted by inserting the resistance cartridge in the same orientation to *fdxCN* grew scarcely on nitrogen gas and displayed acetylene reduction activity slightly lower than that by MSA1. To confirm the functional difference among the three ferredoxins FdxN, FdxC and FdxA, the three strains MSA1, MSA2 and MSB1 were subjected to complementation experiments using the *R. capsulatus* genomic fragments presented in Fig. 1. b.

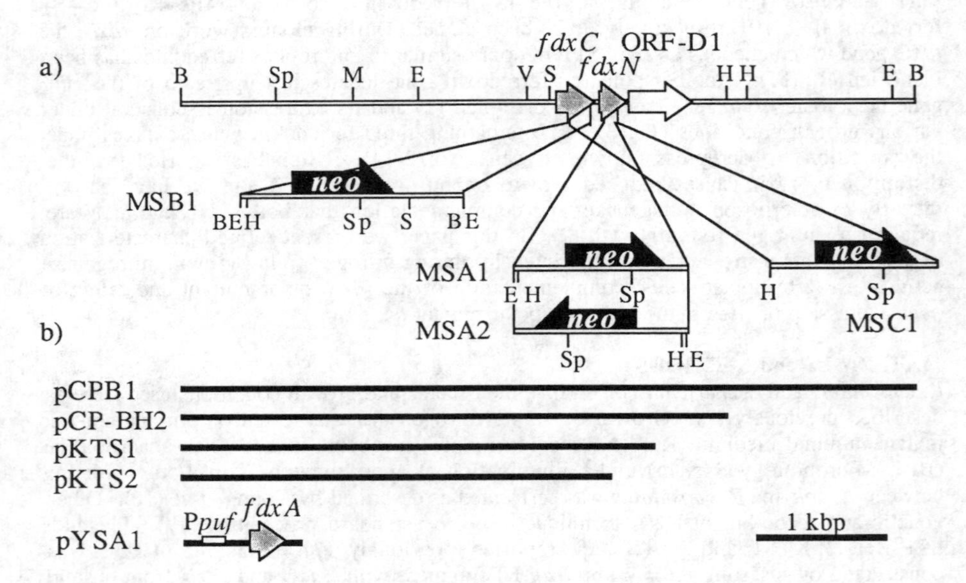

FIGURE 1. a) Physical map around the two *R. capsulatus* ferredoxin genes, *fdxN* and *fdxC* in wild-type and interposon mutants, MSA1, MSA2, MSB1 and MSC1. Ferredoxin genes are symbolized by gray arrows; downstream unidentified open reading frame (ORF-D1) by a white arrow; kanamycin resistance genes by black arrows with *neo* by *inverse contrast*. P*puf* indicates *R. capsulatus puf*-promoter. Restriction enzyme sites: B, *Bam*HI; E, *Eco*RI; H, *Hin*dIII; M, *Mlu*I; S, *Sal*I; Sp, *Sph*I; V, *Eco*RV. b) The DNA fragments used for construction of complementation plasmids.

Table 1. Complementation experiments of *R. capsulatus fdxC* and/or *fdxN* mutants.

Strain	Plasmid	Growth on nitrogen gas *	Nitrogenase Activity (μmol C_2H_2 reduced /h•OD_{660}•ml)	Relative value (%)
SB1003	none	+++	1.398	(100)
MSA1	none	±	0.063	4.5
	pCP-BH2	+++	1.308	93.6
	pKTS1	+++	1.139	81.5
	pKTS2	±	0.048	3.4
	pYSA1	±	0.094	6.8
MSA2	none	–	0.021	1.5
	pCPB1	+++	1.225	87.7
	pCP-BH2	–	0.016	1.1
MSB1	none	+	0.136	9.8
	pCP-BH2	+++	1.464	104.8
	pKTS2	+++	1.445	103.4
MSC1	none	–	0.054	3.8

* Ability to grow on nitrogen-depleted medium, RCV-NF, under illuminated and anaerobic conditions. The light intensity was approximately twice of that in our previous study (7). +++, growth within 3 days at a rate comparable to that of wild-type SB1003; +, slight growth after 5 to 7 days; ±, trace of growth after 7 days; –, no growth after 7 days.

3.2 Complementation of *fdxN* mutant MSA1: The strain MSA1 could be complemented by the plasmids pCP-BH2 and pKTS1. Because the latter contained *fdxN* but only a part of the unidentified open reading frame downstream (ORF-D1), the *fdxN* disruption in MSA1 is non-polar and its phenotype might be caused solely by loss of FdxN. Thus *R. capsulatus* ferredoxin I should have a quite important role in nitrogen fixation if not essential. The plasmid pKTS2 which contained only *fdxC* could not complement the strain confirming the functional difference between FdxN and FdxC.

This strain has the intact *fdxA* gene which encodes [4Fe-4S][3Fe-4S] ferredoxin II, however, the cellular concentration of the protein is known to be approximately 1/20 (mol/mol) of that of 2[4Fe-4S] ferredoxin I under *nif* derepressed conditions (3,4) and possibly too low to support growth by fixing nitrogen. To test the effect of raising its concentration, plasmid pYSA1 was designed to over-express *fdxA* by *R. capsulatus puf*-promoter for the photosynthetic reaction center subunits and light harvesting proteins operon (16). The purification yield of ferredoxin II from SB1003 cells which harbored pYSA1 and grew under illuminated anaerobic conditions was at least 10-times as that from the cells which did not harbored the plasmid (Suetsugu and Saeki in preparation). This indicates that the cellular concentration ratio mentioned above might be raised to at least 1/2 (mol/mol) and the nitrogenase activity by MSA1 harboring the plasmid would become 50% of that by SB1003 if the reactivity of ferredoxin II with the physiological partner of ferredoxin I. MSA1 harboring pYSA1 showed slightly higher acetylene reduction activity suggesting that the [4Fe-4S][3Fe-4S] ferredoxin can substitute ineffectively the physiological function of 2[4Fe-4S] ferredoxin.

3.3 Complementation of *fdxN* mutant MSA2: In contrast to MSA1, the strain MSA2 could not be complemented by the plasmid pCP-BH2 which contained both *fdxN* and ORF-D1. The mutant harboring another plasmid pCPB1 which contained additional 1.5 kbp region downstream fully recovered the capability to grow on nitrogen gas and nitrogenase activity. These indicate that the *fdxN* disruption in MSA2 is polar and entrapped the functional expression of unknown gene essential for *R. capsulatus* to fix nitrogen.

3.4 Complementation of *fdxC* mutant MSB1: The strain MSB1 harboring the plasmid either pCP-BH2 or pKTS2 fully recovered the ability to fix nitrogen gas. The latter plasmid contains *fdxC* but only a portion of *fdxN*. Hence, the [2Fe-2S] ferredoxin encoded by the gene might have roles to enhance the ability to fix nitrogen gas, even if it is not absolutely needed for *R. capsulatus* nitrogen fixation system.

4 CONCLUSION

The three *R. capsulatus* ferredoxins, FdxN of 2[4Fe-4S] type, FdxA of [4Fe-4S][3Fe-4S] type and FdxC of [2Fe-2S] type are not functionally interchangeable: each protein might have a specialized physiological role(s). Another gene which is absolutely required for nitrogen fixation is located downstream of the ORF-D1.

Portions of the study presented at the conference but not included in this proceeding have been submitted to *Plant Cell Physiol.*

REFERENCES

1 Matsubara, H. and Saeki, K. (1992) Adv. Inorg. Chem. 38, 223-280
2 Hallenbeck, P. C., Jouanneau, Y. and Vignais, P. M. (1982) Biochim. Biophys. Acta 681, 168-176
3 Yakunin, A. F. and Gogotov, I. N. (1983) Biochim. Biophys. Acta 725, 298-308
4 Saeki, K., Suetsugu, Y., Yao, Y., Horio, T., Marrs, B. L. and Matsubara, H. (1990) J. Biochem. 108, 475-482
5 Jouanneau, Y., Meyer, C., Gaillard, J. and Vignais, P. M. (1990) Biochem. Biophys. Res. Commun. 171, 273-279
6 Schatt, E., Jouanneau, Y. and Vignais, P. M. (1989) J. Bacteriol. 171, 6218-6226
7 Saeki, K., Miyatake, Y., Young, D. A., Marrs, B. L. and Matsubara, H. (1990) Nucleic Acids Res. 18, 1060
8 Saeki, K., Suetsugu, Y., Tokuda, K., Miyatake, Y., Young, D. A., Marrs, B. L. and Matsubara, H. (1991) J. Biol. Chem. 266, 12889-12895
9 Duport, C., Jouanneau, Y. and Vignais, P. M. (1990) Nucleic Acids Res. 18, 4618
10 Duport, C., Jouanneau, Y. and Vignais, P. M. (1992) Mol. Gen. Genet. 231, 323-328
11 Grabau, C., Schatt, E., Jouanneau, Y. and Vignais, P. M. (1991) J. Biol. Chem. 266, 3294-3299
12 Moreno-Vivian, C., Hennecke, S, Pühler, A. and Klipp, W. (1989) J. Bacteriol. 171, 2591-2598
13 Suetsugu, Y., Saeki, K. and Matsubara, H. (1991) FEBS Lett. 292, 13-16
14 Hallenbeck, P. C. (1991) Biochim. Biophys. Acta 1057, 97-101
15 Klipp, W. (1990) in Nitrogen Fixation: Achievements and Objectives: Proceeding of the 8th International Congress on Nitrogen Fixation (Gresshoff, P. M., Roth, L. E., Stacey, G. and Newton, W. E. ed.), pp.467-474, Chapman and Hall, New York.
16 Young, D. A., Bauer, C. E., Williams, J. C. and Marrs, B. L. (1989) Mol. Gen. Genet. 218, 1-12
17 Sambrook, J., Fritsch, E. F. and Maniatis, T. (1989) Molecular Cloning: a Laboratory Manual, 2nd ed., Cold Spring Harbor Laboratory Press, New York

APPLICATION OF THE FLUX CONTROL THEORY TO THE GS/GOGAT CYCLE IN ISOLATED BARLEY CHLOROPLASTS

[1]ANITA C. BARON, [2]ROGER M. WALLSGROVE & [1]ALYSON K. TOBIN,
[1]Department of Cell & Structural Biology, Williamson Building, University of Manchester, Manchester M13 9PL, U.K. [2]I.A.C.R. Rothamsted, Harpenden, Herts., AL5 2JQ, U.K.

1. INTRODUCTION

In barley leaves ammonia assimilation occurs in the chloroplast via two enzymes glutamine synthetase (GS2) and glutamate synthase (GOGAT), together termed the GS/GOGAT cycle. This activity may be measured in isolated chloroplasts by monitoring the rate of oxygen evolution in the light in the presence of the substrates ammonium, 2-oxoglutarate (2.OG) and glutamine (gln). This is light-dependent as the photosynthetic electron transport chain is necessary to meet the requirement for ATP and reduced ferredoxin:

GS: Glu + ATP + NH_3 ---> Gln + ADP + P_i

GOGAT: Gln + 2.OG + Fd_{red} ---> 2 Glu + Fd_{ox}

A flux control analysis has been carried out on this pathway to try to quantify the extent to which each reaction contributes to the control of ammonia assimilation. According to the flux control theory (1) if an enzyme (E_1) is controlling a pathway then, at steady state, a fractional change in its activity (dE_1/E_1) will result in a corresponding change in pathway flux (dJ_m/J_m). The ratio of these two values gives the flux control coefficient ($C^{J_m}_{E_1}$) for the enzyme.The sum of all flux control coefficients in a pathway equals unity hence if only one enzyme controls flux then its coefficient is 1. Flux control coefficients may be determined by titrating a pathway with specific inhibitors of individual enzymes. In this study the pathway (ammonia-2.OG-gln-dependent oxygen evolution by isolated chloroplasts) was titrated with phosphinothricin (PPT, an irreversible inhibitor of GS) and azaserine (aza, an irreversible inhibitor of GOGAT).

2. MATERIALS AND METHODS

Chloroplasts (>90% intact) were isolated from 8-10 day old barley (*Hordeum vulgare* cv Maris Mink) leaves (2) and illuminated for 3 minutes in an O_2

N. Murata (ed.), Research in Photosynthesis, Vol. IV, 47–50.

electrode at 25°C in electrode medium (0.33M sorbitol, 50mM Tricine, pH 8.2, 2mM EDTA, 1mM $MgSO_4$, 1mM $MnSO_4$) with inhibitor (0-50μM PPT or 0-200μM aza). Substrates were added (2.OG (5, 10, or 20mM), gln (10, 20mM) and 0.5mM NH_4Cl) and rates of O_2 evolution measured at steady-state (5 mins after substrate addition) when the reaction mixture was centrifuged through silicone oil (3) to separate the chloroplasts from the medium. Measurement of GS (4) and GOGAT (5) activities in the resuspended pellets then evaluated the inhibition by PPT and aza in the intact chloroplasts at steady-state.

3. RESULTS AND DISCUSSION

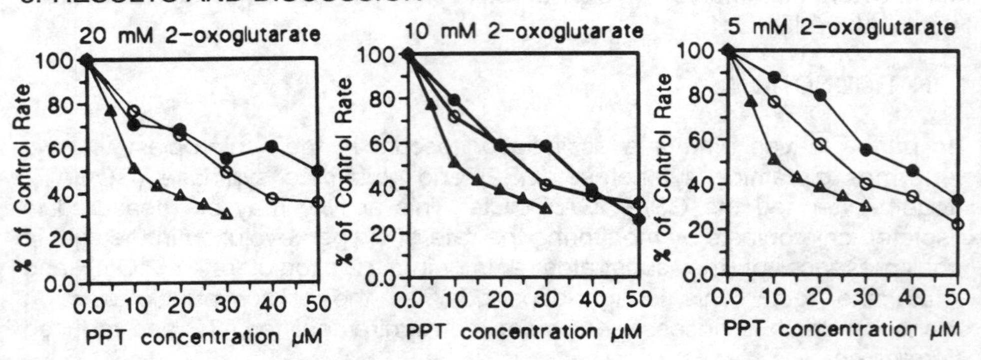

FIGURE 1. Inhibitor (PPT) titration of NH_3-gln-2.OG-dependent O_2 evolution (●) in barley chloroplasts at 20mM gln, 0.5mM NH_4Cl and 2.OG concentrations as shown. (○) GS activity in the chloroplasts at steady-state; (△) isolated GS activity. 100% rates (μmoles h^{-1} mg^{-1} Chl):- O_2 evolution: a) 11.8, b) 11.7, c) 9.5; GS (in chloroplast): a) 19.0, b) 21.3, c) 18.9; GS (isolated): a-c) 14.0.

Figure 1 shows PPT titrations of NH_3-gln-2.OG-dependent O_2 evolution, at steady-state, in isolated barley chloroplasts. Two titration curves are shown for GS. In one (●), GS activity was measured following silicone oil centrifugation of the chloroplasts sampled from the electrode at steady-state (see Methods). This removes any PPT outside the chloroplasts so that subsequent extraction and assay of activity quantifies GS inhibition by PPT during the O_2 electrode measurements. In the other (△) PPT was added to a partially-purified (14-fold) GS2 preparation to determine the inhibitor effect on the isolated enzyme, which is generally used to calculate control coefficients (1). Corresponding aza titrations were performed (Fig 2).Flux control coefficents for GS and GOGAT were calculated using 3 methods (Table 1). The general equation (1) for determining the control coefficient from inhibitor titration curves is:

$$C^J_E = \text{(gradient of flux inhibition curve)/(gradient of enzyme inhibition curve)}$$

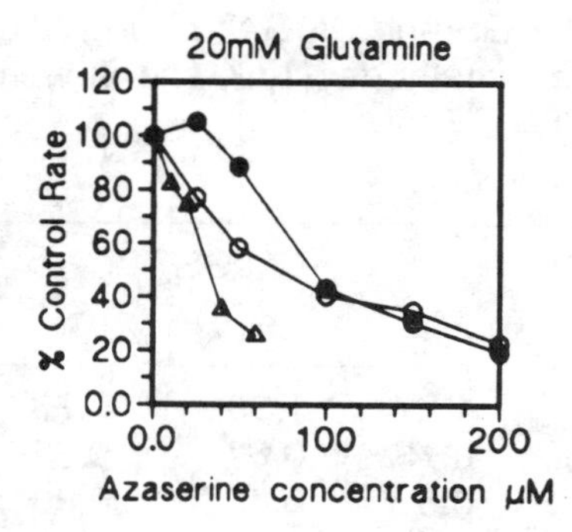

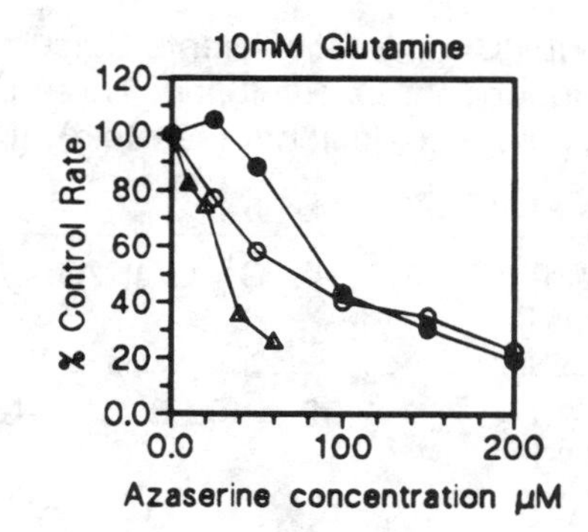

FIGURE 2. Inhibitor (Aza) titration of NH_3-gln-2.OG-dependent O_2 evolution (●) in barley chloroplasts at 20mM 2.OG, 0.5mM NH_4Cl and gln concentrations as shown. (○) GOGAT activity in the chloroplasts at steady-state; (△) isolated GOGAT activity. 100% rates (μmoles h^{-1} mg^{-1} Chl):- O_2 evolution: a) 12.6, b) 6.9; GOGAT (in chloroplast): a) 0.18, b) 0.28; GOGAT (isolated): 0.85.

The initial slope is calculated from a tangent to the curve at the 100% point. Method 1 calculated the gradient between the first two points (0 and 10μM PPT or aza) and used the titration curve on intact chloroplasts (○) as the enzyme inhibition curve. This approach assumes that the curve is linear between these two points. Method 2 assumes a hyperbolic, rather than linear, relationship- a procedure used previously to calculate flux control coefficients using mutants with relatively large changes in enzyme activity (6). Method 3 used the 'traditional' approach (1) where, instead of using the titration curve for GS and GOGAT in intact chloroplasts, as in methods 1 and 2, the isolated enzyme titration curve (△) was used to calculate dE/E. For a number of reasons method 3 produces lower coefficients than methods 1 and 2. First, at a given concentration of inhibitor added to the assay the actual concentration at the active site of the enzyme is significantly lower when added to intact chloroplasts than when added to the isolated enzyme. Stromal PPT concentrations (measured using ^{14}C-PPT and silicone oil centrifugation, data not shown) were only 65% of that added to the electrode. This only accounts in part for the greater inhibition of the isolated enzyme at the same added concentration of inhibitor. An additional factor is that ATP is required for PPT binding to GS (7). ATP was added in excess to the isolated enzme assay (GS synthetase) whereas only endogenous ATP generated during the pre-incubation period, was available for GS in the isolated chloroplasts and this may have limited PPT inhibition. This illustrates a discrepancy between techniques to estimate enzyme inhibition. We conclude that measurement of activity following extraction of rapidly-sampled chloroplasts (Methods 1 & 2) gives a better estimate of the effect of the inhibitor on the pathway than does titration of the isolated enzyme (Method 3) providing the inhibitor is irreversible. Control coefficients for GS are always greater than those for GOGAT and at 20mM 2.OG they exceed 1 (Table 1).

TABLE 1. Flux Control Coefficients Calculated for GS and GOGAT during NH_4-2.OG-gln-dependent O_2 Evolution. Three different methods *(1, 2, and 3) were used to calculate coefficients (see text). $[NH_4Cl]$= 0.5 mM.

[2-OG] mM	[gln] mM	C^J_E GOGAT *1	2	3	C^J_E GS *1	2	3
20	20	-0.32	-0.28	-0.64	1.27	1.38	0.73
10	20				0.73	0.67	0.52
5	20				0.52	0.46	0.30
20	10	-0.22	-0.16	-0.10			

As 2.OG concentrations decrease so do the coefficients for GS. The explanation may be, in part, due to the influence of the ATP/Fd balance on rates of O_2 evolution. Although all of the substrates for GOGAT (2.OG, gln and Fd_{red}) are present, O_2 evolution is inhibited by PPT, particularly at high 2.OG concentrations (Fig 1). This may be due to increases in ATP concentration (due to GS inhibition) decreasing O_2 evolution. This effect may be greater at high 2.OG concentrations because GOGAT rates are then higher and Fd_{red} demand is also high. The ATP/Fd imbalance may then be more significant. As 2.OG concentrations decrease the decreasing coefficient for GS indicates that control of flux is moving to another part of the pathway, although the high coefficent for GS means that it exerts a major control under all conditions. Two reactions become increasingly important at low 2.OG concentrations- dicarboxylate transport and GOGAT. Without specific inhibitors of 2.OG transport it was not possible to measure coefficients for the translocator. The negative coefficient for GOGAT under all conditions results from the stimulation of O_2 evolution when GOGAT is inhibited with aza (Fig 2). This is a reproducible but unexpected result and may be due to a redress of the balance between ATP/Fd_{red} consumption (Baron et al, in preparation).

REFERENCES

1 Kacser, H. (1987) in The Biochemistry of Plants (Davies, D.D., ed.), Vol. 11, pp. 39-67, Academic Press, London
2 Wallsgrove, R.M. et al (1986) Planta 168, 324-329
3 Proudlove, M.O. et al (1987) Prog. Phot. Res. 3. 589-592
4 Rhodes, D. et al (1975) Planta 125, 201-211
5 Wallsgrove, R.M. et al (1982) Planta 154, 473-476
6 Manderscheid, R. and Wild, A. (1986) J. Plant Physiol. 123, 135-142

A DIFFERENT ROLE FOR REDOX REGULATION OF ENZYMES: RESPONSE OF PRK AND G6PDH IN N-LIMITED *CHLAMYDOMONAS* TO NITROGEN RESUPPLY

Heather C. Huppe, Tracy J. Farr and David H. Turpin, Department of Botany, University of British Columbia, Vancouver, B. C. Canada, V6T 1Z4

1. INTRODUCTION

Phosphoribulosekinase (PRK) and several other key enzymes in the reductive pentose phosphate (RPP) pathway are activated by reduction in the presence of light while glucose 6-phosphate dehydrogenase (G6PDH), the first step in oxidative pentose phosphate (OPP) pathway degradation of starch, is inhibited. This regulatory strategy separates diurnally the pathways of carbon reduction and oxidation which coexist in the chloroplast thus preventing futile cycling between them (1).

When unicellular green algae growth is limited by nitrogen (N), the cells store large amounts of starch which is oxidized upon N readdition, even in the light (6). Upon resupply of N stored carbon is oxidized, even in the light. In many algae, including *Chlamydomonas reinhardtii*, starch degradation is accompanied by the suppression of photosynthetic reduction of carbon, a behavior which recalls the biochemical response to light/dark transitions (2). Is redox regulation also involved in the activation of carbon respiration and the suppression of photosynthetic carbon fixation when N is resupplied to N-limited green algae? We have examined the activities of PRK and G6PDH during light/dark transitions and N resupply to compare enzyme response under these two conditions.

2. MATERIALS AND METHODS

Cultures of *Chlamydomonas reinhardtii* cw-15 cc-1883 (nit+) from the Chlamydomonas Genetics Center (Duke University) were grown at a dilution of 0.3 d^{-1} in chemostats using a modified HS media containing 1 mM NO_3^-. Cells were injected into breaking buffer containing 0.05% Triton-X 100, frozen immediately in liquid N_2, and later thawed in a microfuge for 3.5 min and assayed immediately. PRK activity was measured as μmol $NADHox \cdot min^{-1} \cdot mg^{-1} chl$ (4) and G6PDH was measured as μmol $NADPred \cdot min^{-1} \cdot mg^{-1} chl$ (5).

N. Murata (ed.), Research in Photosynthesis, Vol. IV, 51–54.

3. RESULTS AND DISCUSSION

3.1 Enzyme activity changes during a light/dark transition: When dark cells were transferred to light a decrease in G6PDH activity and activation of PRK was measured which confirms that our sampling technique can monitor redox modulation of these enzymes (Fig 1).

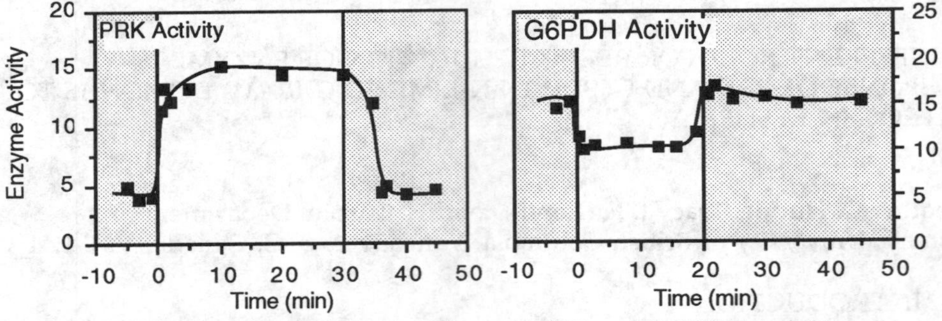

Figure 1: Effect of light/dark transition on PRK and G6PDH activity.

Reduced PRK was stable to atmospheric oxygen in the first hour after extraction (data not shown), however the activity of G6PDH increased with oxidation. The oxidation rate of dark G6PDH was linear for the initial 5 min whereas the light enzyme activity increase was linear for 20 min (Fig. 2). Since the initial oxidation rates of light and dark enzymes are similar, the difference measured in their initial activities reflects a real activation difference and not just a faster oxidation by the dark enzyme during extraction.

Incubation with 10 mM DTT reduced the activity of both the light and dark G6PDH to a similar level within 10 min indicating that G6PDH was not totally reduced under light treatment. Some of the light activity may reflect oxidation occurring during the preparation of the extract. In fact, air oxidation would activate G6PDH to the level of the light sample in only 6 minutes, which is comparable to the time required to prepare extracts.

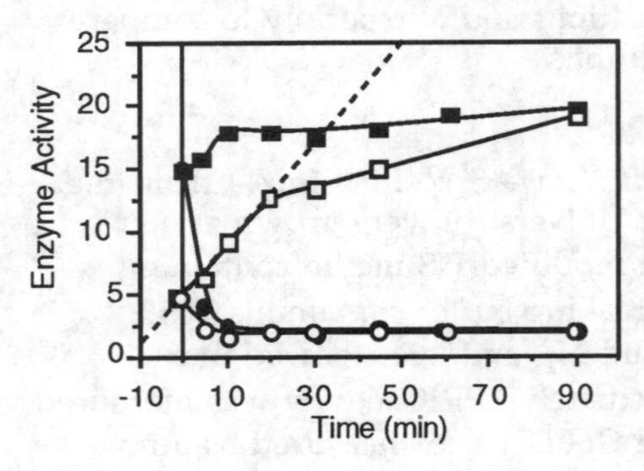

Figure 2: Oxidized and reduced activity of G6PDH extracted in the light (open) and dark (closed). The rate of air oxidation is estimated from the increased light enzyme activity in the initial 20 min (---).

3.2 Time course of enzyme activity during N resupply: Whereas NH_4^+ addition had little effect on either enzyme, NO_3^- caused an increase of

G6PDH activity (Fig 3A) and an inhibition of PRK (Fig 3B).

The addition of both N sources stimulates starch degradation, but in NH_4^+ assimilation the respiration of starch is primarily to produce carbon skeletons whereas NO_3^- assimilation initially requires electrons to reduce NO3- to NH_4^+(7). In N-limited *S. minutum*, NO_3^- causes a rapid drop of the NADPH/NADP ratio and a corresponding increase in 6-phosphogluconate indicative of the activation of the OPP pathway which would produce NADPH (3). The increased activity of G6PDH activity upon addition of NO_3^- to N-limited *C reinhardtii* cells further supports the hypothesis that the OPP pathway is activated during the assimilation of NO_3^- (Fig. 3A).

The suppression of photosynthetic carbon fixation during N assimilation is related to a drop in the level of ribulose 1,5-bisphosphate, the product of PRK (2). The marked drop in PRK activity upon the addition of NO_3^- but not NH_4^+ to *C reinhardtii* indicates that the regulation of photosynthetic suppression depends on the N source used (Fig. 3B).

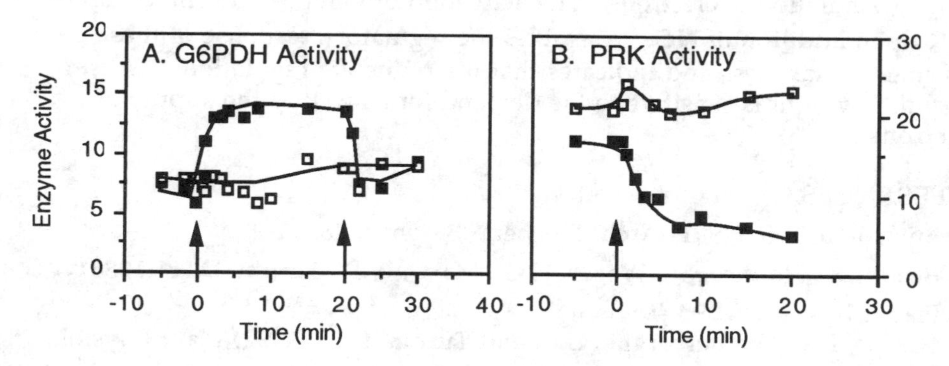

Figure 3 (A, B): Effect of photosynthetic assimilation of NO_3^- (■) or NH_4^+ (□) on the activity of G6PDH and PRK. N was added at time 0; at 20 min. NO_3^- was added to NH_4^+ treated cells and NH_4^+ to NO_3^- treated cells.

3.3 Nitrate addition resembles the effect of dark treatment: PRK deactivation and G6PDH activation at the start of photosynthetic NO_3^- assimilation resembles the enzyme response to oxidation during light/dark transitions. Incubation of extracts with DTT caused similar activation of the dark and NO_3^- PRK and reversed the effects of either NO_3^- or darkness on G6PDH which supports the involvement of a redox regulation mechanism during NO_3^- assimilation similar to that involved during light/dark transitions (Table 1). Further, the total reduced PRK activity and total oxidized G6PDH activity indicate that the activity differences resulted from regulation of existing enzymes, not their induction or degradation.

Table 1: Activity of PRK and G6PDH under different treatments

Extract	PRK			G6PDH		
	Activity	DTT reduced	Oxidized Activity	Activity	DTT reduced	Oxidized Activity
Light	11.3	14.8	0.7	4.8	1.9	22.2
Dark	3.3	13.0	0.7	14.9	1.8	22.3
Nitrate	4.5	12.5	1.4	14.5	1.9	22.3

* PRK activity in μmol NADH ox · mg^{-1} chl · min^{-1}; G6PDH activity in μmol NADPHred · mg^{-1}chl · min^{-1}

CONCLUSION

The different demands on carbon respiration from assimilation of NO_3^- and NH_4^+ are reflected in the effect that these two N sources have on the activation of G6PDH and PRK. Whereas NH_4^+ assimilation requires mobilization of starch to provide carbon skeletons, the primary demand of NO_3^- assimilation is electrons. The activation of G6PDH and inhibition of PRK upon addition of NO_3^- resembles the regulatory response of these enzymes to darkness and indicates that the reductive regulation of these enzymes by light is sensitive to the demand for as well as the supply of electrons.

REFERENCES

1. Buchanan, B.B. (1991) Arch. Biochem. Biophys. 288, 1-9.
2. Elrifi, I.R., Holmes, J.J., Weger, H.G., Mayo, W.P., Turpin, D.H. (1988) Plant Physiol. 87, 395-401.
3. Huppe, H.C., Vanlerberghe, G.C. and Turpin, D.H. (1992) Plant Physiol., in press.
4. Porter, M.A., Milanez, S., Stringer, C.D., Hartman, F.C. (1986) Arch. Biochem. Biophys. 245, 14-23.
5. Scheibe, R., Geissler, A. and Fickenscher, K. (1989) Arch. Biochem. Biophys. 274, 290-297.
6. Smith, R.G., Vanlerberghe, G.C., Stitt, M. and Turpin, D.H. (1989) Plant physiol. 91, 749-755.
7. Vanlerberghe, G.C., Huppe, H.C., Vlossak, K.D.M. and Turpin, D.H. (1992) Plant Physiol. 99, 495-500.

(Supported by NSERC)

REGULATION OF ASPARTATE-FAMILY AMINO ACID BIOSYNTHESIS: STUDIES USING ISOLATED PEA CHLOROPLASTS

W. RONALD MILLS, BRIAN W. STEPHENS and MICHELE REEVES, Departments of Biological Sciences and Chemistry, UNIVERSITY OF HOUSTON, CLEAR LAKE, HOUSTON, TEXAS 77058-1062, U.S.A.

1. INTRODUCTION

Evidence gained over the last decade or so [1-3] strongly suggests that the chloroplast is the main site for the biosynthesis of the nutritionally essential aspartate-derived amino acids in plants leaves (Fig. 1). This may be considered a photosynthetic process since ATP and NADPH produced in light are used directly to drive the synthetic reactions [4]. Further evidence for the role of plastids in essential amino acid synthesis comes from recent studies using transgenic plants [5]; in this case a bacterial enzyme in lysine biosynthesis is expressed in plants only when targeted to the plastids.

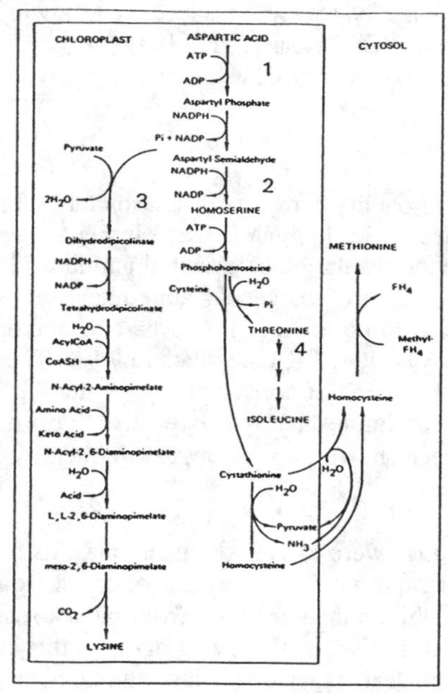

Fig. 1. Biosynthetic pathways for essential amino acid synthesis. Numbers represent: 1, aspartate kinase; 2, homoserine dehydrogenase; 3, dihydrodipicolinate synthase and 4, threonine syntase.

Knowledge about the regulation of aspartate-family amino acid synthesis should be useful both in understanding basic plant metabolism and in possibly modifying the nutritional value of crops. The first enzyme in the pathway (Fig. 1) is aspartate kinase (AK). AK is thought to be important in controlling aspartate-family amino acid biosynthesis [1-3]; forms subject to feedback inhibition by lysine (lys), threonine (thr) and S-adenosylmethionine have been described [6]. In addition, the first enzymes in the lys and thr branches of the pathway, dihydrodipicolinate synthase (DS) and homoserine dehydrogenase (HSDH) respectively, are also believed to be controlled by their endproducts [1-3]. Despite this, the importance of AK and HSDH in regulating the pathway have been questioned recently [7].

During the development of plant leaves, the requirement for amino acid production changes [8]. Because the demand for the aspartate-family amino acids varies with time, one might expect the ability of chloroplasts to synthesize these compounds to fluctuate accordingly. Indeed, isolated

N. Murata (ed.), Research in Photosynthesis, Vol. IV, 55–58.

chloroplasts from young leaves are much more active in amino acid biosynthesis than those from older tissues [9]. Here we describe studies in which we have used intact chloroplasts from young tissues, as well as plastid extracts, to further examine the regulation of essential amino acid biosynthesis.

2. MATERIALS and METHODS

2.1 Chloroplast isolation and characterization: Plastids were prepared from 6-16 day old pea (*Pisum sativum* L.) as described by Mills and Joy [10]. Chlorophyll and protein were determined as in [11] and [12] respectively.

2.2 Chloroplast amino acid synthesis: Isolated chloroplasts were incubated in light in the following medium: 300 mM sorbitol, 50 mM EPPS, 30 mM KCl and [^{14}C]aspartic acid [4]. Reactions were stopped by addition of one-fifth volume 50% trichloroacetic acid. Following centrifugation to clarify the samples, the supernatants were mixed with amino acid standards and analyzed by two dimensional paper (Whatman 3MM) chromatography. The first dimension was run in butanol:acetone:water:diethylamine: triethylamine (10/10/5/1/1; v/v) for 14 hours and the second in isopropanol:water: formic acid (10/5/2; v/v) for 11 hours. After visualizing amino acids by spraying with ninhydrin, spots were cut out and radioactivity determined by scintillation spectrometry; counting efficiency was assessed by channels ratio.

2.3 Enzyme assays: Aspartate kinase in chloroplast lysates was assayed by following the formation of [^{14}C] L-aspartylphosphate from [^{14}C]L-aspartic acid [13]. Dihydrodipicolinate synthase in the extracts was measured as described by Wallsgrove and Mazelis [14].

3. RESULTS AND DISCUSSION

Isolated chloroplasts from young pea leaves readily converted [^{14}C]aspartate into lys and homoserine (hse), a metabolic intermediate [15] which is made in unusually high amounts in peas (Table 1). To investigate the regulation of essential amino acid synthesis in isolated plastids, we tested the effect of exogenous amino acids. Lys or lys plus thr (0.2-2 mM) markedly reduced incorporation of [^{14}C]aspartate into hse. These data support the view that, in intact plastids, AK is regulated by lys. These results are also consistent with the idea AK or HSDH are controlled by thr [1]. By contrast, label incorporation into lys was not diminished by exogenous lys or thr (Table 1). As DS purified from pea has been shown to be strongly inhibited by 50 μM lys [16], this result was unexpected.

Since the biosynthetic studies described above were carried out using plastids from young plant tissues, we asked the following question: are enzymes obtained from young leaves less sensitive to feedback inhibition than enzymes from older tissues. Thus, we examined AK and DS obtained from tissues of varying ages. In this case, chloroplasts were isolated from each of four leaf stages of 12 day-old plants (see Fig. 2). Both lys and thr sensitive forms of AK appear to be present in pea plastids, since 2 mM lys and 2 mM thr, both singly and in combination, reduced AK activity (Fig. 3). Lys inhibited AK activity more strongly than thr, regardless of tissue age. Moreover, extracts from younger leaves were somewhat less sensitive to lys and thr than those from the oldest tissues. DS activity was also examined (Fig. 4). Thr tested

Table 1. Influence of exogenous lysine and threonine on amino acid biosynthesis in isolated intact chloroplasts.

Amino acid supplement	% of control	
	Labeled compound	
	Homoserine	Lysine
Lys 0.2 mM	35	103
Lys 0.2 mM + Thr 0.2 mM	22	105
Lys 2.0 mM	22	113
Lys 2.0 mM + Thr 2.0 mM	18	117

Activity in plastids from 7 day old plants expressed as nmol/mg chl/hr were as follows: hse, 10 and lys, 0.9.

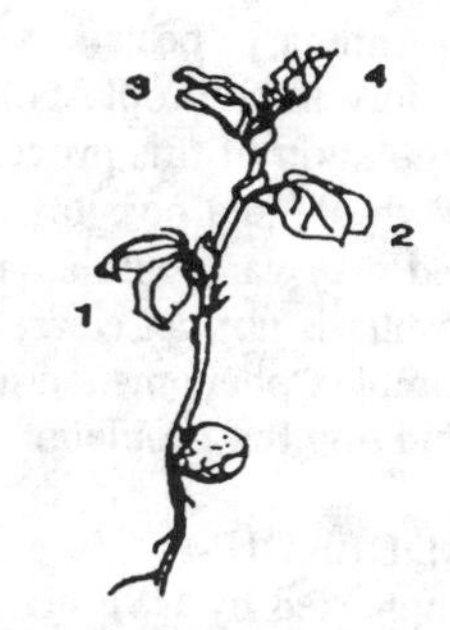

Fig. 2. Drawing of 12-day old pea seedling at the four leaf stage. Leaf 1 is the oldest while leaf 4 is the youngest,

at 2 mM had little effect on the enzyme. By contrast, 2 mM lys sharply lowered activity. For example, activity in lysates from plastids prepared from intermediate age leaves (stages 2 and 3) was almost completely inhibited by 2 mM lys. However, samples from the oldest leaves (stage 1) and the youngest tissues (stage 4) were not totally inhibited by 2 mM lys. The addition of 2 mM thr did not enhance the lys inhibition, rather activity was slightly higher in lys plus thr mixtures compared to lys alone.

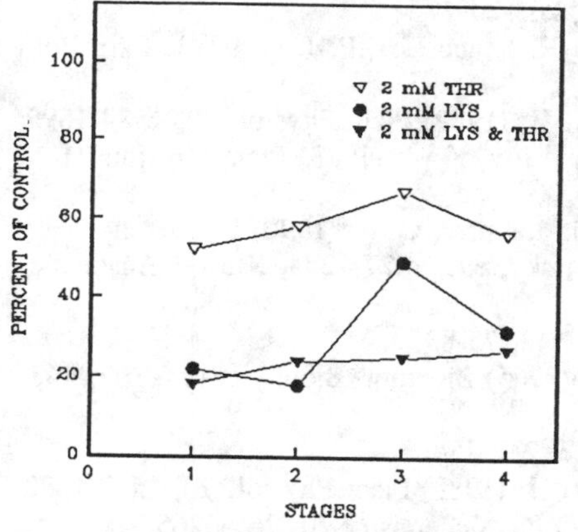

Fig. 3. Influence of leaf age as well as lysine and threonine on aspartate kinase activity.

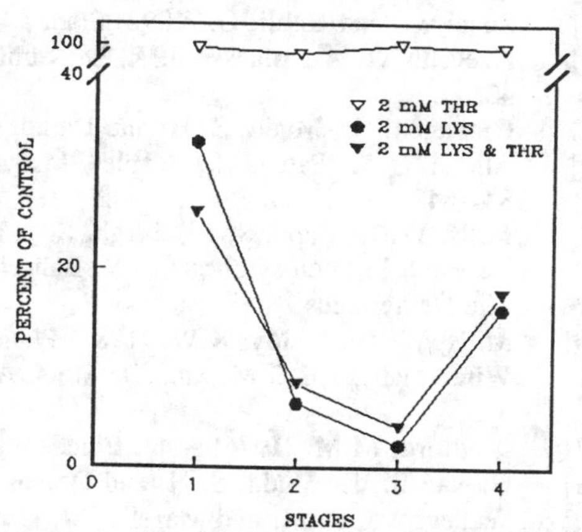

Fig. 4. Influence of leaf age as well as lysine and threonine on dihydrodipicolinate synthase activity.

In summary, because aspartate-family amino acid biosynthesis is thought to occur mainly in chloroplasts [1-5], we have used isolated plastids and extracts to study the regulation of this process. These data suggest that the control of dihydrodipcolinate synthase, and possibly other enzymes, changes markedly during leaf development and and may vary with assay conditions. Although the physiological significance of these results is not yet clear, the data suggest that essential amino acid biosynthesis is a complex phenomenon and that multiple approaches will be necessary in effectively studying the problem.

4. ADDENDUM

Supported by NSF grant (DCB-8904262), the Robert A. Welch Foundation and the UHCL FRS fund.

REFERENCES

[1] Lea, P.J., Wallsgrove, R.M. and Miflin, B.J. (1985) in Chemistry and Biochemistry of Amino Acids, (G.C. Barrett, ed) pp 197-226, Chapman and Hall, London.
[2] Mills, W.R., and Wilson, K.G. (1987) in Models in Plant Physiology and Biochemistry, (D.W. Newmann and K.G. Wilson eds) pp. 19-24, CRC Press, Inc., Boca Raton, Florida.
[3] Bryan, J. K. (1990) in The Biochemistry of Plants, (B. J. Miflin and P. J. Lea, eds), vol. 16, pp. 161-195, Academic Press, New York.
[4] Mills, W.R., Lea, P. J. and Miflin, B.J. (1980) Plant Physiol. 65, 1166-1172.
[5] Shaul, O. and Galili, G. (1992) Plant J. 2, 203-209.
[6] Azevedo, R. A., Blackwell, R. D., Smith, R. J. and Lea, P. J. (1992) J. Exp. Bot., 43S, 67.
[7] Giovanelli, J., Mudd, S. H. and Datko, A. H. (1989) Plant Physiol. 90, 1584-1599.
[8] Atkins, C.A., Pate, J.S., Peoples, M.B. and Joy, K.W. (1983) Plant Physiol. 71, 841-848.
[9] Mills, W.R., Capo, S. F., Bergh, S. A and Lassiter, C. B. (1990) in Current Research in Photosynthesis, (W. Baltscheffsky, ed) pp 271-274, Kluwer Academic, The Netherlands.
[10] Mills, W.R. and Joy, K.W. (1980) Planta 148, 75-83.
[11] Wintermans, J.E.G.M., and De Mots, A. (1965) Biochim. Biophys. Acta 109, 448-453.
[12] Bradford, M.M. (1976) Anal. Biochem. 72, 248-254.
[13] Giovanelli, J., Mudd, S. H. and Datko, A. H. (1989) Plant Physiol. 90, 1577-1588.
[14] Wallsgrove, R. M. and Mazelis, M. (1991) Phytochemistry 20, 2651-2655.
[15] Lawrence, J.M. (1973) Phytochemistry 12, 2207-2209.
[16] Dereppe, C., Bold, G., Ghisalba, O., Ebert, E., and Schär, H.-P. (1992) Plant Physiol. 98, 813-821.

PROPERTIES OF NITRATE REDUCTASE FROM A MARINE RED ALGA *PORPHYRA YEZOENSIS*

YOSHIKO NAKAMURA and TOMOYOSHI IKAWA

Institute of Biological Sciences, University of Tsukuba, Tsukuba, Ibaraki 305, Japan

1. INTRODUCTION

Assimilatory nitrate reductase (NR) from fungi, green algae and higher plants has been intensively characterized with respect to molecular, catalytic and regulatory properties. However, little investigation has been undertaken concerning NRs of nonchlorophyll b species. *Porphyra yezoensis* is a marine red alga and phylogenically distant from not only higher plants but also from green algae. Thus it is of much interest to investigate NR from *P.yezoensis* with respect to NR molecule evolution. Previous study on enzymatic character of NR from *P. yezoensis* has revealed that the enzyme has lower optimal temperature of 25°C and higher pH optimum of 8.5 than those from other sources (1). Moreover, since NR from *P. yezoensis* never binds to well-known affinity gel, blue Sepharose, essentially in the same conditions ever reported, the enzyme is expected to have some compositional difference among those from other sources.

2. MATERIALS AND METHODS

2.1 Plant Material. *Porphyra yezoensis* UEDA f. narawaensis MIURA was cultivated at Nagai, Yokosuka in Japan. The algal thalli were freezed with liquid nitrogen and stored at -80°C.

2.2 Purification of NR. All procedures were carried out at 4°C. Purification was performed by a combination of polyethylene glycol (PEG) treatment, ammonium sulfate fractionation, chromatography on butyl Toyopearl 650 M, blue Sepharose CL-6B, DEAE-cellulose (DE 52), hydroxyapatite columns and Sephacryl S-400 gel filtration.

2.3 Protein Determination. Protein concentrations were determined spectophotometrically using Serva Blue G at 595 nm as described by Read and Northcote (2).

2.4 Electrophoresis. Nondenaturing PAGE was carried out using 7.5 % cross-linked gels and Tris-barbital buffer system (pH 7.0) (3). SDS-PAGE was performed by using Laemmli's buffer system (4).

2.5 Determination of Native Molecular Weight. Native molecular weight of the purified enzyme was determined by a modification of the method of Siegel and Monty (5). Stokes radius was detemined using a Sephacryl S-300 column. The sedimentation coefficient was determined by sucrose density gradient centrifugation. Centrifugation was performed at 4 °C for 15 hours at 40,000 g in a Beckman L8-55M ultracentrifuge equipped with SW 60 Ti rotor.

2.6 Spectral Measurements. UV/visible spectra were measured at room temperature using a SHIMADZU UV-2200 spectrophotometer.

2.7 Enzyme Assays. In determinig K_m values for KNO_3 and NADH, NADH:NR activity was measured following the decrease in absorbance at 340 nm. In the other case NADH:NR activity was measured by the amount of produced NO_2^-. NADH:ferricyanide reductase (NADH:FR) activity was assayed by monitoring ferricyanide dependent NADH oxidation at 340 nm. NADH:cytochrome c reductase

N. Murata (ed.), Research in Photosynthesis, Vol. IV, 59–62.

TABLE 1. Purification of nitrate reductase from *Porphyra yezoensis.*

Step	Total Protein	Total Activity	Specific Activity	Recovery	Purification
	mg	units	units/ mg protein	%	fold
Crude extract	10,393	23.0	0.0022	100	1.0
PEG treatment	1,632	16.4	0.010	71	4.5
$(NH_4)_2SO_4$ precipitate	1,071	16.7	0.016	73	7.3
Butyl Toyopearl	113	18.8	0.169	82	77
Blue Sepharose CL–6B	57	17.4	0.31	76	141
DEAE–cellulose (DE 52)	8.6	9.4	1.1	41	500
Hydroxyapatite	1.7	5.0	3.0	22	1360
Sephacryl S–400	0.16	2.0	12.5	9	5681

(NADH:CR) activitiy was assayed by monitoring the reduction ofcytochrome c at 550 nm. $FMNH_2$:NR and MV:NR activities were measured by the amount of produced NO_2^-.

3 RESULTS AND DISCUSSION

3.1 Purification of NR. The purification of NR from *P.yezoensis* is summarized in Table 1. The purified enzyme had a specific activity of 12.5 units/mg protein and gave a purification of 5700–fold and an overall recovery of 9%. This preparation gave a single protein band on native PAGE and this band also corresponded to a positive stain for MV–NR activity (Fig.1). The success of the purification of NR from *P. yezoensis* is mainly dependent on two steps. The first is PEG treatment, in which a great deal of contaminating proteins such as phycocyanin, phycoerythrin and Rubisco could be effectively eliminated from the enzyme solution. NR protein was soluble in 12% (w/v) PEG solution. Large amount of contaminating proteins in the 12 % PEG solution were discarded as precipitate by the addition of $(NH_4)_2SO_4$ to 15 % saturation. When the concentration of $(NH_4)_2SO_4$ in the 12 % PEG solution increased to 20% saturation, the solution separated into two phases. Most of pigment proteins moved to the upper PEG–rich phase, and NR remained in the lower salt–rich phase (Fig.2). The second is affinity chromatography on blue Sepharose CL–6B with the help of hydrophobic interactions. NR from *P. yezoensis* never bound to blue Sepharose in the same manners as those reported in green alga or higher plants. However addition of 750 mM $(NH_4)_2SO_4$ to 300 mM K–phosphate buffer (pH 7.8) gave almost complete adsorption of NR to the gel. The other chromatographic procedures were chosen to eliminate remains of contaminating proteins.

3.2 Native and Subunit Molecular Weight. The Stokes radius (r_s) of NR from *P. yezoensis* was estimated to be 6.0 nm with calibrated Sephacryl S–300. And the average sedimentation coefficient ($s_{20,w}$) of 8.7 S was obtained. From these two values, and the assumption that the partial specific volume was 0.725 cm^3/g, a molecular weight of 220,000 was calculated for the native enzyme by use of the equation: $M_r = 6\pi r_s \eta N s_{20,s}/(1-v\rho)$ described by Siegel and Monty (5). In the equation N is Avogadro's number, η is the viscosity of the medium, v is the partial specific volume of the protein, and ρ is the density of the medium. The result of SDS–PAGE showed that the molecular weight for the NR subunit was 100,000. Deduced from native and subunit molecular weight, the probable structure for NR from *P. yezoensis* is a dimer of 100,000 subunits. NR from *P. yezoensis* has similar compositional character to those from other eukaryotic NRs.

3.3 Absorption Spectrum. The oxidized enzyme showed, in addition to a protein peak at 276 nm,

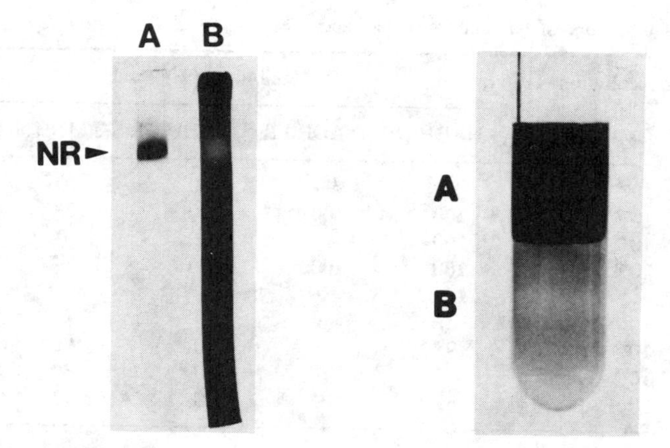

Fig 1. (*left*) Native PAGE of purified NR. A, 10 μg protein was loaded and the gel was stained for protein; B, 1.0 unit of reduced methyl viologen–NR activity was loaded and the gel was stained for the activity. Fig 2.(*right*) Separation of NR protein from large amount of phycobiliproteins and Rubisco by PEG treatment of the crude extract from *Porphyra yezoensis*. A, Upper PEG–rich phase; B, Lower salt–rich phase containing NR.

absorption maxima at 413 nm (Soret). On reduction of the enzyme with dithionite, the Soret band intensified and shifted to 422 nm, and at the same time α– and ß– bands appeared at 527 nm and 557 nm, respectively. NR from *P. yezoensis* has b–type cytochrome like all assimilatory NRs tested.

3.4 Kinetic Properties. The K_m values for NADH and KNO_3 were estimated to be 23 μM and 64 μM, respectively. Though NADPH was tested as an electron donor using potassium phosphate buffer in the pH range 6.0–8.5, no activity was detected. NR from *P. yezoensis* was revealed to be NADH specific.

Since ionic strength has been shown to influence full and partial activities of NR (6,7), the pH dependence was determined under constant ionic strength (μ = 100 mM) in the pH range 6.0–10.0 (Fig.3). The pH optimum of full, NADH:NR activity (Fig.3A) was determined to be pH 8.3. There are no other eukaryotic NR reported to have such high pH optimum. For the NADH–utilizing,

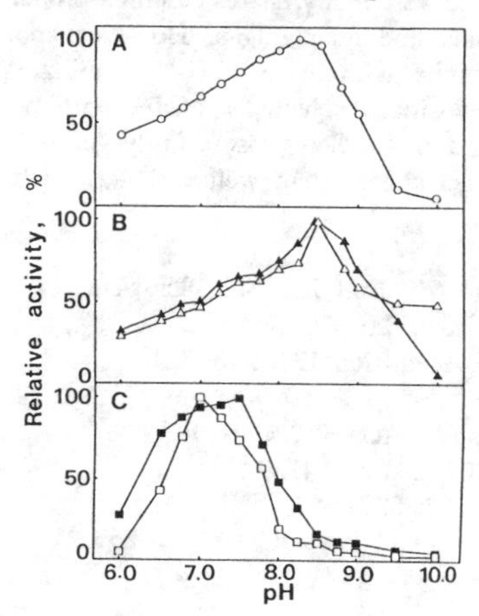

Fig 3. Effect of pH on the full and the partial activities of NR from *Porphyra yezoensis* under constant ionic strength. A, Full activity [NADH:NR (○)]; B, diaphorase activities [NADH:FR (△), and NADH:CR (▲)]; C, nitrate–reducing activities [$FMNH_2$:NR (□), and MV:NR (■)].

Table 2. Effects of inhibitors of NR and its partial activities.

Inhibitor	Concentration (M)	Inhibition (%)				
		NADH:NR	NADH:FR	NADH:CR	$FMNH_2$:NR	MV:NR
p–HMB	10^{-6}	94	93	100	0	0
	10^{-5}	100	100	100	78	36
NEM	10^{-4}	100	49	100	0	0
	10^{-3}	100	100	100	87	15
KCN	10^{-4}	37	0	0	45	67
	10^{-3}	95	0	0	90	98
NaN_3	10^{-4}	62	0	0	80	86
	10^{-3}	85	10	21	93	100

NADH:FR and NADH:CR partial activities (Fig.3B) both exhibited pH optima of 8.5. These values are very close to pH optimum of full activity. Thus higher pH optimum of full activitiy could be ascribed to diaphorase activities. This result is characteristic of NR from *P. yezoensis*, and may show that the enzyme has unique compositional character on the portion related to NADH reduction. The pH optima for the nitrate–utilizing activities, $FMNH_2$:NR and MV:NR activities (Fig.3C) were pH 7.0 and 7.5, respectively.

3.5 Effect of Inhibitors. As shown in Table 2, both sulfhydryl reagents: *p*–HMB and NEM, and metal–binding reagents: KCN and NaN_3, inhibited full activity of NR. It is well–known for NR that and NADH–utilizing partial activities are inhibited by sulfhydryl reagents and nitrate–reducing activities are inhibited by metal–binding reagents (8). Result of the inhibitors on partial activities of NR from *P. yezoensis* follows well this acquaintance. However nitrate–reducing partial activities are partially inhibited by higher concentration of *p*–HMB (10^{-5} M) and NEM (10^{-3} M) than those crytical for NADH–utilizing partial activities. There may be sulfhydryl groups on nitrate–reducing portion of the enzyme which are less accessible than those on diaphorase moiety.

4. CONCLUSION

Our investigation has revealed that NR from *P. yezoensis* essentially shares common properties with other NADH specific NR reported for higher plants and green algae. However approximate coincidence of higher pH optimal value of full activity with those of NADH–utilizing partial activities suggests that the enzyme has unique compositional character on the portion which is related to NADH reduction. As NR is supposed to bind to blue Sepharose affinity gel on its NADH binding site, little adsorption of the enzyme to the gel is consistent well with the result.

REFERENCES

1. Araki, S., Ikawa, T., Oohusa, T. and Nisizawa, K. (1979) Bull Jpn. Soc. Sci. Fish. 45, 919–924
2. Read, S.M. and Northcote, D.H. (1981) Anal. Biochem. 116, 53–644
3. Williams, D.E. and Reisfeld, R.A. (1964) Ann. NY Acad. Sci. 121, 373–381
4. Laemmli, U.K. (1970) Nature 227, 680–685
5. Siegel, L.M. and Monty, K.J. (1966) Biochim. Biophys. Acta 112, 346–362
6. Kay, C.J. and Barber, M.J. (1986) J. Biol. Chem. 261, 14125–14129
7. Barber, M.J. and Notton, B.A. (1990) Plant Physiol. 93, 537–540
8. Solomonson, L.P. and Barber, M.J. (1990) Ann. Rev. Plant Physiol. 41, 225–253

AUTOPHOSPHORYLATION OF MAIZE LEAF NADH:NITRATE REDUCTASE

Wilbur H. Campbell* and Björn Ingemarsson
Botany Department, Stockholms University, Stockholm, S10691 SWEDEN
*On Sabbatical Leave from Michigan Technological Univ., Houghton MI 49931 USA

1. INTRODUCTION

Recent in vivo experiments have demonstrated that NADH:nitrate reductase (NR) is phosphorylated on serine residues (1; N. Crawford, personal communication). These investigations have shown that NR has two types of phosphorylated sites: 1) fixed sites; and 2) changeable sites. Although the changeable sites have been associated with reversible light/dark regulation of NR activity, none of the actual serine residues phosphorylated in NR has been identified. Maize leaf NADH:nitrate reductase (EC 1.6.6.1) has been the subject of many biochemical and physiological studies. In a general way, maize leaf NR is representative of the group of higher plant NADH:NRs which have been characterized. Since maize leaf NR can be easily purified to homogeneity using monoclonal antibody-based immunoaffinity chromatography, it is ideal for investigation of the potential phosphorylation sites in NR. In a first attempt to determine the sites of phosphorylation, purified NR was incubated with a crude extract of maize leaves and gamma ^{32}P-ATP. In the controls for this experiment, maize leaf NR was phosphorylated in the absence of crude extract, which suggested that NR could phosphorylate itself. We have characterized the autophosphorylation of NR and made a preliminary determination of the region of the protein phosphorylated.

2. MATERIALS AND METHODS

2.1 NR Purification: Maize (Zea mays L. cv W64AxW1182E) leaves were harvested and extracted as previously described (2). NR was purified using a Zm2(69) monoclonal antibody column. After elution at pH 11, the buffer was exchanged to 50 mM MOPS, pH 7.5, which restored the enzyme to full activity. Homogeneity was checked by SDS-PAGE as previously described (3). NR activity was assayed using a standard method and modified method with 10 mM $MgCl_2$ (1).

2.2 NR Phosphorylation: Homogeneous NR was added to a mixture containing gamma ^{32}P-ATP (3000 µCi/mmol, Amersham) and $MgCl_2$. The assay mixture contained gamma ^{32}P-ATP (4000 cpm/pmol) in 25 mM Mops, pH 7, 10 mM $MgCl_2$, 0.1 mM EDTA and in some cases BSA was added at 50 µg/ml. When incorporation of ^{32}P was analyzed directly, the reaction mixture was spotted on a filter paper square after 15 min of incubation and then soaked in 10% trichloroacetic acid, followed by 10% Pi (4). After the square was dried, the incorporation was determined by scintillation counting. When the samples were analyzed by SDS-PAGE, an equal volume of 2X treatment buffer was added and the sample heated at 100°C for 2 min prior to loading on the gel. After electrophoresis, the gel was stained, dried and autoradiographed.

2.3 Tryptic Digestion of NR: Samples of NR were phosphorylated as described above and then incubated with 5 ng of trypsin per µg of NR at 15°C for 1 H. Then 2X SDS treatment buffer

N. Murata (ed.), Research in Photosynthesis, Vol. IV, 63–66.

was added and the samples heated. After electrophoresis the gels were stained, dried and autoradiographed. The dried gel was divided into 10 sections and the radioactivity of each section determined by scintillation counting. Unlabelled NR samples were carried along as controls in these experiments.

3. RESULTS AND DISCUSSION

3.1 Autophosphorylation of NR: Maize leaf NADH:NR was labeled by simply incubating it with gamma ^{32}P-ATP in the presence of Mg^{2+}. Adding different buffers (Tris, Hepes or Mops) had no effect on the level of ^{32}P incorporation. However, if Mg^{2+} were omitted, no incorporation was found. As shown below in Table I, among a variety of additives tried only NADH or NAD+ inhibited ^{32}P incorporation into NR with NADH being the most effective. Analysis of the time course of incorporation of ^{32}P showed a fairly steady rate of incorporation. The rate of autophosphorylation was found to be 1 to 3 pmol of ^{32}P incorporated/min/nmol of NR. This rate compares well to that reported for autophosphorylation of protein kinases (5).

Table I. Autophosphorylation of NR: Effects of Additives
Results are shown as CPM incorporated into ~1 μg NR band on an SDS-PAGE gel.

Components	Expt 1	Expt 2	Expt 3
All (NR + Mg^{2+} + ^{32}P-ATP)	1700	2310	7555
All minus ^{32}P-ATP	72	87	40
All minus Mg^{2+}	133	180	--
All plus 1 mM Gln	1900	--	--
All plus 1 mM Glu	1890	--	--
All plus 1 mM NADH	600	1050	870
All plus 1 mM NAD+	--	--	3500

3.2 The Effect of MgATP on NR Activity: When NR was preincubated with MgATP at various concentrations ranging from 25 μM to 0.5 mM for up to 30 min, no effect was found on the enzyme activity. However, when 5 mM MgATP was used, the NR activity was decreased by 20%. But this effect appeared to be due to the competition between MgATP and NADH and not due to phosphorylation of NR, since similar inhibition was found by 5 mM MgATP in the absence of preincubation. These results agree with the findings of Kaiser and Spill (6), who reported that partially purified spinach NR was not inhibited by preincubation with MgATP. As a general observation, the inhibition of NR by addition of Mg^{2+}, which has been found in crude extracts (1,7), is not found with highly purified NR, which may be the result of protein phosphatases operating on NR during the purification.

3.3 Tryptic Digestion of NR after Phosphorylation: To determine a general location for the site of the ^{32}P label in NR, mild tryptic digestion was used. This type of treatment is known to cleave the NR into several large fragments. NR was degraded into 4 major fragments: a doublet near 55 kD, a single band at ~40 kD and a single band at ~30 kD. In addition, 2 very weak bands can be observed in the range of about 15 kD. The autoradiograph of the trypsin degradation products revealed that most of the label had been released as very small peptides which ran at the front of the gel. There was also a small amount of radioactivity in the range of 15 kD where some weakly staining bands were also found on the stained gel. A small amount of label was associated with the 30 kD fragment also. To compare more carefully the labeling patterns of the native and tryptic-digested NR, the dried gels were cut into 10 sections and each section was counted. The results from this analysis are presented in Figure 1. While the quantitative results from scintillation counting agree with those in the autoradiogram in that most of the label is found at the front of the gel after tryptic digestion, these must be considered preliminary and sequencing of peptide fragments will be needed to determine the exact location of the ^{32}P label in NR.

Figure 1. Localization of the ^{32}P label in NR before and after mild trypsin treatment of the enzyme using SDS-PAGE to separate the protein and its fragments followed by liquid scintillation counting of sections of the dried gel to quantify the label.

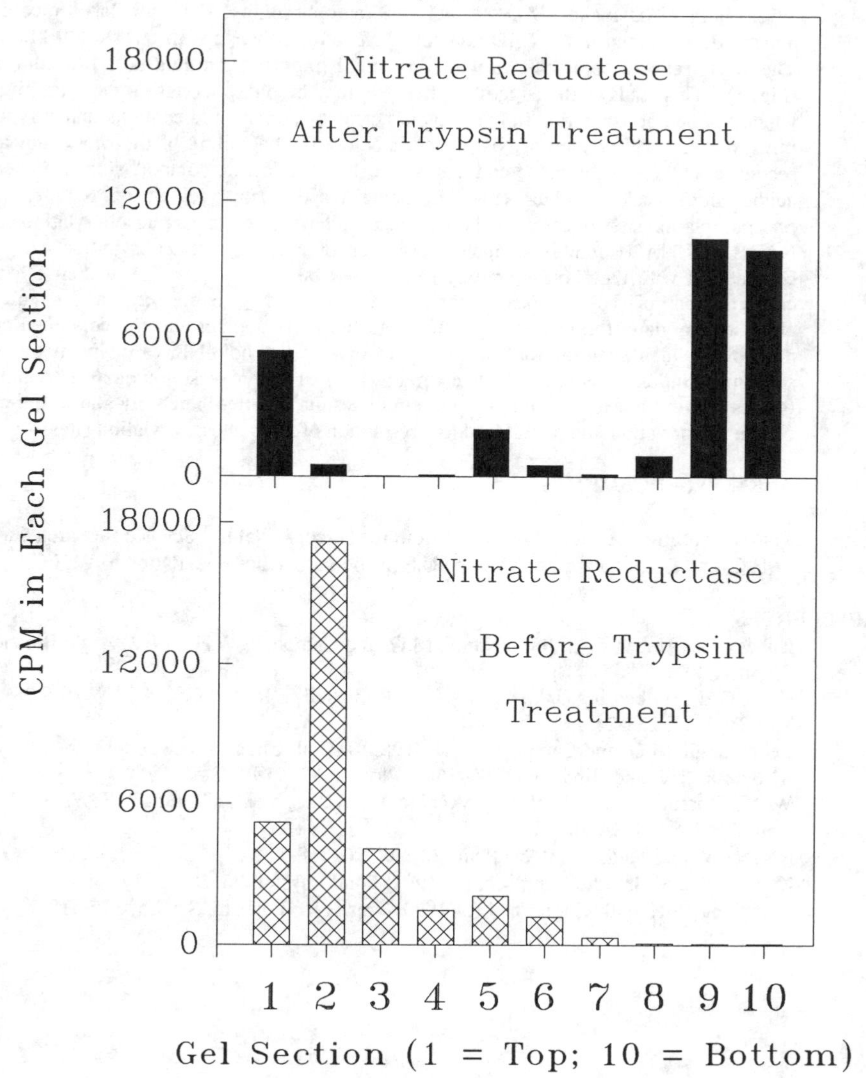

4. CONCLUSIONS

4.1 Homogeneous maize leaf NADH:NR is capable of phosphorylating itself using Mg-ATP. The low rate of incorporation of ^{32}P into NR is consistent with the process being one of autophosphorylation. If the phosphorylation of NR were due to a contaminating protein kinase, one might expect to see a much more rapid incorporation of label as has been observed with phytochrome where some investigators feel the apparent autophosphorylation is due to a contaminating kinase.

4.2 While both NADH and NAD+ inhibit NR autophosphorylation, the label incorporated is apparently not found in the FAD domain of NR after cleavage with trypsin (30 kD fragment). The label seems to be associated with very small fragments running near the front of the gel (Fig. 1). This leads to the suggestion that NR may be phosphorylating its N-terminal region, which has no know function in the enzyme's catalytic activity and contains many tryptic targets in most NRs. This region of NR, which is before the beginning of the MoCo domain in the sequence, is the most variable and has been called the "acidic domain" since it is very rich in acidic amino acid residues (8). In some respects this region of NR resembles the phosphorylation sites in casein and does appear to have potential as phosphorylation site. Since NADH and NAD+ inhibit autophosphorylation of NR, their effect is unlikely to be due to competition with the "kinase activity site" of NR but more likely due to their effects on the conformation of NR. Furthermore, domains of NR expressed in E. coli do not autophosphorylate (this applies specifically to the FAD domain and the combined cyt b/FAD domains), which suggests that this is a property of the holo-NR. Finally, if one looks for sequence similarity between NR and protein kinases, only weak homology is found and this resides within the MoCo domain. Hence, our results reported here only add to the mystery of NR phosphorylation and do not lead to a resolution of NR's phosphorylation sites.

5. ACKNOWLEDGEMENTS

This research was supported by grants from the Swedish Natural Science Research Council to W.H.C. and B.I., and a grant from the U.S. National Science Foundation to W.H.C.

REFERENCES

1 Huber, J.L., Huber, S.C., Redinbaugh, M.G. and Campbell, W.H. (1992) Arch. Biochem. Biophys., 296, 58-65
2 Hyde, G.E., Wilberding, J.A., Meyer, A.L., Campbell, E.R. and Campbell W.H. (1989) Plant Mol. Biol. 13, 233-246
3 Redinbaugh, M.G. and Campbell, W.H. (1985) J. Biol. Chem. 260, 3380-3385
4 Klimczak, L.J. and Hind, G. (1990) Plant Physiol. 92, 919-923
5 Wu, J., Rossomando, A.J., Her, J., Vecchio, R., Weber, M.J. and Sturgill, T.W. (1991) Proc. Natl. Acad. Sci. USA 88, 9508-9512
6 Kaiser, W. and Spill, D. (1991) Plant Physiol. 96, 368-375
7 Kaiser, W. and Brendle-Behnisch, E. (1991) Plant Physiol. 96, 363-367
8 Campbell, W.H. and Kinghorn, J.R. (1990) Trends in Biochem. Sci. 15, 315-319

CHARACTERIZATION OF GLUTAMINE SYNTHETASE PURIFIED FROM *CHLOROBIUM LIMICOLA F. THIOSULFATOPHILUM* NCIB 8327

Jong-Uk Na, Ji-Yoon Kim, Hwan Youn, Sa-Ouk Kang, and Yung-Chil Hah, Department of Microbiology, College of Natural Sciences, and Research Center for Molecular Microbiology, Seoul National University, Seoul 151-742, Korea

1. INTRODUCTION

Glutamine synthetase [L-glutamate : ammonia ligase (ADP-forming), EC 6.3.1.2] has a key role in ammonia assimilation. The enzyme from *Escherichia coli* has been studied extensively and its activity has shown to be regulated by gene expression, multiple feed-back inhibition, kinetic control and adenylation with AMP (20). With respect to patterns of feedback inhibition and adenylation, the glutamine synthetases of the *Rhodobacter capsulata* (10, 16), *Rhodopseudomonas palustris* (1, 2), *Rhodobacter sphaeroides* (6, 14) and *Rhodospirillum rubrum* (21) are very similar to that of *E. coli*. However, with respect to magnesium ion effect, the adenylation system of glutamine synthetases in *Rhodospirillaceae* (2, 4, 6, 7, 10, 17) has some differences from that of *E. coli*. Among photosynthetic bacteria, glutamine synthetase has been purified and characterized in *R. rubrum* (19, 22), *R. palustris* (1, 2), *R. sphaeroides* (6), and *R. capsulatus* (4, 10). However, glutamine synthetases of *Chlorobiaceae* are not reported yet, except that of *Chl. vibrioforme f. thiosulfatophilum* (12). In the present paper, we report the purification and the characterization of ***Chlorobium limicola f. thiosulfatophilum*** NCIB 8327 which was grown on glutamate as major nitrogen source.

2. MATERIALS and METHODS

Materials. All chemicals were standard commercial products of high purity.
Strains. *Chlorobium limicola f. thiosulfatophilum* NCIB 8327 used in this experiment was a kind gift from Dr. Sirievag (Department of Biology, University of Oslo, Norway).
Growth of cells. *Chl. limicola f. thiosulfatophilum* NCIB 8327 maintained in the ATCC medium (18) was cultured photoautotrophically at 30 ℃ in the modified Pfennig's medium (9) with glutamate instead of ammonia as nitrogen sources.
Buffers. The 10 mmol m^{-3}, 100 mmol m^{-3}, and 50 mmol m^{-3} Tris-HCl (pH 7.9) buffers were used in the anion exchange chromatography, the gel permeation chromatography and the preparative HPLC chromatography respectively. The buffers were evacuated and flushed with nitrogen gas, and then dithiothreitol was added to the buffers.
Purification procedures The resuspended cells were broken by ultrasonicator. After ultracentrifigation, the supernatant was eluted with a linear gradient of 0.1 - 0.45 M NaCl on a DEAE-Sepharose CL-6B column (4.4 x 15 cm). The active pool concentrated by Amicon PM-10 membrane was eluted on an Sephacryl S-300 column (2.6 x 140 cm). The concentrated active pool was eluted with a linear gradient of 0.25 - 0.4 M NaCl on an Protein-Pak DEAE 5PW column.
Enzyme assays. Glutamine synthetase activity was determined as γ-glutamyl transferase activity (12). The amount of γ-glutamylhydroxamate formed was estimated by the absorbance at 540 nm. For the assays of adenylation, 60 mmol m^{-3} $MgCl_2$ was added to the reaction mixtures (17). One unit of enyme activity was defined as the amount of enzyme producing 1 μmol m^{-3} min^{-1} of γ-glutamylhydroxamate under the conditions of the

N. Murata (ed.), Research in Photosynthesis, Vol. IV, 67–70.

assay.
Protein determination. Protein concentration was determined according to the method proposed by Lowry *et al* (1951) or Bradford (1976), with bovine serum albumin as a standard.
Molecular weight. The molecular weight of native enzymes was determined by gel permeation chromatography (Sephacryl S-300). Catalase (240,000), alcohol dehydrogenase (150,000), and chymotrypsinogen A (25,000) were used.
Electrophoresis. For gradient SDS-PAGE, 5 - 10 % acrylamide (13) and for native PAGE, 8 % acrylamide (5) were used.
Km values. Km values for substrate such as L-glutamine or hydroxylamine were estimated by Lineweaver-Burk plot.
Effect of amino acids on enzyme ***activity.*** Effect of amino acids on enzyme activity was estimated by the addition of 10 mmol m^{-3} amino acids to the reaction mixtures.

3. RESULTS and DICUSSION

The glutamine synthetase/glutamate synthase pathway appeared to be the principal route of assimilation at low levels of ammonia upto 30 mmol m^{-3} in *Chl. vibrioforme f. thiosulfatophilum* (12), 20 mmol m^{-3} in *Chl. limicola f. thiosulfatophilum*, strain L (11), and 1 mmol m^{-3} in *E. coli.* and *Chl. limicola f. thiosulfatophilum*, NCIB 8327 (9). Adenylated glutamine synthetase from this strain shows 65 % decrease of γ-glutamyltransferase activity only in the presence of 60 mmol m^{-3} Mg^{++}. This result indicate that the adenylated glutamine synthetase is similar to that of *E. coli.*

Glutamine synthetase was purified through 4 steps (Table 1, Fig. 1). Native gel stained for protein and activity show only one band. The purified enzyme shows a single band on SDS-PAGE. The molecular weight of the subunit was 30,000 dalton which was determined by 5 - 10 % gradient SDS-PAGE (Fig. 2).

TABLE 1. Purification step of glutamine synthetase from *Chl. limicola thiosulfatophilum* NCIB 8327

Purification Step	Total Protein (mg)	Enzyme Activity (unit)	Specific Activity (unit/mg)	Recovery (%)	Purification Fold
Crude Extract	651.00	8659.00	13.30	100.00	1.0
Ultracentrifugation	238.00	6966.00	29.30	80.45	2.2
DEAE-Sepharose CL-6B Chromatography	13.00	916.40	70.49	10.6	5.3
Sephacryl S-300 Chromatography	3.25	684.40	199.50	7.50	15.0
Preparative HPLC Chromatography	0.28	173.20	615.80	2.0	46.3

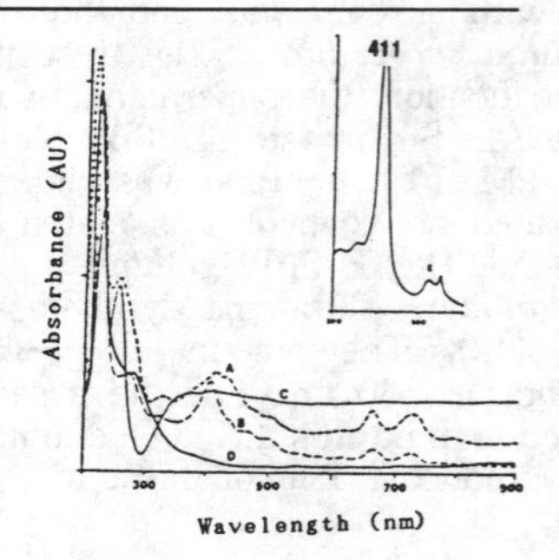

FIGURE 1. UV-visible absorption spectra of enzyme fractions after ion exchange chromatograph (B), gel permeation chromatograph (C), preparative HPLC (D), and that of cytochrome C (E) compared with that of crude enzyme (A).

The enzyme activity by γ-glutamyl transferase assay was inhibited by 21 % and 18 % on 50 mmol m^{-3} NH_4Cl and L-glutamate respectively. These results consist in the inhibition effects of NH_4Cl and L-glutamate on the enzymes of *Anabaena cylindica, Nitrosomonas europaea* and *Chl. vibrioforme f. thiosulfatophilum.* These results support the postulated model of Gass and Meister (8) that L-glutamine interacts with the enzyme so that its NH_2 group occupies the ammonia binding site while the oxygen binding site, to which glutamate is bound, is required for the attachment of the oxygen group of glutamine.

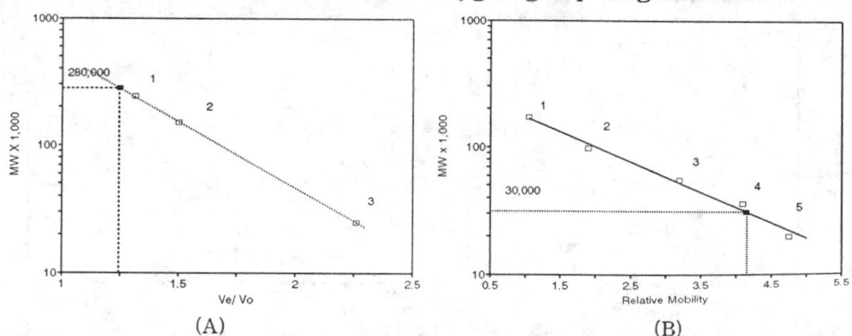

(A) (B)

FIGURE 2. Molecular weight estimation of glutamine synthetase by Sephacryl S-300 (A) and by linear gradient SDS-PAGE B). Molecular weight markers were used 1 (catalase: 240,000), 2 (alcohol dehydrogenase: 150,000), and 3 (chymotrypsinogen A: 25,000) (A); 1 (reduced α_2-macroglobulin: 170,000), 2 (phosphorylase: 97,500), 3 (glutamate dehydrogenase: 55,400), 4 (lactate dehydrogenase, 36,500), and 5 (trypsin inhibitor: 20,100) (B).

The enzyme activity was inhibited considerably by 10 mmol m^{-3} of alanine, glycine, and tryptophan, but was not affected by asparagine, lysine, leucine, and valine (Table 2).

TABLE 2. Effects of amino acids on the purifed glutamine synthetase activity.

Substrate (10 mmol m^{-3})	Relative activity (%)	Inhibition rate (%)
none	100	0
asparagine	100	0
lysine	100	0
leucine	100	0
valine	100	0
glycine	70	30
alanine	57	43
tryptophane	38	62

1,000/ T (1/K)

pH

Temperature (C)

pH

(A) (B) (C) (D)

FIGURE 3. Effect of temperature (A), and pH (B) on the enzyme activity in 0.1 M citrate-borate-phosphate buffer; thermal (C) and pH (D) stability of the enzyme.

The optimal temperature and pH of the enzyme were 30 ℃ and 7.0. In the optimal temperature, the activation energy of the reaction was 8.1 kcal/mol from 5 ℃ to 20 ℃ and 6.3 kcal/mol from 20 ℃ to 25 ℃. The enzyme was very stable up to 50 ℃ and at pH 8.0, respectively as shown in Fig. 3.

Km value was 27.9 mmol m^{-3} for L-glutamine and 0.92 mmol m^{-3} for hydroxylamine-HCl (Fig. 4), whereas 15.7 mmol m^{-3} and 4.5 mmol m^{-3} for L-glutamine and hydroxylamine-HCl in *Chl. vibrioforme f. thiosulfatophilum*, respectively (12).

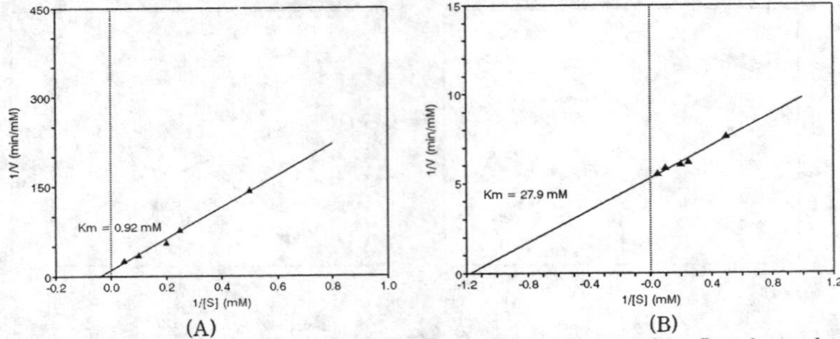

FIGURE 4. Lineweaver-Burk plot of glutamine synthetase for L-glutamine (A) and hydroxylamine-HCl (B).

4. REFERENCES

1. Alef, K., H.-J. Burkardt, H.-J. Horstmann and Zumft, W.G. (1981) Z. ***Nat*** 36(c) : 246 - 254
2. Alef, K.E. and Zumft, W.G. (1981) Z. ***Nat*** 36(C) : 784 - 789
3. Bradford, M.M. (1976) ***Anal. Biochem.*** 72 : 248 - 254
4. Caballero, F. J., F. J. Cejudo, F. J. Florencio, J. Cardenas and Castilo, F. (1985) ***J. Bact.*** 162 : 804 - 809
5. Davis, B.J. (1964) ***Ann. NY Acad. Sci.*** 121 : 404 - 427
6. Engelhardt, H. and Klemme, J.H. (1982) ***Arch. Microbiol.*** 133 : 202 - 205
7. Falk, G., B.C. Johansson and Nordlund, S.(1982) ***Arch. Microbiol.*** 132 : 251 - 253
8. Gass, J.D. and Meister, A. (1970) ***Biochemistry*** 9 : 1380 - 1389
9. Heda, G.D. and Madigan, M.T. ((1986) ***Arch. Microbiol*** 143 : 330 - 336
10. Johansson, B.C. and Gest, H. (1977) ***Eur. J. Biochem.*** 81 : 365 - 371
11. Keppen, O.I., N.V. Lebedeva, S.A. Petukhov and Rodionov, Y.V. 1985 ***Microbiol.*** 54 : 28 - 32
12. Khanna, S. and Nicholas, D.J.D. (1983) ***Arch. Microbiol.*** 134 : 98 - 103
13. Lambin, P.C. (1978) ***Ann. Biochem.*** 85 : 114 - 123
14. Lee, H.J. (1986) Ph. D. theses in Seoul National University.
15. Lowry, O.H., N.J. Rosebrough, A.L.Farr, and Randall, R.J. (1951) ***J. Biol. Chem.*** 193 : 265 - 275
16. Michalski, W.P, D.J.D. Nicholas and Vignais, P.M. (1983) ***Bioch. Biophys. Acta.*** 743 : 136 - 148
17. Nordlund, S., R.H. Kanemoto, S.A. Murre and Ludden P.W. (1985) ***J. Bacteriol.*** 161 : 13-17
18. Pfennig, N. 1984 in Bergey's Mannual of Systematic Bacteriology (Pfennig N., ed), Vol. 3. 1635 - 1709, Williams and Wilkins, Baltimore
19. Soliman, A. and Nordlund, S. (1989) ***Bioch. Biophys. Acta.*** 994 : 138 - 141
20. Stadtman, E.R. and Ginsberg, A (1974) The Enzymes (Boyer, P.D., ed.) Vol. 10, 755 - 807, Academic Press, New York and London
21. Woehle, D.L., B.A. Lueddecke and Ludden P.W. (1990) ***J. Biol. Chem.*** 265 : 13741 - 13749
22. Yoch, D.C, M. Cantu and Zhang Z.M. (1983) ***J. Bacteriol.*** 154 : 632 - 639

EFFECTS OF LIGHT AND NITRATE ON EXPRESSION OF GENES FOR GLUTAMINE SYNTHETASES AND FERREDOXIN-DEPENDENT GLUTAMATE SYNTHASE IN MAIZE.

Hitoshi Sakakibara and Tatsuo Sugiyama

Department of Agricultural Chemistry, School of Agriculture, Nagoya University, Nagoya 464-01, Japan

INTRODUCTION

In most of plants, glutamine synthetase (GS) and glutamate synthase (GOGAT) compose a metabolic route called the GS/GOGAT cycle, and they play a central role in the assimilation of ammonia (1). GS is classified as having two distinct isoforms with different subcellular localizations. There is a cytosolic form, GS1, and a plastidic form, GS2 (2). In leaves, GS2 and ferredoxin-dependent GOGAT (Fd-GOGAT) are responsible for the assimilation of ammonia derived from the reduction of nitrate and the photorespiratory nitrogen pathway. In roots, GSs and Fd-GOGAT also exist, and are mainly involved in the assimilation of ammonia derived from reduction of nitrate. However, details of expression of the enzymes in these tissues are not well understood.

Recently, cDNA clones for maize Fd-GOGAT and GS isoproteins were isolated (3, 4). This enabled us to study the expression of the genes for GS and Fd-GOGAT at the molecular level. In this report, we studied the effects of light and nitrate on the expression of these genes in different organs of maize seedlings by analyzing the changes in the levels of the respective polypeptides and mRNAs. We found differences in terms of combinations and amounts of GS isoproteins and Fd-GOGAT in roots, and these differences seem to be of importance to the physiological characteristics of GS/GOGAT cycle.

MATERIALS AND METHODS

Plant materials and growth conditions--- For the analysis of induction by light, maize (*Zea mays* L. cv. Golden Cross Bantam T51) seedlings were grown on vermiculite with a nitrogen-free 0.1 x Hoagland solution in a dark room for 6 days. Etiolated seedlings were then illuminated continuously under fluorescent light for the indicated times. For the analysis of induction by nitrate, the seeds were initially grown in an aerated hydroponic system that contained a 0.1 x Hoagland solution, without a nitrogen source, under continuous fluorescent light. Then, the nutrient solution was changed to 0.1 x Hoagland solution that contained 16 mM $NaNO_3$ and the seedlings were allowed to grow under the same conditions for the indicated times.

Extraction of proteins and Western blot analysis--- Analysis of crude extracts of leaf or root tissues by Western blotting was carried

N. Murata (ed.), Research in Photosynthesis, Vol. IV, 71–74.

out as described previously (4). Plastids were prepared from roots by the method of Emes and England (5). Soluble fractions of the plastids were obtained by rupturing the plastids in a glass homogenizer and centrifuging to remove the membrane fraction. The amounts of protein were measured by the methods of Bradford (6).

Extraction of RNAs and Northern blot analysis--- Poly(A)$^+$RNAs were prepared from roots of non-induced, nitrate-induced, and ammonia-induced seedlings (7). Details of Northern blot analysis, including specific probes for Fd-GOGAT and GS mRNAs, and conditions for hybridization and washing of the filters, have been described previously (3, 4).

RESULTS AND DISCUSSION

The changes in the steady-state levels of GS isoproteins and Fd-GOGAT in leaves during induction by light were analyzed. Both GS2 and Fd-GOGAT polypeptides showed a marked increase with a similar kinetics (Fig. 1A). The patterns of accumulation of their transcripts were well corresponded to those of respective proteins (Fig. 1B). The levels of GS1 changed less markedly. These results strongly suggest that the expression of GS2, not that of GS1, is regulated coordinately with the expression of Fd-GOGAT probably at the transcriptional level during induction by light.

Figure 2 shows the effects of nitrate on the accumulation of GSs and Fd-GOGAT in leaves and roots. In leaves, the level of neither GS nor Fd-GOGAT were changed essentially during induction by nitrate. In roots, the behavior of GS2 was completely different from that observed in leaves. The level of GS2, which was initially very low, appeared to increase in response to addition of nitrate. Furthermore, a novel GS molecule, designated GSr, also accumulated to a considerable extent. By contrast, the levels of Fd-GOGAT and GS1 did not change significantly during this treatment. Thus, the nitrate gives different effect on the accumulation of GS isoproteins between leaves and roots.

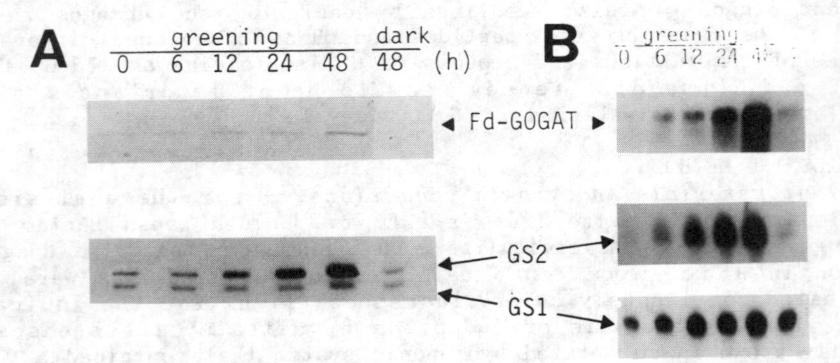

Figure 1. Effects of light on the expression of genes for Fd-GOGAT and GS isoproteins during induction by light (4). Total proteins and RNAs were extracted from greening leaves at the indicated times after the start of illumination and analyzed by Western (A) and Northern blottings (B). pGS112 was used as a representative probe for GS1 gene family (4).

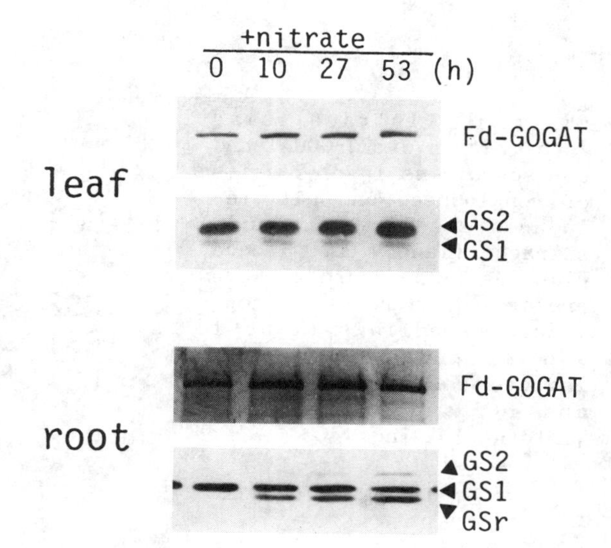

Figure 2. Effects of nitrate on the accumulation of Fd-GOGAT and GS isoproteins in maize seedlings. Total proteins were extracted from leaves and roots at the indicated times after the addition of nitrate to cultures of seedlings and analyzed by Western blotting.

Subcellular location of Fd-GOGAT and GS isoproteins was examined by fractionating root cells (Fig. 3). Both GS2 and Fd-GOGAT were found to be concentrated in the plastid fraction (lane 2 and 4). The level of GS2 only became very high in the plastids after induction by nitrate. Neither GS1 nor GSr was localized in the plastids, suggesting that GSr is an extra-plastidic isoprotein as well. It is clear that the ratio of the amounts of Fd-GOGAT and GS2 in the plastids is variable. The two enzymes are known to constitute a cooperative ammonia-assimilatory cycle in chloroplasts, and they have been shown to accumulate coordinately during induction by light (4). Such coordination did not appear to occur in the root plastids, at least, during induction by nitrate. Figure 4 shows the changes in the levels of mRNAs for Fd-GOGAT and the GS isoproteins in roots that had been treated with nitrate or ammonia. An almost constant signal for the Fd-GOGAT transcript was obtained, while the GS2 transcript was only detected in roots of nitrate-treated seedlings (lane 2). These results agree well with the results obtained at the protein level (Figure 2) and suggest that the induction by nitrate of GS2 can be attributed to increased activity at the transcriptional level. Ammonium ions were not effective for the induction of GS2 and Fd-GOGAT (lane 3).

Without addition of nitrate, glutamine must be mainly produced by cytosolic GS, and upon addition of nitrate, plastidic GS, in turn, contribute to the formation of glutamine. Thus, Fd-GOGAT is able to use glutamine produced by cytoplasmic and plastidic GS isoenzymes. Such metabolic communication between two compartments of a cell in the assimilation of nitrogen has been reported (8, 9). The amount of Fd-GOGAT is kept constant regardless of nitrate supply. This may imply that the catalytic ability of Fd-GOGAT is not limitting, or that enzymes other than Fd-GOGAT contribute to the metabolism of glutamine especially in nitrate-induced roots.

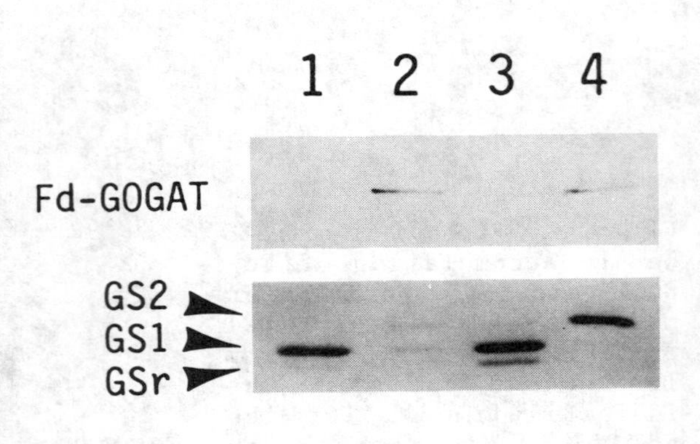

Figure 3. Intracellular localization of Fd-GOGAT and GS isoproteins in root cells of non-induced and nitrate-induced seedlings. Crude extracts (lane 1 and 3) and plastids (lane 2 and 4) were prepared from roots of non-induced seedlings (lane 1 and 2) and of nitrate-induced seedlings (lane 3 and 4), and analyzed by Western blotting.

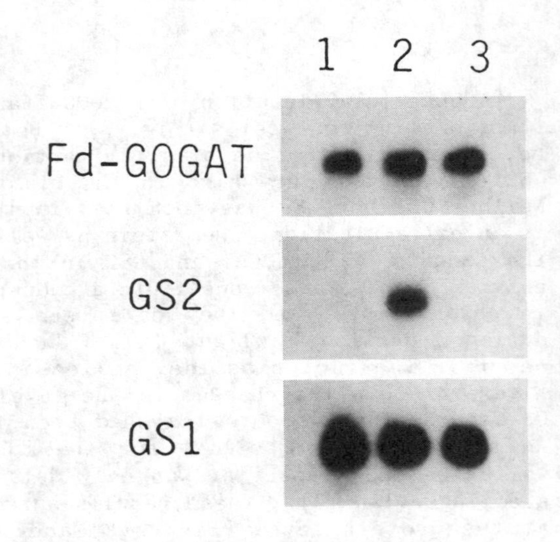

Figure 4. Effects of nitrate and ammonia on the accumulation of transcripts for Fd-GOGAT and GS2 in roots. Poly(A)$^+$RNAs were prepared from roots of non-induced (lane 1), nitrate-induced (lane 2), and ammonia-induced (lane 3) seedlings and analyzed by Northern blotting. pGS112 was used as a representative probe for GS1 gene family.

REFERENCES

1 Miflin, B. J. and Lea, P. J. (1980) *In* The Biochemistry of Plants Vol. 5. Edited by Miflin, B. J. pp. 169-202, Academic Press, Inc., NY.
2 Hirel, B. and Gadal, P. (1980) *Plant Physiol.* 66, 619-623
3 Sakakibara, H., Watanabe, M., Hase, T. and Sugiyama, T. (1991) *J. Biol. Chem.* 266, 2028-2035
4 Sakakibara, H., Kawabata, S., Takahashi, H., Hase, T. and Sugiyama, T. (1992) *Plant Cell Physiol.* 33, 49-58
5 Emes, M. J. and England, S. (1986) *Planta* 168, 161-166
6 Bradford, M. (1976) *Anal. Biochem.* 72, 248-254
7 Sambrook, J., Fritsch, E. F. and Maniatis, T. (1989) *Molecular Cloning: A Laboratory Manual Ed. 2.* Cold Spring Harbor Laboratory Press, Cold Spring Harbor, NY.
8 Yu, J. and Woo, K. C. (1988) *Plant Physiol.* 88, 1048-1054
9 Chen, F. L. and Cullimore, J. V. (1989) *Planta* 179, 441-447

GENE EXPRESSION AND REGULATION OF NITRATE ASSIMILATING ENZYMES IN *SYNECHOCOCCUS* PCC7942

IWANE SUZUKI[1], TATSUO OMATA[2] AND TATSUO SUGIYAMA[1]
[1]AGRIC. CHEM. DEPT., AGR. SCH., NAGOYA UNIV., NAGOYA 464- 01, JAPAN AND [2]SOLAR ENERGY RES. GROUP, THE INST. PHYS. CHEM. RES., WAKO, SAITAMA 351-01, JAPAN

1. INTRODUCTION

Nitrate is a major source of nitrogen for cyanobacteria. The process of nitrate assimilation includes (i) Uptake of nitrate into the cells mediated by an active transport system; (ii) Two-step reduction of nitrate to ammonium mediated by nitrate reductase and nitrite reductase; and (iii) Incorporation of ammonium into carbon skeletons via glutamine synthetase/glutamate synthase cycle. The genes involved in nitrate uptake (*nrtA-nrtD* [1,2,3]) and reduction (*narB* [4] and *nirA* [2]) are organized into a cluster *nirA-nrtA,B,C,D-narB* in the genome of *Synechococcus* PCC7942 [3] (Fig.1). Since the activities of nitrate transport, nitrate reductase and nitrite reductase are all subject to nutritional repression by ammonium in *Synechococcus* [5-8], there seems to be a co-ordinated regulation of the genes in the *nirA-narB* culster. We therefore studied the expression and regulation of the six genes by means of Northern hybridization, using probes specific to each of the genes. We reported here that the six genes from *nirA* to *narB* are cotranscribed as an operon and that the transcription is inhibited by ammonium.

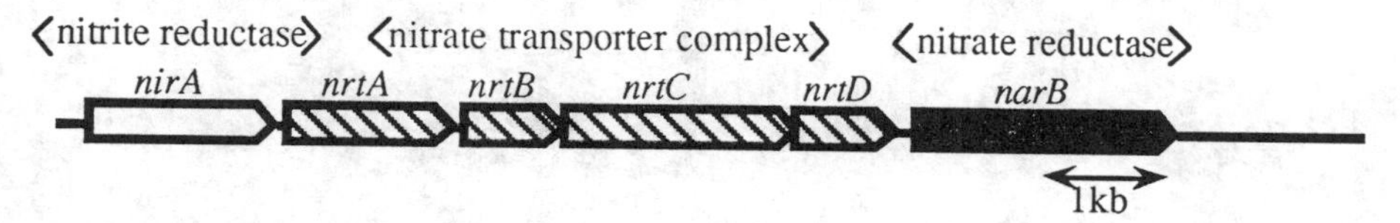

Fig.1 Physical map of the *nirA-narB* region of the genome of *Synechococcus* PCC7942.

2. MATERIALS AND METHODS

Cells of *Synechococcus* PCC 7942 were grown at 30°C in liquid media during aeration with air, under constant illumination provided by fluorescent lamps (approximately 5,000 lx). The basal medium used was a nitrogen-free medium obtained by replacing $NaNO_3$, $Co(NO_3)_2$ and ferric ammonium citrate in medium BG-11[9] with NaCl, $CoCl_2$ and ferric citrate, respectively. An ammonium-containing medium and a nitrate-containing medium were prepared by adding $(NH_4)_2SO_4$ (3.75mM) and KNO_3 (15mM), respectively, to the basal medium. All media were buffered with 20mM HEPES-KOH(8.0).

N. Murata (ed.), Research in Photosynthesis, Vol. IV, 75–78.

For induction of the genes involved in nitrate assimilation, cells grown in the ammonium-containing medium were harvested at mid-logarithmic phase of growth by centrifugation at 3,500 × *g* for 5 min, washed twice with the nitrogen-free medium by resuspension and recentrifugation, and incubated in the nitrate-containing medium under the growth conditions. Total RNA was extracted and purified from *Synechococcus* cells according to Aiba et al. [10] before and after the transfer of the cells from the ammonium-containing medium to the nitrate-containing medium. Northern hybridization analysis was performed according to Church and Gilbert [11], using internal fragments of *nirA, nrtA,B,C,D* and a synthetic 18-mer oligonucleotide complementary to bases -3 to +15 of the *narB* coding region as probes. In a control hybridization experiment, an internal fragment of *psbAI*, one of the three-copy genes encoding the D1 protein of PSII reaction center [12], was used to probe the transcripts from the *psbA* genes. The hybridization signals were detected by autoradiography or by using a BIO-IMAGE Analyzer (Fuji Photo Film). The 5' terminus of the mRNA was determined by S1 mapping, using a single-stranded DNA probe complementary to nucleotides -173 to +21 of the *nirA* coding region.

3. RESULTS AND DISCUSSION

Northern analysis of total RNA from *Synechococcus* cells was performed to determine the size and amount of the transcript from the *nirA-nrtA,B,C,D-narB* gene cluster (Fig. 2). There were no detectable amounts of the transcript in RNA from the ammonium-grown cells (Fig. 2, lanes A). The transcription from the genes was induced when cells

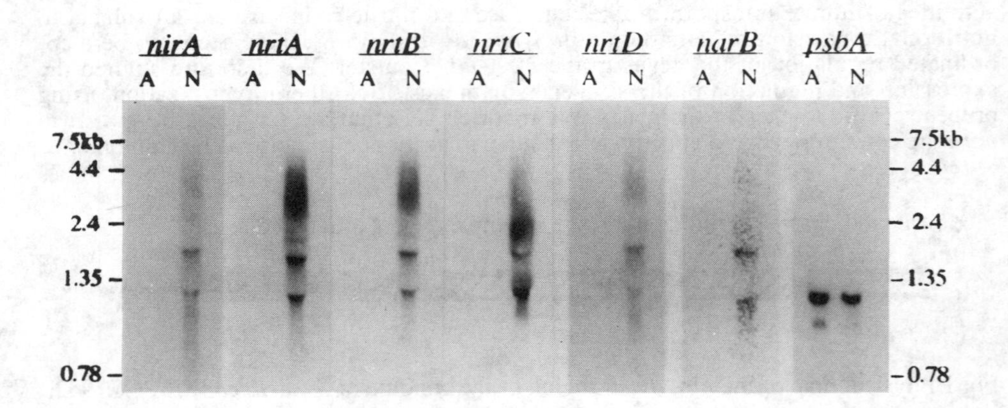

Fig.2 Northern analysis of RNA from ammonium-grown cells of *Synechococcus* PCC7942 before (A) and after (N) 15 min incubation in the nitrate-containing medium. RNA samples (10μg each) were denatured with formaldehyde, resolved by electrophoresis on a 1.2% agarose gel and transferred to positively-charged nylon membranes (Hybond N+, Amersham). The Northern blots were hybridized with the gene-specific probes as indicated. The *narB*-specific oligonucleotide probe was detected by using a BIO-IMAGE Analyzer (Fuji Photo Film), while the other probes were detected by autoradiography.

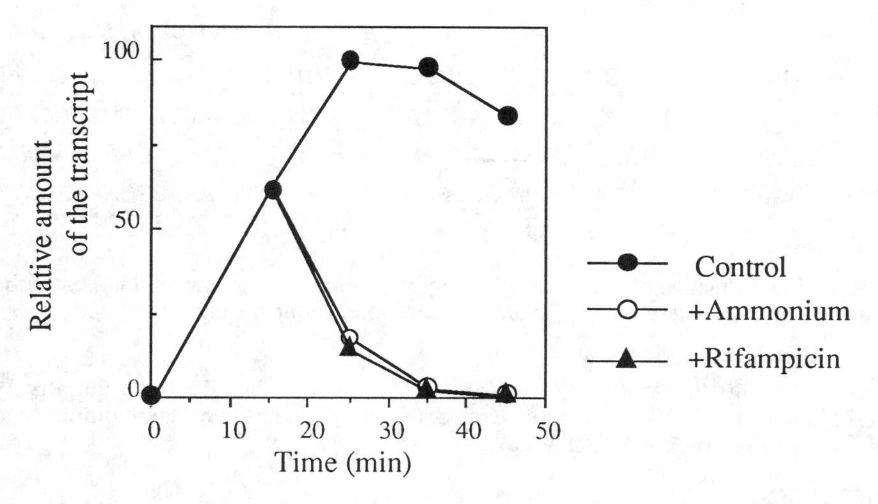

Fig.3 Changes in the amount of the transcript from the *nirA-narB* operon after transfer of the ammonium-grown *Synechococcus* to the nitrate-containing medium. RNA samples were denatured, electrophoresed, blotted to Hybond-N+ as in Fig. 2, and hybridized with the *nrtC*-specific probe. The amount of the probe hybridized to each of the lanes on the blot was quantified by a BIO-IMAGE Analyzer.

were incubated in the nitrate-containing medium (Fig. 2, lanes N). The results clearly demonstrated that the expression of the proteins involved in nitrate assimilation is controlled at the level of transcription. The hybridization profiles obtained with the probes specific to *nirA*, *nrtA,B,C,D* and *narB* were very similar to one another; Each of the probes yielded a smeared signal ranging from 0.5kb to >7.5kb in size. No hybridization signal was obtained when a DNA fragment from the chromosomal region 1kbp downstream from *narB* was used as the probe (not shown). These results showed that the genes *nirA*, *nrtA,B,C,D* and *narB* are cotranscribed into a large mRNA. The smeared hybridization signals were not to be ascribed to inadvertent breakdown of the transcript during the extraction and analysis of RNA, because clear spots were obtained with the *psbA*-specific probe (Fig. 2). The transcript from the *nirA-narB* operon seems to be rapidly degraded *in vivo*.

Figure 3 shows the changes in the amount of the transcript from the *nirA-narB* operon after the transfer of the cells from the ammonium-containing medium to the nitrate-containing medium. The transcript accumulated rapidly upon transfer of the cells from the ammonium-containing medium to the nitrate-containing medium. The amount of the transcript reached a plateau in 30 min and decreased gradually. Addition of rifampicin (50μg/ml) caused a rapid decrease in the amount of the transcript, indicating that the degradation rate of the transcript is high. A simmilar time course was obtained when ammonium (7.5mM) was added to the culture. This suggests that ammonium inhibits the transcription from the *nirA-narB* operon.

By S1 nuclease protection experiments using the RNA sample from cells incubated in the nitrate-containing medium for 15 min, the transcription start site of the *nirA-narB* operon was mapped at 29 nucleotides upstream from the initiation codon of *nirA* (Fig. 4).

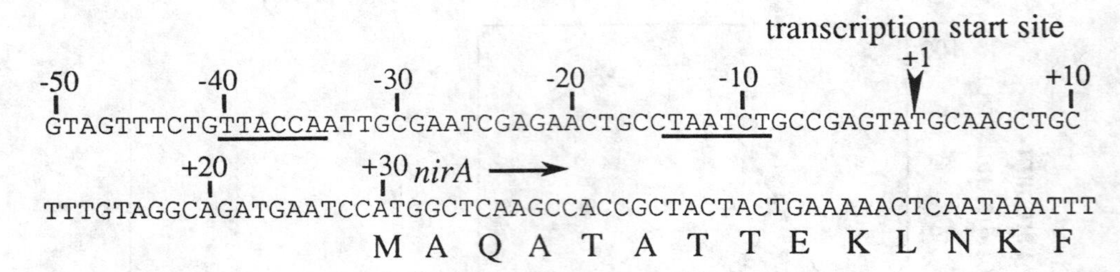

Fig.4 Nucleotide sequence of the 5' flanking region of *nirA*. The arrowhead indicates the transcription start site. The putative -35 and -10 promoter sequence are underlined.

The nucleotides -40 to -35 (TTACCA) and -14 to -9 (TAATCT) were tentatively identified as the -35 and -10 promoter sequence, respectively, based on their similarity to those of *E. coli* (TTGACA and TATAAT).

4. CONCLUSION

The *nirA*, *nrtA-D* and *narB* genes involved in nitrate assimilation of *Synechococcus* PCC7942 are cotranscribed as an operon. The transcription starts at -29 bases upstream from the *nirA* coding region and terminates within 1 kb downstream from the *narB* coding region. Ammonium, when added in the culture medium, represses the transcription from the operon.

This work was supported by Grants-in-aid for Scientific Research in Priority Areas (no. 04273221 to T.O. and no. 04273103 to T.S.) from the Ministry of Education, Science and Culture, Japan.

REFERENCES

1. Omata, T., Omori, M., Arai, N., Ogawa, T. (1989) Proc. Natl. Acad. Sci. USA 86, 6612-6616
2. Omata, T. (1991) Plant Cell Physiol. 32, 151-157
3. Omata, T., Andriesse, X., Hirano, A. (1992) Mol. Gen. Genet. in press
4. Andriesse, X., Bakker, H., Weisbeek, P. (1990) in Inorganic Nitrogen in Plants and Microorganisms (Ullrich, W. R., Rigano, C., Figgi, A., Aparicio, P. J., eds.) pp. 303-307, Springer, Berlin
5. Lara, C., Romero, J.M., Guerrero, M.G. (1987) J. Bacteriol. 169, 4376-4378
6. Herrero, A., Flores, E., Guerrero, M.G. (1981) J. Bacteriol. 145, 175-180
7. Herrero, A., Guerrero, M.G. (1986) J. Gen. Microbiol. 132, 2463-2468
8. Madueño, F., Borrias, W.E, Van Arkel, G.A., Guerrero, M.G. (1988) Mol. Gen. Genet. 213, 223-228
9. Stainer, R.Y., Kunisawa, R., Mandel, M., Cohen-Bazire, G. (1971) Bacteriol. Rev. 35, 171-205
10. Aiba, H., Adhya, S., De Crombrugghe, B. (1981) J. Biol. Chem. 256, 11905-11910
11. Church, G.M., Gilbert, W. (1984) Proc. Natl. Acad. Sci. USA 81, 1991-1995
12. Golden, S.S., Brusslan, J., Haselkorn, R. (1986) EMBO J. 5, 2789-2798

"AIR-POLLUTANT-PHILIC PLANTS" FROM NATURE

HIROMICHI MORIKAWA[1], ASA HIGAKI[1], MASAKO NOHNO[1], MITSUNORI KAMADA[1], MASASHI NAKATA[1], GENTARO TOYOHARA[1], KONOSUKE FUJITA[2] AND KOHEI IRIFUNE[1], DEPARTMENT OF BOTANY, FACULTY OF SCIENCE, HIROSHIMA UNIVERSITY[1], HIGASHI-HIROSHIMA 724, JAPAN AND FACULTY OF APPLIED BIOLOGICAL SCIENCE, HIROSHIMA UNIVERSITY[2], HIGASHI-HIROSHIMA 724, JAPAN

1. INTRODUCTION

Nitrogen dioxide (NO_2) is a main cause of acid rain which is one of the most important global environmental problems. Plants are reported to assimilate NO_2 (1). However, little studies have been made on screening plants that have high NO_2-assimilation ability. Production of "NO_2-philic plants" that can grow with atmospheric NO_2 as a sole nitrogen source may provide a solution for global air-pollution problems from the side of plant science, or plant biotechnology. Here we report on screening of possible "candidates of NO_2-philic plants" from various wild and cultivated plants, involving 52 wild herbaceous plants from roadside, 60 cultivated herbaceous plants, and 37 cultivated woody plants.

2. MATERIALS and METHODS

2.1 Plant materials: Wild herbaceous plants were collected from roadside highly polluted with NO_2, transferred to pots containing sand, and grown for 1-2 weeks without any fertilizer in a greenhouse. Seeds of wild herbaceous plants collected from roadside were sown in the pots containing vermiculite and supplied with tap water. The plants were grown for 1-2 months supplied with 1/1000 hyponex solution (N:P:K=5:10:5) every 3 days in a greenhouse. Cultivated herbaceous and woody plants (provided by Hiroshima City Botanical Garden, Japan) were cultivated in a similar way as for seedlings of wild plants.

2.2 NO_2 fumigation: Fumigation of plants with $^{15}NO_2$ was carried out in a fumigation chamber (50 x 100 x 50 cm) as reported elsewhere (1). Plants were placed in the chamber. The surface of the pot was completely covered with a plastic bag to avoid dissolving of NO_2 in soil-water.

The plants were fumigated with 4 ± 1 ppm $^{15}NO_2$ for 8 h during daytime (9:00-17:00) in the light (10 klx at the top of the chamber). The temperature in the chamber was kept at 24 to 28°C. The NO_2 concentration in the chamber was monitored with a NO_2 gas detection tube every 15 min, and appropriate amounts of $^{15}NO_2$ were added every 10 min to keep the concentration in the chamber. The

N. Murata (ed.), Research in Photosynthesis, Vol. IV, 79–82.

air in the chamber was circulated by an electric fan.

2.3 Analysis of NO_2-assimilation ability of plants: After fumigation, plants were harvested, washed with tap water, rinsed with distilled water, and dried at 80°C for 3 days. Dried plants were ground into fine powder by a mill. The total reduced nitrogen content in the plants was determined after Kjeldahl digestion. $^{15}N/^{14}N$ ratio in the reduced nitrogen fraction was determined by mass spectrometry, and NO_2-derived reduced nitrogen content (NO_2-assimilation ability) in the plants was estimated.

2.4 Analysis of stomatal response of plants to NO_2: In accordance with the method of Black (2) with slight modification, the stomatal response of plants to NO_2 was determined by directly measuring the decrease in the weight of the plants in the presence or absence of NO_2. $^{15}NO_2$ was used for fumigation so that the relationships between stomatal response to NO_2 and NO_2-assimilation ability can directly be studied for individual plants.

A plant in a plastic pot was placed onto an electronic balance in the fumigation chamber. The surface of the pot was completely covered with a plastic bag as described above. The decrease in the weight of the plant was monitored before (2 hr) and after continuous fumigation with $^{15}NO_2$ (for 8hr). The fumigation condition was the same as described above except that the humidity in the chamber was kept at 55±5% using silicagel. The fumigated plant was recovered and its NO_2-assimilation ability was determined as described above.

3. RESULTS and DISCUSSION

Total of 149 plants involving 52 wild herbaceous plants, and 60 cultivated herbaceous plants and 37 cultivated woody plants, were analyzed for NO_2-derived reduced nitrogen content (NO_2-assimilation ability). NO_2-assimilation ability of the plants markedly varied among both wild and cultivated plant species. The highest NO_2-assimilation ability was obtained with *Erechtites hieracifolia* (5.72 mg/g dw) while the lowest value with *Tillandsia ionantha* (0.006 mg/g dw). The difference in NO_2-assimilation ability between these two species was close to 1000-fold. In general, *Asteraceae* such as *Erechtites hieracifolia*, *Crassocephalum crepidioides*, *Carthamus tinctorius* were of the highest ability, while *Poaceae* such as *Paspalum dilatatum*, *Bromus unioloides* and *Eragrostis ferruginea* were of low ability.

When the ratio of NO_2-derived reduced nitrogen to total reduced nitrogen was plotted against the NO_2-derived nitrogen content, almost linear relationship was obtained (Fig. 1). In 15 out of 149 plants, NO_2-derived nitrogen comprised more than 7% of total reduced nitrogen in these plants (Table 1). Because free amino acids in plants are considered to turn over within a week, some of these plants, if not all, could be "candidates of NO_2-philic plants".

Nine species (3 individual plants for each species), involving 3 species (*Erechtites hieracifolia*, *Bidens frondosa* and *Erigeron annuus*) of high NO_2-assimilation ability and 6 species (*Eragrostis ferruginea*, *Kyllinga breviforia* subsp. *leiolepis*, *Plantago lanceolata*, *Hemerocallis fulva* var. *longituba*, *Erigeron pusillus* and *Rumex acetosa*) of low NO_2-assimilation ability, were analyzed for stomatal responses to NO_2 and for NO_2-assimilation. No direct relationships between NO_2-assimilation ability of plants and their stomatal responses to NO_2 were observed at present. It is conceivable that at least for these plants the opening and closure of stomata is not a limiting step of NO_2-assimilation but that other factors such as membrane permeability of nitrate and/or nitrite and biochemical activities related to nitrate metabolism may play a key role for assimilation of NO_2 in plants.

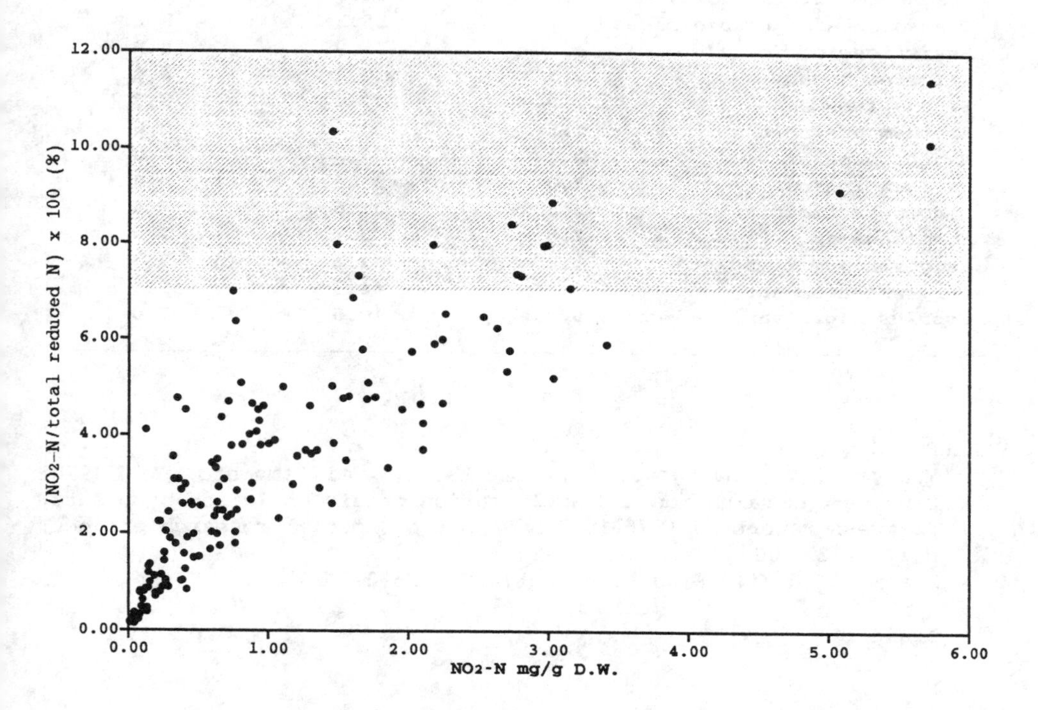

Figure 1. Relationship between NO_2-derived reduced nitrogen and the ratio of NO_2-derived reduced nitrogen to total reduced nitrogen in 149 plants. Each dot corresponds to individual plant species (see text for details).

Table 1. List of plants in which NO_2-derived reduced nitrogen comprised more than 7% of total reduced nitrogen in plants.

Plants	(1) NO_2-N (mg/g DW)	(2) total reduced N (mg/g DW)	(1)/(2) x100 (%)
Nicotiana tabacum BY-2	5.7	50.0	11.4
Borago officinalis	1.5	14.0	10.4
Erechtites hieracifolia	5.7	56.5	10.1
Crassocephalum crepidioides	5.1	55.3	9.2
Levisticum officinale	3.0	33.9	8.9
Erigeron annuus	2.7	32.5	8.4
Bidens frondosa	3.0	37.4	8.0
Anethum graveolens	1.5	18.6	8.0
Mentha piperata	2.2	24.2	8.0
Lactuca indica	3.0	37.2	8.0
Oenothera biennis	2.8	37.6	7.4
Impatiens sp.	2.8	38.1	7.3
Erigeron sumatrensis	1.6	22.4	7.3
Chrysanthemum sp.	3.2	44.5	7.1
Populus nigra var.*italica*	0.7	10.6	7.0

REFERENCES

1 Yoneyama, T., Sasagawa, H., Totsuka, T. and Yamamoto, Y. (1978) Studies on evaluation and amelioration of air pollution by plants. Progress report in 1976-1977. Report of special research project, NIES R-2 103-111

2 Black, C. R. (1979) J. Exp. Bot. 30, 235-243

TRANSGENIC "AIR-POLLUTANT-PHILIC PLANTS" PRODUCED BY PARTICLE BOMBARDMENT

MITSUNORI KAMADA[1], ASA HIGAKI[1], YUKIO JIN[1], MOTOAKI SEKI[1], TATSUYA SAWASAKI[1], SHOJI IDA[2], GENTARO TOYOHARA[1], KOHEI IRIFUNE[1] AND HIROMICHI MORIKAWA[1], DEPARTMENT OF BOTANY, FACULTY OF SCIENCE, HIROSHIMA UNIVERSITY[1], HIGASHI-HIROSHIMA 724, JAPAN AND RESEARCH INSTITUTE FOR FOOD SCIENCE, KYOTO UNIVERSITY[2], UJI 611, JAPAN

1. INTRODUCTION

Plants are reported (1) to assimilate nitrogen dioxide in their leaves through nitrate assimilation pathway. We have been studying on NO_2-assimilation ability of a number of wild and cultivated plants (Proceeding of this Congress). The eventual aim of this study is to produce "Air-Pollutant-Philic Plants" that will give a solution of global environmental problems such as acid rain.

The activities of the enzymes related to nitrate assimilation, including nitrite reductase, are thought to change due to the circadian rhythm (2). When plants are fumigated with NO_2, nitrite and/or ammonia are accumulated in plants during nighttime, which results in lethal damages to plants (1). It is conceivable that when plants are transformed with NiR gene under the control of foreign promoters and terminators the expression of this gene in transformed plants may become independent of the circadian rhythm and that NO_2-assimilation ability of the plants can be much increased.

To test this hypothesis, we first studied production of transgenic *Arabidopsis* plants that are transformed with spinach NiR cDNA under the control of a foreign promoter and terminator because among almost 150 plants analyzed *Arabidopsis thaliana* had a high NO_2-assimilation ability and this plant can easily be transformed by particle bombardment (3). Results are described in the following part of this report.

2. MATERIALS and METHODS

2.1 Plant material: *Arabidopsis thaliana* genotype C24 were aseptically grown from surface-sterilized seeds on Gamborg B-5 agarose (0.6%) medium for 4-6 weeks under 16/8 h light-dark cycle at 26°C. This culture condition was used throughout this study unless otherwise specified. Roots were harvested from the plants and excised into sections (0.5-1.0 cm long), and the sections were placed to form a circle (3.5 cm diameter) on a filter paper (Advantec Toyo no. 2, 5.5 cm diameter) on 0.5/0.05 medium (3). After being cultured for 3 days, they were subjected to particle bombardment.

N. Murata (ed.), Research in Photosynthesis, Vol. IV, 83–86.

2.2 Plasmids: Plasmid pMK48, which contains spinach NiR cDNA (provided by Dr. S. Rothstein, University of Guelph, Canada) (4), the cauliflower mosaic virus (CaMV) 35S promoter at its 5′ end, and nopaline synthase (NOS) polyadenylation region at its 3′ end, was constructed. Plasmid pARK22 (provided by Dr. H. Anzai, Meiji Seika Kaisha, Ltd., Japan), in which transcription of the bar gene is controlled by the CaMV 35S promoter and NOS terminator, was used as selectable marker. The bar gene cassette (1.8 kb) was inserted to the SphI site of pMK48 and the resulting plasmid having both bar gene and NiR cDNA was designated as pMKB17.

2.3 Gene delivery to the cells: The particle acceleration device and the methods for gene delivery to the cells using this device were essentially as reported previously (5, 6). The gold particles (1.1 um in diameter, Tokuriki Honten Co., Ltd., Tokyo, Japan) were coated with plasmid DNA (pMKB17 alone or equal mixture of pMK48 and pARK22) by co-precipitation in ethanol as reported previously (7). Bombardment was made under the following conditions: accelerating pressure of 200 kg/cm^2; sample-to-stopper distance of 10 cm; 4 ug DNA/mg gold particles; reduced pressure of 60 mm Hg. Two bombardments were given to each sample of root sections.

2.4 Selection of transformed calli and plant regeneration: After being shot, the filter papers with sections were transferred onto 0.5/0.05 medium (callus-forming medium), and incubated for 48 h at 26°C. The sections were then transferred onto 0/5 medium (shoot-forming medium) (3) supplemented with 2 mg/l bialaphos (Meiji Seika Kaisha, Ltd., Japan), and cultured for 2 weeks. Bialaphos-resistant calli formed were subcultured on fresh 0/5 medium containing 2 mg/l bialaphos every 2 weeks for 1 month. Regenerated bialaphos-resistant shoots were transferred to Murashige and Skoog (MS) agar (0.8%) medium lacking bialaphos. This facilitated the elongation of the shoots. The elongated shoots were then transferred to bialaphos-free MS agar (0.8%) medium containing 1 mg/l 3-indolebutyric acid (IBA) (root-forming medium).

2.5 Southern blot analysis: Total DNA was isolated from bialaphos-resistant plant by the method of Mettler (8), electrophoresed through a 0.7% agarose gel (2 ug DNA/lane) and transferred to a nylon membrane (NEN Research Products, Boston, Mass., USA) as described by Southern (9). The blots were hybridized with a 2.0-kb EcoRI fragment from pCIB400 (4) containing spinach NiR cDNA that had been ^{32}P-labelled by the random primer method (Pharmacia, USA). After being washed, they were autoradiographed using X-ray film for 24 h.

2.6 Dot blot analysis: Total DNA from bialaphos-resistant plant was isolated as described above and blotted on a nylon membrane (0.2 ug DNA/lane). The blots were hybridized with the EcoRI-fragment of pCIB400 containing NiR cDNA as described above after being biotinylated by the random primer method (Sumitomo Metal, Co., Ltd., Japan). After being washed, the DNA hybridized with the biotin-conjugated and alkaline phosphatase-conjugated probe was detected chemiluminescently using X-ray film with an intensifying screen for 30 minutes.

3. RESULTS and DISCUSSION

Transgenic plants from root sections bombarded with pMKB17:

Eight green bialaphos-resistant calli developed in the presence of 2 mg/l bialaphos on root sections bombarded with pMKB17-coated gold particles (14-17 days after bombardment). No calli were formed from non-bombarded root sections in the presence of the same amount of bialaphos. The bialaphos-resistant calli developed were transferred onto 0/5 medium containing 2 mg/l bialaphos and every 2 weeks transferred onto a fresh bialaphos-containing medium of the same composition. A number of bialaphos-resistant shoots were regenerated from each of the bialaphos-resistant callus clones (1 month after bombardment). They were then transferred to MS agar medium lacking bialaphos, and cultured another for 1 to 2 weeks. The elongated shoots were transferred to MS agar medium containing 1 mg/l IBA, and rooted (2 months after bombardment) (Fig. 1. a). About 5 plants per each of eight clones were kept for further analysis.

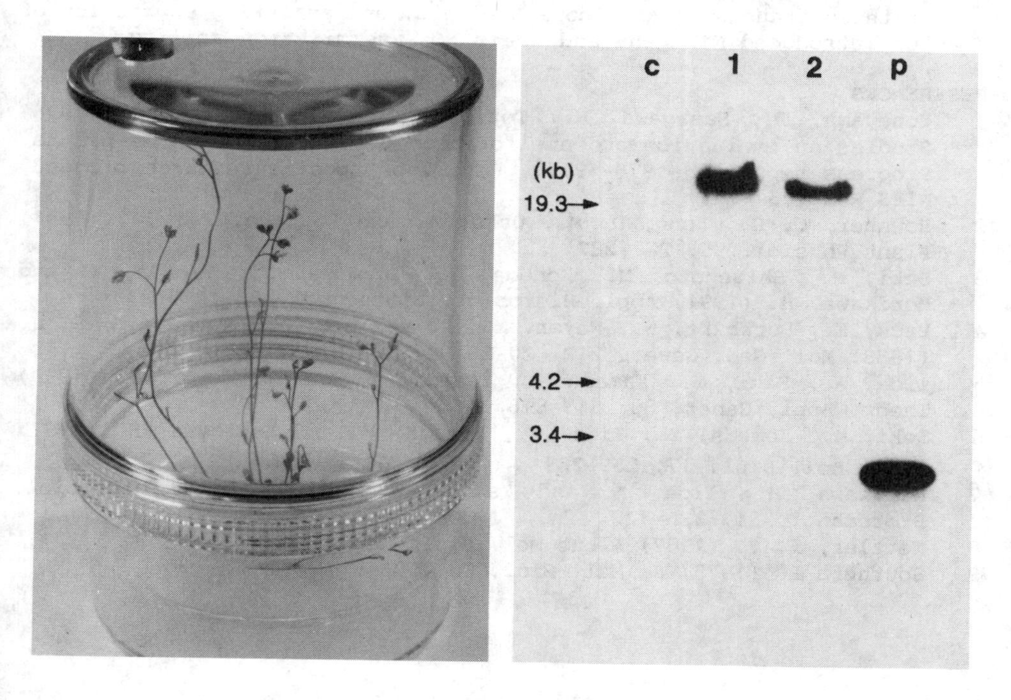

Figure 1. a. A transgenic Arabidopsis thaliana plant that have spinach NiR cDNA (see text for details).
b. Southern blot analysis of DNA from transgenic A. thaliana plants. Total DNAs from a non-transformant (lane C) and from a putative transformant (lanes 1 and 2), without being digested with restriction enzymes, were hybridized with spinach NiR as a probe. Lane P corresponds to plasmid pMK48.

Integration of the introduced NiR gene in the genome of the putative transgenic _A. thaliana_ plants was confirmed by Southern blot analysis (Fig. 1. b). Total DNA from each of the bialaphos-resistant plants, without being digested with restriction enzymes, was hybridized with a probe of spinach NiR cDNA as described in Materials and Methods. The probe hybridized only with high-molecular-weight DNA of the putative transformants, whereas it did not hybridize with the DNA of non-transformed control _A. thaliana_ plants as shown in Fig. 1. b.

Transgenic plants from root sections co-bombarded with pMK48 and pARK22:

From root sections bombarded with gold particles coated with mixture of pMK48 and pARK22, twelve clones of bialaphos-resistant plants (5 plants for each clone) were obtained. Dot blot analysis of the genomic DNA of these plants indicated that 4 clones had spinach NiR cDNA in their genome (data not shown).

We are currently collecting R_1 and R_2 seeds after self-pollination of these transgenic Arabidopsis plants, and analyzing expression of the introduced NiR gene and their NO_2-assimilation ability.

REFERENCES

1 Yoneyama, T., Sasagawa, H., Totsuka, T. and Yamamoto, Y. (1978) Studies on evaluation and amelioration of air pollution by plants. Progress report in 1976-1977. Report of special research project, NIES R-2 103-111

2 Bowsher, C. G., Long, D. M., Oaks, A. and Rothstein, S. J. (1991) Plant Physiol. 95, 281-287

3 Seki, M., Shigemoto, N., Komeda, Y., Imamura, J., Yamada, Y. and Morikawa, H. (1991) Appl. Microbiol. Biotechnol. 36, 228-230

4 Back, E., Burkhart, W., Meyer, M., Privalle,L. and Rothstein, S. J. (1988) Mol. Gen. Genet. 212, 20-26

5 Iida, A., Seki, M., Kamada M., Yamada, Y. and Morikawa, H. (1990) Theor. Appl. Genet. 80, 813-816

6 Seki, M., Komeda, Y., Iida, A., Yamada, Y. and Morikawa, H. (1991) Plant Mol. Biol. 17, 259-263

7 Morikawa, H., Iida, A. and Yamada, Y. (1989) Appl. Microbiol. Biotechnol. 31, 320-322

8 Mettler, I. J. (1987) Plant Mol. Biol. Reporter 5, 346-349

9 Southern E. (1975) J. Mol. Biol. 98, 503-517

Lysine and threonine sensitive isozymes of aspartate kinase in rice and pea.

Seiichiro Kiyota and Katsuhiro Sakano.
Laboratory of nitrogen metabolism, National Institute of Agrobiological Resources, Tsukuba, Ibaraki 305 Japan.

1. Introduction

Aspartate kinase(AK) catalyzes the first reaction of biosynthetic pathway of amino acids of aspartate family. Depending on sensitivity to inhibitory amino acids, AKs are assorted to threonine sensitive (Thr-AK) and lysine sensitive (Lys-AK).

Lys-AKs have been purified from suspension culture cells of carrot (1) and maize (2). But difference between Thr-AK and Lys-AK has not been characterized well. During carrot root tissue culture, the amounts of Thr-AK and Lys-AK and their proportion changed (3). This was accompanied by endogenous free amino acid (4). In the present study, we report that similar changes occur in Thr-AK and Lys-AK during growth of rice plants. In addition, we have purified pea Thr-AK to apparent homogeneity on SDS-PAGE and studied the molecular relationship between Thr-AK and Thr-sensitive homoserine dehydrogenase (HSDH).

2. Materials and methods.

Leaves were harvested from 9-day old pea seedling (*Pisum sativum* L. c.v. Nankaimidori) grown on vermiculite under continuous light. Rice (*Oryza sativa* L. c.v. Koshihikari) was grown on fertilized soil (Bonsol-1, Sumitomo Chemical, Japan) under continuous light. Leaves were harvested every week from the plants during the periods of 2-5 weeks after sowing.

Rice leaves were powdered in liquid nitrogen. The powder was extracted in 2 parts of extraction buffer (50mM Mes-KOH buffer pH6.3, containing 15% glycerol, 1mM $MgCl_2$, 0.1mM Lys, 0.1mM Thr and 14mM mercaptoethanol) by Physcotron homogenizer (Niti-on, Japan). The extract was filtrated through 4 layers of cheese cloth and centrifuged at 15000g

N. Murata (ed.), Research in Photosynthesis, Vol. IV, 87–90.

for 30min. The supernatant was passed through a Sephadex G-25 column which had been equilibrated with 50mM potassium phosphate buffer pH7.6, containing 15% glycerol, 1mM $MgCl_2$, 0.1mM Lys, 0.1mM Thr and 14mM mercaptoethanol. Protein fraction was collected and applied to a DEAE Toyopearl column pre-equilibrated with the same buffer and eluted by NaCl gradient. Pea leaves were extracted in the same way as for rice and details of purification procedures for pea Thr-AK will appear elsewhere (S. Kiyota and K. Sakano, manuscript in preparation).

AK activity was measured by hydroxamate method (5). To determine Thr-AK and Lys-AK separately, either 10mM Lys or Thr was added in the reaction mixture. One unit of AK activity is defined as 1 nmol of aspartylhydroxamate formed per min under standard condition. HSDH activity was visualized on PAGE gel plate by the method of Matthews and Widholm (6).

3. Results and discussion

1. ***Changes in AK isozymes in rice leaves during plant growth.*** Rice leaves were harvested at 2, 3, 4 and 5 weeks after sowing. AK isozymes in the extracts of rice leaves were separated by DEAE Toyopearl chromatography (Fig. 1). One Thr-AK and two Lys-AK activities were found. Thr-AK activity was highest at week 2 and decreased thereafter. One Lys-AK which was eluted at lower NaCl concentration was also high at week 2 and then decreased gradually. But another Lys-AK did not change throughout the whole growth period.

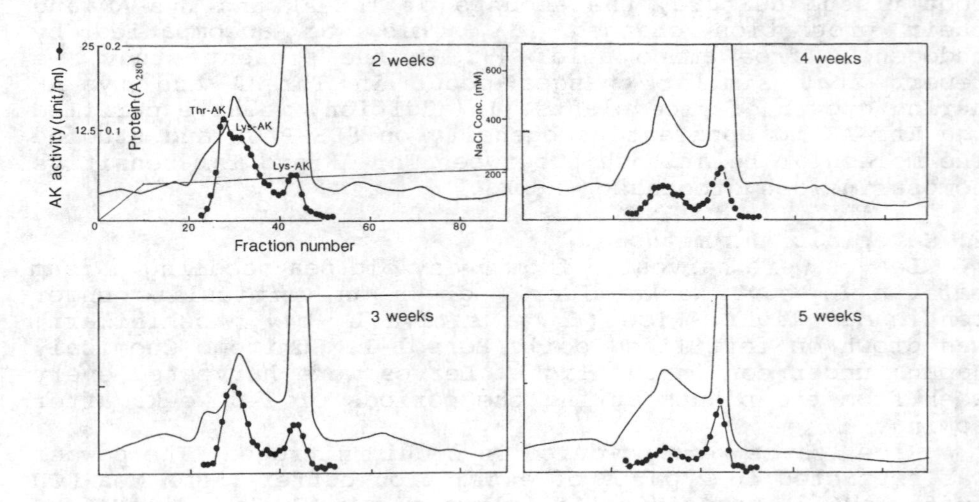

Fig. 1 Profiles of AK from 2 to 5-week old rice leaves.

2. ***Purification of pea Thr-AK.*** Thr-AK from pea leaves was purified to homogeneity on SDS-PAGE (Table 1.).

Table 1. Summary of pea Thr-AK purification

column	total activity units	protein mg	specific activity u/mg	purification folds	yield %
Sephadex G-25	371	5100	0.073	1	100
Sephacryl S-300	125	936	0.13	1.8	34
DEAE Toyopearl	96.8	10.5	9.2	126	26
Mono Q HR5/5	15.6	0.442	35.3	484	4.2
HA-1000	1.28	0.040	32	438	0.3
Mono P HR5/5	0.22	0.001	220	3014	0.06

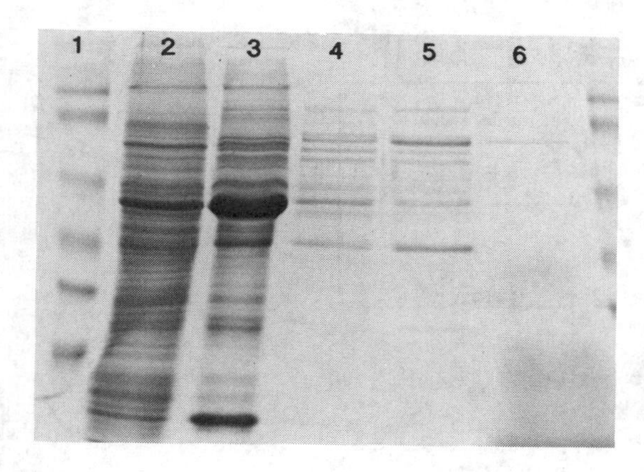

Fig. 2 SDS-PAGE of Thr-AK preparations during purification. lane 1:MW marker 2:after Sephadex G-25, 3:Sephacryl S-300, 4:DEAE Toyopearl, 5:Mono Q, 6:Mono P

Apparent molecular weight as determined on SDS-PAGE was 90kD. As the molecular weight on Sephacryl S-300 gel filtration was approximately 500kD, native Thr-AK may be consisted of 6 identical subunits. Thus molecular construction of pea Thr-AK is different from the maize Lys-AK which has been reported to be composed of 49 and 60kD (2).

3. ***Thr-AK and HSDH activities.*** Thr-AK and Thr-sensitive HSDH activities were coeluted from Sephacryl S-300 column as shown in Fig. 3. In the subsequent column chromatography on DEAE Toyopearl, both were coeluted again. These results confirm those by Aarnes and Rognes (7).
However, none of the Lys-AK was coeluted with HSDH (Fig.3) in contrast to carrot enzyme (8). Also molecular weight of the Thr-AK we purified is similar to that of HSDH of maize (9) and of carrot HSDH (10). Thus, pea Thr-AK is a bifunctional enzyme having AK and HSDH as in carrot enzyme (8).

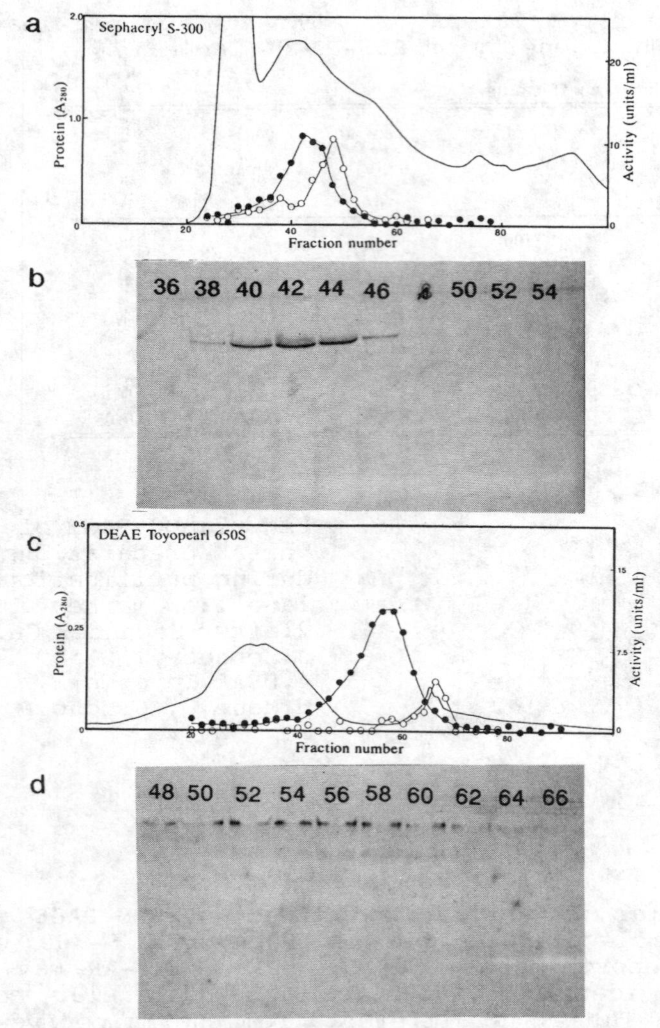

Fig.3 Profiles of a) AK and b)HSDH on Sephacryl S-300, c)AK and d)HSDH on DEAE Toyopearl.

References

1 Relton, J. M., P. L. Bonner, R. M. Wallsgrove and P. J. Lea (1988) BBA 953,48-60.
2 Dotson, S. B.,D. A. Somers and B. G. Gengenbach (1989) Plant Physiol. 91,1602-1608.
3 Sakano, K. and A. Komamine (1978) Plant Physiol. 61,115-118.
4 Sakano, K. (1979) Plant Physiol. 63,583-585.
5 Bryan, P. A., R. D. Cawley, R. D, Brunner and J. K. Bryan (1970) Biochem. Biophys. Res. Commun. 41,1211-1217.
6 Matthews, B. F. and J. M. Widholm (1978) Planta 141,315-321.
7 Aarnes H. and S. E. Rognes (1974) Phytochemistry 13,2717-2724.
8 Wilson B. J., A. C. Gray and B F. Matthews (1991) 97,1323-1328.
9 Krishnaswamy S. and J. K. Bryan (1986) Arch. of Biochem. Biophys. 246,250-262.
10 Matthews B. F., M. J. Farrar and A. C. Gray (1989) Plant Physiol. 91,1569-1574.

PURIFICATION AND PROPERTIES OF ATP-PHOSPHORIBOSYL-TRANSFERASE FROM WHEAT GERM

Silvia Münzer, Rosarin Hashimoto-Kumpaisal, Alfred Scheidegger, Daisaku Ohta
Int. Res. Lab., Ciba-Geigy, Takarazuka, Hyogo 665, Japan

INTRODUCTION

Histidine is an essential amino acid in animals but can be synthesized by most microorganisms and higher plants. The histidine biosynthetic pathway of *Salmonella typhimurium* has been studied extensively by Ames et al. (1). It consists of 10 enzymatical steps catalyzed by 9 different enzymes. The first of these enzymes, ATP-PR-transferase (*N*-1-(5'-phosphoribosyl)-ATP:pyrophosphate phosphoribosyl transferase, EC 2.4.2.17) catalyzes the synthesis of ATP phosphoribose from phosphoribosyl pyrophosphate (PRPP) and ATP as substrates.

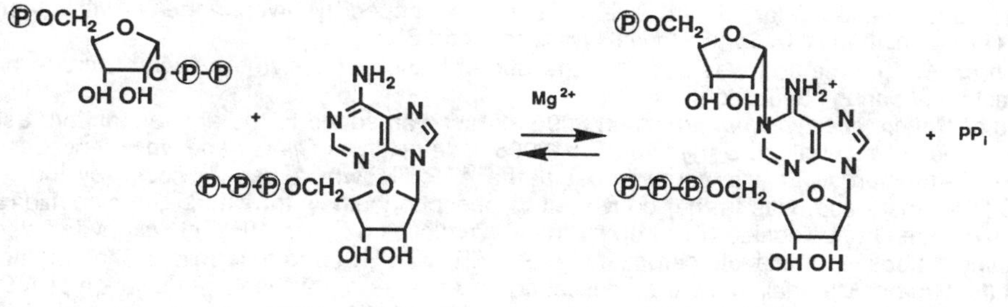

PRPP + ATP $\xrightarrow{Mg^{2+}}$ PR-ATP + PP_i

A histidine biosynthetic pathway similar to that in *Salmonella* is assumed to exist in plants. To investigate the ATP-PR-transferase in plants was the scope of this work.

MATERIALS AND METHODS

Preparation of plant enzyme extracts:
2 to 3 week old plant seedlings or wheat germ were used as enzyme sources. The seedlings were frozen in liquid nitrogen, ground with seasand and polyclar AT using a mortar and a pestle and extracted in ice cold buffer A (100 mM potassium phosphate pH 7.5, 100 mM NaCl, 1 mM L-histidine, 5 mM EDTA, 30 mM β-mercaptoethanol). Wheat germ was homogenized with a Polytron blender in aceton in a methanol/dry ice bath, dried under reduced pressure and extracted in buffer A. After centrifugation the extract solutions were saturated to 80% with ammonium sulfate, the precipitate was redissolved in buffer B (100 mM tris/HCl pH 7.5, 30 mM β-mercaptoethanol) and desalted on Sephadex G-25. These extracts were used for the detection of ATP-PR-transferase activity with enzyme assay A.

N. Murata (ed.), Research in Photosynthesis, Vol. IV, 91–94.

Purification:
All purification steps were carried out at 4°C. Usually about 1 kg wheat germ aceton powder was extracted for 30 min in 6 l extraction buffer A . After removal of the wheat germ residues by centrifugation the extract solution was fractionated by ammonium sulfate precipitation. The precipitate of the 27-47% saturated fraction was redissolved in 50 mM potassium phosphate buffer pH 7.5. Again ammonium sulfate was added to give 25% saturation and the precipitate was centrifuged off. The supernatant solution was applied to a Butyl-Toyopearl 650M column (5 x 51 cm) (Tosoh, Tokyo, Japan) in 50 mM phosphate buffer pH 7.5 with 1 M ammonium sulfate and eluted with a decreasing gradient of ammonium sulfate. Each fraction was desalted on Sephadex G for activity determination, because ammonium disturbs the enzyme assay. The combined active fractions were dialyzed against 50 mM Tris/HCl pH 7.5 , applied to a DEAE-Toyopearl 650M column (5 x 25 cm) (Tosoh) equilibrated with the same buffer and eluted with a gradient of NaCl (0-0.5M). The active fractions were concentrated and dialyzed against 20 mM potassium phosphate buffer pH 7.5. The dialyzed solution was applied to a Heparin-Sepharose CL-6B column (2.5 x 8 cm) (Pharmacia) and eluted with increasing buffer concentration (20-400 mM potassium phosphate buffer pH 7.5). After concentration the active fractions of the previous column were applied to a Superdex 200 26/60 column (Pharmacia) and eluted in 20 mM Tris (pH 7.5) / 0.2 M NaCl buffer. The active fractions of the previous column were concentrated and the buffer exchanged to 20 mM Tris/ HCl pH 7.5 with a PD10 column. The enzyme solution was applied to a 1 ml HiTrap Blue column (Pharmacia) and eluted isocratically with 20 mM Tris/HCl pH7.5.

Enzyme assay:
The standard assay mixture contained 11.4 mM Tris/HCl pH 9.0, 22.8 mM $MgCl_2$, 85.7 mM KCl, 5.7 mM ATP (Sigma), 0.57 mM PRPP (Sigma) and enzyme in 175 µl solution. The mixture was incubated at 30°C for 15 min. The reaction was stopped by lowering the pH with either 50 µl 1 N HCl (method A) or 35 µl 1 M NaH_2PO_4 (method B).
Method A: This method was used for the determination of enzyme activity in crude plant extracts and during purification.
10 µl of *Salmonella typhimurium* strain 3095 extract was added to the above standard assay mixture before incubation. *S. typhimurium* 3095 is defect in its *His G* gene which encodes the ATP-PR-transferase. In this coupling assay the ATP-PR, which was produced by the plant ATP-PR-transferase, was further converted to phosphoribulosyl formimino-5-aminoimidazole carboxamide ribonucleoside (BBM III) by the *Salmonella* enzymes. BBM III was hydrolyzed to 5-amino-1-ribosyl-4-imidazole carboxamide (AICAR) with HCl and determined photometrically with the Bratton-Marshall method as described by Ames et al. (2). A 10 µM solution of AICAR gave an absorbance of 0.270 at 550 nm (2). 1 unit of ATP-PR-transferase activity is defined as the amount of enzyme producing 1 µmol AICAR per minute under standard conditions with excess amount of *Salmonella* enzyme extract.
Method B: All activity determinations for enzyme characterization were performed with partially purified enzyme after Superdex 200 chromatography using method B.
After terminating the enzyme reaction with 35 µl 1 M NaH_2PO_4 15 µl of the reaction mixture were injected into an HPLC system and the compounds isocratically eluted from a QAE-2SW column (Tosoh) with 0.5 M NaH_2PO_4 at a flow rate of 1 ml/min. In this method the peak area at 260 nm was used as a measure for the enzyme activity.

RESULTS AND DISCUSSION

Screening for ATP-PR-transferase in plants:
8 different plant materials were examined for ATP-PR-transferase activity, which could be detected in all preparations except soybean seedlings (Tab.1). The highest specific activity was found in cucumber seedlings and the highest extractable activity per g plant material in locally purchased wheat germ. Because of easy access in large amounts and relatively high extractable activity wheat germ from Sigma was chosen for purification and further studies.

Tab.1: Distribution of ATP-PR-transferase activity in plants

Plant species	specific activity mU/mg[a)]	extractable activity mU/g[b)]
Soybean seedlings *(Glycine max)*	0	0
Corn seedlings *(Zea mays)*	0.051	0.059
Rice seedlings *(Oryza sativa)*	0.054	0.087
Wheat seedlings *(Hordeum vulgare)*	0.018	0.019
Barley seedlings *(Triticum aestivum)*	0.025	0.018
Wheat germ (local) *(Triticum aestivum)*	0.037	1.460
Wheat germ (Sigma) *(Triticum aestivum)*	0.018	0.595

Enzyme activities were determined by method A
a) activity per mg protein *b) activity per g plant material;*

Purification of ATP-PR-transferase from wheat germ:
The ATP-PR-transferase from wheat germ was purified over 30,000 fold in 5 chromatographic steps as summarized in Tab.2. In the last step, chromatography on Blue Sepharose, virtually all impurities were bound to the gel whereas the ATP-PR-transferase was not retained. The SDS PAGE gel of the unbound fraction showed only one major band (see Fig. 1).

Tab.2: Purification of ATP-PR-transferase from wheat germ

fraction	activity mU	act. recov. %	protein mg	spec. act. mU/mg	purification
Crude	2592	100.0	143500	0.018	1.0
Ammonium sulfate	1331	51.3	30740	0.040	2.4
Butyl-Toyopearl	1244	47.8	4100	0.30	16.7
DEAE-Toyopearl	1538	58.3	820	1.90	103
Heparin-Sepharose	700	27.0	59.6	11.8	647
Superdex 200	378	14.6	12.9	29.4	1617
HiTrap Blue	187	7.2	0.34	549	30250

The table shows a representative purification from 1 kg wheat germ aceton powder. Enzyme activities were determined by method A

Properties of the ATP-PR-transferase from wheat germ:
The native molecular weight of the enzyme was determined by gel filtration and native PAGE to be about 220,000 Da. After SDS PAGE one single band of 37,000 Da could be observed, indicating the enzyme to be a hexamer.
The enzyme could be stored frozen at -80°C for at least 6 months without loss of activity. At 4°C the activity decreased about 20% in one week. The enzyme showed highest activity at pH 8.9 and 40°C However, as the enzyme stability at 40°C was poor the standard enzyme assay was incubated at 30°C activity. Under standard reaction conditions the K_m values for ATP and PRPP were determined as 780 µM and 125 µM, respectively. The ATP-PR-transferase was specifically inhibited by L-histidine with an IC_{50} of 70 µM in the standard assay, whereas D-histidine did not inhibit the enzyme activity even at a level of 1 mM.

Tab.3 shows a comparison of the ATP-PR-transferase from wheat germ and *Salmonella typhimurium*. Both enzymes are of similar size. They both require Mg^{2+} ions for activity, and their kinetic parameters are in the same range. No significant differences between the plant and the bacterial enzyme have so far been observed. Histidinoldehydrogenase, the last enzyme in the histidine biosynthetic pathway, has been isolated from cabbage. As in the case of ATP-PR-transferase the structural and functional properties of the plant enzyme were rather similar to those from microbial origin (6). Now both the first and the last enzyme of the histidine biosynthetic pathway have been purified from plant sources, confirming a corresponding pathway in microorganisms and plants.

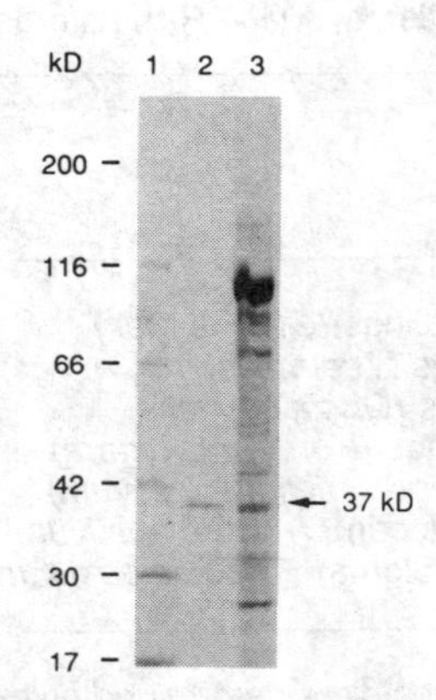

Fig.1: SDS gel of the last purification step

The proteins were separated on an 4/20 SDS-polyacrylamide gel and stained with coomassie blue.
lane 1: molecular weight markers
lane 2: unbound enzyme after HiTrap Blue
lane 3: enzyme solution applied to the HiTrap Blue column. The ATP-PR-transferase appears as a single band of 37 kD.

Tab.3: Comparison of ATP-PR-transferase from wheat germ and *Salmonella typhimurium*

	ATP-PR-transferase wheat germ	*Salmonella typhimurium*	reference
molecular weight	220,000	215,000	4
subunit molecular weight	37,000	34,000-35,000	4, 5
apparent K_m (ATP)	780 µM	200 µM, 430µM	3, 5
apparent K_m (PRPP)	125 µM	67 µM, 56 µM	3, 5
IC_{50} of L-histidine	75 µM	60-80 µM	4, 5

REFERENCES

1. Brenner, M., Ames, B. N. (1971), in Methabolic Pathways, (Vogel, H. J., ed.), Vol. 5, p 349-307, Academic Press, New York
2. Ames, B. N., Martin, R. G., Garry, B. J. (1961), J. Biol. Chem. 236, 2019-2026
3. Martin, R. G. (1963), J. Biol. Chem. 238, 257-268
4. Voll, M. J., Appella, E., Martin, R. G. (1967), J. Biol. Chem. 242, 1760-1767
5. Whitfield, H. J. Jr. (1971), J. Biol. Chem. 246, 899-908
6. Nagai, A., Ward, E., Beck, J., Tada, S., Chang, J.-Y., Scheidegger, A., Ryals, J. (1991), Proc. Natl. Acad. Sci. USA 88, 4133-4137

HISTIDINOL DEHYDROGENASE IN HIGHER PLANTS. PURIFICATION, CLONING, AND EXPRESSION

A. Nagai, K. Suzuki, E. Ward[1], M. Moyer[1], J. Mano, J. Beck[1], S. Tada, M. Hashimoto, J-Y.Chang[2], J. Ryals[1], A. Scheidegger, D. Ohta Intl. Res. Labs., CIBA-GEIGY (JAPAN) Ltd., Hyogo 665, Japan, CIBA-GEIGY Corp. NC 27709, USA[1], and CIBA-GEIGY AG, CH-4002 Basel, Switzerland[2]

1. INTRODUCTION

Histidine (His) biosynthetic pathway has so far been extensively studied in prokaryotic and eukaryotic microorganisms. Bacterial histidinol dehydrogenase (HDH, EC 1.1.1.23) is known to be involved in the His biosynthesis and to catalyze the last two step oxidation reactions in the pathway to produce the end product His from histidinol during the reduction of two moles of NAD^+ (1). On the other hand, although circumstantial evidence suggests the existence of a plant His biosynthetic pathway similar to that in bacterial cells (2), neither biochemical nor physiological aspects of plant HDH have been elucidated. Here we report purification and characterization of HDH from cabbage plants (*Brassica orelacea*). Molecular cloning of a cabbage HDH cDNA and its expression by using the baculovirus expression vector system are also described.

2. MATERIALS AND METHODS

Spring cabbage shoots were selected as the starting material for HDH purification because they possesed the highest specific content of the enzyme activity in the tissue among several plant species examined (3). HDH purification was performed in a series of chromatographic steps including a newly developed histidinol sepharose 4B affinity column (3). The enzyme activity was assayed spectrophotometrically by measuring the increase in absorbance at 340 nm due to the reduction of NAD^+ in the reaction mixture described as previously (3).

Partial amino acid sequences of HDH were determined by automated Edman degradation in peptide fragments obtained either by lysyl endopeptidase digestion or CNBr cleavage of the purified protein (4). A high degree of sequence similarity was found between the peptide fragments of cabbage HDH and various parts of the *HIS4C* gene product of *Saccharomyces cerevisiae*, which corresponds to the yeast HDH (5). Therefore, relative positions and orientations of these peptides in cabbage HDH were deduced by aligning their sequences with that of the yeast HDH, and degenerated oligonucleotides were designed as primers for a polymerase chain reaction to amplify a HDH cDNA fragment in a cabbage cDNA library. A 1-kb cDNA fragment amplified was used as a probe for cloning of a full length HDH cDNA from the same cabbage cDNA library. The cabbage leaf tissue cDNA library was constructed in a λ zapII phage plasmid using a ZAP cDNA gigapack II Gold synthesis kit (Stratagene) (4).

A full-length HDH cDNA cloned from the library was expressed in cultured insect cells (Sf9: *Spodoptera frugiperda* cells) by using the baculovirus expression vector system according to the methods described (6). Briefly, a 1645 bp cDNA fragment containing an entire coding region of cabbage HDH was isolated from pBSHDH (4) by digesting using *Kpn*I and *Bam*HI restriction enzymes, and ligated with the *Kpn*I-*Bam*HI double digested transfer vector pVL1393 to construct pVL1393/HDH. The plasmid pVL1393/HDH was then used to obtain recombinant baculovirus carrying the cDNA encoding HDH precursor protein (AcNPV/HDH) (7). Wild type baculovirus (*Autographa californica* polyhedrosis virus: AcNPV) and the transfer vector pVL1393 were provided by M. D. Summers (Texas A&M University).

N. Murata (ed.), Research in Photosynthesis, Vol. IV, 95–98.

3. RESULTS AND DISCUSSION

3.1 Purification and properties of the enzyme.

HDH was purified 2116 fold from a fraction of cabbage crude extracts precipitated with 45-65% saturation of ammonium sulfate. The purified HDH gave a single band on SDS-PAGE with an apparent molecular mass of 52-kDa (Fig.1, lane 3). An apparent molecular mass in a native form was determined to be 103-kDa by gel filtration suggesting that cabbage HDH consists of two identical subunits. Apparent K_m values for L-histidinol and NAD^+ were 15.5 and 42 μM, respectively. HDH activity was stimulated by the addition of Mn^{2+}, but was inhibited in the presence either of Ba^{2+}, Mg^{2+}, Ni^{2+}, Ca^{2+}, Zn^{2+}, or Cu^{2+}. Optimum pH for the activity was 9.2 in glycine-NaOH buffer. When L-histidinol was used as a substrate for the cabbage HDH, 2 moles of NAD^+ were stoichiometrically reduced during the formation of 1 mol L-histidine. These results indicate that higher plants share the pathway for the synthesis of His with bacteria; at least for the reactions catalyzed by HDH. The purified cabbage HDH was separated into six protein bands showed equal HDH activities upon activity staining analysis using nitroblue tetrazolium and phenazine methosulfate, suggesting the existence of HDH isozymes.

3.2 Cloning.

A full length cDNA was isolated from the cabbage cDNA library by using the amplified 1-kb cDNA fragment as a probe.The cDNA was predicted to encode a HDH precursor protein with a putative 31-amino acid chloroplast transit peptide at its N-terminus and a mature molecular mass of 47.5-kDa (Fig. 2). The transit peptide was rich in serine and threonine (32%) specifically, and also in lysine and arginine (19%), showing general properties for chloroplast transit peptides (8).

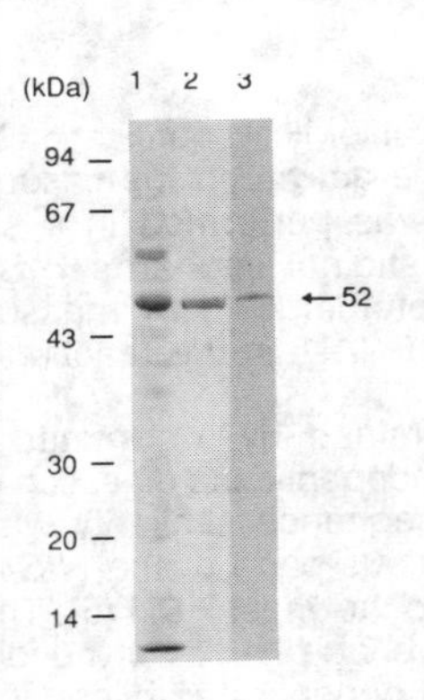

Fig. 1. Comparison of cabbage HDH and rHDH
1. Infected cell
2. rHDH
3. cabbage HDH

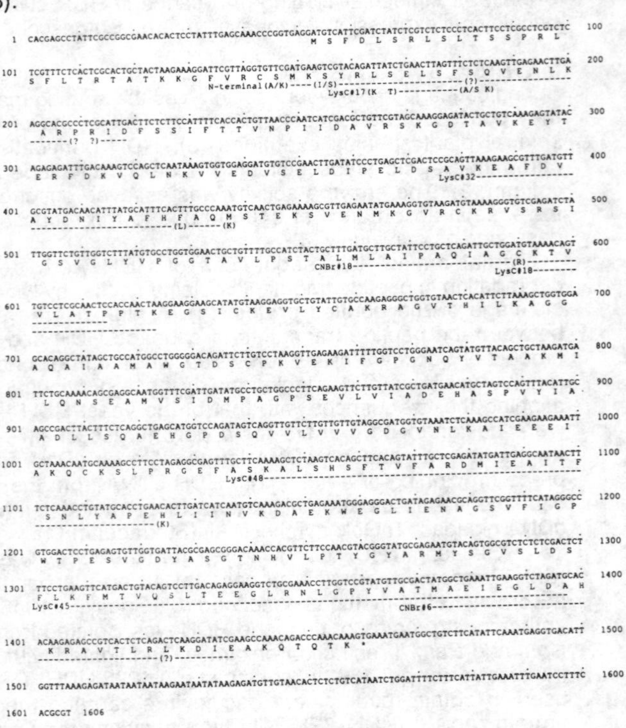

Fig. 2. DNA sequence and deduced amino acid sequence of cabbage HDH cDNA clone. Regions corresponding to the amino acid sequences of the peptides determined from the purified protein were underlined with dotted lines.

The predicted primary structure of the mature HDH was 51% and 49% identical to the *Escherichia coli* (9) and the yeast HDH (5), respectively (Fig. 3). It should be noted that several regions were absolutely conserved across kingdoms and that a cysteinyl residue proposed to locate in a region adjacent to the substrate binding site of *Salmonella* HDH (10) was also found in the cabbage HDH at a position of 143 (Fig. 3).

For southern blotting analysis, cabbage genomic DNA was digested with various restriction enzymes lacking recognition sites within the cDNA clone. The HDH cDNA hybridized with more than one genomic fragment, indicating that the hybridizing region contains introns, or that more than just one gene coding for closely similar but different HDH proteins are present in the cabbage genome. The latter case may explain the existence of several forms of cabbage HDH displayed on the isoelectoric focusing.

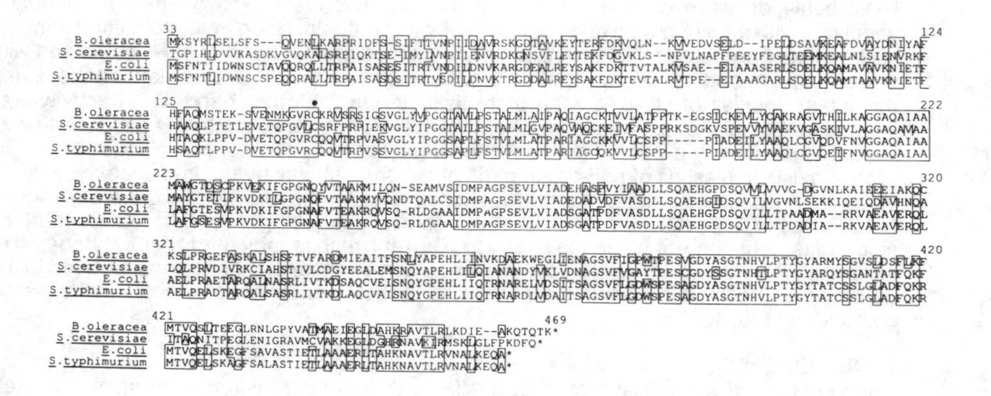

Fig. 3. Comparison among deduced HDH protein sequences from plant and microbial sources.

3.3 Expression.

On the 5th day after the infection of the Sf9 cells with AcNPV/HDH, HDH activity was detected in the cell homogenate (Fig. 1, lane 1) at a level of 1.3 mU/ 1×10^3 cells. One step Mono-Q anion-exchange FPLC (Pharmacia) afforded total purification of rHDH from the cell homogenate. In the purified preparation, there were two forms of rHDH with molecular masses of 52- and 53-kDa on SDS-PAGE, respectively. In the 52-kDa form, Cys 31 (Table 1) was detected as the N-terminus of a major protein and Met 33 as that of a minor one suggesting the second translation origin at this residue.

TABLE 1. N-terminal amino acid sequences of HDH purified from cabbage and rHDH

	20 25 30 35
Cabbage HDH	
Deduced from cDNA	. . L T R T A T K K G F V R C S M K S . .
Determined from purified protein	S M K S . .
rHDH	
52-kDa form (major protein)	C S M K S . .
52-kDa form (minor protein)	M K S . .
53-kDa form	T A T K K G F V R C S M K S . .

Threonine 22 was determined as the sole N-terminus of the 53-kDa form, indicating that the 53-kDa rHDH contained unprocessed peptide at the N-terminus consisting of 10 amino acids derived from the transit peptide. However, the 53-kDa form was processed to a 52-kDa form (Fig. 1, lane 2) by a 2-hour incubation of the cell homogenate at 30 °C. Apparent K_m values for histidinol and those for NAD^+ of the 52- and 53-kDa rHDHs were virtually identical to those of cabbage HDH. Other enzymatic properties of rHDHs were identical to those of the purified enzyme from cabbage plants. These results indicate that the cabbage HDH transit peptide was posttranslationally cleaved by non-specified proteases in the insect cells and that the functional expression of catalytically active cabbage HDH was achieved by the insect cell/baculovirus system.

3.4 Localization studies.

HDH activities were detected in leaves, stems, and roots of two-week-old cabbage seedlings with a comparable level of HDH specific contents. Upon immunoblotting analysis of the extract prepared from each plant part, a single protein band of 52-kDa reacted with polyclonal antibodies raised against rHDH, suggesting the expression of the same molecular species of HDH in each plant tissues. On the other hand, HDH activity was located in the chloroplast fractions, when extracts from both spinach and cabbage leaves were fractionated by a density gradient centrifugation. In addition, it was clarified that HDH protein exists in plastids of non-green parts of cabbage shoots by the immunoblot analysis. While it is a well known fact that many of chloroplastic dehydrogenase generally require $NADP^+$ as a cofactor, there are some reports describing NAD(H) requirement by chloroplast locating enzymes (11, 12, 13). Current results indicated that cabbage HDH requiring NAD^+ locates in chloroplast as well as some higher plant enzymes involved in the amino acid biosynthetic pathways that have so far been established to locate in the plastid compartment (8, 13, 14).

4. CONCLUSIONS

Cabbage HDH has catalytic properties similar to those of the bacterial enzymes. It is likely that higher plant HDH is located in plastids and is involved in the His biosynthetic pathway in higher plants as well as in the bacterial cells.

REFERENCES

1 Adams, E. (1955) J. Biol. Chem. 217, 325-344
2 Wong, Y. -S., and Mazelis, M. (1981) Phytochem. 20, 1831-1834
3 Nagai, A., and Scheidegger, A. (1991) Arch. Biochem. Biophys. 284, 127-132
4 Nagai, A., Ward, E., Beck, J., Tada, S., Chang, J.-Y., Scheidegger, A., and Ryals, J. (1991) Proc. Natl. Acad. Sci. USA 88, 4133-4137
5 Donahue, T. F., Farabaugh, P. J., and Fink, G. R. (1982) Gene 18, 47-59
6 Summers, M.D., and Smith, G. E. (1987) A Manual of Methods for Baculovirus Vector and Insect Cell Culture Procedures, Bulletin No. 1555, Trxas Agricultural Experiment Station and Texas A & M University, Vollege Station, TX
7 Nagai, A., Suzuki, K., Ward, E., Moyer, M., Hashimoto, M., Mano, J., Ohta, D., and Scheidegger, A. (1992) Arch Biochem. Biophys. 295, 235-239
8 Schmidt, G. W., and Mishkind, M. L. (1986) Ann. Rev. Biochem. 55, 879-912
9 Carlomagno, M. S., Chiariotti, L., Alifano, P., Nappo, A. G., and Bruni, C. (1988) J. Mol. Biol. 203, 585-606
10 Grubmeyer, C. T., and Gray, W. R. (1986) Biochemistry 25, 4778-4784
11 Ellerstrom, M., Josefsson, L-G., Rask, L. K., and Ronne, H. (1992) Plant Mol. Biol. 18, 557-566
12 Kater, M. M. , Koningstein, G. M., Nijkamp, H. J. J. , and Stuitje, A. R. (1991) Plant Mol. Biol. 17, 895-909
13 Matoh, T., and Takahashi, E. (1981) Plant Cell Physiol. 22, 727-731
14 Niyogi, K. K., and Fink, G. R. (1992) Plant Cell (4), 721-733

KINETIC ANALYSIS OF CABBAGE HISTIDINOL DEHYDROGENASE

Junichi Mano, Atsuko Nagai[†], Nobuko Uodome[†], Atsuko Kosaka[†], Genji Iwasaki[†], Azadeh Kheilrolomoon[†], Alfred Scheidegger[¶] and Daisaku Ohta[†]
The Research Institute for Food Science, Kyoto Univ., Uji, Kyoto 611, Japan, [†]International Research Laboratories, CIBA-GEIGY (Japan) Ltd., Takarazuka PO Box1, Hyogo 665, Japan and [¶]Swiss Scientific Computing Center, 6928 Manno, Switzerland

1. INTRODUCTION

Histidinol dehydrogenase (HDH; EC 1.1.1.23) catalyzes the final step of histidine biosynthetic pathway, the four-equivalent oxidation of histidinol to histidine by reducing $2NAD^+$ to 2NADH. We have isolated HDH from cabbage (*Brassica oleracea*) (1), and succeeded HDH cDNA cloning from a cabbage cDNA library (2) and expression of active enzyme in the baculovirus-insect cell expression system (3). The cloned cDNA encoded a proenzyme having a putative chloroplast transit peptide, indicating an occurrence of the hisidine biosynthesis pathway in the chloroplast. For further investigations and understanding of the pathway in plants, it is important to obtain a set of kinetic constants of the enzyme at a physiologically reasonable pH, since our knowledge of the kinetics of HDH is confined to that for the HDH in *Salmonella typhimurium* and most of those kinetic studies have been done at pH 9.2 (4, 5). In this study the buffer pH was set at 7.2, representing a typical physiological value both in the cytosol and the chloroplast in plant cells (6). The experiment at neutral pH made it easier to analyze the partial reaction of HDH by the use of the alkaline-labile histidinaldehyde as a substrate. Unlike many biosynthetic dehydrogenases in chloroplasts, the cabbage HDH preferred NAD^+ 870 times more specifically to $NADP^+$, as judged on k_{cat}/K_m.

2. MATERIALS AND METHODS

2.1. Materials: All kinetic studies on HDH were carried out using recombinant cabbage HDH expressed by the baculovirus expression vector system. The enzyme, appearing as a single 52-kDa band on SDS-PAGE, comprised two kinetically identical isoforms differing by two-amino-acid length at the N-termini (3). L-Histidinaldehyde synthesized from L-histidine as previously reported (7), was obtained as a hygroscopic HCl-salt and stored at -30 °C. Concentration of a solution of L-histidinaldehyde was calculated from the dry weight, using the molecular weight of 212.08. L-Histidinol, NAD^+ and $NADP^+$ were purchased from Sigma. NADH was from Nakalai tesque (Kyoto, Japan). Other chemicals were of analytical grade.

2.2. Enzyme Assay: The reaction mixture contained 50 mM Hepes-NaOH, pH 7.2, 0.5 mM $MnCl_2$, NAD^+ or $NADP^+$ at various concentration, and the enzyme. The reaction was started by adding either L-histidinol or L-histidinaldehyde. In the product inhibition studies, inhibitors were added prior to the start of the reaction. The rate of total reaction, the oxidation of histidinol to histidine, was determined on the absorbance increase at 340 nm of NADH or NADPH. The later-half reaction, the oxidation of histidinaldehyde to histidine, was monitored by fluorescence increase of the produced NADH at emission wavlength at 455 nm with excitation at 340 nm.

N. Murata (ed.), Research in Photosynthesis, Vol. IV, 99–102.

Standard curve of the NADH fluorescence intensity was determined on each day of the experiments. Amount of enzyme was calculated by using the dimeric molecular mass of 94,548 and the value $A^{1\%}$(280 nm) of 7.98, which was calculated from the Trp and Tyr contents using extinction coefficients of 5800 and 1450 for the two residues, respectively (8). All data points were the average of duplicate assays.

2. 3. Treatment of Kinetic Data: Theory and nomenclature of Segel (9) were used to interpret the results. Data were analyzed with the computer program GraFit, for curve-fitting and determination of inhibition constants. Difinition of inhibition modes was according to Duggleby (10).

3. RESULTS AND DISCUSSION

3.1. Cabbage HDH shows higher specificity to NAD^+ than to $NADP^+$: From the substrate dependence curves at an excess concentration of histidinol, K_m and k_{cat} values for NAD^+ and $NADP^+$ were determined (Table I). The recombinant HDH of cabbage (rHDH) showed lower K_m value and higher k_{cat} value for NAD^+ than for $NADP^+$. Comparison of k_{cat}/K_m values, which is an indicator of substrate specificity of an enzyme (11) gave that the enzyme is 870 times more specific to NAD^+ than to $NADP^+$. Thus the cabbage HDH, localized in chloroplasts (2), utilizes NAD^+ as the physiological cofactor. Such preference for NAD^+ to $NADP^+$ of a dehydrogenase in chloroplasts is rare although there are several ones reported to prefer NADH to NADPH functioning in the reduction of the substrates in lipid biosynthesis and chlorophyll biosynthesis (12).

TABLE I: Comparison of specificities to NAD^+ and $NADP^+$: Histidinol concentration was fixed at 1.0 mM. Enzyme concentrations in the reaction media were 1.04×10^{-8} M for NAD^+ measurements and 1.04×10^{-7}M for $NADP^+$ measurements.

Coenzyme	K_m (M)	k_{cat} (s^{-1})	k_{cat}/K_m ($s^{-1}M^{-1}$)
NAD^+	8.14×10^{-5}	3.24	4.0×10^4
$NADP^+$	1.41×10^{-3}	6.54×10^{-2}	4.6×10^1

3. 2. The total reaction (from histidinol to histidine): Product inhibition pattern of the total reaction (Table II) was consistent with the BiUniUniBi Ping Pong mechanism (Scheme 1, the upper route) as reported for the *Salmonella* enzyme (4), but unexpectedly NADH showed a clear uncompetitive inhibition against histidinol,with the linear intercept replot pattern. This can be interpreted that the second binding con

TABLE II: Product inhibition pattern in the total reaction (from histidinol to histidine)

Inhibitor	Substrate		Curve shape*			Inhibition mode**	K_i
	variable	saturating	Lineweaver -Burk plot	Intercept replot	Slope replot		
NADH	histidinol	-	l	l	p	UC	4.8 μM
	NAD^+	-	p	l	l	-	-
histidine	histidinol	-	l	-	l	C	0.2 mM
	NAD^+	-	l	l	l	MT	0.9 mM
		histidinol	l	l	l	MT	46 mM

* l, linear; p, parabolic. ** UC, uncompetitive; C, competitive; MT, mixed-type.

stant for NADH, $K_{ip2} = k_{-5}/k_5$, is much smaller than the first one, $K_{ip1} = k_{-3}/k_3$, which is accordingly neglectable.

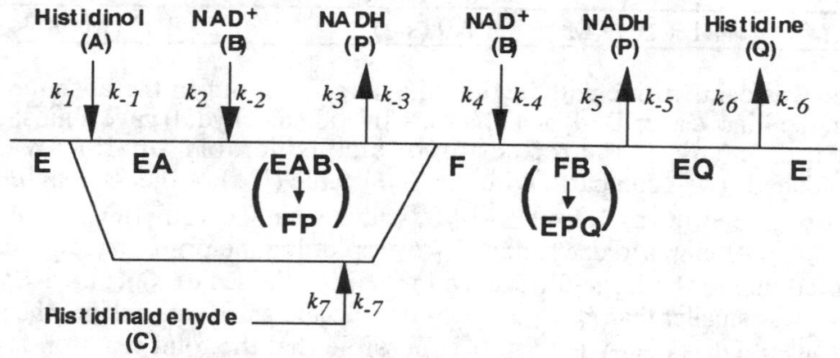

Scheme 1: The reaction sequence of HDH. E, free enzyme; F, the intermediate state which is binding histidinaldehyde.

3. 3. Kinetic constants for the reaction from histidinol to histidine: The initial velocity equation at the enzyme concentration $[E]_0$ in the absence of the products can be derived from the corresponding one formulated for a trisubstrate/triproduct reaction (9), regarding the second and the third substrates are the same, and so are the first two products, as follows;

$$v = \frac{V_{f(\text{total})}[A][B]}{K_{ia}K_{mB1} + (K_{mB1} + K_{mB2})[A] + K_{mA}[B]},$$

where $V_f(\text{total})/[E]_0 = k_{cat}(\text{total}) = \dfrac{k_3k_5k_6}{k_3k_5 + k_3k_6 + k_5k_6}$, $K_{ia} = \dfrac{k_{-1}}{k_1}$,

$K_{mB1} = \dfrac{k_5k_6(k_3 + k_{-2})}{k_2(k_3k_5 + k_3k_6 + k_5k_6)}$, $K_{mB2} = \dfrac{k_3k_6(k_5 + k_{-4})}{k_4(k_3k_5 + k_3k_6 + k_5k_6)}$, and

$K_{mA} = \dfrac{k_3k_5k_6}{k_1(k_3k_5 + k_3k_6 + k_5k_6)}$. The limiting K_m value for NAD^+, $K_mB(\text{total})$, is given; $K_mB(\text{total}) = K_mB1 + K_mB2$ and practically K_mB1 and K_mB2 are not separable. The kinetic constants obtainable for the total reaction are summarized in Table III.

TABLE III: Kinetic constants for the total reaction (from histidinol to histidine).

K_mA	K_mB(total)	k_{cat}(total)	K_{iq}	$k_1 = k_{cat}(\text{total})/K_mA$
3.2×10^{-6} M	5.3×10^{-5} M	$3.6\ s^{-1}$	2.1×10^{-4} M	$5.6 \times 10^{5}\ M^{-1}s^{-1}$

3. 4. The later-half reaction (from histidinaldehyde to histidine): The reaction mechanism of histidinaldehyde oxidation is Ordered BiBi (the lower route in Scheme 1), and the initial velocity equation is given as follows;

$$v = \frac{V_f(\text{later})[B][C]}{K_{ic}K_{mB'} + K_{mB'}[C] + K_{mC}[B]},$$ where $V_f(\text{later})/[E]_0 = k_{cat}(\text{later}) = \dfrac{k_5k_6}{k_5 + k_6}$,

$K_{ic} = \dfrac{k_{-7}}{k_7}$, $K_{mB'} = \dfrac{k_6(k_{-4} + k_5)}{k_4(k_5 + k_6)}$ and $K_{mC} = \dfrac{k_5k_6}{k_7(k_5 + k_6)}$.

The kinetic constants for the later-half reaction are listed in Table IV.

TABLE IV: Kinetic constants for the later-half reaction.

K_mC	K_mB'	k_{cat}(later)	$k_7 = k_{cat}$(later)/K_mC
2.3×10^{-5} M	4.1×10^{-6} M	2.9 (s^{-1})	1.2×10^5 ($M^{-1}s^{-1}$)

Histidine was competitive with histidinol as expected, but in the absence of any inhibitor, the Lineweaver-Burk plot (1/*v* *vs.* 1/[histidinaldehyde]) gave almost parallel lines (Fig. 1). This is the reflection of a considerably small K_i value for histidinaldehyde (K_{ic}) compared with the K_mC value (9). For the *Salmanella* HDH K_{ic} value was reported as 1.4×10^{-11} M, which was 3.5×10^5 times smaller than the K_mC (13). Attempts to determine K_{ic} by replotting the primary reciprocal plots were failed due to the large difference in the magnitudes of K_mC and K_{ic}. That k_{cat}(later) was smaller than k_{cat}(total) was unexpected when we consider the relation $1/k_{cat}$(total) = $1/k_{cat}$(later) + $1/k_3$. It is possible that the total reaction is not the simple sum of the two half reactions since the dimeric structure was required for the total reaction but was not essential for the half reactions (14).

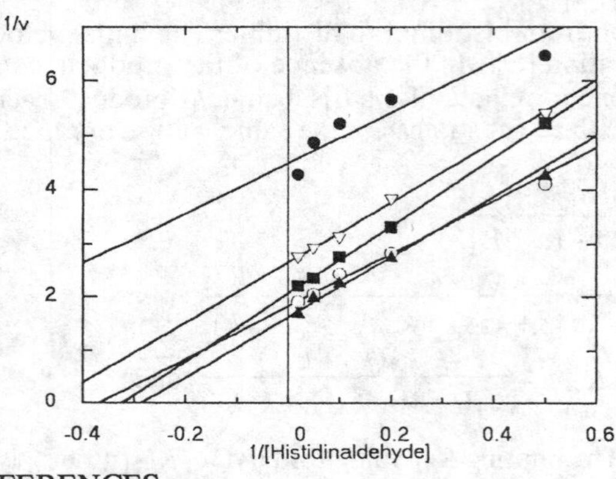

Figure 1. Lineweaver-Burk plot for the later half reaction: NAD+ concentrations were 2 μM (●), 5 μM (▽), 10 μM (■), 20 μM (○) and 40 μM (▲).

REFERENCES

1 Nagai, A. and Scheidegger, A. (1991) Arch. Biochem. Biophys. 284, 127-132
2 Nagai, A., Ward, E., Beck, J., Tada, S., Chang, J.-Y., Scheidegger, A. and Ryals, J. (1991) Proc. Natl. Acad. Sci., USA, 88, 4133-4137
3 Nagai, A., Suzuki, K., Ward, E., Moyer, M., Hashimoto, M., Mano, J., Ohta, D. and Scheidegger, A. (1992) Arch. Biochem. Biophys., 295, 235-239
4 Bürger, E. and Görisch, H. (1981) Eur. J. Biochem. 116, 137-142
5 Grubmyer, C. T., Chu, K.-W. and Insinga, S. (1987) Biochemistry 26, 3369-3373
6 Raven, J. A. (1985) Sci. Prog. Oxf. 69. 495-509
7 Bürger, E. and Görisch, H. (1981) Eur. J. Biochem. 118, 125-130
8 Kuramitsu, S., Hiromi, K., Hayashi, H., Morino, Y. and Kagamiyama, H. (1990) Biochemistry 29, 5469-5476
9 Segel, I. H. (1975) in Enzyme Kinetics, Wiley-Interscience
10 Duggleby, R. G. (1988) Biochem. Med. Metabolic Biol. 40, 204-212
11 Fersht, A. (1977) in Enzyme Structure and Function, Freeman
12 Kirk, J. T. O. and Tilney-Bassett, R. A. E. (1978) in The Plastids, Elsevier
13 Görisch, H. and Hölke, W. (1985) Eur. J. Biochem. 150, 305-308
14 Eccleston, R. G., Thayer, M. L. and Kirkwood, S. (1979) J. Biol. Chem. 254, 11399-11404.

LIGHT-DEPENDENT MAINTENANCE OF ACTIVE NITROGENASE IN THE NON-HETEROCYSTOUS CYANOPHYTE *TRICHODESMIUM* sp. NIBB1067

Kaori Ohki* and Yoshihiko Fujita
Department of Cell Biology, National Institute for Basic Biology, Okazaki, Aichi 444, Japan. (* Present address; Department of Marine Science, School of Marine Science and Technology, Tokai University, Shimizu, Shizuoka 424, Japan).

1. INTRODUCTION

Nitrogenase (N_2ase) in cyanophytes has been known to be protected from O_2 produced by photosynthesis in two ways; spatial separation from photosynthesis by differentiation of heterocysts, and temporal separation by alternative occurrence of N_2-fixation and photosynthesis in a light/dark cycle (1). *Trichodesmium* is a non-heterocystous cyanophyte, but the activity of N_2ase is strictly light-dependent (2). Thus, N_2-fixation and photosynthesis occur simultaneously in this organism. When *Trichodesmium* is grown under 12 hr light/12 hr dark cycles, N_2ase is completely inactivated in the dark phase, and activated upon shift to the light phase (3). Our previous study has also indicated that light-dependent activation of N_2ase occurs in this organism and enables simultaneous occurrence of N_2-fixation and photosynthesis. Reported here are results from further analysis of the mechanism for light-dependent activation of N_2ase in *Trichodesmium.*

2. MATERIAL AND METHODS

Trichodesmium sp. NIBB1067 is the same strain used in our previous studies (cf. 4,5). Cells were grown in AQUIL medium (6) without KNO_3 (cf. 7) under fluorescent light (daylight type, 10 W m^{-2}) in 12 hr light/12 hr dark cycles at 26 °C. Cultures at the exponential growth phase after more than 5 light/dark cycles were used for the experiments. Potential activity of N_2ase was ascertained by acetylene reduction *in vivo* under illumination with white light (2). Fe-protein was determined by Western immunoblot analysis as reported previously (8). Chl *a* concentrations were determined spectrophotometrically in methanol extracts using the absorption coefficient of Mackinney (9)

3. RESULTS AND DISCUSSION

N_2ase is inactive in the dark phase in 12 hr light/12 hr dark cycles. Upon shifting from dark to light, activation of the enzyme occurred with a lag of about 1 hr (Fig.1A). Activation was completely suppressed when chloramphenicol (CAP), a translation inhibitor, was added before light-on (Fig.1A). Addition of CAP during the light activation suppressed further activation. Streptomycin (500 μM) also showed the same inhibitory effect (data, not shown). Rifampicin, a transcription inhibitor, added before light-on also completely inhibited the activation in light. However, addition of rifampicin 1 hr after light-on did not immediately suppress

N. Murata (ed.), Research in Photosynthesis, Vol. IV, 103–106.

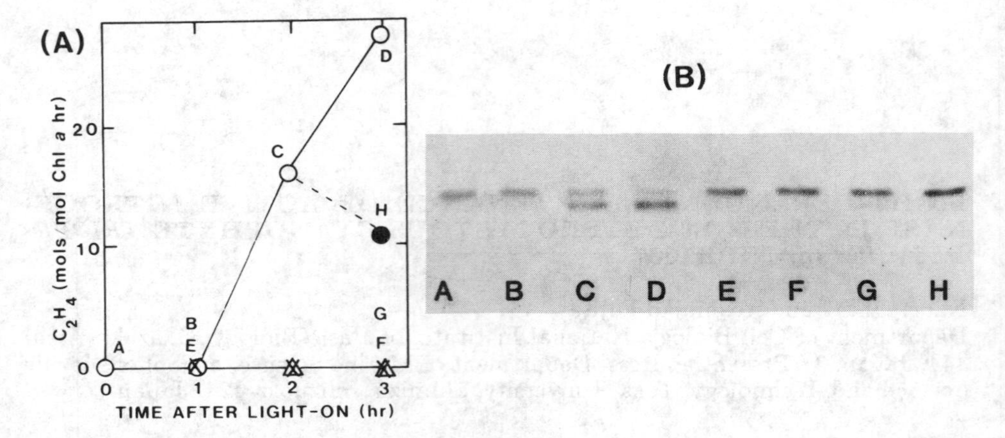

Fig.1 Effect of CAP on light-dependent activation of nitrogenase (A) and a molecular state of Fe-protein of nitrogenase (B) in cells grown under 12 hr light/12 hr dark cycles. In (A), cells were collected at indicated times and rates of acetylene reduction were measured under illumination: Open circles, control; crosses, CAP (15 μM) was added 30 min before light-on; triangles, CAP was added 1hr after light-on; closed circles, CAP was added 2 hr after light-on. In (B), Western immunoblot analysis of Fe-protein. The symbol for each lane indicates the sample with the same symbol in (A).

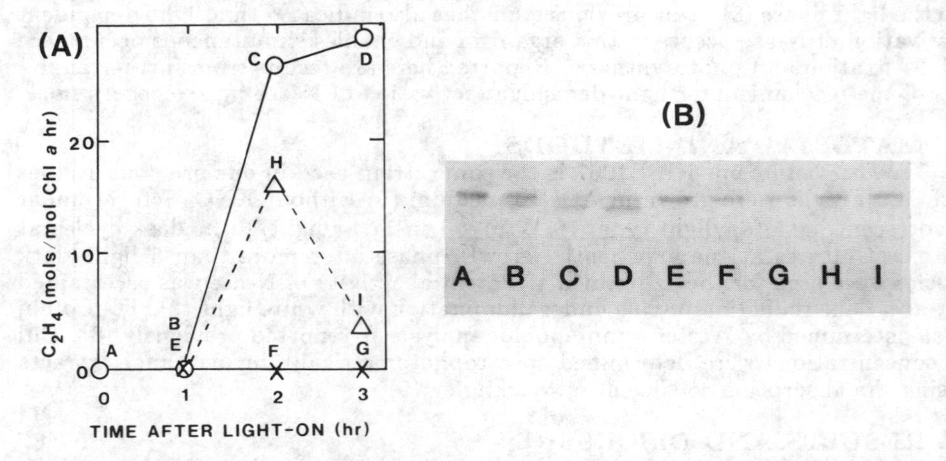

Fig.2 Effect of rifampicin on light-dependent activation of nitrogenase (A) and a molecular state of Fe-protein of nitrogenase (B) in cells grown under 12 hr light/12 hr dark cycles. In (A), open circles, control; crosses, rifampicin (100 μM) was added 30min before light-on; triangles, rifampicin was added 1 hr after light-on. In (B), the symbol for each lane indicates the sample with the same symbol in (A). Experimental details, see the legend for Fig.1.

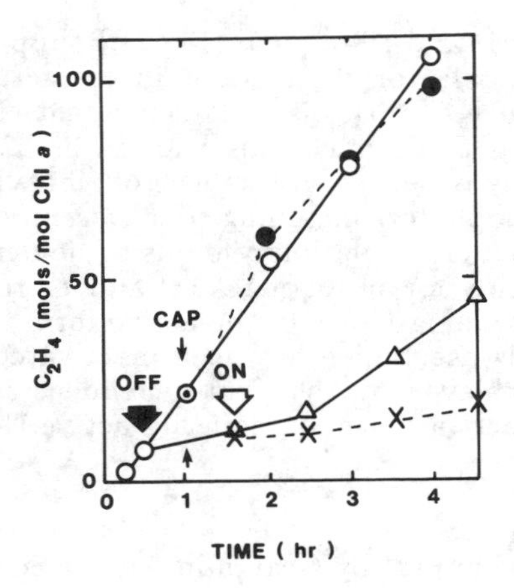

Fig.3 Effect of CAP on light-dependent activation of nitrogenase inactivated by a short dark pulse. Dark pulse for 1 hr was given 30 min after start of acetylene reduction. CAP (15 μM) was added middle of the dark pulse: Open circles, control (without dark pulse and CAP addition); closed circles, without dark pulse, but CAP was added; triangles, with dark pulse but without CAP addition; crosses, with dark pulse and CAP was added.

the activation but inhibition occurred gradually (Fig. 2A). These results indicate that light-dependent activation of N_2ase in *Trichodesmium* involves *de novo* synthesis of protein(s), and that such proteinous factor(s) turns over rather rapidly. If rifampicin and CAP respectively inhibit transcription and translation of the same protein, then the turnover rate of *m*RNA must be slower than that of protein.

N_2ase activity was maximul in the middle of the light phase in 12 hr light/12 hr dark. However, the high activity was diminished by a short dark pulse (Fig.3). Illumination of more than 1 hr was required for complete activation (Fig.3). Addition of CAP inhibited the light activation. Streptomycin and puromycin also showed the same inhibitory effect (data, not shown). However, CAP did not show any effect on the enzyme activity for at least 3 hr when it was added to the cells without a dark pulse (Fig.3). These results suggest that a proteinous factor(s) is rather stable under illumination but rapidly degraded or inactivated in the dark. Rifampicin did not affect the activation process after a short dark pulse (data, not shown).

Involvement of protein synthesis in the light-dependent activation suggests the possibility that synthesis of N_2ase itself is induced by the light. However, since the Fe- and the MoFe-proteins of N_2ase are present in cells at high level even in the dark (3), it is unlikely that synthesis is responsible for the observed changes. A more probable explanation is that the change in activity is correlated with states in the Fe-protein of N_2ase. The Fe-protein has a higher molecular mass (ca. 40 kDa) on SDS-PAGE when the enzyme is inactive and a lower molecular mass (ca. 38k Da) when active (cf.8, and Figs.1B and 2B, A vs. D), which correlates with the CAP (Fig.1B) and rifampicin (Fig.2B) suppression. It is possible to suggest that a proteinous factor(s) functions in the activation of Fe-protein, and that stabilization of such factor(s) is light-dependent. If activation of N_2ase in *Trichodesmium* is similar to the mechanism found in *Rhodospirillum rubrum* (10), then the factor(s) may be active at the level of ribosylation/deribosylation of the Fe-protein. In cyanophytes, including *Trichodesmium*, a modification of Fe-protein via ribosylation/deribosylation remains to be demonstrated.

Light is necessary not only for supplying ATP and/or reducing power to N_2-fixation, but also for maintaining N_2ase in the active form in *Trichodesmium* sp. NIBB1067. Activation of N_2ase, which has been inactivated by O_2 produced by photosynthesis, may be achieved by the light-dependent activating mechanism found in this study. This activation may maintain active N_2ase at high levels in light in this organism.

ACKNOWLEDGEMENTS

This work was supported in part by Grants-in-Aid for Scientific Research from the Ministry of Education, Science and Culture, Japan (to K.O. and Y.F.) and by The Inamori Foundation (to K.O.). We thank Dr.Paul Ludden for the generous gift of antiserum used in this study.

REFERENCES

1. Fay,P. (1992) Microbiol. Rev. 56, 340-373
2. Ohki,K. and Fujita,Y. (1988) Mar. Biol. 98, 111-114
3. Ohki,K., Zehr,J.P. and Fujita,Y. J. Gen. Microbiol. in press
4. Ohki,K., Falkowski,P.G., Rueter,J.G. and Fujita,Y. (1991) In Marine Biology, its Accomplishment and Future Prospect (eds. Mauchline,J. and Nemoto,T.) pp. 205-216, Hokusensha, Tokyo
5. Ohki,K., Zehr,J.P. and Fujita,Y. (1992) In Marine Pelagic Cyanobacteria: *Trichodesmium* and Other Diazotrophs (eds. Carpenter,E.J., Capone,D.G. and Rueter,J.G.) pp.307-318, Kluwer Academic Publishers, Netherlands
6. Morel,F.M.M., Rueter,J.G., Anderson,D.M. and Guillard,R.R. (1979) J. Phycol. 15, 135-141
7. Ohki,K., Rueter,J.G. and Fujita,Y. (1986) Mar. Biol. 91, 9-13
8. Ohki,K., Zehr,J.P., Falkowski,P.G. and Fujita,Y. (1991) Arch. Microbiol. 156, 335-337
9. Mackinney,G. (1941) J. Biol. Chem. 140, 315-322
10. Ludden,P.W. and Roberts,G.P. (1989) Curr. Top. Cell. Reg. 30, 23-56

THE EFFECTS OF ABSCISIC ACID AND INDOLE ACETIC ACID ON NITROGEN FIXATION AND ANTHOCYANIN FORMATION IN AZOLLA PINNATA

CADIZ, N.M. AND A.A. ALEJAR. INSTITUTE OF BIOLOGICAL SCIENCES, UNIVERSITY OF THE PHILIPPINES AT LOS BAÑOS, COLLEGE, LAGUNA, PHILIPPINES

INTRODUCTION

The red anthocyanin pigment in azolla is a stress symptom induced either by high irradiance (1,2) or phosphorus deficiency (3). This condition results in reduced biomass production, total nitrogen and nitrogenase activity (4,5). Certain growth-regulating substances have also been reported to affect the growth and productivity of azolla (6) but no conclusive study has yet been reported on the influence of growth substances on nitrogen fixation, and more specifically on its effect on alleviating the phosphorus deficiency-induced production of anthocyanin. This study investigates the effect of abscisic acid (ABA) or indole acetic acid (IAA) on the overall nitrogen fixation of the symbiosis and its influence on anthocyanin production.

MATERIALS AND METHODS

One-tenth gram of Azolla pinnata (UPLB accession No. 5) was grown in nitrogen-free (N) and nitrogen free, phosphorus free (-N,-P) culture solutions (7) with IAA or ABA added at the range of 10^{-8}M to 10^{-5}M. Azolla grown in the basal medium (i.e. without the hormone) served as control. After 7 days in the greenhouse, Azolla samples were analyzed for total nitrogen (7) nitrogenase activity (8) anthocyanin (9) and chlorophyll content (10).

RESULTS AND DISCUSSION

Nitrogen accumulation by the fronds was significantly decreased by 33% when grown in the absence of phosphorus and almost 50% when grown under high light intensity; i.e. field condition (data not presented). It is conceivable therefore that lower light intensity (greenhouse condition) coupled with lack of phosphorus contributed to the lower nitrogen fixation of the Azolla-Anabaena symbiosis compared with data on the field-grown red azolla. Incorporation of small amount of ABA or IAA can effectively enhance nitrogenase activity of the control plants (Tables 1 and 2). The increase in nitrogenase activity observed in -N treatment with increasing concentration of the hormones is not, however, consistently reflected in the amount of nitrogen accumulated by the fern. The decrease in the enzyme activity by withdrawing phosphorus from the culture solution can likewise be reversed, and even higher activity than that observed in the control can be induced by amending the growth medium with 10^{-6}M or 10^{-5}M ABA (Table 1). These concentrations also gave corresponding small increase in the nitrogen content of azolla. It is speculated that ABA can enhance heterocyst formation which parallel nitrogenase activity. It should not be discounted, however, that lack of phosphorus for ATP production could also limit nitrogenase activity (11,12) and/or ammonia assimilation (15) and as such the observed reduction in nitrogen fixation in azolla cultures without phosphorus. Interestingly, the treatment of phosphorus-deficient azolla with ABA caused thicker, darker blue green

N. Murata (ed.), Research in Photosynthesis, Vol. IV, 107–110.

color and smaller reduction in chlorophyll content than the minus nitrogen, ABA treated azolla cultures (Table 1, Figure 1). This could possibly be attributed to the pigments (chlorophyll and phycobilins) of the symbiont which are speculated to be increased by ABA concommitant to possible increase on the number of algal cells. The enhance nitrogenase activity with addition of IAA does not consistently reflect increase in total nitrogen (Table 2) and was observed to be more effective in the control plants or nitrogen-free azolla cultures than in the phosphorus-deficient set-up. This merely indicates that IAA cannot alleviate the constraint brought by phosphorus deficiency on nitrogen fixation as effectively as ABA treatment.

TABLE 1. Comparative analysis of A. pinnata grown in nitrogen free (control) or phosphorus free culture solutions with various levels of ABA. In a column, means followed by the same letter are not significantly different at 0.05 level.

ABA (M)	Total N (%)	Nitrogenase Activity (nmoles $h^{-1}g^{-1}$)	Anthocyanin (Optical Density A279-A495)	Total Chlorophyll (mgl^{-1})
-N				
0	3.75 b	81.2 d	0.43 c	65.8 a
10^{-8}	2.66 c	84.2 d	0.49 a	24.8 d
10^{-7}	2.96 e	107.7 c	0.46 b	49.3 c
10^{-6}	3.75 b	119.5 b	0.43 c	57.7 b
10^{-5}	4.08 a	147.5 a	0.31 d	58.3 b
-N, -P				
0	2.51 bc	53.2 b	0.54 c	39.7 a
10^{-8}	1.92 d	22.6 d	0.55 c	27.4 c
10^{-7}	2.40 c	47.1 c	0.58 c	29.7 c
10^{-6}	2.66 b	89.6 a	0.63 b	34.1 b
10^{-5}	3.06 a	23.5 d	0.65 a	31.7 b

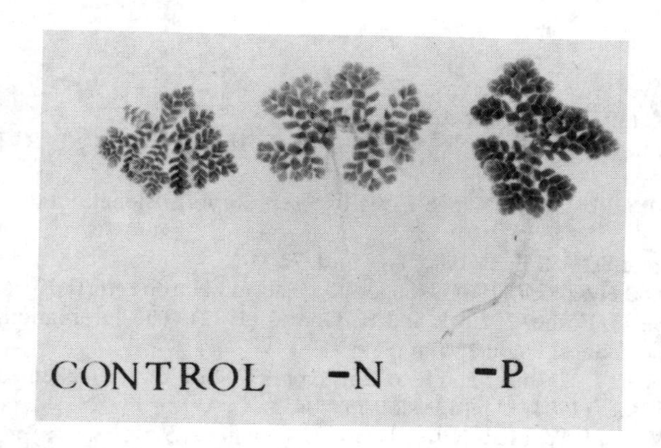

FIGURE 1. Azolla grown in ABA amended -N and -P culture solutions as compared with the control.

TABLE 2. Comparative analysis of A. pinnata grown in nitrogen free (control) or phosphorus free culture solutions with various levels of IAA. In a column, means followed by the same letter are not significantly different at 0.05 level.

IAA (M)	Total N (%)	Nitrogenase Activity (nmoles $h^{-1}g^{-1}$)	Anthocyanin (Optical Density A279-A495)	Total Chlorophyll (mgl^{-1})
-N				
0	3.75 b	81.2 d	0.43 c	65.8 a
10^{-8}	2.22 d	124.9 d	0.26 d	41.2 c
10^{-7}	3.55 c	169.2 a	0.33 c	47.1 b
10^{-6}	3.92 a	138.5 c	0.38 b	51.6 d
10^{-5}	3.60 bc	151.1 b	0.38 b	50.1 d
-N, -P				
0	2.51 a	53.2 a	0.54 c	39.7 a
10^{-8}	1.75 d	9.1 c	0.62 a	16.4 b
10^{-7}	2.92 c	19.0 b	0.61 b	15.2 b
10^{-6}	2.19 b	12.7 c	0.45 d	16.8 b
10^{-5}	1.70 b	10.9 c	0.42 e	14.8 c

REFERENCES

1. Moore, A.W. (1969) Bot. Rev. 35:17-34.
2. Holst, R.W. (1977 Amer. Fer. J. 67(4):99-100.
3. Watanabe, I., C.R. Espinas, N.S. Berja and B.V. Alimagno (1977) IRRI Res. PaperSeries. No. 11.15 p.
4. Ashton, P.J. (1974). The Orange River Progress Report. Bloemfontain, South Africa, pp. 123-138.
5. Tally, SN. and D.W. Rains. (1980) Agron. J. 72:11-18.
6. Kim, J.K. and H.K. Kim (1967) Nongop Kwahakwon Harbo (North Korea) 5:12-17.
7. Yoshida, S., D. Forno, J. Cock and K. Gomes (1972). The International Rice Research Institute. Los Baños, Laguna. 70 p.
8. Hardy, R.W.F., R.C. Burns and R.S. Holsten (1973) Soil Biol. Biochem. 5:47-81.
9. Mancinelli, A.L. (1984) Plant Physiol. 75:44-453.
10. Shoaf, T.W. and B.W. Luim (1976) Limol. Oceanogr. 21:926-928.
11. Yatazawa, M., N. Tomomatsu, N. Hosada and K. Nunome (1980) Soil sci. Plant Nutr. 26(3):415-426.
12. Jakobsen, I. (1985) Physiol. Plant. 64:190-196.

20. Temperature Stress

THE MOLECULAR BASIS FOR THE ACCLIMATION OF PHOTOSYNTHESIS TOWARD TEMPERATURE

N. MURATA, H. WADA, I. NISHIDA, Z. GOMBOS, Y. NISHIYAMA, H. HAYASHI, T. SAKAMOTO, O. ISHIZAKI-NISHIZAWA and S. HIGASHI
National Institute for Basic Biology, Okazaki 444, Japan

1. INTRODUCTION

It has been long suggested that the unsaturation of membrane lipids highly contributes to the temperature acclimation of photosynthetic organisms (1-3). When plants were grown at two different temperatures, the level of unsaturation of membrane lipids is increased in plants grown at low temperature compared with those grown at high temperature. The heat stability and the low-temperature sensitivity are more enhanced in plants grown at high temperature than those grown at low temperature, whereas the photosynthetic activities measured at physiological temperature are higher in plants grown at low temperature than in those grown at high temperature. It has been argued that the enhancement of heat stability and low-temperature sensitivity with the increase in growth temperature is related to the increase in the level of saturation of membrane lipids, and that the change in photosynthetic activity is also related to the level of unsaturation of membrane lipids. However, experimental results to date have not proved the direct contribution of unsaturation of fatty acids to the high-temperature stability, low-temperature stability and the photosynthetic activity at the physiological temperatures.

Since acclimation to temperature is accompanied not only by changes in unsaturation of membrane lipids but also by a number of other metabolic factors, it is possible that such metabolic changes, but not the unsaturation of membrane lipids, allow plants to be tolerant to low or high temperature. In order to verify whether the unsaturation of fatty acids contributes to the temperature tolerance and the photosynthetic activity, it is necessary to establish a system in which only the unsaturation of membrane lipids can be altered without any effect on other metabolic factors.

Recently we isolated a gene, *desA*, for desaturation at the Δ^{12} position of fatty acids of membrane lipids from the cyanobacterium *Synechocystis* PCC6803 (4). It is now possible to obtain strains of *Synechocystis* PCC6803 that contain membrane lipids with defined levels of unsaturation of fatty acids by mutation and transformation with *desA*. For the present experiments we grew, at the same temperature, the wild type that contains mono- di- and triunsaturated fatty acids (5), a mutant, designated Fad6, that contains mono- and diunsaturated fatty acids (5) and a transformant of Fad6, designated Fad6/*desA*::Km^r, that contains monounsaturated but no polyunsaturated fatty acids (6). Our experimental results suggest that the unsaturation of fatty acids, at the Δ^{12} position in particular, enhances the protection against low-temperature photoinhibition.

N. Murata (ed.), Research in Photosynthesis, Vol. IV, 113–119.

In higher plants, we have found that the level of *cis*-unsaturated fatty acids (18:1+18:2+18:3) in phosphatidylglycerol from chloroplast membranes is well correlated with their chilling sensitivity (7,8,9). The level of *cis*-unsaturated fatty acids in the phosphatidylglycerol is highly dependent on the substrate selectivity of acyl-ACP: glycerol-3-phosphate acyltransferase (hereinafter glycerol-P acyltransferase) which transfers the acyl group from acyl-ACP to the C-1 position of glycerol 3-phosphate (10,11). Therefore, it is predicted that the gene engineering of this enzyme can convert plants from chilling-sensitive to chilling-resistant and *vice versa*. Since cDNAs for glycerol-P acyltransferase have been cloned from a chilling-sensitive plant, *Cucurbita moschata* (squash) (12), and a chilling-resistant plant, *Arabidopsis thaliana* (13), it is now possible to transform higher plants such as tobacco with respect to the fatty acid unsaturation of phosphatidylglycerol, and therefore to the chilling sensitivity.

2. MATERIALS AND METHODS

2.1 Organisms and culture conditions: The cyanobacterium *Synechocystis* PCC6803 was mutagenized to produce a Fad6 mutant which is defective in desaturase activity specific for the Δ^6 position (5). The Fad6 mutant was transformed with a *desA* gene which had been disrupted by inserting a Kanamycin-resistant gene cartridge, to produce a double mutant Fad6/*desA*::Km^r, which is defective in introducing the second double bond into fatty acids (6). The wild type and Fad6 strains were grown photoautotrophically in medium of BG-11 as described previously (5), and the Fad6/*desA*::Km^r strain was grown in the same medium but with supplementation by Kanamycin (6). The transformation of tobacco plants with cDNAs for glycerol-P acyltransferases from *Arabidopsis* and squash was described elsewhere (14). The transformations were first *in vitro* cultivated in plastic boxes, and then transferred to the ground in pots. Chloroplasts were isolated from leaves of the non-transformed and transformed tobacco plants.

2.2 Lipid analysis: Extraction and analysis of membrane lipids of *Synechocystis* were performed as described previously (15). Lipids of tobacco leaves were extrated and were analyzed as described previously (14).

2.3 Photosynthetic activity: The oxygen-evolving activity of photosynthesis of cyanobacterial cells and isolated chloroplasts was measured as described previously (16). The oxygen-evolving activity of leaves was measured as described previously (14). The cyanobacterial cells were incubated at high temperature in darkness for 60 min (17), and were incubated at low temperature for 20 min in the light (16). The treatment of the intact leaves was performed as described previously (14).

3. RESULTS AND DISCUSSION

3.1 Temperature acclimation in *Synechocystis*: The thylakoid membranes from *Synechocystis* PCC6803 contain monogalactosyl diacylglycerol, digalactosyl diacylglycerol, sulfoquinovosyl diacylglycerol, and phosphatidylglycerol as major lipid components (5). Major fatty acids, which are esterified to the *sn*-1 and *sn*-2 positions of the above membrane lipids, are 16:0, 18:1(9), 18:2(9,12), 18:3(6,9,12) or 18:3γ, 18:3(9,12,15) or 18:3α, and 18:4(6,9,12,15).

When cells of *Synechocystis* grown at 22°C were compared with those grown at 34°C, the composition of lipid classes did not significantly change. On the other hand, the composition of molecular species, which can be specified by the combination of fatty acids at *sn*-1 and *sn*-2 positions, was markedly affected by growth temperature. As the 22°C-grown cells were compared to the 34°C-grown cells, proportions of 16:0/16:0, 18:1/16:0 and 18:2/16:0 were lowered whereas 18:3α/16:0 and 18:4/16:0 newly appeared. This suggests that the level of unsaturation of membrane lipids was enhanced at low temperature (Table 1).

The photosynthetic activities of the 22°C-grown cells and the 34°C-grown cells were assayed at different temperatures such as 18°C, 25°C, and 34°C. As shown in Fig. 1.a, the 22°C-grown cells were always more active than the 34°C-grown cells at all the three temperatures of assay.

The heat stabilities of these cells were compared. In this experiment, the cells grown either at 22°C or 34°C were exposed to various temperatures and then the photosynthetic activity was assayed at 30°C. Temperatures for the 50% inactivation appeared at 46°C and 49°C in cells grown at 22°C and 34°C. This result clearly demonstrates that cells grown at 34°C are more resistant to heat than those grown at 22°C. We further compared the two kinds of cell with respect to their low-temperature stability. In this experiment, cells grown at 22°C or 34°C were exposed to various low temperatures in the light for 60 min, and then the photosynthetic activity was assayed at 30°C. There was no marked difference between the two kinds of cell in the inactivation at 10°C and 20°C. However, the cells grown at 34°C suffered much higher damage than those grown at 22°C when they were exposed to 0°C. This result demonstrates that cells grown at 22°C are more tolerant toward low temperature than those grown at 34°C.

This series of experiments demonstrates that when the growth temperature is increased, the fatty-acid unsaturation decreased, the photosynthetic activity decreased, and the heat stability

Table 1. Effect of growth temperature and mutation on the composition of molecular species of membrane lipids in *Synechocystis* PCC6803

Strain	Growth temp.	Molecular species					
		16:0 16:0 X	18:1 16:0 X	18:2 16:0 X	18:3γ 16:0 X	18:3α 16:0 X	18:4 16:0 X
		(mol %)					
WT	22°C	2	4	22	42	16	16
WT	34°C	8	14	28	40	0	0
Fad6	34°C	15	25	60	0	0	0
Fad6/*desA*$^-$::Km^r	34°C	10	90	0	0	0	0

increased. Now we can raise questions; whether the fatty-acid unsaturation of membrane lipids affects the photosynthetic activity; whether the unsaturation of membrane lipids affects the heat stability of photosynthesis; whether the unsaturation of membrane lipids affects the low-temperature stability of photosynthesis.

In order to answer these questions it is necessary to establish a system in which the unsaturation of membrane lipids can be modified while the growth temperature is kept constant. It is possible by mutation of fatty-acid desaturation.

3.2 Genetic manipulation of fatty-acid unsaturation in *Synechocystis*: Fatty acids of total glycerolipids were analyzed for the wild type, the mutant, and the transformant of *Synechocystis* PCC6803, each grown at 34°C (Table 1). The most abundant fatty acids in the wild type were 16:0, 18:1(9), 18:2(9,12) and 18:3(6,9,12). The major fatty acids in Fad6 were 16:0, 18:1(9) and 18:2(9,12), indicative of a defect in desaturation of fatty acids at the Δ^6 position. The transformant, Fad6/*desA*::Km^r, was defective in desaturation at the Δ^6 and Δ^{12} positions. Consequently this strain

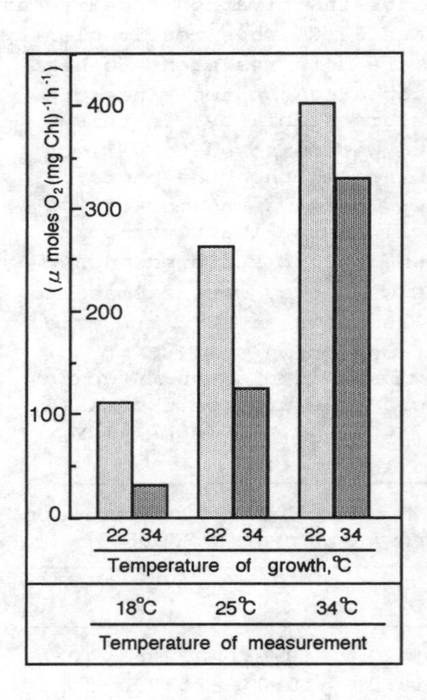

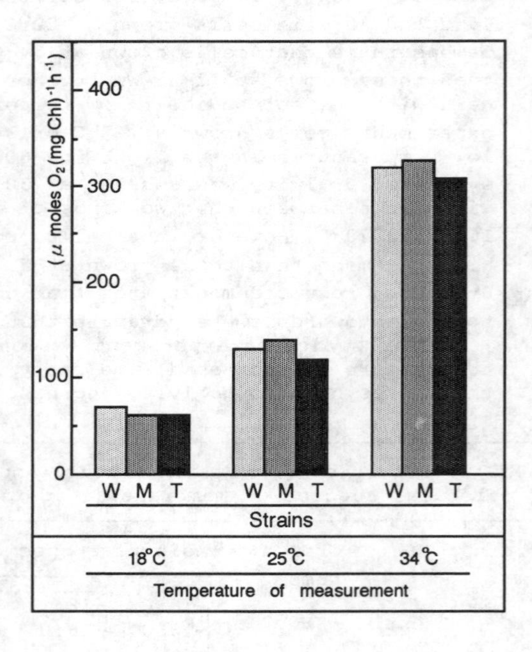

Fig. 1. Effects of growth temperature and mutation on the photosynthetic oxygen-evolving activity in *Synechocystis* PCC6803. (a) Cells were grown at either 22°C or 34°C, and the oxygen-evolving activity was measured at 18°C, 25°C and 34°C. (b) Cells of wild type, Fad6 and Fad6/*desA*::Km^r were grown at 34°C, and their oxygen-evolving activity was measured at 18°C, 25°C and 34°C. W, M and T stand for wild type, Fad6 and Fad6/*desA*::Km^r.

did not contain polyunsaturated fatty acids and possessed only 16:0 and 18:1(9) as the most abundant fatty acids. As a result, Fad6/*desA*::Km^r contained only monounsaturated lipids, Fad6 contained mono- and diunsaturated lipids, and the wild type contained mono-, di-, and triunsaturated lipids (Table 1). Using these three strains, we studied the effects of unsaturation of fatty acids on the photoinhibition at low temperatures with minimum interference by other factors.

The photosynthetic activities at 18°C, 25°C and 34°C of wild-type, Fad6, and Fad6/*desA*::Km^r cells, grown at 34°C, were compared (Fig. 1.b.). Under saturating light, the oxygen-evolving activity of photosynthesis was highly dependent on the temperature of measurement. In all strains the photosynthetic activity at 34°C was 5-fold higher than that at 18°C, while the electron-transport activity from H_2O to benzoquinone at 34°C was about 4-fold higher than that at 18°C. However, despite the considerable differences in unsaturation of fatty acids among the three strains, no significant differences among them in either their photosynthetic or their electron-transport activities were observed at the three temperatures of measurement.

The heat stability of photosynthesis was studied among the three strains. In this experiment, the cells of wild type, Fad6, and Fad6/*desA*::Km^r grown at 34°C were exposed to various temperatures in a range from 40°C to 55°C for 20 min in darkness, and the oxygen-evolving activity at 34°C was measured after immediate cooling. The temperature for 50% inactivation was 48°C in all the strains. A similar type of experiment was done with supplementation of benzoquinone to investigate the heat stability of the oxygen-evolving photosystem 2 activity. Again no significant difference was observed in temperature for 50% inactivation of oxygen evolution. These findings suggest that the elimination of unsaturation, step by step, by mutation of Δ^6 desaturation and disruption of Δ^{12} desaturation has no significant effect on the heat stability of photosynthesis and oxygen evolution.

Time courses of photoinhibition of wild-type and Fad6/*desA*::Km^r cells, at 10°C, 20°C and 30°C, were compared in the light of 2.5 mEin/m^2/sec. At 10°C the photoinhibition of photosynthesis occurred very rapidly in both wild type and Fad6/*desA*::Km^r. However, Fad6/*desA*::Km^r lost its photosynthetic activity much more rapidly than the wild type. At 20°C, the rate of photoinhibition of photosynthesis decreased markedly in the wild-type strain. Nevertheless, Fad6/*desA*::Km^r was inhibited more rapidly than the wild type. At 30°C the wild type was resistant to photoinhibition for as much as 2 hours of illumination. Fad6/*desA*::Km^r still experienced photoinhibition, but the photoinhibition occurred less rapidly than at 10°C and 20°C. The results for Fad6 were the same as for the wild type at the three temperatures. These observations suggest that Fad6/*desA*::Km^r is much more susceptible to photoinhibition than the wild type and Fad6.

In the present study, we demonstrate that the photoinhibition of all strains of *Synechocystis* PCC6803 was more pronounced at low temperature than at growth temperature. The photoinhibition at low temperatures is accelerated further by elimination of polyunsaturated fatty acids from membrane lipids. However, it was also observed that the photoinhibition at 30°C was faster in Fad6/*desA*::Km^r than in wild type and Fad6. Therefore, it is very likely that the fatty-acid unsaturation is related to the tolerance to photoinhibition, although this effect appears more pronounced at low temperature.

3.3 Genetic manipulation of fatty-acid unsaturation in tobacco: Analysis of lipids from leaves of transgenic tobacco plants revealed that no discernible change was observed in overall fatty-acid compositions between transformed and non-transformed plants. Analysis of individual lipid classes demonstrates that only phosphatidylglycerol is significantly altered in its fatty-acid composition by transformation with cDNAs for glycerol-P acyltransferases. When the squash cDNA was introduced, the level of *cis*-unsaturated fatty acids in phosphatidylglycerol was significantly lowered. In contrast, introduction of the *Arabidopsis* cDNA caused a small but significant increase in these fatty acids.

Chilling sensitivity experiment was performed by exposing a leaf disk of the transgenic tobacco plants to 1°C for 4 hours under illumination, returning it to 27°C in the darkness and monitoring the photosynthetic oxygen evolution affected by these treatments (Table 2). The transformant with pBI-121 alone and wild-type tobacco showed some chilling sensitivity. Upon introduction of the cDNA for glycerol-P acyltransferase from squash, this sensitivity was markedly increased. However, introduction of the cDNA for glycerol-P acyltransferase from *Arabidopsis* increased chilling tolerance. Notably, the degree of sensitivities toward chilling of tobacco plants transformed with cDNA for the enzymes from *Arabidopsis* (chilling-resistant) and squash (chilling-sensitive) were similar to those of spinach and squash (Table 2).

Exposure of whole plants to 1°C for 10 days clearly produced different appearance of leaves, such as chlorosis and total deterioration, among transformants with different constructs (14). The leaf damages appeared more clearly when the plants were kept at 25°C for 2 days after the chilling treatment. Leaves of wild

Table 2. Effect of chilling treatment on the photosynthetic activity of tobacco plants transformed with cDNAs for glycerol-P acyltrans-ferases from *Arabidopsis thaliana* and *Cucurbita moschata* (squash)

Plant	Extent of inactivation of photosynthesis during treatment at 1°C for 4 h
	(%)
Spinach	7
Squash	82
Transgenic tobacco plants with	
pBI121 (vector plasmid, control)	25 ± 11
cDNA for *Arabidopsis* enzyme	7 ± 3
cDNA for squash enzyme	88 ± 12

type and transformants with pBI-121 suffered partial chlorosis by the chilling treatment. Transformants with cDNA for the squash enzyme were severely damaged and some leaves were completely dead. In contrast, transformants with cDNA for the squash enzyme were much more resistant to chilling than the wild type and transformants with the plasmid alone. These differences in the chilling sensitivity were well correlated with the extents of fatty-acid unsaturation of phosphatidylglycerol.

4. CONCLUSION

In the present study it was possible to significantly alter the fatty-acid unsaturation of lipids of thylakoid membrane by disruption of desaturase gene or introduction of glycerol-P acyltransferase. The results demonstrate that *in vivo* the acyltransferase and the desaturase play key determinants for the fatty-acid composition of membrane lipids. Apart from the alteration of fatty-acid unsaturation of membrane lipids by genetic engineering, modification of the fatty-acid unsaturation results in alteration of the chilling sensitivity of the plants and cyanobacteria. Other factors could contribute to chilling sensitivity, but these experiments provide the direct evidence that the fatty-acid unsaturation of membrane lipids is a major contributor.

REFERENCES

1 Murata, N. (1989) J. Bioenerg. Biomembr. 21, 61-75
2 Murata, N. and Nishida, I. (1989) in Chilling Injury of Horticultural Crops (Wang, C.Y., ed.), pp. 181-199, CRC Press, Boca Raton, Florida
3 Raison, J.K., Roberts, J.K.M. and Berry, J.A. (1982) Biochim. Biophys. Acta 688, 218-228
4 Wada, H., Gombos, Z. and Murata, N. (1990) Nature 347, 200-203
5 Wada, H. and Murata, N. (1989) Plant Cell Physiol. 30, 971-978
6 Wada, H., Gombos, Z., Sakamoto, T. and Murata N. (1992) Plant Cell Physiol. 33, 535-540
7 Murata, N., Sato, N., Takahashi, N. and Hamazaki, Y. (1982) Plant Cell Physiol. 23, 1071-1079
8 Murata, N. (1983) Plant Cell Physiol. 24, 81-86
9 Roughan, P.G. (1985) Plant Physiol. 77, 740-746
10 Frentzen, M., Heinz, E., McKeon, T.A. and Stumpf, P.K. (1983) Eur. J. Biochem. 129, 629-636
11 Frentzen, M., Nishida, I. and Murata, N. (1987) Plant Cell Physiol. 28, 1195-1201
12 Ishizaki, O., Nishida, I., Agata, K., Eguchi, G. and Murata, N. (1988) FEBS Lett. 238, 424-430
13 Nishida, I., Tasaka, Y., Shiraishi, H. and Murata, N. (1992) Plant Mol. Biol., in press
14 Murata, N., Ishizaki-Nishizawa, O., Tasaka, Y., Hayashi, H., Higashi, S. and Nishida, I. (1992) Nature 356, 710-713
15 Sato, N. and Murata, N. (1988) Methods Enzymol. 167, 251-263
16 Gombos, Z., Tasaka, Y., Shiraishi, H. and Murata, N. (1992) Proc. Natl. Acad. Sci., in press
17 Gombos, Z., Wada, H. and Murata, N. (1991) Plant Cell Physiol. 32, 205-211

MOLECULAR AND CELLULAR ACCLIMATION OF PLANTS TO COLD

Helen Ougham, Petra Schünmann, Andrea Quigley and Catherine Howarth
AFRC Institute Of Grassland & Environmental Research, Plas Gogerddan, Aberystwyth, Dyfed SY23 3EB, Wales, U.K.

1. INTRODUCTION

Higher plants are essentially immobile organisms which are forced to survive and function under the full range of environmental conditions which may occur in their habitats. To do so requires metabolic and physiological flexibility, which for an individual plant may be achieved in three ways: either (a) the plant's existing cellular machinery is inherently capable of tolerating a range of conditions; or (b) changes in the external environment may lead to alterations in gene expression which facilitate survival and function under the altered circumstances; or (c) the plant will grow new tissue more accurately matched to its environment. The plant community as a whole has, of course, two additional resources available: (d) adaptation by evolution of a species' genotype, and (e) succession of species in one geographical location as its environment changes.In practice, plants make full use of all these acclimatory and adaptive strategies. However, the short time-scale over which some environmental variables can fluctuate means that in these cases, only the first two strategies will be of value in protecting plants. Temperature is one such rapidly-changing variable. Fig. 1 shows the diurnal temperature changes in air, soil surface and 5cm soil depth, in a field in Rajasthan, N. India during June.

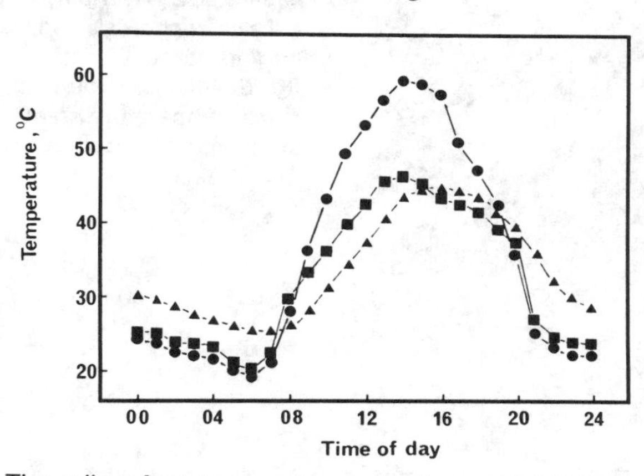

Figure 1. Diurnal temperature variations, measured using thermocouples, in air 150 mm above the soil surface (■), 5 mm below soil surface (●), and 5 cm soil depth (▲), in a farmer's field in Rajasthan, India, over a 24 h period in June

The soil surface temperature varies by up to 40°C between day and night, at a time

N. Murata (ed.), *Research in Photosynthesis, Vol. IV*, 121–128.

when young pearl millet seedlings would be emerging through this surface. That such seedlings do emerge, survive and grow to mature plants is an indication of their resilience and adaptability. The survival and expansion of photosynthetic leaf tissue is the primary requirement for effective functioning of the plant as a whole. Indeed, for most crop plants, green leaf area duration is likely to be a more important determinant of overall crop productivity than photosynthetic performance in mature leaf tissue (1). This paper will concentrate on factors which contribute to the survival and the continued development of photosynthetic leaf tissue at non-optimal temperatures; a description of the high-temperature response will be followed by a discussion of two different aspects of plant behaviour at low temperatures.

2. RESPONSES TO HIGH TEMPERATURE

The heat-shock response is a near-ubiquitous phenomenon in higher eukaryotes, and is characterised by two main components: alteration in gene expression, and development of thermotolerance. When tissue grown at a temperature at or near the optimum is subjected to a non-lethal temperature increase of 8-10°C, there is a major reprogramming of gene expression in which normal cellular protein synthesis is repressed and a set of proteins known collectively as the heat-shock proteins (HSPs) is synthesised. This process is mediated primarily at the transcriptional level, and can be brought about by either a sudden temperature increase (a true "heat-shock"), or a more gradual rise in temperature akin to the kind of variation likely to occur in a plant's natural environment.

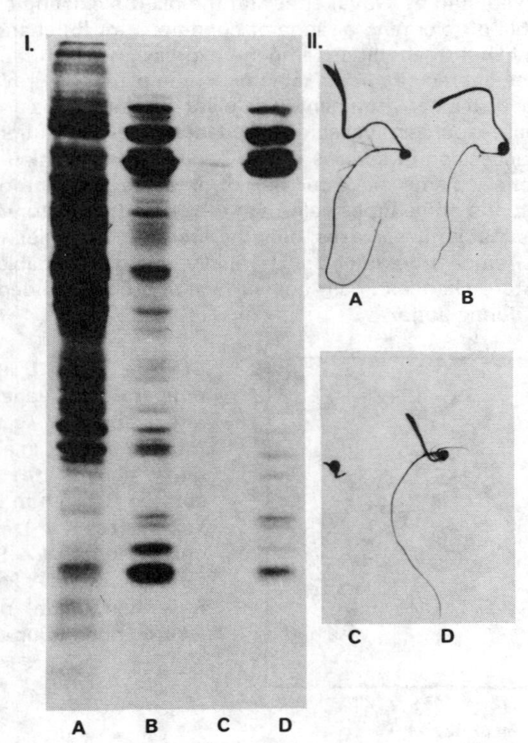

Figure 2. (I) Protein synthesis by 40h-old millet seedlings, germinated at 35°C and incubated in the presence of [^{35}S-methionine for 2h at 35°C (A), 45°C (B) or 50°C (C), or at 50°C following a 30 min pretreatment at 45°C (D). Radiolabelled proteins were separated by SDS-polyacrylamide gel electrophoresis and visualised by fluorography.
(II) Seedlings subjected to the same temperature treatments as in (I) and returned to 35°C for 24h to recover.

Plant HSPs fall into two main size classes (high and low molecular weight); the high mol. wt. HSPs (70-90 kDa) are highly conserved across the whole range of eukaryotic organisms, while the low mol. wt. group (16-25 kDa) are more characteristic of plants. The actual temperature at which HSP synthesis occurs maximally depends primarily on the genetic background and geographical origin of the plant species; for example, it is 45°C in the tropical cereal sorghum (2), whereas it is 35°C in the temperate grass *Lolium temulentum* (3). The heat-shock response is rapid; heat-shock mRNAs can be detected within 10 minutes of the heat-shock (4), and HSP synthesis within 15-20 minutes. Much evidence has been accumulated which indicates that the synthesis of certain of the HSPs is correlated with the ability of plants to develop thermotolerance. For example, millet seedlings grown at 35°C and exposed to 45°C for 30 minutes are capable of withstanding a subsequent treatment of 50°C which kills unacclimated seedlings (Fig.2). During the 45°C treatment, normal protein synthesis is repressed and HSPs are synthesised; this pretreatment permits the seedlings to continue protein synthesis when they are transferred to 50°C, whereas untreated 35°C-grown plants cannot carry out protein synthesis at 50°C (5). Further evidence for the link between HSP synthesis and induced thermotolerance comes from work on other treatments, such as arsenite, which have been shown to induce synthesis of at least a subset of HSPs; these treatments can also confer increased thermotolerance upon plant tissues without the need for exposure to elevated temperature.

To summarise, heat-shock protein synthesis in higher plants is:
- extremely rapid
- dependent upon altered gene expression at the transcriptional level
- observed in almost all plant tissues
- correlated with increased thermotolerance, though continued synthesis of HSPs is required to maintain thermotolerance
- inducible by sudden or gradual temperature increases, and by certain other treatments

3. ACCLIMATION TO LOW TEMPERATURE

For many perennial plant species and autumn-sown crops, the ability to withstand periods at or below the freezing point is essential for survival. In freezing-susceptible plants, formation of extracellular ice can lead to freeze dehydration of cells; ice crystals can also cause physical damage by disrupting membranes. Green leaf tissue is particularly susceptible to freezing damage. Many, but not all, plant species are capable of developing freezing tolerance during an appropriate acclimation treatment; this increase in freezing tolerance is known as hardening. There are certain points of similarity between hardening and the heat-shock response in plants. Firstly, tolerance of an otherwise lethal freezing treatment can be induced by a period of exposure to a low but non-injurious temperature. However, whereas heat tolerance can be significantly increased by a few minutes' exposure to a high, non-damaging temperature, cold hardiness develops over a period of days or weeks. Fig. 3a shows the increase in freezing tolerance (measured as depression of LT_{50}, the temperature at which 50% of plants are killed) for two contrasting varieties of winter oats, exposed to a hardening treatment of 2°C. Both varieties take more than a week to attain maximum hardiness, starting from a similar initial freezing tolerance (-5 to -6°C), though much of this hardiness is achieved within the first two days. The freezing-tolerant variety Kentucky is able to develop much greater tolerance than the variety Bulwark. Hardiness is reversible; Fig. 3b shows the loss of freezing tolerance by the same two varieties after return to a higher non-hardening temperature. Within 5 days, the susceptible variety Bulwark has lost most of its acquired freezing tolerance, whereas Kentucky retains about 50% of the induced freezing-tolerance for at least 20 days.

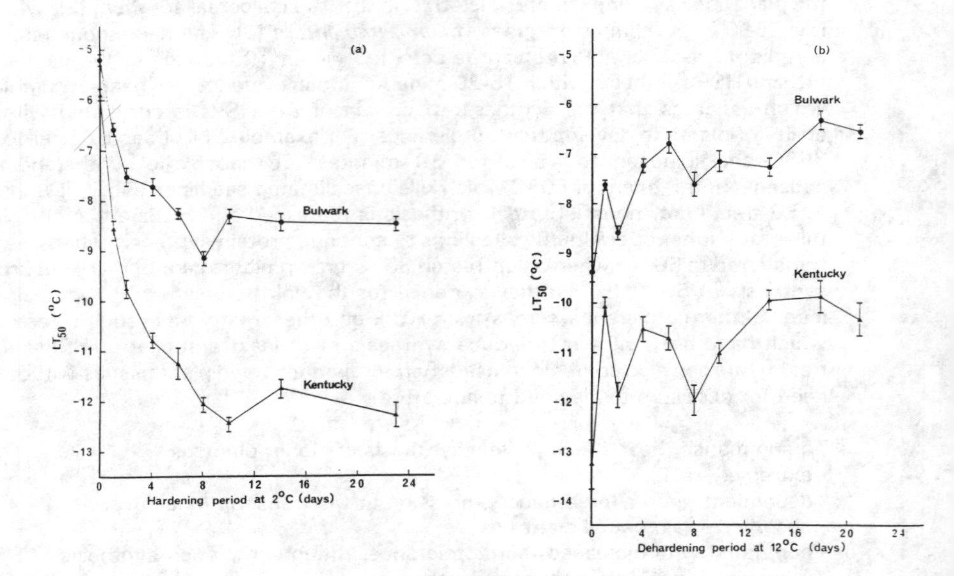

Figure 3. (a) Time course of hardening, measured by change in LT_{50} (temperature required to kill 50% of plants), for two contrasting varieties of oat seedlings. Seedlings were grown to the 2nd leaf stage at 15°C and exposed to a hardening treatment of 2°C for 24d. (b) Time course of dehardening for the two varieties shown in (a), following transfer to 10°C.

Like the heat-shock response, the process of hardening requires an alteration in gene expression, and in most cases this includes increased or *de novo* transcription of certain genes, and down-regulation of others. However, unlike the heat-shock response, there is no general repression of normal cellular protein synthesis, except insofar as lowered temperature reduces the rate of all biochemical processes. Many of the genes expressed during the hardening period are as yet of unknown function, but some have been demonstrated to have homology with fish "antifreeze" proteins (6) or drought-induced gene products (7). While attempts to show any homology between heat-shock proteins and cold-induced proteins have in general been unsuccessful, drought and related treatments (e.g. osmotic stress, abscisic acid) do induce synthesis of a subset of the cold-induced proteins. Abscisic acid or drought can also increase plant cold-hardiness without exposure to low temperature (8,9). This may well be a consequence of the fact that much of the damage caused by freezing plant tissue is due to intracellular dehydration.

While heat-shock proteins are synthesised in most parts of the plant, cold-hardening in grasses and cereals seems to be mainly a property of meristematic tissue.

Alterations in gene expression correlated with hardening are most pronounced in the meristem region (10). Following a severe freezing treatment, a plant often survives as a whole by regrowth of leaves from the protected shoot apex, even though all the original leaf tissue has been killed. Therefore the graminaceous plant may be unable to protect its photosynthetic tissue from freezing damage directly, depending instead upon regrowth from surviving meristems. The time required for such a plant to make good its losses due to freezing may greatly reduce effective leaf area duration.

In summary, cold acclimation or hardening in higher plants:
- is slower than the heat-shock response (requires days or weeks for full development)
- depends upon altered gene expression at the transcriptional level, though post-transcriptional processes are also important
- in grasses and cereals, occurs mainly in meristematic tissues
- can be induced by a low but non-lethal temperature treatment and by certain other treatments
- has no apparent homology with the heat-shock response

4. THE RESPONSE OF LEAF EXTENSION GROWTH TO LOW TEMPERATURES

The leaf of a graminaceous plants represents a linear gradient of cell age and development. Cell division occurs in the meristematic zone at the leaf base; above this region cells expand and mesophyll cells develop functional chloroplasts; and the leaf blade consists of mature, fully-differentiated cells which cannot normally be induced to differentiate or undergo division. Thus the photosynthetic area of a leaf is determined largely by processes which occur towards its base and, except for the primary leaf, usually within the sheath formed by older leaves. Temperature is one of the many environmental factors which can influence the rate of leaf extension growth. The duration of the cell division cycle in plants is increased at low temperature, hence reducing the rate at which new cells are formed (11); however, cell extension is both more sensitive to temperature changes and capable of responding more rapidly. If localised cooling is applied to the base of a grass or cereal leaf, extension growth rate decreases within seconds (12). The growth rate increases again equally rapidly upon rewarming. The speed of this response suggests that it is mediated by existing components of the tissue concerned, rather than requiring de novo gene expression. The leaf base is the site for temperature perception as well as extension growth in grasses and cereals, since if the basal meristem and extension zone are held at a constant temperature while the leaf blade is cooled or warmed, growth rate does not change (13).

For any given graminaceous plant species and genotype, extension growth continues to decline with temperature until a characteristic threshold temperature is reached at which growth ceases (12). For most temperate grasses and cereals, this temperature is between 1 and 5°C; for tropical cereals it is higher (e.g. 8°C for sorghum; (5)). A plant held for prolonged periods at its threshold temperature generally undergoes no tissue damage, and resumes growth at the original or a higher rate when returned to its former growth temperature. The ability to perceive, and stop growing at, an appropriate threshold temperature seems to be an essential survival character in temperate grasses and cereals. For example, work on 15 species of temperate grasses (genera *Lolium* and *Dactylis*) showed a strong inverse correlation between the relative growth rate at low positive temperatures, and the ability of unhardened plants to survive freezing (14). In other words, plants which cease growing at relatively high temperatures have better intrinsic freezing tolerance than those which continue growing down to lower temperatures. Is this correlation obligatory, or a coincidence brought about by close genetic linkage between freezing tolerance and temperature sensitivity of extension growth? In the latter case, it should be possible to develop plants with the advantage of early spring growth, greatly enhancing the overall canopy area duration, without suffering the penalty of increased susceptibility to freezing damage.

The *slender* mutation in barley is a useful experimental tool for investigating this problem. A recessive mutation in a single nuclear gene gives rise to a plant with elongated, attenuated leaves. The phenotype in some respects mimics the appearance of a normal plant which has been treated with exogenous gibberellic acid, but *slender* plants do not contain abnormally high levels of biologically-active gibberellins (15). Instead, it appears that the constraints upon extension growth which can be released by gibberellin application have been permanently abolished in *slender*, giving an absolute growth rate (at 20°C) 150% that of normal barley leaves, and a final leaf length twice that of normal plants (16). The threshold temperature for cessation of leaf extension in unhardened normal barley is approximately 5°C, and plants held at this temperature will resume extension growth at a temporarily-increased rate when rewarmed. However, slender plants grown under the same conditions do not stop growing until the temperature is reduced to about -5°C, and when rewarmed they are unable to undergo normal extension growth because intercellular ice formation has caused irreversible damage. Thus slender barley apparently lacks the capacity to perceive an appropriate threshold temperature by arresting leaf extension growth. This mutant should therefore give some clues to the way in which production of leaf area is limited by low temperature.

Detailed analysis of growth rates in different regions of the barley leaf base has shown (Fig. 4) that the increased overall leaf extension rate in *slender* is due not to a greater extension rate at any one point, but rather to the ability of cells to continue extending for a longer period as they move up from the leaf base.

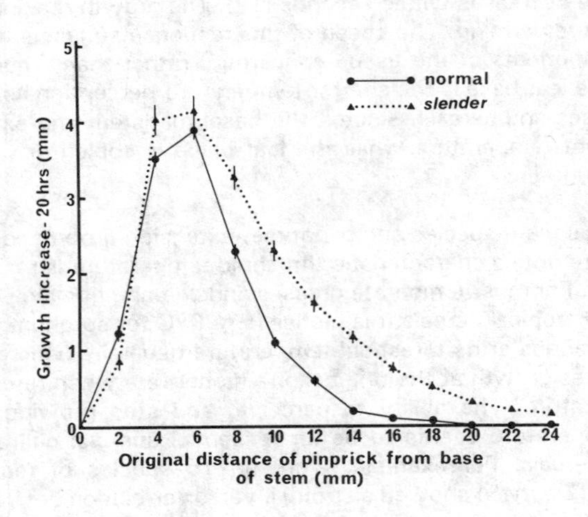

Figure 4. Rate of extension growth in successive 2mm segments of *slender* and normal barley primary leaves at 20°C. Pinpricks were made at 2mm intervals up the leaf, and distances between pinpricks were measured again 20h later. Bars represent standard errors.

Cell-free translation of mRNAs extracted from different parts of the leaf has enabled us to identify physiologically-equivalent parts of the leaf, and cDNA libraries have been constructed using mRNA from extension zone tissue of both genotypes. Differential screening has led to the isolation of cDNA clones showing altered levels or patterns of expression in the *slender* mutant. Sequence analysis of two of these clones has so far revealed no homology with other known sequences, but the third has been identified as the mRNA encoding NADPH-protochlorophyllide oxidoreductase (17). Protochlorophyllide reductase mRNA in *slender* barley grown at 20°C is present at less than half the levels in the corresponding tissues of normal barley (Figure 5).

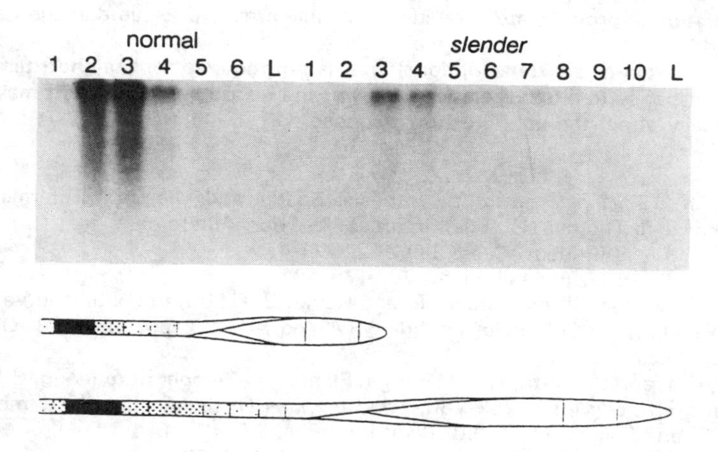

Figure 5. Comparison of levels of protochlorophyllide oxidoreductase mRNA (transcript size 1.6 kb) in successive segments of extending *slender* and normal barley leaves. Segments were numbered from the leaf base upwards; a section of expanded leaf blade tissue (L) was also taken from each genotype for comparison. Total RNA was extracted from leaf tissue grown at 20°C and subjected to northern blot analysis. The diagrams illustrate leaves of the two genotypes (showing the much greater leaf length in *slender*); shading indicates regions where the message is present, and intensity of shading is proportional to relative level of message.

Dark-grown leaf tissue of both genotypes contains much more of the mRNA than light-grown tissue; but again *slender* barley, which continues to grow more rapidly than the normal genotype in the dark, has a lower level than normal. Treating normal barley seedlings with exogenous gibberellic acid causes them to grow at a rate similar to that of *slender* seedlings, and the level of protochlorophyllide reductase mRNA in these seedlings is greatly reduced following gibberellin treatment (P.H.D. Schünmann, unpublished).

What is the likely significance of this observation? The nuclear-encoded enzyme protochlorophyllide reductase catalyses a key step in chlorophyll biosynthesis, the light-dependent conversion of protochlorophyllide to chlorophyllide (18). Levels of the enzyme and its mRNA are also light-regulated: illumination of etiolated seedlings causes a rapid decline in concentration of both the message and the protein, and this decline is mediated by phytochrome (19). It has been proposed (20) that protochlorophyllide reductase may be involved in the light-regulated development of chloroplasts as well as in chlorophyll biosynthesis. Our results suggest that (at least in barley) the enzyme or its message may participate in yet another developmental process: the control of leaf extension during the transition from growth to photosynthesis, and the regulation of this extension process by temperature.

To summarise:
- extension growth rate in grasses and cereals responds to temperature changes within seconds
- the leaf base (division and extension zone) is the site of temperature perception
- the alteration in growth rate is rapidly reversible provided tissue damage has not occurred
- gene expression at the transcriptional level is not required for the short-term growth response to altered temperature, but the genotype of the plant may dramatically affect the nature of the response.

REFERENCES

1 Thomas, H. (1992) in Crop Photosynthesis: Spatial and Temporal Determinants (Baker, N.R. and Thomas, H., eds.) in press, Elsevier, Amsterdam
2 Howarth, C.J. (1989)Plant, Cell & Env. 12, 471-477
3 Ougham, H.J. (1987) Physiol. Plant. 70, 479-484
4 Nagao, R.T., Kimpel, J.A., Vierling, E. and Key, J.L. (1986) in Oxford Surveys Of Plant Molecular And Cell Biology (Miflin, B.J., ed.) Vol. 3, pp. 384-438, Oxford University Press, Oxford
5 Ougham, H.J. and Howarth, C.J. (1988) in Plants and Temperature (Long, S.P and Woodward, F.I., eds.), pp. 259-280, The Company Of Biologists Ltd., Cambridge
6 Kurkela, S. and Franck, M. (1990) Plant Mol. Biol. 15, 137-144
7 Hahn, M. and Walbot, V. (1989) Plant Physiol. 91, 930-938
8 Robertson, A.J., Gusta, L.V., Reaney, M.J.T. and Isikawa, M. (1988) Plant Physiol. 86, 344-347
9 Siminovitch, D. and Cloutier, Y. (1982) Plant Physiol. 69, 250-255
10 Hughes, M.A. and Pearce, R.S. (1988) J. Exp. Bot. 39, 1461-1467
11 Francis, D.F. and Barlow, P.W. (1988) in Plants and Temperature (Long, S.P and Woodward, F.I., eds.), pp. 181-201, The Company Of Biologists Ltd., Cambridge
12 Stoddart, J.L., Thomas, H., Lloyd, E.J. & Pollock, C.J. (1986) Planta 167, 359-363
13 Watts, W.R. (1974) J. Exp. Bot. 25, 1085-1096
14 Pollock, C.J. and Eagles, C.F. (1988) in Plants and Temperature (Long, S.P and Woodward, F.I., eds.), pp. 157-180, The Company Of Biologists Ltd., Cambridge
15 Croker, S.J., Hedden, P., Lenton, J.R. & Stoddart, J.L. (1990) Plant Physiol. 94, 194-200
16 Pollock, C.J., Ougham, H.J. & Stoddart, J.L. (1992) in Barley: Genetics, Biochemistry, Molecular Biology and Biotechnology (Shewry, P.R., ed.), pp. 265-276, C.A.B. International, Wallingford
17 Schulz, R., Steinmüller,K., Klaas, M., Forreiter, C., Rasmussen, S., Hiller, C. and Apel, K. (1989) Mol. Gen. Genet. 217, 355-361
18 Apel, K., Santel, H.-J., Redlinger, T.E. and Falk, H. (1980) Eur. J. Biochem. 111, 251-258
19 Santel, H.-J. and Apel, K. (1981) Eur. J. Biochem. 120, 95-103
20 Harpster, M. and Apel, K. (1985) Physiol. Plant. 64, 147-152

GENETIC APPROACHES TO THE FUNCTION OF THE CHLOROPLAST LOW MOLECULAR WEIGHT HEAT SHOCK PROTEIN

Katherine W. Osteryoung and Elizabeth Vierling, Department of Biochemistry, University of Arizona, Tucson, AZ 85721, USA.

INTRODUCTION

Plants, as all other organisms, produce heat shock proteins (HSPs) in response to high temperature and other stresses. Five major classes of HSPs have been identified in eukaryotes: HSP100, HSP80-90, HSP70, HSP60, and low molecular weight (LMW) HSPs (15-30 kD) (1,2). Each class comprises a nuclear gene family, specific members of which encode proteins targeted to different cellular compartments. Members of the HSP100 (3), HSP70 (4), HSP60 (5) and LMW HSP (6) families have been shown to be present in the chloroplasts of higher plants. Other members of these families are found in the cytoplasm and in some cases in the ER or mitochondria (7). Presumably, all proteins within an HSP class perform similar functions but with some degree of specialization depending on their unique structural features and location within the cell. A large body of evidence indicates that HSPs of the high molecular weight classes act as "molecular chaperones" which mediate conformational changes involved in protein folding, transport and activity (7). The function of the LMW HSPs is unknown.

Our laboratory has been studying the major chloroplast-localized LMW HSP in order to understand how this protein functions to protect chloroplasts, and also as a model system to understand the function of LMW HSPs in general. We refer to this HSP as HSP21 after its apparent molecular weight in *Pisum sativum* (pea) and *Arabidopsis thaliana*, the experimental plants used in the laboratory. Sequence analysis of HSP21 from several higher plant species, including both dicots and monocots, has revealed a high degree of evolutionary conservation in the structure of the protein (8,9) (Fig. 1). The protein is encoded in the nucleus

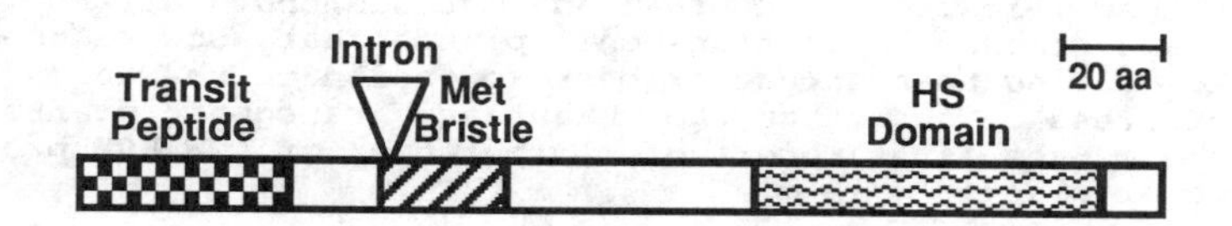

Figure 1. Generalized structure of the chloroplast-localized LMW HSP (HSP21). The position of a 164 bp intron in the genomic copy of HSP21 from *A. thaliana* is indicated. The scale bar indicates the length of 20 amino acids.

N. Murata (ed.), Research in Photosynthesis, Vol. IV, 129–136.

and has an amino-terminal transit peptide required for transport into the chloroplast. A carboxyl-terminal domain of approximately 80 amino acids shares homology with LMW HSPs found in other plant cell compartments and in other eukaryotes (6,8). Towards the amino terminus of the mature protein, HSP21 also has an interesting domain of 28 amino acids that is not found in other LMW HSPs, but is the most highly conserved region among the chloroplast HSPs (20 identical amino acids comparing 5 species (8,9)). This domain is rich in Met residues and is predicted to form an amphipathic α-helix similar to the "methionine bristle" helices of a 54 kD component of signal recognition particle (8). The genomic copy of HSP21 in *A. thaliana* contains a single intron directly preceding the Met domain (K. Osteryoung, H. Sundberg & E. Vierling, manuscript in preparation). It is interesting to speculate that HSP21 evolved from a nuclear gene which acquired sequences encoding a transit peptide and that the Met domain and intron were inserted in the same evolutionary event.

HSP21 is strongly regulated by high temperature. The mRNA and protein cannot be detected in tissues of plants grown at normal temperatures, but they accumulate in proportion to temperature above 32-34° C in pea (10). In contrast to the mRNA, which decays rapidly following return to normal temperature, the protein is quite stable with a half-life of 52 hrs (10). HSP21 accumulates not only in chloroplasts, but also in root tissues where it is found in the plastid fraction (9). Localization of HSP21 to non-photosynthetic plastids suggests that this protein protects functions common to all plastids, and may only indirectly protect the photosynthetic apparatus from heat damage.

Investigating the structure of HSP21 and its association with other components in the chloroplast is important for understanding the function of the protein during response to heat stress. HSP21 is recovered as a soluble protein from the chloroplast stroma and shows little specific association with thylakoids (9,10). In its native state the protein is found in a high molecular weight particle between 200 and 300 kD depending on the plant species (9, unpublished observations). The HSP21 particle is resistant to treatment with high salt and non-ionic detergent, suggesting hydrophobic interactions contribute significantly to its structure (9). When HSP21 is imported *in vitro* into isolated chloroplasts, the particle will assemble provided that the chloroplasts have been obtained from plants that were previously heat stressed (9, Q. Chen, K. Osteryoung & E. Vierling, manuscript in preparation). Failure of the particle to assemble in chloroplasts from control plants is probably due to the lack of a pool of endogenous HSP21 rather than to a requirement for additional heat-inducible factors (unpublished observations). Preliminary data suggest that the high molecular weight particle is composed primarily, or solely, of HSP21. Further studies of this particle are in progress.

Our molecular and biochemical analyses of HSP21 have provided the necessary foundation to initiate genetic experiments aimed at elucidating HSP21 function. In *A. thaliana* HSP21 is encoded by a single gene, facilitating the use of genetic methods to study the protein. Here we report identification of *A. thaliana* mutants that fail to express HSP21, and generation of transgenic plants that show reduced HSP21 expression during heat stress or overexpression in the absence of stress. Our progress in analyzing the mutant and transgenic plants is discussed. This is the first report of manipulation of LMW HSP protein levels in a higher plant.

MATERIALS and METHODS

Mutant seed stocks

Arabidopsis thaliana ("Columbia" ecotype) M2 seeds produced from an EMS mutagenized M1 generation were gifts from Drs. M. Estelle (Indiana University, Bloomington) and D. Mount (University of Arizona,

Tucson). M2 seed from a gamma-irradiated M1 generation were purchased from Lehle Seeds, Inc. (Tucson, Arizona).

Vector construction and plant transformation

Nearly the entire transcribed region of the *A. thaliana* HSP21 gene was amplified from a genomic clone by the polymerase chain reaction (PCR) and used for the construction of vectors for plant transformation. To obtain constitutive expression of antisense RNA, the AtHSP21 PCR fragment was ligated in the antisense orientation to the CaMV 35S promoter and nopaline synthase polyadenylation signal in the binary T-DNA transformation vector pMON530 which also incorporates a gene conferring resistance to kanamycin (kan^r)(11). A heat-regulated antisense gene was also constructed in the same vector by ligating the strong heat shock promoter sequence from the soybean GmHSP17.5-E gene (12) 5' to the AtHSP21 fragment. A vector to produce constitutive overexpression of the AtHSP21 protein was made by placing the gene fragment in the sense orientation behind the CaMV 35S promoter in pMON530. Constructs were introduced into *Agrobacterium tumefaciens* strain GV3111SE (13) by direct transformation.

A root transformation procedure modified from Valvekens et al. (14) was used to introduce the transgenes into *A. thaliana* ecotypes Landsberg erecta, Norway and RLD. Control transformants were generated by transformation with pMON530 alone. Seeds obtained from selfed, primary transformants (T_1 seeds) were germinated on kanamycin and scored for segregation of the kan^r phenotype. Kan^r T_1 individuals were transplanted to soil, grown, and tested for HSP21 protein expression following heat stress as described below.

Plant growth and heat stress

Mutant seeds were planted in flats and grown for about 3 wks under a 16 hr daylength at approximately 23-24° C. Kan^r T_1 seedlings transplanted to soil were grown similarly. Whole plants were subjected to heat stress by increasing the temperature gradually to 40° C as described by Chen et al. (10). In some cases, heat stress was carried out on individual excised leaves placed on moist filter paper in petri dishes. A 40° C treatment gives strong induction of HSP21 and does not impair growth or subsequent flowering of wild-type seedlings. Leaf protein extracts were prepared as described below either directly after the end of the 40° C treatment, or on the following morning.

Protein extraction and immunoblotting

Leaf proteins were extracted from single leaves directly in SDS-PAGE sample buffer (60 mM Tris-HCl pH 8.0, 60 mM DTT, 2% SDS, 15% sucrose, 5 mM ϵ-amino-N-caproic acid, 1 mM benzamidine, 0.01% bromophenol blue) (approximately 10 $\mu l\ mg^{-1}$ tissue). Extracts were boiled for 3 min and insoluble debris was removed by centrifugation for 5 min at 12,000 x *g*. Proteins were separated by SDS-PAGE and blotted to nitrocellulose by standard methods. Blots were reacted with crude antiserum at a 1:1000 dilution and processed for antibody detection using a chemiluminescent method (Amersham) according to the manufacturer's directions.

Antibodies against *A. thaliana* chloroplast AtHSP21 (8) and cytoplasmic AtHSP17.6 (15) were prepared against fusion proteins produced in *E. coli* basically as described by Vierling et al. (16). Details of the individual fusion protein constructs and antibody characterization are to be published elsewhere.

RESULTS

Identification of HSP21 mutants

Rosette-stage plants grown from mutagenized seed stocks were heat-stressed at 40° C, and leaf protein extracts were prepared and analyzed by western blotting using *A. thaliana* HSP21 antibodies. Screening of 3,593 individual plants by this method has been completed, including plants from both EMS-treated (2,530) and gamma-irradiated (1,063) seed stocks. Three plants, mutants 1, 2 and 3, were identified which did not show high levels of AtHSP21 following heat stress. Mutants 1 and 2 were from EMS seed stock and mutant 3 was from gamma-irradiated stock. These plants were retested by western analysis using antibodies against the cytoplasmic class I LMW HSP, AtHSP17.6. All three mutants accumulated AtHSP17.6 indicating they were not impaired in their overall ability to respond to heat stress. No plants have been identified which failed to express both AtHSP21 and AtHSP17.6. Western analysis of two of the HSP21 mutants (1 and 3) is shown in Figure 2. Mutant 2 (not shown) was similar to mutant 3 in that it had two immunoreactive bands of lower molecular weight than AtHSP21.

Unfortunately, no seed were obtained from any of these mutants. Mutant 1 was grown for five months and never flowered, even after treatment in the cold and by spraying with giberellic acid. Mutant 2 was both male and female sterile. Because these plants were grown from mutagenized seed which has multiple mutations per individual, it is unlikely that the late flowering and sterility phenotypes are related to the HSP21 deficiency. Mutant 3 was lost to an aphid infestation prior to flowering. Screening of additional mutant stock is in progress.

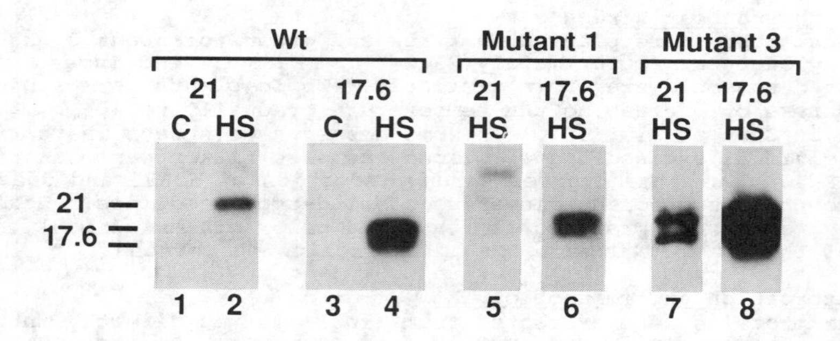

Figure 2. Western analysis of *A. thaliana* mutants that do not express AtHSP21 during heat shock. Lanes 1-4: Control (C) or heat shock (HS) leaf extracts from wildtype (Wt) plants. Lanes 5 and 6: HS leaf extracts from mutant 1. Lanes 7 and 8: HS leaf extracts from mutant 3. Western blots were reacted with either AtHSP21 or AtHSP17.6 antibodies as indicated above each lane. The positions of AtHSP21 and AtHSP17.6 are indicated at the left. The AtHSP17.6 antibodies react with two bands corresponding to related gene family members.

Generation of transgenic mutants

Transformation and regeneration of plants with the antisense gene constructs have been carried out to obtain 29 lines with the "constitutive" CaMV 35S antisense gene and 29 lines with the heat shock (HS) inducible antisense gene. Preliminary analysis of segregation for kan^r suggests that about 80% of these lines have insertions at a single locus. Southern analysis will be performed on lines of interest to examine the organization of the transgenes.

Western analysis has been performed on heat-stressed leaf extracts from 25 of the 35S and 21 of the HS antisense lines to test for reduced AtHSP21 expression. At least six kan^r T_1 individuals were tested from each line. For the analysis, western blots were probed simultaneously with the AtHSP21 and AtHSP17.6 antibodies and examined for a decrease in the ratio of AtHSP21 to AtHSP17.6 as compared to wild type plants or to control plants transformed with the vector alone. Two of the 35S and two of the HS antisense lines showed reduced expression of AtHSP21 relative to AtHSP17.6. The greatest reduction was obtained in a line with the HS antisense gene as shown in Fig. 3. Visual estimates based on band intensities from autoradiograms suggest that AtHSP21 expression is reduced about 80% in this line. More rigorous quantification of the inhibition is in progress. Under normal growth conditions plants from this line show no obvious phenotypic alterations in morphology and flower normally. Homozygous seed stocks are being established for further testing of the phenotype following heat stress.

Sixteen transgenic lines have been produced with the AtHSP21 35S overexpression construct. Eight of these lines have been tested for constitutive AtHSP21 expression by western analysis of T_1 plants. Seven lines showed little or no constitutive expression of AtHSP21, while all kan^r T_1 plants from the remaining line showed very high levels of constitutive expression (Fig. 3). We estimate that AtHSP21 accumulates to significantly higher levels in these plants than are observed following a day of heat stress at 40° C. Segregation analysis of kan^r in the overexpression line suggests it has a single insertion of the transgene. Observations of the phenotype of twelve T_1 plants from this line indicate that all are greatly reduced in size and flower earlier than either control transformants or those exhibiting a very low level of constitutive expression.

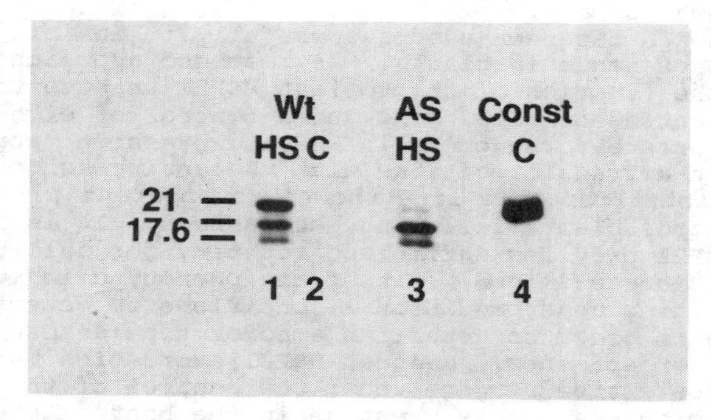

Figure 3. Western analysis of AtHSP21 expression in transgenic plants. Blots of leaf extracts from control (C) or heat-stressed (HS) plants were probed simultaneously with AtHSP21 and AtHSP17.6 antibodies. Lanes 1 and 2: wild type plants (Wt); Lane 3: antisense plant (AS); Lane 4: constitutively overexpressing plant (Const). Antibody-reactive bands are indicated at the left as in Fig. 2.

DISCUSSION

We have initiated both classical genetic and transgenic approaches to obtaining *A. thaliana* plants deficient in the synthesis of chloroplast HSP21. Using a screen to detect plants that fail to express HSP21 during heat stress, we hoped to obtain HSP21 null mutants.

Because there is no evidence that HSP21 is expressed during any stage of plant growth and development in the absence of stress, it is reasonable to assume that null mutants would be viable under normal growth conditions. Screening of the first approximately 3600 mutagenized *A. thaliana* M2 seedlings yielded three mutants with undetectable levels of HSP21, but which were fully capable of synthesizing cytoplasmic HSPs. Although the sample size is small, this is a surprisingly high frequency of mutations if all are in the HSP21 gene itself. These results demonstrate the feasibility of the screening method. A major disadvantage to our method is the need to grow individual plants for several weeks prior to testing, limiting the rate at which plants can be screened. Another drawback is the possibility that desired mutant plants are killed by the heat stress used for the screen. However, only a very small percentage of the mutants which have been heat stressed die prior to flowering. The death of these individuals could be due to other mutations and be unrelated to the stress treatment. All three HSP21 mutants identified survived the heat stress. Further analysis of the mutants would be necessary to determine the nature of the genetic lesion, and in what way lack of HSP21 affects the plant during and following stress. Unfortunately, as stated above, it was not possible to obtain seed from the mutants so far identified.

Continued screening of mutagenized seedlings is in progress. Although from our initial results it appears that lack of HSP21 expression during heat stress is not lethal under the conditions tested, to avoid having to stress entire plants, future testing will be done by heating excised leaves. All identified mutants will be backcrossed to wildtype as well as selfed to determine the genetic basis of the HSP21 deficiency and to separate the HSP21 mutation from other mutations. Analysis of HSP21 RNA levels and PCR amplification of the HSP21 gene followed by DNA sequencing will be used to examine the molecular basis of the mutation. Once a stable line containing the mutation has been established plants will be tested for their response to different conditions of heat stress.

Antisense RNA has been used successfully to inhibit the expression of a wide range of genes in plants. As a second approach to investigating the function of chloroplast HSP21 we have transformed plants with an antisense HSP21 gene under control of either a 35S or HS promoter. The greatest reduction in HSP21 expression (approximately 80%) was seen in a transformed line with the antisense gene under HS control. T_1 plants from this line showed no apparent differences as compared to control plants following heat stress. It is possible that the residual HSP21 provides sufficient activity for full protection under the conditions examined, or that the phenotype is more subtle and will require testing under additional conditions to detect. T_2 plants are being grown in order to establish a homozygous antisense line to be used in further experiments. Reduced HSP21 expression has also been obtained with the antisense gene under the control of the 35S promoter, although inhibition was not as great as in the best case with the HS promoter. It is likely that in *A. thaliana* the 35S promoter has reduced activity at elevated temperatures so that maximum levels of the antisense RNA are not present when required for inhibition of HSP21 expression. Schöffl et al. (17) reported that the 35S promoter produced high levels of RNA encoding a soybean LMW HSP in transgenic tobacco when plants were maintained at 20° C, but that RNA levels dropped approximately 50% after a two-hour heat shock at 40° C. To date the antisense plants have only been tested using a 40° C heat stress treatment. Inhibition of HSP21 expression, in particular in the 35S plants, may be more effective at lower temperatures. A greater degree of inhibition might also be achieved by crossing 35S and HS antisense transformants to obtain lines expressing both antisense genes. The presence of antisense RNA prior to heat stress (produced from the 35S promoter), as well as high levels during heat stress, should further reduce HSP21 levels. These experiments will be initiated with the most promising antisense lines.

A. thaliana plants that overexpress HSP21 constitutively have also been produced. It is not surprising that only one of eight transformed lines showed high levels of HSP21; large differences in expression of transgenes are typical in higher plants. It is interesting that the level of HSP21 in the overexpressing plants appears greater than that following a 40° C heat stress. Other researchers have shown that translation of HS mRNAs is not efficient at control temperatures, and that HSP mRNAs are unstable at control temperatures (1). The gene construct used in our experiments added a few nucleotides from the 35S transcript to the HSP21 5' leader, and truncated the gene at the 3' end with addition of the nopaline synthase polyadenylation site. These changes may alter the stability and translatability of the transcript relative to the endogenous AtHSP21 transcript, allowing a high level of expression at non-stress temperatures. Alternatively, the stability and translatability of different HSP transcripts may vary. It is also possible that the RNA level in the overexpressing line is actually low, but that the long half-life of HSP21 allows a large amount of protein to accumulate. The level of HSP21 RNA in these plants has not been examined. The HSP21 protein appears normal as determined by the formation of a high molecular weight particle that comigrates on native gels with authentic AtHSP21 (unpublished observations).

Preliminary results suggest that constitutive expression of HSP21 is detrimental. All individuals from the overexpressing line were small and flowered early. The molecular basis of this phenotype is unclear, but may be related to the reason why the protein is normally present only during periods of stress. We have not yet performed extensive analysis of the phenotype of the constitutive plants during stress. It will be important to analyze independent overexpressing transgenic lines, and to outcross these lines in order to confirm that the phenotype is not due to the site of transgene insertion or to somatic mutation resulting from tissue culture.

HSPs are hypothesized to be necessary for the development of thermotolerance (1). Acquired thermotolerance is the ability to withstand normally lethal temperatures following some type of pretreatment, usually at a high, but non-lethal temperature. Pretreatments which induce thermotolerance are correlated with the production of HSPs in plants and other organisms (1,2). If HSP21 is involved in thermotolerance, the HSP21-deficient mutants and antisense plants should be unable to develop thermotolerance, while the constitutive plants may exhibit thermotolerance without a pretreatment. Because HSP21 is plastid localized, we would expect thermotolerance to be restricted to plastid functions and may not be detected by observation of whole plants. Manipulation of HSP genes to increase overall plant thermotolerance is clearly a complex problem due to the number of different HSP genes. Our results suggesting that constitutive expression of these proteins is deleterious further complicates potential attempts to engineer HSP expression for plant improvement.

Our investigations of plants with altered LMW HSP expression, along with biochemical analysis of LMW HSP structure and activity, should enable us to determine the role of these proteins in plant responses to stress. We hypothesize the LMW HSPs may also act as a type of molecular chaperone as has been shown for the other classes of HSPs.

ACKNOWLEDGEMENTS

We thank L. Lauzon and C. Doherty for excellent technical assistance, H. Sundberg and L. Hernandez for production of AtHSP21 and AtHSP17.6 antibodies, respectively, and Monsanto Co. for the gift of pMON530. Support for this project has been provided by a grant from the National Institutes of Health to E.V.

REFERENCES

1) Lindquist, S.L. and Craig, E. (1988) Annu. Rev. Genet. 22,631-677
2) Vierling, E. (1991) Ann. Rev. Plant Physiol. Plant Mol. Biol. 42,579-620
3) Squires, C. and Squires, C.L. (1992) J. Bact. 174,1081-1085
4) Marshall, J., DeRocher, A.E., Keegstra, K., Vierling, E. (1990) Proc. Natl. Acad. Sci. USA 87,374-378
5) Hemmingsen, S.M., Woolford, C., van der Vies, S.M., Tilly, K., Dennis, D.T., Georgopoulos, C.P., Hendrix, R.W., Ellis, R.J. (1988) Nature 333,330-334
6) Vierling, E., Nagao, R.T., DeRocher, A.E., Harris, L.M. (1988) EMBO J. 7,575-581 (1988)
7) Gething, M-J. and Sambrook, J. (1992) Nature 355,33-45
8) Chen, Q. and Vierling, E. (1991) Mol. Gen. Genet. 226,425-431
9) Chen, Q. (1992) Ph.D. Dissertation, University of Arizona, Tucson, AZ.
10) Chen, Q., Lauzon, L.M., DeRocher, A.E. Vierling, E. (1990) J. Cell Biol. 110,1873-1883
11) Rogers, S.G., Klee, H.J., Horsch, R.B., Fraley, R.T. (1987) Meth. Enzymol. 153,253-277
12) Ainley, W.M. and Key, J.L. (1990) Plant Molec. Biol. 14,949-967
13) Rogers, S.G., Horsch, R.B., Fraley, R.T. (1986) Meth. Enzymol. 118,627-641
14) Valvekens, D., Van Montagu, M., Lijsebettens, M. (1988) Proc. Natl. Acad. Sci. USA 85,5536-5540
15) Helm, K. and Vierling, E. (1989) Nuc. Acids Res. 17,7995
16) Vierling, E., Harris, L.M., Chen, Q. (1989) Molec. Cell. Biol. 9,461-468
17) Schöffl, F., Rieping, M., Baumann, G. (1987) Devel. Genet. 8,365-374

THE ADAPTATION OF PHOTOSYNTHESIS TO HIGH TEMPERATURE IN *SYNECHOCOCCUS* PCC7002

Yoshitaka Nishiyama[1,2], Eszter Kovács[1], Hidenori Hayashi[1], Tadashi Watanabe[2] and Norio Murata[1]
[1]National Institute for Basic Biology, Okazaki 444, Japan
[2]Institute of Industrial Science, University of Tokyo, Tokyo 106, Japan

1. INTRODUCTION

When plants are exposed to heat, their photosynthesis is irreversibly inactivated. The plants, however, have ability to adapt to high-temperature environment and to enhance the thermal stability of photosynthetic apparatus (1). These phenomena are observed in several species of plants (1-3), while the mechanism for the adaptation is so far unclear. It has been recognized that PS2 activity is the most sensitive to heat among a number of photosynthetic activities (1). Since the oxygen-evolving process is particularly sensitive to heat (4-6), the protection of the PS2 oxygen-evolving complex against heat inactivation is regarded as the mechanism for the photosynthetic adaptation to high temperature. To understand the mechanism for the adaptation, we examined the effect of growth temperature on the thermal stability of photosynthesis both in cells and in isolated thylakoid membranes of the cyanobacterium, *Synechococcus* PCC7002.

2. MATERIALS AND METHODS

The cells of *Synechococcus* PCC7002 were grown photoautotrophically in medium A of Stevens et al. (7) at designated temperatures with aeration by 1% CO_2 in air under illumination from incandescent lamps (70 $\mu E\ m^{-2}\ s^{-1}$). The cells of *Synechocystis* PCC6803 were grown under the condition as described in (8).

Thylakoid membranes were prepared by breakage of cells with glass beads in the medium containing 50 mM Hepes-NaOH (pH 7.5), 1.0 M glycinebetaine (betaine, hereinafter), 800 mM sorbitol, 30 mM $CaCl_2$ and 1 mM 6-amino-n-caproic acid. The thylakoid membranes were isolated according to (8).

For heat treatment of cells, the suspension of cells at a concentration of 5 μg Chl ml^{-1} was incubated for 60 min at designated temperatures in darkness in the medium A. Thylakoid membranes were incubated for 20 min at designated temperatures in darkness in the medium containing 50 mM Tricine-NaOH (pH 7.5), 1.0 M betaine, 600 mM sucrose and 30 mM $CaCl_2$ (medium B) at a concentration of thylakoid membranes corresponding to 10 μg Chl ml^{-1}. After the incubation, the suspension was quickly cooled to 25°C, and then the photosynthetic oxygen evolution was measured.

N. Murata (ed.), Research in Photosynthesis, Vol. IV, 137–140.

Photosynthetic oxygen evolution was measured with a Clark-type oxygen electrode as described in (8). Photosynthesis in intact cells was measured at 30°C in the medium A in the absence of exogenously added electron acceptor. The PS2-mediated electron transport from H_2O to BQ in intact cells was measured at 30°C in the medium A supplemented with 1 mM BQ and 1 mM $K_3Fe(CN)_6$. The PS2-mediated electron transport from H_2O to PBQ in thylakoid membranes was measured at 25°C in the medium B supplemented with 100 μM PBQ.

3. RESULTS AND DISCUSSION

Figure 1a shows the profiles of heat inactivation of photosynthesis measured by oxygen evolution in cells of *Synechococcus* PCC7002 grown at 25°C and 40°C. The growth temperature had a distinct effect on the thermal stability of photosynthesis. The temperature for 50% inactivation appeared at 46°C and 50°C in cells grown at 25°C and 40°C, respectively. This observation indicates that cells grown at 40°C acquired the enhanced thermal stability of photosynthesis as compared with cells grown at 25°C.

A similar shift of the profile of heat inactivation was observed in another cyanobacterial strain, *Synechocystis* PCC6803, as shown in Figure 1b. This strain is a freshwater origin, while *Synechococcus* PCC7002 is a saltwater origin. It is of interest that these organisms living in different environment show a similar adaptive response to high temperature.

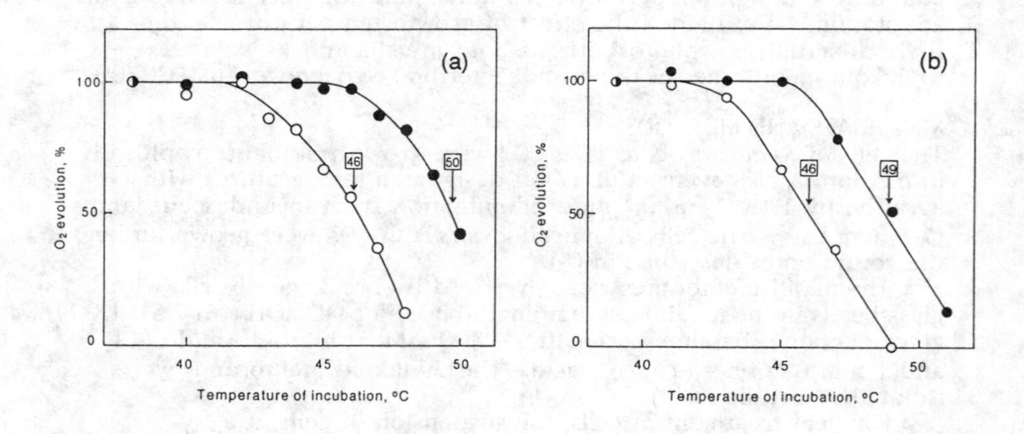

Figure 1. (a) Heat inactivation of photosynthesis in cells of *Synechococcus* PCC7002; o——o , cells grown at 25°C; ●——● , cells grown at 40°C.
(b) Heat inactivation of photosynthesis in cells of *Synechocystis* PCC6803; o——o , cells grown at 22°C; ●——● , cells grown at 36°C. The numbers in rectangles are temperatures for 50% inactivation.

For the PS2-mediated electron transport from H_2O to BQ in cells, a similar shift of the profile of heat inactivation was observed. The temperature for 50% inactivation appeared at 44°C and 48°C in cells grown at 25°C and 40°C, respectively (Table 1). Although the midpoint temperature was slightly lower than that of photosynthesis, the difference by 4°C was also observed in this reaction.

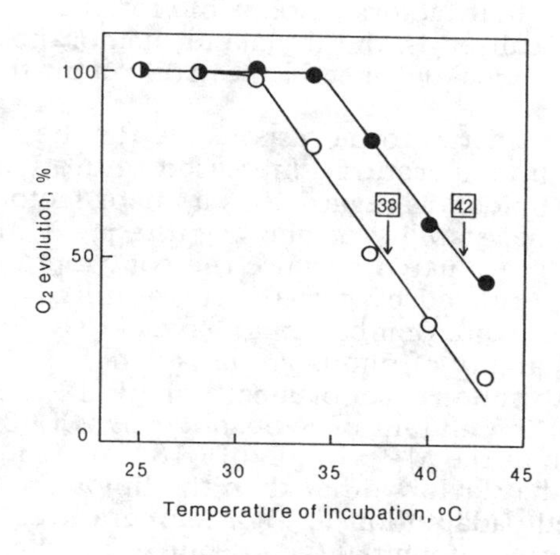

Figure 2. Heat inactivation of PS2-mediated electron transport from H_2O to PBQ in thylakoid membranes of *Synechococcus* PCC7002; o—o , thylakoid membranes from 25°C-grown cells; ●—●, thylakoid membranes from 40°C-grown cells.

Figure 2 shows the profiles of heat inactivation of the PS2-mediated electron transport from H_2O to PBQ in thylakoid membranes isolated from cells grown at 25°C and 40°C. The temperature for 50% inactivation was 38°C and 42°C in the thylakoid membranes from cells grown at 25°C and 40°C, respectively. The difference of the midpoint temperature by 4°C was the same as that observed in intact cells. Thus, the thylakoid membranes from 40°C-grown cells retained a greater thermal stability of the PS2 activity than those from 25°C-grown cells.

Table 1 Effect of growth temperature on thermal stability of photosynthetic activities in cells and thylakoid membranes of *Synechococcus* PCC7002

		Temperature for 50% inactivation, °C		
Sample	Activity	Grown at 25°C	Grown at 40°C	Δ
Cells	Photosynthesis	46	50	4
Cells	PS2 (H_2O→BQ)	44	48	4
TM	PS2 (H_2O→PBQ)	38	42	4

TM: Thylakoid membranes

In Table 1 the temperatures for 50% inactivation by heat treatment in cells and thylakoid membranes are summarized. The profiles of heat inactivation in thylakoid membranes were shifted toward low temperature as compared with those in intact cells. This shift might be attributed to the loss of the interaction between the thylakoid membranes and the cytosol. Nevertheless, the shift of the thermal stability acquired by the cells was retained in the thylakoid membranes. This result indicates that factors responsible for the enhanced thermal stability are localized in the thylakoid membranes, and that even after isolation, the thylakoid membranes still retain the factors.

Several factors have been considered to be responsible for the photosynthetic adaptation to high temperature. Increased saturation level of fatty acids of membrane lipids was regarded as a major factor for the enhancement of the thermal stability of photosynthesis (2, 3). This notion, however, should be reevaluated because the contribution of other factors, which are also regulated by growth temperature, cannot be excluded. On the other hand, Gombos et al. have clearly demonstrated that the thermal stability of photosynthesis is not affected by the change in the saturation level of membrane lipids, using isothermally grown cells of the mutant of *Synechocystis* PCC6803 which is defective in desaturation at the Δ^{12} position of C18 fatty acids (9, 10). These findings suggest that factors other than the lipids are responsible for the photosynthetic adaptation to high temperature. Heat shock proteins could be another potential factor, but so far there is no direct evidence for their role in the thermal stability of photosynthesis. Our results suggest that the factors for the adaptation to high temperature exist in thylakoid membranes, and their nature will be clarified.

REFERENCES

1 Berry, J. and Björkman, O. (1980) Annu. Rev. Plant Physiol. 31, 491-543
2 Pearcy, R. (1978) Plant Physiol. 61, 484-486
3 Raison, J. K., Roberts, J. K. M. and Berry, J. A. (1982) Biochim. Biophys. Acta 688, 218-228
4 Katoh, S. and San Pietro, A. (1967) Arch. Biochem. Biophys. 122, 144-152
5 Yamashita, T. and Butler, W. L. (1968) Plant Physiol. 43, 2037-2040
6 Nash, D., Miyao, M. and Murata, N. (1985) Biochim. Biophys. Acta 807, 127-133
7 Stevens, S. E. Jr., Patterson, C. O. P. and Myers, J. (1973) J. Phycol. 9, 427-430
8 Mamedov, M. D., Hayashi, H., Wada, H., Mohanty, P. S., Papageorgiou, G.C. and Murata, N. (1991) FEBS Lett. 294, 271-274
9 Wada, H., Gombos, Z. and Murata, N. (1990) Nature 347, 200-203
10 Gombos, Z., Wada, H. and Murata, N. (1991) Plant Cell Physiol. 32, 205-211

HEAT STABILITY OF PHOTOSYNTHETIC ELECTRON TRANSPORT IN THYLAKOID MEMBRANES FROM THE CYANOBACTERIUM

Mahir D. MAMEDOV, Hidenori HAYASHI and Norio MURATA,
Department of Regulation Biology, National Institute for Basic Biology,
Myodaiji, Okazaki 444, Japan

1. INTRODUCTION

The heat stability of electron-transport reactions in cyanobacterial photosynthesis has been studied [1-3]. However, there have been no systematic study to compare the heat stabilities of various electron-transport and phosphorylation reactions. It has been shown that the high concentration, such as 1.0 M, of glycinebetaine (betaine, hereinafter) protects the oxygen-evolving activity by stabilizing the binding of the extrinsic proteins to the PS2 complex [4-6]. Therefore, we may ask whether or not betaine also protects various electron transport and phosphorylation reactions against heat inactivation.

Recently, we obtained mutants of the cyanobacterium *Synechocystis* PCC6803 which is defective in the activity of fatty-acid desaturases [7]. One of such strain, designated Fad6/desA::Km^r, is defective in desaturation at the $\Delta 6$ and $\Delta 12$ positions of C18 fatty acids and, therefore, contains only monounsaturated lipid molecules, in contrast to wild type which contains mono- di- and triunsaturated fatty acids [8]. So, it would be important also to examine the effect of unsaturation of fatty acids on any of the electron-transport and phosphorylation reactions.

2. MATERIALS and METHODS

Wild-type and Fad6/desA::Km^r strains of *Synechocystis* PCC6803 were described previously by Wada et al. [8]. Cells were grown at 34°C and thylakoid membranes were prepared with and stored in solutions that contained 1.0 M betaine according to Mamedov et al. [9].

The thylakoid membranes were incubated for 25 min at designated temperatures in darkness in a medium containing 600 mM sucrose, 50 mM Tricine-NaOH (pH 7.5) and 30 mM $CaCl_2$. Then the suspension was cooled to 25°C. After addition of various electron acceptors, donors and cofactors, photosynthetic activities were measured at 25°C.

The transport of electrons from H_2O to PBQ, from H_2O to MV, from DQH_2 to MV and from $DADH_2$ to MV were quantitated by polarographic monitoring of the concentration of oxygen in the reaction medium with a Clark-type oxygen electrode. The transport of electrons from H_2O to DCIP and from DPC to DCIP as well as phosphorylation coupled to the cyclic transport of electrons were measured as described in [9].

In all experiments, thylakoid membranes were added to give a final concentration that corresponded to 10 μg of Chl/ml.

N. Murata (ed.), Research in Photosynthesis, Vol. IV, 141–144.

3. RESULTS and DISCUSSION

Figure 1 shows the dependence on temperature of the inactivation by heating of the transport of electrons from H_2O to PBQ in the thylakoid membranes isolated from wild-type cells. Betaine stabilized the evolution of oxygen at high temperatures. Temperatures for 50% inactivation were 42°C and 36°C in the presence of 1.0 M betaine and in its absence, respectively. Betaine also enhanced the oxygen-evolving activity, as demonstated previously [9]. This result was confirmed in the experiment in which thylakoid membranes were incubated first in the absence of betaine and then the activity was measured in the presence of 1.0 M betaine (dashed line in Fig.1). The temperature for 50% inactivation was 36°C, indicating that betaine added after the incubation at high temperature did not affect the stability to heat.

In Table 1 the temperature for 50% inactivation by heat treatment of the various photosynthetic reactions are summarized. The dependence on temperature of inactivation by heat of the electron-transport reactions from H_2O to MV and from H_2O to DCIP were similar to those from H_2O to PBQ.

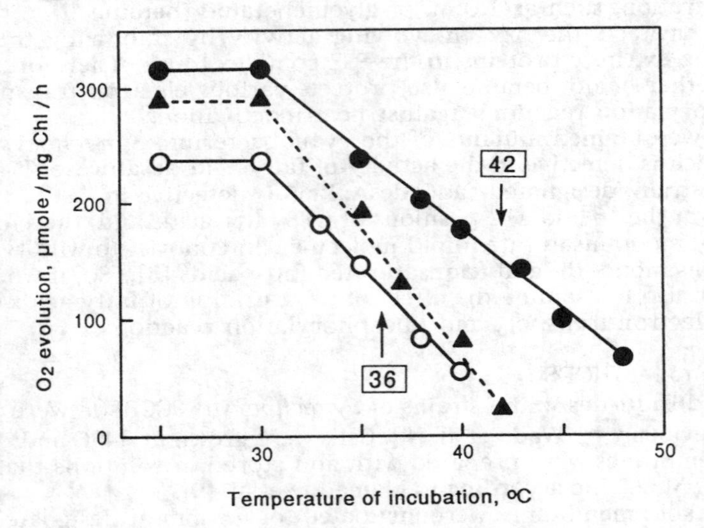

Figure.1. Dependence on temperature of inactivation by heat of the transport of electrons from H_2O to PBQ in thylakoid membranes from wild-type cells. The numbers in rectangles are temperatures in degrees C at which the activities were reduced to 50% of the original levels. o——o, No betaine was added to both the incubation and the reaction mixtures; ●——●, 1.0 M betaine was added to these mixtures; ▲— —▲, 1.0 M betaine was added only to the reaction medium after heat treatment in the absence of betaine.

The electron-transport reaction from DPC to DCIP was the next sensitive to heat. Since DPC by-passes the oxygen-evolving site, these findings suggest that the oxygen-evolving machinery is particularly sensitive among all other reactions of PS2. The phosphorylation reaction coupled to the cyclic electron-transport was as sensitive as the reaction from DPC to DCIP. On the other hand, the transport of electrons from $DADH_2$ to MV which involves the PS1 reaction, was the most resistant to heat. The transfer of electrons from DQH_2 to MV, which involves both PS1 and cytochrome b_6/f complexes was more sensitive to heat than the PS1 reaction, suggesting that the electron-transport reaction of the cytochrome b_6/f complex is more sensitive to heat than the PS1 reaction. From all these data together, the rank order of the sensitivity to heat of the photosynthetic reactions is: evolution of oxygen > PS2 reaction ≈ synthesis of ATP > cytochrome b_6/f reaction > PS1 reaction.

Table 1. Temperature for 50% inactivation by heat of specific reactions in thylakoid membranes from wild-type and Fad6/desA::Km^r strains of *Synechocystis* PCC6803.

Reaction	Betaine (1.0 M)	Temperature for 50% inactivation	
		Wild type	Fad6/desA::Km^r
$H_2O \rightarrow$ PBQ	-	36	36
	+	42	42
$H_2O \rightarrow$ MV	-	36	36
	+	41	41
$H_2O \rightarrow$ DCIP	-	37	37
	+	42	42
DPC $\rightarrow$ DCIP	-	47	46
	+	47	47
$DQH_2 \rightarrow$ MV	-	56	55
	+	56	55
$DADH_2 \rightarrow$ MV	-	59	59
	+	60	60
ATP synthesis	-	48	47
	+	48	48

The data in the present study also indicate that betaine stabilizes the oxygen-evolving reaction but no other reactions examined. As we demonstrated previously [4,5], betaine stabilizes the structure of the extrinsic proteins of PS2 complex of spinach. It is very likely that betaine stabilized the binding of the 33-kDa extrinsic protein to the PS2 complex also in the thylakoid membranes from *Synechocystis* PCC6803. However, it is rather surprising that betaine had no effect on the heat stability of other complexes.

Thylakoid membranes of *Synechocystis* PCC6803 contain a high level of polyunsaturated lipid molecules. The present study has provided a clear evidence against the role of lipid saturation on the heat stability of electron transport and phosphorylation reactions. The finding that no differences were observed in the heat stability of photosynthetic activities between the wild type and Fad6/desA::Km^{r} strains suggests that the extent of saturation of fatty acids in the thylakoid membranes is not related to the heat stability of the photosynthetic activities.

REFERENCES

1 Fork, D.C., Sen, A. and Williams, W.P. (1987) Photosynth. Res. 11, 71-87
2 Vigh, L., Lehel, C., Torok, Z., Gombos, Z., Balogh, N. and Horvath, I. (1990) in: Plant Lipid Biochemistry, Structure and Utilization (Quinn, P.J. and Harwood, J.L., eds.), pp. 373-381, Portland Press Ltd., London
3 Gombos, Z., Wada, H. and Murata, N. (1991) Plant Cell Physiol. 32, 205-211
4 Papageorgiou, G.C., Fujimura, Y. and Murata, N. (1991) Biochim. Biophys. Acta 1057, 361-366
5 Murata, N., Mohanty, P., Hayashi, H. and Papageorgiou, G.C. (1992) FEBS Lett. 296, 187-189
6 Williams, W.P. and Gounaris, K. (1992) Biochim. Biophys. Acta 1100, 92-97
7 Wada, H., Gombos, Z. and Murata, N. (1990) Nature 347, 200-203
8 Wada, H., Gombos, Z., Sakomoto, T. and Murata, N. (1992) Plant Cell Physiol. (in press)
9 Mamedov, M.D., Hayashi, H., Wada, H., Mohanty, P.S., Papageorgiou, G.C. and Murata, N. (1991) FEBS Lett. 294, 271-274

DAYTIME EXPRESSION OF A 35 kDa CHLOROPLAST PROTEIN IS DELAYED IN TOMATO BY CHILLING

Tamara L. Jones and Donald R. Ort, Photosynthesis Research Unit, USDA/ARS & Department of Plant Biology, University of Illinois, Urbana, IL 61801 USA

1. INTRODUCTION

Many tropical and subtropical plants, including some agriculturally significant crop plants, are susceptible to chilling-induced inhibition of photosynthesis from exposure to low, but non-freezing temperatures. For example, tomato shows as much as a 60% inhibition of net photosynthesis after 16 h at 4°C in the dark (1). This is in contrast to chilling-insensitive plants, such as spinach, in which photosynthesis is unaffected by such treatments. Although greater than 70% of the dark chilling-induced inhibition of photosynthesis in tomato can be assigned to a dysfunction at the level of the chloroplast (1), the inhibition is <u>not</u> caused by direct disruption of water oxidation (2), electron transfer (3), photophosphorylation (4) or activation/regulation of the carbon reduction cycle enzymes (5). Thus, while the inhibition of net photosynthesis caused by dark chilling can be substantial in species such as tomato, it is apparently caused by a relatively subtle mechanism.

Patterns of tomato leaf protein synthesis following dark chilling revealed that while the net synthesis of most leaf proteins remained unchanged, there was an apparent induction of a 35 kDa protein as well as a marked decline in the accumulation of chlorophyll a/b binding proteins of photosystem II (cab) and in the net synthesis of three thylakoid proteins (6). The chill-induced decline in cab synthesis was explained by the recent discovery that low temperature halts the progression of the circadian clock (7) controlling the transcription of certain nuclear-encoded chloroplast proteins (e.g. 8). The effect of dark chilling is to suspend the endogenous rhythm for an amount of time equivalent to the period of low temperature exposure. For the nuclear-encoded chloroplast proteins rubisco activase (rca) and cab, the normal rhythms in both transcription and translation were delayed (7). Thus, the result of chilling is that the expression of these genes and their products can become drastically out of phase with the actual time of day.

The delay of the endogenous clock by low temperature may be a breakthrough in elucidating the mechanism of dark-chill induced inhibition of photosynthesis in chilling-sensitive plants. To date however, these effects have been shown only for cab and rca. Both of these proteins have large, stable pools in the chloroplast, which make it unlikely that transitory disruption in their synthesis would have any significant direct effects on photosynthesis. Instead, we view the effect that chilling has on the expression of these genes as a potential model how the expression of other, much less abundant, proteins may be influenced by low temperature exposure. Since the 35 kDa protein that is induced in tomato by chilling (6) is a low abundance, rapidly turning over polypeptide (9) it is interesting in this regard and the focus of this brief paper.

N. Murata (ed.), Research in Photosynthesis, Vol. IV, 145–148.

2. MATERIALS AND METHODS

2.1 Leaves of tomato plants (*Lycopersicon esculentum* Mill. cv Floramerica) were labeled with ^{35}S-methionine as described elsewhere (7). The protein extracts were run on SDS-PAGE (10), electroblotted to PVDF transfer membrane and visualized by autoradiography (7).

2.2 *Staphylococcus aureus* V.8 protease was used for limited digestion of proteins according to the method of Cleveland et al. (11). Protein bands were cut from SDS-PAGE and loaded into the stacker portion of a linear gradient slab gel in which V.8 protease had been incorporated. The protein fragments were separated on the linear gradient, electroblotted onto PVDF transfer membrane and the peptide map was detected by autoradiography.

3. RESULTS AND DISCUSSION

In our previous work it was shown that a 35 kDa protein is heavily labeled following a 16h dark chilling period when the chill period is initiated in the late afternoon. However, this protein was undetectable in plants maintained in the dark at $25^{\circ}C$ during the same period. It was observed that the net synthesis of this 35 KDa protein persisted for only 3-4 h following the chill. Sensitivity to protein synthesis inhibitors, showed that this chill-induced protein is synthesized on cytoplasmic ribosomes and is nuclear encoded (6,9).

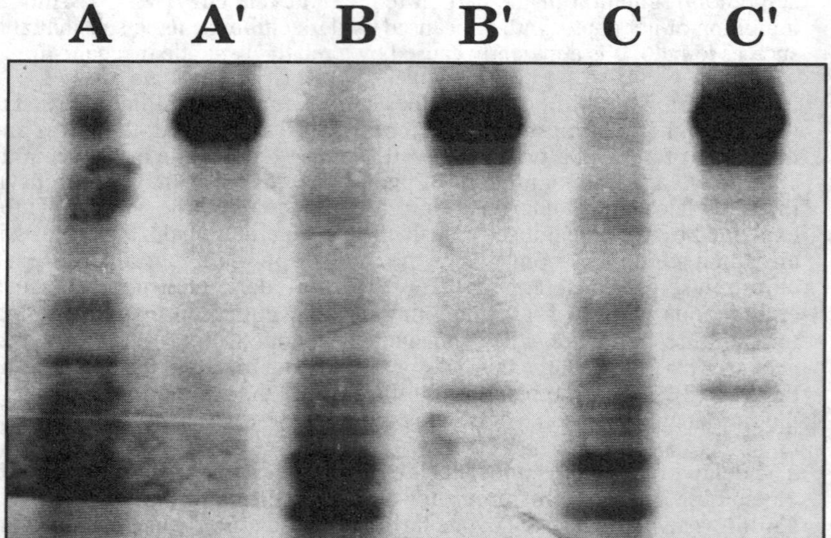

A A' B B' C C'

FIGURE 1. Proteolytic digests of the 35 kDa protein from tomato plants (A) incubated in the dark for 16h beginning at 15:00 hours, (B) chilled in the dark for 16h beginning at 15:00 hours or (C) sampled at 15:00 hours. Lanes A', B' and C' are the undigested controls of their corresponding lanes. This experiment demonstrates that the normal afternoon expression of the 35 kDa protein is delayed by chilling.

The recent discovery that chilling interrupts the circadian control of transcription in tomato raised the question of whether the apparent induction of the 35 kDa protein was actually a mistiming of expression similar to that observed for cab and rca. To investigate this issue, *in vivo* -labeled protein samples were isolated from control plants in the afternoon at the time when the chill treatment is generally initiated. These were compared to samples taken 16h later following the chill. A seemingly identical radioactive protein as that seen after chilling was evident in the leaf the afternoon prior to the chill treatment (data not shown). To confirm that the 35 kDa protein present in the afternoon sample was identical to that seen after the 16h chill treatment, peptide maps of both proteins were compared (Fig 1). Whereas the protein is absent in the 16h dark control (cv lane A with lanes B and C), the peptide maps for the chill-induced (lane B) and the protein normally expressed in the afternoon (lane C) indicate that they are indeed the same polypeptide. This finding indicates that this 35 kDa protein is normally expressed in the afternoon and that the apparent chilling-induction of synthesis is actually a delay in expression caused by chilling similar to that we observed previously for cab and rca (7).

The normal diurnal expression pattern of this protein is shown in Figure 2, again relying of peptide maps to verify the identity of the protein. Individual tomato plants were labeled for 30 min at 3h intervals. The data show that the net synthesis of this protein became detectable about 15:00 hours, reached a maximum 3h later and thereafter declined until net synthesis was no longer detectable after 21:00 hours. Although this protein was one of the most intensely labeled proteins during this interval in the afternoon, it is important to note that it never accumulated to a level that was visible by either Coomassie blue or silver staining.

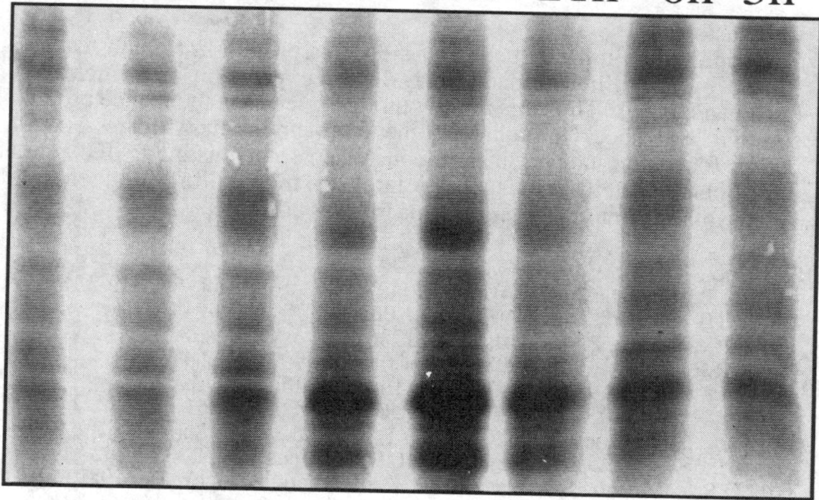

FIGURE 2. Peptide map demonstrating the diurnal expression of the 35 kDa protein. The data show that this protein is normally synthesized for only a relatively brief period in the afternoon with maximum expression at 18:00 hours.

FIGURE 3. The 35 kDa protein co-isolates with intact chloroplasts. Total leaf protein (lanes A & B) and protein from intact chloroplast (lanes C & D) were isolated from tomato plants incubated at room temperature in the dark for 16 h (lanes A & C) or chilled at 4°C in the dark for 16 h (lanes B & D).

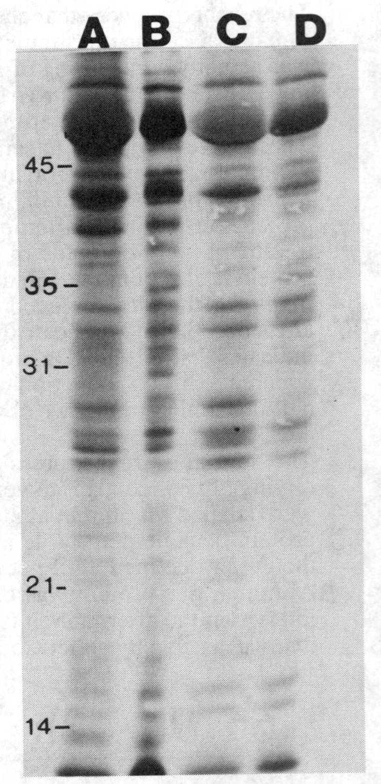

We reported previously that the chill-induced 35 kDa protein did not co-isolate with thylakoid membranes (6) but the autoradio-graphs presented in Figure 3 show that this protein does co-isolate with intact tomato chloroplasts indicating that it may be a stromal or outer membrane localized protein. Peptide maps confirmed that the totalleaf 35 kDa protein (lane B) and intact chloroplast 35 kDa protein (lane D) were identical (data not shown).

4. Conclusions

The apparent chilling induction of a 35 kDa protein in tomato leaves is actually caused by a chilling-induced delay in the expression of a nuclear gene under circadian control. Thus this rapidly turning over, low abundance protein is not any sort of a "chill shock" protein but rather a protein normally expressed with a diurnal pattern for a short interval in afternoon. Whether the mistiming of expression of this chloroplast protein is casually related to the chilling-induced inhibition of photosynthesis in tomato remains uncertain at this time.

REFERENCES

1. Martin, B., Ort, D.R. and Boyer, J.S. (1981) Plant Physiol. 68, 329-334
2. Martin, B. and Ort, D.R. (1982) Plant Physiol. 70, 689-694
3. Kee, S.C., Martin, B. and Ort, D.R. (1986) Photosyn. Res. 8, 41-51
4. Wise, R.R. and Ort, D.R. (1989) Plant Physiol. 90, 657-664
5. Sassenrath, G.F. (1988) PhD. Thesis (Univ. of Illinois, Urbana)
6. Cooper, P. and Ort, D.R. (1988) Plant Physiol. 88,454-461
7. Martino-Catt, S. and Ort, D.R. (1992) Proc. Natl. Acad. Sci. USA 89, 3731-3735
8. Nagy, F., Kay, S.A. and Chua, N.-H. (1988) Genes Dev. 2, 376-382
9. Ort, D.R., Martino, S., Wise, R.R., Kent, J. and Cooper, P. (1989) Plant Physiol. Biochem. 27, 785-793
10. Laemmli, U.K. (1970) Nature 227, 680-685
11. Cleveland, D.W., Fisher, S.G., Kirschner, M.W. and Laemmli, U.K. (1977) J. Biol. Chem. 252, 1102-1106

PLASTICITY OF THE STRESS TOLERANCE OF PHOTOSYSTEM II IN VIVO

Michel HAVAUX[1] and **Reto J. STRASSER**[2], DPVE, CEN CADARACHE[1], F-13108 SAINT-PAUL-LEZ-DURANCE, FRANCE and LABORATOIRE de BIOENERGETIQUE[2], UNIVERSITE de GENEVE, CH-1254 JUSSY, SWITZERLAND

1. INTRODUCTION

Photosystem II (PSII) is believed to be one of the most sensitive component of the photosynthetic apparatus towards several major environmental stresses including heat stress. *In vivo* measurements of the temperature-dependence of chlorophyll fluorescence in 25°C-grown potato leaves (Fig. 1) indicated that, indeed, the threshold temperature (T_c) above which PSII denatures is rather low - around 38°C - with temperatures higher than T_c causing a rapid loss of PSII activity (inset of Fig. 1). Heat-induced deactivation of PSII appears to involve denaturation of certain functional proteins, dissociation between the peripheral light-harvesting pigments and the PSII complex and release of two of the four manganese atoms of the oxygen-evolving complex (1-4). Presumably, those denaturation events result from changes in lipid-protein interactions associated with increased fluidity of the thylakoid membranes at elevated temperatures (4).

The experiments presented here demonstrate that, for a given plant material, the heat-tolerance level of PSII (*i.e.* T_c) is highly flexible. In particular, it is shown that the presence or the absence of light, the leaf water status and the recent 'thermal history' of the leaf samples markedly influence the heat tolerance of the photochemical apparatus of photosynthesis.

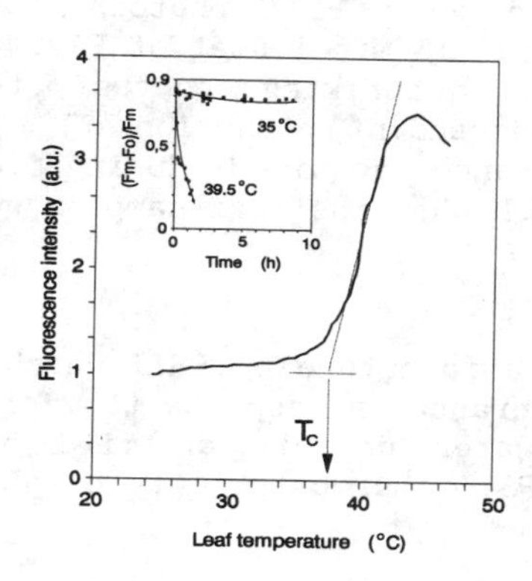

Fig. 1. Chlorophyll fluorescence emission under low exciting light in potato leaves heated at a rate of 1°C min^{-1}. The Tc value is indicative of the PSII thermotolerance (2). Inset: (Fm-Fo)/Fm in leaves placed in the dark at 35°C (<Tc) or 39.5°C (>Tc).

N. Murata (ed.), Research in Photosynthesis, Vol. IV, 149–152.

2. MATERIALS and METHODS

Chlorophyll fluorescence was measured in weak modulated light using either a MFMS-fluorometer (Hansatech Ltd., UK) or a PAM-fluorometer (H. Walz GmbH, FRG) as described in a previous paper (5). Leaf temperature was adjusted and monitored during fluorescence measurements as described in Ref. (6). The maximal photochemical efficiency of PSII (ϕ) was calculated from the initial (Fo) and maximal (Fm) levels of chlorophyll fluorescence as: ϕ=(Fm-Fo)/Fm. Photosynthetic oxygen evolution by leaf discs was measured at 25°C with a Clark-type oxygen electrode (Yellow Springs Instruments, USA).

3. RESULTS

3.1 *Heat pretreatment*

When the fluorescence-temperature experiment shown in Fig. 1 was done after preheating the leaf at 35°C for a relatively short period of time (2h), a marked shift of T_c towards higher values was observed (Fig. 2A) indicating increased thermostability of PSII. As a consequence, heat stress conditions which caused an almost complete and irreversible inhibition of PSII photochemistry in control leaves had considerably less effects on the photochemical efficiency of PSII in preheated leaves (Fig. 2B). Heat-induced acquisition of PSII thermotolerance was fast, with a half-time $t_{1/2}$ of around 30 min (inset of Fig. 2A) and slowly reversible upon return of the leaf samples at 25°C ($t_{1/2} > 6$ h, data not shown).

3.2 *Light*

Fig. 3 demonstrates that light also protects photosynthesis against heat injury of PSII: when applied in darkness, heat stress (40°C) caused a dramatic reduction of the rate of photosynthetic oxygen evolution in pea leaves whereas, in the presence of light, the same heat treatment had no influence on oxygen evolution. Those contrasting heat-responses of illuminated and non-illuminated leaves were also observed when variable chlorophyll fluorescence was measured (data not presented).

3.3 *Water stress*

The stability of PSII to heat was observed to increase during water stress as indicated by the upward shift of T_c during leaf dehydration (Fig. 4). When control, well-hydrated leaves were placed at 42°C in the dark, the quantum yield ϕ of PSII photochemistry rapidly decreased and reached zero after *ca.* 15 min (inset of Fig. 4), indicating complete deactivation of PSII. In striking contrast, this treatment caused only a slight, time-independent reduction of ϕ in water-stressed leaves. PSII thermotolerance acquired during leaf dehydration was reversible within about 5 h when the leaf samples were transferred into water (data not shown).

4. DISCUSSION

The presented data illustrate the dynamic nature of PSII which is able to noticeably increase its thermotolerance in response to various environmental stimuli such as light, water deficit or mild heat conditions. In this study, increases in PSII thermostability of about

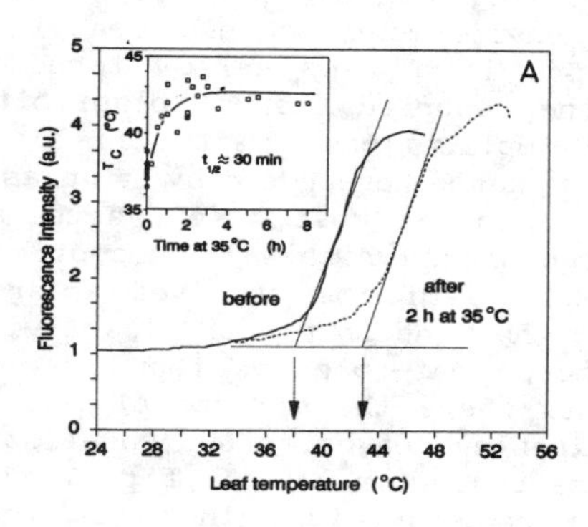

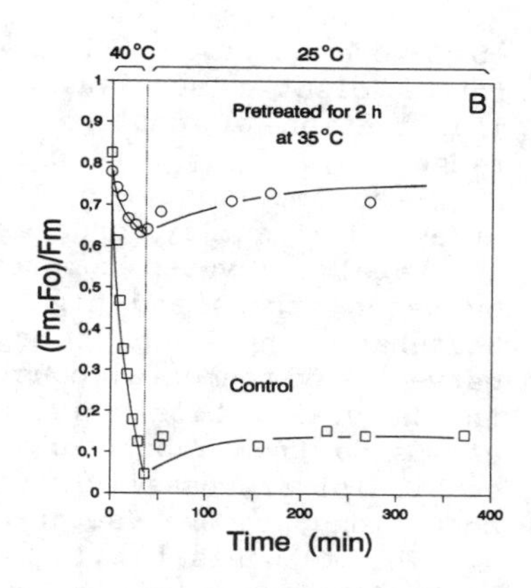

Fig. 2. **A)** *Temperature-dependence of chlorophyll fluorescence in potato leaves before and after 2-h exposure to 35°C. Inset: time course of the changes in Tc during pretreatment at 35°C.* **B)** *(Fm-Fo)/Fm in potato leaves heated at 40°C in the dark for 40 min and then transferred at 25°C.*

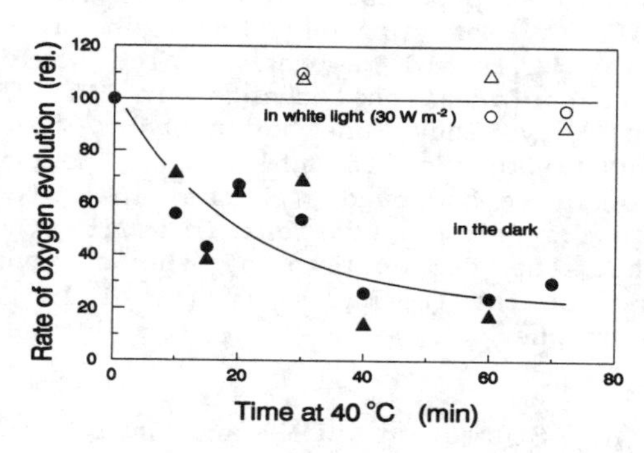

Fig. 3. Light-limited (triangle) and light-saturated (circle) rates of oxygen evolution in pea leaves preheated at 40°C in darkness or in the light.

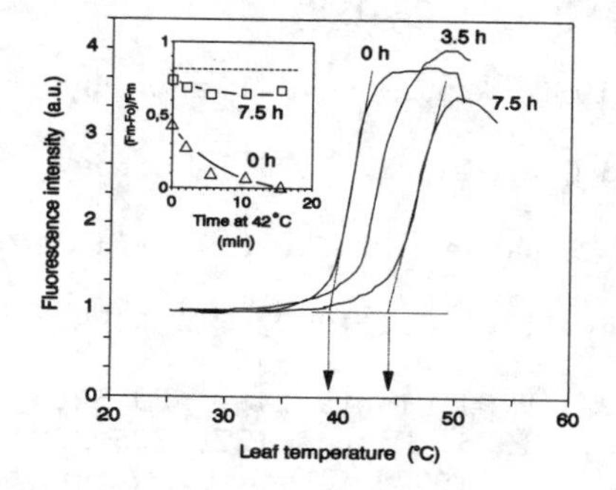

Fig. 4. Temperature-dependence of chlorophyll fluorescence in tomato leaves dehydrated in air for various times. Inset: (Fm-Fo)/Fm in control and dehydrated (for 7.5 h) leaves placed at 42°C in the dark. The dotted line indicates the (Fm-Fo)/Fm value in control and dehydrated leaves before heat stress.

+5°C were observed (Figs. 2 and 4); this can be extremely important for a plant's survival in a hot environment because heat-induced inactivation of photochemistry occurs in a very narrow temperature range (Fig. 1). It is clear that the reported thermal plasticity of PSII has important ecophysiological implications: in the field, heat stress is usually progressive (and hence preceded by a phase of moderately elevated temperatures) and is, in most cases, accompanied by water stress and high solar irradiances which are susceptible of heat-hardening PSII. A major consequence of the observed antagonism between environmental constraints is that the *in vivo* PSII activity in the natural habitats is probably more heat-tolerant than previously estimated from laboratory experiments where the effects of a defined constraint are usually studied by exposing leaves, grown under optimal conditions, to one factor-one reponse tests (as *e.g.* in Fig. 1).

The mechanism(s) by which PSII can rapidly adjust its thermal stability remain(s) to be elucidated and will be studied in future work. If the current perception of heat injury of photosynthetic membranes is correct (see Introduction), increased thermostability of PSII should imply stabilization of lipid-protein interactions in this photosystem. Changes in the lipid phase of thylakoid membranes can result in a modification of the PSII heat-tolerance (7). However, the characteristics of the above-described processes (fast induction, slow reversal) exclude the possibility of profound changes in the lipid/protein composition of the thylakoid membranes which would be much slower (*cf.* Ref. 8). A mere conformational changes in PSII (more rapidly reversible) is also unlikely. Thus, one has probably to look for adaptive changes in the surroundings of the chloroplast membranes (*e.g.* accumulation of thermoprotective compounds, changes in proton or metal cations concentration) as suggested by various *in vitro* studies (9,10 and others) showing that the composition of the suspension medium exerts a strong influence on the thermal stability of isolated thylakoids and PSII core preparations.

REFERENCES

1 Thompson, L.K., Blaylock, R., Sturtevant, J.M. and Brudvig, G.W. (1989) Biochem. **28**, 6686-6695
2 Schreiber, U. and Berry, J.A. (1977) Planta **136**, 233-238
3 Nash, D., Miyao, M. and Murata, N. (1985) Biochim. Biophys. Acta **807**, 127-133
4 Berry, J. and Björkman, O. (1980) Annu. Rev. Plant Physiol. **31**, 491-543
5 Havaux, M., Strasser, R.J. and Greppin, H. (1991) Photosynth. Res. **27**, 41-55
6 Havaux, M., Greppin, H. and Strasser, R.J. (1991) Planta **186**, 88-98
7 Kunst, L., Browse, J. and Somerville, C. (1989) Plant Physiol. **91**, 401-408
8 Santarius, K.A. and Müller, M. (1979) Planta **146**, 529-538
9 Krause, G.H. and Santarius K.A. (1975) Planta **127**, 285-299
10 Williams, W.P. and Gounaris, K. (1992) Biochim. Biophys. Acta **1100**, 92-97

D1 PROTEIN METABOLISM IN MAIZE AT LOW TEMPERATURES

Guy J. Bredenkamp and Neil R. Baker, Department of Biology, University of Essex, Colchester, CO4 3SQ, Essex, U.K.

1. Introduction

Photosynthetic productivity of maize in temperate regions is limited by low temperatures experienced in the early growing season (1). A particular problem is the susceptibility of the photosynthetic apparatus to photoinhibition during periods of chilling involving damage to the D1 protein of PSII and the slow recovery of the D1 after removal of the chill (2,3). Recent studies on maize leaves grown at low temperatures have shown that chloroplast-encoded gene products, including the D1 protein, are markedly under-represented relative to nuclear-encoded polypeptides in the thylakoid membranes of mesophyll cells (4). Consequently, it is evident that chilling perturbs the co-ordination of thylakoid membrane biogenesis in maize. This could have important implications for the photoinhibition of photosynthesis since the processes involved in the accumulation of D1 in the thylakoid membrane appear to be impaired at low temperatures (4). In this study we investigate the effects of temperature on the *in vitro* synthesis, assembly and degradation of the D1 protein in maize mesophyll chloroplasts.

2. Materials and Methods

Maize (*Zea mays* cv. LG11) was grown in controlled environment cabinets at 14 or 25°C for the 16 h photoperiod (PPFD 230 μmol m^{-2} s^{-1}) and at 12 or 20°C, respectively, at night. Intact mesophyll chloroplasts were prepared as previously described (5) and resuspended in protein synthesis buffer (330 mM sorbitol, 50 mM tricine/KOH, pH 8.4). Samples containing 200 μg chl ml^{-1} were illuminated at 600 μmol m^{-2} s^{-1} with *ca.* 50 μCi ml^{-1} [^{35}S]-methionine (1200 Ci mol^{-1}, NEN/DuPont) simultaneously at a range of temperatures between 13 and 26°C in a series of water-jacketed glass vessels. After labelling for various times (see figure legends), chloroplast samples (100 μl) were lysed by adding 500 μl ice-cold 10 mM $MgCl_2$. Thylakoid membrane fractions were then pelleted, washed in 10 mM $MgCl_2$ and solubilised in SDS buffer for gel electrophoresis. SDS gels were loaded with 20 μg Chl per track. After running, gels were stained in Coomassie blue, infiltrated with Autofluor (National Diagnostics), dried and autoradiographed by exposure to Kodak XAR-5 film. For quantitation of incorporated

N. Murata (ed.), Research in Photosynthesis, Vol. IV, 153–156.

label, autoradiographs were scanned densitometrically using a Molecular Dynamics gel scanner with ImageQuant software: the amount of label in each band on the autoradiographs was measured by volume integration of the entire band.

For pulse-chase analysis, chloroplasts were illuminated as above for 10 min at 25 °C or 40 min at 14°C in the presence of *ca.* 0.25 µCi [^{35}S]-methionine mg^{-1} chl. Cold methionine was then added to 5 $nmol^{-1}$ µg chl and the suspension divided into aliquots which were incubated with illumination for 20-80 min at six different temperatures between 13 and 25°C. 500 µl of ice-cold 10 mM $MgCl_2$ was added to each 50 µl time point sample and the thylakoid membranes centrifuged, washed and solubilised for SDS-PAGE and autoradiography as above.

3. Results

The temperature dependency of ^{35}S-label incorporation into the D1 protein in chloroplasts isolated from 25°C-grown leaves at 10 min intervals during a 40 min synthesis period is shown in Fig. 1. After 10 min, label incorporation follows a conventional pattern of temperature dependency, with a Q_{10} of approximately 2.6. During the remainder of the incubation period, protein accumulation at 13°C continues at an approximately linear rate, whereas between 15 and 21°C the amount of incorporated label appears to reach a maximum after 20 to 30 minutes. At 23 to 25°C, a large proportion of the newly-synthesised protein is degraded in the 40-minute sample. It is clear from these data that the rates of both synthesis and degradation of D1 are enhanced at higher temperatures. An additional complication, however, is the possibility of a strong temperature dependence of the rate of chloroplast lysis *in vitro*. In lysed chloroplasts, degradation of D1 will proceed, but not synthesis, resulting in a spurious decline in labelled protein in chloroplasts incubated at higher temperatures for long periods. The degradation of newly synthesised D1 was examined by pulse-chase analysis.

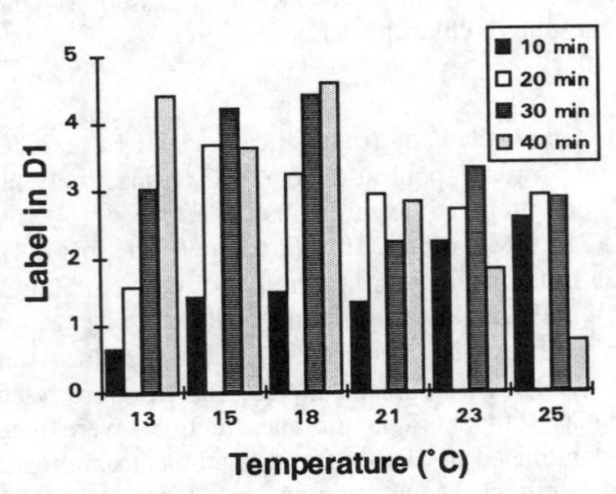

Fig. 1. Time course of ^{35}S-methionine incorporation into D1 protein (in arbitrary units) in thylakoids of chloroplasts isolated from leaves grown at 25 °C as a function of incubation temperature. Data are the means of three experiments and standard errors were less than 7% of the mean.

The effect of temperature on the kinetics of D1 degradation during an 80-min chase period *in vitro*, for chloroplasts isolated from 25°C-grown plants and pulse-labelled at 25°C for 10 min was examined (Fig. 2). As might be expected from Fig. 1, degradation of newly-synthesised D1 protein is clearly more rapid at higher temperatures; at 13°C, 67% of the original label is still present after 20 min, whereas at 25°C, only 29% remains after the same time. In contrast, when pulse-labelling is carried out at 13°C for 40 min (Fig. 3), the labelled D1 appears to be much more stable in the chase period, and the rate of its degradation is not so markedly dependent on temperature. This raises the possibility that D1 synthesised at low temperatures may be assembled into the membranes in such a way that its subsequent turnover is inhibited. In chloroplasts isolated from leaves grown at 14°C and pulse-labelled at 13°C, this effect is even more pronounced (Fig. 4). Degradation of the D1 protein is substantially slower than for chloroplasts from 25°C-grown leaves under the same experimental conditions; 53% of label is still present after 80 min chase at 25°C in the chloroplasts from 14°C-grown leaves, compared to 32% in chloroplasts from leaves grown at 25°C.

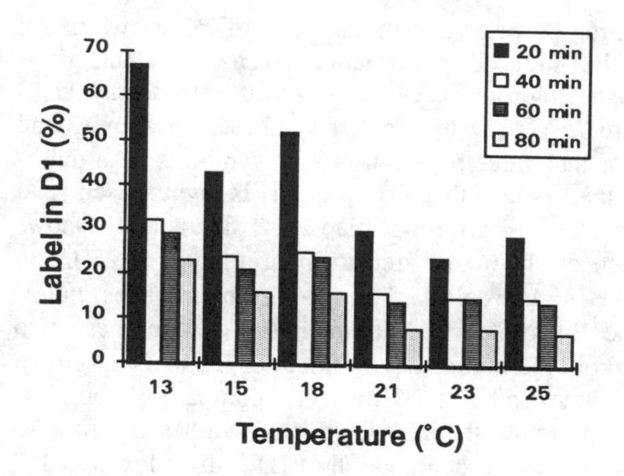

Fig. 2. Chase of ^{35}S-methionine in D1 protein in the thylakoids of mesophyll chloroplasts isolated from leaves grown at 25°C as a function of temperature. Label in D1 is expressed as a percentage of that present immediately after the 40 min pulse of ^{35}S-methionine given to the intact chloroplasts at 25°C, and the chase was carried out over 80 min.

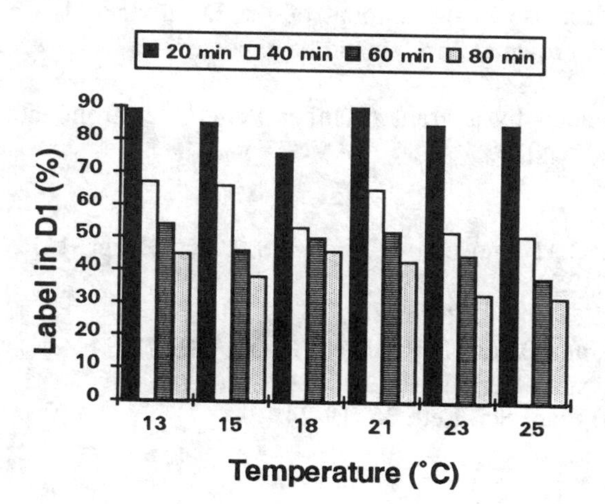

Fig. 3. Chase of ^{35}S-methionine in D1 protein in the thylakoids of mesophyll chloroplasts isolated from leaves grown at 25°C as a function of temperature. Label in D1 is expressed as a percentage of that present immediately after the 40 min pulse of ^{35}S-methionine given to the intact chloroplasts at 13°C, and the chase was carried out over 80 min

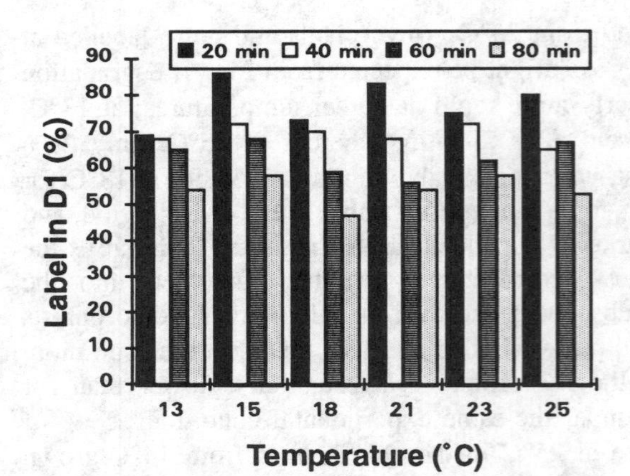

Fig. 4. Chase of ^{35}S-methionine in D1 protein in the thylakoids of mesophyll chloroplasts isolated from leaves grown at 14°C as a function of temperature. Label in D1 is expressed as a percentage of that present immediately after the 40 min pulse of ^{35}S-methionine given to the intact chloroplasts at 13°C, and the chase was carried out over 80 min.

4. Conclusions

The previously observed deficiency of the D1 protein in thylakoids of 14°C-grown maize would not appear to result from chill-induced perturbation to the mechanism of chloroplast protein synthesis, since maize chloroplasts can clearly synthesise the D1 at 13 °C albeit at a reduced rate compared to 25°C. The Q_{10} for D1 synthesis between 13 and 25°C was determined at 2.6, not an unusual value for plant protein synthesis. The pulse-chase data presented demonstrate that when the D1 protein is synthesised and incorporated at 13°C into thylakoids from 14°C-grown plants, its degradation shows remarkably little temperature-dependence when compared to incorporation at 25°C in chloroplasts from 25°C-grown leaves. In chloroplasts from 25°C-grown leaves, pulse-labelled at 13°C, the stability of the D1 protein is intermediate between these two situations. This suggests that the thylakoid membrane environment of D1 in 14°C-grown maize tends to stabilise newly synthesised D1. However, comparing the low temperature-dependence of D1 degradation with the high Q_{10} for its synthesis, it follows that the ratio of the rate of synthesis to the rate of degradation of D1 will be lower at 13° C than at 25°C. Consequently, a net decrease in the amount of the D1 thylakoids of leaves grown at 14°C compared to leaves grown at 25°C would be expected.

Acknowledgement. This study was funded by a grant (number PG84/502) from the Agricultural and Food Research Council to NRB.

References

1. Stirling, C.M., Nie, G.Y., Aquilera, C., Nugawela, A., Long, S.P. and Baker, N.R. (1991) Plant Cell Environ. 14, 947-954.
2. Long, S.P., East, T.M. and Baker, N.R. (1983) J. Exp. Bot. 34, 177-188.
3. Ortiz-Lopez, A., Nie, G.Y., Ort, D.R. and Baker, N.R. (1990) Planta 181, 78-84.
4. Nie, G.Y. and Baker (1991) Plant Physiol. 95, 184-191.
5. Jenkins, C.L.D. and Russ, V.J. (1984) Plant Sci. Lett. 35, 19-24.

HEAT SHOCK PROTEINS AND THERMAL RESISTANCE OF PHOTOSYSTEM II

Nathalie MILLER and Robert CARPENTIER, Centre de recherche en photobiophysique, Université du Québec à Trois-Rivières, C.P. 500, Trois-Rivières, Québec, G9A 5H7, Canada.

1. INTRODUCTION

Upon heat stress, all organisms can induce the synthesis of a family of proteins called the heat-shock proteins (hsp) (1). In higher plants, the occurrence of these polypeptides is proposed to be associated with thermal tolerance because in the presence of hsp plants seedlings can grow above 40°C, at temperatures which are usually lethal (2-5). Several hsp have been located inside the chloroplast and some are found to be associated with the thylakoid membranes (3,6-9). However there is no report of an increased resistance of the photosynthetic functions to heat-stress in the presence of hsp.

Photosystem II (PSII) is the most sensitive photosystem to elevated temperatures. Because hsp associated with thylakoid membranes have been found mostly associated with the grana-membrane fraction (9) a relation between an increase resistance of PSII to heat-stress and the occurrence of hsp can be suggested. In this paper, we show a direct relationship between the synthesis of hsp an the acclimation of PSII function to heat-stress.

2. MATERIALS AND METHODS

Barley seeds (*Hordeum vulgare*) were grown in vermiculite for seven days at 25°C in a 16:8 light/dark cycle at a light intensity of 30 W/m^2. Seven days old leaves were harvested and soaked in distilled water containing the specified additives during heat shock treatments (3 h at 40°C). Thylakoid membranes and intact chloroplasts were isolated as previously described (10-11).

Oxygen evolution was monitored at 22°C with a Clark-type electrode as described elsewhere (12). The media contained thylakoid membranes at a Chl concentration of 11 μg/ml, 20 mM tricine (pH 7.6),

N. Murata (ed.), Research in Photosynthesis, Vol. IV, 157–160.

10 mM NaCl, 5 mM $MgCl_2$ and 240 μM 2,6-dichlorobenzoquinone (DCBQ) as artificial electron acceptor. The samples were incubated at 30°C for the specified period of time and then transfered to the electrode chamber.

3. RESULTS AND DISCUSSION

Acclimation of PSII to elevated temperature is demonstrated in Fig. 1. In these experiments, thylakoid membranes were isolated from plants either untreated or acclimated 4 h at 40°C. The initial rate of oxygen evolution of these preparations measured at 20°C was similar (180 ± 20 μmol O_2/mg Chl•h). However, if the samples were incubated at 30°C prior to oxygen evolution measurements, there was a noticeable decline of activity that was much more pronounced in thylakoids isolated from untreated plants in comparison to thylakoid obtained from plants that were acclimated at 40°C. This difference was especially clear after at 5 h incubation of the isolated membranes where the samples obtained from acclimated plants still retained about 70% of their control activity.

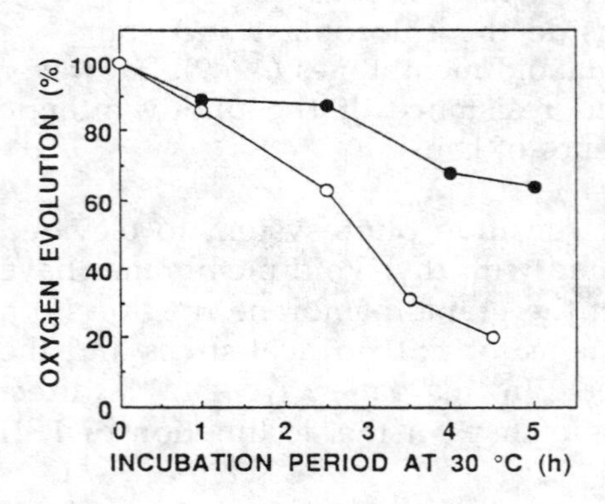

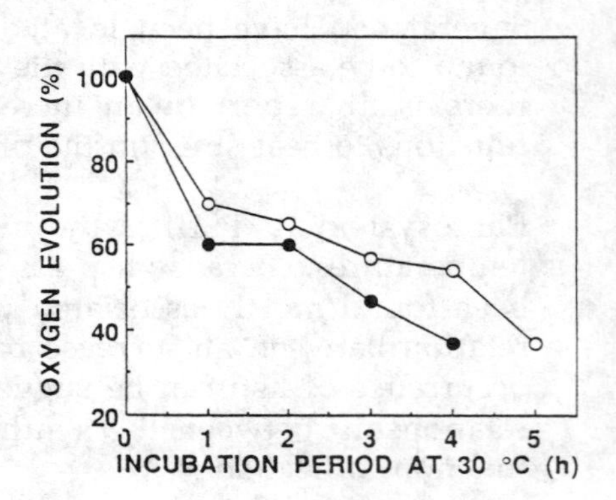

FIGURE 1. (Left) Oxygen evolution in thylakoid membranes isolated from plants either untreated (O) or acclimated 3 h at 40°C (●). The samples were preincubated at 30°C for the specified period of time before measurements.

FIGURE 2. (Right) Oxygen evolution in intact chloroplasts either untreated (O) or acclimated 3 h at 40°C (●). The samples were preincubated at 30°C for the specified period of time before measurements.

On the other hand, if intact chloroplast isolated from untreated barley leaves were subjected to a heat-stress of 3 h at 40°C, these chloroplasts could not acquire the thermal stability they obtained when this treatment was performed with whole leaves. In fact, the chloroplasts acclimated at 40°C and non-acclimated chloroplasts presented a similar decline of their oxygen evolving activity after incubation at 30°C (Fig. 2).

Thus, it appears that the factor that provided the thermal resistance of PSII after the acclimation period of whole leaves originated from the cytosol and was imported into the organelle. Under the acclimation conditions, radio-labelled methionine was added to the watering media to follow the formation of hsp. The 22 and the 70 kDa hsp were found in the thylakoid membrane fractions obtained from plants treated 3 h at 40°C (results not shown). Therefore, the acclimation conditions were appropriate the produce the hsp and the latter must be good candidates as a factor that produced thermal adaptation.

In Table 1, it is shown that thermal adaptation was inhibited by cycloheximide and chloramphenicol. The former inhibit the synthesis of nuclear-encoded proteins and its inhibitory effect indicated the involvement of hsp of nuclear origin in the induced thermal tolerance of PSII.

TABLE 1. Oxygen evolution activity of thylakoid membranes isolated from seedlings either untreated or acclimated 3 h at 40°C. Activities where measured after a 2 h and a 5 h incubation of the isolated thylakoids at 30°C

Additives[a]	Oxygen evolution (%)[b]			
	Control		Acclimated	
	2 h	5 h	2 h	5 h
None	55	41	86	68
Cycloheximide (5 mM)	63	38	57	45
Chloramphenicol (5 mM)	56	25	56	23

[a] Leaves were cut and soaked in distilled water containing the additives during heat acclimation.

[b] Rates represent the extent of activity retained after the incubation of thylakoid membranes at 30°C and are expressed as a percentage of the maximal rate (100%) obtained before incubation. This maximal rate was similar in all experiments (180 ± 20 μmol O_2/mg Chl•h).

The action of chloroamphenicol, an inhibitor of the synthesis of chloroplast-encoded polypeptides, suggests that a chloroplast factor is also required to confer thermotolerance. However, hsp were detected in the chloroplast stroma even in the presence of this inhibitor (7). The above indicates that an intra-organelle processing of the hsp is required to obtain the active form of the nuclear-encoded hsp or that the action of the nuclear-encoded hsp must be combined with that from a chloropalst-encoded polypeptide to produce thermotolerance.

In conclusion, the inhibition of the thermal adaptation of PSII by inhibitors of protein synthesis and the occurrence of hsp during this process provide a good correlation to attribute a role of hsp in the acquisition of thermotolerance of the photosynthetic functions. This is in line with the location of hsp in the grana fractions of the thylakoid membranes (9).

REFERENCES

1 Lindquist, S. and Graig, E.A. (1988) Annu. Rev. Genet. 22, 631-677
2 Lin, L.-Y., Roberts, J.K. and Key, J.L. (1984) Plant. Physiol. 74, 152-160
3 Restivo, F.M., Tassi, F., Maestri, E., Lorenzoni, L., Puglisi, P.P. and Marmiroli, N. (1986) Curr. Genet. 11, 145-149
4 Krishnan, M., Nguyen, H.T. and Burke, J.J. (1989) Plant Physiol. 90, 140-145
5 Marmiroli, N., Lorenzoni, L., Cattivelli, L., Stanca, A.M. and Terzi, U. (1989) J. Plant Physiol. 135, 267-273
6 Kloppstech, K., Meyer, G., Schuster, G. and Ohad, I. (1985) EMBO J. 4, 1901-1909
7 Vierling, E., Mishkind, M.L., Schmidt, G.W. and Key, J.L. (1986) Proc. Natl. Acad. Sci. USA 83, 361-365
8 Krishnasamy, S., Mannan, R.M., Krishnan, M. and Granam, A. (1988) J. Biol. Chem., 263, 5104-5109
9 Adamska, I. and Kloppstech, K. (1991) Eur. J. Biochem. 198, 375-381
10 Carpentier, R., Leblanc, R.M. and Mimeault, M. (1987) Enzyme Microb. Technol. 9, 489-493
11 Cerovic, Z.G. (1984) Biochem. J. 223, 543-545
12 Carpentier, R., Larue, B. and Leblanc, R.M. (1984) Arch. Biochem. Biophys. 228, 534-543

CHILLING DAMAGE OF DARK STORED CUCUMBERS (*Cucumis sativus* L.) AFFECTS THE MAXIMUM QUANTUM YIELD OF PHOTOSYSTEM 2.

OLAF VAN KOOTEN, Manon G.J. Mensink, Els C. Otma, Alex C.R. van Schaik and Simon P. Schouten, Agrotechnological Research Institute (ATO-DLO), P.O. Box 17, NL-6700 AA Wageningen, The Netherlands.

1. INTRODUCTION

The chilling sensitivity of fruits of tropical origin prohibits the long term storage of these commodities at temperatures well below 10 °C (1). In freshly harvested fruits of *Cucumis sativus* L. stored in darkness for a prolonged period at temperatures below 10 °C lipid peroxidation is induced upon rewarming at temperatures above 10 °C (2). Fruits stored at 4 °C for up to 14 days do not reveal any visually assessable symptoms of chilling injury upon retrieval from cold storage. However after several days at 20 °C the fruits reveal the symptoms of chilling injury ranging from shriveling or pitting of the peel to depressions in the peel, internal browning, up till tissue collapse and incipient decay. Accurate measurements of the components capable of impeding oxidative stress in the chloroplasts of cold stored cucumber fruits revealed the occurrence of oxidative stress long before the onset of lipid peroxidation (3).

Pulse amplitude modulated chlorophyll fluorescence has been shown to be a sensitive technique to investigate events occurring at the thylakoid membrane (4). Effects resulting from chilling (5), air pollutants (6) and water deficit (7) on the photosynthesis of plants have been readily detected by this method. This technique could be very useful to asses chlorophyll containing vegetables and fruits during storage at low temperatures.

2. MATERIALS AND METHODS

Cucumbers: a group of 240 high quality cucumbers were obtained from the auction. The fruits were grown in a glass house. Fully developed fruits had been harvested on the day of purchase. The cucumbers were genetically homogenous. The fruits were put in storage facilities after visual inspection at 4, 7, 10 of 13 °C, i.e. in darkness. After 2 weeks of storage the fruits were retrieved and visually inspected for signs of incipient decay. Fruits with no defects were scored 0. Fruits with one spot of browning were scored 1. Fruits with multiple spots of internal browning were scored 2. The percentage rot was determined by adding the scores of 60 fruits in one treatment and dividing the result by 1.2. This results in a classification which correlates well with chilling injury as determined by other techniques (2). After cold storage the fruits were kept in darkness at 20 °C and 60% relative humidity for 6 days. Then again the percentage rot was determined.

Chlorophyll fluorescence measurements: dark adapted cucumbers were placed at 4 mm distance from the end of the quadrufurcated light guide of a modulated chlorophyll fluorescence measuring device (PAM 101, 103, Effeltrich, Germany). The averaged intensity of the modulated measuring beam ($\lambda \sim 650$ nm) at the peel was less than 0.2 μmol m^{-2} s^{-1}. This allows an accurate measurement of the minimal fluorescence level F_0 (8). The addition of

N. Murata (ed.), Research in Photosynthesis, Vol. IV, 161–164.

10 W m^{-2} of continuous far red light ($\lambda \sim$ 730 nm) did not influence this level, therefore we assume that the redox components of the electron transport chain were fully oxidized. Then a saturating light pulse was supplied via the light guide by a halogen lamp. The light intensity at the peel during the pulse was 13500 μmol m^{-2} s^{-1} PAR. The pulse duration was 1 s and a cut off filter blocking light above 700 nm was used. During the pulse the maximum level of modulated chlorophyll fluorescence was determined F_m. In this manner the averaged fluorescence levels of $\sim$ 120 mm^2 peel tissue was determined. From the two levels the quantum yield of photosystem 2 was inferred by calculating F_v/F_m (9). Thus the cucumbers were measured at three points in time. Within a day after harvest, after 14 days of cold storage and after 6 more days at 20 °C.

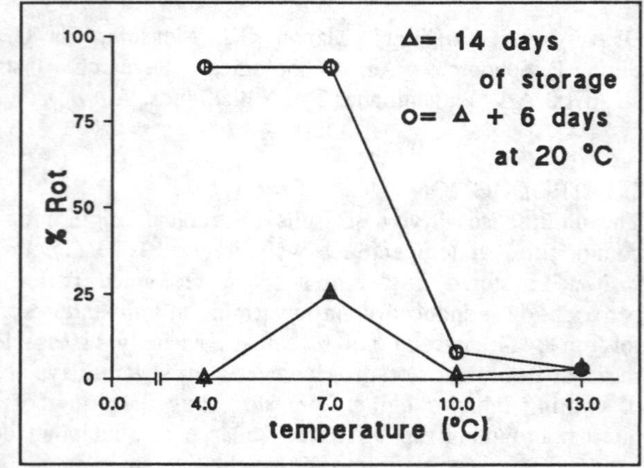

Figure 1 The percentage rot or incipient decay determined by visual inspection as described in the materials and methods.

3. RESULTS

Upon arrival the cucumbers were visually inspected. Fruits that were damaged or showed signs of discoloration or incipient decay were removed. A sample of 48 cucumbers selected at random was used to measure the initial value of the fluorescence yield. The quantum yield of PS II as determined by F_v/F_m appeared to be remarkably uniform $F_v/F_m = 0.77 \pm 0.01$, the last value is the normal standard variation for a population of 48 samples. The variance in absolute values of F_0 or F_m was larger due to small variations in the distance between the peel and the light guide.

After two weeks of storage at the different temperatures the cucumbers were visually inspected and the average amount of chilling injury was determined as % rot (fig. 1, Δ). The few small spots of discoloration found at 10 and 13 °C were probably caused by damage due to handling during harvest and transport, which had not been detected before storage. No chilling injury could be detected on cucumbers stored at 4 °C, while considerable decay could be detected in cucumbers stored at 7 °C. The

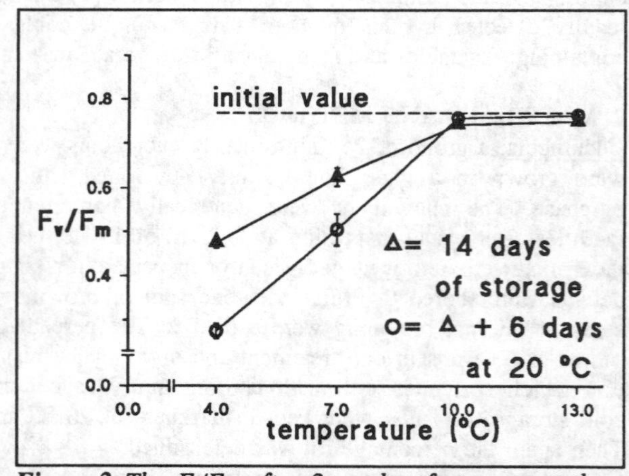

Figure 2 The F_v/F_m after 2 weeks of storage at these temperatures and upon rewarming for 6 days. Error bars are standard deviation. The initial value was measured at the start of the experiment.

cucumbers were then left at 20 °C in darkness for the duration of 6 days. After this period the chilling injury had increased considerably in the fruits stored below 10 °C (fig. 1, O). The injury in the other fruits did not increase during this rewarming period.

The F_v/F_m of the cucumbers stored at 10 and 13 °C did not change during the storage period. The fruits stored below these temperatures experience a significant decrease in F_v/F_m (fig. 2, Δ). The decrease appears to be temperature dependent and is even more pronounced after 6 further days of storage at 20 °C (fig. 2, O). The decay in F_v/F_m was not caused by enhancement of the F_o level (fig. 3). No significant increase could be detected except after 2 weeks of storage at 4 °C plus 6 days at 20 °C. The decrease in F_v/F_m appears to be caused by a decrease in the F_m level (fig. 4). In the case of 2 weeks at 4 °C + 6 days at 20 °C the F_m seems to have increased again.

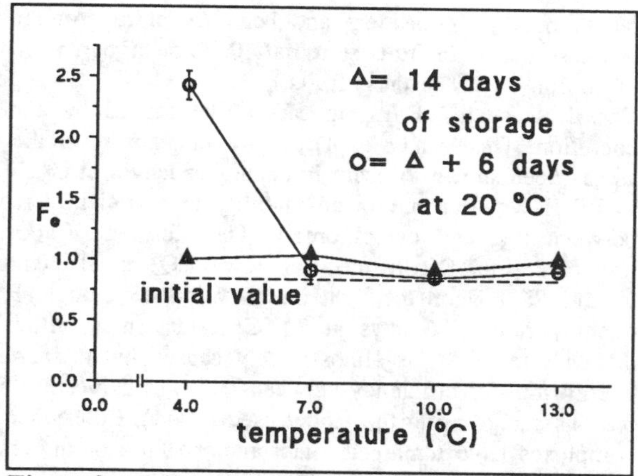

Figure 3 Minimal fluorescence yield measured before (initial value) and after 2 weeks of storage at these temperatures. And after rewarming for 6 days. The yield is expressed in volts.

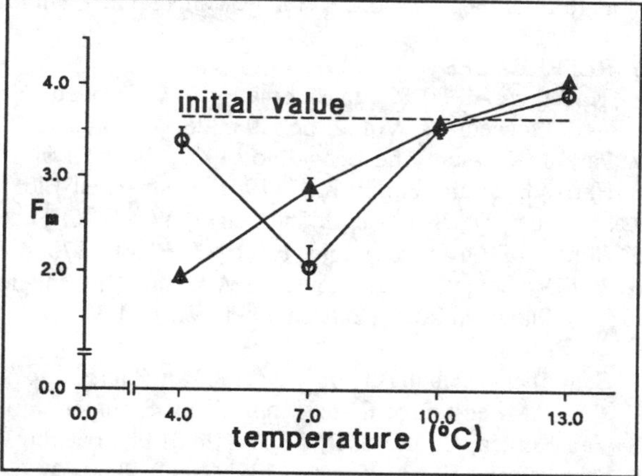

Figure 4 Maximal fluorescence yield F_m at the same moments as in figs. 2 and 3. These values together with those in fig. 3 were used to calculate the data for fig. 2.

4. DISCUSSION

After 2 weeks of storage there appears to be a considerably higher % rot in cucumbers stored at 7 °C than at 4 °C. This is mainly caused by the temperature sensitivity of the biological processes involved in decay and senescence. These cucumbers had also slightly turned yellow as opposed to the cucumbers stored at 4 °C, which could not be distinguished from the cucumbers stored above 10 °C. Therefore the visible effects of chilling injury, e.g. discoloration or incipient decay, should be regarded as a secondary proces enhanced by higher temperatures. While the actual damage characterized as leakage of the membranes caused by insufficient scavaging of radicals (3) formed during or directly after the cold treatment, can be regarded as the primary proces of chilling injury. This last proces is augmented by lower temperatures and seems to be well correlated with F_v/F_m as shown in fig. 2. It seems that cold storage induces changes in the thylakoid membranes resulting in a decreased quantum yield of PSII. The decrease appears to be temperature dependent and becomes more pronounced after 6 days at 20 °C. While no decrease occurs in fruits stored at 10 °C or higher, which correlates well with the total absence of chilling injury in these fruits.

The decrease in F_v/F_m appears to be caused by a decrease in F_m in all but one storage condition. This can be explained by an inability of the oxygen evolving complex to function as has been shown to occur in cucumber leaves at 0 °C (10). Such an inactivation of the donor to PS II would result in an inability to sufficiently reduce the electron carrying redox pool between P_{680} and cytochrome f. The fact that F_o does not change under most conditions implies that the flux of electrons toward Q_A is sufficiently compensated by a drain of electrons toward PS I when the light intensity is low enough. However, storage at 4 °C and a subsequent period of 6 days at 20 °C results in a further change in the membrane. Now the decrease in F_v/F_m is almost solely caused by an increase in F_o. This could imply a loss of energy transfer efficiency between the light harvesting complex and the reaction center if one reasons according to the model used in (11). Consequently one would conclude that few PS II complexes have remained intact and the bulk of the emitted fluorescence originates from the light harvesting complexes directly.

The present study reveals the possibility to use F_v/F_m as a parameter to detect the effect of chilling on temperature sensitive fruits and vegetables in an early stage. The quantum yield of PS II seems to correlate well with the amount of chilling injury on the membrane level. We are investigating the possibility to apply this technique as an on-line measurement during storage in order to minimize storage temperatures, while preventing chilling damage.

5. REFERENCES

1. Kader, A.A. (1989) in International Controlled Atmosphere Research Conference, Fifth Proceedings, Vol. 2, pp. 303-328, Wenatchee, Washington, USA.
2. Parkin, K.L. and Shu-Lung Kuo (1989) Plant Physiol. 90: 1049-1056
3. Hariyadi, P. and Parkin K.L. (1991) Postharvest Biol. Technol. 1: 33-45
4. Schreiber, U., Schliwa, U. and Bilger, W. (1986) Photosynth. Res. 10: 51-62
5. Björkman, O. and Demmig, B. (1987) **Planta** 170: 489-504
6. Van Kooten, O., Van Hove, L.W.A. and Vredenberg, W.J. (1990) in Current Research in Photosynthesis (Baltscheffski, M., ed.) Vol. IV, pp 611-614, Kluwer Acad. Publ., Dordrecht
7. Schreiber, U. and Bilger, W. (1987) in Plant Response to Stress (Tenhunen J.D., Catarino F.M. en Lange O. red.) pp. 27-53, Springer Verlag, Berlin
8. Van Kooten, O. and Snel, J.F.H. (1990) Photosynth. Res. 25: 147-150
9. Sommersalo, S. and Krause, G.H. (1989) Planta 177: 409-416
10. Shen, J-R., Terashima, I. and Katoh, S. (1990) Plant Physiol. 93: 1354-1357
11. Genty, B., Briantais, J.M. and Baker N.R. (1989) Biochim. Biophys. Acta 990: 87-92

FREEZING DAMAGE AND PROTECTION OF PHOTOSYSTEM II PARTICLES BY SUCROSE AND TREHALOSE

EMILIA APOSTOLOVA, MIRA BUSHEVA AND BORIS TENCHOV
Central Laboratory of Biophysics, Bulgarian Academy of Sciences,
Sofia 1113, Bulgaria

1. INTRODUCTION

Plant cell membranes are extremely frost sensitive (1). The increase in frost resistance in many plants is correlated with changes in the carbohydrate content; i.e. various sugars and sugar derivatives accumulate in cells (2). Recently it has been shown that such differences exist in the protective efficiency of different sugars during freezing of isolated chloroplast membranes and photosystem II (PS II) particles. Trehalose was the better cryoprotectant in comparison with other sugars at short freezing times (3,4,5,). The aim of this study was to show the cryoprotective effects of sucrose and trehalose on the PS II particles depending on the rate and length of time of freezing.

2. MATERIALS AND METHODS

Isolation of PS II particles from pea leaves was performed according to Yamamoto et al. (6). Suspension of PS II particles, containing 450 μmol chl/ml, 100 mM NaCl and 300 mM sucrose or trehalose were frozen to -27 ^{o}C. Two rates of freezing have been studied: rapid freezing (11.7 ^{o}C per minute) and slow freezing (1.5 ^{o}C per minute). After various length of freezing the samples were thawed in a water bath at 20 ^{o}C. The PS II activity and 77K fluorescence emission spectra were measured immediately after thawing.
Photochemical activity of PS II (from H_2O to 3,4-dichlorphenolindophenol /DCPIP/; from 1.5 diphenylcarbazide /DPC/ to DCPIP) was monitored spectrophotometrically by measuring the DCPIP photoreduction at 580 nm. The reaction medium contained: 10 mM MES-NaOH (pH 6.5), 0.33 M sucrose, 4 mM $MgCl_2$ 0.01 mM DCPIP and 20 μg chl/ml. In some samples DPC was added to a concentration of 0.5 mM.
The 77K chlorophyll fluorescence was measured in a cylindrical quartz cuvette of a Jobin Yvon JY3 spectrofluorimeter, equipped with a red-sensitive photomultiplier and low temperature device. Chlorophyll fluorescence was excited at 436 nm (slit width = 4 nm). The chlorophyll concentration in the sample was 10 μg chl/ml.

3. RESULTS AND DISCUSSION

The chlorophyll emission spectra of higher plant chloroplasts at 77K are characterized by three main bands near 685, 695 and 735 nm. They are believed to originate from the light-harvesting chlorophyll a/b protein complex of PS II (LHCP II), PS II and PS I complexes, respectively (7,8). The 77K chlorophyll fluorescence of PS II fragments is used to study excitation energy transfer between LHCP II and PS II core complex. Freezing of fragments in

N. Murata (ed.), Research in Photosynthesis, Vol. IV, 165–168.

100 mM NaCl results in an increase with 18% of F_{695}/F_{685} ratio in comparison with to unfrozen particles (Table 1), which indicates some changes in the interaction between LHCP II and PS II complexes. The changes of this ratio are smaller in the presence of sucrose or trehalose. It is clear that the excitation energy transfer between LHCP II and PS II is preserved to a considerable degree in the presence of these disaccharides and that the cryoprotective effect of sucrose is higher than that of trehalose. The comparison of the data at slow and rapid freezing shows that in both cases the F_{695}/F_{685} ratio of PS II particles in the respective solution are similar; i.e. the changes in exitation energy transfer between LHCP II and PS II of the particles are independent of the rate of freezing.

Fig. 1A shows DCPIP-photoreduction of PS II particles subjected to slow freezing in different solutions. Approximately 30% of the capacity of DCPIP-photoreduction rate is retained after freezing for 19h at -27° C in the presence of only 100 mM NaCl. Storage of the particles under the same conditions leads to full inhibition of PS II mediated electron transport after 188h. The activity of the particles frozen in the presence of 300 mM sucrose or trehalose are protected in different degree. Increase of the length of freezing time leads to a decrease of the ability for DCPIP-photoreduction. The particles frozen in the presence of disaccharides after 312h preserve 50-80% from the activity of the freshly isolated particles . Trehalose is more effective than sucrose in preserving the PS II mediated electron transport independantly on the length of freezing period. On the other hand it has been shown that trehalose prevents the release of the soluble electron transport protein plastocyanine from the thylakoid membranes during freeze-thaw treatment (4,5). It can be concluded that the cryoprotective effect of trehalose is better for both the chloroplast membranes and PS II particles at long and short freezing time.

Fig. 1B shows DCPIP-photoreduction of PS II particles subjected to a fast freezing in different solutions. In this case also 50-80% of PS II mediated electron transport flow is preserved after freezing for 312 h in the presence of studied disaccharides. Comparing the data of Fig. 1A and Fig. 1B it is evident that in both cases (at slow and rapid frezing rate) DCPIP-photoreduction rate of PS II particles in respective solution are similar. It is clear that the changes in PS II

Table1.Effect of freezing rate on F695/F685 chlorophyll fluorescence ratio of PS II particles. The particles are frozen for 19h at -27 ^{o}C. The F_{695}/F_{685} ratio of freshly isolated PSII particles was 0.695± 0.013. The data are average from seven independent experiments.

Sample	F_{695}/F_{685}	
	Slow freezing	Rapid freezing
100 mM NaCl	0.810 ±0.013	0.812 ±0.019
100 mM NaCl + 300 mM sucrose	0.732 ±0.023	0.758 ±0.015
100 mM NaCl + 300 mM trehalose	0.772 ±0.015	0.780 ±0.040

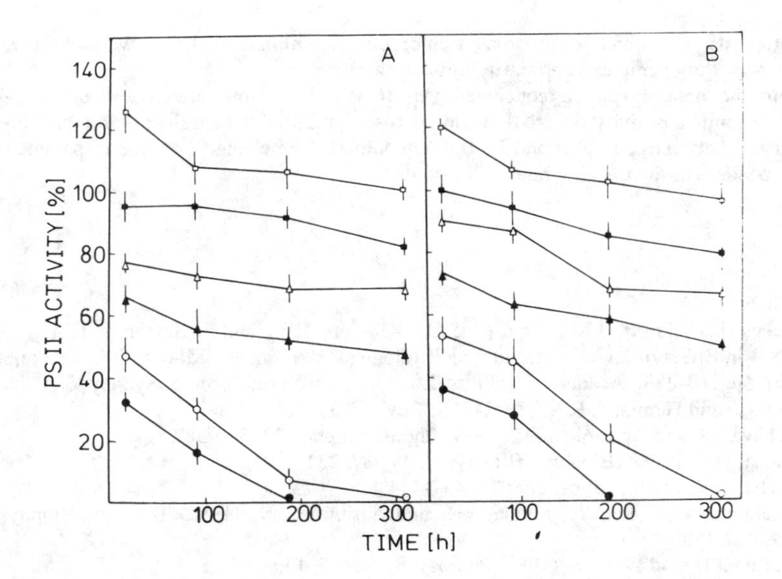

FIGURE 1. Effect of length of freezing on DCPIP-photoreduction of PS II particles. (A) slow freezing rate; (B) rapid freezing rate. The partiles are frozen in: (● ○) 100 mM NaCl; (▲ △) 100 mM NaCl and 300 mM sucrose; (■ □) 100 mM NaCl and 300 mM trehalose. DCPIP photoreduction from H_2O to DCPIP (● ▲ ■) and from DPC to DCPIP (○ △ □). 100% corsponds to the rate of DCPIP photoreduction of freshly isolated PS II particles from H_2O to DCPIP (9.91 μmoles DCPIP /mg chl per h). The data are average from seven independent experiments.

mediated electron transport are independent of the rate of freezing. Increase of the length of freezing time leads to a decrease of the PS II activity. The presence of trehalose or sucrose preserves the PS II activity to a considerable degree.

Addition of DPC (electron donor to PS II) leads to an increase in PS II reducing capacity with 15 to 30% both in the presence and absence of disaccharides (Fig. 1). Hence the observed inhibition of PS II activity (independently on the rate of freezing) was most probably due to changes in both the electron donor site/s/ (water splitting complex) of PS II and chlorophyll-protein complex of PS II core. These changes do not dependent on the rate of freezing. It can be concluded that water-oxidizing system of PS II particles was influenced not only by freeze-thaw treatment. The alterations in the oxidizing side of PS II are not decisive for the inhibition of the electron transport activity of PS II. Our results for PS II particles are in contradiction with the data obtained during freeze-thaw treatment of intact leaves (9), protoplasts (10) and even isolated chloroplast membranes (9,11) which show that the water-splitting complex is primarily influenced.

From the data it can be concluded that trehalose is more effective than sucrose for the photochemical activity of PS II while sucrose is better than trehalose for the direct energy transfer between LHCP II and PS II core complex. The changes of these parameters are independent of the freezing rates.

REFERENCES

1 Heber, U., Schmitt, J.M., Krause, G.H., Klosson, R.J. and Santarius, K.A. (1981) in Effect of low temperature on Biological membranes (Morris, G.J., Clarke, A., eds.), pp. 263-283, Academic Press, London, New York, Toronto, Sydney, San Francisco
2 Alden, J. and Hermann, R.K. (1971) Bot. Rev. 37, 37-141
3 Busheva, M. and Apostolova, E. (1989) Photosynthetica 23, 380-382
4 Hincha, D.K. (1989) Biochim. Biophys. Acta 987, 231-234
5 Hincha, D.K. (1990) Cryo-Letter 11, 437-444
6 Yamamoto, Y., Yeda, T., Shinkai, H. and Nishimura, N. (1982) Biochim. Biophys. Acta 579, 347-350
7 Krause, G.H. and Weis, E. (1984) Photosynth. Res. 5, 139-157
8 Krause, G.H. (1991) Ann. Rev. Plant Physiol. Plant Mol. Biol. 42, 313-349
9 Heber, U., Tyankova,L. and Santarius, K.A. (1973) 291, 223-37
10 Rumich-Bayer, S. and Krause, G.H. (1989) Photosynth. Res. 8, 61-174
11 Grafflage, S. and Krause, G.H. (1986) Planta 168, 67-76

EFFECTS OF LIGHT AND HIGH TEMPERATURE ON THE LEAVES OF A RICE MUTANT SENSITIVE TO SOLAR RADIATION

Takuichi Fuse[1], Koh Iba[1], Hikaru Satoh[2] and Mitsuo Nishimura[1], Dept. of Biol., Fac. of Sci., Kyushu Univ.[1], Fukuoka 812, Japan and Plant Breeding Laboratory, Fac. of Agr., Kyushu Univ.[2], Fukuoka 812, Japan

1. INTRODUCTION

Responses of plants to excessive or detrimental factors such as high light intensity, high and low temperatures, and active oxygen species have been recognized to be important in agriculture and productivity of plants in general. Effects of light and high temperature were studied in a spontaneous mutant KL808 (*spl-2*) of rice, which is sensitive to solar radiation. Spotted dead areas are observed in the leaves of KL808 plants when the leaves are irradiated with solar light. Both KL808 and the wild type became susceptible to irradiation after the dark incubation for one day. The preincubation under weak illumination lessened the irradiation-induced damage, which suggested the protective effect of light acclimatization. The damages of KL808 leaves were most marked under irradiation by blue light at high temperature. Activities of the O_2^-- and H_2O_2-scavenging enzymes and the content of ascorbic acid (AsA) in KL808 leaves were not much different from those in the wild type, before and after the irradiation at high temperature.

2. MATERIALS and METHODS

2.1 *Plant materials* — KL808 (*spl-2*) and the parental wild type, "Kinmaze", were obtained from the Laboratory of Plant Breeding, Faculty of Agriculture, Kyushu University. The *spl-2* locus has been mapped on chromosome 2 (1). Rice seedlings were grown as described by Yoshida *et al.* (2). The rice plants was cultured under cool-white fluorescent light (3,000 lux) at 25 °C. Eighth or ninth leaves grown for about two months were used for this study.

2.2 *Measurement of damages by irradiation with visible light* — For the time course studies, the rice leaves were irradiated with white light (10,000 or 3,000 lux) at 40 °C. For fluence-response relationship analyses, the rice leaves were irradiated with monochromatic lights in the presence of weak white light (3,000 lux) at 40 °C. The monochromatic lights were obtained by passage of white light from a halogen lamp through interference filters, which were combined with appropriate glass filters to eliminate second-order diffractive light. Intensity of monochromatic irradiation was measured by a calibrated thermopile. Light intensity was varied by neutral density filters. The extent of the damage by light is expressed as follows;

$$\text{damage (\%)} = L_d/L_a \times 100$$

N. Murata (ed.), Research in Photosynthesis, Vol. IV, 169–172.

where L_d is the damaged area of the leaves caused by irradiation, and L_a is the total area of the leaves irradiated by light.

3. RESULTS and DISCUSSION

3.1 Almost no damage was found in the KL808 leaves cultured under white light (3,000 lux) at 25 °C. The damage on the mutant leaves become more conspicuous when cultured under stronger light and at higher temperature. Spotted dead areas appeared on the surface of the mutant leaves by a two-day irradiation of white light (10,000 lux) at 40 °C. The areas were dispersed on the whole surface of the mutant leaves (Fig. 1A). In the leaves of the wild type a similar damage was observed after the two-day irradiation of white light (10,000 lux) at 40 °C when the the plants were preincubated in the dark for one day (Fig. 1B), but no damage was observed when the wild-type leaves were irradiated without dark preincubation (Fig. 1A).

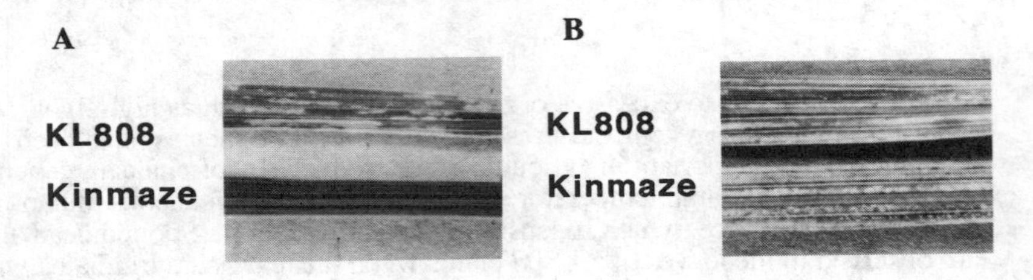

FIGURE 1 Damages on the rice leaves caused by irradiation with white light (10,000 lux) at 40 °C. A: leaf blades were irradiated for two days. B: leaf blades were irradiated for two days following the preincubation in the dark for one day.

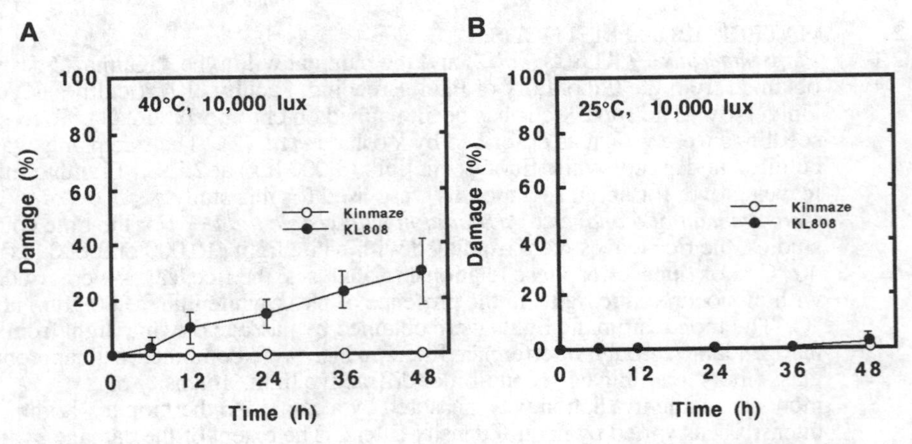

FIGURE 2 Time-courses of damage on the leaves caused by white-light irradiation (10,000 lux). A: irradiated at 40 °C. B: irradiated at 25 °C.

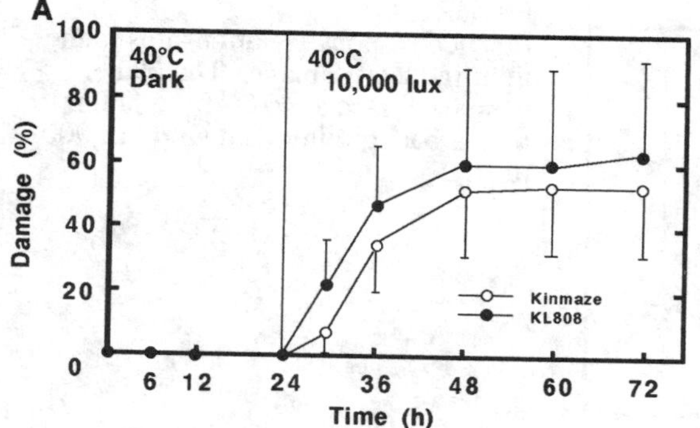

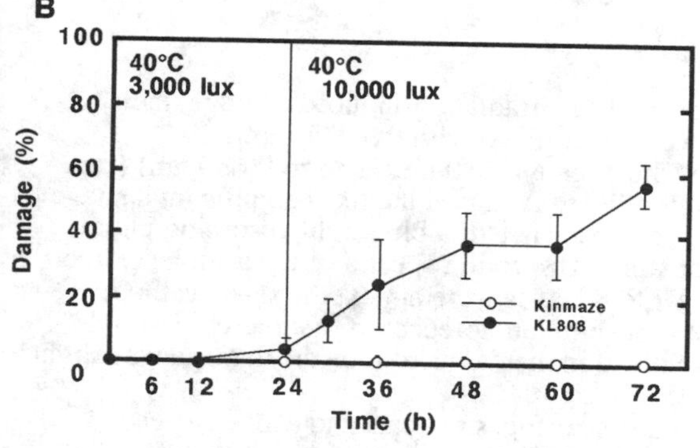

FIGURE 3
Time-courses of damage on the leaves caused by white-light irradiation (10,000 lux) at 40 °C for two days following the preincubation for one day. A: preincubated in the dark at 40 °C. B: preincubated under white light (3,000 lux) at 40 °C.

3.2 Time-courses of irradiation-induced damage at 25 °C and 40 °C are shown in Fig. 2. The spotted dead areas, dispersed on the whole surface, linearly increased with the time of strong irradiation (10,000 lux white light) at 40 °C in KL808 (Fig. 2A). No damage occurred in the wild type when the leaves were irradiated by 10,000 lux white light at 25 °C or 40 °C (Fig. 2A, B). only a slight damage was observed in KL808 at 25 °C (Fig. 2B). The wild-type leaves preincubated in the dark at 40 °C for one day were damaged by irradiation of white light (10,000 lux) for two days (Fig. 3A). The pattern of the damage was similar to that of the mutant. Under the same conditions, the damage of KL808 was even stronger. In the wild type that had a preincubation under the low-intensity (3,000 lux) white light at 40°C for one day, the irradiation of 10,000 lux white light at 40 °C caused no damage. However, the mutant leaves preincubated under the low light condition (3,000 lux) at 40 °C for one day were moderately damaged by irradiation of white light (10,000 lux) at 40 °C for two days (Fig. 3B). The wild-type leaves preincubated in the dark at 25 °C for one day had some damage by irradiation of white light (10,000 lux) at 40 °C for two days (data not shown). Thus, the irradiation-induced damage of KL808, which were more prominent at higher light intensities and higher temperatures, became even larger when preincubated in the dark. The wild-type leaves became irradiation-sensitive after the dark pre-incubation. With the preincubation under weak light, the irradiation-induced damage was less prominent in the wild type. These results suggest that the acclimatization to light has an protective effect against the strong irradiation.

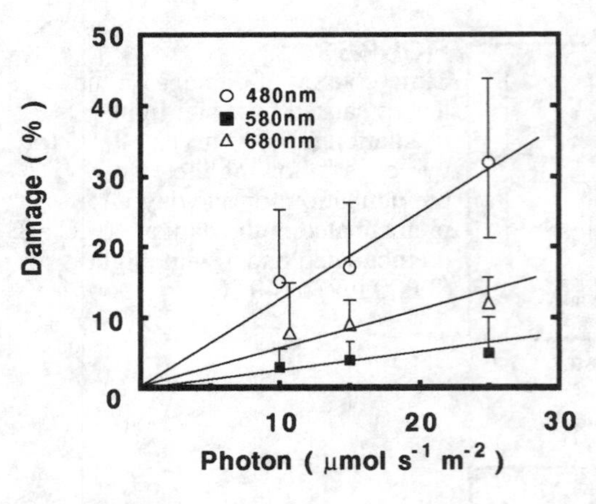

FIGURE 4
Fluence-response relationships in the light-induced damage. The plants were irradiated at 40 °C for 6 hours with a background white light (3,000 lux).

3.3 To find the wavelength dependence of the irradiation-induced damage, the fluence-response relationships were determined with three different monochromatic lights, blue (480 nm), green (580 nm), and red (680 nm) (Fig. 4). The blue monochromatic light (480 nm) caused the most significant damage on the mutant leaves, suggesting the existence of a blue-light absorbing photo-sensitizer responsible for the damage. Absorption spectra of the acetone extract and the methanol extract of the KL808 leaves were almost the same as those of the wild-type leaves. Red-light absorbing photoreceptors such as chlorophyll and phytochrome may not be involved in the damage since the damage was slight under the irradiation of red light.

3.4 AsA acts as a reductant in plants and scavenges radicals and active oxygen species that are produced under strong irradiation (3). The AsA content of the mutant was not much different from that of the wild type, and there was almost no difference in the level of AsA between KL808 and the wild type after an irradiation with the strong white light (10,000 lux) at high temperature (40 °C). It is possible that the damages were not directly related to the decrease of AsA content. The SOD and peroxidase activities of the mutant were not much different from those of the wild type, both before and after the irradiation, suggesting that the damages were not directly related to the decrease of the levels of SOD and peroxidase activity.

REFERENCES

1. Iwata, N., Omura, T. and Satoh, H. (1978) *J. Fac. Agr. Kyushu Univ.* 22, 243-251
2. Yoshida, S., Forno, D. A., Cock, J. H. and Gomez, K. A. (1976) Laboratory Manual for Physiological Studies of Rice. 3rd ed. pp. 61-66. The International Rice Research Institute, Los Banos
3. Asada, K. and Takahashi, M (1987) in Photoinhibition (Kyle, D. J., Osmond, C. B. and Arntzen, C. J., eds.), pp. 227-287, Elsevier, Amsterdam

CHARACTERISTICS OF THE PHOTOSYNTHESIS IN ALPINE PLANTS ON QINGHAI PLATEAU

Guiying Ben, Cunfu Lu *, Fa Han and Shengbo Shi
Northwest Plateau Institute of Biology, the Chinese Academy of Sciences, Xining 810001, China
* Department of food science, Shandong Agricultural University, Taian 271018

INTRODUCTION

Numerous studies have demonstrated that the physiological processes of plants were closely correlated with their indigenous environments. The distribution of apline plants are beyond timberline, the regions characterized by cold or cool summers, low air pressure, and low perennial herbaceous or dwarf shrubby vegetation. The net assimilation and respiration of alpine plants are different from that of low elevation species. They can capture, store and utilize energy within low temperature environments (Bliss, 1985).

The characteristics of photosynthesis were studied for many species, such as *Trifolium repens* (Machler et al. 1978), *Eucalyptus pauciflora* (Slatyer et al. 1977) and *Oxyria digyna* (Billings et al. 1961, Chabot et al. 1972). It was indicated that the photosynthetic rates were higher and the abilities to utilize low CO_2 concentration were greater in higher altitude populations compared with that at low elevations. Some results, however, relating photosynthetic rates to elevtions might be conflicting. Mooney (1964) found no significant difference in the net photosynthesis at 70 KLux and 20℃ in the plants from various altitudes between 1350m and 3800m. The quantum requirenments of wheats in Qinghai Plateau was higher than that in lowland (Shanghai), and the experiments showed that the low atmospheric pressure might be the main cause accounting for the higher quantum requirement in Qinghai Plateau (Xu 1988).

The objectives of this study were to examine the quantum yields, maximum rates of photosynthesis. The photosynthetic temperature responses, the leaf conductance, and chloroplast pigments were measured. We attepted to discover the photosynthetic responses of alpine plants to their enviroments.

MATERIALS AND METHODS

This investigations were conducted in the regions of Haibei Research Station of Apline Meadow Ecosystem (37°29′—37°45′ N., El. 3200—3400m) and Daban Mountain ridge (El. 3980m). The alpine plants of *Koberesia humilis*, *Lagotis brevituba* and *Elymus nutans* were collected from different altitudes in July and August, 1991.

It is more difficult to determine the photosynthesis in the field of the alpine or mountain ridge due to environmental factors changing frequently. In most cases we measured photosynthetic capacities under optimum conditions in the laboratory. Plants were collected in form of sod blocks which several plants were taken together in a cohesive mass of soil. The *L. brevituba* was taken from Daban Mountain ridge (3980m) and *K. humilis* from three elevation sites: 3980m, 3200m and 2300m. The sod blocks were potted in pots and then were brought into the laboratory or transferred to the growth room (15/10℃

N. Murata (ed.), Research in Photosynthesis, Vol. IV, 173–176.

day/night, 80—100 μE $m^{-2}s^{-1}$ light.). Before the photosynthesis measuring some plants were made pretreatments with cold stress between — 5℃ to — 14℃. The photosynthetic gas exchanges were measured using the liquid oxygen electrode. The electrolyte solution is 0. 1 mol/L $NaHCO_3$.

RESULTS

The maximum rates of photosynthesis(saturated light and CO_2, 25℃)and quantum yields were influenced by the indigenous conditions. When measuring under standard conditions the apparent quantu yields in *K. humilis* were decreased with the increasing elevations of plant native sits, but the maximum rates of photosynthesis, light saturation and compensation points were increased with the altitudes(Table 1).

Table 1. Comparisons of photosynthetic gas exchange in *K. humilis* and *E. nutans* from different altitudes

Location elevations (m)	Species	P* (μmol O_2 m^{-2} s^{-1})	Quantum yields
3200 (Haibei station)	*K. humilis*	2. 04	0. 032
	E. nutans	1. 72	0. 032
3980 (Daban Mt.)	*K. humilis*	2. 48	0. 028
	E. nutans	5. 11	0. 024

* P is apparent photosynthesis which made using liquid oxygen electrode, 25℃.

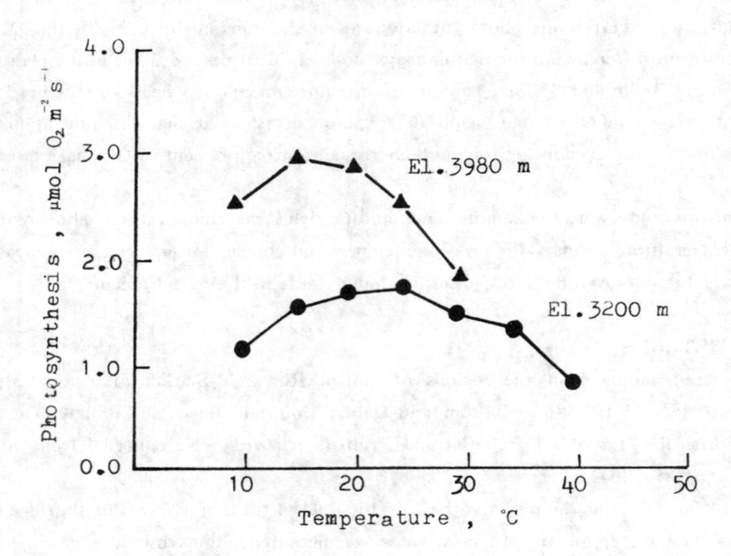

Fig. 1. Temperature—response curves of photosynthetic O_2 evolution in *K. humilis* from 3980m(▲) and 3200m(●)growing in the growth room(15/10℃ day/night, 80—100μE $m^{-2}s^{-1}$ light)

The temperature dependence of photosynthesis response curve showed that the maximum rates of photosynthetic O_2 evolution were higher in *K. humilis* taken from 3980m than that from 3200m when plants growning at lower temperature regimes(15/10℃ day/nigh)(Fig. 1).

Difference in photosynthetic optima among the altitudinal ecotypes are more pronounsed. The optimum temperatures of *K. humilis* collected from 3980m, 3200m, and 2260m were 15℃, 20℃ and 25℃. The temperature responses of the photosynthetic rates in alpine species are affected by the origin, growth and the measurmental temperatures. When measured at 5℃ the photosynthetic O_2 evolution rates in the both grown at 15/10℃ and 24/13℃ were inhibited, while the value(1.16μmol O_2 m^{-2} s^{-1})plant grown at 24/13℃ was lower than the value (2.01μmol O_2 m^{-2} s^{-1}) of plant grown at 15/10℃. Whereas measured at 25℃. the plant growm at 24/13℃ had higher value(20.50μmol O_2 m^{-2} s^{-1}) compared with the value(11.05μmol O_2 m^{-2} s^{-1})grown at 15/10℃.

The effects of cold stress on photosynthesis in *K. humilis* and *L. brevituba* were made under control conditions(Table 2). In alpine areas the minimal nocturnal air temperatures were sometimes below 0℃ during the plant growing season, thus the leaves were stiffly frozen in the early morning. The data presented in Table 2 showed the resistences of *K. humilis* and *L. brevituba* hardy tissues to frost temperatures. Photosynthetic O_2 evolution rates were inhibited when plants in low temperatures between −5 to −15℃ and dark pretreatments for several hours, while the O_2 evolutions were still observed even under −13℃ for 2h.

Table 2. Effects of cold stress on photosynthetic O_2 evolution of alpine plants *

Species and Location El.	Pretreatment temperature (℃)	P (μmol O_2 m^{-2} s^{-1})	Quantum yields
K. humilis (3880m)	control	4.45	0.033
	−5——6℃, 12h	2.95	0.030
	control	4.15	0.059
	−10——11℃, 5h	3.68	0.044
L. brevituba (3980m)	control	12.69	0.016
	−5——6℃, 7h	6.06	0.012
	control	3.68	0.014
	−13——14℃, 2h	1.49	0.011
	−13——14℃, 5h	* *	* *

* 1. The data were made using liquid oxygen electrode, 25℃

2. Before measurments of photosynthesis the stressed plants were transferred to the growth room for 1h

* * No photosynthetic O_2 evolution

DISCUSSION

The photosynthesis of alpine plants adapted to, but limited by their living conditions. When measurements made under the condition of lower temperature and lower CO_2 concentration, the photosynthetic rates of the species of apline ecotypes increased with increasing elevations (Machler et al. 1978, Berry and

Bjokman, 1980). The abilities of plants at high altitude regions to utilize low CO_2 concentrations were greater than those in the lower elevations. Chabot et al. (1972) suggested that the temperature optima for both RuBPcase activity and apparent photosynthesis be similar, and the optima were 10—20 C for an alpine grass.

That of the alpine plants can make even better use of the available light quantities had been confirmed, the high values of photosynthetic light saturation points ascribed to the thickness of palisad tissues (Glagolva, 1962). The quantum yields showed lower values with increasing elevations seems, at least in part, to be related to the lower CO_2 partial pressure at high altitude regions. The maximum values and the daily sum of the leaf diffusive conductances in *E. nutans* grown at 3200m were higher compared with that grown at 2260m, but the time of reached to peak values lagged for 2h (Ben et al., in press).

REFERENCES

1. Bliss, L. C. (1985) in Physiological Ecology of North American Plant Communities (Chabot, B. F., Mooney, H. A., eds), pp. 41—60, Chapman and Hall, New York London
2. Machler, F. and Nosberger, J. (1977) Oecologia 31, 73—78
3. Statyer, R. O., Morrow, P. A. (1977) Aust. J. Bot. 25, 1—20
4. Billings, W. D., Clebsch, E. E. C., Mooney, H. A. (1961) Science B3, 1834
5. Chabot, B. F., Chabot, J. F. and Billings, W. D. (1972) Photosynthetica 6(4): 364—369
6. Mooney, H. A, Wright, R. D. and Strain, B. R (1964) Amer. Midl. Nat. 72, 281—197
7. Xu, D. Q. (1988) Plant Physiology Communications 5, 1—7
8. Mochler, F., Nosberger, J. (1978) Oecologia 35, 267—276
9. Berry, J., Bjokman, O. (1980) Ann Rev Plant Physiol 31, 491—534
10. Glagolva, T. A., (1962) Akad. Nauk sssk. Batan. J. 47, 1567

THE CHLOROPHYLL FLUORESCENCE TEMPERATURE CURVE AS A PLANT DAMAGE AND LIGHT ACCLIMATION DIAGNOSTIC TOOL

KUROPATWA R., NAUS J., KLINKOVSKY T., ILIK P., KALINA J., MASLAN M., ZAK D., LATTOVA J., PAVLOVA Z.
Department of Experimental Physics, Palacky University, CS-771 46 Olomouc; Research Institute for Vegetable Growing and Breeding, S-772 35 Olomouc, CZECHOSLOVAKIA

1. INTRODUCTION

The dependence of chlorophyll fluorescence intensity or quantum yield of a photosynthetic system on linearly increasing temperature in the range from 20 °C to about 70 °C is in this text called the Fluorescence Temperature Curve (FTC). Measurements of FTC have been mostly realized under very weak light excitation (referred to also as Fo conditions) and two characteristic points (Tp and Tc or Tt) of the first FTC band were evaluated revealing high temperature or drought tolerance of plants [1 - 4].

Our experimental conditions correspond to the steady state conditions (T or Fs level) caused by weak actinic light [5, 6]. Two maxima of the curve are usually clearly discernible [7 - 9] situated at about 52 °C and 62 °C respectively depending on the heating rate, plant species and the functional state. Three additional parameters may be determined from these curves:

- M1/F(T30) - the ratio of fluorescence intensity at the first maximum (M1) to the intensity at 30 °C (F(T30));
- M1/M2 - the ratio of fluorescence intensity at the first FTC maximum to that at the second peak;
- M1'/M2' - the ratio of the relative heights of fluorescence intensity at the first FTC maximum to that at the second maximum taken above the fluorescence intensity at 30 °C i.e.

$$M1'/M2' = (M1 - F(T30))/(M2 - F(T30)).$$

2. MATERIALS AND METHODS

2.1. Plant material

Barley (Hordeum vulgare L., cv. Zenit). The seedlings were grown in a cultivation chamber under the light intensity of 20 W.m(-2) at a regime: light 16 h/22°C and dark 8 h/18°C. In the growth phase of the second leaf (1.2 according to Feekes macrophenological scale) the central segment of the primary leaf blade was measured.

N. Murata (ed.), Research in Photosynthesis, Vol. IV, 177–180.

Spruce (Picea abies (L.), Karst.) trees of 35-years old canopy grown at the Experimental Research Station Bily Kriz (943 m a.s.l., Beskydy Mountains, Czechoslovakia) and five years old spruce saplings grown on soil in pots.

Tomato (Solanum licopersicum L. cv. Marathon). Two weeks old seedlings of tomato were transplanted to a perlite and watered by Cooper solution of various concentrations. The cultivating conditions were the same as those of the barley plants. The youngest grown-up leaves of 56 days old plant were measured.

In all cases the fluorescence was excited and detected from the adaxial (upper) leaf side.

2.2. FTC method

A laboratory-made spectrofluorimeter with a computer driven system of the linear heating and fluorescence detection was used [7]. Weak actinic light (2-4 W.m(-2)) of 436 nm wavelength with 15 nm spectral half-width was used for the chlorophyll fluorescence excitation. The fluorescence emission was detected at 685 nm (emission of PS II) with the spectral resolution 4 - 6 nm. A leaf segment or needles were immersed in stirred distilled water and heated at the constant rate of 4 °C/min.

In addition, the fluorescence spectrum at 77 K or Fv/Fm fluorescence induction parameter at room temperature were measured [7].

3. RESULTS AND DISCUSSION

3.1. Stress detection - M1/F(T30) parameter

Three types of stress have been applied, heat and high light affecting directly and the nutrition stress indirectly the PS II function.

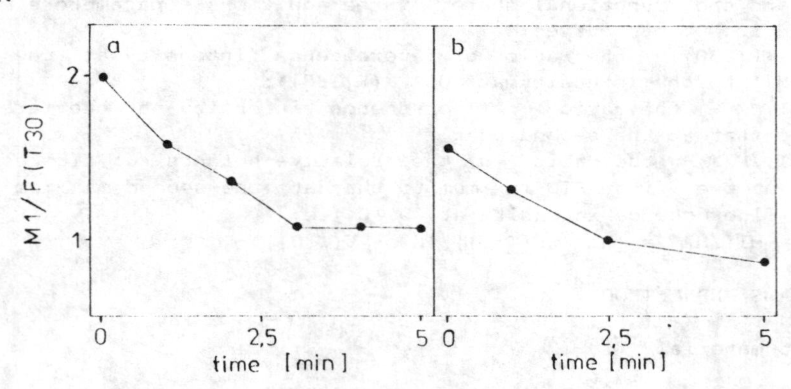

FIGURE 1. The dependence of M1/F(T30) parameter of barley primary leaf on a) the incubation time at 49 °C;
b) the duration of high-light (1500 W.m(-2) exposure).

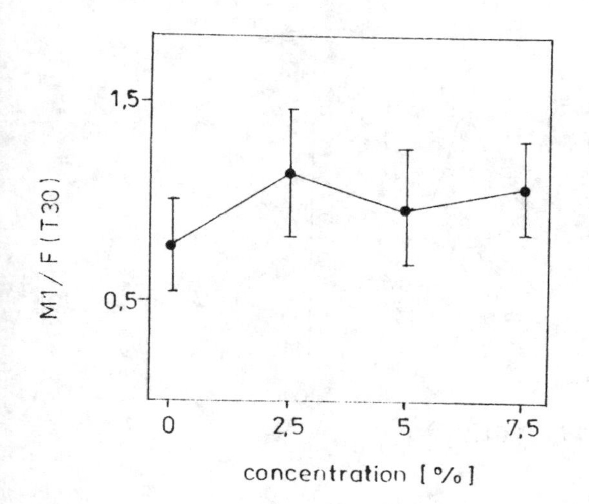

FIGURE 2. The dependence of M1/F(T30) parameter of young tomato leaf on the concentration of standard Cooper nutrient solution.

Heat stress. Upon incubation of the barley leaf at 49 °C in distilled water the M1/F(T30) ratio decreased with increasing time of incubation. It was shown that this decrease correlates with changes in Fv/Fm and (Fpl-Fo)/(Fm-Fo) values of fluorescence induction and the F735/F685 band ratio of 77 K fluorescence spectrum [7].

High-light stress. The decrease of M1/F(T30) with increasing time of white light exposition (about 1500 W.m(-2)) is shown in Fig. 1b. This decrease was found to proceed in parallel to the increase of F735/F685 band ratio of fluorescence spectrum at 77 K indicating a photoinhibitory damage [10, 11].

Nutrition stress. The nutrition stress of tomato plants was in evidence mainly at very low and zero nutrient concentrations predominantly in the growth parameters (results not shown). The measured photosynthetic parameters were less influenced. As shown in Fig. 3, the M1/F(T30) parameter revealed a slight tendency to increase with the increasing concentration of the nutrient solution. A similar tendency was in this ontogeny phase and young leaf found for the Fv/Fm quantity. Similar results were obtained for paprika plants. The results depended on the plant growth phase and the age of the measured leaves.

3.2. Acclimation to light level - M1'/M2' parameter.

The current-year needles, grown at the sun exposed upper crown layer of the spruce canopy, revealed in summer a lower ratio of the first to the second FTC peak (the M1/M2 or M1'/M2' ratios) than the needles situated in the lower shaded crown zone (Fig. 3). The values of M1'/M2' were 1.07 + 0.08 and 2.80 + 0.67 respectively. The needles of higher M1'/M2' ratio had a higher Chl (a+b) content and lower Chl a/b ratio.

Similarly the five-year old spruce saplings exposed for three weeks, in natural conditions, to full summer sun light had reproducibly lower M1'/M2' ratio than the saplings kept in low light level.

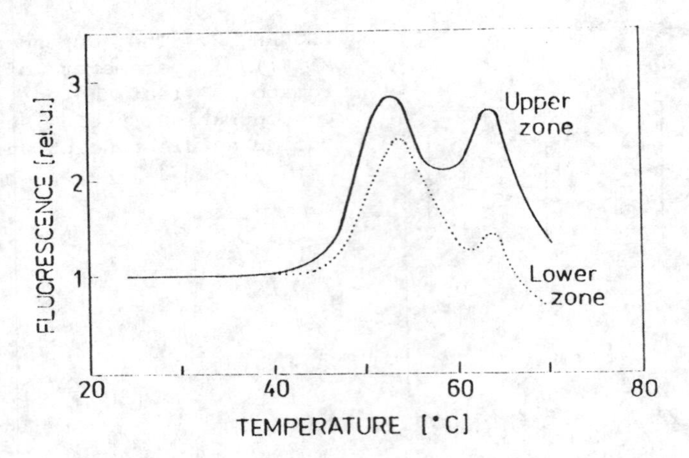

FIGURE 3. Typical FTC's of needles from the upper and lower crown zones of spruce canopy.

These results are in accordance with [12] but in disagreement with [13]. For the case of spruce trees, the M1'/M2' (M1/M2) value may be suggested to serve as a rough estimate of the light level adaptation of the needles.

REFERENCES

1 Smillie, R.M. and Nott, R. (1979) Aust. J. Plant Physiol. 6, 135-141

2 Bilger, H.W., Schreiber, U., Lange, O.L. (1984) Oekologia 63, 256-262

3 Havaux, M., Ernez, M., Lannoye, R. (1988) J. Plant Physiol. 133, 555-560

4 Hugly, S., Kunst, L., Browse, J., Somerville, Ch. (1989) Plant Physiol. 90, 1134-1142

5 Schreiber, U. and Berry, J.A. (1977) Planta 136, 236-238

6 Weis, E. (1985) Biochim. Biophys. Acta 807, 118-126

7 Naus, J., Kuropatwa, R., Klinkovsky, T., Ilik, P., Lattova, J., Pavlova, Z. (1992a) Biochim. Biophys. Acta (In Press)

8 Naus, J., Dvorak, L., Kuropatwa, R., Maslan, M. (1992b) Photosynthetica 27, (In Press)

9 Kuropatwa, R., Naus, J., Maslan, M., Dvorak, L. (1992) Photosynthetica 27 (In Press)

10 Oquist, G. (1986) J. Plant Physiol. 122, 169-179

11 Nedbal, L., Setlikova, E., Masojidek, J., Setlik, I. (1986) Biochim. Biophys. Acta 848, 108-119

12 Downton, W.J.S., Berry, J.A. (1984) Biochim. Biophys. Acta 679, 474-478

13 Mannan, R.M., Periyanan, ,S., Kulandaivelu, C., Bose, S. (1986) Photosynth. Res. 8, 87-92

THE EFFECT OF LEAFSTALK CHILLING ON PHOTOSYNTHESIS OF INTACT LEAF IN PLANTS WITH DIFFERENT TYPE OF PHLOEM LOADING.

Natalya I.Filatova & Natalya S.Mamyshina, Dept. of Photosynthesis, Botanical Institute, the USSR Acad. of Sci. Prof. Popov Str., 2, St.Peterburg, 197376 RUSSIA

1. INTRODUCTION

1.1 It is known that the leafstalk chilling (<6°C) leads to inhibition of assimilate transport. As a result of this inhibition the abundance of assimilates in mesophyll cells takes place. It may be the cause of decreasing and in some cases of stopping of leaf photosynthesis.(Gamalei,1990)

1.2 As it was shown in works by Pickord et al., (1978), Minchin et al.,(1983) that there was the complete inhibition of phloem translocation if the temperature of leafstalk or stem decreased below 10°C, after 10 - 20 min temperature shock. Similar profiles were found to occur after a sudden heat shock (Tompson,1986) or sudden hypoxia stress (Grodzinski et al., 1984) were applied to petiole or stem. It is nessesary underline that in these works it was investigated the effect of different sudden stress (chilling or heating) on movement of photoassimilates only. The main task of our work was to investigate the effect of leafstalk chilling on photosynthesis of intact leaf in plants with different type (symplast or apoplast) of phloem loading. It is important from the point of view the investigation very complex problem of sink - sourse relations in green leaf.

2. MATERIALS and METHODS

2.1 The main objects was the next plants - Prunella vulgaris, with symplast or open type of loading and Leucanthemum vulgare with apoplast or close type of phloem. These plants were grown on dry meadow of the protected South - Taiga Reservation in Central Europeanen part of Russia, where the experiments were done.

2.2 Photosynthesis were measured by portable system LI-COR 6200 in natural conditions on intact leaf with minimal change to environment of plant. The net exchange of CO_2 and transpiration were measured by enclosing 3 or 4 leaves in hermetic chamber with specific sensors - leaf thermocouple,

N. Murata (ed.), Research in Photosynthesis, Vol. IV, 181–184.

a humidity sensor and air temperature thermistor. The data from measurement are automatically logged into the strateh pad in the LI - 6200's memory. All of the computations are done at the end of an observation and take about 1 sec. Our data are based on 60 sequential observations, so the time of exposure was equal 1 min.

2.3 Cold treatment was done by application the piece of ice to 1 - 1,5 cm of petiole intact leaf of plant. The maesurements of net - photosynthesis were made every hour during long chilling (12 hours - from 8 till 20 p.a.), and also every 5 minutes after short chilling (60 min). The control variants in the experiment were the leaves of the other plant grown near.

3. RESULTS AND DISCUSSION

3.1 The response of photosynthesis (Pn) in the plant with symplastic type of loading (Prunella vulgaris) during the cold treatment of leafstalk was studied into (10 hours). The rate of photosynthesis at 8 o'clock before afternoon (the start of experiment) was the same in both leaves (control and chilling). Then we can see the great difference in diurnal course of net - photosynthesis between control and experimental variants. It is observed in the control the natural diurnal course of photosynthesis with depression from 14 till 15 o'clock . The reason of this depression was perhaps the high temperature of leaf (38°C). However, in the case of leaf with chilling treatment of petiole the decrease of net - photosynthesis was begining over three hours after cold effect and reached 51% from control. At 1 o'clock a.p. the inhibition of photosynthesis in cold variants was about 60%. This decreasing continued during five hours and then the reparation of photosynthesis occured. Then over ten hours the value of net - photosynthesis reached the control one. It was shown by Gamalei (1990) under investigation of ultrastructure of mesophyll cells (electron microscopy) that after 3 hours the cold treatment of leafstock Cucurbito pepo with symplast type of loading there was an inhibition of assimilate transport. It was observed that the vacuole of the mesophyll cells became greatly, and simulteniously the grain of starch appeared in chloroplasts of leaf after petiole chilling. It was suggested that the inhibition of net - photosynthesis after 3 hours of petiole chilling in Prunella vulgaris also with, the symplast type of loading was influenced by increasing of soluble carbohydrate in mesophyll cells of leaf.

3.2 The investigation the short dynamics of net - photosynthesis at 12 o'clock in control and experimental variants also demonstrated that there was sharp inhibition of photosynthesis (on 90%) during 50 min after petiole chilling, and then a small increasing of photosynthesis took place during 20 minutes.

3.3 It was be studied also the response of net - photosynthesis in the plant with apoplastic type of loading Leucanthemum vulgare during the cold treatment of petiole (12 hours). There are no the great differences in the diurnal course of net - photosynthesis between control leaf and leaf with chilling petiole in this plant.

3.4 The investigations the dynamics of net - photosynthesis during short cold treatment of petiole in Leucanthemum vulgare also showed that there was an inhibition of photosynthesis (on 44%) during 20 minutes, and then the rate of photosynthesis reached the rate one of control leaf over 40 min.

3.5 The study of ultrastructure of mesophyll cells and thin vems in Pisum sativum (apoplast type of loading) was undertaken by Gamalei (1990). It was shown that transport of photoassimilates in the leaf with apoplast type of loading is less sensitive to cold shock than in the case of leaf with symplastic type. It was appeared that after 3 hours of cold treatment the number of starch grains in chloroplasts of mesophyll cells and transfercells sharp increased. It was suggested that carbon utilised during photosynthesis in this leaf was used mainly to the starch synthesis, and less degree to soluble carbohydrate synthesis.

3.6 The next suggestion may be put forward. The net - photosynthesis does not reacted on chilling of leafstock in plant with apoplastic type of loading. May be it depends on the next circumstances:
a) the less sensivity of photoassimilate transport to cold shock in the case of this type loading;
b) the capability of mesophyll cells synthesized the starch very active during the photosynthesis.
The last idea needs in detailed experimental investigation.

4. CONCLUSION

4.1 The obtained data let us to underline that the question about the relationship between of photosynthesis and photoassimilate transport appears rather complex one. Under the investigation of this problem it is nessesary to take into consideration the type of assimilate loading. As it was shown that the reaction of photosynthesis on cold shock of petiole was a sharply different in plants with symplastic or apoplastic type of loading.

REFERENCES

1. Gamalei Y.V. (1990) Leaf Phloem.(in Russian) Nauka 144p.
2. Grodzinski B., Jahnke S. and Thompson R.G. (1984) J. Exp. Bot., 35, pp678 - 690.

3. Minchin P.E.H., Lang A. and Thorpe M.R. (1983) J. Exp. Bot., 34, pp 156 - 162.
4. Pickard W.E., Minchin P.E.H. and Troughton J.H. (1978) J. Exp. Bot., 29, pp 993 - 1001.
5. Thompson R.G. (1986) In "Short - Lisotopes in Biology." Wellington pp 80 - 86.

TEMPERATURE BEHAVIOR OF PHOTOSYSTEM II IN CHILLING-RESISTANT AND CHILLING-SUSCEPTIBLE PLANT SPECIES, STUDIED BY FLUORESCENCE AND LUMINESCENCE METHODS.

Anne Glémin, Teresa Miranda and Jean-Marc Ducruet
INRA/CEA, Section de Bioénergétique, DBCM, CEA Saclay.
91191 Gif-sur-Yvette cedex, France.

1. INTRODUCTION

Fluorescence and luminescence emission reflects the state of both the charge stabilisation and the pigment antenna in photosystem II. Their properties are strongly influenced by temperature, in a way which depends on the plant species and on the heat or cold hardening procedures to which plants are submitted. The composition of thylakoid membranes is an important factor in the behavior of photosystem II according to temperature (1), including cold or heat. Using 14 crop plants species and cultivars with an already known degree of chilling tolerance, we studied some characteristic parameters of leaf fluorescence and thermoluminescence emissions from 0°C to 60°C, in order to examine their relationship with the cold-tolerance trait.

2. MATERIAL AND METHODS

2.1 Plants were grown in chambers at 22°C, under 25O μE m^{-2} s^{-1}, 16 hours. Then, part of them were submitted to a progressive hardening: the temperature was first lowered at 12°C for 3 days then at 5°C for 2 to 5 days. Light was 100 μE m^{-2} s^{-1} and leaves were harvested at the end of dark periods, in order to limit photoinhibition.

Measurements were done on the upper face of leaves.

2.2 Thermoluminescence emission (0.5°C/s temperature gradient) and Fo fluorescence emission excited by an ultra-weak 480 nm light (0.05°C/s) were recorded on the same set-up and quantitatively analyzed, as described elsewhere (2).

Fluorescence rise kinetics were induced by a continuous 633 nm excitation (110 or 700 μE m^{-2} s^{-1}).

Low temperature emission spectra were recorded under strong 480 nm front excitation after grinding pieces of leaves in liquid nitrogen with water and quartz particles (3).

3. RESULTS

In the 0°C to 40°C range, the Fo fluorescence level only shows a small increase above 30°C, concomitant to a weak dark

N. Murata (ed.), Research in Photosynthesis, Vol. IV, 185–188.

thermoluminescence emission, ascribable to a heat-induced Q_B -> Q_A reverse electron transfer (4). The high-temperature rise (LHCII disconnection) above 40°C peaked at a maximum Fom near 50°C. The peak temperature was not shifted by cold treatment, but the maximum value of Fom was much more decreased in chilling-susceptible than in -tolerant plants (it was already lower at 22°C) after a progressive hardening to 5°C (Fig. 1).

The Fp level was slightly higher in chilling-susceptible than in -tolerant plants below 20°C, but the decrease of Fp above 20°C (5) was similar in both cases. After hardening in low light conditions, Fp was lower only in susceptible plants.

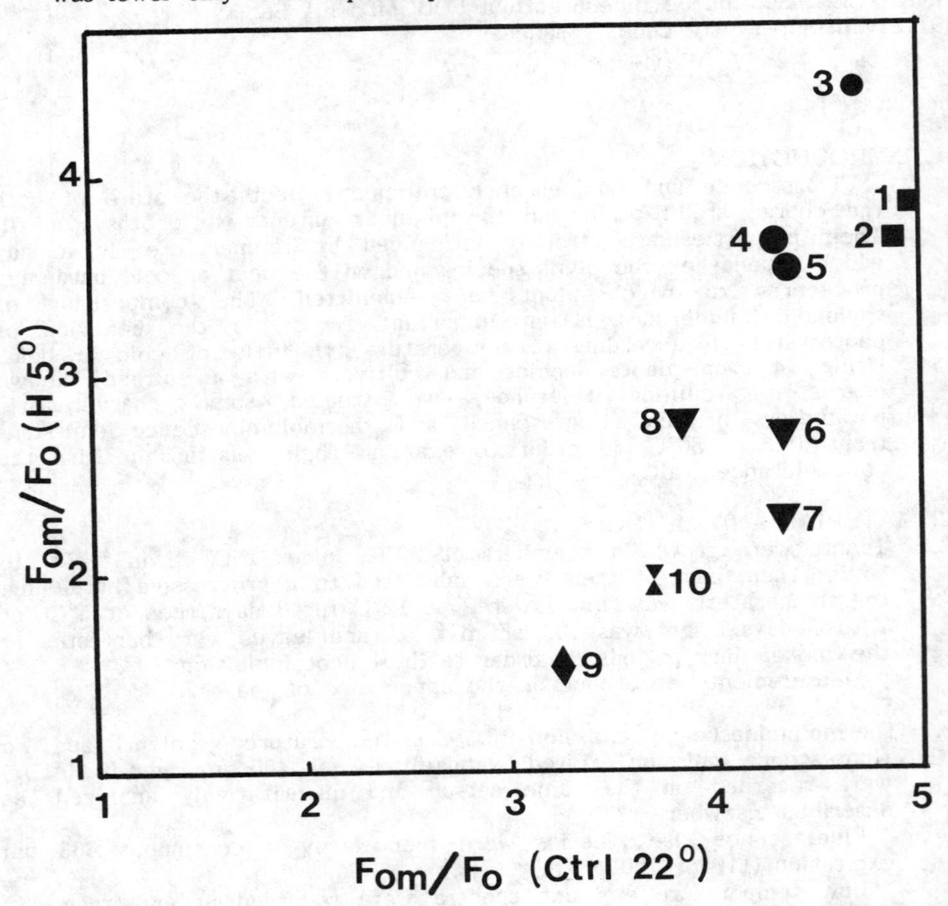

FIGURE 1. Maximum Fom (near 50°C) related to Fo (10°C) fluorescence (excitation: 480 nm, emission: › 650nm), in control and cold-hardened plants: rape ( ), pea ( ), soybean ( ), tomato ( ), cucumber ( ). n°: see table 1.

TABLE 1: peak temperature (Tm) and activation energy (EA) of the B band (S_2 Q_B^-) of thermoluminescence in leaves after one flash. TL gradient: 0.5°C/s. n: number of replicates. R: ratio of EA hardened / unhardened. Dicotyledonous plant species and cultivars are listed by order of decreasing chilling tolerance.

	Control 22°C			Hardened 12°C-> 5°C			
Species	n	EA	Tm	n	EA	Tm	R
<u>Rapeseed</u>							
1-Regent	4	0.88	32.8	6	0.87	32.1	0.99
C.I 5%		*0.15*	*0.99*		*0.08*	*1.2*	
2-Stellar	4	0.73	30.7	6	0.75	32.7	1.03
C.I 5%		*0.12*	*2.51*		*0.08*	*0.89*	
<u>Pea</u>							
3-Kazar	4	0.85	35.4	7	0.75	31.7	0.88
4-Wirtenb.	2	0.73	33.9	3	0.68	29.6	0.93
5-Kelvedon	4	0.80	34.0	7	0.75	27.5	0.94
Mean sp.	*10*	*0.80*	*34.4*	*17*	*0.73*	*29.6*	
C.I 5%		*0.04*	*1.17*		*0.03*	*1.59*	
<u>Soybean</u>							
6-Verdon	4	0.95	34.8	3	0.65	23.5	0.68
7-Labrador	4	0.92	34.1	3	0.64	17.2	0.69
8-M. Arrow	4	0.91	34.8	5	0.64	23.8	0.70
Mean sp.	*12*	*0.93*	*34.6*	*11*	*0.67*	*21.9*	
C.I 5%		*0.03*	*1.64*		*0.04*	*2.59*	
<u>Tomato</u>							
9-Marmande	5	0.93	36.7		-	-	
C.I 5%		*0.08*	*3.81*				
<u>Cucumber</u>							
10-Prodig.	7	0.98	32.0	5	0.75	25.5	0.76
C.I 5%		*0.07*	*0.94*		*0.10*	*7.08*	
<u>Maize</u>							
W64A	2	1.27	17.0	3	1.25	17.3	0.98
F244	3	1.38	17.2	3	1.30	16.9	0.94
B73	3	1.38	18.2	3	1.35	19.6	0.98
Mean sp.	*8*	*1.36*	*17.5*	*9*	*1.30*	*17.9*	
C.I 5%		*0.11*	*0.71*		*0.07*	*2.63*	

Thermoluminescence showed that a progressive hardening decreased both the maximum temperature of the B band and its apparent activation energy E_A (Table 1). In chilled cucumber and tomato, thermoluminescence emission was suppressed between 0 and 50°C. The high E_A values for maize was also observed for other graminaceous plant species.

Low temperature emission spectra showed a decrease of the PS-II emission (685 and 695 nm) compared to PS-I (730-740 nm) only in chilled cucumber and tomato, at a stage which corresponds to visible damages in leaves.

No significant effects of a short 20 h cold incubation in the dark could be detected by fluorescence and thermoluminescence measurements, at the exception of cucumber.

4. DISCUSSION

The maximum fluorescence Fm (or Fp) becomes equal to Fo (Fom) at high temperatures and this is linked to the phase separation of non-bilayer membranes lipids (5). Fom was generally lower in the chilling-susceptible plants and was further decreased by a progressive cold hardening, but also Fm, to an extent which seems to be correlated with the chilling-susceptibility. Variations of the Fom/Fo ratios could reflect changes in the properties of LHC II and its interactions with membrane lipids.

The characteristics of the B band of thermoluminescence gives an insight in the charge stabilisation between S_2 and Q_B^- in PS-II. In chilling-susceptible plants, recombination becomes easier after cold-hardening. However, it cannot be excluded that photoinhibition plays a role even under 100 μE m^{-2} s^{-1}. A cold incubation in total darkness for 20 h did allow a change in the B band parameters to be observed. In addition to a lower Fv/Fm, a decrease of E_A and Tm have been previously observed in cold-tolerant spinach progressively hardened to 5°C, but under 220-250 μE m^{-2} s^{-1} (6).

However, other mechanisms that those here examined may be involved in the temperature behavior of photosystem II, among which the cold-induced proton leakiness of the thylakoid membrane in chilling-susceptible plants.

TM is supported by a grant from INIA (Madrid).

REFERENCES

1 Murata, N. and Yamaya, J. (1984) Plant Physiology 74, 1016-1024.
2 Ducruet, J.M. and Miranda, T. (1992) Photosynthesis Res., in press.
3 Weiss, E. (1985) Photosynthesis Res., 6, 73-86.
4 Bilger, W., Schreiber, U. and Lange O.L. (1984) Oecologia 63, 256-262.
5 Williams, J.P., Brain, A.P.R. and Dominy P.J. (1992) Biochim.Biophys. Acta 1099, 137-144.
6 Briantais, J.M., Ducruet, J.M., Hodges, M. and Krause, G.H. (1992) Photosynthesis Res. 31, 1-10.

A NEW KIND OF INDUCTION RESPONSE FOUND IN TWO RAINFOREST SPECIES.

JENNIFER WATLING AND IAN WOODROW, DEPARTMENT OF BOTANY, JAMES COOK UNIVERSITY, TOWNSVILLE, QUEENSLAND, 4811, AUSTRALIA.

1. INTRODUCTION.

Plants growing in rainforest understoreys are exposed to large variations in PFD (Photon Flux Density). Low levels of background shade light can rapidly change to higher intensities as direct sunlight penetrates the overlying canopy (see Figure 1.). These patches of light, or sunlfecks, vary in intensity and duration depending on the position of the sun and canopy architecture. Constituting up to 80% of total daily PFD (1), sunflecks are an important source of light energy for understorey plants. However, efficient utilisation of this fluctuating light requires that plants respond quickly to increased PFD. Recent studies have shown that the speed of this response is, under certain conditions, largely limited by the rate of Rubisco (Ribulose bisphosphate carboxylase-oxygenase) activation (2). Further, this activation process has been found to be limited by a preceding light dependent process, thought to be activation of the enzyme rubisco activase (3). In *Spinacea oleracea* the first activation step (activase activation) has been shown to saturate at PFDs of 135 μmol quanta $m^{-2}s^{-1}$ (3). Since a faster response time would increase the amount of carbon fixed during a sunfleck, saturation of the first process would place a plant in a better position, biochemically speaking, to utilise a sunfleck.

This induction process was studied in two rainforest species to determine the effect of background PFD levels on the rate of the assimilation rise.

N. Murata (ed.), Research in Photosynthesis, Vol. IV, 189–192.

Figure 1. Sunfleck activity in the understorey of a North Queensland rainforest. Measured with a quantum sensor (LI-COR 190SA) on the 9/9/91 on a clear day.

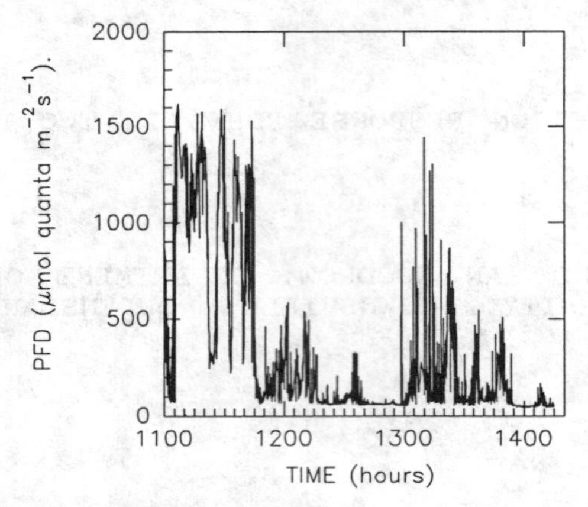

2. MATERIALS AND METHODS.

The plants studied were *Alocasia macrorrhiza* and *Omalanthus novoguinensis*, both of which are native to the rainforests of North Queensland, Australia. *A. macrorrhiza* can be found in both understorey and open sites, while *O. novoguinensis* typically grows in sunny positions in large gaps and on forest edges. Plants were grown in pots in a glass-house where maximum daily PFD was 1800 μmol quanta $m^{-2}s^{-1}$, and air temperature was 25°C day and night.

Photosynthetic responses to increasing PFD were measured using a gas exchange system (MPH-1000 open, differential system with mass-flow controllers, and an ADC infra-red gas analyser). Plants were placed in the gas exchange system at 25°C, 70% relative humidity and 500 μmol quanta $m^{-2}s^{-1}$ until maximum assimilation rates were reached. Photosynthetic enzymes were then deactivated by reducing PFD to 10 μmol quanta $m^{-2}s^{-1}$ for 50 minutes. Blue light was used to prevent stomatal closure during the low light period. After 50 minutes PFD was raised to a higher level (20, 30, 50, 70, 90, or 130 μmol quanta $m^{-2}s^{-1}$) for 25 minutes before being finally increased to 500 μmol quanta $m^{-2}s^{-1}$ (white light). The response of assimilation to changes in PFD was recorded at 5 second intervals until the maximum rate was reached. Assimilation rates were corrected to a c_i (internal CO_2 concentration) of 250 ppm as described by Woodrow and Mott (2).

3. RESULTS AND DISCUSSION.

The response of assimilation to the 10-500 μmol quanta $m^{-2}s^{-1}$ PFD rise was similar in both species (see Figure 2.). The sigmoid curve obtained is qualitatively different from previously reported induction responses for *A. macrorrhiza* (4) and other plants (3, 4, 5) in which a sharp rise in assimilation rate followed by a gradual increase to a maximum is typical. However, this exponential type of response was obtained when the initial PFD was increased. For *A. macrorrhiza* the change in response from the sigmoid to the exponential rise occurred at starting PFDs of 50 μmol quanta $m^{-2}s^{-1}$ and above, and for *O. novoguinensis* at PFDs of 90 μmol quanta $m^{-2}s^{-1}$ and above (see Figure 3.)

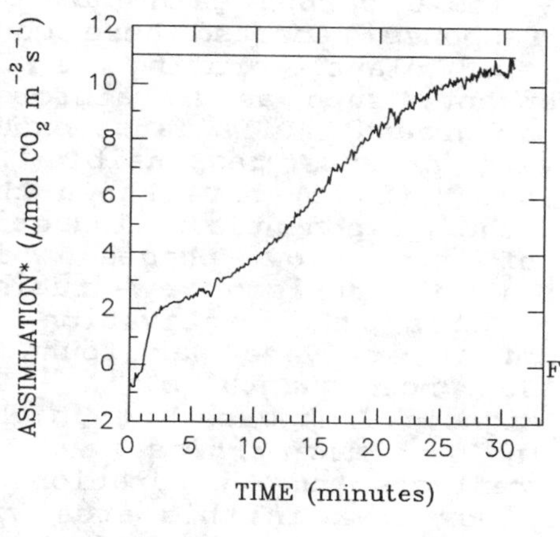

Figure 2. Photosynthetic induction response in *O. novoguinensis* after a rise in PFD from 10–500 μmol quanta $m^{-2}s^{-1}$. *Assimilation corrected to c_i of 250ppm.

Forgone assimilation = 8.93 mmol CO_2 m^{-2}

Figure 3. Photosynthetic induction response in *O. novoguinensis* after a rise in PFD from 90–500 μmol quanta $m^{-2}s^{-1}$.

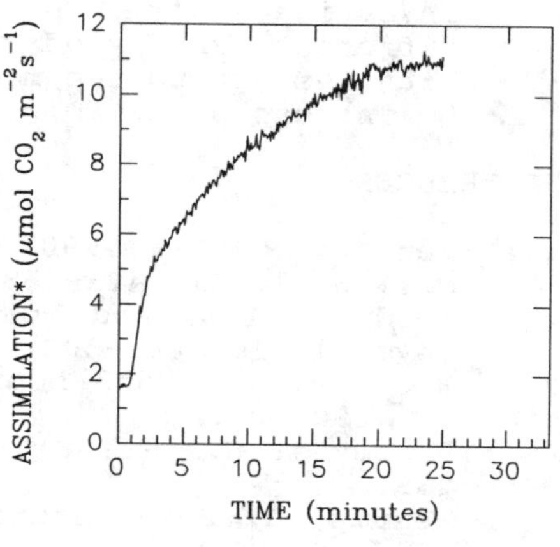

Forgone assimilation = 4.04 mmol $co_2 m^{-2}$

The significance of the two different responses can be best illustrated by comparing the amount of forgone assimilation resulting from a particular transient. Forgone assimilation is a quantitative expression of the lost opportunity for carbon gain experienced by a plant after a rise in PFD. It arises because the assimilation rate does not rise instantaneously with the rise in PFD. Forgone assimilation can be calculated by integrating the area above the curve in any induction transient. For the transients shown in Figures 2 and 3 forgone assimilation is greater when the response is sigmoid. For example forgone assimilation, during the transient, is reduced from 8.93 to 4.04 mmol CO_2 m^{-2} when the sigmoid response is removed by a higher initial PFD.

The time required for rubisco activation after a rise in PFD can significantly limit carbon gain during a sunfleck. The sigmoid response reported here could seriously disadvantage a plant growing in a fluctuating light environment, such as a rainforest understorey, unless the background PFD is large enough to saturate the underlying process responsible for this response. Woodrow and Mott (3) have shown that in *Spinacea oleracea* the exponential induction response is composed of two slow phases which represent the activation of rubisco by rubisco activase and preceding this the activation of activase. The activation of activase was found to saturate at PFDs of 135 μmol quanta $m^{-2}s^{-1}$. The disappearance of the sigmoid response at higher starting PFDs found in *A. macrorrhiza* and *O. novoguinensis* probably reflects the saturation of activase activation. Further work in this area will investigate the ability of plants to adapt to different levels of background light, in particular with respect to the mechanisms underlying the response to increases in PFD.

REFERENCES.

1 Pearcy, R.W. (1990) Ann. Rev. Plant Physiol. Plant Mol. Biol. 41, 421-453.

2 Woodrow, I.E. and Mott, K.A. (1989) Aust. J. Plant Physiol. 16, 487-500.

3 Woodrow, I.E. and Mott, K. A. (1992) Plant Physiol. 99, 298-303.

4 Pearcy, R.W. (1988) Aust. J. Plant Physiol. 15, 223-238.

5 Pearcy, R.W. and Seemann, J.R. (1990) Plant Physiol. 94, 628-633.

21. Water and Salt Stresses

DIVERSE GENETIC RESPONSES TO ENVIRONMENTAL STRESS IN A SALT-TOLERANT PLANT: CLASSES OF TRANSCRIPTS

JOHN C. CUSHMAN[1], E. JAY DEROCHER[2], DANIEL M. VERNON[3], JOHN C. THOMAS, CHRISTINE B. MICHALOWSKI, HANS J. BOHNERT, DEPARTMENT OF BIOCHEMISTRY AND DEPARTMENTS OF MOLECULAR AND CELLULAR BIOLOGY AND OF PLANT SCIENCES, THE UNIVERSITY OF ARIZONA, TUCSON, AZ 85721, U.S.A.

1. INTRODUCTION

We have developed a model to study the multi-faceted responses of plants to abiotic stresses. Our main emphasis is to characterize mechanisms responsible for salt, drought and low temperature tolerance of the common ice plant (*Mesembryanthemum crystallinum).* The advantages of this plant are its small genome, abundant physiological, biochemical and developmental knowledge about the plant, and the well-characterized gene expression changes that occur during development and in response to a variety of environmental stresses. Particularly well characterized is the physiology and molecular biology of CAM (Crassulacean Acid Metabolism) induction (2, 33, 42). Since the ice plant can be regenerated (19) and transformed using *Agrobacterium* vectors (J.C. Cushman, unpublished), new avenues of research can be initiated that will lead to in-depth analysis of the mechanisms that are naturally present in this drought- and salt-tolerant plant and that appear to be missing in glycophytic plants.

Using several examples that document gene expression changes we demonstrate how the ice plant responds to stress changes during its life time. We think that whole plant analysis, rather than analyses of, for example, suspension cells or excised leaves, is more suitable to study environmental stress and the adaptive, stress-ameliorating responses of this plant. We show here that a number of genes in the ice plant undergo a phase change in expression at age five to six weeks after germination when the plant becomes developmentally oriented towards CAM induction (4). Before this time point is reached, CAM inducibility is minimal and photosynthesis-related proteins are expressed at highest levels (23). With increasing age, the primary leaves (even in the absence of stress) gradually express CAM-related genes (4, 7) and increasingly show the physiological characters indicative of CAM switching (13, 38). Stress accelerates this transition dramatically (2, 4). Having characterized a large number of genes, it is now possible to distinguish the developmentally programed processes of CAM induction and long-term adaptations to water stress from reactions of the plant that establish stress tolerance in the short-term (31, 35, 36). One crucial short-term response is osmotic adaptation. As the ice plant accumulates NaCl under stress conditions in the vacuole, adjustments must occur in the cytoplasm. It appears that the accumulation of proline (8, 31) and the accumulation of pinitol (27) may be sufficient for adjustment. An observation that supports this notion has been the recent identification of a stress-inducible gene encoding a methyl transferase involved in pinitol biosynthesis (34). In contrast to CAM genes, the gene encoding this methyl transferase is

[1]present address: Department of Biochemistry and Molecular Biology, Oklahoma State University, Stillwater, OK 74078-0454; [2]present address: MSU-DOE Plant Research Laboratory, E. Lansing, MI; [3]present address: Department of Botany, Oklahoma State University, Stillwater, OK 74078-0454.

N. Murata (ed.), Research in Photosynthesis, Vol. IV, 195–202.

stress-inducible at any time point during the lifetime of the ice plant (35) representing a new class of transcripts.

While some progress has been made in understanding the time course and the stress-ameliorating mechanisms of salt stress protection in the leaves of the ice plant, several aspects need more attention. First, we have recently obtained evidence indicating that the polyol biosynthetic capacity of the ice plant is more complex than previously thought. The epidermal bladder cells of the ice plant (28) contain different polyols (1), in addition to pinitol. Second, we have evidence for dramatic stress-induced gene expression changes in the root system which may be more pronounced than those changes observed in the aerial parts of the plant.

2. MATERIALS AND METHODS

General techniques used for the growth of plants and tissue harvesting, for the isolation of DNA, RNA and protein, the generation and use of gene or transcript libraries and subtracted cDNA libraries, and for DNA sequencing have been published previously (2, 3, 5, 6, 10, 23, 34). Root cDNA libraries were established from root tissue of hydroponically-grown plants salt-stressed for 6 and 30 h. These libraries were analyzed for transcripts whose expression was enhanced under stress. Slot blot filters and filters for northern-type hybridizations were prepared from RNA isolated at different times during development of the primary leaves of the ice plant (from two to nine weeks of age) from either control plants (no stress) or plants stressed by the addition of 500 mM NaCl (soil grown plants) or 400 mM (hydroponically grown plants) for various lengths of time, or drought-stressed plants, or plants stressed by maintenance at $5^{O}C$ for several days (Table 1).

3. RESULTS AND DISCUSSION

In this short overview we will discuss a few selected topics illustrating different types of stress-adaptive responses that act synergistically to form the basis of the ice plant's tolerance to environmental stresses. The sections indicate that **(i)** the photosynthetic apparatus is largely protected against the effects of stress as judged by the expression of genes for photosynthesis-related functions, **(ii)** CAM induction gives rise to long-term protection by providing a highly water-use efficient mode of nocturnal carbon uptake and fixation, **(iii)** polyol production is the major protection mechanism against osmotic stress both long and short term, and **(iv)** root-specific changes in gene expression in response to salinity stress may make a major contribution towards the ability of this facultative halophyte to withstand osmotic stress. We show that various environmental stresses, depending on the agent producing the osmotic stress and other environmental conditions (such as light intensity and quality; 18), affect a very large number of genes, whose expression is up-regulated, maintained, or down-regulated. We propose that many of these changes in gene expression, including down-regulation, have adaptive significance. By using a direct screening approach, we estimate the magnitude of changes in gene expression to be on the order of 100-200 genes up-regulated and about three times this number down-regulated in response to salt stress (20). Part of the gene expression changes that are shown here (Figures 1 & 2, Table 1) exemplify the flexibility of the ice plant in coping with different stresses in different ways. Some responses are dependent on the tissue type, the cell type, and/ or the developmental status of the plant (1, 4, 18, 31, 32, 36). It will be important in the future to focus on cell specificity of stress reponses, how specific responses are integrated in tissues, and how communication is achieved between organs, for example the root and leaf systems.

3.1. Photosynthesis-Related Genes. In *Mesembryanthemum,* there is no evidence of any pronounced change in the photosynthetic apparatus or electron transport activities during CAM induction brought about by salt stress (8, 15). Despite this apparent resiliency, photosynthetically related genes generally exhibit a down-regulation in expression in response to salt stress. For example (Table 1), the *rbc*S gene family which encodes the small subunit proteins of Rubisco shows a dramatic decline in steady state transcript levels in response to salt stress (9, 10, 11). Similarly, the expression of chlorophyll a/b binding protein (21) and *pet*H (ferredoxin $NADP^+$-oxidoreductase) (22) suffer a (transient) decline in transcript levels. Transcription rates for these genes as measured by *in vitro* transcription run-on assays may increase, remain constant, or decline upon salt stress (4, 11, 23). Ferredoxin-$NADP^+$-reductase (FNR) transcription rates decline almost two-fold during salt stress (23) despite constant levels of steady state messenger RNA (22). In contrast, transcription rate for the chloroplast localized phosphoribulokinase

----

Table I. Genes from *Mesembryanthemum crystallinum* and changes in transcript expression depending on developmental and environmental cues.

Gene	Clones	Size (kbp)	Enzyme/Protein	Protein Localization	Expression (Salt Stress)
Ppc1	cDNA/ gene	3.3	phosphoenolpyruvate carboxylase	cytosol	induced
Ppdk1	cDNA/ gene	3.4	pyruvate orthophosphate dikinase	chloroplast	induced
Gpd1	cDNA/ gene	2.1	NAD-glyceraldehyde 3-P dehydrogenase	cytosol	induced
Mod1	cDNA/ gene	2.2	NADP-malic enzyme	cytosol	induced
Mdh1	cDNA/ gene	1.8	NAP-malate dehydrogenase	chloroplast	induced
Imt1	cDNA	1.6	Myo-inositol O-methyl transferase	cytosol	induced
Sep1	cDNA	1.3	sulfhydryl endopeptidase	cytosol	induced
Ppc2	cDNA/ gene	3.3	phosphoenolpyruvate carboxylase (housekeeping)	cytosol	repressed
RbcS1-5	cDNA/ gene	~0.8	small subunit Rubisco	chloroplast	repressed
Prk1	cDNA	1.5	phosphoribulokinase	chloroplast	transiently repressed
PetH	cDNA/ gene	1.5	ferredoxin-$NADP^+$-oxidored.	chloroplast	constitutive
Cab1-?	cDNA	0.8	chlorophyll a/b-binding protein	chloroplast	repressed
Act	cDNA/ gene	n.d.	actin	cytosol	constitutive
Tub	cDNA/ gene	n.d.	tubulin	cytosol	constitutive

A selection of genes and transcripts and their expression characteristics in the ice plant. For references, see: Cushman et al. (1989; 1990); Bohnert et al. (1992); Vernon & Bohnert (1992); Cushman (1992a,b); Michalowski et al. (1989, 1992); DeRocher et al. (1992); DeRocher & Bohnert (1992). n.d. = not determined.

(PRK), remains relatively unaffected by the salt stress treatment (23). *RbcS* transcription increases or remains constant (depending on the time point in development at which the plants are stressed), while the corresponding mRNAs decline drastically during salt stress treatment (11). These studies targeting the expression of photosynthesis-related genes allow two conclusions. The mode of expression of these genes, transcriptional control, regulation of mRNA stability, or translation, may be different for each gene, and may vary in the context of plant development. It is also important to realize that transcription is not the only expression control mechanism during salt stress of the ice plant. Strict transcriptional control has been shown for some genes (3, 5, 6, 34, 36), while other genes (*Ppc1*; 3, 4) are regulated transcriptionally and, possibly, by modulation of mRNA stability. For other genes, such as the *RbcS* genes (11) transcription is probably not the most important regulatory mode of expression.

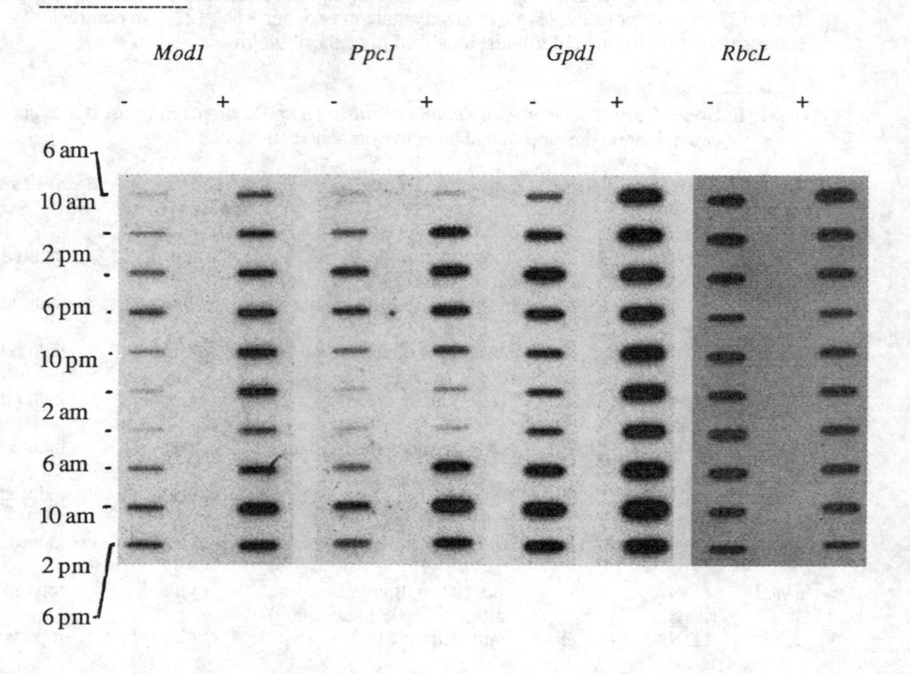

FIGURE 1. Selected transcripts exemplifying diurnal rythmicity of transcript amounts in unstressed and stressed primary leaves.
(- = no stress; + = salt-stressed for 5 days). Equal amounts of total RNA were loaded on nitrocellulaose filters which were probed by hybridization with radioactively labelled DNA from clones of genes or cDNAs as indicated. The signals documented do not reflect relative transcript abundance since the filters were exposed to X-ray film for different time periods. Autoradiograms were analyzed using a Macintosh "Onescanner".

3.2. CAM-Induction. In response to salinity or drought stress, *M. crystallinum* will shift from a C_3 to a CAM mode of photosynthesis (42). This transition provides a unique opportunity to study the molecular basis of CAM photosynthetic carbon fixation. In CAM plants the majority of CO_2 uptake and fixation into C_4 acids (malate) occurs at night. During the day, plants close their stomata, which results in reduced evaporative water loss, and they draw upon the stored malate as a carbon source for refixation via the Calvin-Benson (C_3) photosynthesis cycle. The net effects of this mode of photosynthetic carbon uptake are increased water use efficiency and a CO_2 concentrating mechanism that serves to limit photorespiration. During the transition from C_3 photosynthesis to CAM, the activities of several enzymes involved in malate metabolism and gluconeogenesis are increased (14, 39, 41).

We have now characterized many of the genes encoding the enzymes that are up-regulated by salt stress (Table 1). First among these is *Ppc*1, the gene that encodes the CAM specific isoform of phophoenolpyruvate carboxylase (PEPC), the enzyme responsible for the primary fixation of CO_2 (3). The increased activity of PEPC is the direct result of increased mRNA accumulation (21, 25) driven by increased transcription rates (3). A second, constitutively expressed gene for PEPC (*Ppc*2) has also been characterized that apparently does not play a role in CAM (Table 1) (3). Steady state mRNA levels for pyruvate orthophosphate dikinase (PPdK), the enzyme that converts pyruvate to PEP, also increase during salt stress (Table 1) (21). Likewise, mRNA levels increase for NAD-glyceraldyde 3-phosphate dehydrogenase (GAPDH), an enzyme of the glycolytic pathway that contributes to the formation of PEP, the substrate for PEPC (26). In addition, the activities of both NADP- and NAD-dependent malic enzyme (ME) increased 4-10 fold by salt stress treatment (14). The increased NADP-ME activity is localized to the cytosol (39, 41) and the increased NAD-ME activity is localized to the mitochondria (40). We have isolated the gene for NADP-ME from *M. crystallinum* and have demonstrated that transcripts from this gene increase 8-10 fold only in leaves during CAM induction strongly suggesting that it plays an important role in malate decarboxylation (5). Further research on the expression pattern of the NAD-dependent form of ME will help to better define the contribuiton of this enzyme to CAM.

The reduction of OAA to malate during dark CO_2 fixation is thought to be catalyzed primarily by an NAD-dependent form of malate dehydrogenase (MDH) in *M. crystallinum.* However, the activities of both a chloroplast localized NADP-MDH activity and an extrachloroplastic (mitochondrial and cytosolic) NAD-MDH activity increase during CAM induction (14). We have cloned and characterized a full-length cDNA clone encoding NADP-MDH from *M. crystallinum* whose expression increases as a result of transcriptional induction during the C_3 to CAM transition (6). Prior to this increase, transcript levels decline transiently in a manner similar to that observed for transcripts of other chloroplast localized proteins such as SSU of Rubisco, chlorophyll a/b binding protein (21) and PRK (23). This transient decline may be the result of changes in transcript stability or a decline in transcription rates immediately after the initial stress treatment. However, other genes (i.e. ME and PEPC) do exhibit diurnal changes in transcript abundance (Figure 1). Roots exhibit no detectable increase in NADP-MDH transcripts during salt stress. The leaf-specific, salt-stress-inducible pattern of expression suggests that NADP-MDH participates in the CO_2 fixation reactions of CAM. CAM plants typically display a "morning burst" of CO_2 uptake and fixation just after illumination. During the early part of this burst, the majority of CO_2 fixation results in malate formation via the combined actions of PEPC and NAD(P)-MDH that can contribute substantially to total net carbon gain (37). The light-induced activation of the NADP-dependent form of MDH in CAM plants (16) suggests that this enzyme may be partially responsible for this burst of CO_2 fixation.

The increased expression of CAM genes and synthesis of CAM enzymes results from increased transcription rates of all genes examined thus far (3, 5, 6, 36). This observation suggests that a common mechanism is involved in the coordinate induction of certain CAM pathway enzymes by salt stress in the common ice plant. Studies are now in progress to isolate additional members of gene families (i.e. NAD-ME and NAD-MDH) encoding enzymes that participate in CAM. The analysis and comparison of the 5'-flanking regions are in the prosess of being dissected to define those descrete elements or regions that confer salt-stress-responsive gene expression. The recent development of a rapid and sensitive transient assay system using microprojectile bombardment of intact leaf tissue (J.C. Cushman, unpublished) should greatly accelerate these analyses and ultimately lead to the identification of the components responsible for the activation of transcription by salt stress in the ice plant. Many CAM-related genes exhibit diurnal changes in transcript abundance, in addition to their stress-induced expression (Figure 1).

3.3 Polyol Production. The accumulation of low-molecular weight metabolites, such as proline, glycine-betaine and sugar alcohols, is a common response to water stress imposed by salinity or drought. It has long been a matter of debate whether these metabolites serve an adaptive role or whether their accumulation signals a pathological response to stress. Pathological accumulation of metabolites could arise from the misdirected action of enzymes, e.g. in peroxisomes, that were already present at the time the stress started.

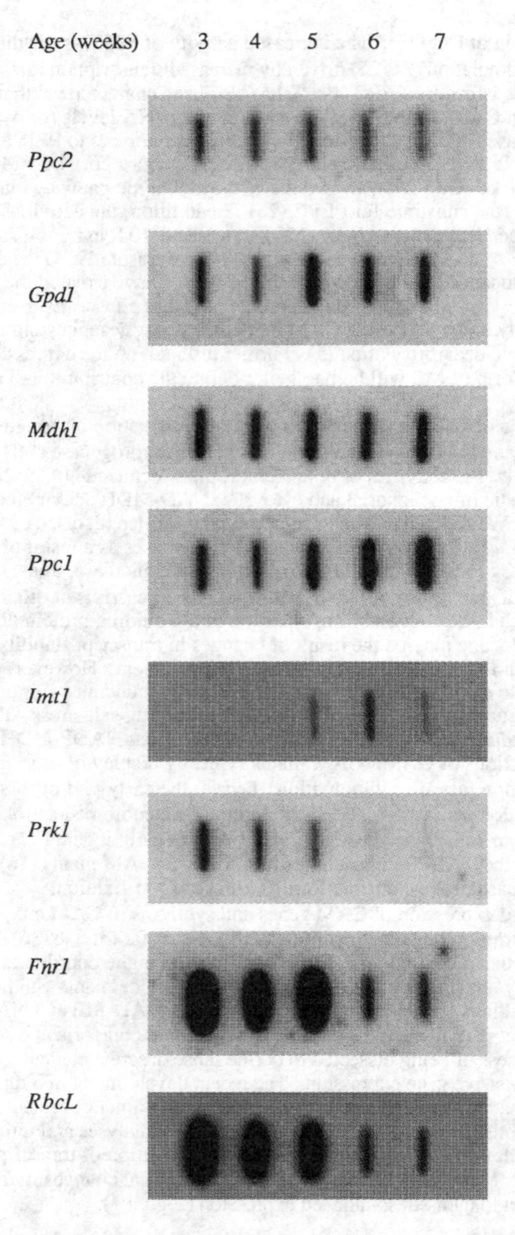

FIGURE 2. Selected transcripts indicating developmentally determined changes in steady-state levels in the absence of stress.

RNA was isolated from unstressed plants at the plant age indicated, equal amounts were blotted and treated as described in Figure 1. Based on total RNA these slot blots demonstrate the existence of several different classes of transcripts the steady-state amounts of which are regulated developmentally.

Opportunistic accumulation could occur in instances of continued synthesis of a metabolite, while its further utilization declined. In contrast, metabolite accumulation may be due to induction of synthesis pathways, which would indicate a likely role in stress adaptation.

We recently identified a dramatically stress-induced gene that plays a role in the biosynthesis of sugar alcohols (34). This gene, *Imt1* (Table 1) encodes a myo-inositol O-methyl transferase that catalyzes the first step in the biosynthesis of pinitol, a cyclic sugar alcohol that accumulates to high amounts in stress ice plants (27). Pinitol has also been detected in other plants that tolerate osmotic stress (12). *Imt1* is transcriptionally induced. This indicates the importance of low-molecular-weight metabolites, such as polyols, to stress adaptation. IMT1 induction is solely dependent on stress and is independent of plant development, in contrast to the inducibility of CAM, which follows a age-dependent gradient (4, 34). This developmental independence, and the ability to be induced by salt and low temperature (35), indicate that Imt1 is controlled by gene regulatory mechanisms distinct from those tyhat control changes in photosynthesis and those that determine CAM switching.

3.4 Gene Expression in Roots. We have recently begun to analyze stress responsive genes in roots of the ice plant based on the assumption that polyol accumulation in leaves and stems can only be one stress-relieving factor and that control over ion fluxes in the root system might contribute as much to the halophytic character of the ice plant as does pinitol accumulation. This assumption needs to be substantiated by future research. However, preliminary results indicate that gene expression changes in the roots are probably much more pronounced than changes in the aerial parts of the ice plant (C.B. Michalowski, unpublished). It appears that the steady-state amounts of transcripts, such as the transcript encoding a germin-like protein (24), change rapidly as the roots experience salt stress. The root-specific salt stress response appears to be complex involving changes in the transcripts for many genes (P. Andolfatto and J.C. Thomas, unpublished; Yamada, S., unpublished).

3.5. Ways to make halotolerant Plants. If polyol accumulation, similar to what is hypothesized for the accumulation of glycine betaine (17), is an adaptive measure to survive salt stress, drought and, possibly also, low temperature, it should be possible to engineer this pathway and accumulate polyols in plants which normally do not accumulate these compounds and which are not tolerant to those stresses. We have begun experiments that test this concept. The incorporation of a bacterial gene specifying mannitol 1-phosphate dehydrogenase into tobacco has been achieved (29) and the resulting transgenic plants are, at least partially, protected from the effects of severe salt stress (30). The mechanisms by which the transgenic tobacco plants are protected from the deleterious effects of high concentrations of sodium are not known. Likely, the protection conveyed by an increased osmotic value of the cytoplasm plays a role, but the increased amount of mannitol may also act as an osmoprotective compatible solute. These plants are only the first generation of transgenic models for the study of environmental stress tolerance. We consider transgenic glycophytes, accumulating such polyols under the control of attuned promoter elements by which the timing of expression and cell and tissue specificity can be regulated, ideal models. Not only can they be used for studying adaptive tolerance mechanisms in order to generate stress-tolerant crop plants, but these plants should also be useful for the study of stress perception and signal transduction.

4. ACKNOWLEDGEMENTS

This work was supported by U.S. Department of Agriculture Competitive Research Grants Program #89-37264-4711 and #91-37100-5872 to HJB, and #90-37280-5662 to JCC.

REFERENCES

1 Adams, P., Thomas, J.C., Vernon, D.M., Bohnert, H.J. and Jensen, R.G. (1992) Plant & Cell Physiology, submitted.

2 Bohnert, H.J., Vernon, D.M., DeRocher, E.J., Michalowski, C.B. and Cushman, J.C. (1992) in Inducible plant proteins (Wray, J.L., ed.), pp.113-138, Cambridge University

Press, Cambridge.
3 Cushman J.C., Meyer, G., Michalowski, C.B., Schmitt, J.M. and Bohnert, H.J. (1989) Plant Cell 1, 715-725.
4 Cushman, J.C., Michalowski, C.B. and Bohnert, H.J. (1990) Plant Physiol. 94, 1137-1142.
5 Cushman, J.C. (1992a) Eur. J. Biochem. In press.
6 Cushman, J.C. (1992b) Photosyn. Res. In press.
7 Cushman, J.C., Vernon, D.M. and Bohnert, H.J. (1992) in Control of plant gene expression (Verma, D.P.S., ed) CRC Press, Boca Raton, in press.
8 Demmig, B. and Winter, K. (1983) Planta 159, 66-76.
9 DeRocher, E.J., Michalowski, C.B. and Bohnert, H.J. (1991) Plant Physiol. 95, 976-978.
10 DeRocher, E.J., Quigley, F., Mache, R. and Bohnert, H.J. (1992a) J. Mol. Biol., submitted.
11 DeRocher, E.J. and Bohnert, H.J. (1992b) in preparation.
12 Dittrich, P. and Brandl, A. (1987) Phytochemistry 26, 1925-1926.
13 Herppich, W., Herppich, M. and von Willert, D.J. (1992) Botanica Acta 105, 34-40.
14 Holtum, J.A.M. and Winter, K. (1982) Planta 155, 8-16.
15 Köster, S. and Anderson, J.M. (1988) Photosyn Res. 19, 251-264.
16 Littlejohn, R.O. and Ku, M.S.B. (1984) Plant Physiol. 74: 1050-1054.
17 McCue, K.F. and Hanson, A.D. (1990) Trends Biotech. 8, 358-362.
18 McElwain, E.F., Bohnert, H.J. and Thomas, J.C. (1992) Plant Physiol. 99, 1261-1264.
19 Meiners, M.S., Thomas, J.C., Bohnert, H.J. and Cushman, J.C. (1991) Plant Cell Rep. 9, 563-566.
20 Meyer, G., Schmitt, J.M. and Bohnert, H.J. (1990) Molec. Gen. Genet. 224, 347-356.
21 Michalowski, C.B., Olson, S.W., Piepenbrock, M., Schmitt, J.M. and Bohnert, H.J. (1989a) Plant Physiol. 89, 811-816.
22 Michalowski, C.B., Schmitt, J.M. and Bohnert, H.J. (1989b) Plant Physiol 89, 817-822.
23 Michalowski, C.B., DeRocher, E.J., Bohnert, H.J. and Salvucci, M.E. (1992) Photosynth Res. 31, 127-138.
24 Michalowski, C.B. and Bohnert, H.J. (1992) Plant Physiol. 100, in press.
25 Ostrem, J.A., Olson, S.W., Schmitt, J.M. and Bohnert, H.J. (1987) Plant Physiol. 84, 1270-1275.
26 Ostrem, J.A., Vernon, D.M. and Bohnert, H.J. (1990) J. Biol. Chem. 265, 3497-3502.
27 Paul, M.J. and Cockburn, W. (1989) J. Exp. Botany 40, 1093-1098.
28 Steudle, E., Lüttge, U., and Zimmermann, U. (1975) Planta 126, 220-246.
29 Tarczynski, M.C., Jensen, R.G. and Bohnert, H.J (1992) Proc. Natl. Acad. Sci. USA 89, 2600-2604.
30 Tarczynski, M.C., Jensen, R.G. and Bohnert, H.J. (1992) Science, submitted.
31 Thomas J.C., DeArmond, R. and Bohnert, H.J. (1992a) Plant Physiol 98, 626-631.
32 Thomas, J.C., McElwain, E.F. and Bohnert, H.J. (1992b) Plant Physiol 100, in press.
33 Ting, I.P. (1985) Ann. Rev. Plant. Physiol. 36, 595-622.
34 Vernon, D.M. and Bohnert, H.J. (1992a) EMBO J 11, 2077-2085.
35 Vernon, D.M. and Bohnert, H.J. (1992b) Plant Physiol 99, 1695-1698.
36 Vernon, D.M., Ostrem, J.A. and Bohnert, H.J. (1992) Plant, Cell & Environment, submitted.
37 Winter, K. (1980) Plant Physiol. 66, 917-921.
38 Winter, K. and Gademann, R. (1991) Plant Physiol. 95, 768-776.
39 Winter, K., Foster, J.G., Edwards, G.E. and Holtum, J.A.M. (1982) Plant Physiol. 69, 300-307.
40 Winter, K., Arron, G.P. and Edwards, G.E. (1986) Plant Cell. Physiol. 27, 1533-1539.
41 Winter, K., Foster, J.G., Edwards, G.E. and Holtum, J.A.M. (1982) Plant Physiol 69, 300-307.
42 Winter, K. (1985) Crassulacean acid metabolism, in Photosynthatic Mechanisms and the Environment (Barber, J. and Baker, N.R., eds), pp. 329-387, Elsevier, Amsterdam.

MECHANISMS OF THE ACID RESISTANCE OF *DUNALIELLA ACIDOPHILA*

Gimmler, Hartmut, Lehrstuhl Botanik I, Universität Würzburg, FRG.

INTRODUCTION

The unicellular green alga *Dunaliella* is well known for its extreme *salt tolerance*, which permits this alga to grow in NaCl concentrations up to saturation. Typical representatives are the species *D. salina, D. parva* or *D. bardawil*. The biochemistry and physiology of these algae have been reviewed recently by Ginzburg (15) and the the late M. Avron (1). Much less it is known that the genus *Dunaliella* comprises also an extreme *adicophilic* species, growing in 0.1 M sulfuric acid: *D. acidophila* exhibits optimal growth and photosynthesis at pH 1.0 (fig.1)(2). Also the biology of this species has been reviewed very recently (3,16). This paper focusses on properties of *D. acidophila*, which are of crucial importance for the survival at acid pH, such as the electrical potentials, the H^+ pump, the permeability of the plasma membrane for H^+ and the uptake of cations and anions. Also the uptake of dissociable solutes, such as inorganic carbon and phosphate, which are present at neutral pH as anions and therefore are also taken up in the anionic form, but which are present at pH 1.0 entirely in the protonated form, is a physiological problem for this alga.

METHODS

For methods see legends of figures and tables and references in the particular chapters of this article..

RESULTS and DISCUSSION

pH homeostasis

A prerequisite for a normal cell metabolism is the maintenance of a constant internal pH. Indeed, both acidophilic and neutrophilic *Dunaliella* species join the property of

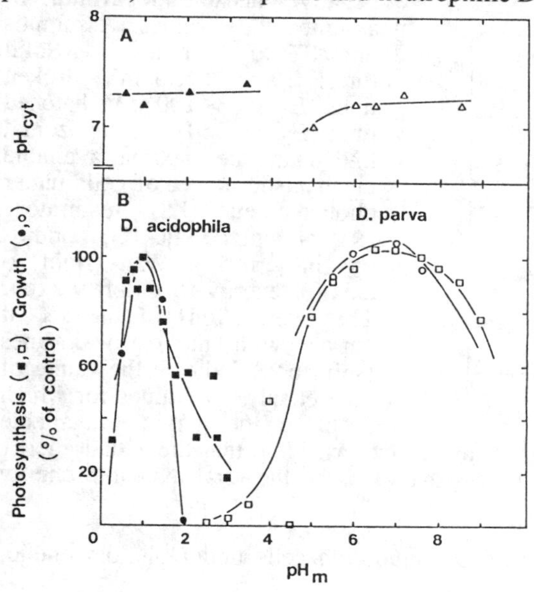

Figure 1. Internal pH (A), photosynthesis and growth (B) of *D. acidophila* and *D. parva* as function of the external pH. The internal pH was measured by ^{31}P-NMR, photosynthesis by light-induced fixation of $^{14}CO_2$, and growth by a Coulter Counter (2,3).

N. Murata (ed.), Research in Photosynthesis, Vol. IV, 203–210.

a strict pH homeostasis (fig. 1a) (1-3). ^{31}P-NMR studies revealed that within the particular pH ranges of growth the cytoplasmic pH is kept constant close to 7.0 in both algal types. The resulting H^+ gradient across the plasma membrane (PM) is up to 100 with the halotolerant species, but up to 3 x 10^6 with *D. acidophila*. How mechanistically the latter gradient can be maintained? The H^+ balance across the PM is determined by the passive H^+ influx ("leak") into the cells on one side and by the active H^+ export (H^+ pump) on the other side. The former is determined by the permeability coefficient of the PM for H^+ (P_H+ value) and the H^+ electrochemical gradient ($\Delta\tilde{u}\, H^+_M$), whereas the latter depends on the activity of the PM - H^+ - ATPase. The question arises whether the PM of *D. acidophila* is less permeable for H^+ than the PM of other plant cells and / or the H^+ - ATPase of this alga is more efficient than that of the neutrophilic *Dunaliella* species.

P_H+ values

Permeability coefficients of the PM for H^+ have been estimated for various plant systems to vary between 10^{-8} and 5 x 10^{-5} m s^{-1}. In *D. acidophila* H^+ fluxes at pH 1.0, measured under different metabolic conditions and using different methods, varied between 2 and 90 x 10^{-9} mol m^{-2} s^{-1}. These fluxes can be converted into apparent P_H+ values of 3 x 10^{-10} to 4 x 10^{-9} m s^{-1}, indicating that the permeability of the PM of *D. acidophila* for H^+ may be significantly lower than that of other membranes. In view of the acid resistance of *D. acidophila* this makes sense. However, the mechanistic reason for this difference it not known, yet. In fig.2 the

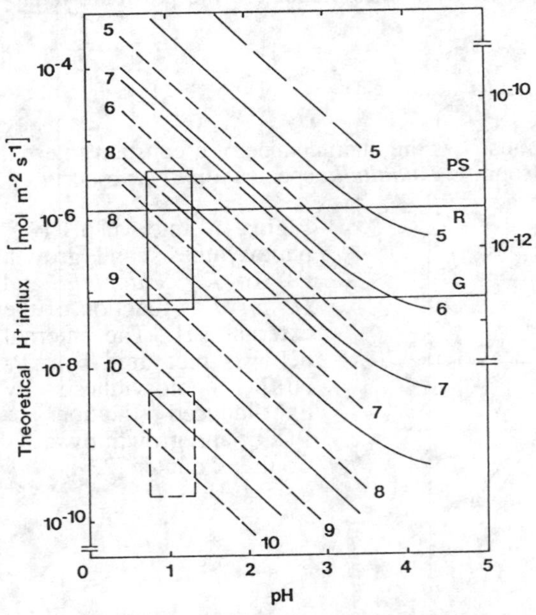

Figure 2. Theoretical H^+ influx (lines, left y-axis) and range of experimentally determined H^+ fluxes (dotted box) as function of external pH. Numbers attached to the set of curves represent the negative decadic logarithm of assumed P_H+ values. Assumption: ATP to H^+ ratio = 1. Solid lines: E_m = + 50 mV, broken lines: E_m = + 100 mV, hatched lines: E_m = - 50 mV. Horizontal lines mark the maximal available mechanistic power of cells under photosynthetic (PS), respiratory (R), and glycolytic (G) conditions in terms of Watt (right y-axis) or energy flux (left y-axis). The intersections of the set of curves with the vertical lines (solid box) indicate the range of theoretical P_H+ values for which at pH 1 the maximal available energy would match the energy required for H^+ export. Note that the actual energy required for H^+ export (dotted box) is less than 1 % of the total available energy (solid box).

maximal available mechanistic power of *D. acidophila* cells under photosynthetic, respiratory and glycolytic conditions is compared with both experimentally determined and theoretical H^+ fluxes across the PM. Both parameters can be compared directly if expressed in terms of fluxes (mol m^{-2} s^{-1}) and an ATP to H^+ ratio of 1 is assumed. Theoretical H^+ fluxes are calculated assuming various membrane potentials between +50 and +100 mV on one side (typical for *D. acidophila*, see below) and -50 mV (typical for neutrophilic *Dunaliella* species) on the other side. P_H+ values were varied corresponding to the data found in the literature for various plant membranes (see above). Data demonstrate that at pH 1.0 less then 1 % of the total available mechanistic power is required for the export of H^+. Furthermore it can be extracted from fig. 2 that only with positive membrane potentials between +50 and +100 mV and P_H+ values between 10^{-10} and 10^{-8} m s^{-1} theoretical and experimental H^+ fluxes match each other. Negative membrane potentials, typical for neutrophilic *Dunaliella* species, would require $P_H{}^+$ values lower than 10^{-10} m s^{-1}, which have not been measured. Data stress the importance of positive membrane potentials for the acid resistance of *D. acidophila* (see below).

Membrane potentials (E_m values)

The membrane potential of *D. acidophila* cells was measured by the insertion of potential sensitive glass microcelectrodes (11). E_m values at an external pH of 1.0 were always positive and varied between + 30 and + 80 mV (fig.3, table 1).

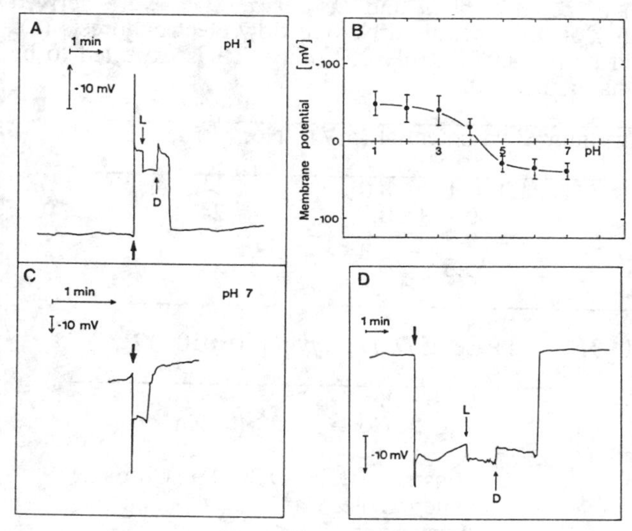

Figure 3. Membrane potentials of *D. acidophila* (A-C) and *D. parva* (D, pH 7.6) as affected by light (L) and dark (D), and the external pH. Membrane potentials were measured by glass microelectrodes with tip diameters between 0.1 and 0.4 µm (11). The bold arrows indicate the insertion of the electrode. Break downs of the E_m after some time are technical artifacts due to the escape of cells from the electrodes.

Table 1. E_m values of *Dunaliella* cells (compare fig.3) (11)

Species	pH	treatment	$E_{m\ dark}$	$E_{m\ light}$
D. acidophila	1.0	---	+ 48.5 ± 17	+ 39.5 ± 5
	1.0	2.8 x 10^{-4} M omeprazole	+ 81.0 ± 24.0	n.d.
	7.0	---	- 36.5 ± 10	n.d.
D. parva	7.6	---	- 32.5 ± 12	- 39.8 ± 12
D. bardawil	7.6	---	- 40.0 ± 14	- 49.0 ± 17

This is in contrast to the negative E_m values measured for neutrophilic *Dunaliella* species (fig.3d, table 1). Light causes a slight hyperpolarization of about 10 mV, indicating a light-induced stimulation of the PM - H^+ - ATPase (table 1). The H^+ - ATPase inhibitor omeprazole (9,10) causes a significant depolarization of the cells. This implies that the E_m of *D. acidophila* is dominated by diffusional processes rather than by active ion pumping: The diffusion potential of this alga is almost unaffected by omeprazole, whereas the H^+ export via the PM - ATPase is reduced. The positive E_m is almost constant at pH values between 0.5 and 3.0, but changes to negative values when cells are transfered to media with pH values between 5 and 7 (fig. 3b,c).

Zeta potentials
The zeta potential of *D. acidophila* cells, which is a measure for the surface potential, can be derived from the electrophoretic mobility of cells as measured by free flow electrophoresis (5). Zeta potentials are positive at acidic pH (+6 mV), but negative at alkaline pH (-30 mV)(table 2). The reason for the excess of positive charges at the outer side of the PM in *D. acidophila* is the complete protonation of phosphate groups of phospholipids at acid pH. Only positively charged groups remain at this pH. A positive zeta potential is certainly of benefit for the acid resistance of

Table 2. Zeta potentials (ZP) of *D. acidophila* and *D. parva*. Data were derived from the electrophoretic mobility of cells measured by free flow electrophoresis (5). For technical reasons ZP could be measured at pH 2.0, only. ZP is expected to be even more positive at pH 1.0 than at pH 2.0.

Species	pH of the medium	Zeta potential (mV)	No. of runs
D. acidophila	2.0	+ 6.1 ± 1.6	24
	7.0	- 30.4 ± 0.9	24
D. parva	5.5	- 29.4 ± 0.4	4
	7.0	- 35.3 ± 0.8	21

Table 3. Properties of the PM - H^+ - ATPase of *D. acidophila* (9, 10, 12).

K_m ATP (mM):	0.06 - 0.07
Me^{2+} specificity	Mg > Co > Mn >> Zn
V_{max} (µmol P_i mg^{-1} protein min^{-1})	2
Inhibitors:	Vanadate, DES, DCCD, erythrosine Omeprazole, Ca^{2+}
Activators	Fusicoccin, K^+
No effect:	SITS, DIDS, nitrate
MW (KDa):	100
pH optimum:	6.0

D. acidophila, because it decreases the passive H^+ influx into the cells and thereby reduces the energy required for active H^+ export. A beneficial side effect of the positive surface charge is a higher resistance of the cells to cationic toxins (e.g. heavy metals) (13).

H^+ - ATPase

Similar as all other plant cells also the PM of *D. acidophila* contains a H^+ exporting ATPase. This enzyme has been isolated, purified and characterized by Sekler and Pick (9,10 12) and resembles basically those ATPase which have been isolated from higher plant cells. It exhibits slight differences to the ATPase from neutrophilic *Dunaliella* species (12). The basic feature of the *D. acidophila* ATPase are summarized in table 3. In comparison to the corresponding ATPase of the neutrophilic relatives, the activity of the *D. acidophila* ATPase *in vitro* is up to 30 fold higher (12). There are indications that this enzyme is overproduced in intact *D. acidophila* cells (10,12).

Thermodynamic considerations

Using the positive E_m values of table 1, an cytoplasmic pH of 7.0 (fig.1), an external pH of 1.0, a phosphorylation potential of 630 mol l^{-1} and a temperature of 293 K, from simple thermodynamic equations and the assumption that the ATP/H^+ ratio is 1, the following parameters can be calculated (11):

1. The ΔG_{ATP} of *D. acidophila* is about -46 kJ mol^{-1}.
2. The H^+ electrochemical gradient (inwards), $\Delta\tilde{\mu} H^+_M$ is between -25 and -29 kJ mol^{-1}.
3. The maximal H^+ electrochemical gradient created by the H^+ - ATPase, $\Delta\tilde{\mu} H^+_P$ is -46 kJ mol^{-1}.
4. The maximal proton motive force of the H^+-ATPase, PMF_P is about -480 mV, whereas the actual potential of the pump (E_P') at an external pH of 1.0 is -131 mV, only.

Calculations demonstrate that the actual potential of the H^+ - ATPase in *D. acidophila* is likely to be significantly lower than that of the PM - H^+ - ATPase in neutrophilic *Dunaliella* species or higher plant cells. If an ATP /H^+ ratio of 2 is put into the equations, the actual potential becomes positive. This excludes this ratio for the export of H^+ by the H^+ - ATPase in *D. acidophila*. All experimental data are in agreement with thermodynamics and indicate that the PM - H^+ - ATPase of *D. acidophila* is indeed able to export protons against a gradient of 6 pH units across the PM, provided the H^+/ATP ratio is 1 and that the membrane potentials are positive and thereby enables the cells to survive at pH 1.0.

Cation and anion uptake

Positive membrane potentials and zeta potentials minimize passive influx of H^+ into

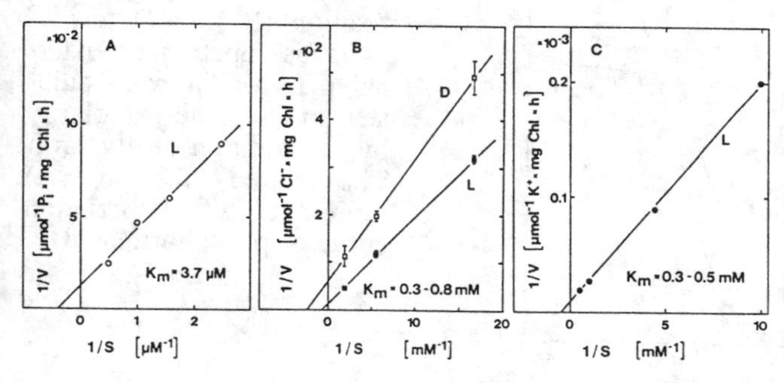

Figure 4. Uptake of K^+ (C), Cl^- (B), and phosphate (A) as function of the external substrate concentration (double reciprocal plot). K^+ uptake was measured with $^{86}Rb^+$,Cl^- with $^{36}Cl^-$, and phosphate with ^{32}P as tracers (6,7). V_{max} values are 1200 (P_i), 1-2 (K^+) and 0.07 (Cl^-) µmol mg^{-1} chlorophyll h^{-1}.

the cells. However, to the same time they create problems for the uptake of other ions: The uptake of the essential K^+ may be hampered, whereas the uptake of anions such as Cl^- may be facilitated. Therefore special mechanism are required to ensure sufficient uptake of K^+ and to prevent possible toxifications by excess uptake of Cl^-.

The K^+ uptake in neutrophilic *Dunaliella* species is dependent on metabolic energy. The negative membrane potential, generated by a vanadate sensitive PM- H^+ -ATPase, is the driving force (8,12). In *D. acidophila*, however, the situation must be different. Nevertheless, in spite of positive E_m values and zeta potentials which tend to exclude K^+, cells are able to accumulate K^+ (e.g. 150 mM inside at 2 mM outside) and to regulate its K^+ content. The uptake clearly proceeds against the electrochemical equilibrium and exhibits Michalis-Menten - kinetics (fig. 4). It is stimulated by light and inhibited by the SH blocker omeprazole (6), which is impermeant at pH 1.0 (9,10). The K^+ uptake is much less sensitive against FCCP than the ATP pool (fig.5). We have to conclude that an externally accessible SH group is involved in

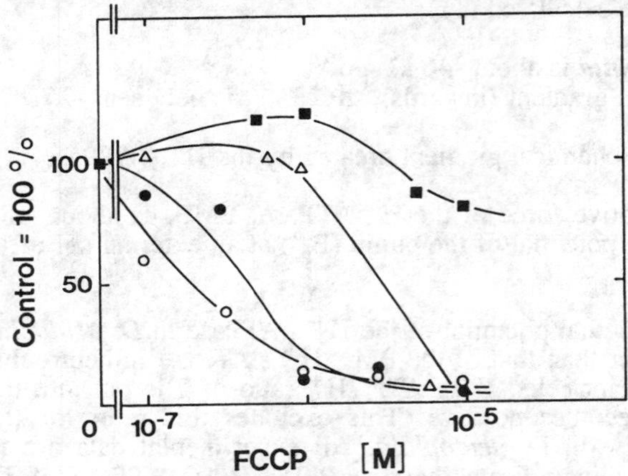

Figure 5. The effect of the uncoupler FCCP on the uptake of Cl^- (■), K^+ (▲), phosphate (o) and the ATP pool (●) of *D. acidophila* (6,7).

the transport reaction and that the uptake is not primarily energized (6). Conditions which depolarize cells, inhibit the uptake of K^+ (6). All *in vivo* findings are in agreement with the existence of a K^+ / H^+ cotransport, which uses the large H^+

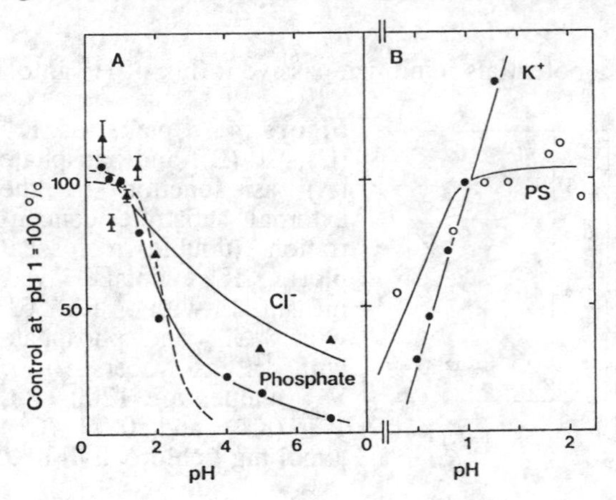

Figure 6. Uptake of phosphate,(A), Cl^- (B), K^+ (B) and photosynthetic CO_2 fixation (B) in *D. acidophila* as function of external pH. Media were adjusted to the same osmolarity by the addition of glycerol. The dotted line in (A) represents the dissoziation curve of phosphoric acid.

gradient across the PM for the transport of K^+ against the electrochemical gradient of K^+ (2). Such a mechanism had been postulated from experiments with PM vesicles isolated from *D. acidophila* and reconstituted plasma membranes (8). In intact cells such a K^+ / H^+ must be controlled by additional, unknown internal factors, since the pH profile (fig. 6) demonstrate an inverse relation between the external H^+ concentration and K^+ uptake.
Also the uptake of Cl^- exhibits Michaelis - Menten - kinetics (fig.4) and is primarily independent on the hydrolysis of ATP (fig. 5)(7). At Cl^- concentrations up to 4 mM the internal Cl^- levels are higher than predicted by the electrochemical equilibrium. This implies uptake by a carrier. The uptake of Cl^- is inhibited by SITS and DIDS at concentrations which do not affect the internal ATP pool and photosynthesis (7). At Cl^- concentration higher than 10 mM internal Cl^- concentrations are lower than predicted by the electrochemical equilibrium, permitting uptake via Cl^- channels. Cl^- uptake ceases with increasing pH (fig. 6). Cl^- efflux may proceed at low external Cl^- through diffusion, at high external Cl^- through an active Cl^- pump. The latter prevents toxic accumulation of Cl^- inside the cells at high external Cl^-. *D. acidophila* tolerates NaCl concentrations up to 700 mM (16). Data suggest tight co-operativity between the systems responsible for Cl^- uptake and Cl^- efflux, with the cytoplasmic pH, the internal Cl^- pool, and the E_m being important mediators.
One interesting question in respect to uptake of cations has not been investigated so far in *D. acidophila*: The neutrophilic *Dunaliella* species possesses a Na^+ / H^+ antiporter in the PM, the function of which is to export H^+ in exchange of external Na^+ (12). If such a antiporter is present also in *D. acidophila*, it could operate energetically only in the direction of H^+ influx in exchange against an internal Na^+. Such a reaction might be lethal for this alga, if it would not be strongly regulated. Preliminary experiments demonstrated that the Na^+ pool of *D. acidophila* is very low (5 mM) and illumination causes a further decrease of the Na^+ pool. The light-induced decrease is prevented by amiloride, an inhibitor of the Na^+ / H^+ antiporter.

Uptake of CO_2 and phosphate

Other difficulties which have to be encountered by acidophiles arises from the fact that solutes, such as inorganic carbon or phosphate, which are dissociated at neutral pH (consequently the substrates for uptake are HCO_3^- and $H_2PO_4^-$), are totally protonated at pH 1.0: Inorganic carbon and phosphate are at pH 1.0 entirely in the form of CO_2 (H_2CO_3) and H_3PO_4, respectively. Therefore special mechanisms for the uptake of these substrates are required in this alga. The permeability coefficient of the PM of *D. acidophila* for CO_2 is relatively low (10^{-7} - 3×10^{-6} m s^{-1} (2) and thereby minimizes internal acidification by excess uptake of the weak acid H_2CO_3. The uptake of CO_2, which must be distinguished from internal CO_2 fixation, is sti-

Table 4. The effect of Na^+ on the uptake of phosphate in *D. acidophila* (1 μM P_i, pH 1) and *D. bioculata* (0.5 μM, P_i, pH 7.6)(light) (Hirsch, Falkner, unpublished).

Species	Na^+ (mM)	Uptake of phosphate (Control - Na^+ = 100 %)
D. acidophila	1	102 ± 13
	5	99 ± 18
	100	111 ± 6
D. bioculata	10	188 ± 5
	100	625 ± 15

mulated by light. Only in the light, but not in the dark, CO_2 uptake satisfies the demand of photosynthetic CO_2 fixation. This demonstrates that the PM of *D. acidophila* contains a special transport system, the substrate of which is CO_2 or H_2CO_3. Thus the uptake can be adapted to the demands of photosynthesis. In neutrophilic *Dunaliella* species it is more likely that the transporter for inorganic carbon uses bicarbonate as substrate. Neutrophilic algae are generally assumed to take up phosphate in the form of a Na^+ / $H_2PO_4^-$ cotransport. This is the reason for the stimulation of phosphate uptake by Na^+. This applies also to neutrophilic species of *Dunaliella* (table 4). However, such a Na^+ effect is totally absent in *D. acidophila*, although this alga does possess a high affinity uptake system for phosphate in the PM (fig.4). The pH profile of phosphate uptake into *D. acidophila* cells (fig. 6a) resembles the dissoziation curve of phosphoric acid. It must be concluded that the uptake mechanism is not a Na^+ / $H_2PO_4^-$ cotransport. Rathermore the transported species must be either H_3PO_4 or the uptake proceeds via an electrically neutral H^+ / $H_2PO_4^-$ cotransport. Results demonstrate that also in respect to the uptake of phosphate, *D. acidophila* is very well adapted to the extreme acidity in its environment by the expression of a special transport system.
In conclusion, *D. acidophila* has evolved efficient mechanisms to cope with very high acidity. Surprisingly, this alga has difficulties when the H^+ stress is diminished (fig. 1) (2). Evolutionary, the adaptation to the ecological niche of low pH, did not create an alga which is less competitive at pH 7, (acid tolerance), but rather a specialist who simply cannot survive at this pH (acidophily).

ACKNOWLEDGEMENTS
This study was supported by the Deutsche Forschungsgemeinschaft (SFB 251).

REFERENCES

1 Avron, M. and Ben-Amotz, A.(1992): *Dunaliella* Physiology, Biochemistry and Biotechnology, CRS Press, Boca Raton.
2 Gimmler, H. and Weis, U.(1992) in *Dunaliella*: Physiology, Biochemistry, and Biotechnology (Avron, M. and Ben-Amotz, A.), pp. 99-133, CRS Press, Boca Raton.
3 Gimmler, H., Kugel, H., Leibfritz, D. and Mayer, A.(1988), Physiol. Plant. 74, 521-530.
4 Gimmler, H., Weiss, C., Kugel, H. and Treffny, B.(1989), New Phytol. 113, 175-184.
5 Gimmler, H., Schieder, M., Kowalski, M., Zimmermann, U., and Pick, U. (1991), Plant, Cell & Environ. 14, 261-269.
6 Carandang, J., Pick, U., Sekler, I., and Gimmler, H. (1992), J. Plant Physiol. 139, 413-421.
7 Hirsch, R., Carandang, J., Treffny, B., and Gimmler, H. (1992), J. Exp.Bot., 43, 887-896.
8 Gläser, U., Sekler, I., and Pick, U. (1990), Biochim. Biophys. Acta, 1019, 293-299.
9 Sekler, I., Gläser, U., and Pick,U. (1991), J. Membr. Biol. 121, 51-58.
10 Sekler, I., Remis, D., Gimmler, H., and Pick, U.(1992), Biochim. Biophys. Acta (submitted).
11 Remis, D., Simonis, W. and Gimmler, H. (1992), Arch. Microbiol. 158, (in press).
12 Pick, U. (1992) in *Dunaliella*: Physiology, Biochemistry, and Biotechnology (Avron, M. and Ben-Amotz, A.), pp. 64-97, CRS Press, Boca Raton.
13 Gimmler, H., Treffny, B., Kowalski, M., and Zimmermann, U. (1991), J. Plant Physiol., 138, 708-716.
14 Zenwirth, D., and Kaplan, A. (1981), Planta, 152, 8-12.
15 Ginzburg, M. (1988), Adv. Bot. Res. 14, 95-183.
16 Fuggi, A., Pinto, G., Pollio, A., and Taddei, R. (1988), Phycologia, 27, 334-339.

THE EFFECT OF TEMPERATURE ON LEAF PHOTOSYNTHESIS OF DEHYDRATED C3 PLANTS.

Gabriel Cornic, Laboratoire d'Ecologie Végatale, Bât. 362, Université de Paris XI, F-91405, Orsay, Cedex, FRANCE.

1. INTRODUCTION

The understanding we have of the effects of dehydration on leaf photosynthesis has changed much during the last few years. It is likely that the photosynthetic system is more resistant to water shortage than previously thought. Stomatal closure appears to be responsible for the decline in net photosynthesis of leaves submitted to mild droughts similar to those which may frequently occur in natural conditions (1,2,3). It is interesting to note the role played by non-destructive techniques in the work which has contributed to this new understanding. Improved gas exchange systems coupled with measurement of chlorophyll fluorescence emission or light scattering at 532 nm have proven particularly useful.

The first evidence for a strong stomatal control on leaf photosynthesis during drought came from experiments in which stomatal resistance was suppressed prior to or after the drying of the leaf. This was achieved either by stripping the lower leaf epidermis (4,5) or by increasing CO_2 concentration (1,2,6,7,8) during measurements to ensure a saturation at the carboxylating sites despite the stomatal closure observed in this situation. Both types of experiments indicate that mechanisms responsible for the maximum photosynthesis are significantly impaired only when leaf water deficit (LWD) is higher than about 30%. Maximum quantum yield of O_2 evolution measured at high CO_2 concentration is also hardly affected within the same range of LWD (6) showing that photosystem activities are resistant to desiccation. Similar conclusions can be drawn from light scattering and chlorophyll fluorescence emission measurements on desiccating leaves (9,10, 11). These observations on whole leaves are consistent with results showing in isolated cells, protoplasts and chloroplasts submitted to an osmotic constraint that photosystem activities are not changed (see 1 for a review).

As a consequence it can be concluded, despite the values usually calculated (6,7), that the average CO_2 concentration at within the leaf cells (Cc) during a mild drought is low. Indeed, (i) the variation of the whole chain electron transfer estimated by chlorophyll fluorescence on bean leaves as a function of net CO_2 uptake when CO_2 concentration is decreased, is

N. Murata (ed.), Research in Photosynthesis, Vol. IV, 211–218.

identical to the same relation when net CO_2 uptake decreases during dehydration of a cut leaf. Furthermore, (ii) the whole chain electron transfer estimated on wilted leaves which have been desiccated slowly (by withholding watering during a couple of weeks) and which do not present a significant CO_2 uptake in normal air, is mainly linked to the reduction of O_2 and still represents about 55% of the maximum capacity (12).

Of course, "non-stomatal effects" eventually occur as a leaf is drying and thus Cc is expected to increase accordingly. As discussed in a review paper (1) those non-stomatal effects are not well identified arising from "few facts and much speculation". Some of those non-stomatal effects could be triggered by the decrease in Cc itself : for instance, during a mild drought (LWD not higher than about 35%) a decline in the activities of extractable nitrate reductase (13) and sucrose phosphate synthase (14) which was reversed when the wilted leaves were exposed to high CO_2 concentrations.

Finally, when looking at the sensitivity of photosynthetic system to drought stress, it is also striking to note the similarity of the relations between photosynthetic capacity (high CO_2 concentration and high light measurements) and leaf water deficit obtained on xero-, meso-and hygrophytes leaves dehydrated either rapidly on the bench or slowly, by withholding plant watering for several days (1,3,8). This similarity strongly suggests that water potential is not a decisive factor to explain the effects of desiccation on photosynthesis : an account has to be taken of the change in water content and thus in cell volume (1,8).

Abscissic acid (ABA) accumulates rapidly in the leaves when a plant is submitted to a drought (15). This accumulation is involved in numerous metabolic changes and contributes at least partly to stomatal closure under such a condition. The ABA induced stomatal closure can be reversed at low temperature (11,16,17). Thus, if ABA plays a role in stomatal closure during a drought stress it is expected (i) that decreasing leaf temperature under mild dehydration (about 30% leaf water deficit) will increase stomatal aperture and (ii) that as a result leaf net CO_2 uptake will increase since in this condition photosynthetic capacity is probably not impaired by water shortage. Such an increase of net photosynthesis by dehydrated leaves at low temperature is also expected because the low CO_2 concentration which are occuring in such a situation will favour the oxygenase activity of the rubisco. We report here results of experiments showing that decreasing temperature of dehydrated leaves does increase stomatal conductance and photosynthetic net CO_2 uptake. These results support the notions that photosynthetic mechanisms are resistant to drought and that Cc is low in a leaf submitted to a mild desiccation.

2. MATERIAL AND METHODS

2.1. The plants were grown in a growth chamber in pots containing an organic soil watered every two days to the field capacity. Photosynthetic photon flux density (PPFD) at the top of the plants was either 220 μmol m^{-2} s^{-1} (Phaseolus vulgaris L., Castanea sativa L.) or 450 μmol m^{-2} s^{-1} (Pisum sativum), photoperiod 16h, air temperature 22° C and relative humidity about 70%. Measurements were performed on the cotyledonary leaves of 15 day old plants (P.vulgaris) or mature leaves of the two other plants. Desiccation of the leaves was always obtained by withholding watering of the plants. A leaf water deficit of about 35% was obtained in 10 days in French bean and C.sativa and in about 2 days in P.vulgaris.

2.2. CO_2 exchange. Measurements of leaf net CO_2 uptake and transpiration were performed using an open system which has already been described (11). Unless otherwise stated the experiments were started after leaf net CO_2 uptake and leaf transpiration reached a steady state rate in air containing 340 ± 10 $\mu l.l^{-1}$ CO_2 under the limiting light of 247 μmol m^{-2} s^{-1} at a leaf temperature of about 25 °C. During the experiments CO_2 and light conditions were the same as during the "equilibration" period. The experiments were carried out either on leaves attached to the plants (drought stress experiments) or on detached leaves with petiole in water or in ABA solution (10^{-4} M in 0.5 % ethanol). When ABA was used the detached leaf was first allowed to reach a steady state net CO_2 uptake in the standard condition described above before ABA was added to the water given to the leaf. Experiments were started after ABA addition when the transpiration rate and leaf temperature were constant.

2.3. Chlorophyll fluorescence measurements. Fluorescence measurements were performed with the PAM chlorophyll fluorometer. The fibre optic system was essentially arranged as in (18). The frequency of modulated light was 1.6 KHz. Saturating pulses (1s) of white light (12500 μmol m^{-2} s^{-1}) were provided by a KL 1500 Schott light source activated by a PAM 103 trigger control unit at intervals of 200 s. Two fluorescence yields were measured : F_s and F_m, where F_s is the steady state fluorescence reached upon continuous illumination and F_m the maximal fluorescence induced by the one second saturating pulse. From these measurements the ratio $\Delta F/F_m$ calculated as $(F_m-F_s)/F_m$ gives a relative measurement of the quantum yield of PS2 electron flow (19).

3. RESULTS

3.1. Modulation of net CO_2 uptake (A) and leaf CO_2 conductance (g_c) by temperature on ABA-treated leaves and dehydrated leaves of French bean. As shown in Fig.1, both g_c and A measured at about 27°C on leaves which had been fed with ABA through the transpiration were very low. Decreasing the temperature of these leaves increased g_c (closed symbol) which was then 7-fold higher at about 13°C than at about 27°C. This effect of low temperature is fully reversible: increasing the temperature of the leaves back to around 27°C caused a stomatal closure. In these experiments vapour pressure deficit (VPD) was maintained constant, though with a wide range of variation (VPD = 1200 ± 400 Pa), despite the changes of temperature. As stomata open, A increased (open symbol) from a relative value close to 0 at about 27°C to 2 at about 13 °C. Fig.2 shows that decreasing the temperature of a wilted leaf at constant VPD, increased both g_c and A. In the example given leaf water deficit (LWD) was about 30% during the experiment. Much as for ABA-treated leaves, this effect of temperature is reversible. The low temperature effect on the opening of stomata and the increasing of A was greater on plants having a LWD 23% (closed symbols) than on those having a LWD of 34% (11).

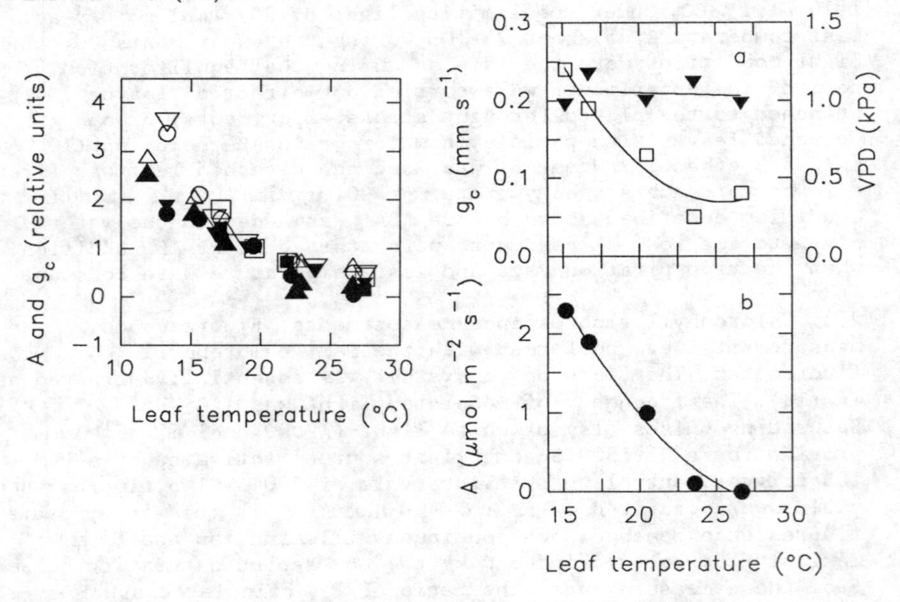

Figure 1 (left). Relations between leaf CO_2 conductance (open symbols), leaf net CO_2 uptake (closed symbols) and leaf temperature. Measurements were performed on cut leaves fed with a 10^{-4}M ABA solution (water containing 0.5% ethanol). The different symbols refer to measurements performed independently on different leaves. Data were normalised to values at 19 °C: leaf CO_2 conductance at 19 °C = 1.48 ± 0.36 mm s^{-1}; leaf net CO_2 uptake at 19 °C =

1.65 ± 0.31 μmol m^{-2} s^{-1}. Measurements on Phaseolus vulgaris.

Figure 2.(right) Relations between a) leaf CO_2 conductance, b) leaf net CO_2 uptake measured on dehydrated leaves (about 32% leaf water deficit and temperature. Measurements were made at constant VPD. Measurements on P.vulgaris.

3.2. Comparison of the effect of temperature on leaves fed with ABA and on wilted leaves (37% LWD); experiments done on French bean. Fig. 3b (close symbol) shows that the optimum temperature for net CO_2 uptake by non-wilted leaves is around 20 °C. Decreasing the temperature of the leaves to 14°C caused about a 25% decline in A. Noteworthy that, as expected from Figs 1 & 2, both in ABA-treated leaves (Fig.3a) and wilted leaves (Fig.3b open symbol), the thermal optimum for leaf net CO_2 shifted to about 14°C. More over, for temperatures below 14°C, in both cases A was very similar to that of the control leaves : for temperatures lower than 14°C leaf photosynthesis is limited by temperature and no longer by water deficit nor by the ABA-induced stomatal closure.

3.3. The above described temperature effect on wilted leaves is also observed on other plants; experiments done on 2 year old seedlings of Castanea sativa. Fig.4 shows the temperature response of g_c and A measured under a limiting photon flux density on a mature leaf of a 2 year old Catanea sativa seedling either well watered (closed symbols) or after dehydration (open symbols; LWD of about 28%) obtained by withholding watering during 10 days. Measurements were done at constant VPD. As in Fig.3b, thermal optimum is about 20°C before dehydration and about 14 °C after dehydration. Below 14 °C, in the dehydrated leaf, A and g_c values were very similar to those measured before desiccation. This effect has also been observed so far in Vigna sinensis L., and Pelargonium zonale L.

3.4. The effect of light intensity and O_2 concentration during the measurements; experiments done using Pisum sativum L. When measurements are done under a PFD of 480μmol m^{-2} s^{-1}. decreasing temperature of a wilted leaf of Pisum sativum did not remove the effect of drought on leaf photosynthesis both in 21% and 2% O_2 nor did it restore stomatal aperture which remained 5- to 7-fold lower than that observed in the control
leaf (data not shown). This is in contrast with the results obtained under a PFD of 170 μmol m^{-2} s^{-1} where the effect of desiccation was removed and leaf conductance nearly restored (data not shown) by lowering leaf temperature to about 10 °C in 21% O_2 and 20 °C in 1% O_2. However in the two light conditions the results were qualitatively similar (lower thermal optimum after desiccation).
Fig.4b and Fig.4d show the variation of $\Delta F/F_m$.

This parameter is a relative measurement of the quantum yield of

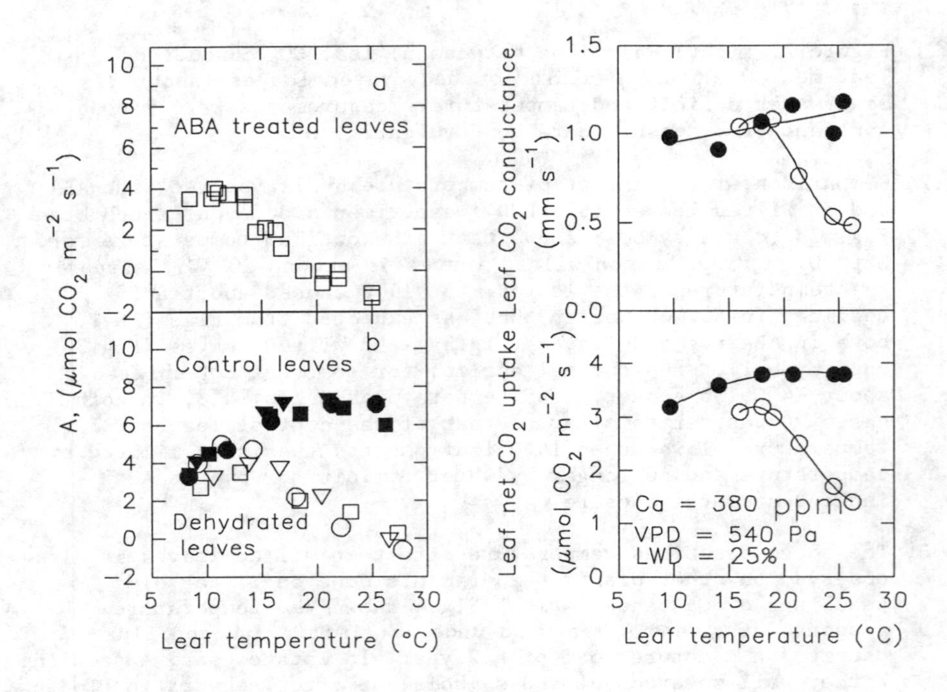

Figure 3.(Left) Relation between leaf net CO_2 uptake measured either on a) ABA-treated leaves (see Fig.1) or b) dehydrated leaves (37% leaf water deficit, open symbols) and temperature. On b) is also shown the thermal response of non-dehydrated leaves (filled symbols). In each condition the different symbols represent measurements performed independently on different leaves. Measurements on P.vulgaris.

Figure 4.(Right) Relations between a) leaf CO_2 conductance, b) leaf net CO_2 uptake and temperature. Closed symbols : non-dehydrated leaf, open symbols : dehydrated leaves (about 29% leaf water deficit). Measurements were made at constant VPD on Castanea sativa.

PS2 photochemistry (19) and can be used to estimate the linear electron flow in intact leaves under divers conditions (11,3) including different temperatures. At constant irradiance $\Delta F/F_m$ is a relative measurement of whole chain electron transfer. Under the two light conditions, whole chain electron transfer estimated on control leaves (closed symbols) decreases regularly as temperature declines being somewhat lower in 2% O_2 in agreement with observations made already made on French bean (11). Under low light, dehydration (open symbols) did not change whole chain electron transfer (Fig.5d) while it was inhibitory under medium light (Fig.5b).

4. DISCUSSION AND CONCLUSION.

The above results show that stomatal conductance can be increased on both ABA-treated leaves and dehydrated leaves of Phaseolus vulgaris when temperature is lowered. This increase is correlated with an increase of Leaf net CO_2 uptake which becomes (even when it is negligible at normal temperature) identical to that of non-treated well hydrated leaves at a temperature around 15°C. As discussed in (17) the nature of the temperature control of the ABA effect on stomatal closure is unknown. However, as a whole the results (i) demonstrate that photosynthetic mechanisms are not impaired by a LWD as high as 30%, (ii) indicate that stomatal closure plays the main role in the inhibition of leaf photosynthesis during dehydration (compare the response of ABA-treated leaves and dehydrated leaves Fig.3) and (iii)

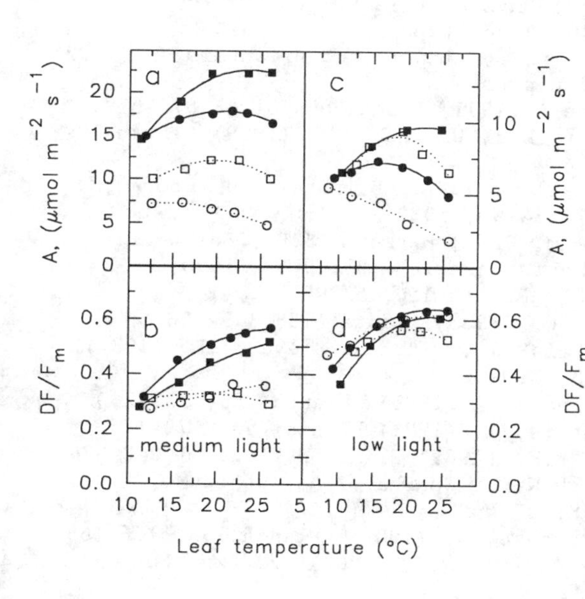

Figure 5. Relation between leaf CO_2 uptake and leaf temperature measured either in 21% O_2 (circles) or in 2% O_2 (square) in control (filled symbols) or dehydrated (open symbols) leaves under a) a medium light or c) a low light (Material and Method). Relation between quantum yield of PS2 photochemistry ($\Delta F/F_m$) and leaf temperature. Conditions during measurements and symbols were the same as above. b)medium ligh d)low light. Vpd was maintained at 600 ±50 Pa. Measurements done on Pisum sativum.

strongly suggest that Cc is low during a mild drought. This effect of low temperature on net photosynthesis of dehydrated leaves is also described here on other C3 plants. Fig.5 shows that this response can be modulated by light intensity. At 10°C in 21% O_2 and 1% O_2 A remains below the value measured at the same temperature on control leaves; this is in contrast to what is observed under low light. However the response in the two light conditions is qualitatively similar, and the strong effect of O_2 on A which is observed on dehydrated leaves show that drought in these conditions induces a low Cc. Under low light, whole chain electron transfer is hardly changed by desiccation (notably in the 21% O_2 condition) : PCR and PCO cycle reactions are electron transport limited and the decrease in Cc brought about by somatal closure and the decrease in O_2 concentration as well result only in a change in the distribution between the PCR and PCO cycles reactions. It is striking to note under the medium light that the estimations of whole chain electron transfer at around 10 °C are the same. This would mean that there is, even at this temperature, a substantial electron flow to O_2 in the dehydrated leaf maintained in 2% O_2. At higher temperature in dehydrated leaves this electron flow would be limited by Cc (because as noted above g_c remains low).

REFERENCES

1 Kaiser, W.M. (1987) Physiol. Plant. 71, 142-149
2 Chaves,M.M. (1991) J. of Exp. Bot. 42, 1-16
3 Cornic,G.,Ghashghaie,J.,Genty,B. and Briantais,J. (1992) Photosynthetica (in press).
4 Graziani,Y.,Livine,A.(1971) Plant Physiol.48,575-579
5 Schwab, K.B., Schreiber, U., Heber, U.(1989) Planta 177, 217-227
6 Cornic,G., Le Gouallec, J.-L., Briantais, J.,Hodges,M. (1989) Planta. 177,84-90, 1989
7 Frederik, J.R., Alm, D.M., Hesketh, J.D., Below, F.E. (1990) Photosynthesis Research. 25:49-57, 1990.
8 Kaiser, W.M.(1982) Planta 154, 538-545
9 Dietz,K-J., Heber,U. (1983) Planta. 158,349-356
10 Genty, B., Briantais, J., Viera Da Silva, J.B. (1987) Plant Physiol. 83, 360-364.
11 Cornic,G., Ghashghaie,J. (1991) Planta 185, 255-260
12 Cornic,G., Briantais, J. (1991) Planta 183, 178-184
13 Kaiser,W., Förster,K. (1989) Plant physiol. 91,970-974
14 Vassey,T.L., Quick,W.P., Sharkey,T.D., Stitt,M. (1991) Physiol. Plant. 81,37-44
15 Pierce, M. and Raschke, K. (1981) Planta 153, 156-165
16 Rodriguez, J.L., Davies, W.J. (1982) J. Exp. Bot. 33,977-987
17 Ward,D.A. Lawlor,D.W. (1990) J.Exp.Bot. 41,309-314
18 Dietz, K.J., Shreiber, U., Heber, U. (1985) Planta 166,219-226
19 Genty, B., Briantais, J., Baker, N.R. (1989) Biochim. Biophys. Acta. 990,87-92.

SALT TOLERANCE IN HIGHER PLANTS: THE IDENTIFICATION OF THE VACUOLAR Na^+/H^+ ANTIPORT.

Bronwyn J. Barkla and Eduardo Blumwald
Department of Botany, University of Toronto,
25 Willcocks St., Toronto, Ontario, Canada M5S 3B2.

1. INTRODUCTION

The transport of Na^+ across the tonoplast, and its compartmentalization into the vacuoles of halophytes and salt tolerant glycophytes is an important mechanism for averting the damaging effects of Na^+ on key biochemical processes in the cytosol [1]. In these plants, the vacuolar Na^+ accumulation is mediated by a Na^+/H^+ antiport that uses the pH gradient generated by electrogenic H^+-pumps to couple the active (uphill) accumulation of Na^+ with the passive (downhill) efflux of H^+ [2]. In plants the operation of a vacuolar Na^+/H^+ antiport has been reported in isolated tonoplast vesicles and intact vacuoles of sugar beet [3], and barley [4]. Although the mammalian protein counterpart, the renal Na^+/H^+ exchanger, has been extensively characterized biochemically and recently several isoforms have been cloned and expressed [5], little progress has been made towards identification of the plant antiport despite the increasing evidence supporting its existence. In this paper we demonstrate that the presence of amiloride (an inhibitor of the antiport [3]), or an increase in the NaCl concentration, in the cell suspension growth media resulted in the enhanced synthesis of a 170 kDa polypeptide which correlated with an increased Na^+/H^+ activity. A 170 kDa polypeptide was also previously shown to specifically incorporate $[H^3]$-MIA, an amiloride analogue. Furthermore, incubation of tonoplast membranes with antibodies raised against this 170 kDa polypeptide resulted in total inhibition of the antiport activity. These observations indicate that the 170 kDa polypeptide is associated with the vacuolar Na^+/H^+ antiport.

2. METHOD AND MATERIALS

2.1 Plant Material: Cell suspension cultures of sugar beet were grown as described previously [6].

N. Murata (ed.), Research in Photosynthesis, Vol. IV, 219–226.

2.2 Isolation of Tonoplast Vesicles and Fluorescence Assays: Purified tonoplast vesicles were prepared by homogenization of sugar beet cell suspensions followed by density gradient fractionation [3]. The fluorescence quenching of acridine orange was used to monitor the dissipation of inside-acidic pH gradients across tonoplast vesicles as previously outlined [3].

2.3 SDS and Two Dimensional Gel Electrophoresis: Protein samples from purified tonoplast were prepared as previously described, and separated by SDS-PAGE and two dimensional electrophoresis [7].

2.4 Antigen and Antiserum Preparation: The 170 kDa was excised from the preparative gels and the protein was electro-eluted, dialyzed and concentrated. The antigen was then emulsified with an equal volume of Freund's complete or incomplete adjuvant and a female, 6-8 week old BALB/c mouse was inoculated as outlined previously [7].

2.5 Western Immunoblotting: Following SDS-PAGE separation tonoplast proteins were electro-blotted onto a nitrocellulose membrane and screened with the 170 kDa antiserum as previously described [7].

2.6 Metabolic Labeling of Tonoplast Proteins: Twenty-four hours prior to labeling, sugar beet cells (25g fresh weight) were used to inoculate fresh medium. Cells grown in MS medium were transferred to MS medium with or without 100 mM NaCl, and cells grown in MS medium in the presence of 100 mM NaCl were transferred to similar medium with the addition of 1 mM amiloride. Following treatment 0.9 μCi of [^{35}S]-methionine was added for 3 hrs and tonoplast proteins were then isolated as described above.

3. RESULTS AND DISCUSSION

3.1 The effect of amiloride and several of its analogues on the Na^+/H^+ antiport was studied [8] in order to find a high affinity radiolabeled probe that could be used for the identification of the antiport subunit(s). The binding of a radiolabeled 5-amino substituted amiloride analogue ([^{3}H]-N^5-methyl-N^5-isobutylamiloride, MIA) to tonoplast proteins upon irradiation was characterized [9]. Tonoplast binding studies using this analogue revealed a high-affinity binding component with a K_d of 1.3 μM which was closely related to the constant of inhibition of the antiport for MIA (2.5 μM [9]), suggesting that this high-affinity component could represent a class of sites associated with the Na^+/H^+ antiport. Incubation of tonoplast with increasing concentrations (10 μM to 1 mM) of [^{3}H]-MIA in the presence or absence of 1 mM amiloride revealed two sets of photolabeled polypeptides which differed in their affinities for amiloride and MIA. A set of polypeptides of molecular masses 170, 38 and 35 kDa with a higher affinity for MIA than for amiloride could be associated with the Na^+/H^+ antiport. While a second set of polypeptides of molecular masses 223, 123, and 32 kDa could be associated with the vacuolar cation channel. Patch-clamp studies in isolated vacuoles from sugar beet cells demonstrated the higher affinity of the channel for amiloride than for MIA (730 nM, 2.5 μM, respectively, [10]).

3.2 In order to confirm the association of the polypeptides labeled by [^{3}H]-MIA, with the vacuolar Na^+/H^+ antiport, amiloride was used to challenge the sugar beet cell suspension cultures grown in the presence of 100 mM NaCl. If the activity of the antiport was inhibited by the presence of amiloride in the growth medium, the cells would be unable to survive the high-salt growth conditions unless they were able to produce more antiport molecules or alter the turnover rate of the antiport. If more antiport molecules were produced, a quantitative increase of this protein would be expected.

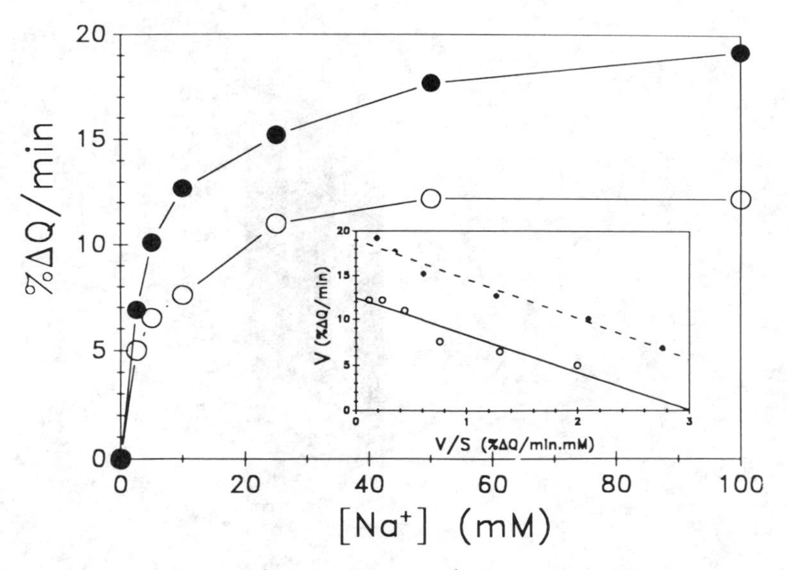

FIGURE 1. Initial rates of Na^+-dependent H^+ flux in isolated tonoplast vesicles from sugar beet cell suspensions. A pH gradient (acidic inside) was generated by activation of the H^+-ATPase. When a steady-state pH gradient was obtained, the H^+-ATPase was stopped and Na^+ (2.5-100 mM) was added and the initial rate of fluorescence recovery (%ΔQ/min, where Q stands for quench) was measured. Tonoplast vesicles were from cell suspensions grown with 100 mM NaCl in the presence (●) or absence (○) of 1 mM amiloride. (*Inset*) Eadie-Hofstee plot of the data [V, velocity (% Q/min); S, substrate concentration (Na^+, mM)].

Although no other significant differences were detected between control and amiloride-grown cells, cells grown in the presence of amiloride displayed an increased vacuolar Na^+/H^+ antiport activity (Fig. 1).The kinetic data indicated that the affinity of the antiport for Na^+ did not change, but the rates for maximal velocity of the reaction were higher (Fig. 1). An increase in V_{max} with no change in apparent K_m suggested either the addition of more antiport molecules to the tonoplast in response to amiloride in the growth medium or an increase in the turnover rate of exchange.
To distinguish and compare the independent effects of NaCl and amiloride on newly synthesized tonoplast proteins, membranes were prepared from sugar beet cells that were metabolically labeled with [^{35}S]methionine and the tonoplast proteins were isolated and resolved by SDS-PAGE as described in Material and Methods (Fig. 2).

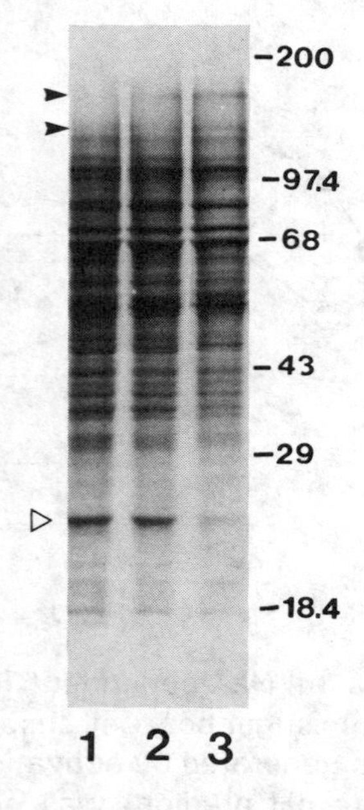

FIGURE 2. Autoradiogram of tonoplast proteins isolated from sugar beet cell suspensions metabolically labeled with [^{35}S]-methionine. Cells grown in MS medium were transferred to MS medium without (*lane 1*) or with (*lane 2*) 100 mM NaCl for 24 hrs prior to adding label. Cells grown in MS medium with 100 mM NaCl were transferred to MS medium with 100 mM NaCl and 1 mM amiloride prior to labeling (*lane 3*).

Neither the addition of salt nor the addition of amiloride to the growth medium resulted in *de novo* protein synthesis, however several polypeptides were seen to show either an increase or decrease in labeling. Notably, two polypeptides of 170 kDa and 130 kDa showed increased labeling when cells were exposed to 100 mM NaCl, and labeling increased even further when the cells were exposed to amiloride.The similarity in molecular masses of the 170 kDa tonoplast polypeptide identified by specific photolabeling [9] and by [^{35}S]methionine *in vivo* labeling (Fig. 2) indicates that the same polypeptide whose synthesis was enhanced by salt and amiloride was also specifically photolabeled by the amiloride analogue [^{3}H]MIA. These results suggest the association of the 170 kDa polypeptide with the vacuolar Na^+/H^+ antiport.

3.3 Polyclonal antibodies to the 170 kDa sugar beet tonoplast polypeptide were produced in mice by immunization with protein electroeluted from bands excised from SDS gels. Western blot analyses of two-dimensional PAGE of tonoplast proteins showed the reactivity of a single 170 kDa polypeptide with a pI = 6.2 (Fig. 3). No reactivity was detected on purified plasma membranes, thus suggesting that the antiport is specifically associated with the tonoplast (not shown).

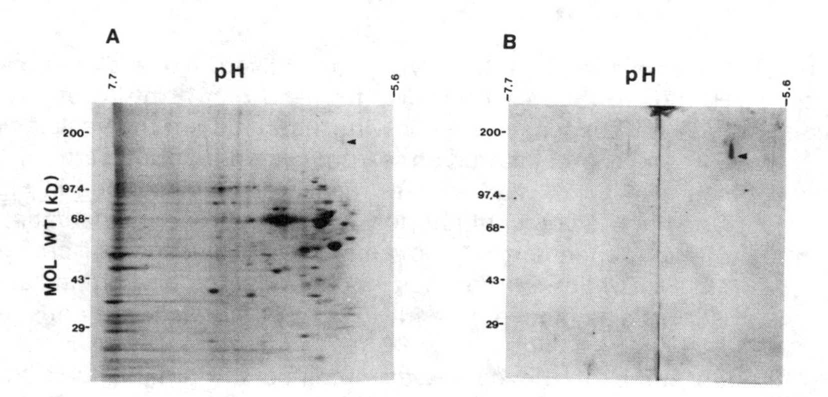

FIGURE 3. Western blot analysis using the antiserum directed against the 170 kDa polypeptide. (*A*) Coomassie blue-stained gel. (*B*) Immunoblot using a 1:2000 dilution of the antiserum. The arrowhead indicates the location of the 170 kDa polypeptide.

Additional evidence that the 170 kDa polypeptide is associated with the vacuolar Na^+/H^+ antiport is based on the effects of incubation of tonoplast with the antibodies to the 170 kDa polypeptide. Fig. 4 shows the IgG-dependent inhibition of the Na^+-dependent H^+ fluxes in purified tonoplast vesicles. A dilution of 1:750 rendered an almost total inhibition of the antiport activity, while mouse non-immune serum showed no effect.

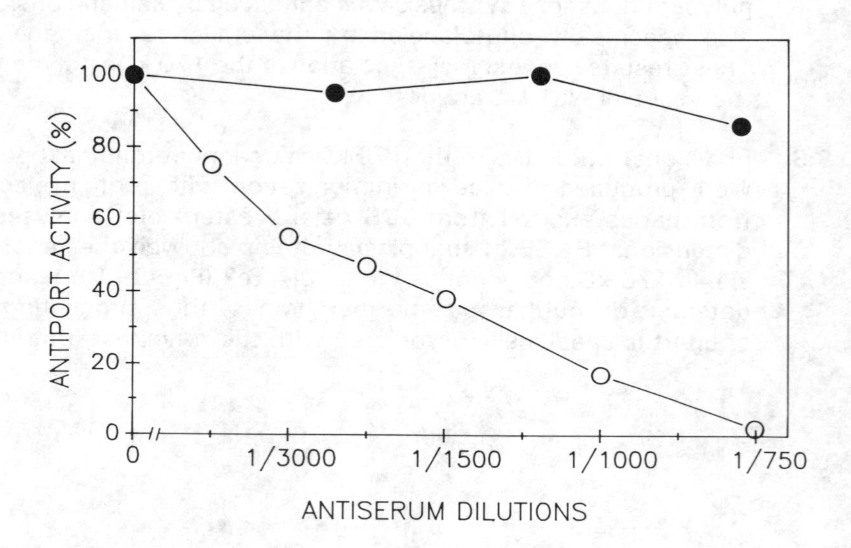

FIGURE 4. Effect of the 170 kDa polypeptide antiserum on Na^+-dependent H^+ flux in tonoplast vesicles from 100 mM NaCl grown sugar beet cell suspensions. Following incubation of the vesicles with $(NH_4)_2SO_4$-precipitated antiserum or non-immune serum for 20 min at 4°C, H^+ fluxes were measured as described in Fig. 1. One hundred percent antiport activity represents the initial rate of Na^+-dependent H^+ movement in the absence of antiserum (11 % Q/min). (●) Vesicles incubated with non-immune serum; (○) vesicles incubated with $(NH_4)_2SO_4$-precipitated antiserum.

3.4 Although some of the data was obtained after many cell culture growth cycles, the effect on protein synthesis was seen 24 hours after exposure to amiloride, before cell division occurred [6]. This indicates that the observed effects do not represent a selection of genetic variants. We have shown previously that the tonoplast antiport activity of sugar beet cells was enhanced by increasing NaCl concentrations in the growth medium, and the cells maintained a constitutive level even in the absence of NaCl [6]. Halophytes grown in the absence of NaCl are known to retain some characteristics related to salt tolerance. We tested the constitutive and inducible levels of the vacuolar Na^+/H^+ antiport protein and correlated those levels with the antiport activity at increasing NaCl concentrations in the growth medium (Fig. 5).

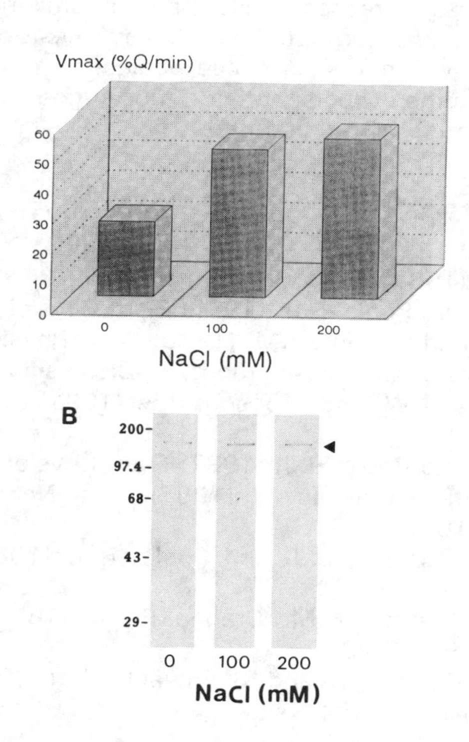

FIGURE 5. Correlation between salinity in the growth medium, maximal velocity (V_{max}), Na^+/H^+ exchange and synthesis of the 170 kDa polypeptide. Cells were grown in the absence and presence of 100 and 200 mM NaCl. Na^+-dependent H^+ fluxes and Western blots of tonoplast proteins were performed as described above. (A) V_{max} (%Q/min); (B) Western blots.

The exposure of the cells to 100 mM NaCl resulted in an increased antiport activity of about twice the control value. A comparable increase in antiport protein could be detected by Western blots. Exposure of the cells to 200 mM NaCl did not result in either a significant increase in activity or protein level. The retention of a constitutive level of the vacuolar Na^+/H^+ antiport in the absence of NaCl may be related to the general pattern observed in halophytes. Although our findings suggest that the growth of sugar beet in increasing NaCl concentrations induced an increased antiport activity that was correlated with the increased synthesis of antiport molecules, an additional effect on the turnover rate of the antiport cannot be ruled out and remains to be investigated.
In conclusion, the vacuolar Na^+/H^+ antiport activity of sugar beet cell suspensions was increased by NaCl and by amiloride. the increased antiport activity was correlated with the synthesis of a tonoplast 170 kDa polypeptide. Antibodies raised against this polypeptide almost totally inhibited the vacuolar activity, thus suggesting the association of this polypeptide with the antiport.

REFERENCES

1 Flowers, T.J., Troke, P.F. and Yeo, A.R. (1977) Annu. Rev. Plant. Physiol. 28,29-121.
2 Blumwald, E. (1987). Physiol. Plant. 69,731-734.
3 Blumwald, E. and Poole, R.J. (1985) Plant Physiol. 78,163-167.
4 Garbarino, J. and Dupont, F.M. (1988) Plant Physiol. 86,231-236.
5 Igarashi, P., Reilly, R.F., Hildebrandt, F., Biemesderfer, D., Reboucas, N.A., Slayman, C.W. and Aronson, P.S. (1991) Kidney Int. 40,S84-S89.
6 Blumwald, E. and Poole, R.J. (1987) Plant Physiol 83,884-887.
7 Barkla, B.J. and Blumwald, E. (1991) Proc. Natl. Acad. Sci. USA 88,11177-11181.
8 Blumwald, E., Cragoe, E.J. and Poole, R.J. (1987) Plant Physiol. 85,30-33.
9 Barkla, B.J., Charuk, J.H.M., Cragoe, E.J. and Blumwald, E. (1990) Plant Physiol. 93,924-930.
10 Pantoja, O., Dainty, J. and Blumwald, E. (1990) Plant Physiol. 94,1788-1794.

CHARACTERIZATION OF GENES RESPONSIVE TO DESICCATION AND THEIR EXPRESSION IN *ARABIDOPSIS THALIANA*

Kazuo Shinozaki, Kazuko Yamaguchi-Shinozaki, Tomohiro Kiyosue, Toshisuke Iwasaki and Satomi Urao.
Laboratory of Plant Molecular Biology, Tsukuba Life Science Center, The Institute of Physical and Chemical Research (RIKEN), 3-1-1 Koyadai, Tsukuba, Ibaraki 305, JAPAN

1. INTRODUCTION

Plants respond to conditions of drought or water deficit by a number of physiological and developmental changes. A number of genes that respond to desiccation at the transcriptional level have been described recently (1, 2). Most of the genes that have been studied to date are also induced by abscisic acid (ABA; 2). Thus, it appears that desiccation triggers the production of ABA, which, in turn, induces various genes. However, several genes that are induced by desiccation are not induced by ABA (3), which indicates the existence of ABA-independent as well as ABA-responsive signal transduction cascades between the initial signal of a water deficit and the expression of specific genes.

In order to learn more about the signal-transduction pathways between desiccation and gene expression, we have cloned and characterized genes that respond to desiccation in *Arabidopsis thaliana*. We have identified nine independent cDNAs and have designated them *r*esponsive to *d*esiccation (RD clones; 4). Northern blot analysis has revealed broad variations in the timing of induction of RD genes and has shown that two of these genes respond to ABA while three do not (4). Transcription of gene(s) that hybridize to RD29 cDNA is induced very rapidly and at a high rate 20 min after the start of desiccation, and this transcription is followed by a second induction phase which begins after about 3 h (4). Two genomic clones corresponding to the RD29 cDNA (*rd29*A and *rd29*B) were isolated and the control of the transcription of the genes was analyzed (5). In the present study we analyzed the expression of *rd29*A in transgenic *Arabidopsis* and tobacco plants that were exposed to desiccation, cold, high-salt conditions and ABA by use of fusions between the 5' flanking region of *rd29*A and the β-glucuronidase (GUS) reporter gene. We found that the *rd29*A promoter contains *cis*-acting elements that are involved in the desiccation-induced expression of this gene. We describe the induction of *rd29*A by desiccation that occurs via at least two signal-transduction pathways: an ABA-independent and an ABA-responsive pathway.

2. RESULTS AND DISCUSSION

2.1 Isolation of cDNA clones corresponding to genes induced by desiccation

We constructed a cDNA library from the poly(A)$^+$ RNA purified from plants that had been desiccated for 10 h using the λgt11 vector. This library was differentially screened using cDNA prepared from poly(A)$^+$ RNA isolated from hydrated plants (control cDNA) and cDNA prepared from poly(A)$^+$ RNA isolated from desiccated plants (dry cDNA). Fifteen plaques produced a stronger hybridization signal with [^{32}P]-labelled dry cDNA. On the basis of hybridization analyses, these 15 cDNA clones were divided into 9 RD (responsive to desiccation) groups (4). The nucleotide sequences of the inserts in all nine clones have been determined. A search was made in a protein sequence database, SWISS PROT, for homologies to these 9 sequences. The results of the homology search are summarized in Table 1.

N. Murata (ed.), Research in Photosynthesis, Vol. IV, 227–230.

We analyzed the induction of expression of RD genes by water deficiency using Northern hybridization. The timing of the accumulation of their mRNAs varies between RD genes, suggesting that there are several signal transduction pathways involved in the induction of these genes (4).

TABLE 1. Characterization of the structure and expression of RD clones.

Gene	Homology	Transcript size (kb)	ABA*
RD28	water channel protein	1.4	-
RD19	thiol protease	1.2	-
RD21	thiol protease	1.5	-
RD22	unidentified seed protein	1.9	+
RD29	*lti*140	2.4	+
RD17	*rab*, dehydrin	1.3	+
RD20		1.1	+
RD26		1.5	+
RD2		1.4	+

*: Genes that are induced by ABA (+) or not induced by ABA (-)

2.2 Northern analysis of the expression of RD29 mRNA

RD29 is induced very rapidly and strongly by desiccation. This induction is a two-phase process with peak levels of the transcript being apparent 1 and 10 h after the start of desiccation (4). However, RD29 mRNA was first detected 2 h after plants had been sprayed with ABA (5). Differences in the time course of induction of RD29 by desiccation and ABA suggest that the first rapid induction of transcription caused by desiccation is not mediated by endogenous ABA. Measurements of levels of endogenous ABA induced by water deficiency in *Arabidopsis* revealed that ABA is detectable 2 h after desiccation and reaches a maximum level at 10 h, providing further evidence that ABA is not responsible for the initial rapid induction of RD29. RD29 was also induced by high-salt conditions within 20 min after the initiation of such treatment. When we transferred plants from agar plates to water, rather than a solution of NaCl, as controls, we also detected rapid expression of RD29. Therefore, it appears that a change in osmotic pressure also triggers rapid induction of RD29. The level of RD29 mRNA induced by desiccation was almost the same in the *aba*-1 and *abi*-1 mutants of *Arabidopsis* (ABA-deficient and ABA-insensitive mutants, respectively) as that in the wild type. By contrast, the level of mRNA induced by application of ABA was considerably lower in *abi*-1 than in the wild type or in *aba*-1 (5). These results suggest that an ABA-independent, as well as an ABA-responsive, signal-transduction pathway exists to link desiccation to the second phase of expression of RD29.

RD29 is induced by cold as well as by desiccation and high-salt conditions and have sequence similarity with cold-inducible *lti*140. The mRNA of *lti*140 accumulates rapidly when plants are exposed to low temperature or water stress or are treated with ABA (6). Although *lti*140 is induced by exogenous ABA and desiccation stress, induction of this gene by low temperature is independent of ABA. Despite the great difference in size between *lti*140 and RD29, they have very similar patterns of induction in response to environmental stress and treatment with ABA.

2. 3 Sequence analysis of two genes corresponding to RD29 and their putative translation products

Genomic Southern analysis revealed that there are several genes for RD29 on *Arabidopsis* genome (5). The RD29 genes described here, *rd29*B and *rd29*A, are located in tandem, in that order, in an 8-kbp region of the *Arabidopsis* genome (Fig. 1). Both the *rd29* genes contain three introns at identical positions. The putative proteins which correspond to *rd29*A and *rd29*B, RD29A and RD29B, respectively, are extremely hydrophilic and contain only one cystein residue, which makes the RD29 proteins similar in structure to the LEA (Late Embryogenesis Abundant) proteins (7). However, the *rd29* mRNA in desiccated seeds was considerably less abundant than in fully hydrated vegetative and flower tissues.

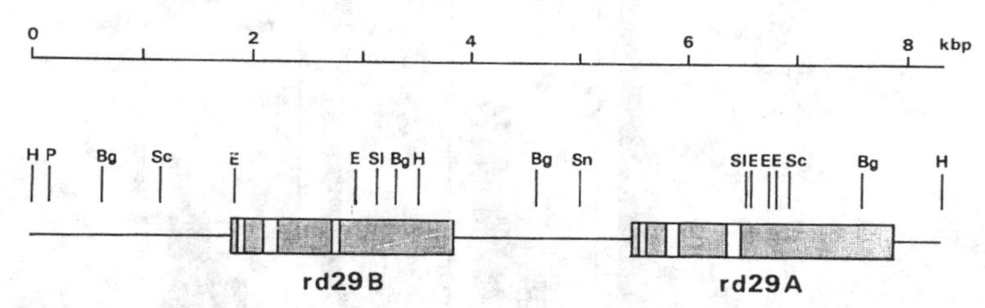

Figure 1. Structure of two genes for *rd29*A and *rd29*B. The shaded and open boxes indicate exons and introns, respectively. Restriction sites are abbreviated as H (*Hind*III), P (*Pst*I), Bg (*Bgl*II), Sc (*Sac*I), E (*Eco*RI), Sl (*Sal*I), and Sn (*Sna*BI).

2.4. Analysis of a *rd*29A promoter-GUS fusion gene induced by desiccation, cold, high salt conditions and ABA treatment in transgenic plants

The gene corresponding to the RD29 cDNA, *rd29*A, is induced within 20 min of the start of desiccation, while *rd29*B is induced 3 h after desiccation has been initiated (5). However, the rapid induction of *rd29*A is not observed after treatment with ABA. These observations suggest that the *rd29*A promoter region has at least two independent *cis*-acting elements, one that is responsive to changes in osmotic potential and is independent of ABA, and another that, perhaps, is involved in ABA-responsive gene expression. The 1640-bp spacer region between *rd29*B and *rd29*A is thought to contain *cis*-acting elements responsible for the induction of *rd29*A by environmental stress and ABA. We tested for the involvement of *cis*-acting elements in the desiccation-responsive expression of *rd29*A by transforming *Arabidopsis* and tobacco with a GUS fusion construct that contained the *rd29*A promoter (Fig. 2A). Significant induction of GUS activity by desiccation, cold and change in osmotic potential were driven by the region upstream of *rd29*A (Fig. 2B). GUS activity was also induced by treatment with exogenous ABA. The time course of induction of GUS coincided with expression of *rd29*A, as determined by Northern blot hybridization, indicating that the promoter region of *rd29*A is sufficient to induce ABA-independent as well as ABA-responsive expression of *rd29*A (5). These results indicate that the induction of *rd29*A by desiccation occurs at the transcriptional level and is not due to increased stability of *rd29* mRNA.

Histochemical analysis of expression of the *rd29*A/GUS fusion gene revealed that GUS activity driven by the *rd29*A promoter was induced by desiccation in almost all the organs and tissues of transgenic *Arabidopsis* rosettes, indicating that the *rd29*A promoter region can function in almost every tissue in rosettes that are exposed to osmotic stress (5). In fully hydrated rosette plants, weak expression of GUS activity was found in several regions, such as trichomes and the major veins of cotyledons. It is not yet clear whether the spatial distribution of the expression of the fusion gene is due to tissue-specific expression or to sensitivity of particular tissues to osmotic stress.

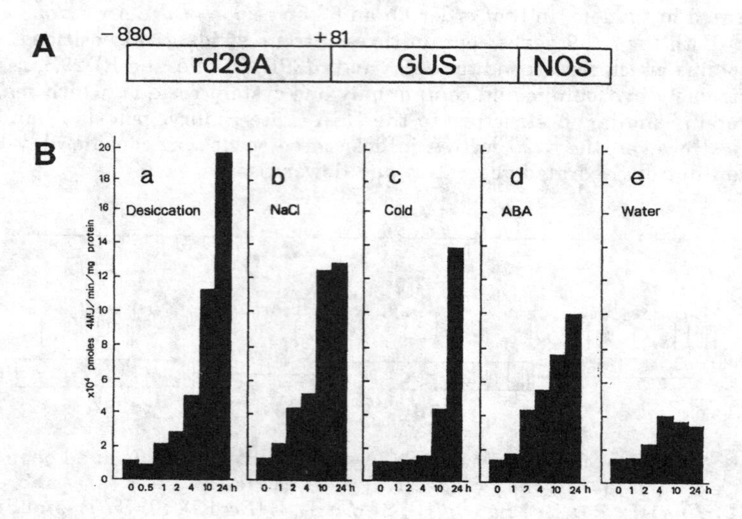

Figure 2. Induction of GUS activity in transgenic *Arabidopsis* plants after exposure to desiccation, cold, salt stress or ABA.
(A) Structure of the *rd29*A/GUS fusion construct. A 961-bp fragment of the *rd29*A promoter region (-880 to +81) was fused to the coding region of the GUS reporter gene.
(B) Average GUS activities in transgenic *Arabidopsis* rosettes exposed to desiccation (a), high-salt condition (b), cold (c), 100 μM ABA (d), or water (e). Numbers on the abscissa indicate the duration of treatment in hours. GUS activity was measured in ten independently obtained transgenic plants.

Acknowledgements. This work was supported by the Special Coordination Fund of the Science and Technology Agency and a Grant-In-Aid from the Ministry of Education, Science and Culture of Japan to K. S.

REFERENCES

1. Skriver, K. and Mundy, J. (1990) Plant Cell 2: 502-512
2. Bray, E.A. (1991) in Abscisic Acid; Physiology and Biochemistry (Davies, W.J. and Jones H.G. eds.), Bios Scientific Publishers, Oxford, pp. 81-98
3. Guerrero, F.D., Jones, J.T. and Mullet, J.E. (1990) Plant Mol. Biol. 15: 11-26
4. Yamaguchi-Shinozaki, K., Koizumi, M., Urao, S. and Shinozaki, K. (1992) Plant Cell Physiol 33: 217-224
5. Yamaguchi-Shinozaki, K. and Shinozaki, K. (1992) Mol. Genet. Genet. in press.
6. Nordin, K., Heino, P. and Palva, E.T. (1991) Plant Mol. Biol. 16: 1061-1071
7. Baker, J., Steele, C. and Dure III, L. (1988) Plant Mol.Biol. 11: 277-291

SELECTION AND CHARACTERIZATION OF STRESS-TOLERANT CULTURED GREEN CELLS OF TOBACCO

FUMIHIKO SATO, KEN-ICHI MUROTA, SATOMI TAKEDA and YASUYUKI YAMADA,
Department of Agricultural Chemistry, Kyoto University, Kyoto 606-01, Japan

1. INTRODUCTION

Cultured green cells of higher plants provide a unique system for photosynthetic research on the cellular basis. Especially, photoautotrophic(PA) cell lines are useful because these cells have developed chloroplasts with relatively high photosynthetic activity even in the presence of organic carbon source and can grow in the light without any addition of organic carbon sources (1, 2). Usefulness of PA tobacco cells have been proven for the investigation of photosynthesis-promoting compounds like choline analogs (3) as well as for the screening of potent herbicidal compounds(2, 4) and selection of herbicide resistant cells (5). Here, We report the cellular responses of PA cells on several environmental stresses, i.e. high salt, sulfite, active oxygen generated by paraquat (methylviologen) and high temperature. Stress tolerant cells were also established to identify specific adaptive responses to stresses on cellular basis, while more complex multicellular processes or mechanisms involving highly specialized cells might be missed.

2. MATERIALS and METHODS

In these experiments, PA tobacco (*Nicotiana tabacum* L. cv Samsun NN) cells were maintained in Linsmaier-Skoog liquid medium containing 10μM naphthaleneacetic acid and 1μM kinetin with 3% sucrose, i.e., under photomixotrophic condition in the light (ca 100μE/m^2/s) at 25±2°C (1). Cells were subcultured every two weeks. Tobacco seedlings grown aseptically were used in some experiments after ca 2 weeks of germination.

Effects of NaCl, sulfite, paraquat and high temperature (55°C) were evaluated by the determination of the increase in fresh weight of cultured cells and seedlings or the chlorophyll content on fresh weight basis. Chlorophyll was extracted with 80% (v/v) acetone and the content was determined spectrophotometrically(6).

Stress tolerant cells were selected by the repeated subculture of cells under the lethal conditions; 0.2M NaCl, 50mM sulfite or 3-10μM paraquat.

Enzymes were extracted in 200mM Tris-HCl buffer (pH 7.8) containing 20mM mercaptoethanol with a mortar and pestle with small amounts of polyclarAT and sea sands. After the centrifugation at 15,000xg for 30min, the supernatant was desalted with PD-10 column and used for enzyme assay. Superoxide dismutase (SOD) activity was determined using SOD-test Wako.

N. Murata (ed.), Research in Photosynthesis, Vol. IV, 231–234.

Ascorbate peroxidase (AsA-POD) activity was determined according to Gerbling et al.(7). Peroxidase (POD) activity was determined using guaiacol as substrate (8). Protein determinations were according to Bradford (9) with BSA as a standard.

3. RESULTS AND DISCUSSION

3.1. Cellular responses of cultured green cells to NaCl, sulfite, paraquat (active oxygen) and high temperature

The responses of cultured cells to NaCl, sulfite, paraquat and high temperature were compared with those of seedlings. Fig.1A-D clearly showed that cultured cells and seedlings responded to stresses in similar manner. Addition of 0.1M NaCl in medium inhibited the growth by 20-50% and 0.2M NaCl almost completely inhibited the growth of both cultured cells and seedlings. Addition of sulfite induced the bleaching of chlorophyll at 20mM. In the presence of 50mM sulfite, most cultured cells and all seedlings were bleached and died. Paraquat induced the photobleaching of chlorophyll at 0.3-1μM. Addition of 3 μM paraquat bleached cells completely. Evaluation of the effect of high temperature was difficult, because the results fluctuated. But, it was commonly observed that the incubation of cultured cells or seedlings at 55°C over 90min was sufficient to kill the cells completely.

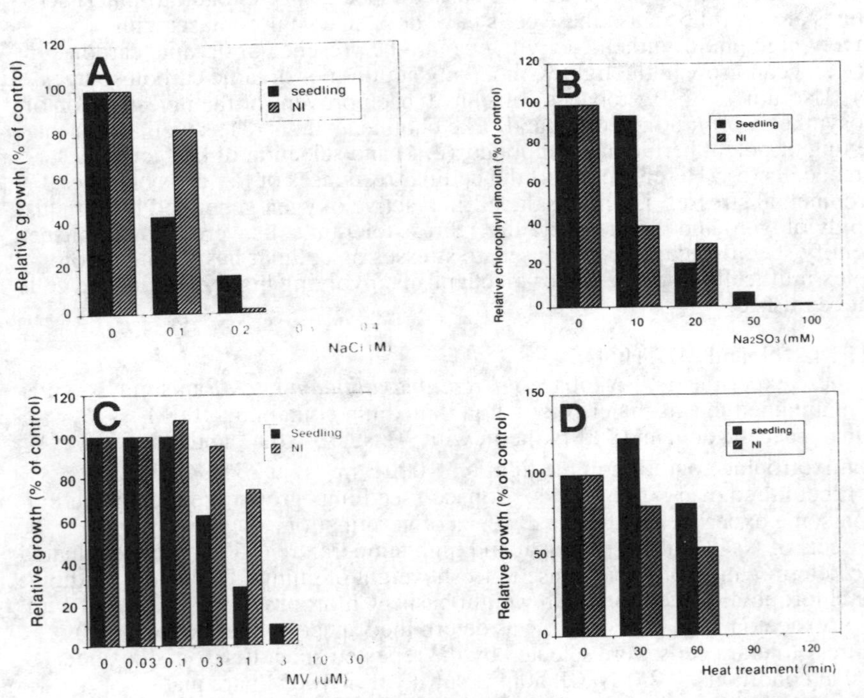

Fig. 1 Cellular responses of cultured green tobacco cells (NI) and seedlings to NaCl (A), sulfite (Na_2SO_3; B), paraquat (MV; C) and high temperature (55°C; D)

3.2 Selection of stress tolerant cells

By the repeated subculture, cell lines which can grow under the lethal stress condition, i.e., 0.2M NaCl, 50mM sulfite, 100μM paraquat were established. However, the tolerant cells which can grow at 55°C over 90min was not established. To examine the growth characteristics of tolerant cells, the cross-tolerance of selected cells were examined. Fig. 2 A-D indicated that the tolerance of each selected cell lines were rather specific to each stresses to which these cells were selected, while sulfite tolerant cells showed some cross-tolerance to 0.2M NaCl, and paraquat tolerant cells were tolerant to 50mM sulfite and to high temperature in some extent. Cross-tolerance of sulfite tolerant cells to high NaCl would be brought by the adaptation of cell to high concentration (50mM) of salt (sulfite). The cross-tolerance of paraquat tolerant cells to sulfite and high temperature suggests that the generation of active-oxygen and its scavenging systems would be involved in the adaptation in sulfite-stress and high temperature, while they are not sufficient for the higher dose of stresses.

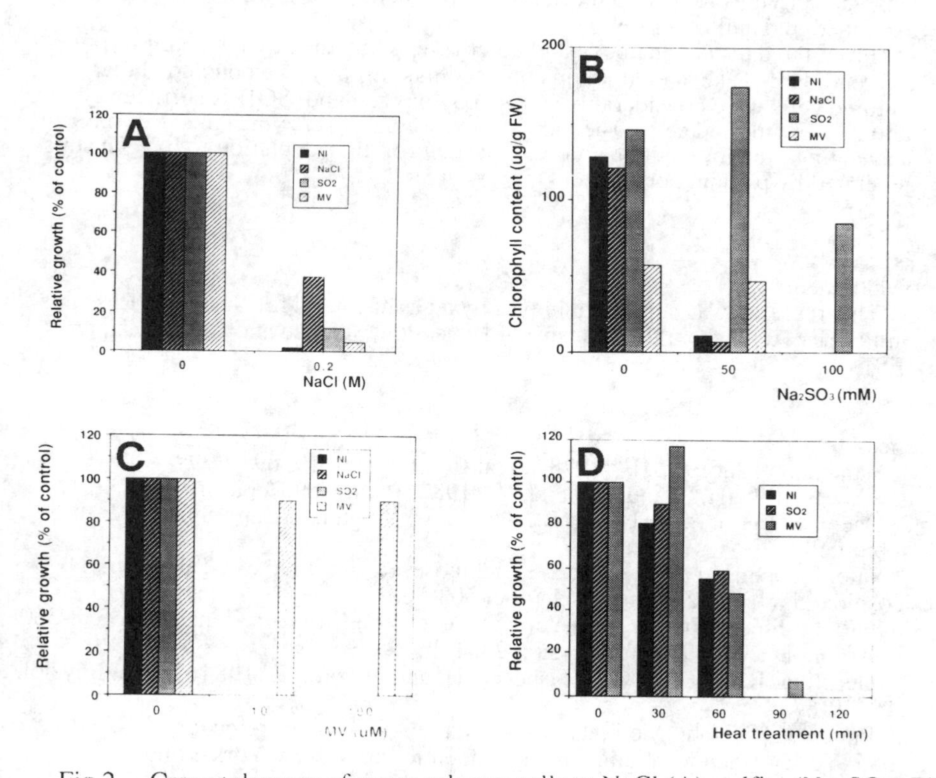

Fig.2 Cross-tolerance of stress-tolerant cells to NaCl (A), sulfite (Na_2SO_3; B), paraquat (MV;C) and high temperature (55°C; D)
Nonselected cells, NaCl adapted cells, sulfite-tolerant cells, and paraquat tolerant cells were referred as NI, NaCl, SO_2 and MV, respectively.

3.3 Active oxygen-scavenging systems

To elucidate the tolerance mechanism of these stress tolerant cells, the activities of some enzymes involved in active oxygen scavenging systems were measured. Cultured cells showed higher enzyme activities of SOD, AsA-POD and POD than leaves on protein basis. When the activities were compared among the cultured cells, the highest SOD was observed in NaCl-tolerant cells and the SOD activity in paraquat-tolerant or sulfite-tolerant cells were comparable to nonselected cultured cells. The activities of AsA-POD were slightly higher in paraquat-tolerant or in sulfite-tolerant cells than those in nonselected or NaCl-tolerant cells, while the activities of guaiacol-dependent POD were much higher in nonselected or NaCl-tolerant cells than paraquat-tolerant or sulfite-tolerant cells.

Active staining of SOD separated by native PAGE indicated that isozyme patterns of SOD were similar among cultured cells, while some isozyme activities were strong in sulfite-tolerant or paraquat-tolerant cells. Whether the different isozyme activities reflect to the adaptation to active oxygen/or sulfite should be examined in detail in future.

From the data shown above and other results obtained by the analyses of carotenoids (S.Takeda et al. in this proceedings; P-051) , we concluded that cultured cells were considerably stressed by oxygen and SOD is sufficiently activated in cultured cells. The increase in associating enzymes in active oxygen scavenging system would be more important for the adaptation to oxygen stress generated by paraquat or sulfite.

Acknowledgments

This research was supported in part by a Grant-in Aid for Scientific Research on Priority Areas from the Ministry of Education, Science and Culture, Japan (FS).

References

1. Yamada, Y. and Sato, F. (1978) Plant Cell Physiol. 19, 691-699
2. Sato, F., Takeda, S. and Yamada, Y. (1987) Plant Cell Rept. 6, 401-404
3. Che, F-S., Sato, F., Hyeon, S-B., Isogai, A., Yamada, Y. and Suzuki,A. submitted
4. Sato, F., Yamada, Y., Kwak, S-S., Ichinose, K., Kishida, M., Takahashi, N., Yoshida, S. (1991) Z.Naturforsch. 46c, 563-568
5. Sato, F., Shigematsu, Y. and Yamada, Y. (1988) Mol.Gen.Genet. 214, 358-360
6. Arnon, D.I. (1949) Plant Physiol. 24, 1-15
7. Gerbling, K.P., Kelly, G.J., Fisher, K.H. and Latzko, E. (1984) J.Plant Physiol. 115, 59-67
8. Putter, J. (1974) in Methods of Enzymatic Analysis (Bergmeyer, H.U., ed.) p685, Verlag Chemie, Weinheim & Academic Press, New York-London
9. Bradford, M.M. (1976) Analyt.Biochem., 72, 248-254

TWO ISOFORMS OF NADP-MALIC ENZYME IN THE FACULTATIVE CAM PLANT *MESEMBRYANTHEMUM CRYSTALLINUM*

KAZUYUKI SAITOU, WAICHI AGATA, YUKO MASUI, MASAE ASAKURA AND FUMITAKE KUBOTA, DEPARTMENT OF AGRONOMY, FACULTY OF AGRICULTURE, KYUSHU UNIVERSITY, HAKOZAKI, HIGASHI-KU, FUKUOKA 812, JAPAN

INTRODUCTION

NADP-malic enzyme (L-malate:$NADP^+$ oxidoreductase [oxaloacetate-decarboxylating], EC 1.1.1.40) is widespread among almost all plants, including C_3, C_4, and Crassulacean acid metabolism (CAM) type species (1), although its metabolic functions are different depending on the organism. NADP-malic enzymes from several plant species and tissues have been separated into two categories (2, 3). It appears that one type of NADP-malic enzyme exists in C_3 and CAM plants and in nongreen tissues of C_4 plants and a second type exists only in green leaves of C_4 plants. We have recently purified NADP-malic enzyme from leaves of *Mesembryanthemum crystallinum* exhibiting CAM (4). The analysis of subunits by SDS-PAGE and the determination of native molecular weight indicated that the enzyme from CAM-*M. crystallinum* was a hexamer of identical subunits. The purified enzyme exhibited no cooperativity for binding of L-malate and cooperativity for binding of $NADP^+$. The NADP-malic enzyme purified from leaves of CAM-*M. crystallinum* had different structural and enzymatic properties from those reported for the enzyme from other plants (4, and references therein). *M. crystallinum* has the capacity to fix carbon in both the C_3 and the CAM modes of photosynthesis. The present paper reports the results of immunochemical studies of NADP-malic enzymes from C_3- and CAM-*M. crystallinum*.

MATERIALS AND METHODS

M. crystallinum plants were grown from seed as previously described (4). CAM was induced under the water culture conditions added 400 mM NaCl for two weeks. The fully developed leaves were harvested during the late daylight period and stored at -55 °C until use.

The NADP-malic enzyme was assayed by following the malate-dependent reduction of $NADP^+$ at 340 nm, as previously described (4).

The specific antiserum against NADP-malic enzyme, purified from CAM-*M. crystallinum*, was obtained by the injection of the purified enzyme into a New Zealand white

N. Murata (ed.), Research in Photosynthesis, Vol. IV, 235–238.

rabbit.

The PAGE was carried out following the method described by Davis (5). The Laemmli (6) system for SDS-PAGE was used. Analytical polyacrylamide gels were blotted onto nitrocellulose membranes using an electroblotting apparatus (Horizblot AE-6670, ATTO Co, Tokyo, Japan) for Western blotting.

Peptide mapping by partial proteolytic cleavage was performed as described by Cleveland et al. (7).

Immunoprecipitation of NADP-malic enzyme with antiserum raised against NADP-malic enzyme from leaves of CAM-*M. crystallinum* was performed by the modified method described by Murata et al. (8). ELISA was performed by the method described by Kawarabata and Hayasaka (9).

RESULTS AND DISCUSSION

After the increase in NaCl concentration in the nutrient solution, the activity of NADP-malic enzyme in extracts from leaves continued to increase until the eighth day and it remained constant thereafter. As a consequence, the activity of NADP-malic enzyme on the twelfth day was twelve-fold higher than the original level. The activity of NADP-malic enzyme in extracts from roots decreased gradually to half of the original level on the sixth day and it remained constant thereafter.

Extracts from leaves and roots were subjected to SDS-PAGE and analyzed by the protein blot method using the antiserum against NADP-malic enzyme from leaves of CAM-*M. crystallinum* (Fig. 2). In extracts from leaves, the intensity of the band which reacted with the antibody increased after the increase in NaCl concentration in the nutrient solution (Fig. 2A). In extracts from roots, the intensity of the band which reacted with the antibody decreased (Fig. 2B).

While extracts from C_3 and CAM tissues showed one NADP-

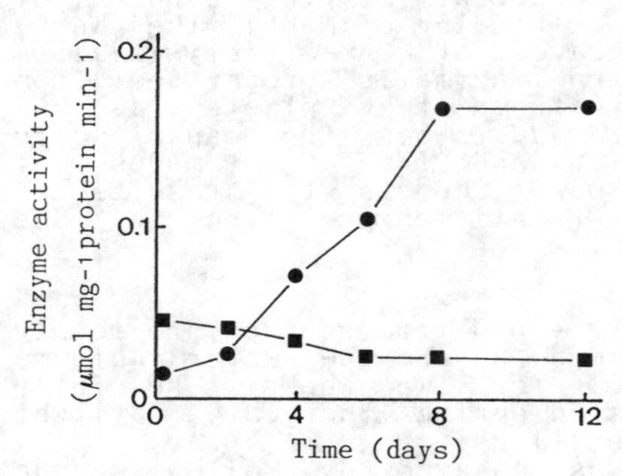

FIGURE 1. Changes in NADP-malic enzyme activities in leaves and roots of M. crystallinum during salt stress. ●, Leaves; ■, roots.

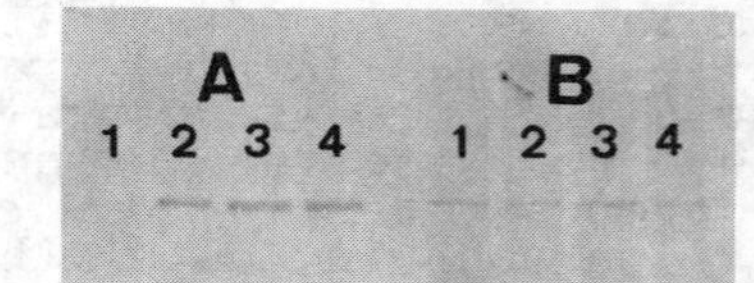

FIGURE 2. Immunodetection of NADP-malic enzyme in leaves (A) and roots (B) during salt stress. Equal amounts of protein were subjected to SDS-PAGE and transferred to nitrocellulose for immunoblotting. Lane 1, extract from unstressed plants; 2, extract from plants stressed for 4 days; 3, 8 days; 4, 12 days.

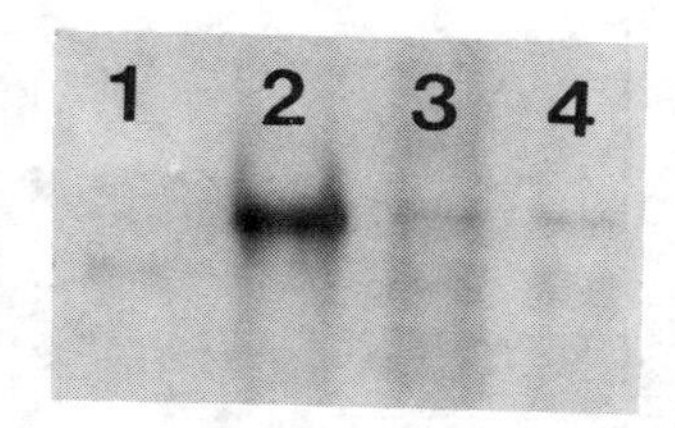

FIGURE 3. Immunodetection of NADP-malic enzyme in C_3- and CAM-M. crystallinum. Extracts from leaves and roots were subjected to electrophoresis under native conditions on 5% gel and transferred to nitrocellulose for immunoblotting. Lane 1, extract from C_3 leaves; 2, CAM leaves; 3, C_3 roots; 4, CAM roots.

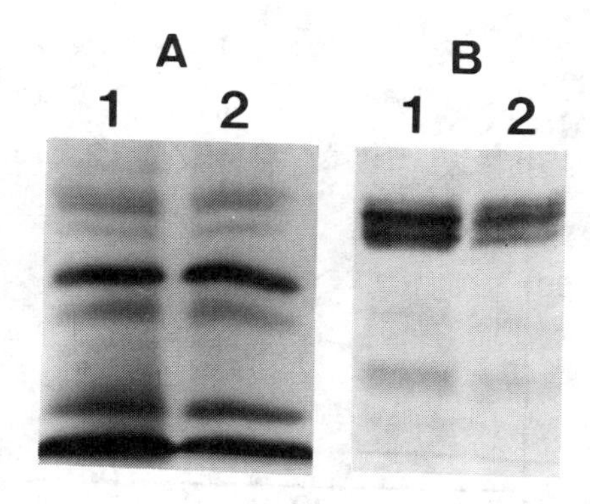

FIGURE 4. Peptide mapping of NADP-malic enzyme from C_3 and CAM leaves. A, The bands were detected by silver staining. B, The bands were detected by protein blotting using antiserum raised against purified NADP-malic enzyme from CAM-M. crystallinum and peroxidase-conjugated secondary antibody. Lane 1, NADP-malic enzyme from C_3 leaves; 2, CAM leaves.

malic enzyme band, respectively, NADP-malic enzyme extracted from C_3 leaves migrated more fast than the enzymes extracted from CAM leaves and C_3 and CAM roots on non-denaturing gels (Fig. 3).

Peptide mapping was carried out to compare the primary structures of the two NADP-malic enzyme proteins in C_3 and CAM leaves (Fig. 4A). The two NADP-malic enzyme proteins had very similar peptide maps and was therefore homologous in sequence. To further examine the similarities among these proteins, we examined the reactivities of the digested peptide fragments and the antibody (Fig. 4B). Almost all peptide fragments from the two NADP-malic enzyme proteins were recognized by the antibody and the patterns of immunoreactive fragments were similar.

The effects of antiserum on the activity of NADP-malic enzymes extracted from C_3 and CAM leaves are shown in Fig. 5. The antiserum inhibited the activity of NADP-malic enzyme in extracts from both C_3 and CAM leaves. The amounts of antiserum required for 50% inhibition were about 10 μl and 16 μl of antiserum per unit of enzyme from C_3 and CAM leaves, respectively.

The ELISA procedure was employed to determine the immunochemical cross-reaction of the NADP-malic enzymes extracted from C_3 and CAM leaves (Fig. 6). The slopes were

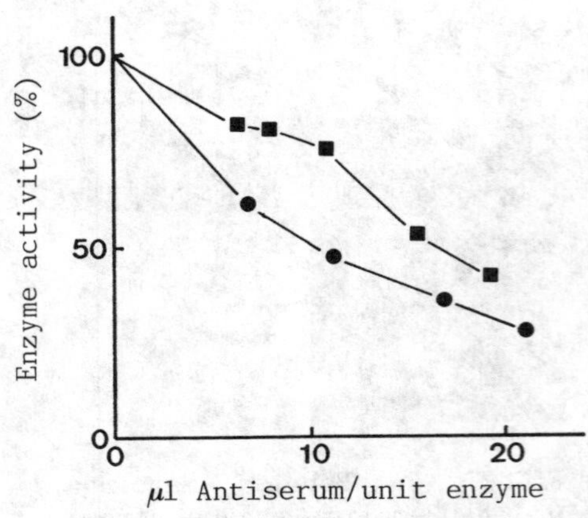

FIGURE 5. Immunoprecipitation curves of NADP-malic enzyme in extracts from leaves of C_3- and CAM-M. crystallinum. ■, C_3; ●, CAM.

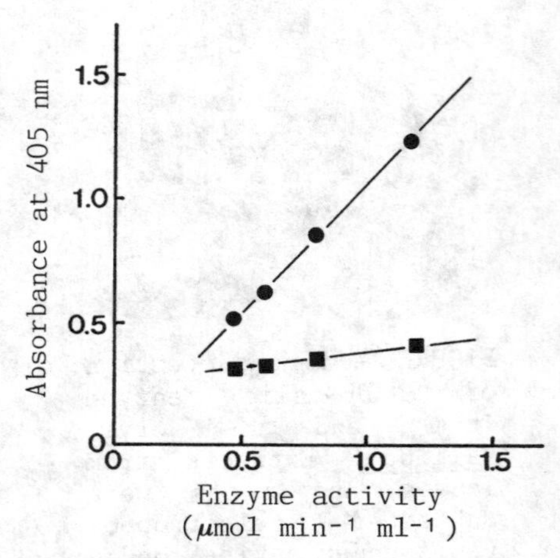

FIGURE 6. ELISA of proteins extracted from C_3- and CAM-M. crystallinum with antiserum raised against purified NADP-malic enzyme from CAM-M. crystallinum. ■, C_3; ●, CAM.

different. This result suggests that antigenicities of the enzyme which depended on the source of enzyme are different.

Further studies are in progress to elucidate the molecular basis for the diversity of the enzyme by comparative analysis of the genes that encode the enzyme in C_3 and CAM leaves.

REFERENCES

1 Asami, S., Inoue, K., Murachi, A. and Akazawa, T. (1979) Arch. Biochem. Biophys. 194, 503-511
2 Nishikido, T. and Wada, T. (1974) Biochem. Biophys. Res. Commun. 61, 243-249
3 Pupillo, P. and Bossi, P. (1974) Planta 144, 283-289
4 Saitou, K., Agata, W., Asakura, M. and Kubota, F. (1992) Plant Cell Physiol. 33, 595-600
5 Davis, B.J. (1971) Ann. New York Acad. Sci. 121,404-427
6 Laemmli, U.K. (1970) Nature 227,680-685
7 Cleveland, D.W., Fisher, S.G., Kirschner, M.W. and Laemmli, U.K. (1977) J. Biol. Chem. 252,1102-1106
8 Murata, T., Ohsugi, R., Matsuoka, M. and Nakamoto, H. (1989) Plant Physiol. 89,316-324
9 Kawarabata, T. and Hayasaka, S. (1987) J. Invertebr. Pathol. 31,280-288

cDNA cloning of betaine aldehyde dehydrogenase from barley and regulation of its expression by osmotic stress.

Manabu Ishitani and Tetsuko Takabe, Res. Inst. Biochem. Reg., Sch. Agr. Sci., Nagoya Univ., Chikusa, Nagoya 464-01, Japan.

1. *INTRODUCTION*

Betaine (glycine betaine) is an osmoprotectant in several families of higher plants subjected to water stress or salt stress (1). Betaine synthesis and accumulation have been best characterized in members of two families, Gramineae (barley, maize) and Chenopodiaceae (spinach, sugar beet). In these plants, betaine biosynthesis occurs by a two-step oxidation of choline via the intermediate betaine aldehyde. Both steps are localized in the chloroplast in spinach (2). The second enzyme in the pathway, betaine aldehyde dehydrogenase (BADH, EC 1.2.1.8.), has been purified to apparent homogeneity (3), and cDNAs encoding this enzyme have been cloned from spinach (4) and sugar beet (5). Our previous work (6,7) revealed that betaine accumulates in both the leaves and roots of barley, a member of the Gramineae, in response to salt stress. In parallel with the accumulation of betaine, salt stress also increases the levels of both BADH activity and BADH protein in barley. To investigate this stress-induced process further, we have cloned BADH cDNA of a nearly full length from barley, and examined the expression of BADH gene in leaves of barley in response to osmotic stress.

2. *MATERIALS AND METHODS*

2.1

Plant material; Barley (*Hordeum vulgare* L. 116 Jeonju Native Korca) was used for all these experiments. Plant growth conditions were as described previously (6). Salt stress was given by raising NaCl concentration in 100 mM steps every second day until a final concentration reached 300 mM, whereas water stress treatment was done by adding 200 g/L of polyethylene glycol 6000 to the hydroponic culture medium. mRNA was isolated from the leaves of control and stressed barley according to the method of Watanabe and Price (8).

2.2 *Construction of cDNA library;* cDNA library was prepared using Predigested Lambda ZAP II/EcoRI Cloning Kit (Stratagene). After screening the barley cDNA library

N. Murata (ed.), Research in Photosynthesis, Vol. IV, 239–242.

using a fragment of BADH cDNA from spinach as probe, three positive clones were obtained. One of them with the largest insert was subjected to further analyses.

2.3 *DNA sequencing*; DNA sequence was determined using Taq Dye Primer Cycle Sequencing Kit from Applied Biosystems.

3. *RESULTS AND DISCUSSION*

3.1 *Isolation and characterization of cDNA clone encoding BADH*; A cDNA library was constructed in bacteriophage λZAP II using poly(A)$^+$ mRNA from salinized barley plants, and the entire cDNA library was screened using a probe that is the fragment of 3' coding region (693 bp) of spinach BADH cDNA, which had been subcloned after amplification by PCR. From 600,000 independent transformants screened, three clones were isolated, of which one nearly full lengh of cDNA clone was sequenced, and was confirmed to encode BADH by its nucleotide sequence and deduced amino acid sequence identity to those of sugar beet and spinach BADH reported previously (4, 5).

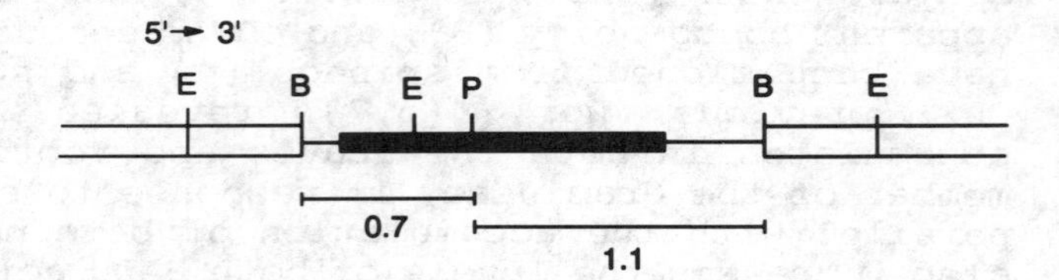

FIGURE 1. Partial restriction map for Barley BADH cDNA. Bold lines indicate the protein-coding region; open boxes are λ vector DNA. The 0.7-kbp BamHl/Apal restriction fragment was used as probe for Northern blot analysis. Cleavage sites by Restriction endonuclease; E, EcoRI; B, BamHI; P, PstI. Fragment sizes are shown in kilobases.

This clone contained a 1819 bp cDNA insert with a single long open reading frame predicting a polypeptide of 496 amino acids with 69 % and 68 % identity to BADH of spinach and sugar beet, respectively. This indicates that BADH gene is conserved between monocot and dicot. In addition, the published amino acid sequence of BADH from *E. coli*(9) was also similar to the barley BADH, showing 37 % identity. Figure 2 shows that regions of identity included the decapeptide motif VTLELGGKSP and residues for NAD$^+$-binding and catalytic sites presumed to be characteristic of various dehydrogenases (4).

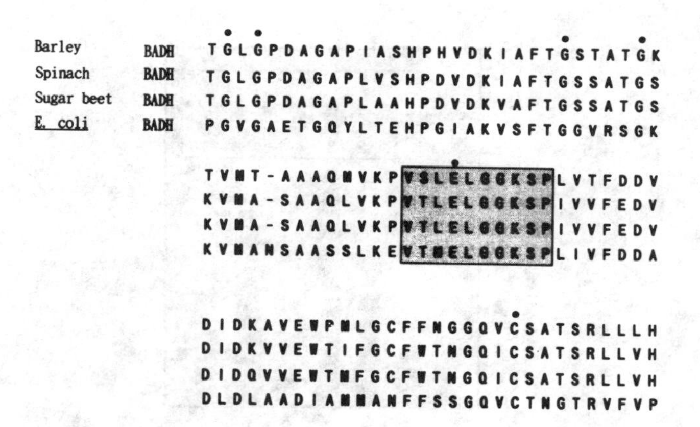

FIGURE 2. Presence in Barley BADH of the common decapeptide motif and residues for $NAD^{\pm}$-binding and catalytic sites presumed to be characteristic of various dehydrogenases. Segments with identical amino acids with respect to barley BADH are shaded. Bold dots show the residues presumed to be associated with NAD^{+}-binding and catalytic site of various dehydrogenases.

3.2 *Northern blot analysis;* The expression of BADH mRNA was examined in leaves of barley under osmotic stress. Total RNAs (30 μg) prepared from leaves subjected to osmotic stress were hybridized with the 0.7 kbp BamHI/ApaI digested fragment of barley BADH cDNA (Figure 1). The RNA gel blot analysis in Figure 3 (inset) showed a single transcript of ca. 1.9 kbp. When the leaves were subjected to salt stress (lanes 3 and 4) or water stress (lanes 5 and 6), the amount of mRNA increased with increasing time of stress, and in samples after 48 h stress (lanes 4 and 6), the signal was 6 and 5-fold greater than that of the control plant (lane 2), respectively. This indicates that BADH mRNA accumulates in response to both salt stress and water stress. This is also in consistent with the accompanying rise in both BADH enzyme activity and BADH protein reported previously by our group (6,7). The level of BADH mRNA level decreased upon 36 h releif from salt stress (lane 7). This led us to conclude that the level of BADH mRNA is regulated by osmotic stress in barley leaves.

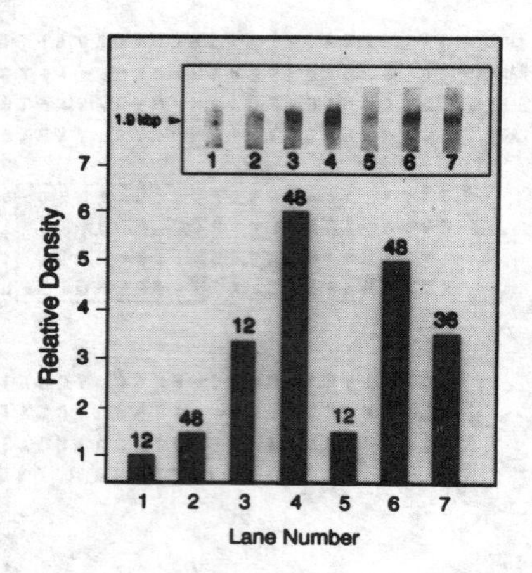

FIGURE 3. RNA gel blot analysis of barley BADH mRNA. Each lane was loaded with 30 µg total RNA from leaves of control and stressed barley plants. The histogram was obtained by densitometric scanning of the individual band of the Northern blot analysis shown in the inset. The value of lane 1 was arbitrarily set to 1.0. Lanes 1, 2: control; lanes 3, 4: salt stress (300mM NaCl); lanes 5, 6: water stress (200 g/L PEG6000); lane 7: after relief from 48-h salt stress. Number on top of each bar indicates time of treatment(h).

REFERENCES

1 Hanson, A. D and Hitz, W, D. (1982) *Annu. Rev. Plant Physiol.* 33: 163-203.

2 Hanson. A. D., May, A. M., Grumet, R., Bode, J., Jamieson, G. C. and Rhodes, D. (1985) *Proc. Natl. Acad. Sci.* USA 82: 3678-3682.

3 Arakawa, A. Takabe, T. Sugiyama, T. and Akazawa, T. (1987) *J. Biochem.* 101: 1485-1488.

4 Weretilnyk, E. A. and Hanson, A. D. (1990) *Proc. Natl. Acad. Sci.* USA 87: 2745-2749.

5 McCue, K. F. and Hanson A. D.(1992) *Plant Mol. Biol.* 18: 1-11.

6 Arakawa, K., Katayama, M. and Takabe, T. (1990) *Plant Cell Physiol.* 31: 797-803.

7 Arakawa, K., Mizuno, K., Kishitani, S. and Takabe, T. (1992) *Plant Cell Physiol.* in press.

8 Watanabe, A. and Price, C. A. (1982) *Proc. Natl. Acad. Sci.* USA 79: 6304-6308.

9 Boyd, L. A., Adam,L., Pelcher, L. E., McHughen, A., Hiriji, R. and Selvaraj, G. (1991) *Gene.* 103: 45-52.

IMMUNOLOGICAL STUDIES OF BETAINE ALDEHYDE DEHYDROGENASE IN BARLEY

Keita Arakawa, Katsuhiko Mizuno and Tetsuko Takabe

Research Institute for Biochemical Regulation, School of Agricultural Sciences, Nagoya University, Chikusa, Nagoya 464-01, Japan.

1. INTRODUCTION

Betaine aldehyde dehydrogenase (BADH) catalyzes the last step of betaine synthesis in higher plants. BADH from chenopods has been well characterized by Hanson's group. Many members of the Gramineae (monocots) were also known to accumulate betaine at various levels in response to salt stress. However, the regulatory mechanism of enzymes involved in the synthesis of betaine in response to salt stress has not been well understood yet in the cereal plants.

We analyzed the changes in the levels of betaine and BADH activities from barley in response to salt stress. The levels of betaine and BADH activities were found to be increased to 7- and 3-fold, respectively, over the course of 7-d salinization at 200 mM NaCl(1). In this study, we describe the immunological analysis of the changes in the levels of BADH protein in barley exposed to osmotic stress (salt and water stresses) and to subsequent removal of the salt stress. In addition, we also describe the presence of BADH protein in nonphotosynthetic tissues, such as roots and etiolated leaves, of barley plants.

2. MATERIALS AND METHODS

2.1 Plant materials: Barley (*Hordeum vulgare* L., cv Harunanijyo) was grown as described previously(1). Salt treatment of 6-d-old plants was initiated by the addition of NaCl to a final concentration of 200 mM. Roots were harvested from 6-d-old plants grown under aseptic conditions on agar plates. Etiolated leaves were harvested from 6-d-old plants that had been grown in the dark at 25°C.

2.2 Preparation of crude BADH fractions from barley: Crude BADH fractions were prepared as 55-70% saturated $(NH_4)_2SO_4$ fractions from barley(1).

2.3 Detection of BADH activity and protein: BADH was assayed

N. Murata (ed.), Research in Photosynthesis, Vol. IV, 243–246.

by the fluorometric method(1). BADH protein was detected by Western blot analysis with polyclonal antibodies raised in rabbit against SDS-denatured BADH from spinach(2). The antibodies were found to also recognize BADH from barley by immunotitration analysis(3).

2.4 Quantification of betaine: The levels of betaine in various tissues of barley were analyzed by ^{1}H NMR spectroscopy as described previously(1).

3. RESULTS AND DISCUSSION

3.1 Induction of BADH protein in barley leaves by osmotic stress: The levels of betaine and BADH protein in leaves of barley that had been subjected to water stress were analyzed (Figure 1, A and B). Water stress was initiated by withholding of water or by addition of polyethylene glycol 6000 to a final concentration of 250 g/l (solute potential: -2.44 MPa) and the plants were grown for one day and three days, respectively, prior to harvest. The level of BADH protein was increased by both the drought and water stresses, just as it was by salt stress. The level of betaine was also increased by osmotic stress.

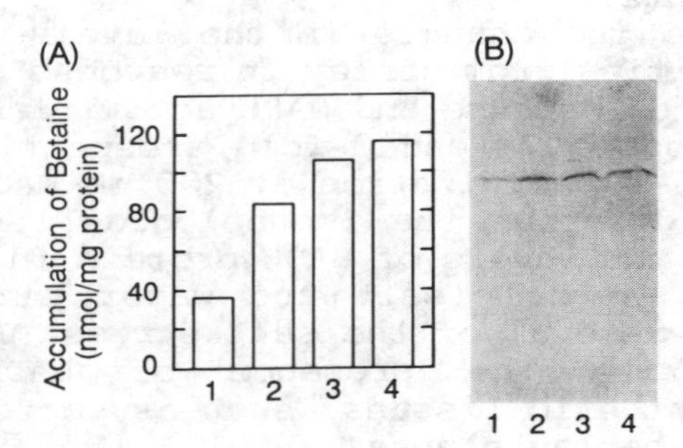

FIGURE 1. Induction of the accumulation of betaine and BADH protein in barley leaves under osmotic stress. (A) Quantification of betaine. (B) Immunoblot analysis of BADH protein. Lane 1, control; lane 2, 200 mM NaCl; lane 3, 250 g/l polyethylene glycol 6000; lane 4, withholding of water.

3.2 The effect of removal of stress on the levels of betaine and BADH protein in salt-stressed barley leave: Changes in the levels of betaine and BADH protein were followed over the course of 3 days in barley plants transferred to a non-salinized medium after a 3-d salinization treatment. Upon termination of salt stress, barley plants began to grow normally. The level of BADH protein fell and the total amount of betaine decreased to about 85% in leaves (Figure 2). Ladyman et al. (4) reported that the total amount of betaine in barley plants is maintained after water-stressed barley plants are rewatered. Furthermore, they also reported that betaine is translocated from mature leaves to younger leaves or roots through the phloem after rewatering in barley. We found that the total amount of BADH protein is maintained after removal of salt stress in leaves, while the level of BADH protein on a total-protein basis is reduced upon the restoration of normal growth (Figure 2, C and D). In addition, since betaine is thought to be a stable end product(4), it is likely that the total amount of betaine in barley leaves decreases via translocation of betaine to roots after termination of salt stress (Figure 2, A and B). Therefore, it appears that BADH is one of the enzymes responsible for osmotic adjustment under osmotic stress in barley leaves.

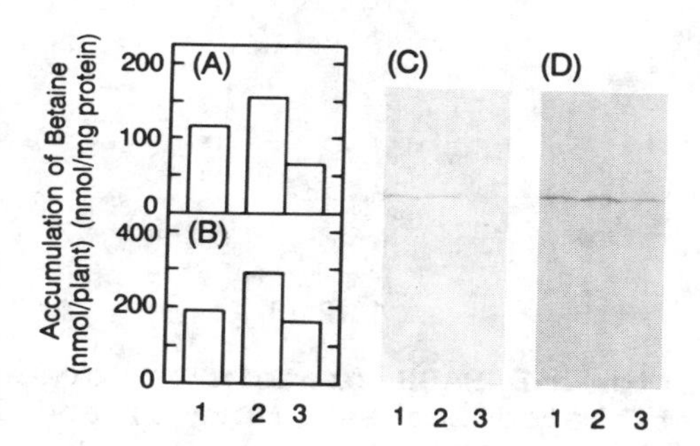

FIGURE 2. Effect of removal of salt stress on the levels of betaine (A, B) and BADH protein (C, D) in salt-stressed barley leaves. Six-d-old barley plants were cultured in the salinized medium (200 mM NaCl) for 3 days (lane 1). The barley plants were then grown in either the salinized medium (lane 2) or in non-salinized normal medium (lane 3) for 3 days. (A) and (C), on the basis of total leaf protein. (B) and (D), on the basis of leaves per plant.

3.3 BADH protein in green leaves, etiolated leaves and roots of barley: The synthesis of betaine is known to occur in chloroplasts (i.e., in green leaves)(5). Hanson's group reported that choline monooxygenase, which catalyzes the first step in the synthesis of betaine, requires reduced ferredoxin as reducing power(6), suggesting that irradiation by light is essential for the synthesis of betaine. However, we detected betaine (62 nmol/g fr wt; ca. 20% of that in green leaves) in etiolated barley leaves(1). In the present study, we also detected BADH protein immunologically in nonphotosynthetic tissues, such as roots and etiolated leaves (Figure 3, A and B). Several reports have suggested that ferredoxin and ferredoxin-$NADP^+$ oxidoreductase are also present in nonphotosynthetic tissues. From these data, it seems that synthesis of betaine and BADH protein does not have an absolute requirement for light.

Many problems remain to be clarified with the regulatory mechanisms of synthesis of betaine in response to osmotic stress. To solve these problems, we must analyze the whole process of the synthesis of betaine at the molecular level in detail.

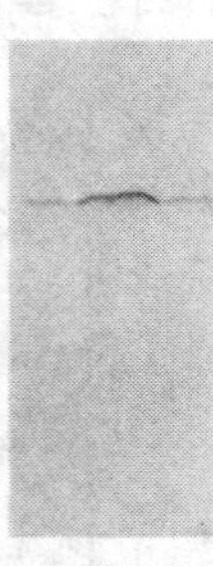

FIGURE 3. Detection of BADH protein in green leaves (lane 1), etiolated leaves (lane 2) and roots (lane 3) of barley plants.

REFERENCES

1 Arakawa, K., Katayama, M. and Takabe, T. (1990) Plant Cell Physiol. 31: 797-803.

2 Arakawa, K., Takabe, T., Sugiyama T. and Akazawa, T. (1987) J. Biochem. 101: 1485-1488.

3 Arakawa, K., Mizuno, K., Kishitani, S. and Takabe, T. (1992) Plant Cell Physiol. in press.

4 Ladyman, J.A.R., Hitz, W.D. and Hanson, A.D. (1980) Planta 150: 191-196.

5 Hanson, A.D., May, A.M., Grumet, R., Bode, J., Jamieson, G.C. and Rhodes, D. (1985) Proc. Natl. Acad. Sci. USA 82: 3678-3682.

6 Brouquisse, R., Weigel, P., Rhodes, D., Yocum, C.F. and Hanson, A.D. (1989) Plant Physiol. 90: 322-329.

BETAINE ALDEHYDE DEHYDROGENASE PROTEIN IS PRESENT IN LEAVES OF BOTH BETAINE ACCUMULATORS AND NONACCUMULATORS IN VARIOUS CEREAL PLANTS

Keita Arakawa, Katsuhiko Mizuno , Sachie Kishitani* and Tetsuko Takabe, Res. Inst. Biochem. Reg., Sch. Agr.- Sci., Nagoya Univ., Chikusa, Nagoya 464-01 and *Laboratory of Plant Breeding, Faculty of Agriculture, Tohoku University, Sendai 980, Japan.

1. INTRODUCTION

All members of the Chenopodiaceae examined and several members of the Gramineae were reported to accumulate glycinebetaine(betaine) as compatible solute for osmotic adjustment. In plants, betaine is synthesized by a two-step oxidation of choline; both steps occur in the chloroplast(1). The first step is catalyzed by choline monooxygenase and the second step is catalyzed by a specific betaine aldehyde dehydrogenase(BADH). In our previous study(2), it was found that spinach BADH is a dimer of two polypeptides of 60kDa each. Weretilnyk et al.(3) reported that high betaine levels are detected in leaves from several distantly related families of dicotyledons and betaine-accumulating species have a BADH enzyme recognized by antibodies raized against BADH from spinach leaves. By contrast, little is known about this enzyme in members of the Gramineae(monocots) except barley(4,5). In this study, we investigated the accumulation of betaine and BADH protein in leaves of various cereal plants.

2. MATERIALS and METHODS

Plants were grown in a growth chamber under a 12-h light(25 °C) and 12-h dark(18 °C) cycle . Plants were illuminated by fluorescent lamps, which provide 100 $\mu E.m^{-2}.s^{-1}$ at plant level. Seeds of the following plants were obtained from commercial sources in Japan: Hordeum vulgare L., cv. Harunanijou; Triticum aestivum L. cv. Gogatsu; Zea mays L. cv. Golden Cross Bantam T-51; Oryza sativa L. cv. Nihonbare; Sorghum bicolor Moench. Seeds of Secale cereale L., Eleusine coracana Gaerth, Panicum miliaceum L. cv. Shinano No. 1, Echinochloa utilis Ohwi and Setaria italica Beauv cv. Rikuu No. 4 were kind gifts from Dr. Yasuhiro Kono(Nagoya University). Hordeum vulgare L. Gondar 1(OUE574) and Hordeum vulgare L. Jeonju Native (OUK116) were bred at Research Institute for Bioresourses, Okayama University(Okayama, Japan). Plants were grown in a 1,000-fold diluted solution of Hyponex for 7 days. When plants were salinized, NaCl was added to the irrigation solution in 50-mM increments every day until tips of the leaves become yellow(ca. 6 days).
Quaternary ammonium compounds were extracted from various cereal leaves with 1 N H_2SO_4, precipitated as their periodides and then analyzed by ^1H NMR spectroscopy in a JEOL-JMN200 Fourier-

N. Murata (ed.), Research in Photosynthesis, Vol. IV, 247–250.

transform NMR spectrometer(4).
In order to detect BADH protein in various cereal plants Western blotting was carried out using antibody raized against pure BADH protein from spinach leaves(5).

3. RESULTS

We examined betaine levels in leaves of members of the Gramineae(Table 1). Hordeum vulgare L., Triticum aestivum L. and

TABLE 1. Betaine levels in leaf extracts of control and salinized plants

Species	Betaine(nmol.(mg total protein)$^{-1}$)	
	Control	Salinized
*Hordeum vulgare L.		
cv. Harunanijou	41	349
cv. Gondar 1(OUE574)	82	325
cv. Jeonju Native (OUK116)	41	336
*Triticum aestivum L.	54	349
*Secale cereale L.	95	173
*Eleusine coracana Gaerth	<2	54
*Sorghum bicolor Moench	49	80
*Panicum miliaceum L.	4	17
*Setaria italica Beauv	14	18
Echinochloa utilis Ohwi	<2	<2
Zea mays L.	<2	<2
Oryza sativa L.	<2	<2

*Betaine-accumulating species

Secale cereale L., which belong to the Tritiaceae, accumulated high levels of betaine, whereas Eleusine coracana Gaerth and Sorghum bicolor Moench accumulated lower amounts of betaine than those species described above. On the other hands, Panicum miliaceum L. and Setaria italica Beauv accumulated only small amounts of betaine and betaine was undetectable in Echinochloa utilis Ohwi, Zea mays L. and Oryza sativa L.. In all the betaine accumulators, the levels of betaine were increased by salinization.
By Western blot analysis BADH protein was detected in both betaine accumulators and nonaccumulators. BADH activity was found in the leaf extract of salinized rice(betaine nonaccumulator under our experimental conditions) to be ca. 10 % of that of barley.

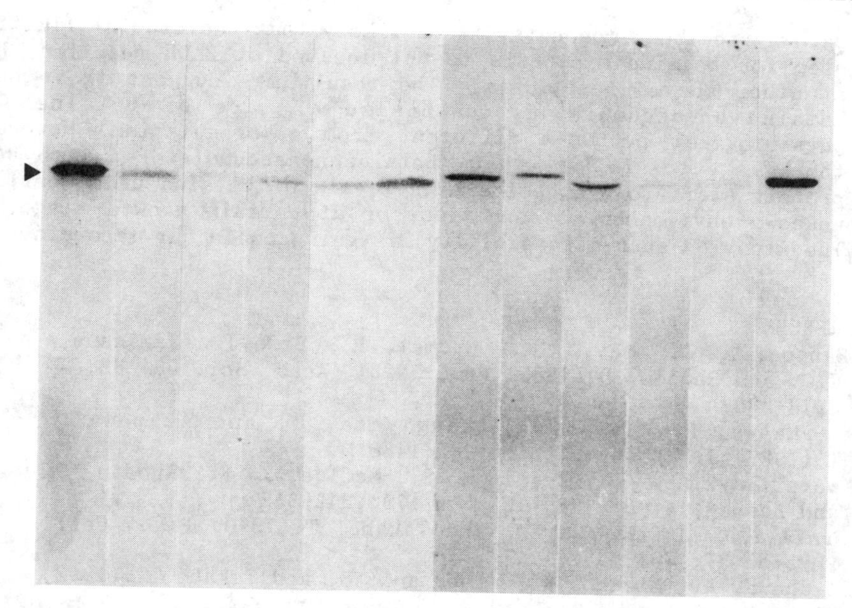

Fig. 1 Western blot analysis using antibodies raized against the 60-kDa polypeptide of BADH from spinach.
Lanes: 1, Hordeum vulgare L.; 2, Triticum aestivum L.; 3, Secale cereale L.; 4, Eleusine coracana Gaerth; 5, Sorghum bicolor Moench; 6, Panicum miliaceum L.; 7, Setaria itarica Beauv; 8, Echinochloa utilis Ohwi; 9, Zea mays L.; 10, Oryza sativa L.; S, spinach.

4. DISCUSSION

In the Gramineae family, some members could accumulate high levels of betaine such as Hordeum vulgare L., Triticum aestivum L., and Secale cereale L., which belong to the Tritiaceae subfamily. However, other members of this same family were found to accumulate much lower or negligible levels of betaine. It has also reported that betaine levels vary widely depending on the members of families in dicots(3). Furthermore, Lerma et al.(6) reported that Zea mays L. accumulates various levels of betaine depending on its genotypes. We could not detect betaine in Zea mays L.(cv. Golden Cross Bantam T-51), indicating betaine deficiency in this specific cultivar of maize. However, all the betaine accumulators and nonaccumulators tested in the present study contained BADH activity as well as BADH protein as shown immunologically using antibody raized against spinach BADH protein(Fig. 1), suggesting the presence of choline-betaine pathway in these monocots. It is likely that the crucial limiting step for betaine synthesis is not located at BADH reaction, but at other enzyme reaction(s). The result may suggest that these betaine nonaccumulators synthesize a trace of betaine for physiological purposes different from osmoregulation. However, there is a possibility that betaine nonaccumulators with BADH protein start to synthesize high levels of betaine under certain unknown environmental conditions or at certain growth stage(s). The study on such a possibility is going on in our laboratory.

REFERENCES

1 Hanson, A. D., May, A.M., Grumet, R., Bode,J., Jamieson, G.C. and Rhodes, D.(1985) Proc. Natl. Acad. Sci. USA 82, 3678-3682
2 Arakawa, K., Takabe, T., Sugiyama, T. and Akazawa, T.(1987) J. Biochem. 101: 1485-1488
3 Weretilnyk, E. A. , Bednarek, S., McClue, K. F., Rhodes, D. and Hanson, A. D.(1989) Planta 178: 342-352
4 Arakawa, K., Katayama, M. and Takabe, T.(1990) Plant Cell Physiol.31: 797-803
5 Arakawa, K., Mizuno, K., Kishitani, S. and Takabe, T.(1992) Plant Cell Physiol. in press
6 Lerma, C., Rich, P. J., Ju, G. C., Yang, W-J., Hanson, A. D. and Rhodes, D.(1991) Plant Physiol. 95: 1113-1119

ACKNOWLEDGMENT

This investigation was supported by a grant from Bio-Media Project of Japanese Ministry of Agriculture, Forestry and Fisheries.

FACULTATIVE HALOPHYTES ACCUMULATE PROLINE AS THE EARLY RESPONSE TO SALT STRESS

Y. Sanada, K. Kuribayashi, T. Andoh, M. Takeda, N. Tamai and K. Wada
Department of Biology, Faculty of Science, Kanazawa University,
Kanazawa, Ishikawa 920-11, Japan.

1. INTRODUCTION

A facultative halophyte, *Mesembryanthemum crystallinum* can shift from C_3 mode metabolism of photosynthesis to Crassulacean Acid Metabolism (CAM) in the presence of a high concentration of salt (1, 2). During the transition, activity and protein of PEPCase increase gradually (3, 4, 5). Rapid proline accumulation is observed prior to CAM transition (6). It appears to be associated with NaCl stress. The physiological role of proline in the stressed plants is not clear. From the results obtained, the function of proline in the stressed plants is discussed.

2. MATERIALS AND METHODS

Plant growth and harvesting : Seeds of *Mesembryanthemum crystallinum* L. were germinated in a mixture of soil and vermiculite in 1:1 ratio in a growth cabinet. Plants were grown under a 12-h light period (light intensity; 300 μ mol quanta/ m^2/s) at 25℃ and a 12-h dark period at 17℃ at 50-60 % relative humidity and watered daily with one-third Hoagland's nutrient solution. The 7- to 8-week old plants were stressed by the ample addition of 400 mM NaCl in nutrient solution. At the fifth day after the start of NaCl stress, some of plants were transferred into continuous darkness in the growth cabinet for 68-h (Temperature cycle is kept at 25℃ for 12 h and at 17℃ for 12 h). Discs (diameter 1.0 cm) were taken from the second or third leaf pair using a cork borer, frozen in liquid nitrogen and stored at -80 ℃ until assay.

Wheat seeds were soaked for 3 days in tap water. Then the germinated seeds were grown on a plastic mesh plate covered with a layer of cheese-cloth in a flat vat containing one-third Hoagland's solution. Two to three-week old plants were subjected to salt stress (138 mM NaCl). The growth conditions were the same as those of *M. crystallinum*.

Extraction of free amino acids : A disc was homogenized with two volumes of

N. Murata (ed.), Research in Photosynthesis, Vol. IV, 251–254.

distilled water and heated in a boiling bath for 6 min. The heat-treated homogenate was cooled down in a ice bath and centrifuged at 9,000 x*g* for 15 min. The supernatant was treated with TCA (final 5 %) and centrifuged again. The resulted supernatant was diluted with two volumes of water. Then, an aliquot was analyzed by amino acid analyzer (IRICA, Kyoto, Japan).

3. RESULTS AND DISCUSSION

Eight-week old *M. crystallinum* plants were subjected to stress of 400 mM NaCl at the early light period. As shown in Fig. 1, proline content increased rapidly after 2- or 3-day lag, as reported by many investigators. On 2nd and 3rd days, proline content of leaves harvested on light period increased gradually. A considerable accumulation of proline (2.4 μ moles/g fresh weight) was shown on the 5th day of stress treatment. Proline accumulation reached the highest level on the 11th day of stress treatment. Thereafter, the highest level of proline was sustained and the carbon metabolism was gradually transferred to CAM (data not shown). On the other hand, proline accumulation of the control plants was hardly discernible even after 10 days.

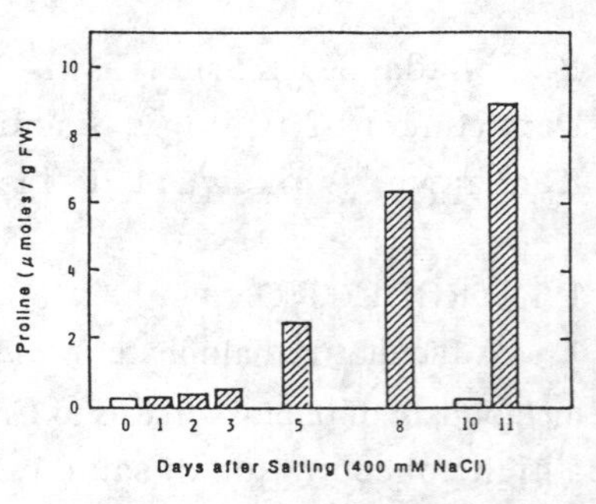

Fig. 1. Changes of proline levels in *M. crystallinum* treated with (-▨-) or without (-□-) NaCl.

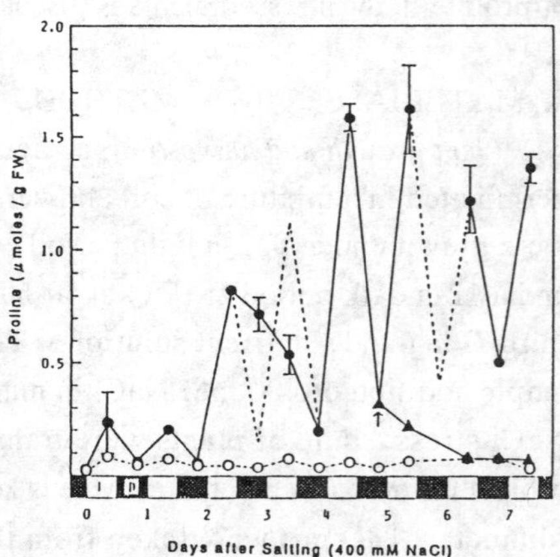

Fig. 2. Changes of proline levels during day/night cycle in *M. crystallinum* stressed (-●-) or unstressed (-○-) with NaCl. Vertical bars indicate standard errorof the mean for three measurements. On 5th-day after treatment (↑), plants were transferred into continuous darkness (-▲-).

In order to investigate the light/dark change of proline content, 8-week old plants were subjected to stress of 400 mM NaCl at the start of light period. Even after 8 hours of the first cycle, proline content of the stressed plants was slightly higher than that of control plants as shown in Fig. 2. After 8 hours of the first dark cycle, it decreased to the level of control plants. On the second light cycle (2nd day), it became higher again. This light/dark change of proline content in the stressed plants became remarkably with cycle. At the third dark cycle, decrease of proline level was a little. It seemed to be consequence of that we forgot to turn off the dim light for operations in the growth cabinet. Broken lines in Fig. 2 indicate the predicted changes on the stressed plants. At the fifth dark cycle, some of the stressed plants were transferred into the continuous darkness. Proline level was kept low as obtained in the control plants during dark period. It means that the light/dark change of proline level is not a circadian rhythm.

Fig. 3 shows the more precise change of proline levels than the experiments above during light/dark cycle. A slow increase of proline level was observed for the first 6 hours and then a remarkable increase in the stressed plants. Proline level quickly decreased with transition to the dark cycle. On the other hand, a steep increase with no lag was observed at start of the second light cycle. Interestingly, a slight light/dark change of proline level was observed even in the unstressed plants.

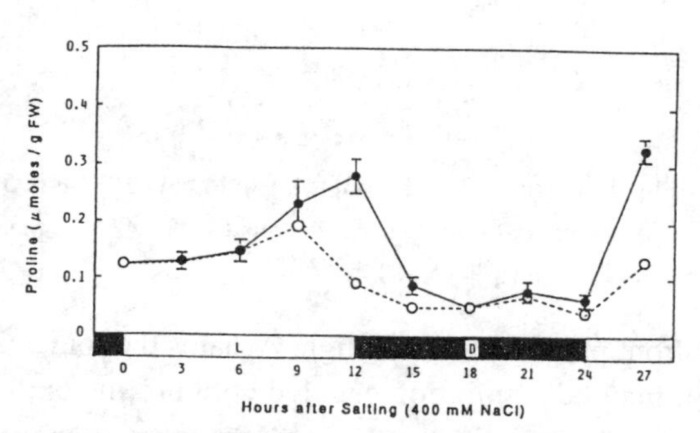

Fig. 3. Changes of proline levels in *M. crystallinum* with (-●-) or without (-○-) NaCl treatment.

Root proline content was also determined as shown in Fig. 4 (panel A). Root of the stressed plants accumulated proline more quickly than leaf and no lag was observed. Although we do not know yet if proline level in root of the stressed plants changes on a light/dark cycle, the quicker response of proline in root to salt stress than that in leaf and the light/dark change of proline level in leaf suggest that proline synthsized in leaves in light is transported to root in which proline is not able to be synthesized (7) and that proline in the stressed cells functions as osmoticum with or without another organic substances such as pinitol proposed by Paul and Cockburn (8).

As shown in Fig. 5, on the other hand, the change of proline level with light/dark cycle was not observed in wheat, which did not make a transition to CAM. In plants under salt stress, a great amount of energy (ATP) and reducing equivalent (NADPH) will be required for maintenance of the normal conditions in cells. They are, of course, supplied

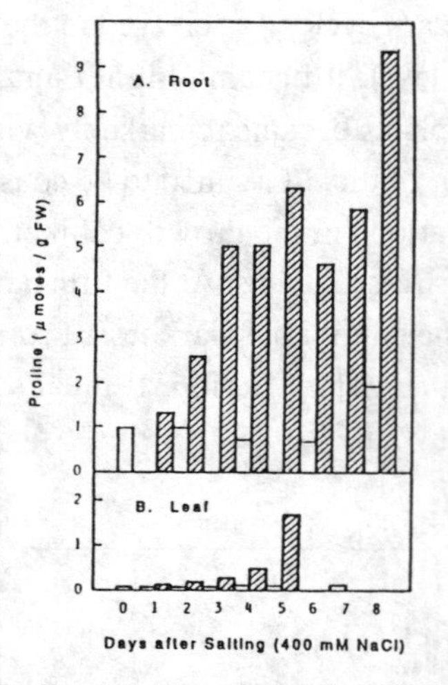

Fig. 4. Proline levels in root (A) and Leaf (B) of *M. crystallinum* during treatment with (-▨-) or without (-□-) NaCl.

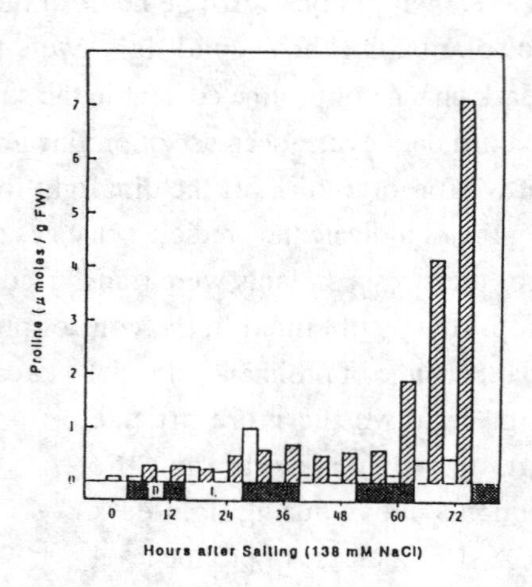

Fig. 5. Proline content in shoots of young wheat plants. Two-week old plants were stressed with (-▨-) or without (-□-) 138 mM NaCl.

from photosynthesis in light. What is the source in dark ? As suggested from this study, it may be respiration coupled with proline oxidation (9) in mitochondria and pentose phosphate pathway. Our preliminary experiments with *M. crystallinum* leaf discs under salt stress did not show the day/night change of proline level. Therefore proline transport from leaves to the other parts of plant must be considered as a cause of the day/night change of proline level in leaf. Anyhow, it is very probable that the day/night change of proline can induce *M. crystallinum* to CAM.

REFERENCES

1 Winter, K. and von Willert, D.J. (1972) *Z. Pflanzenphysiol*. 67; 166-170.

2 Winter, K. and Lüttge, U. (1976) In *Water and Plant Life, Ecological Studies* 19,(Lange, O.L. et al. eds.), 323-334, Spriger-Verlag, Berlin.

3 Greenway, H., Winter, K. and Lüttge, U. (1978) *J. Exp. Bot*. 29; 547-559.

4 Holtum, L.A.M. and Winter, K. (1982) *Planta* 155; 8-16.

5 Hofner, R., Vazquez-Moreno, L., Winter, K., Bohnert, H.J. and Schmitt, J.M. (1987) *Plant Physiol*. 83; 915-919.

6 Ostrem, J.A., Vernon, D.M., Olson, S.W. and Bohnert, H.J. (1987) *Plant Physiol*. s83; 280.

7 Chang, H.-H. (1987) *Plant Physiol*. s83; 274.

8 Paul, M.J. and Cockburn, W. (1989) *J. Exp. Bot*. 40; 1093-1098.

9 Boggess, S.F., Koeppe, D.E. and Stewart, C.R. (1978) *Plant Physiol*. 62; 22-25.

SALT STRESS-INDUCED CELL INJURY AND H^+-GRADIENT BETWEEN THE CYTOPLASM AND THE VACUOLE IN SUSPENSION-CULTURED PLANT CELLS.

Kazuyuki Kuchitsu, Kunihiro Kasamo[1] and **Naoto Shibuya**, *Department of Cell Biology, National Institute of Agrobiological Resources and* [1]*Molecular Function Lab., National Food Research Institute, Kannondai, Tsukuba, Ibaraki 305, JAPAN*

1. INTRODUCTION

Many plants, including most crops, are sensitive to salt stress. Though the main mechanism for salt injury has been attributed to increase in intracellular Na^+, target site of Na^+ still remains unclear. Compartmentation of H^+ and other ions are important factors to maintain the homeostasis of various functions in cells (1). To understand the cellular and molecular mechanisms involved in the damage due to salt, we have investigated changes in intracellular compartmentation of ions with special reference to H^+ (2). *In vivo* ^{31}P-NMR (nuclear magnetic resonance) spectroscopy allowed noninvasive simultaneous measurement of physiological parameters such as pH and quantity of phosphate compounds in different compartments (cytoplasm and vacuoles), and revealed that the vacuoles are acidic compartments in higher plants (3), algae (4) and fungi. In both salt-tolerant and salt-sensitive algal species, NaCl stress induced intracellular pH changes, which may play physiological roles in salt adaptation and salt injury. In a salt-tolerant unicellular green alga *Dunaliella tertiolecta*, salt stress induced cytoplasmic alkalization (5), which may function as one of the possible effectors for the rapid activation of the synthesis of osmoticum during the adaptation. On the contrary, salt stress-induced cytoplasmic acidification and vacuolar alkalization were observed in a salt-sensitive alga *Nitellopsis obtusa*. (6)

In higher plants, the vacuole is the main intracellular compartment that occupies most of the cell volume, and the gradient of ions between the cytoplasm and the vacuole is assumed to affect various stress responses (2). Little is known, however, for the intracellular pH change in response to salt stress. In this article, salt-induced pH change in the cytoplasm and the vacuole as well as its possible molecular mechanism were studied using suspension-cultured plant cells. The significance of H^+-gradient between the cytoplasm and the vacuole to the stress response is discussed.

2. MATERIALS and METHODS

2.1 *Plant Materials:* Suspension-cultured cells of rice (*Oryza sativa* L. var Musashikogane) and tobacco (*Nicotiana tabacum* L.) were kindly provided by Dr. Yuko Ohashi (National Institute of Agrobiological Resources, Tsukuba, Japan). Rice cells were grown in AA medium (7) containing 3 % (w/v) sucrose in the dark at 25 °C. The growth of the cells was monitored by measuring the fresh weight and the dry weight.

2.2 In vivo *^{31}P-NMR Spectroscopy of the Cells:* Cells were transferred to a NMR tube and suspended in the AA medium depleted with phosphate and minor elements, unless otherwise stated. This medium contains 3 mM of Ca^{2+}. In order

N. Murata (ed.), Research in Photosynthesis, Vol. IV, 255–258.

to avoid oxygen starvation, the cell suspension was bubbled with oxygen at a rate of 3 mL/min during the measurement. ^{31}P-NMR spectra were obtained with a Varian VXR-500S spectrometer, operating at 202.3 MHz. Temperature was kept at 26°C. Each spectrum was acquired with 45° pulses at a repetition rate of 0.2 s. As an external reference, 1.8% (w/v) methylene diphosphonic acid (MDP) in Tris-HCl buffer (pH 8.9) in a capillary tube was used, and the chemical shift value of each signal was expressed in ppm relative to the MDP signal. The intracellular pH was deduced from a standard reference curve of chemical shift established as a function of pH.

2.3 *Preparation of Tonoplast Vesicles:* Right-side out tonoplast vesicles were prepared from rice cells as described previously (**8**) with some modifications. In brief, the microsomal membrane fraction suspended with 0.25 M sucrose was layered over 6 % (w/w) dextran T-70 and centrifuged at 120,000 x g for 90 min. The tonoplast-enriched membranes were collected in the interface.

2.4 *Measurement of Enzyme Activities and Proton Transport Activity:* The assay mixture for tonoplast ATPase activity consisted of 3 mM Tris-ATP, 3 mM $MgSO_4$, 50 mM KCl and 30 mM MES-Tris (pH 6.5), sodium azide, ammonium molybdate and vanadate. The pyrophosphatase was assayed in 1 mM Tris-pyrophosphate, 1 mM $MgSO_4$ and 40 mM MES-Tris (pH 8.0) in the presence of various ions. For both assays, after 30-min incubation, the reaction was terminated by trichloroacetic acid and the released Pi was determined (**9**).

The decrease in internal pH of membrane vesicles was estimated by measuring the quenching of quinacrine fluorescence. Tonoplast membrane vesicles were added to a solution consisting of 0.25 M sucrose, 50 mM choline-Cl, 10 µM quinacrine, 10 mM MES-Tris (pH 8.0) in the presence of various salts. After adding 1 mM Tris-pyrophosphate and 1 mM $MgSO_4$, the decrease in fluorescence at 500 nm was monitored with an excitation wavelength of 425 nm.

3. RESULTS and DISCUSSION

3.1 *Salt Stress-Induced Leakage of H^+ out of the Vacuole to the Cytoplasm.*

NaCl stress caused serious inhibition of cell growth in suspension-cultured cells of rice and tobacco. In rice, salt stress of 0.05-0.1 M NaCl reduced the growth rate, and cells showed almost no growth under 0.15 M of NaCl. The growth of tobacco cells was more sensitive to salt. Severe NaCl stress caused even cell death. The viability of the rice cells estimated by the colorimetric assay with MTT (3-(4,5-dimethyl-2-thiazolyl)-2,5-diphenyl tetrazolium bromide) decreased within several hours in the presence of more than 0.2 M of NaCl.

By aerating the cell suspension with oxygen during the NMR measurement, we monitored the time courses of cytoplasmic and vacuolar pH changes under salt stress by *in vivo* ^{31}P-NMR spectroscopy. A typical ^{31}P-NMR spectrum of intact rice cells is shown in Fig. 1. The signals for cytoplasmic and vacuolar inorganic phosphate were always separated, and the pH values of the two compartments were deduced from their chemical shift values. Under normal growth conditions, the pH values of cytoplasm and vacuoles were about 7.5 and 5, respectively, indicating that H^+ had accumulated in the vacuole at levels several hundred times higher than that in the cytoplasm.

When NaCl (0.1-0.4 M) was applied to the medium, pH of the vacuole increased to about 6 (Fig. 2). Under severe NaCl stress (0.4 M), the cytoplasmic pH decreased, correspondingly and finally the H^+-gradient between the two compartments disappeared after several hours. Similar results were obtained with tobacco cells under 0.2 M NaCl. These alkalization of the vacuole and the acidification of the cytoplasm indicate that H^+ leaked across the tonoplast after the salt stress.

When the rice cells were suspended in 0.1-0.14 M NaCl, vacuolar pH increased while the cytoplasmic pH remained almost constant. This indicates that protons leaked out of the vacuole, but the homeostasis of the cytoplasmic pH was maintained when the salt stress was not severe. It is assumed that the pH regulating mechanisms in the cytoplasm such as the H^+-pump in the plasma membrane and/or biochemical pH stat (2) could compensate the influx of H^+ from the vacuole in this case.

When the rice cells were suspended in the Ca^{2+}-depleted medium (1 mM KCl, 2 % glucose), both the acidification of the cytoplasm and the alkalization of the vacuole were induced by 0.2 M NaCl. This result is consistent with the previous observation that Ca^{2+} in the medium reduced the effect of NaCl stress (**10, 11**).

In conclusion, protons concentrated in the vacuole leaked out to the cytosol after salt stress. The cytoplasmic pH is assumed to be determined by the balance of the influx of H^+ from the vacuole and the active pH-regulating mechanisms. When the NaCl stress is not serious, the cytoplasmic pH is maintained, but cytoplasmic pH decreased under severer critical stress. Since the disturbance of cytoplasmic pH should have serious consequence on the cellular regulation, we propose that this salt-induced pH change is one of the initial and significant steps that lead to cell damage in higher plants just as in *Nitellopsis* (**6**).

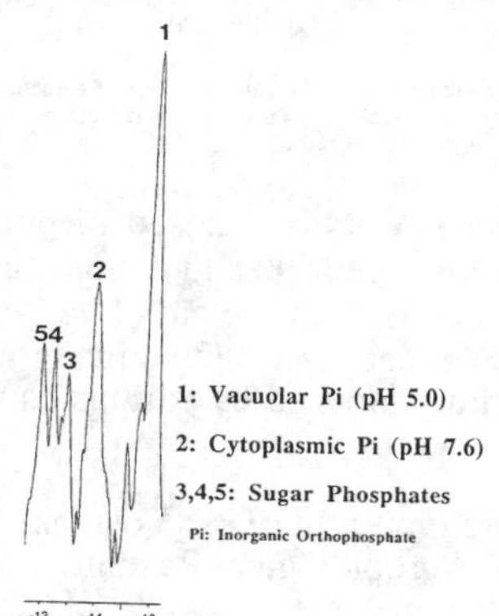

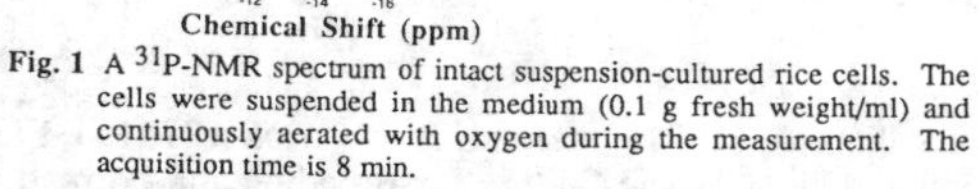

Fig. 1 A ^{31}P-NMR spectrum of intact suspension-cultured rice cells. The cells were suspended in the medium (0.1 g fresh weight/ml) and continuously aerated with oxygen during the measurement. The acquisition time is 8 min.

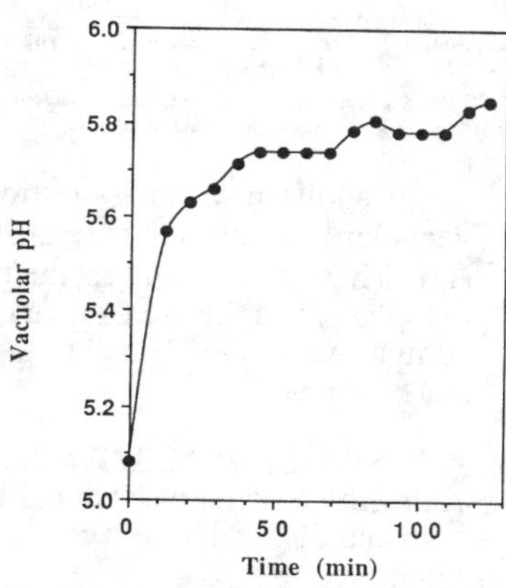

Fig. 2 Vacuolar pH Change Induced by NaCl Stress (0.14 M) in Suspension-Cultured Rice Cells.

3.2 *Inhibition of Pyrophosphate-Dependent H^+-Transport across the Vacuolar Membrane under Salt Stress.*

To investigate the molecular mechanism for salt-induced leakage of H^+ out of the vacuole, the effects of various ions on the activities of the two kinds of H^+-pumps (ATPase and pyrophosphatase (PPase)) in the tonoplast were characterized. Tonoplast H^+-ATPase activity was not so much affected by Na^+ in the presence of K^+. In contrast, H^+-PPase activity, as well as pyrophosphate-dependent H^+-transport, were strictly K^+-dependent, and strongly inhibited by Na^+ in the presence of K^+ (Fig. 3). Rb^+ activated PPase like K^+, whereas Li^+, F^- and Ca^{2+} inhibited PPase activity. The effects of ions on the tonoplast H^+-PPase activity are summarized in Fig. 4.

Under salt stress, it is supposed that Na^+ increases and K^+ decreases in the cytoplasm (10). Actually, the efflux of K^+ from the rice cells under salt stress was confirmed with a K^+-specific microelectrode. Considering the opposite effects of Na^+ and K^+ on PPi-dependent H^+-transport activity (Fig. 3), this proton pump is assumed to be seriously inhibited under salt stress. Thus we speculate that tonoplast H^+-PPase is one of the important target sites under salt (Na) stress in plant cells (Fig. 4).

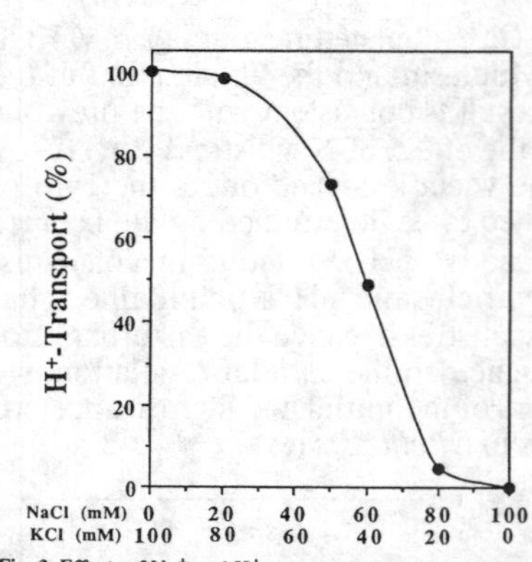

Fig. 3 Effects of Na^+ and K^+ on pyrophosphate-dependent H^+-transport activity in the tonoplast vesicles.

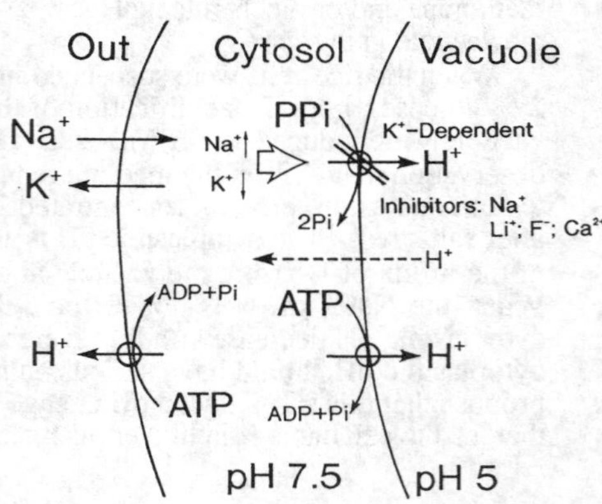

Fig. 4 A possible mechanism for the inhibition of pyrophosphate-dependent H^+-transport and the lealage of protons from the vacuole under salt (Na) stress in plant cells.

In addition to the salt stress, chilling stress also caused the inhibition of vacuolar H^+-pumps in suspension-cultured rice cells (8) and mung bean seedlings (12). These results suggest the possibility that H^+-leakage out of he vacuole to the cytoplasm and the breakdown of H^+-gradient between the two major intracellular compartments are critical steps for cell injury induced by various environmental stress in plants.

4. ACKNOWLEDGMENT: The authors are grateful to Drs. Yoshiaki Yazaki and Katsuhiro Sakano of National Institute of Agrobiological Resources for valuable help and discussion for *in vivo* NMR measurement.

REFERENCES

1. Guern, J., Felle, H., Mathieu, Y. and Kurkdjian, A. (1991) Internatl. Rev. Cytol. 127, 111-173
2. Kuchitsu, K. (1992) in Gene Manipulation and Plant Tissue Culture for Breeding and Formation of Phytochemicals (Oono, K. et al., ed.), pp. 127-132 NIAR, Tsukuba
3. Roberts, J.K.M. (1984) Annu. Rev. Plant Physiol. 35, 375-386
4. Kuchitsu, K., Oh-hama, T., Tsuzuki, M. and Miyachi, S. (1987) Arch. Microbiol. 147, 83-87
5. Kuchitsu, K., Katsuhara, M. and Miyachi, S. (1989) Plant Cell Physiol. 30, 407-414
6. Katsuhara, M., Kuchitsu, K., Takeshige, K. and Tazawa, M. (1989) Plant Physiol. 90, 1102-1107
7. Toriyama, K. and Hinata, K. (1985) Plant Sci. 41, 179-183
8. Kasamo, K. (1988) Plant Cell Physiol. 29, 1085-1094
9. Kasamo, K. (1979) Plant Cell Physiol. 20, 281-292
10. Katsuhara, M. and Tazawa, M. (1986) Protoplasma 135, 155-161
11. Nakamura, Y., Kasamo, K., Shimosato, N., Sakata, M. and Ohta, E. (1992) Plant Cell Physiol. 33, 139-149
12. Yoshida, S., Matsuura-Endo, C. (1991) Plant Physiol. 95:504-508

SALT STRESS RESPONSES IN CULTURED GREEN TOBACCO CELLS

Fumihiko Sato[1], Ken-ichi Murota[2], Sueo Aso[2] and Yasuyuki Yamada[1]
[1]Dept. of Agric. Chem., Facul. of Agric., Kyoto Univ., Kyoto, 606-01, [2]Dept. of Agric. Chem., Facul. of Agric., Tokyo Univ. of Agriculture, Tokyo 156, Japan

1. INTRODUCTION

Osmotic adjustment is a fundamental adaptive response of plant cells which are exposed to salinity and is necessary for survival and growth under saline conditions (1). The *in vitro* isolation of cells of glycophytes with enhanced salt tolerance has facilitated the study of cellular responses to salinity (2). These salt tolerant cells are especially useful in studies to identify specific adaptive responses of glycophytes to salinity because they provide a system with which to separate those processes which are involved in salinity adaptation as opposed to those which are a response to the imposition of the stress. Utilizing isolated cells does restrict studies to salt tolerance mechanisms which are characteristics of individual cells and does not lend itself to examination of the contributions to salt tolerance of more complex multicellular processes or mechanisms involving differentiated highly specialized cells. However, these studies have been limited to heterotrophically cultured cells, which growth is solely dependent on the organic carbon source added in medium.

Photoautotrophy is one of the primary target of salt stress. Photoautotrophically (PA) cultured cells that grow only by photosynthesis provide the suitable material for the study of cellular responses on photosynthesis to salinity. Here we report the growth and photosynthetic characteristics of cultured tobacco (*Nicotiana tabacum* cv. Samsun NN) cells which can grow photoautotrophically in the medium containing 0.2 M NaCl, under which saline condition unadapted cells can not grow and their photosynthesis was inhibited considerably. We also describe the characteristics of polypeptides accumulating in thylakoid membranes of unadapted and adapted cells to get some informations about the molecular basis in adaptation of photosynthesis under NaCl stress.

2. MATERIALS AND METHODS

2.1 Selection of a cell line adapted to 0.2M NaCl

Photoautotrophic (PA) cultures of tobacco (*Nicotiana tabacum* cv. Samsun NN) were maintained in modified Linsmaier and Skoog liquid media without sucrose in air enriched with CO_2 (1-2 %) as described elsewhere (3), except that two-tier flasks were used as described by Hüsemann and Barz (4). A cell line adapted to 0.2 M NaCl was selected by the repeated subculture of PA cells in 0.2 M NaCl containing medium. Both adapted and unadapted cells were subcultured every two weeks at 26±2°C with reciprocal shaking (100 rpm) under continuous light (ca. 8,000 lux).

N. Murata (ed.), Research in Photosynthesis, Vol. IV, 259–262.

2.2 Isolation of stroma-free chloroplast thylakoid membranes

Chloroplasts were isolated with the method described previously (5). Both cells (100 g) were homogenized in 150 ml of 0.4 M sucrose, 50 mM Tricine-KOH (pH 7.8), 10 mM NaCl, 2 mM $MgCl_2$ and 5 mM mercaptoethanol in a Waring blender for 5 sec 3 times. The homogenates were filtered through four layers of gauze, the filtrates centrifuged at 400 g for 2 min, and the supernatants recentrifuged at 2000 g for 8 min. The chloroplasts pelleted were further purified by sucrose density gradient centrifugations (60 %, 48 %, 35 %, 25 % (w/v)) containing 50 mM Tricine-KOH (pH 7.8) solution at 21,000 rpm (Beckman SW-28 rotor) for 1 hr. Purified chloroplasts were suspended in extraction solution and centrifuged at 10,000 g for 10 min. The sedimented chloroplasts were resuspended in destilled water for 3 min and centrifuged at 12,000 g for 10 min. The pellet was washed with distilled water once. All procedures were carried out at 0-4°C. The Chl concentration was calculated using the equations of Mackinney (6).

2.3 Polypeptides extraction from thylakoid membranes

Polypeptides of thylakoid membranes were extracted according to Schuster and Davies (7). Hundred mg of thylakoid membranes was suspended in 1.5 ml of ice-cold extraction buffer (0.7 M sucrose ; 0.5 M Tris ; 30 mM HCl ; 50 mM EDTA; 0.1 M KCl ; 2 % (v/v) mercaptoethanol). Proteins were extracted from the suspension with an equal volume of phenol saturated with water, then precipitated by mixing them with 0.1 M ammonium acetate in methanol. The precipitate was air dried and redissolved in 9.5 M urea; 2 % Nonidet P-40; 2 % ampholines (pH 2.5-4 : pH 3.5-10 : pH 5-8 : pH 9-11=1 : 20 : 3 : 3) ; 5 % mercaptoethanol.

Protein was measured by the Coomassie-blue protein quantification method described by Bradford (8) and compared to values for Bovine serum albumin standards, which also had been dissolved in the lysis buffer.

2.4 Electrophoresis

Two-dimensional gel electrophoresis was done with slight modifications, according to the method of O'Farrell (9). Each 1.5 mg sample of protein were loaded for the first dimension. Molecular weight markers (Amersham) that ranged from 14,300 to 97,400 were used to determine the molecular weights of the polypeptide spots. The pH range of the isoelectric focusing gels was obtained by pI marker (Oriental yeast).

Gels were stained with 0.1 % Coomassie brillant blue R-250 in 25 % ethanol : 10 % acetic acid, and destained in 25 % ethanol : 10 % acetic acid.

3. RESULTS AND DISCUSSION

3.1 Growth and photosynthetic characteristics of NaCl-adapted cells

The growth of unadapted cultured green cells was completely inhibited by the addition of 0.2 M NaCl in medium, while they increased about 200 % in the control culture without NaCl after 3 weeks of culture. NaCl adapted cells could increase their dry weight more than 100 % after 3 weeks of inoculation. The photosynthetic oxygen evolution activity of adapted cells was less affected than that of unadapted cells by the addition of NaCl in assay buffer. The tolerance of photosynthetic activity in adapted cells was also observed in isolated thylakoid membranes (K. Murota et al., details will be published elsewhere.).

3.2 Characterization of polypeptides in thylakoid membrane

To understand the molecular mechanism of salt tolerance, we examine the polypeptide accumulation in the thylakoid membrane by polyacrylamide gel electrophoresis. While one dimensional PAGE showed little differences between adapted cells and unadapted cells, 2D-PAGE analysis of the protein of thylakoid membranes clearly showed that the polypeptides of thylakoid membranes of unadapted cells differed in several respects from those of adapted cells (Figure 1, Table 1). Proteins P2, P4, P5 and P7 were present in remarkably large amounts in thylakoid membranes of unadapted cells than in those of adapted cells, whereas the amounts of protein P15, P16, P17 were remarkably abundant in the thylakoid membranes of adapted cells. Further investigation to get information about these polypeptide accumulating differently in adapted cells and unadapted cells was not successful at this moment, because their NH_2-terminal amino acid sequences were blocked. We are continuing the characterization of polypeptides in thylakoid membranes using specific antibody. Our latest results indicated that 23 kD polypeptide of water-splitting complex may be involved in salt tolerance (K.Murota et al., unpublished data). Further investigation is in progress to understand the molecular mechanism of salt tolerance in photosynthesis.

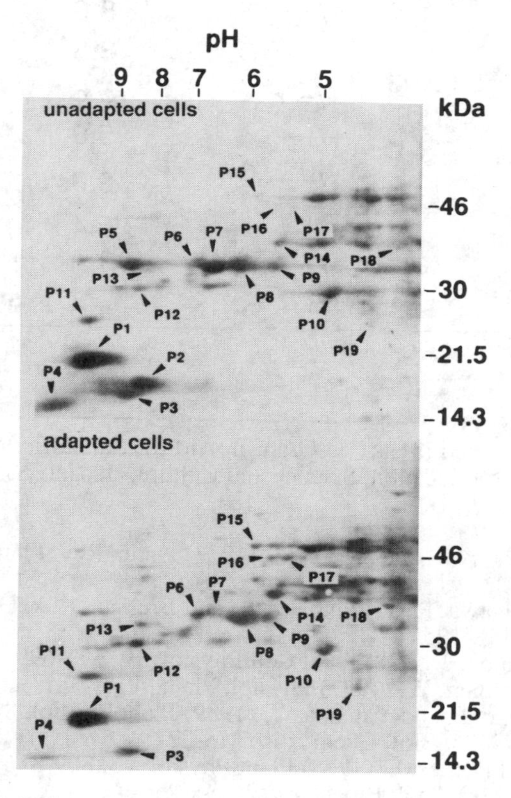

Figure 1 Two dimensional polyacrylamide gel electrophoresis of thylakoid membrane polypeptides of unadapted and adapted cells to 0.2 M NaCl.

Table 1 Differences in polypeptides accumulation in thylakoid membranes of unadapted and adapted cells to 0.2 M NaCl.

Polypeptide	Presence in unadapted / adapted	pI	M.W.(kD)
P2	+ + + +/-	8.4	18
P4	+ + +/+	10.7	16
P5	+ + +/-	8.8	33
P7	+ + + +/+	6.7	33
P8	+ +/+ + +	6.2	33
P12	+/+ +	8.6	30
P13	+/+ +	8.3	33
P14	+/+ +	5.6	38
P15	+/+ +	5.9	48
P16	-/+ +	5.6	45
P17	+/+ +	5.4	45
P18	+/+ +	4.3	37
P19	+/+ +	4.5	25

ACKNOWLEDGMENT

This work is supported in part by Grant-in Aid for Scientific Research on Priority Areas from Ministry of Education, Science and Culture, Japan(FS).

REFERENCES

1 Flowers, T.J., Troke, A.R. and Yeo, A.R. (1977) Annu. Rev. Plant Physiol. 28, 89-121
2 Binzel, M.L., Hasegawa, P.M., Handa, A.K. and Bressan, R.A. (1985) Plant Physiol. 79, 118-125
3 Yamada, Y. and Sato, F. (1978) Plant Cell Physiol. 19, 691-699
4 Hüsemann, W. and Barz, W. (1977) Physiol. Plant. 40, 77-81
5 Shigematsu, Y., Sato, F. and Yamada, Y. (1989) Plant Physiol. 89, 986-992
6 Mackinney, G. (1941) J. Biol. Chem. 140, 315-322
7 Schuster, A.M. and Davies, E. (1983) Plant Physiol. 73, 809-816
8 Bradford, M.M. (1976) Anal. Biochem. 72, 248-254
9 O'Farrell, P.H. (1975) J. Biol. Chem. 250, 4007-4021

CHANGE OF PROTEIN PHOSPHORYLATION OF *DUNALIELLA TERTIOLECTA* CELLS IN OSMOTIC SHOCK

TAKASHI YUASA AND SHOSHI MUTO, INSTITUTE OF APPLIED MICROBIOLOGY, UNIVERSITY OF TOKYO, BUNKYO-KU, TOKYO 113, JAPAN

1. INTRODUCTION

Dunaliella tertiolecta is an extremely halotolerant unicellular green alga. The cells have no rigid cell wall and are enclosed only within a thin plasma membrane; thus are able to change rapidly their volume and shape in response to external osmotic changes. The cells can rapidly recover their volume and shape by varying the intracellular concentration of glycerol. As the adaptation process for osmotic stress was not affected by inhibitors of protein synthesis (1), the reactions involved are not controlled at the level of gene expression. Instead, enzymatic activation *via* regulatory cofactors or posttranslational protein modifications may particiate in the osmoregulation of *Dunaliella*.

We have partially purified and characterized Ca^{2+}-dependent protein kinase (CDPK) from *D.tertiolecta* (2). The CDPK is greatly activated by a micromolar Ca^{2+}. The activated enzyme associated to the microsomes and phosphorylated the membrane proteins, suggesting possible involvement of the CDPK in osmoregulation.

In the present study, changes in protein phosphorylation in *Dunaliella* cells after osmotic shock were investigated in relation to the role of CDPK in osmoregulation of the algae.

2. MATERIALS AND METHODS

2.1 Algal culture: *D.tertiolecta* was precultured as described (2) in the medium containing 0.5 M NaCl, and diluted with 2 volumes of the medium lacking Pi, and then incubated for 15 h at room temprature under continuous light (20 W/m^2). The cells were incubated for 1 h with $KH_2{}^{32}PO_4$ (final 20 μM and 74 kBq/ml). During the incubation ^{32}P was completely incorporated into the algae.

2.2 Osmotic shock: The labeled cells were diluted with 1.5 volumes of medium containing 0, 0.5 or 1.5 M NaCl.

2.3 Inhibitor treatment: The labeled cells were preincubated for 30 min with inhibitors before osmotic shock.

2.4 Analysis of labeled proteins: At intervals after osmotic shock, cells were treated with 10% CCl_3COOH, 20 mM NaF and 1 mM phenylmethylsulfonyl fluoride (PMSF) at 0°C and centrifuged at 16,000*g* for 15 min. After rinsing with chilled 0.25 M sucrose, the precipitates were dis-

N. Murata (ed.), Research in Photosynthesis, Vol. IV, 263–266.

solved in SDS-PAGE sample buffer containig 8.5 M urea and subjected to SDS-PAGE. Gels were stained with Coomassie blue and autradiographed.

2.5 *In vitro* protein phosphorylation: Microsomal fraction of the cells was phosphorylated with purified CDPK as described (2).

2.6 Enzyme treatment of phosphorylated samples: CCl_3COOH-precipitated samples were suspended in 1% SDS and 1% β-mercaptoethanol, neutralized with 1M NaOH and solubilized by heating at 100°C for 5 min. Samples were diluted with 4 volumes of 50 mM citrate-NaOH (pH 5) for endoglycosidase H (Boehringer), glycopeptidase A, mixed glycosidases (Seikagaku Kogyo) and V8 protease (Sigma), 50 mM Tris-HCl (pH 8) for pronase E (Kaken Kagaku) or 50 mM citrate-Na_2HPO_4 (pH 5), 1% Triton X-100 and 1 mM PMSF for phospholipase D (Boehringer) and phospholipase A_2 (Sigma). Each enzyme was used at 250 mU/ml and incubated for 15 h at 37 °C. The reaction was stopped by adding 1/4 volume of 4x SDS-PAGE sample buffer. After heating for 3 min, samples were subjected to SDS-PAGE.

3. RESULTS AND DISCUSSION

3.1 Effects of inhibitors on recovery of cell shape after osmotic shock: A protein kinase inhibitor K252a (5 μM) inhibited the recovery of cell shape after hypoosmotic shock, whereas it had no effect on the recovery after hyperosmotic shock. This suggests the involvement of protein phosphorylation in the recovery of cell shape after hypoosmotic shock. On the contrary, 10 nM calyculin A, a protein phosphatase inhibitor, inhibited the recovery of cell shape after hyperosmotic shock (data not shown), suggesting the involvement of protein dephosphorylation in the recovery after hyperosmotic shock.

3.2 Change of protein phosphorylation after osmotic shock: After incubating cells with ^{32}Pi for 1 h, ^{32}P was incorporated into bands corresponding to 100, 70, 64, 38 and 28 kDa. The pattern of phosphoprotein did not change during further 90-min incubation, but the total ^{32}P incorporation slightly increased with time (Fig.2A). Upon hypoosmotic shock (Fig.2B), the 28-kDa band markedly increased during 2—5 min and returned to the original level after 20 min. Concurrently several bands appeared at 30—32 kDa. Patterns of other radioactive bands were essentially same as in control. A remarkable smear band broadly ranging 30—100 kDa appeared immediately after hyperosmotic shock; it retained high radioactivity for 1 h and slightly decreased after 1.5 h. A similar change was

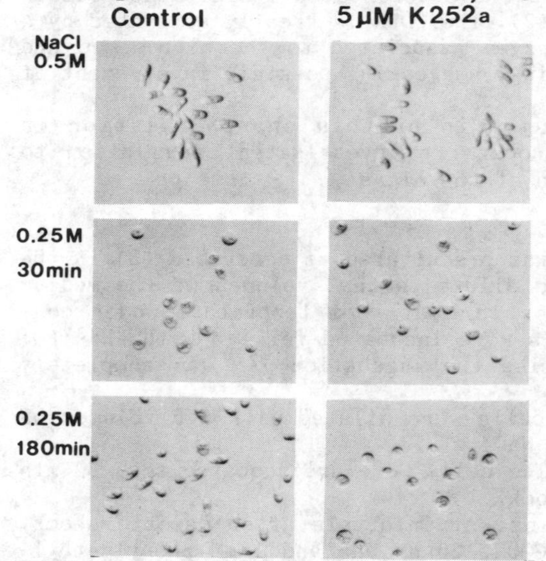

FIGURE 1. Effect of K252a on recovery of cell shape after hypoosmotic shock.

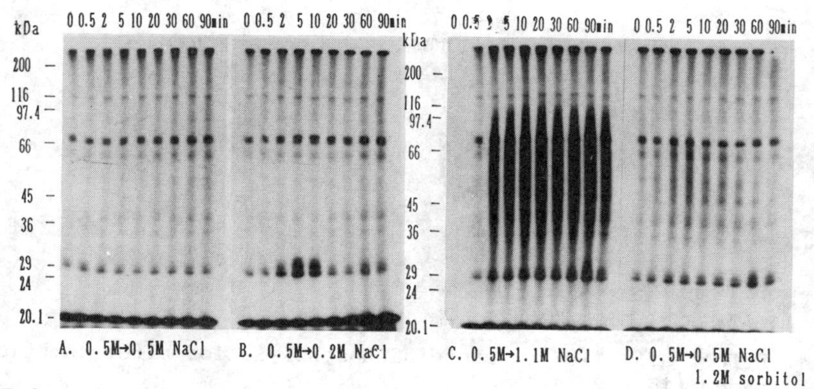

FIGURE 2. Change of protein phosphorylation after osmotic shock.

observed in the 28-kDa band. When hyperosmotic shock was given with sorbitol instead of NaCl, the increase in smear band was mostly suppressed (Fig.2D). When concentration of $MgCl_2$ (9→40 mM) or $CaCl_2$ (1.5→30 mM) was increased under isoosmotic condition, the observed change in phosphorylation pattern was very similar to that under hyperosmotic shock (data not shown). These results suggest that the phosphorylation of smear band and 29-kDa band may be caused by the increase of salt concentration rather than by the increase of osmolarity. The divalent metal salts seem more effective than NaCl.

3.3 Effects of inhibitors of protein kinase and phosphatase, and A23187 on protein phosphorylation after osmotic shock: The hypoosmotic shock-induced increases of 28—32-kDa bands were completely inhibited by 5 μM K252a (Fig.3B). On the other hand, the hyperosmotic shock-induced increase of smear band had no effect (Fig.3C). In the presence of 10 nM calyculin A, a part of smear band ranging 50—70 kDa disappeared under hyperosmotic shock, whereas the increases of 28—32-kDa bands under hypoosmotic shock had no effect (data not shown). Possible involvement

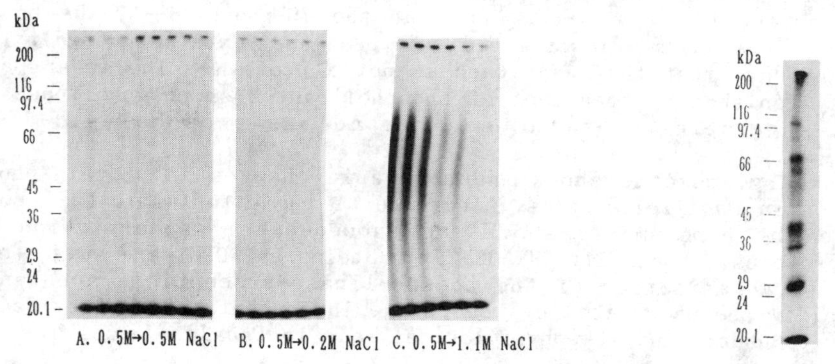

FIGURE 3. Effect of K252a on protein phosphorylation after osmotic shock (left).

FIGURE 5. *In vitro* phosphorylation of microsomal proteins (right).

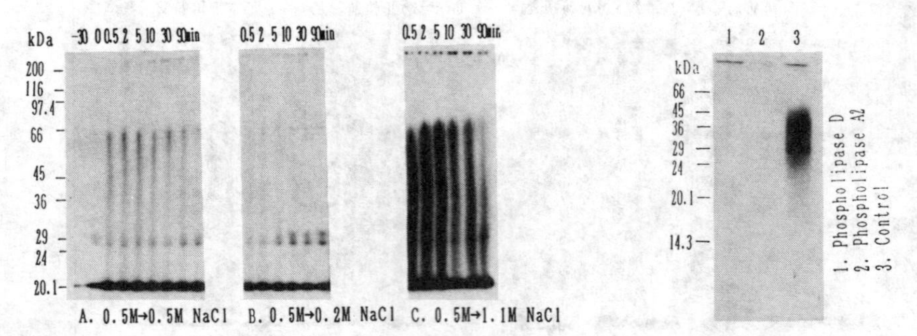

FIGURE 4. Effect of A23187 on protein phosphorylation after osmotic shock (left).

FIGURE 6. Effect of phospholipase treatment on the smear band.

of CDPK in osmotic shock-induced protein phosphorylation was examined using Ca^{2+} ionophore A23187. During preincubation with 10 μM A23187, phosphorylation of 70- and 28—32-kDa bands increased (Fig.4A, 0 min). This suggests that A23187 caused the increase in cytoplasmic Ca^{2+} concentration and subsequently activated CDPK which phosphorylated 70- and 28—32-kDa bands, and that the Ca^{2+} increase was caused by hypoosmotic shock. Hypoosmotic shock gradually increased the 28—32-kDa bands (Fig.4B). The smear band increased rapidly by hyperosmotic shock.

3.4 *In vitro* phosphorylation of microsomal proteins by CDPK: When the microsomal fraction of *Dunaliella* was incubated with CDPK, several proteins were phosphorylated in a Ca^{2+}-dependent manner as previously reported (2) (Fig.5). Among them 100-, 36-, and 28-kDa bands had similar molecular masses to those phosphorylated *in vivo* (Fig.2B).

3.5 Enzyme treatment of phosphorylated proteins: Since glycoproteins behave as smear bands in SDS-PAGE, phosphorylated samples were treated with glycopeptidase, glycosidases or proteases, and analyzed by SDS-PAGE in order to identify the hyperosmotic shock-induced smear band. No effect was observed in the smear band but the 70- and 28—32-kDa bands disappeared from the samples treated with protease (data not shown). The results indicate that the smear band is not a protein. The smear band completely vanished by treatment of phospholipase D or phospholipase A_2 (Fig.6), suggesting that the smear band has phospholipid-like structure(s).

In summary, osmotic shock induced rapid changes in protein phosphorylation in *Dunaliella* cells. Increase of the cytoplasmic Ca^{2+} concentration by hypoosmotic shock and subsequent phosphorylation of several proteins, especially 28—32-kDa proteins by CDPK were suggested. Further characterization of the phospholipase-susceptible substance which rapidly phosphorylated by the change in concentration of salts is necessary to understand its physiological role in *Dunaliella* cells.

REFERENCES

1. Sadka,A.,Lers,A.,Zamir,A.,and Avron,M.(1989) FEBS Lett. 244, 93-98
2. Yuasa,T.,and Muto,S.(1992) Arch. Biochem. Biophys. 296, 175-182

PHOTOFIXATION OF $^{14}CO_2$ AND PHOTOSYNTHETIC ELECTRON TRANSPORTS IN A DESICCATION TOLERANT CYANOBACTERIUM SCYTONEMA GEITLERI

S.N. TRIPATHI AND B.S. TIWARI, CENTRE OF ADVANCED STUDY IN BOTANY, BANARAS HINDU UNIVERSITY, VARANASI-221 005 INDIA

1. INTRODUCTION

The cyanobacteria from building surfaces express marked tolerance to extremes of environmental stresses, particularly, desiccation (1). The prokaryotic cell organization and capacity for higher plant type photosynthesis tender a suitable model system for the study of desiccation tolerance particularly photosynthetic aspects. Photosynthetic behaviour of Scytonema geitleri, one of the potent desiccation tolerant cyanobacterium from the roof top, has been investigated by measuring photofixation of $^{14}CO_2$ and electron transports (PS II, PS I and whole-chain) at different time course and water potentials in the present study.

2. MATERIALS AND METHODS

Mats of Scytonema geitleri in almost unialgal state were scrapped from roof tops of tropical building of Banaras Hindu University (see ref. 1 for climatic details), and gently washed with distilled water to remove attached building materials. The washed mats were stored in atmosphere of conc. H_2SO_4 at 25°c in dark and used for experiments.

2.1 Isolation of thylakoids and measurements of photosynthetic electron transports were made following the methods reported by Samuelsson and Prezelin(2) and Allen and Holms (3) using clark type oxygen electrode (Hansatech instruments Ltd. U.K.) with certain modifications. $^{14}CO_2$ fixation studies were made employing Conway dish method(4).

3. RESULTS AND DISCUSSION

Mats of S. geitleri, osmotically saturated at 0 bar for different time intervals, showed a gradual increase upto 24 h followed by decline in $^{14}CO_2$ fixation, it was negligible in dry mats (Fig.1). Scherer et.al. (5) have shown evolution of photosynthetic oxygen within 60 minutes of rewetting and reached its maximum within 7-9 h in species of Nostoc, a terrestrial cyanobacterium. In a species of Oscillatoria recovery of $^{14}CO_2$ fixation reached its maximum after 17 h of wetting (6). Whereas, mats of S. geitleri osmotically equilibrated at different water potential solutions

N. Murata (ed.), Research in Photosynthesis, Vol. IV, 267–270.

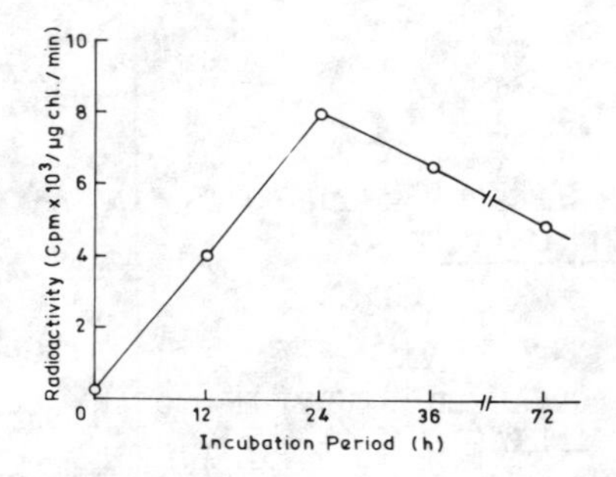

Fig. Photofixation of $^{14}CO_2$ by S.geitleri mats incubated at 0 bar (osmotically) for different time course under growing conditions.

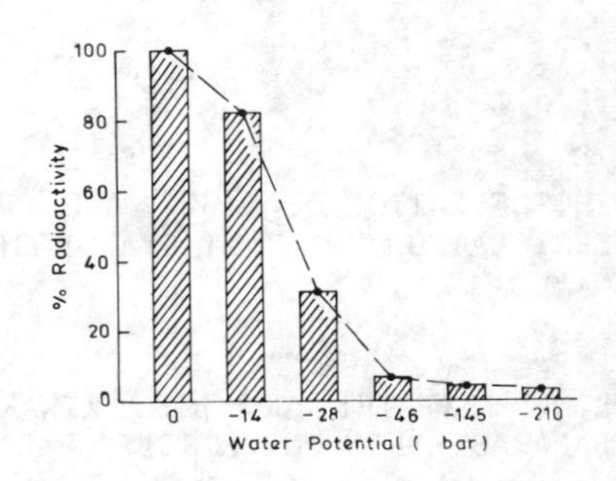

Fig.2. Photofixation of $^{14}CO_2$ by S.geitleri mats treated at different water potential for 24 h under gorwing conditions.

TABLE 1 : Photosynthetic electron transport activity in thylakoids of S.geitleri incubated osmotically at 0 bar for different time course at growing conditions.

Incubation time (h)	O_2 evolution/consumption mM/µg chl/min			% Activity		
	*PS-II	PS-I	Whole Chain	PS II	PS I	Whole Chain
1. 0	.026	.058	.001	100	100	100
2. 12	.032	.061	.008	123.07	105.17	800
3. 24	.044	.077	.021	169.23	132.75	2100.
4. 72	.099	.037	.019	380.76	63.79	1900.

*PS II($H_2O \rightarrow$ DAD/FeCN), PS I(DCPIP/Asc$\rightarrow$ MV), Whole Chain($H_2O \rightarrow$ MV).

TABLE 2 : Electron transport activity in thylakoids isolated from S.geitleri treated with different osmotic potential solutions for 24 h at growing conditions.

Treatment (12 h)	O_2 evolution/consumption mM/µgchl/min			% Activity		
	PS II	PS I	Whole Chain	PS II	PS I	Whole Chain
0 bar	.044	.077	.021	100	100	100
-28 bar	.031	.054	.009	64.4	70.12	47.36
-145 bar	.0246	.046	.006	55.9	65.25	31.57

*PS II($H_2O \rightarrow$DAD/FeCN), PS I(DCPIP/Asc$\rightarrow$ MV), Whole Chain ($H_2O \rightarrow$ MV).

for 24 h under growing conditions showed a maximum $^{14}CO_2$ fixation at 0 bar which reduced by 82, 81 and 6.5% at -14, -28 and -46 bars, respectively (Fig.2). Further lowering of water potential, has shown the least $^{14}CO_2$ fixation. $^{14}CO_2$ fixation in soil algae Microcoleus (7) and cyanidium coldarium (8) has been reported to be less sensitive upto -14 bar but markedly inhibited at/below -24 bar, further revealing higher adaptability of S. geitleri under water stress conditions as compared to the soil algae. The mats of S. geitleri have shown similar pattern of $^{14}CO_2$ fixation under various treatments of water potential as it has been reported for in other roof-top cyanobacteria (1,4,9).

3.1 Thylakoids isolated from dry mats and mats incubated for different time course at 0 bar under growing conditions reflected presence of considerable photochemical activity of electron transports (Table-1). Maximum activity was observed in mats grown for 24 h showing an increment of 21, 77 and 44% in whole chain, PS II, and PS I, respectively. On the basis of stoichiometries of 0_2 evoluation / uptake (see ref. 3) it may be said that activity of PS II is considerably high in the thylakoids of dry mats. The stability of thylakoid membranes under dry conditions may be attributed to carbohydrates specially Trehalose (10) and Glycine Betaine (11). However, stoichiometric relationship between electron transport follows almost usual pattern in the thylakoids of 24 h grown mats probably due to a gradual recovery in PS I on wetting of the mats. Though, almost zero $^{14}CO_2$ fixation has been recorded, a considerable activity of electron transport has been observed in dry mats. The presence of such high activity of electron transport in thylakoids of dry mats may be said to be due to quick recovery of electron transport on addition of reaction medium used in 0_2 evolution technique, However, a recovery in peak fluorescence and fluorescence yield has been reported in dry pea cotyledons containing water content even below 12% (13). Table (2) shows that lowering of water potential considerably lowered the activity of all electron transport systems with greater reduction in PS II. This could be due to impairing of water molecules at the water splitting site. The reduction in activity of PS I on lowering in water potential may be due to partial impairment of energy transfer mechanism in chlorophyll/PSI (13).

3.2 In tropics, building surfaces cyanobacteria are subjected to very low humidity (upto 20% R.H during hot summers) besides high temperature (45°c ambient and upto 68°c surface) and high light intensity (437 cal/cm/day) during hot summer. In addition to dry conditions of hot summer and cold winter season, even during rainy season the algae are frequently exposed to drying and wetting. Accumulation of hydrophobic proteins, rich in SH groups (14) high chlorophyll stability index (15) accumulation of water stress proteins (16) and carbohydrates specially Trehalose (17) have been suggested for tolerance of the algae under extremes of desiccation.

ACKNOWLEDGEMENTS
Thanks are due to CSIR New Delhi and Head department of Botany, Banaras Hindu University Varanasi for financial assistance and facilities.

REFERENCES

1. Tripathi, S.N., Tiwari, B.S., Talpasayi, E.R.S. (1991) Energy and Buildings 15-16, 499-505.
2. Samuelsson & Prezelin (1985), J. Phycology, 21, 453-457.
3. Allen, J.F., Holms, N.G. (1986) In: Photosynthesis Energy Transduction - A practical approach (Eds. Hipkins, M.F., Baker, N.R.) 103-141.IRL. Press, Oxford
4. Tripathi S.N. Talpasayi, E.R.S. (1982) In: Proc. Natl. Symposium on Biological Nitrogen Fixation. IARI, New Delhi, 138-149.
5. Scherer S., Ernst, A., Chen., T.W., Boger, P. (1984), Oecologia 62, 418-423.
6. De Winder, B, Hans, C.P., M and Mur, L.R. (1989) Arch. Microbiol 152, 458-462.
7. Brock, T.D. (1975) J. Phycology, 11, 316-320.
8. Smith, D.W., Brock, T.D. (1973) J. Phycology, 9, 33.
9. Talpasayi, E.R.S., Tripathi, S.N. (1987) Proc. Natl. Acad Sci.B. 527-529
10. Crowe, J.H. Crowe, L.M. Carpenter, J.F. Wistrom, C.A. (1987) Biochem. J., 242, 1-10.
11. Mamedov, M.D., Hayashi, H. Wada, N. Mohanty P.S. Papageorgiou, G.C. Murata, N. (1991) FEBS Letters, 294, 271-275.
12. Vertucci, C.W., Ellenson, J.L., Leopold, A.C. (1985) Plant Physiol, 79, 248-252.
13. Valcke, R., Poucke, M.V. (1983) In: Effect of Stress on Photosynthesis (Eds. Marcelle, R. Clijster, H. Poucke, M.V.), 141-150. Martinus Nijhoff/Dr. W. Junk Publishers, Hague, Netherlands.
14. Tripathi S.N., Talpasayi, E.R.S. (1980) Curr Sci, 49, 31-32.
15. Tripathi, S.N. (1983) Z.Allge. Mikrobiol., 23, 443-446.
16. Scherer, S. and Potts, M. (1989) J. Biol. Chem., 264, 12546-12553.
17. Hershkovitz, N. Oren, A. Cohen, Y. (1991) Applied and Environmental Microbiol 57, 645-648.

THE EFFECTS OF DROUGHT AND UV-RADIATION UPON CHLOROPHYLL FLUORESCENCE AND CO_2 ASSIMILATION

H. NONAMI, M. KOHCHI, T. FUKUYAMA, and Y. HASHIMOTO, Dept. of Biomechanical Systems, College of Agriculture, Ehime University, Tarumi, Matsuyama 790, Japan

1. INTRODUCTION

Photosynthesis is inhibited by severe water stress and exposure to UV radiation. Recent changes occurring in the earth's ecosystem may increase the likelihood for plants to be subjected to water stress and exposed to UV radiation. Because photosynthesis involves the two processes of photophosphorylation and CO_2 fixation through the Calvin cycle, photosynthesis has not been studied well under conditions of water stress and exposure to UV radiation simultaneously. In the present study, interactions of both physiological functions were studied by measuring chlorophyll fluorescence, CO_2 uptake rates and water status simultaneously when leaves of *Tradescantia* plants were subjected to water stress and exposure to UV radiation.

2. MATERIALS AND METHODS

2.1 Plant material: *Tradescantia virginiana* L. plants were cloned from one stock by root cutting and were grown in pots (humus 45%, perlite 30%, clay 15%, sand 5% and peat 5%) in a greenhouse and fertilized weekly with a nutrient solution. One week prior to chlorophyll fluorescence measurements, plants were transferred to a growth room in which air temperature was kept at 25 ± 1 °C and air humidity was maintained at 50 ± 10% RH. Photosynthetically active photon flux density was set to 200 $\mu mol \cdot m^{-2} \cdot s^{-1}$ during the experiment in the growth room. Fluorescence measurements and CO_2 uptake measurements were conducted under conditions similar to growing conditions in the growth room. Water stress was given by excising the base of the leaf. UV radiation was applied prior to fluorescence and CO_2 uptake measurements by using a 20W–UV lamp (GL–20, Toshiba Co.) having a peak at 254 nm. Distance between the UV lamp and the leaf surface was kept at 0.30 m. Time of the UV exposure ranged from 10 min to 10 h.

2.2 Chlorophyll fluorescence induction kinetics measurements: Chlorophyll fluorescence was measured by using a Plant Stress Meter (BioMonitor S.C.I. AB). A leaf cuvette of the Plant Stress Meter was clamped adjacent to a CO_2 assimilation chamber (ADC) on a leaf. Before chlorophyll fluorescence measurements, leaf tissue in the cuvette was treated in the dark for 20 min. During dark adaptation of the leaf and fluorescence measurements, CO_2 uptake could be measured without interruption in the same leaf simultaneously. Output from the Plant Stress Meter was fed into a computer (PC–9801vm, NEC Co.) through an A/D converter, and fluorescence intensity was plotted with a logarithmic function of time during fluorescence induction so that the fast kinetics could be visualized more easily.

2.3 Water status measurements: Water potential, osmotic potential and turgor of leaves used for chlorophyll fluorescence CO_2 assimilation measurements were measured with isopiestic psychrometers (1). Cell turgor was measured with a cell pressure probe according to Nonami et al. (2) and Nonami and Schulze (3).

N. Murata (ed.), Research in Photosynthesis, Vol. IV, 271–274.

3. RESULTS AND DISCUSSION

Using the nomenclature of Papageorgiou (4), the fluorescence rises from an initial level (O) to a peak (P) within a few seconds, reflecting the photoreduction of the primary stable electron acceptors Q in photosystem II (5, 6) (see notations in Fig. 1.a.). The fluorescence then decreases, largely as a consequence of electron–transport–mediated reoxidation of Q and build–up of trans–thylakoid ΔpH (7, 8). Before the low steady–state level (T) is attained, a fluorescence oscillation with the minimum S and the maximum occurs (Fig. 1.a.).

When leaf water potential decreased from –0.24 MPa to –0.81 MPa, fluorescence intensity of the first peak (P) of the induction kinetics curve decreased, and that of the second peak (M) was not influenced by the water stress (Fig. 1.a.). When leaf water potential decreased further from –0.81 MPa to –0.96 MPa, fluorescence intensity of the second peak decreased (Fig. 1.a.). A further decrease of leaf water potential caused both peaks to be flattened (Fig. 1.a.). This indicates that water stress first causes a decrease of the early reaction detected in the first peak of chlorophyll fluorescent induction kinetics.

When leaves were exposed to UV for 5 h, the water potential was not affected by the UV radiation, but the fluorescence intensity decreased to 1/2 of the intensity before the UV exposure (Fig. 1.b.). This indicates that chlorophyll fluorescence was inhibited by the UV radiation.

In order to compare differences between effects of water stress and UV radiation on photosynthetic functions, CO_2 uptake, chlorophyll fluorescence and water status were measured simultaneously. When leaf water potential decreased, CO_2 uptake decreased almost linearly and became zero at –1.0 MPa of water potential (closed circles in Fig. 2.a.). When plants were exposed to UV, CO_2 uptake was inhibited and further became negative (open circles in Fig. 2.a.). This indicates that CO_2 was released from leaves exposed to UV.

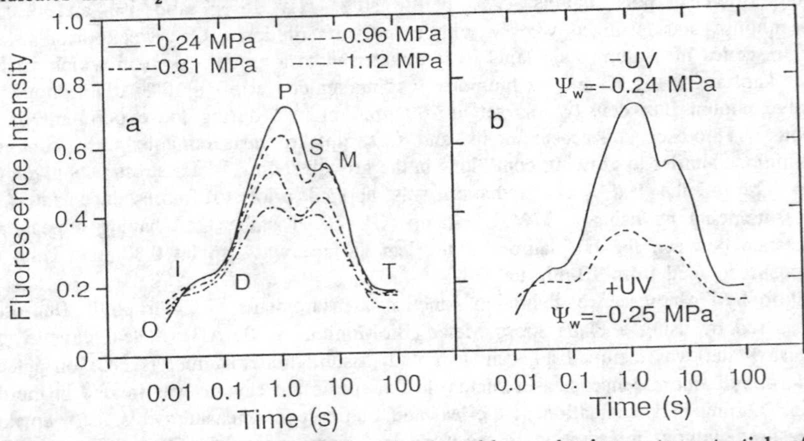

FIGURE 1.a) Chlorophyll fluorescence induction kinetics of leaves having water potentials of –0.24 MPa (solid line), –0.81 MPa (dashed line), –0.96 MPa (one–dotted chain line) and –1.12 MPa (two–dotted chain line). Characters O, I, D, P, S, M, T indicate characteristics of a fluorescence induction curve according to Papageorgiou (4). b) Chlorophyll fluorescence induction kinetics when leaves were exposed to UV (+ UV; dashed line) or not (–UV; solid line). Leaf water potential (Ψw) of plants without UV radiation was –0.24 MPa and that of plants exposed UV for 5 h was –0.25 MPa.

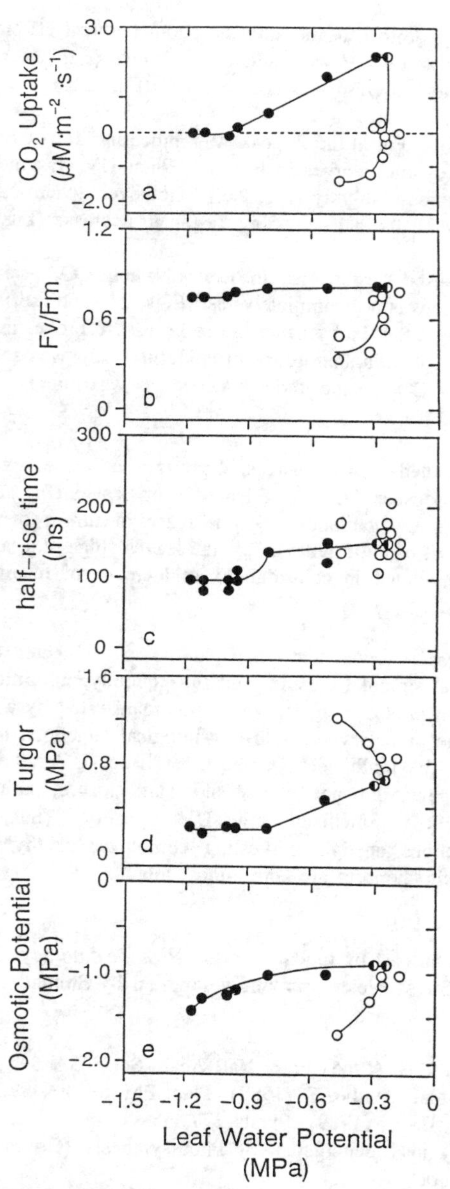

FIGURE 2.a) Comparison of effects of low water potentials and UV radiation on CO_2 uptake, b) Fv/Fm of chlorophyll fluorescence induction kinetics, c) half-rise time from Fo to Fm of chlorophyll fluorescence induction kinetics, d) leaf turgor, and e) leaf osmotic potential. Open circles indicate leaves exposed to UV, and closed circles indicate leaves exposed to low water potentials.

The ratio of Fv/Fm, which is known to measure the photochemical efficiency of photosystem II (9), decreased significantly when UV was radiated on leaves (Fig. 2.b.). In the case of water stress, a significant decrease in Fv/Fm was not observed (Fig. 2.b.).

The half–rise time from Fo to Fm at the P–peak was indicating 1/2 of time duration between O and P of chlorophyll fluorescence curves in Fig. 1. When UV was radiated on to leaves, the half–rise time tended to increase slightly (Fig. 2.c.). However, when leaf water water potential became lower than –0.8 MPa, the half–rise time began to decrease (Fig. 2.c.).

Although water stress caused turgor loss in leaves, when CO_2 assimilation was inhibited completely, turgor of leaves was not completely lost (Figs. 2.a. and 2.d.). When cell turgor was measured in leaves having –1.0 MPa by using the cell pressure probe, turgor of mesophyll cells was between 0.3 MPa and 0.4 MPa, and turgor of epidermal cells was zero or almost zero. This indicates that a decrease of CO_2 uptake under water stress was mainly responsible for stomatal closure.

In contrast to leaves subjected to water stress, the turgor of leaves exposed to UV increased significantly (Fig. 2.d.). Because CO_2 was released from leaves (Fig. 2.a.), stomates were not closed by exposure to the UV radiation. An increase of turgor of leaves exposed to UV coincided with a decrease of osmotic potential of the leaves (Figs. 2.d. and 2.e.). This indicates that soluble matters accumulated in cells due to an increase of respiration, resulting in low osmotic potentials in cells.

In the present study, it was observed that when plants were subjected to water stress, the first event to occur was gradual stomatal closure, and subsequently, inhibition of photoreduction of the electron acceptors Q in photosystem II, which was manifested by a decrease in the P–peak. When water stress became more severe, both physiological functions related to photosynthesis and respiration seemed to be inhibited. On the other hand, UV radiation did not inhibit the functions of respiration and did not induce stomatal closure, although the functions of photosynthesis were inhibited immediately after UV exposure. Thus, UV radiation seems to damage specifically functions of light–harvesting complexes or thylakoid membranes while membrane functions in mitochondria are kept almost intact.

ACKNOWLEDGEMENTS

This work was supported in part by funds from the New Technology Development Foundation to H. Nonami. A Plant Stress Meter was kindly supplied by Shimadze Co.

REFERENCES

1 Boyer, J.S. and Knipling, E.B. (1965) Proc. Natl Acad. Sci. USA 54, 1044–1051
2 Nonami, H., Boyer, J.S. and Steudle, E. (1987) Plant Physiol. 83, 592–595
3 Nonami, H. and Schulze, E.–D. (1989) Planta 177, 35–46
4 Papageorgiou, G. (1975) in Bioenergetics of Photosynthesis (Govindjee, ed.) pp. 319–371, Academic Press, New York
5 Duysens, L.N.M. and Sweers, H.E. (1963) in Studies on microalgae and photosynthetic bacteria, pp. 353–372, Japan Soc. Plant Physiol. ed. Univ. of Tokyo Press, Tokyo
6 Bradbury, M. and Baker, N.R. (1983) Proc. R. Soc. London B 220, 251–264
7 Krause, G.H., Vernotte, C. and Briantais, J.–M. (1982) Biochim. Biophys. Acta 679, 116–124
8 Quick, W.P. and Horton, P. (1984) Proc. R. Soc. London B 220, 371–382
9 Öquist, G. and Wass, R. (1988) Physiol. Plant. 73, 211–217

ASPECTS OF PHOTOSYNTHETIC CARBON METABOLISM ON SOYBEAN UNDER WATER STRESS.

ALBERTO BATTISTELLI[1], MARCELLO GUIDUCCI[2] and TIZIANA SCHIAPPA[1].
(1) Inst. for Agroforestry, CNR Viale Marconi 2, 05010 PORANO, ITALY. (2) Inst. of Agronomy, Univ. of Perugia, Borgo XX Giugno, 06100 PERUGIA, ITALY.

INTRODUCTION

Water deficit could determine a variety of modifications of the photosynthesis, depending on its intensity, duration and on the specie to which it is imposed. When appropriate measurement systems are used, it is possible to distinguish between stomatal and non-stomatal limitation of the photosynthetic process induced by water stress (1). When non-stomatal limitations are present, aspects of the biochemical regulation of photosynthesis are likely to have been modified.
It has been postulated that non-stomatal limitation of photosynthesis could arise from a decreased sucrose synthesis and export capability, (2). Sucrose phosphate synthase (SPS), (EC 2.4.1.14) is a key enzyme in the regulation of the sucrose synthesis pathway, (3), and substantial differences have been found to exist in the regulation and properties of this enzyme in different species (4, 5). Recent papers have shown that the activity and the activation state of SPS in spinach and bean could vary under water stress. The spinach enzyme is activated under short term water stress, (6), while, in bean, (7), the total SPS activity is decreased and the enzyme is deactivated under water stress imposed over a period of days, this could determines a feedback-induced limitation on photosynthesis, (8). The SPS of soybean, (*Glycine max* L.), unlike the spinach and bean enzyme, does not undergo light activation (4, 7), and shows different response to substrates and effectors concentration, this makes it possible that the coordination of CO_2 fixation and sucrose synthesis in soybean is different than in species like spinach or bean, (5).

The aim of our work was to characterize i) the effect of field imposed water stress on soybean photosynthesis, ii) the speed of recovery after rewatering and iii) the effect of water stress on the activity of the SPS in relation to photosynthetic activity.

MATERIALS AND METHODS

A Soybean (*Glycine max* L., cv Evans) crop was grown in the field at the experimental station of the Agronomy Institute of the University of Perugia (Italy, 43° N lat.) during summer 1991. In a randomized blocks design with 3 replications, two irrigation treatments were imposed: i) C= 100% re-integration of the crop evapotranspiration (ETc); ii) S= 33% re-integration of ETc. An irrigation to fully re-integrate the soil water content on both the treatment was done the 25th of August. Measurements were made on the 20th and the 21th of August (Before Irrigation) and on the 29th of August (After Irrigation) with the crop at the beginning of pod filling. All the measurements and samples were taken from the central leaflet of the youngest fully expanded leaf.
Gas exchange was measured in the field at high photon flux density (PFD, 400-700 nm) with an open system (LCA-3, ADC, U.K.), at ambient CO_2 concentration and temperature. The relative water content (RWC= % of actual over saturated leaf water content) was measured using four

N. Murata (ed.), Research in Photosynthesis, Vol. IV, 275–278.

10 cm^2 leaf disc per plot.

The occurrence of non-uniform photosynthesis was not directly investigated in this study. Although there are scarce evidences of this phenomenon in chronically water stressed plants in the field, (1), to verify the occurrence of a non-stomatal limitation of photosynthesis under our conditions, the CO_2 and light saturated photosynthetic capacity, Amax, was measured at 25 ˚C, 10% CO_2 (verified to be saturating for both treatment, data not shown) and PFD of 1800 µmol quanta m^{-2} s^{-1}, using 10 cm^2 leaf discs in a Clark type oxygen electrode (LD2, Hansatech, U.K.), to overcome any stomatal limitation. Measurement of Amax on the two treatments were sequentially replicated from morning to late afternoon, Amax values obtained at different time were averaged for each treatment and eventual effect of the time of the day was not taken into account. The same system was used to measure the maximum apparent photon yield (ϕ_i), (incident light), of O_2 evolution, as the slope of the linear portion, at low PFDs, of the O_2 evolution vs PFD relationship. After the measurements of Amax and ϕ_i,the leaf discs were used for spectrophotometric measurement of the chlorophyll a and b.

Samples for SPS measurement were taken between 1.00 and 3.00 p.m.. 10 cm^2 leaf discs were freeze clamped *in situ* using copper rods pre-cooled at liquid nitrogen temperature and were stored at -80 ˚C. For extraction, leaf portions were ground in liquid nitrogen and the powder quickly transferred to a glass-glass homogenizer containing ice cold extraction buffer. The extraction and assay buffers and conditions used were as in (4), with minor modifications: shortly Hepes-KOH buffer was used instead of Mops-NaOH, the enzyme was assayed under conditions for maximum activity, with concentration of fructose 6-phosphate (F6P), glucose 6-phosphate (G6P) and UDPglucose (UDPG) being 6 mM, 30 mM and 10 mM in this order. One aliquot of each extract was used for measurement of chlorophyll. Each extract was assayed in triplicate. Averages of the two treatment were compared, separately for the two times, using the Student t test.

RESULTS AND DISCUSSION

Field imposed water shortage strongly affected the soybean photosynthesis. The water content in the soil decreased gradually over the season allowing for a gradual raise of the water deficit in the S treatment, (data not shown). Measurements were started 6 weeks after the starting of the water shortage, when clear differences in the RWC of the two treatments were present (Fig. 1). Interestingly, despite of the low water content in the upper soil layer (50 cm), plants were able to fully recover their water content during the night.

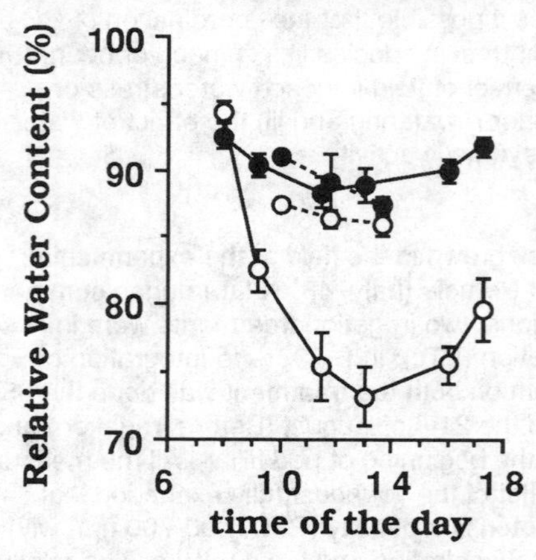

FIGURE 1. Diurnal variation of Relative Water Content (+/- SD, n=3) of field grown soybean under water stress, before (continuous lines) and after (dashed lines) the rewatering. Plain circles= control, open circles= water stress.

Before the irrigation, the strongest differences in gas exchange parameters over the day (data not shown) were recorded between 1.00 and 2.00 p.m. and those data are shown in table 1. The assimilation rate at ambient CO_2 concentration and temperature, (A), was decreased of about 55% in S with respect to C. The decrease in A, was accompanied by a statistically significant decrease of the calculated sub-stomatal CO_2 concentration C_i indicating a stomatal limitation of A. A statistically significant decrease in Amax (-33%) was also observed, (Tab.1), indicating a clear and strong non-stomatal limitation of photosynthesis induced by water stress. These results are similar when expressed on chlorophyll basis (data not shown).

TABLE 1. Photosynthetic parameters of field grown soybean, under long term water stress, before and four days aftre rewatering. Within each period with respect to irrigation, * and ** indicate statistically significant differences at $P \leq 0.05$ and 0.01 level, respectively.

	BEFORE IRRIGATION		AFTER IRRIGATION	
	control	stress	control	stress
A (μmol CO_2 $m^{-2} s^{-1}$)	21.9	9.8 **	23.8	21.2 **
C_i (μl CO_2 l^{-1})	197.9	172.2 **	201.6	206.2 ns
A_{max} (μmol O_2 $m^{-2} s^{-1}$)	74.0	49.7 *	75.0	68.2 ns
SPS (μmol mg chl.$^{-1}$ h^{-1})	54.9	45.5 *	55.0	42.6 **

The value of ϕ_i was not significantly different between the treatments and it was similar to published values for healthy C_3 plants, (9), (0.0908 and 0.0875 for C and S respectively), indicating that no photoinhibition was induced by water stress. It should be noted that the decrease in the RWC during the day was accompanied by paraheliotropic leaf movements which drastically reduced the intensity of light impinging upon the leaf surfaces.No statistically significant differences were also recorded for the chlorophyll content and the chlorophyll a/b ratio, (data not shown) indicating that no differential senescence stage was induced by the two water regimes in the leaf used, (10). The extractable SPS activity was significantly lower in the water stressed plants (-17%) than in the control.

Four days after rewatering, the differences on RWC were almost cancelled, (fig. 1). A in the S treatment was only 10% lower than that in the control, while the C_i value between the two was similar. Assuming the absence of non-uniform stomatal aperture, this would indicate a small residual non-stomatal limitation of A. However the difference in Amax between the two treatment was not statistically significant. On chlorophyll basis the two values were practically the same (data not shown). Surprisingly, despite of the almost complete recovery of all the other parameters, the SPS activity remained unchanged after the rewatering.

Our experiment clearly demonstrate that under field conditions long lasting water deficit determines both stomatal and non-stomatal limitation of soybean photosynthesis. Although the RWC did not decrease under the 70%, and the plants were able to fully recover the water content at night, the effect on soybean photosynthesis could be defined as severe. Other authors have not found non-stomatal limitation of A under water shortage on soybean in the field, (11), it is possible that the water stress in their experiment was less severe, or that the CO_2 concentration they used (1800 μl l^{-1}), was not sufficient to saturate photosynthesis. Actually the maximum assimilation rates they measured were similar to the values obtained in our case for the S treatment before rewatering. Four days after rewatering 90% of photosynthesis had already recovered, although the SPS had not. This indicates that not only a sufficient stomatal

conductance was rapidly restored but also that the causes of the non-stomatal limitation of A were overcome. The fact that SPS activity was decreased under water shortage and did not recover at all while most of the limitations of A were eliminated after rewatering deserves more attention. As a first, like in bean, (7), the SPS is decreased following the decrease in A and evidently the decrease in the availability of fixed carbon for sucrose synthesis. The soybean SPS activity is regulated on a diurnal basis, by a system thought to involve changes in the amount of protein or post-translational modification affecting only the maximum velocity, (12). The time scale involved on the modification of SPS under water stress seems to be much longer, and it remains to be elucidated if any relation exists between the regulation of SPS under the two conditions. As a second, it is evident that the large modifications of A and Amax, observed following the recovery after water stress are scarcely paralleled by changes in SPS activity. In species like spinach and bean, changes in SPS activity are part of regulatory system that coordinate the sucrose synthesis to the availability of fixed carbon (13), such a system is necessary to attain maximum rate of photosynthesis. A coordinate control of photosynthesis, assimilate export and SPS activity operates in soybean on a diurnal basis, (12). No coordinate control of photosynthesis and SPS activity is evident following the changes in A and Amax due to recovery from water stress, this could means that the export rate was also not coordinate with such a changes or that the coordination of flux toward sucrose and the assimilation rate was obtained by modifying the levels of SPS substrates and, eventually, effectors.
Our results demonstrate the importance of the duration of water stress on the photosynthetic response of soybean, and the ability of this specie to recovery its photosynthetic capability after prolonged and severe water shortage. It is also clear that changes in SPS activity could be interpreted as a response to the decrease in photosynthesis, more than a cause of it. Our results support also the finding that strong differences in SPS regulation and in the coordination between photosynthesis and sucrose synthesis could exist in different species.

REFERENCES

1 Terashima, I (1992) Photosynt. Res. 31: 195-212.
2 Kaiser, W. M. (1987) Physiol. Plantarum 71:142-149.
3 Stitt, M., Huber, S. and Kerr, P. (1977) in The Biochemistry of Plants. A Comprehensive Treatise. (Stumpf, P.K and Conn, E. E., eds) Vol. 10, pp. 327-409. Academic Press, New York.
4 Huber, S.C., Nielsen, T.H., Huber, J.L. and Pharr, D.M. (1989) Plant Cell Physiol. 30: 653-658.
5 Nielsen, T.H. and Huber, S.C. (1989) Phisiol. Plant. 76: 309-314.
6 Quick, P., Siegl, G., Neuhaus, E., Feil, R. and Stitt. M. (1989) Planta 177:535-546.
7 Vassey, T.L., Quick, W. P.., Sharkey, T. D. . and Stitt, M. (1991) Physiol. Plant. 81:37-44.
8 Vassey, T. L. and Sharkey, T. D. (1989) Plant. Physiol. 89:1066-1070
9 Björkman, O. and Demmig, B. (1987) Planta 170: 489-504.
10 Eskins, K. and McCarthy, S. (1987) In: Plant Senescence: Its Biochemistry and Physiology. (Thomson, W. W., Nothnagel, E. A. Huffaker, R.C. Eds.) The American Society of Plant Physiologists. Rockville.
11 Frederick, J. R., Alm, D. M., Hesketh, J. D. and Below, F. E. (1990) Photosynt. Res. 25: 49-57.
12 Kerr, P. K. and Huber, S. C. (1987) Planta 170:197-204.
13 Battistelli, A., Adcock, M. D. and Leegood, R.C. (1991) Planta 183: 620-622.

SOME ASPECTS OF CARBOHYDRATE METABOLISM IN BEAN PLANTS UNDER WATER DEFICIT

MARISOL CASTRILLO AND ANIUSKA KAZANDJIAN
DEPTO. BIOLOGIA DE ORGANISMOS. UNIVERSIDAD SIMON BOLIVAR. APTO. POSTAL 89000. CARACAS 1080A. Venezuela.

1. INTRODUCTION

Under drought conditions, the low carbon supply could induce to a shift in chemical partitioning of carbon in favor of sucrose synthesis or starch remobilization may be necessary (1). During drought conditions the carbon supply is lower and allocation of some carbon to osmotic adjustment, survival would require that adjustment be made in sink demand and source to sink ratio. In plants which osmotically adjust with sucrose, such as vean, osmotic adjustem and export will both depend on sucrose levels in the leaf mesophyll cells (1). The decrease in sucrose phosphate syntase activity (SPS) (EC 2.4.1.14) in Phaseolus vulgaris as an effect of moderate (-0.9 MPa) water deficit has been reported (2,3). It has been reported that the effect of water stress on SPS activity was a consequence of the inhibition of phptpsynthesis caused by stomatal closure (3). The present work studied the effect of moderate (-0.80 MPa) and severe (-1.45 MPa water deficit on sucrose metabolism in bean plants, Tacarigua variety. To this extent, plants were deprived of water and, in young leaves, the activities of the enzymes involved in the metabolisms of sucrose were measured; thus, assays were made on the SPS activity in conditions of substrate saturation (total) and limiting substrate plus inorganic phosphate (Pi - insensitive). Other assays performed were those on the activities of sucrose synthase (SS), soluble acid and neutral invertases. Contents of sucrose, glucose, fructose, starch and protein were also measured.

2. MATERIALS AND METHODS

Seeds of Tacarigua variety were germinated in trays with blotting paper. Seven days seedlings were transferred to 4 L platic pots containing a mixture of clay and sand (3:2). These plants were watered daily and mantained in a greenhouse under the following climatic conditions: 29.5 $\pm$ 2.3° C maximun average tempetature; 18.5 $\pm$ 1.7°C minimum average temperature; 96% maximun relative humidity (RH); 43% minimum RH; 655.7 $mol^{-2}s^{-1}$ average sun radiation. After the seedling had been grown for 25 days, they were divided into two

N. Murata (ed.), Research in Photosynthesis, Vol. IV, 279–282.

groups, 40 of such plants were deprived of water (water deficit plants); the remaining 40 plants were watered as usual (control plants). Measurements of parameters took place at two day intervals for a total of eight days in both group of plants. Each measurement consisted of four replicates of four plants each and only the second and / or third (from the apex) expanded leaf was used in the analysis.
Measurements of water potential (Y_W) were taken as in (4). The method of (5) was used to measure thr RWC.
One gram of leaf (without midvein) was ground 1:5 (w/v) in 50 mM HEPES -NaOH pH 7.5; 5mM $MgCL_2$; 1mM EDTA; 0.5 mg ml^{-1} BSA; 2% (v/v) glycerol; 0.05% (v/v) Triton X-100; 2.5mM DTT; 2% (w/v) PVPP. The homogenate was centrifuged at 10,000g for 30s. The supernatant was desalted and concentrated using Centricom 10 (Amicon, GB) tubes. The desalted and concentrated extracts were used in the enzymatic assays.
The activities of SPS (total and Pi-insensitive), SS and Neutral and Acid Invertases were assayed following the method reported by (6). The SPS assays were performed at the same time each measurement day (2). The method reported by (7) for starch determination eas used. The method reported by (8) and modified by (9) was used for soluble sugars determination. The protein estimation was done in crude extracts using the method reported by (10).

3. RESULTS AND DISCUSSION

Table 1 shows the average values for Y_W and RWC in both control and water deficit plants. A decrease in these values is observed in water stressed plants. Table 2 show the values of the enzyme activities tested. Total and Pi-insensitive SPS activities showed a decrease in their activities as the water deficit is increased. The decrease in Pi-insensitive SPS activity, however, is relatively lower than for total SPS activity. The decrease in activities could be due to a decrease in protein content, but it seems that the activation state increased during the water deficit period.

TABLE 1. Minimum values of water potential and relative water content reached in water deficit plants and average values of control bean plants of Tacarigua variety. Each value is mean of four replicates ± standard deviation.

Treatment	Y_W (MPa)	RCW (%)
Controls	-0.30 ± 0.10	98 + 2.00
Water	-1.45 ± 0.10	48 ± 5.00

Table 2 also ahows the values for sucrose synthase (SS) activity. It can be observed that as the water deficit is increased, the activity of this enzyme increases. the levels of SS are often low in mature leaves, as previously reported (11). In our work, we found that the SS activity of control plants was low, but it increased in water -

stressed plants. This activity was measured as syhtnesis of sucrose, - although it has been reported that this enzyme is more active in the hydrolisis of this sugar (12).
The activities of soluble acid and neutral invertases (Table 2) were - higher at moderate water deficit (-0.80 Mpa) and decreased at severe water deficit (-1.45 MPa), being lower for the neutral invertase.

TABLE 2. Percentages obtained with respect to control values of Sucro se-P-Synthase (SPS) total and Pi-insensitive, Sucrose Synthase (SS) - and soluble Acid (A) and Neutral (N) Invertases in leavaes of bean - plants of Tacarigua variety, under water deficit.

Treatment	Y_w	SPS Total	SPS Pi-insensitive	SS	Invertases A	Invertases N
Control	-0.30	100	100	100	100	100
	-0.80	44	90	108	184	136
Water deficit	-1-45	12	22	192	144	44

The ratio starch/sucrose (Table 3) decreased implying that, under water deficit, the rate of increase of starch hydrolisis could be higher than the rate of decrease of sucrose synthesis. The ratio total Fru (Table 3) increased as a redult of the water deficit. This increase may be related to the production of glucose from a relatively - higher starch hydrolysis. Table 3 also presents the values for protein content. A decrease in this parameter is observed at moderate water, slightly increasing, at severe water stress. The latter increase in protein content has been previously reported (13).
In the present work, the effect of the water deficit on the assayed-leaf tissue was evidenced by: 1) a decrease in both SPS activity and the starch/sucrose ratio 2) an increase in both SS activity and the total Glc/total Fru ratio and 3) an increase subsequent decrease, at severe water stress, of the acid invertase activity.
During drought conditions, sucrose export out to the leaves is expected to decline quantitatively due to the decline in sucrose levels in the transport pool(1). It is conceivable that a newly formed sucrose is rapidly sequestered in the vacuoles not only to prevent the inhibition of sucrose phosphate synthase but to be removed from the transport (export) pool and to contribute to osmotic adjustment (1). On - the other hand, export maintenence under limited carbon supplies may result from remobilization of starch in the leaf (chloroplast). It - was reported by (14) that under water stress in soybean, the carbon exchange rate was reduced and the export rates were buffered by leaf starch hydrolisis.
In the present work, it could be possible that the produced sucrose - would contribute to the osmotic adjustment in the studied water stres

sed leaf tissue, then, its export out would decline. The relatively higher starch hydrolisis would buffer the export rate and the increased SS and initially acid invertase activities could contribute to double the osmotic potential, as indicated by the total Glc/total Fru ratio.

TABLE 3. Percentages obtained, with respect to control values, of starch/sucrose and total glucose/total fructose ratios and protein content in leaves of bean plants, Tacarigua variety under water stres

Treatment	Y_w (MPa)	starch/sucrose (%)	total Glc/totalFru (%)	Protein (%)
Controls	-0.30	100	100	100
	-0.80	30	170	28
Water deficit	-1.45	28	156	38

REFERENCES

1. Daie, J. (1988) Critical Rev. PL.Sciences 7(2). 117-137
2. Vassey, T.L.and Sharkey, T.D.(1989) Pl.Physiol.89,1066-1070.
3. Vassey, T.L., Quick,P., Sharkey,T.D. and Stitt, M., (1991) Physiol Plant., 81,37-44.
4. Castrillo, M., and Trujillo I. Photosynyhetica 26 (1) In Press.
5. Turner, N.C., (1981). Plant and Soil, 58,339-366
6. Castrillo, M., Kruger, N.J. and Whatley,F.R. (1992).Plant Sci. In Press
7. Hubbard, N.L., Pharr, D.M., and Huber, S.C., (1990) Plant Physiol. 94, 201-208.
8. Blakeney, A.B., and Mutton, L.L., (1980) Jr.Sci.Food Agric., 31, 889-897.
9. Tawfik, A.M., and Mardon, C.J., (1985).Jr. Sci. Food Agric. 36, 621-627
10. Bradford, M.M., (1976) Anal. Bioch, 72, 248-254.
11. Vassey, T.L., (1989) Plant Physiol. 89, 347-351.
12. Fieuw, S., and Willenbrink, J., (1987) Jr. Plant Physiol. 131., 153-162.
13. Castrillo, M., Fernandez, D., Fernandez, P., Molina, B., and Kazandjian, A. (1990) Turrialba, 40, 515-519.
14. Huber, S.C., Rogers, H.H. and Mowry, F.L. (1984) Pl. Physiol. 76, 244-247.

THE RELATIONSHIP BETWEEN RESISTANCE TO WATER TRANSPORT AND THE MIDDAY DEPRESSION OF PHOTOSYNTHETIC RATE IN RICE PLANTS

Tadashi HIRASAWA and Kuni ISHIHARA, Faculty of Agriculture, Tokyo University of Agriculture and Technology, Fuchu, Tokyo 183, Japan

1. INTRODUCTION

In rice plants, even though they grow under submerged soil conditions, the stomatal conductance and the photosynthetic rate decrease due to leaf water deficits under intense transpiration in the afternoon on a clear day (Fig. 1)(1). The degree of depression in the photosynthetic rate under sufficient sunlight is supposed to depend on the water uptake ability of roots from many observations. However, the actual relationship between water uptake capacity of roots and the degree of the midday depression was not known because there was no useful indicator for estimating the capacity quantitatively. In a previous report(2), it was clarified that water uptake capacities of crop plants can be compared by calculating resistance to water transport. The present study was conducted to investigate the relationship between water uptake capacity and the degree of the midday depression in photosynthetic rate.

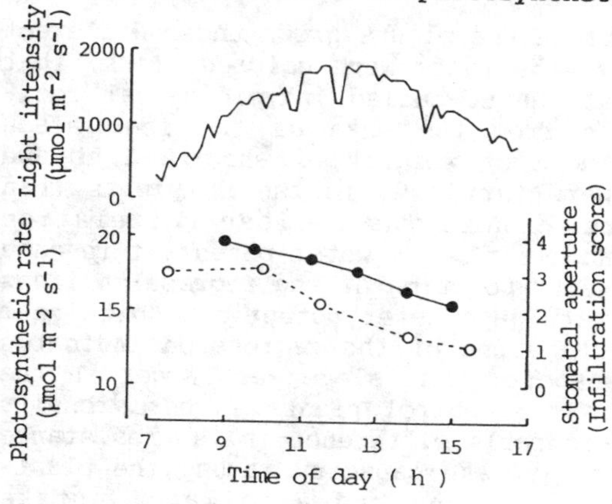

FIGURE 1. Diurnal changes of light intensity, stomatal aperture (open circles) and photosynthetic rate (solid circles) in rice plants growing in the field.

2. MATERIALS and METHODS

Rice plants (Oryza sativa L., cv. Nipponbare) were grown in the University farm under submerged soil conditions. Rice plants (cv. Manryo) grown in 1/2000 a Wagner pots filled with soil under submerged soil conditions were also used for measurements. In the potted plants, three plots were prepared; one was a control and the others were as follows: (i) a plot where soluble

N. Murata (ed.), Research in Photosynthesis, Vol. IV, 283–286.

starch and additional ammonium sulfate were applied to soil in a pot several days before measurements to make the soil reductive and to decrease the physiological activity of roots without decreasing the nitrogen content of the leaves (SA plants); (ii) a shaded plot where rice plants were grown in a greenhouse with low light intensity and high humidity compared to outdoors for about 6 weeks before measurements to decrease the root-top ratio (SP plants).

Stomatal aperture was measured by the improved infiltration method (3). Transpiration and photosynthetic rates of the intact uppermost fully expanded leaf was measured with an assimilation chamber in the field. Humidity- and CO_2 concentration-controlled air was pumped into the assimilation chamber. After ensuring that the transpiration rate had reached a constant rate, the leaf was excised and sealed in a pressure chamber for measuring leaf xylem water potential. Transpiration measurements were done by the weighing method in the potted plants. Since the rice plants were grown under submerged soil conditions, the water potential of the soil could be regarded as 0 MPa. Consequently, the resistance to water transport through the roots to the leaves (R) was calculated, according to a previous report (2), as follows:

$$R = -\Psi_x / T$$

where Ψ_x is the leaf xylem water potential and T the transpiration rate on the basis of the leaf area.

3. RESULTS and DISCUSSION

3.1 Resistance to water transport in the plants grown under different conditions: In the SA plants, the roots were colored black, that is, they developed a sign of the so-called "physiological root-rot" and the exudation rate from the base of the leaf blade decreased markedly. Both the root weight per shoot weight and root weight per leaf area were far lower in the SP plants than those in the control plants. There was a close correlation between transpiration rate and leaf xylem water potential in each plot(Fig. 2). The linear extrapolation of the regression lines down to zero transpiration rate gave water potentials quite near to the origin. Therefore, the slope of the regression indicates the resistance to water transport. The slope was larger in the SA and the SP plants than in the control plants. These results indicate that there was considerable difference in the resistance to water transport, i.e. water uptake capacity, among the plants grown under the different conditions and also water uptake capacity was lower in rice plants in which " root-rot " occurred as well as in those which developed a small root system.

3.2 Relationship between resistance to water transport and the degree of the midday depression in stomatal aperture and photosynththic rate: To decrease root water uptake capacity, part of the root system was excised in rice plants grown in the field. The

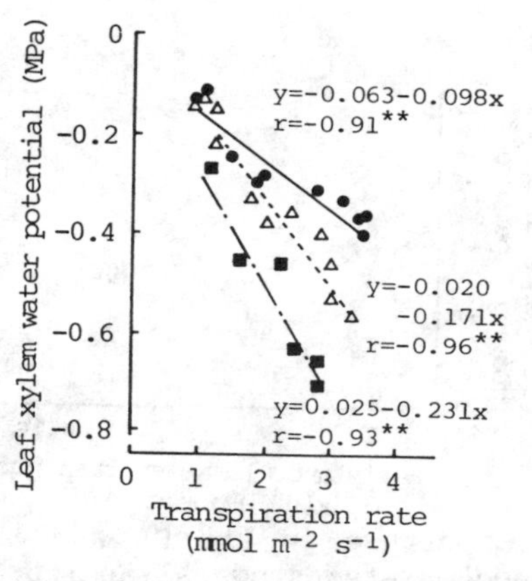

FIGURE 2. Relationship between transpiration rate and leaf xylem water potential in rice plants grown in (i) a plot supplied with soluble starch and additional ammonium sulfate (SA)(solid squares), (ii) a shaded plot (SP)(open triangles) and (iii) a control plot (solid circles).

excision was done by running a knife into the soil to a depth of about 8 cm (ME plants) and 16 cm (SE plants) at a distance of 5 - 6 cm around a hill. Resistance to water transport increased significantly due to the excision (Fig. 3.A.). And the resistance in the SE plants was larger than that of the ME plants. The differences in stomatal aperture and photosynthetic rate were not clear among these plants in the early morning (Fig. 3.B.). However, large significant differences in the midday stomatal aperture and photosynthetic rate were observed among the plants. The degree of the midday depression was larger in the plants whose resistance to water transport was higher.

Midday stomatal closure was remarkable in the SA and the SP plants compared to that in the control plants. To get the figure indicating the degree of midday stomatal closure, the difference in the stomatal apertures of the treated and the control plants was accumulated during the daytime under intense transpiration and sufficient solar radiation as shown in Fig. 4.A. There was a close correlation between resistance to water transport and the accumulated stomatal closure in the plants grown under different

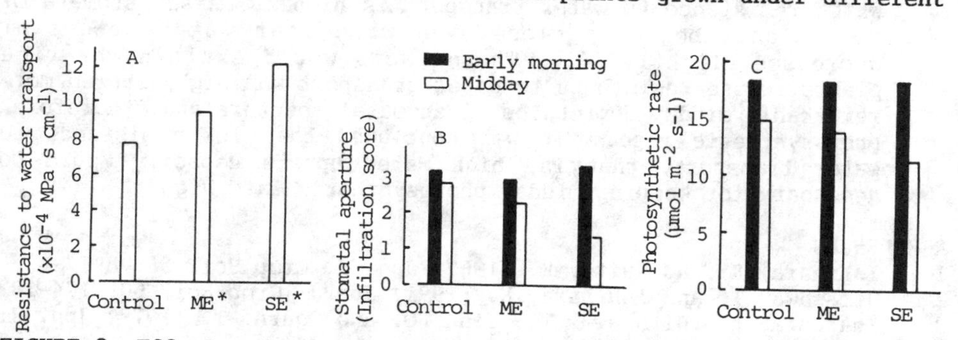

FIGURE 3. Effects of partial excision of root system on resistance to water transport(A), stomatal aperture(B) and photosynthetic rate(C) in rice plants grown in the field. * See the text.

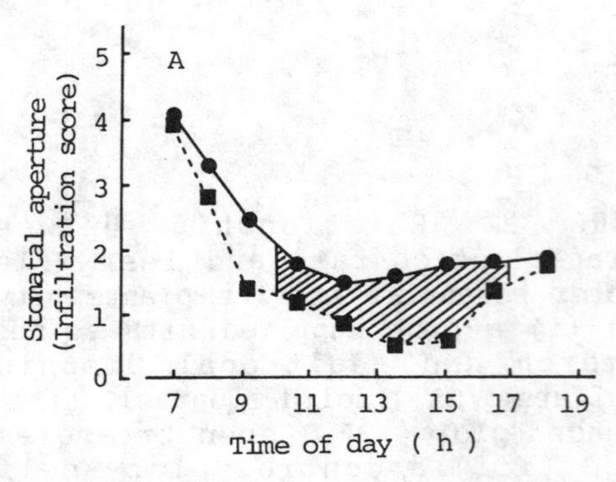

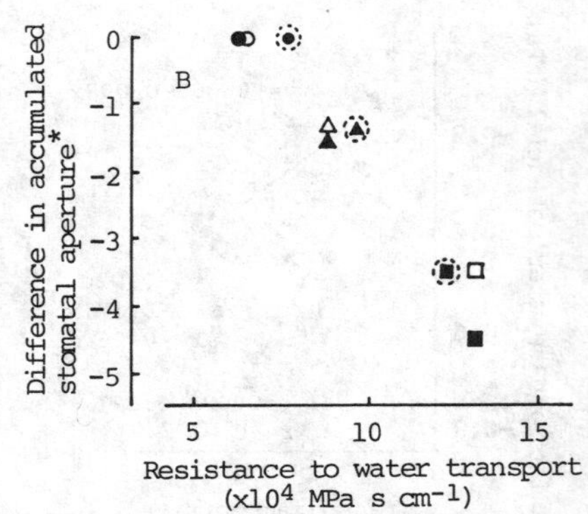

FIGURE 4.A) Diurnal changes of stomatal aperture in the SA and the control plants and the difference in accumulated stomatal apertures of the two plants during the daytime (hatched portion). B) Relationship between resistance to water transport and midday stomatal aperture. Squares, triangles and circles represent the SA, the SP and the control plants, respectively. Closed and encircled symbols, closed symbols and open symbols represent the measurement taken on the same day, respectively. * Negative values mean the accumulated stomatal aperture in the treated plants was smaller than that in the control plants.

conditions (Fig. 4.B.). As there is a close correlation between stomatal aperture and photosynthetic rate, Fig. 4.B. also indicates that there should be a close correlation between the resistance and the degree of the midday depression in photosynthetic rate.

It was clarified from the results mentioned above that water uptake capacity affects the degree of the midday depression in stomatal aperture and photosynthetic rate. As transpiration rate increases, leaf water potential decreases more in the plants in which resistance to water transport is higher. Also, stomata of rice plants begin to close even when leaf water potential decreases slightly (4). These facts would explain why rice plants, whose resistance to water transport was high, showed more remarkable midday depression of stomatal aperture and, therefore, photosynthetic rate. It was concluded that low resistance to water transport, that is, high water uptake capacity would be necessary for keeping midday photosynthetic rate high.

REFERENCES

1 Ishihara, K. and Saito, K. (1987) Jpn. J. Crop Sci. 56, 8-17
2 Hirasawa, T. and Ishihara, K. (1991) Jpn.J. Crop Sci. 60, 174-183
3 Ishihara, K., Hirasawa, T., Iida, O. and Ogura, T. (1979) Jpn. J. Crop Sci. 48, 319-320
4 Hirasawa, T., Iida, Y. and Ishihara, K. (1988) Jpn. J. Crop Sci. 57, 112-118

EFFECTS OF DROUGHT ON WATER RELATIONS OF FIELD-GROWN DOUGLAS FIR

E. STEINGRÖVER, W. van ORDEN, G. van ROEKEL, R. BLIKMAN, J. van der BEEK and W. JANS, IBN-DLO, INSTITUTE FOR FOREST AND NATURE RESEARCH, P.O. Box 23, 6700 AA, WAGENINGEN, THE NETHERLANDS

1. INTRODUCTION

During the Dutch national program on acidification the effect of air pollution on Douglas fir was studied. The effects of ozone on photosynthesis were highly dependent upon the environmental conditions (1). Using meteorological techniques, the transpiration of a Douglas fir crown appeared to be constant in relation to changes in water vapour deficit (VPD), and decreased with soil water potentials below -3 Bar (2). In the third phase of this program the combined effects of air pollution and drought are studied and therefore more detailed information about the trees water relations and gas exchange are necessary. In a preliminary study needle water relation as dependent on the needles position within the crown was determined (3). In the current study the effect of several environmental parameters on the water relation of Douglas fir needles are presented.

2. MATERIALS and METHODS

2.1. Stand description: The research site is located at the Veluwe, in the central part of the Netherlands. Two year old Douglas fir seedlings of the provenance Arlington were planted in 1962. The stand is located on a sandy loam soil with different textures at short intervals. Ground water is found at a depth of 40 meters. The climate is moderately humid with an average rainfall of 800 mm per year. The stand is of average vitality and covers an area of 2.5 ha. Stem density is 785 trees per ha, average DBH in 1991 was 239 mm and average tree height was 21.01 meters.

2.2 Sampling: All measurements were carried out in 1991 between 12:00 and 16:00 h on 3 trees. The trees were divided into 5 levels. Levels 1 and 2 in the shade adapted part of the crown, levels 4 and 5 in the sun adapted part and level 3 around the crown's closure. At each level one dominating first order branch

N. Murata (ed.), Research in Photosynthesis, Vol. IV, 287–290.

directed to the sun was used. On each first order branch 3 third order, current-year branch parts were measured. The data from levels 4-5 and 2-1 are presented.

2.3 Methods: A steady state porometer (ADC, LCA-2) was used to measure transpiration (E), stomatal resistance (Rs), temperature, relative humidity and PAR. Needle water potential was determined with a pressure bomb (PMS, model 650).

3. RESULTS and DISCUSSION

3.1 Temporal variation: 1991 could be roughly divided into a relative dry period (unto day 250) and a normal wet period. Soil water potentials became more negative during the drier period of the year, but no relation to needle water potential was found. E was higher at level 5 than at level 2 (Fig. 1). Stomatal resistance at level 5 did not exceed 2000 s/m, and no midday reduction in transpiration was observed, indicating that the stomata in the sun adapted needles did not close on the days of measurements. At level 2 resistances were above 2000 s/m, but transpiration still continued at low rates. Needle water potential was more negative at level 5 than at level 2.

3.2 Effect of environmental parameters: In contrast to the crown transpiration rate measured by Bosveld et al. (2), E was not constant with changing VPD. At level 5 transpiration rate increased with increasing VPD and Rs was kept con-

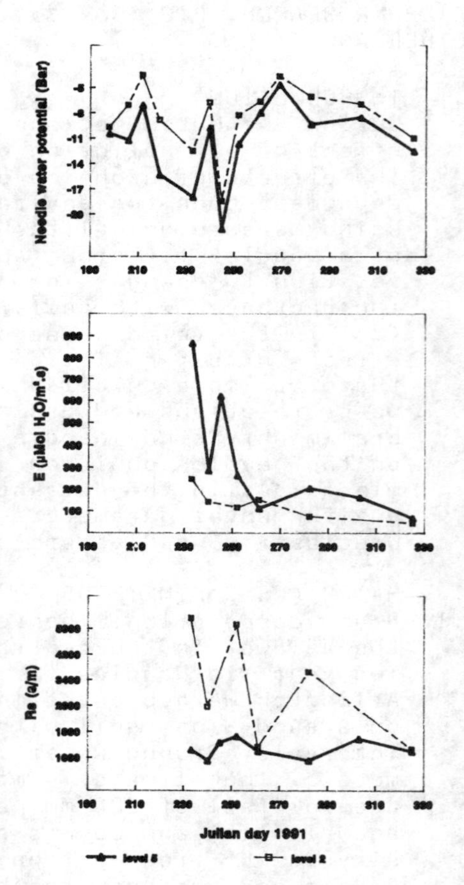

Fig 1: Needle water potential, transpiration rate (E) and stomatal resistance (Rs) measured between 12:00 and 16:00 h.

stant independent of both VPD and PAR (Fig. 2). Rs was also independent of needle water potential, both in the relative dry and in the wetter period of the year. In the dry period, needle water potentials were more negative, but despite values below -20 Bar, assumed to be the threshold level for stomatal closure in Douglas fir (4), no closure was observed (Fig. 3).
At level 1-2 however, E was not dependent upon VPD, and no relation between Rs and VPD or PAR was found (Fig. 2). Rs was however highly correlated to needle water potential both in the relative dry and the wetter period of the year (Fig. 3). Assuming the needles are closed at Rs values above 2000 s/m, the threshold value of needle water potential for

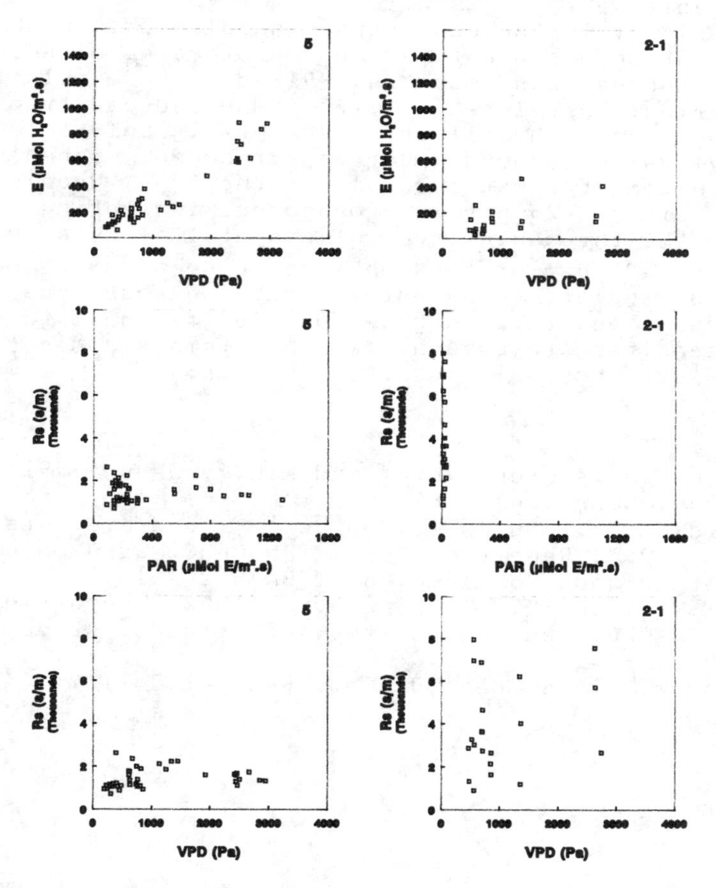

Fig 2: The relation between transpiration rate (E) and VPD, between stomatal resistance (Rs) and PAR and between stomatal resistance (Rs) and VPD, at level 5 and 2-1.

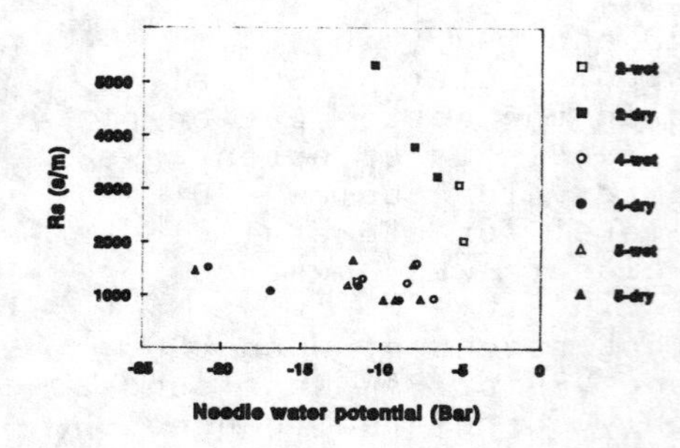

Fig. 3: The relation between stomatal resistance (Rs) and needle water potential at level 5, 4 and 2-1 in a wet and relative dry period in 1991.

stomatal closure in the shade adapted needles must be less negative than -20 Bar.

3.3 Conclusions: In the sun adapted needles E is highly dependent upon ambient VPD and no stomatal closure during the day was found in 1991, despite a relative dry period. Bosveld et al. (2) found reduced transpiration rates with soil water potentials below -3 Bar. In 1991 values around 3 Bar were reached, probably not limiting the water supply to the tree. Needle potentials of -25 Bar were measured, indicating that either the threshold level of stomatal closure must be below -25 Bar or the sun adapted needles are not able to regulate their water loss. The shade adapted needles of adult field-grown Douglas fir seem to be more sensitive to drought, as the stomata close at less negative needle water potentials.

REFERENCES

1. Evers P., Steingröver E.G. and W.W.P. Jans (1992) Acta Bot. Neerl. 41(1)89-101
2. Bosveld, F.C., Bouten W., Noppert F. and E.G. Steingröver (1991) Report nr. 623, IBN-DLO, Wageningen, the Netherlands, pp:163-186, ISBN 0924-9141
3. Jans W.W.P. and E.G. Steingröver (1992), Report nr. 695, IBN-DLO, Wageningen, the Netherlands, 42 pp, ISBN 0924-9141
4. Running W. (1976) Can. J. For. Res. 6:104-112

ANALYSIS OF THE PHOTOSYNTHESIS/TRANSPIRATION RATIO OF PLANT CANOPY BY COMPUTER SIMULATION

Wang, Tian-duo, He, Dong-xiang, Shi, Jian-zhong, and Fu, Wei.
Shanghai Institute of Plant Physiology, Chinese Academy of Sciences, Shanghai, 200032, China

1. INTRODUCTION

Photosynthesis (P)/transpiration (T) ratio is the basis of the consideration of water use efficiency (WUE) in agriculture in any region with less than adequate supply of water. In addition to the differences in the effects of environmental conditions on the two processes, the additional mesophyll/carboxylation resistance involved in the transport of CO2, and the differences in response of the two processes to temperature and radiation, make the P/T ratio dependent also on the leaf area indices (LAI). Computer programs are needed to simulate P and T for canopies with different LAI's.

In the simulation of the two processes using data about meteorological variables, the relative merits of the "big leaf model" and multi-layer models are under debate for quite a long time[1]. When one is dealing with fields with different irrigation/fertilization levels or along the whole growth period, considering the range of LAI encountered, no single canopy resistance value is applicable to all cases, and, therefore, the use of multi-layer models is inevitable. Raubach and Finnigan[1] argued convincingly that multi-layer models can be not only correct, but also useful.

A set of programs simulating P and T using multi-layer models were designed, basing on the knowledge of physical and physiological laws, and the data of radiation, air temperature, and wind speed are used as inputs, or forcing functions. Plant characteristics with respect to stomatal and photosynthetic behaviors are the main parameters.

Since this work is a part of the efforts to design programs for the assessment of crop productivity of large areas, a balance is to be struck between completeness and simplicity. The programs take into consideration of the large difference between leaf layers with respect to radiation and turbulent transfer conductivity, but omit the transient changes in conductivity associated with changing wind speed. The change in soil moisture profile and availability of water to the roots are also omitted at the present stage.

The results of preliminary simulation with the programs were checked against those measured with a weighing lysimeter, and with eddy correlation technique.

2. MATERIALS AND METHODS

Maize plants grown at the Yucheng Comprehensive Experimental Station were used for the measurements of plant characteristics, lysimeter readings, and eddy correlation measurements. The days of measurements were taken on Aug. 31 and Sept. 6, 1991, at the stage of grain filling.

N. Murata (ed.), Research in Photosynthesis, Vol. IV, 291–294.

The values of stomatal conductances (g) and of P of different leaves were measured by the leaf chamber analyzer of Analytical Development Corporation, Inc.

To calculate T, the interdependence of leaf temperature and T under given radiation and wind speed is based on the Penman-Monteith equation. The formula used was that given by Goudriaan[2] where the boundary resistance was a function of wind speed and leaf width. The radiation received by a leaf in any layer in the canopy is calculated according to Beer's Law[3], and that of wind speed as a negative exponential function of depth in the canopy. The transfer of momentum, water vapor, CO_2 and heat is all taken to be by turbulent transfer down to the boundary layer above leaf surface with the same turbulent conductivity (K). The canopy was taken as horizontally uniform, and only vertical transfer was considered.

The canopy was divided into 4 layers, and the T and P of each layer were calculated. Since steady state was assumed, no efforts were made to take into account the transition between varying wind speeds.

Two programs were used in this work. Both programs include the soil evaporation (E) and get evapotranspiration (ET) and the H_2O flux measured by both the lysimeter and eddy correlation is also ET. Program SET simulated only ET. Stomatal conductances of the different layers were inputted from measurements. Net radiation data at different time in a day were used. Program SPET simulated both P and ET. The stomatal conductances were calculated from P using a linear regression equation of it on P. Net radiation (R_n) was calculated from the daily sunshine hours and the latitude.

The P of each leaf layer was calculated by the approach of Monsi and Saeki[3], except that the equation proposed by Causton and Pamela Dale[4] was used for the P/I (light intensity) equation, and the maximum P (P_{max}), dark respiration (R_d) and a parameter α were obtained from measured data of P for different leaf layers.

The equations used in the programs will be published elsewhere.

The evapotranspiration (ET) of the canopy was checked by a weighing lysimeter with a diameter of 3 m^2, taken every 2 h. The CO_2 exchange rates of the canopy were checked by the simultaneous measurements using eddy correlation equipment, taken every 15 min.

3. RESULTS AND DISCUSSION

The diurnal change of ET of the maize canopy on Sept. 6, 1992, has been calculated, and the results are shown in Fig. 1, together with the data from the weighing lysimeter. The matching is quite good.

The diurnal changes of R_n calculated by the program PSET are shown in Fig. 2, together with the data measured with radiometer.

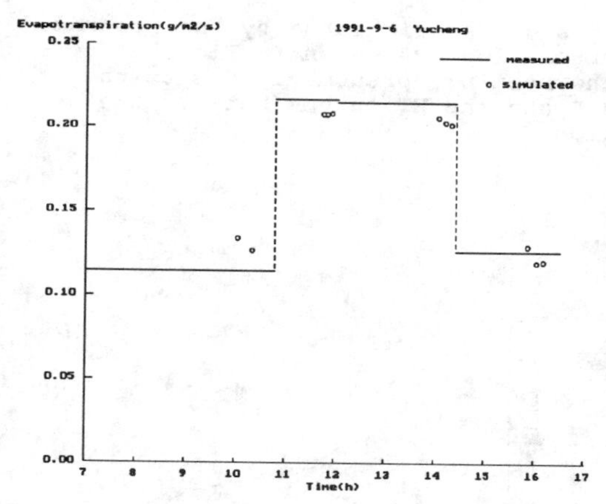

FIGURE 1. Calculated ET by program SET compared with the results obtained with weighing lysimeter.

FIGURE 2. Calculated R_n by the program SPET compared with measured values.

The values of ET calculated by the program SPET for Aug. 31, 1991, are shown in Fig. 3, together with the measurements by eddy correlation. Though the general trends are the same, there are important differences, both in the magnitude of the peaks, and in the time phase, the cause of which need be clarified in the future.

The canopy P for the same day was also calculated by the program SPET, and the results of diurnal changes of P are shown in Fig. 4, together with the CO2 flux rate obtained with eddy correlation. The agreement was quite good, except that the former rose earlier than the latter.

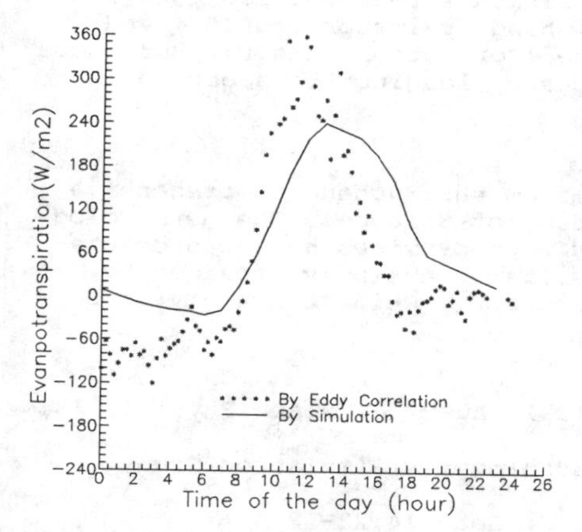

FIGURE 3. Calculated ET by program SPET compared with the results of eddy correlation.

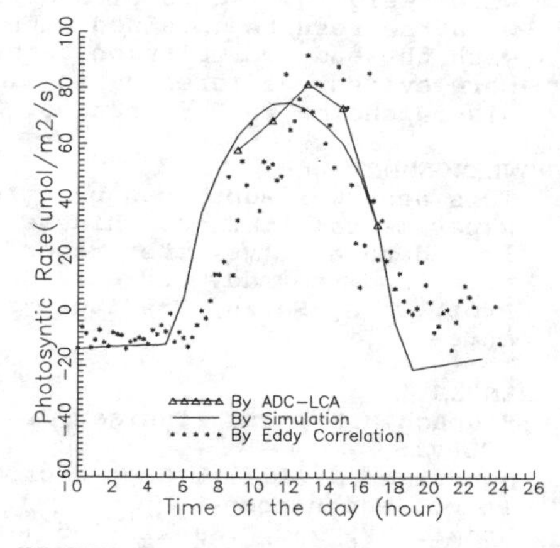

FIGURE 4. Calculated P by program SPET compared with the results of eddy correlation.

The P/ET ratio changes during a day as simulated by the program SPET and measured by eddy correlation are shown in Fig. 5. There are large discrepancies in the morning, presumably due to the phase difference of both the P and the ET curves between the simulation and eddy correlation.

Under the wide range of radiation, and narrower ones of temperature and wind speed, provided by the diurnal changes, the programs gave simulations which coincided roughly with the measurements taken using different techniques, even with the many simplifications involved in the programs. This provided us with confidence about the usefulness of these and similar programs.

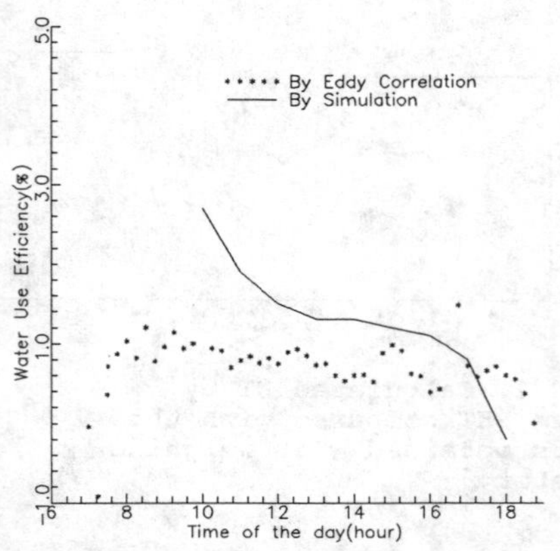

FIGURE 5.Calculated P/ET ratio by program SPET as compared with the results of eddy correlation.

With longer simulation periods for the assessment of regional productivity, frequent measurements of photosynthetic characteristics are to be avoided. Then the changes of them with age and season, and also the growth of canopy as dependent on P, are also to be simulated.

4. CONCLUSIONS

The programs for simulation of ET and P for maize canopy using multi-layer models based on known physical and physiological laws were designed. The results of simulation agreed tolerably well with the results obtained with weighing lysimeter (for ET) and with the eddy correlation technique (for both ET and P). But there were evident differences in time phase, leading to larger discrepancies in P/ET ratios.

ACKNOWLEDGEMENT

This work was supported by a fund from the Yucheng Comprehensive Experimental Station, Chinese Academy of Sciences. The meteorological data and lysimeter recordings were provided by the same station, and the eddy correlation results were kindly provided by Prof. Chen, Fa-zu, Institute of Geography, Chinese Academy of Sciences.

REFERENCES

1 Raupach,M.R., and Finnigan,J.J. (1991) Aust. J. Plant Physiol. 15, 705-716
2 Goudriaan,J.(1977): Crop Micrometeorology: A Simulation Study. Pudoc, Wageningen
3 Monsi, M., and T.Saeki (1953) Jap. J. Bot. 14,22-52
4 Causton,D.R., and Pamela Dale, M. (1990) Ann. Bot. 65,389-394.

GAS EXCHANGE AND WATER USE EFFICIENCY IN WATER STRESSED <u>SETARIA SPHACELATA</u>

J. Marques da Silva and M.C. Arrabaça, Departamento de Biologia Vegetal, Faculdade de Ciências da Universidade de Lisboa, Portugal.

1. INTRODUCTION

Stomata control the income of CO_2 into the leaf and hence are the first control step in the overall process of photosynthesis. Species greatly differ in the way they control stomatal opening in response to environmental conditions [1]. Knowledge of how plants control stomata under water deficit conditions is important to understand plant strategies of survival to drought.

2. MATERIAL AND METHODS

Setaria sphacelata was grown in pots with a mixture of peat and soil (1:2) in a greenhouse. Sun light was supplemented by halogen incadescent light which provided, per si, a photon flux density (PFD) of 135 $\mu mol\ m^{-2}s^{-1}$ (PAR) at intermediate canopy level. Pots were abundantly watered three times a week. First youngest fully-expanded leaves collected from randomly selected pots were used for experiments. Leaves were excised and rapidly dehydrated by exposure to laboratory atmosphere. Water stress was monitored by measurements of relative water content (RWC). Carbon exchange rate (CER) and transpiration rate (E) were measured under atmospheric CO_2 concentrations with a portable IRGA (LCA2, ADC, U.K.) at approximately 25 ^oC under a PFD of 1850 $\mu molm^{-2}s^{-1}$ (PAR) provided by a Bjorkman lamp (LSI, Hansatech Ltd., U.K). Both gas exchange rates, stomatal conductance to water vapour (g_swa) and sub-stomatal CO_2 concentration (C_iCO_2) were calculated using a synthesis of the equations from [2] and [3]. Instantaneous water use efficiency (WUE) was calculated according to [4]. O_2 evolution under saturating CO_2 (5%) was measured in a Clark-type leaf disc electrode (LD2, Hansatech Ltd., U.K.) at 25 ^oC and an irradiance of 1850 $\mu molm^{-2}s^{-1}$. All values were expressed as percentage of values obtained at nearly full saturation.

3. RESULTS AND DISCUSSION

Fig. 1a shows that there is a rapid decline of CER when RWC falls from 100 to 85. At RWC 79, CER reaches its lowest value, about 2% of initial value. Fig. 1b ilustrates the decline of E with declining RWC. Though the overall pattern of change is similar, E is not as sensitive as CER to RWC. Fig 1c shows a sharp decrease of WUE as water deficit increases. At full saturation WUE was about 0.0058 ± 0.0008 $molCO_2\ mol^{-1}H_2O$. Fig. 1d ilustrates the decline of g_swa with declining RWC, with a pattern of variation similar to E. Fig. 1e presents C_iCO_2 measured at different RWC. Correlation between RWC and C_iCO_2 is poor, but yet statisticaly significant ($p<0.05$). Fig. 1f indicates the decline of O_2 evolution with declining RWC under saturating CO_2. The shape of the curve is opposite to the one obtained with photosynthesis measured under ambient CO_2 (CER). The decrease of O_2 evolution is slower at the begining of stress, and faster at the end. When measured at ambient CO_2, photosynthesis is much more affected by dehydration than when measured at saturating CO_2. From data in Fig. 1a and Fig. 1f we could estimate the diffusional and non-diffusional contribution for photosynthesis decline. The

N. Murata (ed.), Research in Photosynthesis, Vol. IV, 295–298.

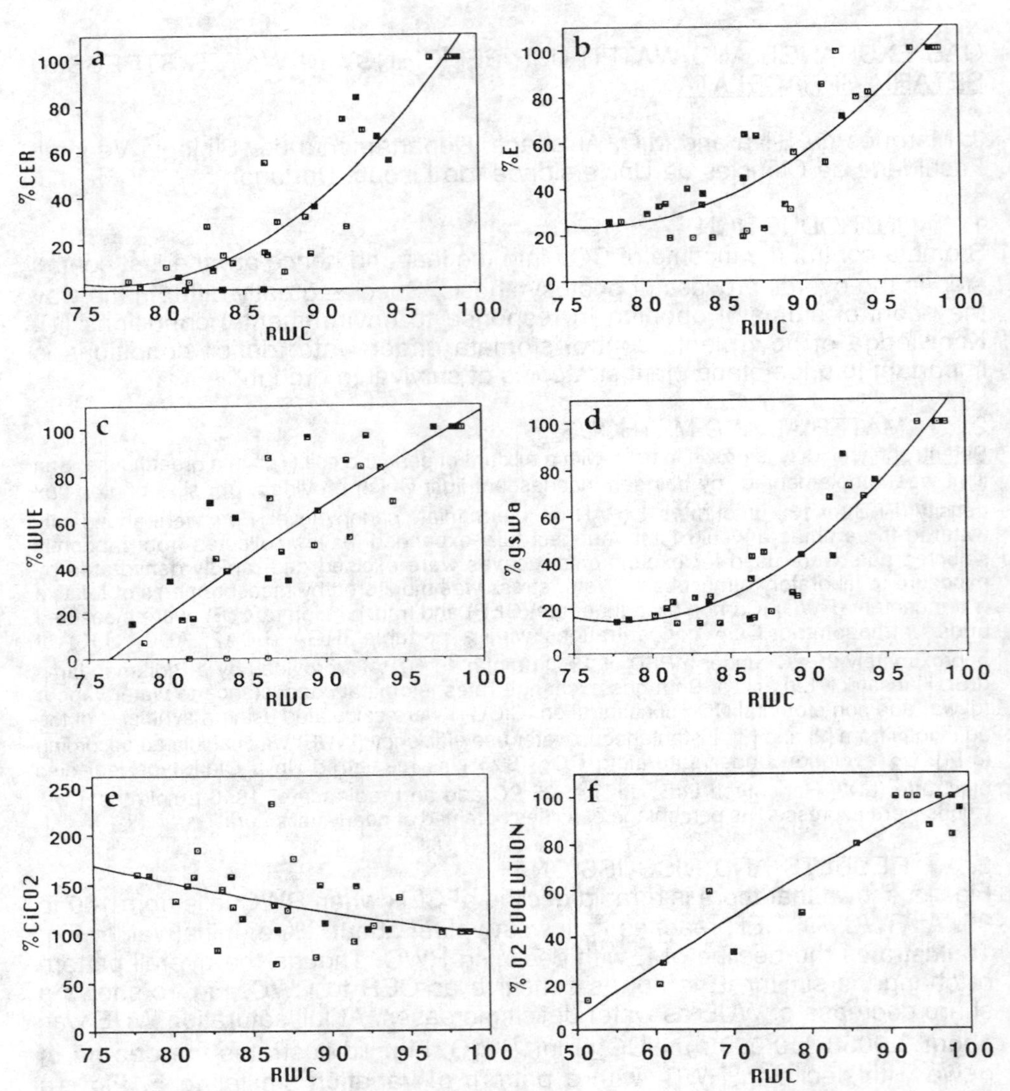

Fig. 1: a, b, c, d, e and f presents, respectively, the variation of carbon exchange rate (CER), transpiration rate (E), instantaneous water use efficiency (WUE), stomatal conductance to water vapour (g_swa), sub-stomatal CO_2 concentration (C_iCO_2) and O_2 evolution with RWC. All parameters are expressed as percentage of values obtained at nearly full water saturation.

method was adapted from [5]. Analysis was performed under 5% CO_2 concentrations and we presume to eliminate all diffusional barriers to CO_2, both from gas and liquid phase. This is why we separate all diffusional barriers from non-difusional barriers, by opposition to analysis performed at C_iCO_2 330 ppm [6] where stomatal limitations are separated from non-stomatal limitations. Results are presented on Table 1.

Table 1: Limitations of photosynthesis at different RWC. Values shown for diffusional and non-diffusional limitation represent the inhibition that each one of these processes could account per si

RWC (%)	Total Limitation	Diffusional Limitation	Non-Diffusional Limitation	Diffusional/Non -Diffusional
95	27%	23%	5%	4.6
85	84%	80%	23%	3.5
75	97%	96%	42%	2.3

Diffusional limitations are always much more important than non-diffusional limitations, although as photosynthesis declines also CO_2 saturated photosynthesis declines. Non-diffusional limitations per si can explain increased limitations. In most analysis, diffusional limitations are usually taken as stomatal limitations. Lets however consider, in a first approach, that diffusional limitations are, indeed, equivalent to stomatal limitations. The decline in photosynthesis due to a decrease in stomatal conductance occurs because the consumption of CO_2 is higher than its supply. In these circumstances, a lowered internal concentration of CO_2 is to be expected. However, in our results C_iCO_2 does not decrease with RWC. Insensitivity of C_iCO_2 to water stress was also found by [7] and [8]. Several explanations could be advanced to this fact. First of all, we have to question the validity of our estimates of the different contributions to the decline in photosynthesis. We must emphasize that these are aproximative calculations, based on the adjustment of equations to the data in Fig. 1a and 1f. However, the predominance of stomatal (diffusional) limitations is so large that we can safely accept its main role on photosynthesis limitations in S. sphacelata. Other explanations have been proposed by different authors to explain the conflicting evidence between C_iCO_2 insensitivity (or increase) to water deficit and predominance of stomatal limitations to photosynthesis. The validity of C_iCO_2 estimates was questioned by [9] who argued that high values of C_iCO_2 found under water stress were wrong estimates due to the effect of patchy stomatal closure. Some authors, however, have also found constant internal CO_2 concentrations in droughted leaves whose stomata closed uniformly ([7],[8]). Furthermore, [10] and [11] using normal models of stomatal closure instead of the bimodal models used before, conclude that patchy stomatal closure has a negligible effect on C_iCO_2 estimation. The non-decrease of C_iCO_2 was explained by increased photorespiration [12]. There would be an internal cycling of CO_2, the rate of assimilation being greatly enhanced [13]. Photorespiration may play an important role in C_3 plants, but it seems unlikely that it could entirely explain what happens with S. sphacelata, a C_4 plant. We propose here a different explanation that takes into account that there are other diffusional barriers to CO_2. Some of those barriers, namely the plasmalemma, have in "normal" circumstances, an effect similar to stomatal resistance [4]. If the limiting step for CO_2 diffusion under water stress is one of those internal diffusional barriers, photosynthesis would be limited mainly by diffusional constraints without decreasing sub-stomatal concentration of CO_2. It would simultaneously explain diffusional limitations and elevated C_iCO_2. It is generally believed that internal barriers do not impose important restrictions to CO_2 diffusion, but this assumption is not so far based on solid support [6]. Also [4] and [14] pointed out that the resistance of internal barriers and the mechanisms of CO_2 diffusion inside the leaf are largely unknown. Complex alterations of internal leaf pH under water stress [15] may be related to increased internal diffusion limitation to CO_2. Indeed, plasmalemma, the internal barrier which under normal conditions presents the highest (though moderate) resistance to CO_2 diffusion, is highly permeable to CO_2, but almost totally impermeable to HCO_3^- [4]. Internal pH change could change the CO_2/HCO_3^- equilibrium [16], changing the plasmalemma (and other internal membranes) resistance to carbon diffusion. Further investigation of internal diffusive resistances to CO_2, under stress conditions, may be of great importance.

REFERENCES

1.Chaves, M.M. (1991) J. Exp. Bot. 42 (234), 1-16.
2.Caemmerer, S and Farquhar, G.D. (1981) Planta 153, 376-387
3.Long, S.P. and Hallgreen, J.E. (1985) in Techniques in Bioproductivity and Photosynthesis (Coombs, J., et al., eds.), pp. 62-93, Pergamon Press, New York
4.Nobel, S.P. (1983) Biophysical Plant Physiology and Ecology, W.H. Freeman and Co., San Francisco
5.Mattews, M.A., and Boyer, J.S. (1984) in Advances in Photosynthesis Research (Sybesma, C., ed.), vol. 4, pp. 383-386, Martinus Nijhoff/Dr W. Junk Publishers, The Hague
6.Farquhar, G.D., and Sharkey, T.D. (1982) Ann. Rev. Plant Physiol. 33, 317-345
7.Stuhlfauth, T., Sultemeyer, D.F., Weinz, S. and Fock, H.P. (1988) Plant Physiol. 86, 246-250
8.Frederick, J.R., Alm, D.M. Hesketh, J.D. (1989) Photosynthetica 23 (4), 575-584
9.Sharkey, T.D., Loreto, F. and Vassey, T.L. (1990) in Current Research in Photosynthesis (Baltscheffsky, M., ed), vol. 4, pp. 549-556, Kluwer Academic Publishers, Dordrecht
10.Cheeseman, J.M. (1991) Plant, Cell and Environment 14, 593-599
11.Kraalingen, D.W.(1990) Plant, Cell and Environment 13, 1001-1004
12.Krampitz, M.J., Klug, K. and Fock, H.P. (1984) Photosynthetica 18 (3), 322-328
13.Krampitz, M.J., and Fock, H.P. (1984) Photosynthetica 18 (3), 329-337
14.Edwards, G., and Walker, D.A. (1983) C_3, C_4: Mechanisms, and Cellular and Environmental Regulation of Photosynthesis, Blackwell Scientific Publications, Oxford
15.Hartung, W. and Radin, J.W. (1989) Current Topics in Plant Biochemistry and Physiology 8, 110-124
16.Umbreit, W.W. (1972) in Manometric and Biochemical Techniques (Umbreit, W.W., et al., eds.), 20-29, Burgess Publishing Company, Minneapolis

22. Light Acclimation

LIGHT ACCLIMATION OF THYLAKOID SYSTEM IN CYANOPHYTES: REGULATION OF PSI FORMATION IN RESPONSE TO LIGHT REGIME

Yoshihiko Fujita, Akio Murakami and Katsunori Aizawa
Department of Cell Biology, National Institute for Basic Biology, Okazaki, Aichi 444, Japan

1. INTRODUCTION

In developing thylakoids, stoichiometric composition of components functioning in the light-energy conversion, represented by PSI/PSII stoichiometry, is regulated in response to photosynthetic conditions such as light regime (1,2). The ratio of PSI to PSII becomes higher under conditions where PSII action exceeds PSI, and the ratio decreases when PSI action exceeds PSII. Anderson (3) named this phenomenon "a long term adaptation of thylakoid system". Indeed, changes in PSI/PSII stoichiometry have been found to maintain the efficiency of light-energy conversion at high level under the light regime, to which the stoichiometry has been adjusted (4,5). Our previous study with the cyanophyte *Synechocystis* PCC 6714 has indicated that (i) stoichiometry regulation is achieved by changes in abundance of PSI complex (6,7) through regulation of PSI synthesis (8), and that (ii) the regulation occurs in response to the redox steady-state of ETS component(s) acting between the two photosystems (9,10), probably Cyt b_6-f complex (10,11); stimulation of PSI synthesis occurs when the component(s) becomes highly reduced, and vice versa.

Based on these findings, we have proposed a work model for the control of PSI synthesis in the stoichiometry regulation such that reduced levels of ETS component(s), probably of Cyt b_6-f, is monitored, transduced through signal transduction system and induces the control of PSI synthesis. Three questions arise from this work model: (i) how is the redox state monitored, (ii) what is the signal transduction, and (iii) which step(s) in PSI synthesis is controlled and how. Reported here are our recent results obtained from the experiments to look for the answers to these questions.

2. MATERIAL AND METHODS

Synechocystis PCC 6714 was grown in the MDM medium (12) after slight modification; phosphate was added at double strength. Cells were grown with 30 mM glucose in a thermostatted reciprocal shaker (26°C) under illumination with a weak orange light (6 W m^{-2}) which excites mainly PSII (PSII light) or a weak red light (12 W m^{-2}) exciting mainly PSI (PSI light) (cf.13). Cells at the exponential growth phase were used for the experiments. Conditions for experimental incubation were the same as those for cell cultures.

Abundance of PSI, PSII and Cyt b_6-f complexes was determined with isolated membranes spectrophotometrically by redox changes in absorptions of P700 for

N. Murata (ed.), Research in Photosynthesis, Vol. IV, 301–308.

PSI, Cyt b_{559} for PSII and Cyt *f* and/or Cyt b_6 for Cyt b_6-*f* complexes, respectively (cf.7). Rates of PSI synthesis were determined by pulse-labeling of psaA/B with ^{35}S-methionine followed by immunoprecipitation. The labeling time was 2 to 24 min. Details for determination will be reported elsewhere (K.Aizawa and Y.Fujita, in preparation).

Redox levels and electron flow around Cyt b_6-*f* complex under steady state of photosynthesis were monitored with intact cells by flash-induced oxidation-reduction of Cyt *f* under background illumination with PSI or PSII light. Details were reported in the previous paper (10).

Chl *a* concentrations were determined in acetone extracts spectrophotometrically using the absorption coefficient of Mackinney (14). Intracellular levels of Pchllide were measured spectrofluorometrically with acetone extracts. The fluorescence intensity at 632 nm was determined under 435 nm excitation. Details for the determination will be reported elsewhere (Y.Fujita and A.Murakami, in preparation). Cell concentrations were determined by counting cells on a haematocytometer under a light microscope.

3. RESULTS AND DISCUSSION

3.1 *Oxidation-reduction of Cyt* b$_6$-f *and regulation of PSI synthesis:* As we reported previously (10), a fast reduction of flash-oxidized Cyt *f* occurs prominently under conditions where PSI increase is induced or high PSI levels are maintained. Amplitude of the fast reduction relative to the total is greater before occurrence of PSI increase than that after reaching a high level of PSI. Thus, the fast reduction seems to correlate closely to the regulation (stimulation) of PSI synthesis. $T_{1/2}$ of the fast reduction is 3 to 5 msec, far faster than that for Cyt *f* reduction by

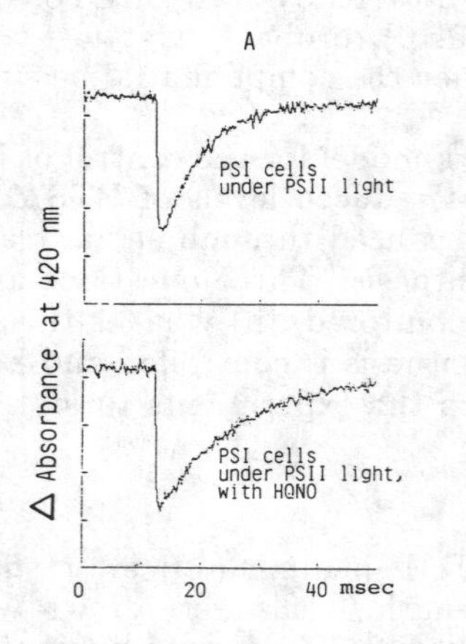

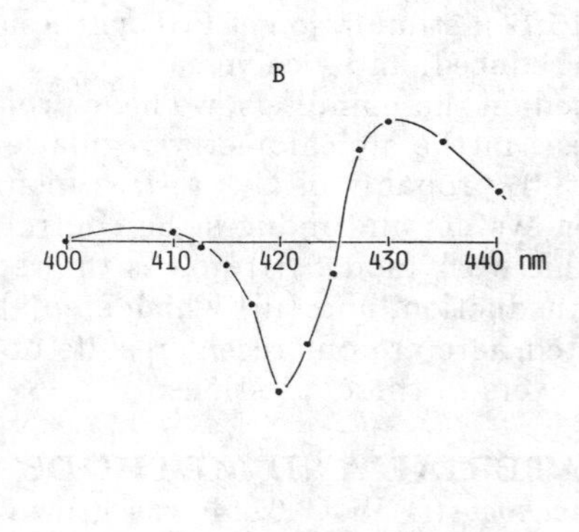

FIGURE 1. Effect of HQNO on reduction of flash-oxidized Cyt *f* (A) and difference spectrum, HQNO-poisoned (50 μM) minus control (B) observed with *Synechocystis* PCC 6714 grown under PSI light. In A, Cyt *f* oxidation was measured at 420 nm under PSII light, and in B, difference spectrum was determined 15 msec after the flash-oxidation.

PQH_2 (10 to 15 msec, cf.10). To characterize the fast reduction, we examined the effect of HQNO, the inhibitor of Cyt b_6 oxidation in Q cycle (cf.15). The reduction was slowed down by HQNO (50 μM) to $T_{1/2}$ of the same level of the reduction by PQH_2 (10 msec, Fig.1A). The difference spectrum, HQNO-poisoned minus control, 15 msec after flash-oxidation (Fig.1B) indicates that in HQNO-poisoned cells, Cyt b_6 remains at reduced state (positive difference around 430 nm) while Cyt f stays at oxidized state (negative difference around 420 nm). Results indicate that the rapid reduction is due to the flash-induced electron flow from Cyt b_6 through Q cycle. Thus, the amplitude of the rapid reduction corresponds to the reduced level of Cyt b_6 under steady state.

If the reduced level of Cyt b_6 is monitored by the HQNO-sensitive Cyt b_6 oxidation, PSI increase (stimulation of PSI synthesis) should be suppressed by HQNO. HQNO is a labile reagent. In the experiments to determine HQNO effect on PSI synthesis, we replaced the incubation medium with the fresh one and added fresh HQNO at every 5 hr. Thus, the cells were intermittently poisoned by HQNO during the incubation. Though cell growth was slowed down, it still occurred exponentially. Suppression was more prominent under PSII light (50% inhibition) than under PSI light (30% inhibition). A high level of PSI in cells grown under PSII light was reduced by HQNO even under PSII light (Fig.2A). However, HQNO-suppression is not so much as that by PSI light. This is probably due to an intermittent treatment with HQNO. Abundance, on a per cell basis, of PSI complex before (5.7 mols per 10^{19} cells) and after (3.3 mols per 10^{19} cells) the 20-hr incubation with HQNO under PSII light indicated that PSI levels were reduced after the incubation. However, abundance of PSII and Cyt b_6-f was not altered (before incubation, 1.7 mols PSII and 1.4 mols Cyt b_6-f per 10^{19} cells; after incubation, 1.5 mols PSII and 1.3 mols Cyt b_6-f per 10^{19} cells). HQNO effect was almost insignificant on the decrease in PSI levels under PSI light (Fig.2B). Results indicate that HQNO suppresses stimulation of PSI synthesis under PSII light. Insignificant effect on PSI light-induced PSI decrease indicates that suppression of PSI synthesis is insensitive to HQNO. HQNO effects on the oxidation

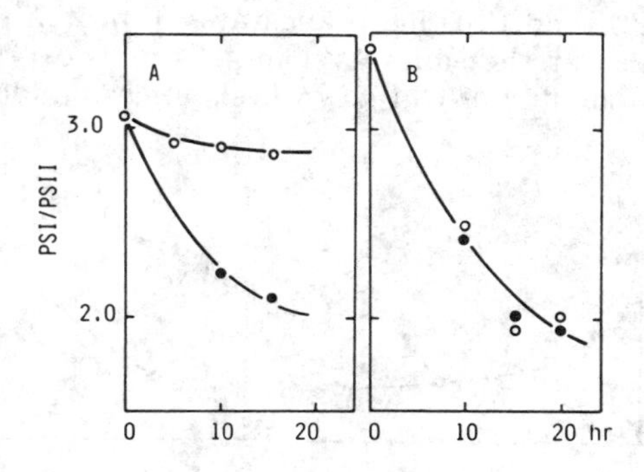

FIGURE 2. HQNO effect on changes in PSI levels under PSII light (A) and induced by shift from PSII to PSI light (B). PSI levels are presented relative to PSII. Open circles, control; closed circles, with HQNO (50 μM).

of Cyt b_6 and on the PSI synthesis suggest that (i) HQNO-sensitive oxidation of Cyt b_6 is monitored and that (ii) PSI synthesis is stimulated in proportional to the size of the signal, the size of Cyt b_6 oxidation.

3.2 *Control of PSI synthesis; a possible involvement of regulation of Chl* a *synthesis:* Stable assembly of PSI complex requires supply of a great number of Chl *a*. Thus, regulation of PSI synthesis can be achieved by control of Chl *a* synthesis as well as by control of apoprotein synthesis. Synthesis of PSI core peptides, psaA/B, has been known to be controlled by Chl *a* supply in developing chloroplasts of barley seedlings (16,17). A similar control mechanism may occur in the regulation of PSI/PSII stoichiometry. Indeed, our previous model experiments have shown that limitation of Chl *a* synthesis by the inhibitor causes a selective suppression of PSI synthesis (18).

Myers et al. (19) have found that Pchllide is accumulated in cells of *Anacystis nidulans* Tx 20 grown under PSI light but rapidly decreases upon shift to PSII light. Their finding suggests that Chl *a* synthesis is regulated in response to light regime. We confirmed their findings with *Synechocystis* PCC6714. Pchllide was accumulated up to 10% of total Chl *a* in cells grown under PSI light. A slight accumulation occurred for Mg-protoporphyrin, but most of this pigment was excreted into medium. Accumulation of Chllide *a* was insignificant. Shift of light regime to PSII light caused a rapid decrease in Pchllide levels (Fig.3A). Pchllide decrease occurred with at least two kinetic phases; initial rapid phase ($T_{1/2}$, around 10 min) followed by a very slow phase. Accumulation induced by PSI light was far slower than PSII light-induced decrease (Fig.3B). Changes in Pchllide levels indicate that PSI light causes suppression of Chl *a* synthesis at the step(s) after Pchllide or acceleration at the step(s) before Pchllide, and that PSII light acts in reverse way. If a step before Pchllide synthesis would be regulated, the flux of Chl *a* synthesis in cells under PSII light should be far smaller than that in cells under PSI light. However, Chl *a* concentrations, on a per cell basis, in the former were 2 to 3 times greater than those in the latter, due to difference in PSI abundance per cell (cf.7). Cell growth under our experimental conditions were almost equal under PSI and PSII light, and rates of protein synthesis, including PSII protein, were also at the same level in cells of two types, except for PSI synthesis (20). Thus, the flux of Chl *a* synthesis in cells under PSII light must

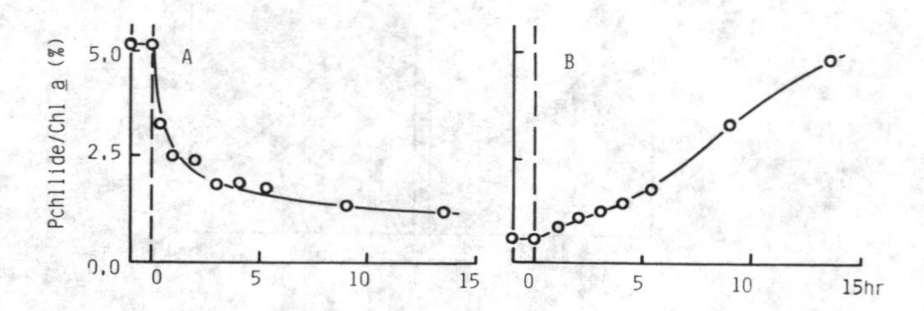

FIGURE 3. Changes in intracellular Pchllide levels induced by shift from PSII to PSI light (A) and from PSI to PSII light (B).

TABLE 1. Correlation between Pchllide decrease (stimulation of Chl *a* synthesis) and PSI increase induced by shift from PSI light to various conditions.

	Shifted to			
Initial rate* of	PSII light	Addition of DCMU(0.1mM) & glucose (30mM)	Dark with glucose (30mM)	PSII light with HQNO (400μM)
Pchllide decrease	1.0	0.5	0.3	0.0
Increase in PSI levels	1.0	0.6	0.4	0.0

Cells grown under PSI light were used.
* Relative to the maximum values observed upon shift from PSI to PSII light.

be greater than that in cells under PSI light, contrary to the latter possibility. Regulation of Chl *a* synthesis must occur at the step(s) after Pchllide synthesis. Decrease in Pchllide under PSII light was suppressed by α,α'-dipyridyl at high concentration, and Chllide *a* was accumulated (data not shown), indicating that Pchllide-Chllide *a* conversion is not the step to be regulated. The regulation must occur at a terminal step(s) associated with Chl *a* transport to the site for PSI and PSII assembly in thylakoid membranes.

Suppression of Chl *a* synthesis under PSI light corresponds to suppression of

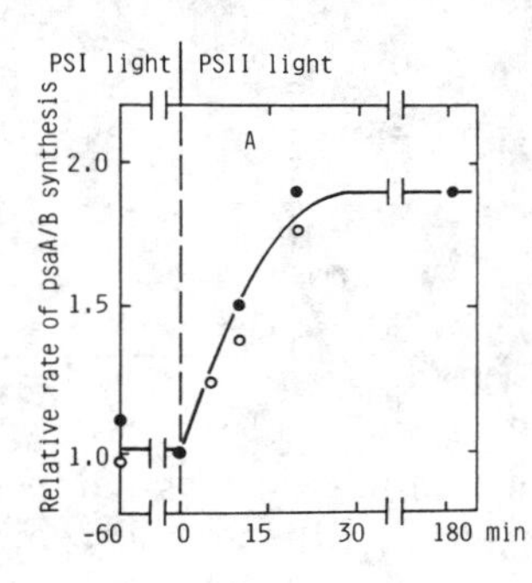

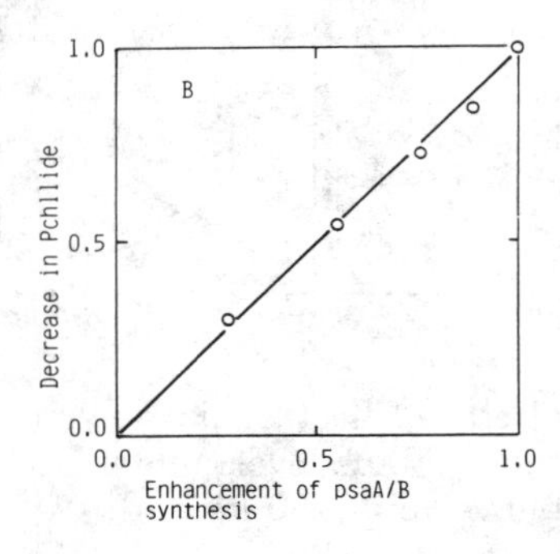

FIGURE 4. Changes in rate of psaA/B synthesis induced by shift from PSI to PSII light (A) and correlation between changes in psaA/B and Chl *a* synthesis indicates by Pchllide levels induced by light shift (B).

PSI synthesis. Indeed, Pchllide decrease (stimulation of Chl *a* synthesis) occurred in all cases, where PSI synthesis was stimulated (Table 1). Further, PSII light-induced stimulation of Chl *a* synthesis was inhibited by HQNO like PSI synthesis though a high concentration (400 μM) was needed in this case. Thus, regulation of Chl *a* and PSI synthesis correlates very closely to each other.

It is possible that Chl *a* synthesis itself is not regulated, but changes in Pchllide levels result from regulation of PSI synthesis at the apoprotein synthesis. Indeed, rates of psaA/B synthesis were accelerated up to twice higher levels upon shift to PSII light (Fig.4A). The change of the rates was identical with that of Pchllide decrease (Fig.4B). Shift from PSII to PSI light slowed down the synthesis to the level under PSI with a similar rapidness (20). If changes in Pchllide levels would be a reflection of regulation of psaA/B synthesis, PSII light-induced decrease in Pchllide levels should not occur when psaA/B synthesis is inhibited. However, puromycin, the translation inhibitor did not suppress Pchllide decrease (Fig.5A). Chloramphenicol, erythromycin and streptomycin also showed no effect. Results indicate an occurrence of regulation of Chl *a* synthesis itself. Enhancement of psaA/B synthesis induced by shift to PSII light was not suppressed by rifampicin (20). The regulation must occur after the transcription. It is very likely that PSI synthesis is controlled by Chl *a* synthesis or supply as similar to the PSI synthesis in developing chloroplasts of barley seedlings.

Further, the translation inhibitor induced a rapid decrease in Pchllide levels, i.e., stimulation of Chl *a* synthesis even under PSI light (Fig.5B). Chl *a* synthesis under PSI light must be suppressed by a proteinous factor which turns over rather rapidly. Pchllide decrease shown in Fig.5B indicates that $T_{1/2}$ for degradation of the suppressive factor is around 10 min.

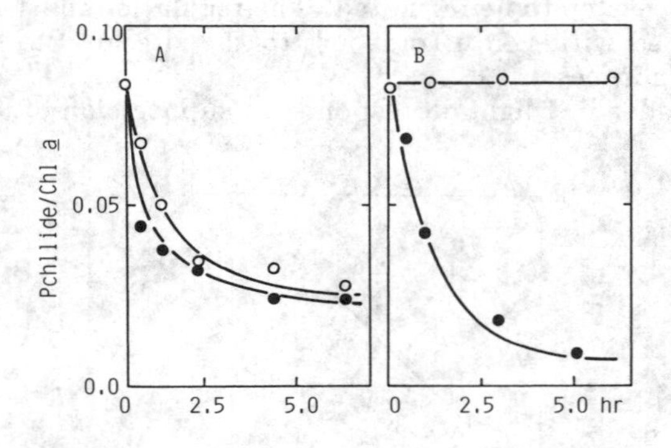

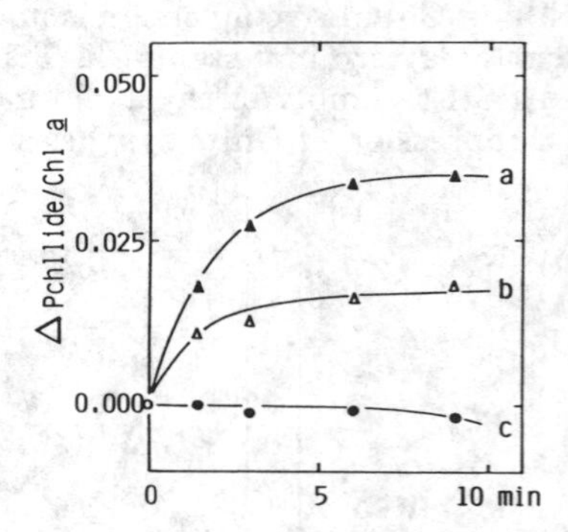

FIGURE 5 (left). Effect of puromycin on Pchllide decrease induced by PSII light (A) and on Pchllide levels under PSI light (B). Open circles, control; closed circles, with puromycin (150 μg/ml).

FIGURE 6 (right). Effect of HQNO and puromycin on Pchllide levels under PSI light. Curve a, with HQNO (400 μM) and puromycin (150 μg/ml); b, with HQNO alone; c, with puromycin alone. Differences from control values at respective times are protted .

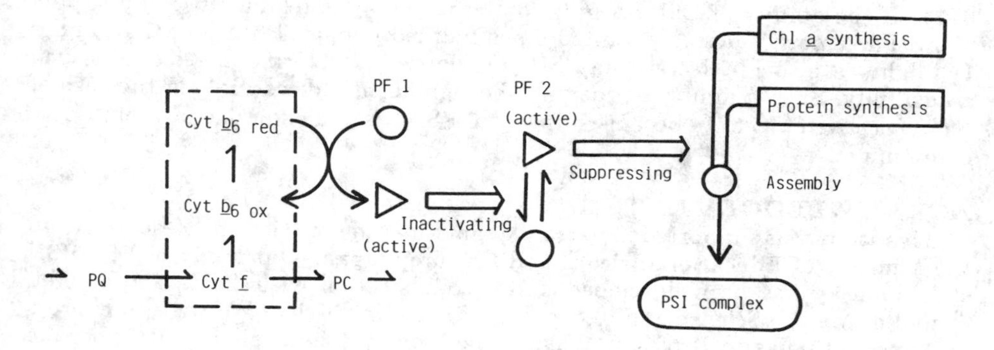

FIGURE 7. A work model for regulation of PSI synthesis in response to photosynthetic conditions.

Under PSI light, HQNO caused an enhancement of Pchllide accumulation (Fig.6, curve b), indicating that HQNO further reduces the signal level which is limited under PSI light. This HQNO effect was enhanced by the translation inhibitor (Fig.6, curve a). Other 3 inhibitors also showed the same effect. Results suggest an occurrence of another proteinous factor in the signal transduction. This factor must function between Cyt b_6 oxidation and the suppressing factor and turns over far more rapidly ($T_{1/2}$, around 3 min).

Based on the results reported here, we can draw a revised work model as shown in Fig.7. Cyt b_6 oxidation, which is sensitive to HQNO, activates a factor (PF1), which turns over very rapidly. The activated factor inactivates a suppressive factor (PF2). Thus, Chl *a* synthesis or supply to the photosystem assembly is stimulated in proportional to the size of Cyt b_6 oxidation. The flux of Chl *a* supply controls selectively PSI synthesis since the affinity for Chl *a* supply is higher to PSII than PSI assembly (cf.18). However, it is also possible that the control occurs in the affinity for Chl *a* supply to PSI assembly through modification of a component acting in Chl *a* supply to photosystem assembly; a low affinity under low signal level (under PSI light) becomes higher with a greater signal (under PSII light). The assumptive suppressing factor (PF2) may be such a component. The model has been drawn under assumption that control of PSI synthesis occurs at the level of Chl *a* synthesis. At present, however, we cannot neglect exclusively a possibility for the control of the apoprotein synthesis.

Cunningham et al. (21) have reported that in *Porphyridium cruentum*, abundance of PSII complex is also changed in reverse way to changes in PSI abundance. We have also observed similar PSII change for *Porphyra yezoensis* (S.Abe, A.Murakami, K.Ohki, Y.Aruga and Y.Fujita, in preparation) and for marine *Synechococcus* strains (K.Ohki, A.Murakami and Y.Fujita, unpublished). In these cases, plural PSII complexes are assembled into one phycobilisome (cf.22) very differently from *Synechocystis* PCC 6714 (one PSII to one phycobilisome). Since number of PSII per one phycobilisome is changed in the former cases, stoichiometry between these two may be more flexible than that in *Synechocystis* PCC

6714. If the affinity of Chl *a* supply to PSI assembly is regulated, Chl *a* supply to PSII assembly is possibly limited much markedly under PSII light than under PSI light, resulting in decrease in PSII abundance in the former cases due to such a flexibility. Such a limitation may not be significantly discernible in the case of *Synechocystis* PCC 6714 because number of PSII assembled in one phycobilisome is minimum.

ACKNOWLEDGEMENTS

This study was supported in part by Grants-in-Aid for Scientific Research from the Ministry of Education, Science and Culture, Japan. Our study of PSI/PSII stoichiometry has been developed under collaboration with Professor K.Ohki, School of Marine Science and Technology, Tokai University. We wish to express our sincere thanks to Professor Ohki for her contribution. Thanks are also due to Miss T.Yoshimi for her technical assistance.

REFERENCES

1. Fujita,Y. (1990) Bot. Mag., Tokyo, special issue 2, 29-42
2. Melis,A. (1991) Biochem. Biophys. Acta 1058, 87-106
3. Anderson,J.M. (1986) Ann. Rev. Plant Physiol. 37, 93-136
4. Murakami,A. and Fujita,Y. (1988) Plant Cell Physiol. 29, 305-311
5. Chow,W.S., Melis,A. and Anderson,J.M. (1990) Proc. Natl. Acad. Sci. U.S.A. 87, 7502-7506
6. Fujita,Y., Ohki,K. and Murakami,A. (1987) Plant Cell Physiol. 28, 227-234
7. Fujita,Y. and Murakami,A. (1987) Plant Cell Physiol. 28, 1547-1553
8. Fujita,Y., Murakami,A., Ohki,K. and Hagiwara,N. (1988) Plant Cell Physiol. 29, 557-564
9. Fujita,Y., Murakami,A. and Ohki,K. (1987) Plant Cell Physiol. 28, 283-292
10. Murakami,A. and Fujita,Y. (1991) Plant Cell Physiol. 32, 213-222
11. Murakami,A. and Fujita,Y. (1991) Plant Cell Physiol. 32, 223-230
12. Watanabe,A. (1960) J. Gen. Appl. Microbiol. 6, 283-292
13. Fujita, Y. Ohki,K. and Murakami,A. (1985) Plant Cell Physiol. 26, 1541-1548
14. Mackinney,G. (1941) J. Biol. Chem. 140, 315-322
15. Matsuura,K., Murakami,A. and Fujita,Y. (1988) Plant Cell Physiol. 29, 1261-1268
16. Klein,R.R., Gamble,P.E. and Mullet,J.E. (1988) Plant Physiol. 88, 1246-1256
17. Eichacker,L.A., Soll,J., Lauterbach,P., Rüdiger,W., Klein,R.R. and Mullet,J.E. (1990) J. Biol. Chem. 265, 13566-13571
18. Fujita,Y., Murakami,A. and Ohki,K. (1990) Plant Cell Physiol. 31, 145-153
19. Myers,J., Graham,J.-R. and Wang,T. (1982) Plant Physiol. 69, 549-550
20. Aizawa,K. and Fujita,Y. (1993) This issue
21. Cunningham,F.X.Jr., Dennenberg,R.J., Jursinic,P.A. and Gantt,E. (1990) Plant Physiol. 93, 888-895
22. Ohki,K., Okabe,Y., Murakami,A. and Fujita,Y. (1987) Plant Cell Physiol. 28, 1219-1226

DEGRADATION PRODUCTS OF THE D1 PROTEIN ARE LOCATED IN THE NON-APPRESSED REGIONS OF THE THYLAKOID MEMBRANE *in vivo*

REETTA KETTUNEN, ELINA LEHTONEN, ESA TYYSTJÄRVI AND EVA-MARI ARO
Department of Biology, University of Turku, SF-20700 Turku, Finland

1. INTRODUCTION

Light can cause an inactivation of PSII electron transport and subsequent degradation of the D1 protein. The exact degradation mechanism and cleavage site of the D1 protein are currently under intense study. Many lines of evidence suggest that degradation of the D1 protein is an enzymatic process both under high and low light (1-3). The primary cleavage site is probably located between the transmembrane segments IV and V of the D1-protein (1). However, the site of primary cleavage may depend on the mechanism of photoinactivation of PSII (3). Recovery from photoinhibition requires degradation of the damaged D1 protein and synthesis of a new copy.

Because photoinhibition mainly concerns PSIIα of the appressed regions (4), whereas synthesis and insertion of the new D1 protein into the PSII complex occur in non-appressed regions (5,6), the PSII complex must cycle between these two membrane regions during photoinhibition and recovery (6,7). The coordinated function of different thylakoid regions may be a prerequisite for a dynamic and well regulated process of D1 protein turnover. We have previously argued that the phosphorylated form of the D1 protein, the D1*, might be involved in regulation of the degradation of the D1 protein (8). In the present communication we present data suggesting that a third thylakoid membrane domain, the intermediate fraction between appressed membranes and stroma lamellae, is involved in D1 protein turnover.

2. MATERIALS AND METHODS

Pumpkin (*Cucurbita pepo* L., cv. "Jättiläismeloni") plants were grown at the PPFD of 1000 (HL-plants, HL = high light) and, when particulary indicated, also at 50 μmol $m^{-2}s^{-1}$ (LL-plants, LL = low light). Before the photoinhibition treatments, the leaves were incubated for three hours in darkness, with their petioles in water or in chloramphenicol (1 mg/ml). It was tested that the main effect of chloramphenicol during high light stress was an inhibition of D1 protein synthesis (9). Photoinhibition treatments of isolated thylakoids were done as in (8).

N. Murata (ed.), Research in Photosynthesis, Vol. IV, 309–316.

Thylakoid subfractions were isolated by digitonin and Triton X-100 digestion essentially as in (10). Treatment of the crude grana fraction with Triton X-100 followed by sentrifugation (40 000 x g, 30 min) separates grana lamellae from the intermediate fraction that was subsequently rescued by sentrifugation (144 000 x g, 90 min) from the supernatant.

Polypeptides of the thylakoid membranes and subfractions were separated by 12 to 22.5 % SDS-UREA-PAGE. After electrophoresis the polypeptides were transferred to Immun-Lite membrane (BioRad) for immunodetection of the D1 protein with a BioRad Chemiluminescent kit. The D1 antibody, a generous gift from A. Soitamo, was raised against a fusion protein containing the 22 first amino acids of the N-terminal end of *Synechococcus* D1 protein.

Turnover of the D1 protein was studied with pulse and chase -technique in leaf discs using [^{35}S]-methionine. The pulse was done by illuminating leaf discs for three hours at the PPFD of 1000 μmol $m^{-2}s^{-1}$ (HL-plants) or at the PPFD of 500 μmol $m^{-2}s^{-1}$ (LL-plants) at room temperature. The chase PPFD was 1000 μmol $m^{-2}s^{-1}$. After isolation of thylakoids, polypeptides were separated by 12 to 22,5 % SDS-PAGE and visualized by autoradiography.

3. RESULTS AND DISCUSSION

3.1 D1* is also found in the intermediate fraction

Thylakoid membrane consists of three membrane domains. Digitonin digests pumpkin thylakoid membranes yielding very pure stroma lamellae but only a crude grana fraction. The latter was further purified with Triton X-100 which separates the appressed lamellae from the 'intermediate' fraction that contains the non-appressed regions of grana discs. See Table 1 for the chlorophyll a/b ratios of the different thylakoid subfractions.

The intermediate fraction contains both PSI and PSII polypeptides and some specific polypeptides (data not shown). The differences in polypeptide composition suggest that the intermediate fraction is a functionally different non-appressed domain of the thylakoid membrane, consisting of the margins of grana stacks and of the fret membranes. Evidence indicating importance of the third domain of thylakoid membrane has been presented by Anderson (11) and Albertsson et al. (12).

TABLE 1. The chlorophyll a/b ratios of the three thylakoid subractions of high-light grown pumpkin leaves.

	chl a/b ratio ± S.E., N = 7
Intact thylakoids	3.8 ± 0.07
Stroma lamellae	8.9 ± 0.24
Crude grana	3.3 ± 0.07
Appressed membranes	2.3 ± 0.07
Intermediate fraction	5.5 ± 0.45

We have previously shown that the D1 protein undergoes *in vivo* a light-induced modification to D1* (13) and the modified form can only be found in the appressed membranes. However, fractionation of thylakoid membranes into grana, stroma and intermediate fractions revealed that D1* was present after illumination both in the grana lamellae and in the intermediate fraction (Fig. 1). D1* was never seen in the stroma lamellae, in accordance with Elich et al. (14).

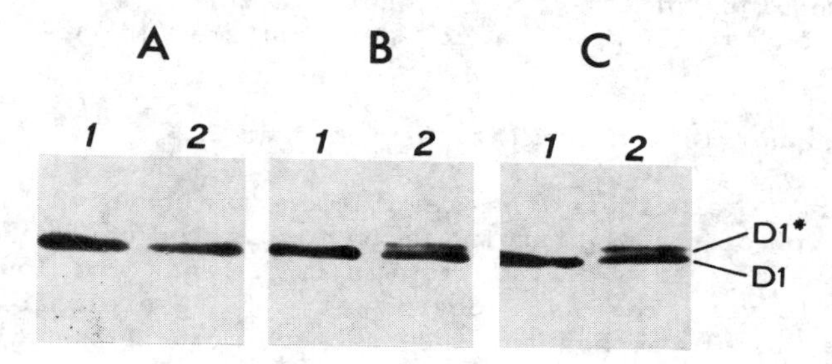

FIGURE 1. An immunoblot of the D1 protein demonstrating the light-induced appearance of D1* in thylakoid subfractions. A: stroma lamellae, B: appressed membranes, C: intermediate fraction. The numbers refer to the treatments of intact leaves; 1: dark incubation for 3 hours at RT, 2: light treatment at 2500 μmol $m^{-2}s^{-1}$ for 3 h at RT.

The proportion of D1* of the total D1 content in intact leaves depends on light intensity and no D1* is present after prolonged dark incubation of leaves. It also seems that the high-light-induced degradation of the D1 protein occurs via D1* in intact leaves (13). D1* is not the D1 protein that is *per se* targetted for degradation (8). D1* is a phosphorylated form of the D1 protein (8,14) and it can be induced in thylakoids under conditions favoring protein phosphorylation, without inactivating PSII electron transport. Phosphorylation-induced D1* appeared to be a poor substrate for the protease, as compared to the nonphosphorylated D1 (Fig 2., see also 8).

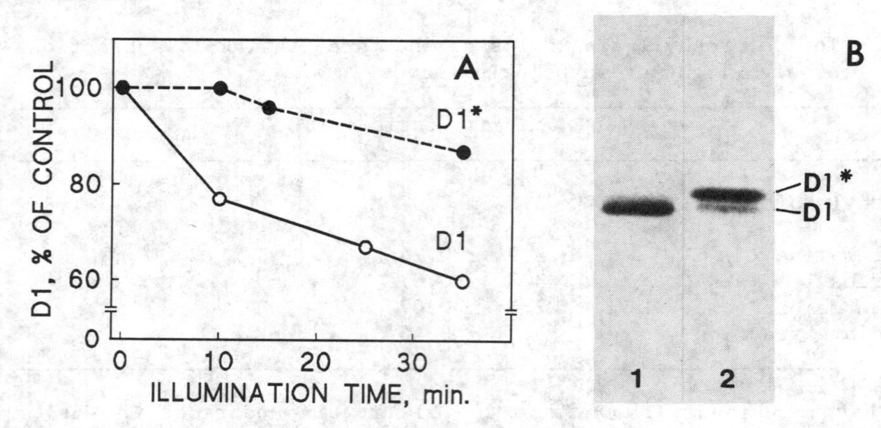

FIGURE 2. A. Loss of phosphorylated (D1*) and nonphosphorylated D1 protein during illumination (1500 μmol $m^{-2}s^{-1}$, 20 °C) of thylakoid membranes. Prior to photoinhibition treatments, thylakoid membranes were illuminated at 100 μmol $m^{-2}s^{-1}$, 20 °C for 20 min in the absence or presence of 0.4 mM ATP.
B. An immunoblot of the D1 protein before (1) and after (2) phosphorylation by illumination (20 min, 100 μmol $m^{-2}s^{-1}$) in the presence of 0.4 mM ATP.

3.2 Does phosphorylation regulate D1 turnover ?

In order to elucidate the regulation of photoinhibition-induced degradation of the D1 protein, we have compared photoinactivation of PSII and D1 protein degradation in high-light and low-light grown pumpkin leaves. The same degree of PSII photoinhibition in the presence of chloramphenicol induced much more degradation of the D1 protein in HL-leaves than in LL-leaves during illumination (Fig. 3). This indicates that degradation of the D1 protein does not directly follow the photoinactivation of electron transport but some regulatory step is involved. Furthermore, the undegraded D1 protein in LL-leaves is in the D1* form. Slower degradation of the D1 protein in LL-leaves can also be demonstrated by pulse and chase experiments (Fig. 4). Illumination at the PPFD of 1000 μmol $m^{-2}s^{-1}$ induces net photoinhibition only in LL-leaves whereas HL-leaves counteract photoinhibition mainly by rapid turnover of the D1 protein.

Phosphorylation of D1 to D1* may slow down degradation of the D1 protein. Such a control mechanism would prevent total disassembly of photoinhibited PSII which could occur if the D1 protein were degraded in appressed regions where synthesis of a new D1 protein cannot follow. We hypotesize that only after entrance to non-appressed regions, D1* becomes susceptible to an intrinsic protease (15). This step may involve dephosphorylation. We tested the hypothesis that the D1 protein is degraded in non-appressed membranes by searching for degradation products in different thylakoid membrane regions.

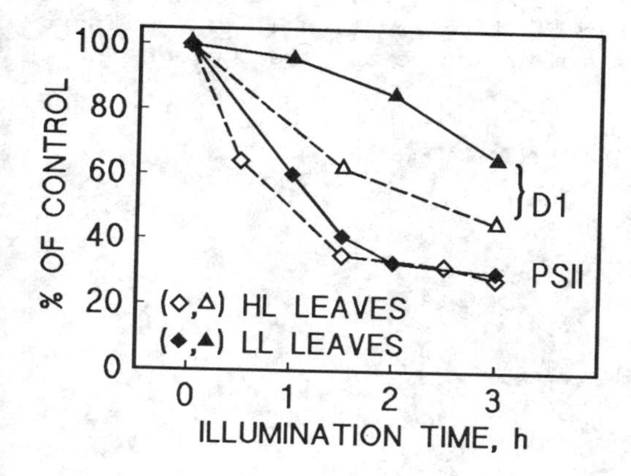

FIGURE 3. Photoinactivation of PSII electron transport and degradation of the D1 protein in HL- and LL-leaves in the course of illumination at RT in the presence of chloramphenicol. D1 protein content and PSII-activity were measured from thylakoids isolated from treated leaves.

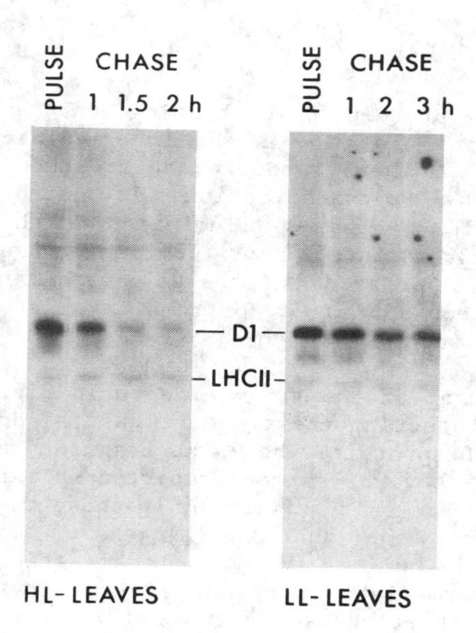

FIGURE 4. An autoradiogram demonstrating the slower turnover of the D1 protein in pumpkin plants grown at low light (LL-leaves) than in plants grown at high light (HL-leaves). Chase was done at a PPFD of 1000 μmol $m^{-2}s^{-1}$ for 1, 1.5, 2 and 3 h at RT.

3.3 A 23 kD D1 fragment is found in the intermediate fraction

After photoinhibition treatments of intact leaves, degradation fragments of the D1 protein were found only in the non-appressed membranes and mainly in the intermediate fraction (Fig. 5). There was not even a trace of a D1 fragment in the appressed membranes.

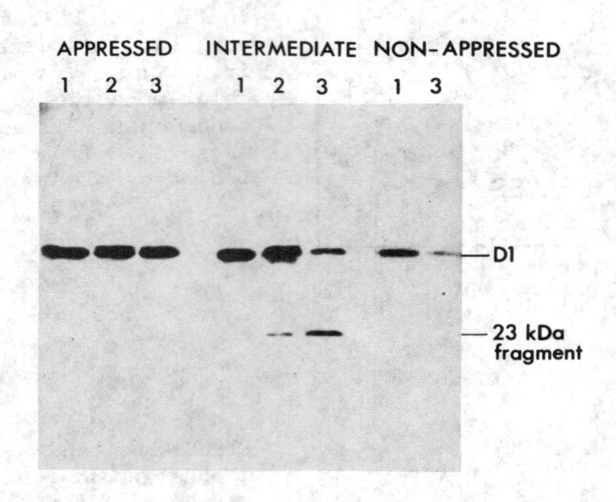

FIGURE 5. An immunoblot of the D1 protein demonstrating that a degradation fragment of the D1 protein is located in the intermediate fraction of the thylakoid membrane. The numbers refer to the treatment of intact leaves prior to isolation of thylakoid subfractions; 1: control leaves, dark-adapted for 11 hours at RT, 2: leaves illuminated at the PPFD of 2500 μmol $m^{-2}s^{-1}$ for 1,5 h at RT, 3: as lane 2 but illumination was done in the presence of chloramphenicol. Appressed = appressed membranes, intermediate = intermediate fraction, non-appressed = stroma lamellae. The wells were overloaded in order to find D1 fragments.

An estimation of the molecular weight of the fragment seen in Fig. 5 is 23 kD. The antibody used in detecting the fragment was raised against the N-terminal end of the D1 protein. The 23 kD fragment in Fig. 5 resembles closely the other *in vivo* fragment reported so far (1), although the light conditions were quite different in these two studies. This fragment supports the view that the D1 protein is cleaved *in vivo* between transmembrane helices IV and V. Localization of the 23 kD fragment in the intermediate fraction gives further support to the proposed cycling of PSII between appressed and non-appressed membranes (6,7) and suggests that degradation of the D1 protein takes place in the non-appressed areas of grana stacks.

3.4 D1* is characteristic to higher plants

We hypothesize that phosphorylation of the D1 protein to D1* is a means to prevent degradation of the damaged D1 protein in appressed membranes and to allow migration of photodamaged PSII centers to non-appressed membranes where insertion of a new copy of the D1 protein can immediately follow the degradation. This, together with fast D1 synthesis, ensures that the number of D1-depleted PSII centers is low. The survival strategy of LL-plants is to slow down degradation of the D1 protein by accumulating D1*. The photoinhibited reaction center could act as a quencher of exitation energy preventing totally irreversible photo-oxidative damage to pigments, proteins and lipids.

The dependence of the rate of D1 turnover on growth light intensity does not seem to hold in lower photosynthetic organisms like *Synechocystis* (16) and *Ceratodon purpureus* (17). Even though grown at a low PPFD (50 μmol $m^{-2}s^{-1}$), they have a high rate of D1 turnover, comparable to that in HL-leaves, when exposed to photoinhibitory illumination (1000-1500 μmol $m^{-2}s^{-1}$). These organisms also lack the ability for D1 protein phosphorylation (no D1* formation, data not shown) and their (thylakoid) membranes are not segregated into well-defined appressed and non-appressed regions. Apparently, these organisms lack the ability to regulate degradation of the D1 protein in photodamaged PSII centers.

The role of the intermediate fraction in photoinhibition is very interesting. The facts that D1* appears in the intermediate fraction after light treatment of intact leaves but not in the stroma lamellae and D1 fragments are mainly located in the intermediate fraction, suggests that the D1 protein is degraded in the intermediate fraction. It remains to be seen whether the intermediate fraction has a specific role in photoinhibition or if it is just a non-appressed membrane region that happens to be near to the appressed regions.

REFERENCES

1 Greenberg, B.M., Gaba, V., Mattoo, A.K. and Edelman, M. (1987) EMBO J. 6, 2865-2869
2 Aro, E.M., Hundal, T., Carlberg, I. and Andersson, B. (1990) Biochim. Biophys. Acta 1019, 269-275
3 De Las Rivas, J., Andersson, B. and Barber, J. (1992) Febs Lett. 301, 246-252
4 Mäenpää, P., Andersson, B. and Sundby, C. (1987) FEBS Lett. 215, 31-36
5 Mattoo, A.K. and Edelman, M (1987) Proc. Natl. Acad. Sci USA 84, 1497-1501
6 Adir, N., Shochat, S. and Ohad, I. (1990) J. Biol. Chem. 265, 12563-12568

7 Guenther, J.E. and Melis, A. (1990) Photos. Res. 23, 105-109
8 Aro, E.-M., Kettunen, R. and Tyystjärvi, E. (1992) FEBS Lett. 297, 29-33
9 Tyystjärvi, E., Kettunen, R., Ali-Yrkkö, K. and Aro, E.-M. (1992) Plant. Physiol, in press
10 Leto, K.J., Bell, E. and McIntosh, L. (1985) EMBO J. 4, 1645-1653
11 Anderson, J.M. (1989) Physiol. Plant. 76, 243-248
12 Albertsson, P.-Å., Andreasson, E., Svensson, P and Yu, S.-G. (1991) Biochim. et Biochen. Acta 1098, 90-94
13 Kettunen, R., Tyystjärvi, E. and Aro, E.-M. (1991) FEBS Lett. 290, 153-156
14 Elich, T.D., Edelman, M. and Mattoo, A.K. (1992) J. Biol. Chem. 267, 3523-3529
15 Virgin, I., Salter, H., Ghanothakis, D. and Andersson, B. (1991) FEBS Lett. 281, 125-128
16 Kallio, T, Aro, E.-M., Jansson, C. and Mäenpää, P. (1992), these proceedings
17 Rintamäki, E., Salo, R. and Aro, E.-M. (1992), these proceedings

ACKNOWLEDMENTS: This work was supported by the Academy of Finland. The authors wish to thank Ms. Virpi Paakkarinen for excellent technical assistance and Mr. A. Soitamo for the D1 antibody.

MECHANISMS OF CHLOROPLAST ACCLIMATION TO SUBOPTIMAL AND ADVERSE IRRADIANCE

Jeong Hee Kim and Anastasios Melis
Department of Plant Biology, 411 Genetics/Plant Bio. Bldg, University of California, Berkeley, CA 94720, U.S.A.

1. INTRODUCTION

1.1 Photosystem stoichiometry adjustments in response to suboptimal irradiance:

Under limiting intensity of illumination, the efficiency of photosynthesis depends on the coordinated interaction of two photosystems in the electron-transport chain. Photosystem-II (PSII) is involved in the oxidation of water and reduction of plastoquinone (PQ), whereas photosystem-I (PSI) enables electron-transport from plastohydroquinone and from the cytochrome *b-f* complex to ferredoxin. The quantum yield of photosynthesis in many plant species from diverse light habitats is about 0.106 ± 0.001 mol O_2 evolved per mol photon absorbed [1-3]. This value is very close to a theoretical upper limit of 0.125 mol O_2 evolved per mol photon absorbed, translating in a photosynthesis efficiency of about 85%, independent of the light climate in which plants grow. This is a remarkable feature of the photosynthetic apparatus, given the contrasting light-qualities that prevail in different plant ecosystems [4-6], and the fact that substantially different pigments absorb light for PSI and PSII in the thylakoid membrane of oxygenic photosynthesis.

It is known that strong variations in light-quality occur within a single leaf [6,7], within the canopy of a single tree or within the canopy of a forest [4], and within the aquatic environment [5]. Some of these environments favor absorption of light by PSI, others favor absorption of light by PSII. Thus, a question was raised as to how plants may perform photosynthesis with maximal efficiency under a variety of contrasting light-qualities. Recent work [8-10] provided direct evidence that adjustment of the photosystem ratio in thylakoids may be a key to the high quantum efficiency of photosynthesis under diverse light-quality conditions. The mechanism for the adjustment of the photosystem ratio appears to be highly conserved in nature since oxygen-evolving organisms from cyanobacteria to higher plant chloroplasts are known to possess it [11-22]. It was inferred that such mechanism performs a highly needed function in oxygen-evolving plants [10].

The dynamic response of thylakoid membranes and the adjustment of photosystem stoichiometry to different light-quality conditions suggests the existence of a mechanism capable of recognizing imbalance in the rate of light utilization by the two photoreactions and directing cellular metabolic activity for photosystem stoichiometry adjustments. Clearly, the acclimation mechanism confers to plants a significant evolutionary advantage

N. Murata (ed.), Research in Photosynthesis, Vol. IV, 317–324.

over that of a fixed PS ratio in thylakoid membranes. The notion of "flexible" or "dynamic" thylakoid membrane of photosynthesis is accepted by most investigators in the field [23-29]. However, the underlying molecular mechanism for the control of the PSII/PSI ratio and the regulation of biosynthesis/assembly of proteins that bring about this effect are not known.

1.2 Response to chronic adverse irradiance:

Chronic irradiance stress (high light-intensity) during plant growth lowers the chlorophyll content of chloroplasts and limits the photosystem light-harvesting antenna size. The adverse irradiance causes photoinhibition [30-33], manifested by the accumulation of damaged PSII units in the thylakoid membrane. These PSII units contain a modified form of D1 (D1*) [34-36] and cannot perform a photochemical charge separation. Recent work from this lab [36,37] reported that, under chronic photoinhibition conditions, thylakoid membranes have a greatly elevated PSII/PSI stoichiometric ratio (PSII/PSI=~12/1). Most of these PSII units are photochemically inert (damaged) [37]. The results suggested enhanced biosynthesis/assembly and enhanced concentration of PSII relative to other thylakoid membrane complexes under chronic photoinhibition. Clearly, an enhanced concentration of a labile component in the thylakoid membrane might serve to counter the adverse effect of irradiance stress. To gain a better understanding on the response of chloroplasts to such chronic environmental stress, we measured the turnover rate of D1 and the steady-state levels of *psb*A, *psb*D and *psa*B gene transcripts under physiological and irradiance stress conditions.

2. MATERIALS AND METHODS

Specific polyclonal antibodies were raised in rabbit against the PSII reaction center D1/32 kDa (*psbA* gene) and D2/34 kDa (*psbD* gene) proteins. Similarly, polyclonal antibodies were raised in rabbit against the PSI reaction center heterodimer (*psaA*/*psaB* gene) proteins. These antibodies were used to quantitate the level of the respective photosystem apoproteins in thylakoids as a function of time during chloroplast acclimation to a particular light regime.

3. RESULTS AND DISCUSSION

3.1 Photosystem Ratio Adjustment During Chloroplast Acclimation to PSI- or PSII-light

Specific polyclonal antibodies were used to quantitate the level of the respective photosystem apoprotein in thylakoids as a function of time during chloroplast acclimation to a particular light regime. In this experimentation, plants were shifted from a PSII-light to a PSI-light environment, and vice versa.

<u>(i) PSI-light ---> PSII-light transition</u>

Quantitation of Q_A (PSII) and P700 (PSI) by spectrophotometry revealed a prompt change in the PSII/PSI ratio (**Fig. 1**, half-time=20 h, initial PSII/PSI=2.5, final PSII/PSI=1.2).
SDS-PAGE and immunoblot analysis revealed a monotonous increase in the PSI reaction center protein content (**Fig. 2**), occurring essentially in parallel with the P700 content in thylakoids. These

results suggested that the absolute amount of PSI protein in the thylakoid membrane closely follows the assembly of functional PSI complexes. Non-functional or unassembled *psaA/psaB* gene products did not accumulate in detectable amounts in thylakoids during a PSI-light ---> PSII-light transition.
Additional SDS-PAGE and immunoblot analysis revealed a decrease in the concentration of both D1 and D2 proteins, occurring essentially

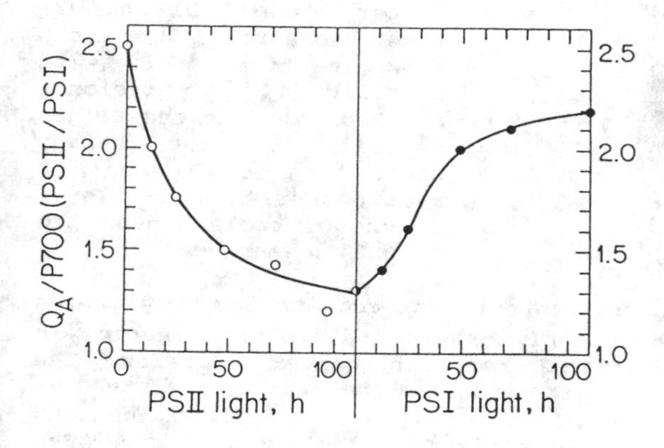

FIGURE 1. The response of photosystem stoichiometry (PSII/PSI ratio) to changes in the light-regime during plant growth. Pea plants were first acclimated to PSI-light. They were switched (at time zero) to a PSII-light environment. After 110 h, the same plants were switched back to a PSI-light environment.

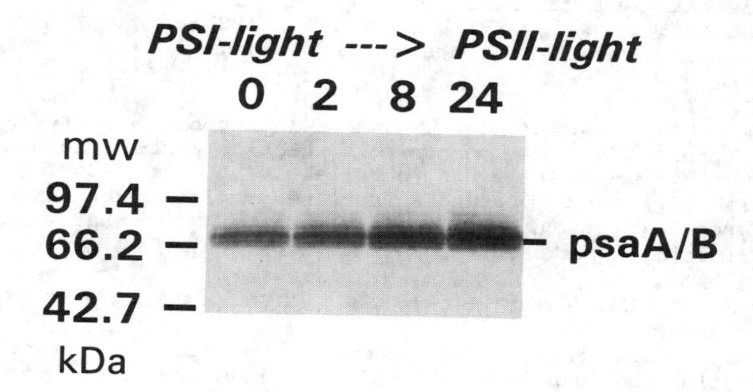

FIGURE 2. Immunoblot analysis of pea thylakoids acclimating (0-24 h) during a PSI-light--->PSII-light transition. Lanes were loaded with 20 nmol Chl (*a+b*). Steady-state levels of PSI reaction center protein were measured from the cross-reaction with specific polyclonal antibodies. Note the ~65% increase in the level of these proteins over the 0 to 24 h period.

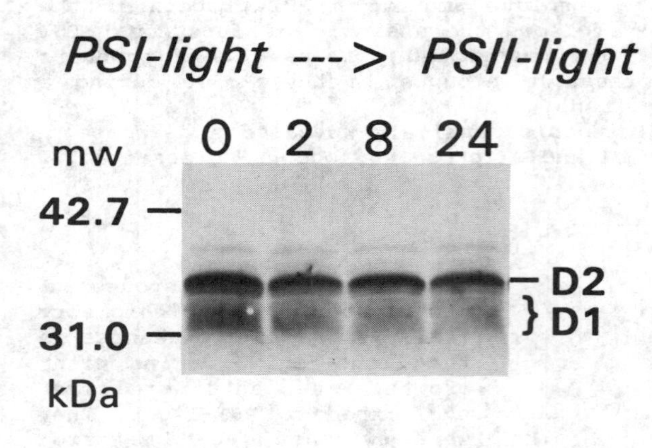

FIGURE 3. Immunoblot analysis of pea thylakoids acclimating (0-24 h) during a PSI-light -----> PSII-light transition. Lanes were loaded with 20 nmol Chl (*a*+*b*). Steady-state levels of PSII reaction center protein (D1 and D2) were measured from the cross-reaction with specific polyclonal antibodies. Note the slight decrease in the steady state level of D2 and the ~40% decrease in the level of the D1 protein over the 0 to 24 h period.

in accordance with the Q_A content in acclimating thylakoids (**Fig. 3**). However, we consistently observed different kinetics in the decrease of the D1 and D2 reaction center proteins. The results suggested a faster rate in the decrease of the D1 relative to the D2 protein (**Fig. 3**). This may reflect enhanced D1 degradation under the predominantly PSII-light conditions. The different response of the D1 and D2 proteins to the PSI-light ---> PSII-light transition suggested different control mechanisms in the regulation of biosynthesis/degradation of the two proteins.

<u>(ii) PSII-light ---> PSI-light transition</u>

Quantitation of Q_A (PSII) and P700 (PSI) by spectrophotometry revealed a reversal of the earlier change in the PSII/PSI ratio (**Fig. 1**, half-time=30 h, initial PSII/PSI=1.2, final PSII/PSI=2.3).

Under these conditions, SDS-PAGE and immunoblot analysis revealed a monotonous decrease in the PSI reaction center protein content, occurring essentially in parallel with the P700 content in thylakoids, and a monotonous increase in the concentration of both D1 and D2 proteins, occurring in parallel with that of Q_A in the acclimating thylakoids.

3.2 Rate of D1 Turnover Under Physiological and Adverse Irradiance

Earlier work from this laboratory revealed different SDS-PAGE migration patterns of D1 from control and irradiance-stressed thylakoids. **Figure 4** shows an SDS-PAGE and immunoblot analysis of the D1/32 kDa reaction center polypeptide of PSII from control (lane 1) and irradiance-stressed thylakoids (lane 2) of *D. salina*. Quantitation of the cross reaction in the two lanes with an LKB-Pharmacia XL laser densitometer (not shown) revealed an estimated 2.5-times greater cross reaction between antibodies and HL-grown sample, suggesting the presence of 2.5 times more PSII-RC protein in lane 2 (HL) than in lane 1 (control). Note that about a third of the total PSII-RC protein in the HL sample migrated at about 160 kDa, indicating the presence of PSII-RC dimers. These results suggested that HL-grown *D. salina* thylakoids contain an excess of PSII complexes which are photochemically inert and, as such, they can not be detected by the Q_A or pheophytin photoreduction.

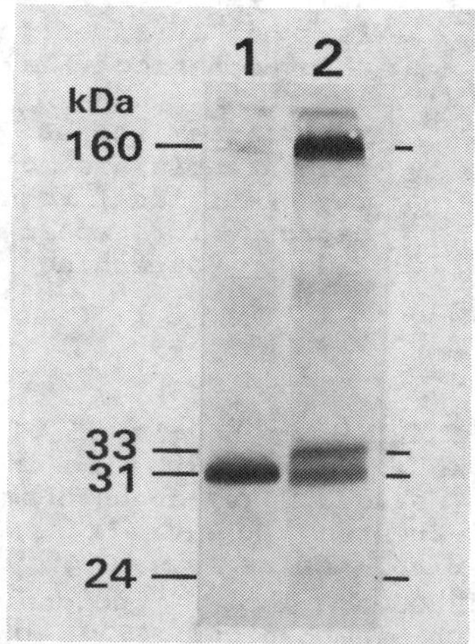

FIGURE 4. Immunoblot analysis of *D. salina* thylakoids, probed with antibodies against the D1/32 kDa reaction center polypeptide of PSII. Lane 1 (thylakoids from control cells grown under 100 µmol photons.$m^{-2}.s^{-1}$) was loaded with 8.4 nmol Chl (19 pmol of photochemically active Q_A). Lane 2 (HL-grown thylakoids grown under 2,000 µmol photons.$m^{-2}.s^{-1}$) was loaded with 4.2 nmol Chl (12 pmol Q_A). The much greater cross reaction with proteins in the HL-grown cells suggested the presence of photochemically inert PSII units in these samples.

The levels of D1 protein shown in **Fig. 4** are steady-state amounts resulting from the continuous biosynthesis and degradation of D1. To assess the rate of D1 turnover under the two different irradiance conditions, the amount of D1 was measured as a function of time in the presence of chloramphenicol. **Figure 5** shows that upon addition of chloramphenicol to low-light *D. salina* cells *in vivo*, the amount of D1 protein declined with a half-time of about 7 hours. This provides a measure of the rate of PSII damage and D1 degradation under these conditions. Since in the absence of chloramphenicol levels of D1 remain constant, it is concluded that the rate of D1 turnover under low-light conditions occurs with a half-time of about 7 h. This is consistent with other estimates on the rate of D1 turnover under low-light plant growth [38].

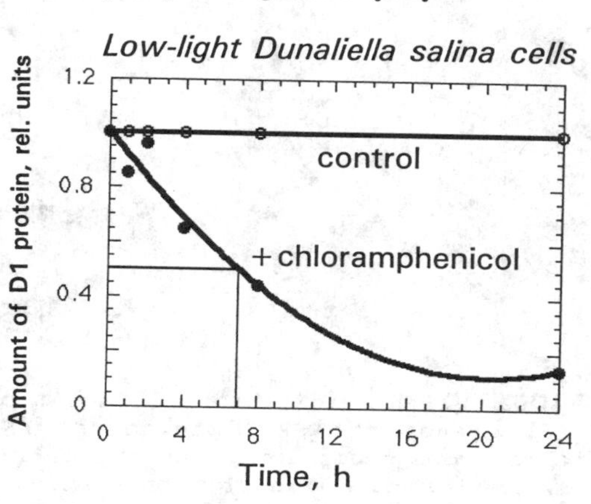

FIGURE 5. Levels of D1 protein as a function of time in control (no additions) or chloramphenicol -treated *Dunaliella salina in vivo*. Cells were grown under 100 µmol photons.$m^{-2}.s^{-1}$. Chloramphenicol (500 µg/ml) was added to the growth medium at 0 time. Similar results were obtained with the protein synthesis inhibitor lincomycin.

Figure 6 shows that, under irradiance-stress conditions, addition of chloramphenicol to *D. salina* cells resulted in a much faster decline in the amount of D1 protein (half-time of only about 20 min). Thus, PSII damage and D1 degradation under irradiance stress is about 20-times faster that those in **Fig. 5**. In the absence of chloramphenicol, levels of D1 remained constant in the chloroplast (**Fig. 6,** control), therefore, the rate of D1 turnover under irradiance stress (including damage/degradation and *de novo* biosynthesis/assembly) must occur with a half-time of about 20 min. Additional results (not shown) suggested that the chloroplast capacity for repair does not exist in the cell *a priori*, but it is induced depending on the light-intensity during plant growth and

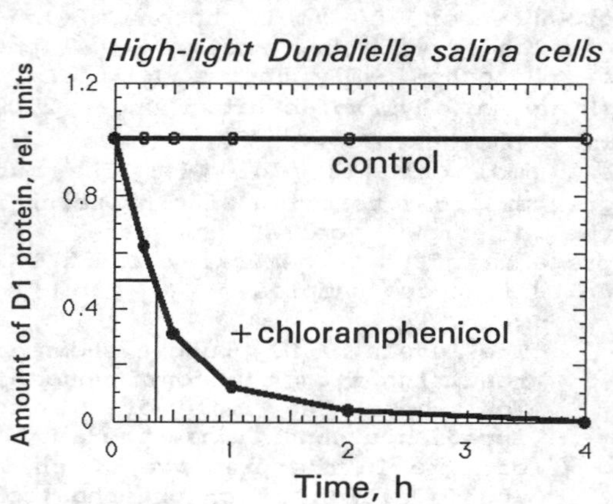

FIGURE 6. Levels of D1 protein as a function of time in control (no additions) or chloramphenicol -treated *Dunaliella salina in vivo*. Cells were grown under 2,000 µmol photons.$m^{-2}.s^{-1}$. Chloramphenicol (500 µg/ml) was added to the growth medium at 0 time. Similar results were obtained with the protein synthesis inhibitor lincomycin.

on the rate of PSII damage. The chloroplast ability to carry out enhanced rates of repair is induced over a period of 36-48 h upon cell placement under high-light conditions. The mechanism for the induction of the capacity for repair is unknown.

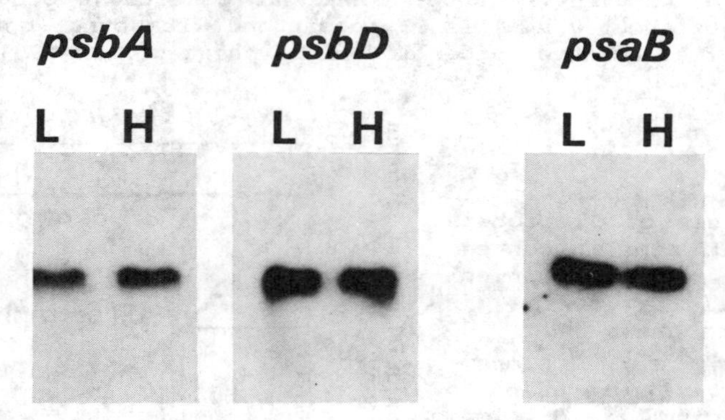

FIGURE 7. Hybridization of random primed *psbA* (D1), *psbD* (D2) or *psaB* (PSI) genes to RNA blots. Total RNA isolated from *Dunaliella salina* cells grown under low-light (L) or high-light (H) conditions. Each lane was loaded with 7 µg of total RNA.

3.3 Steady-state Levels of *psbA*, *psbD* and *psaB* mRNA Under Physiological and Irradiance Stress Conditions

Irradiance-dependent modifications in gene expression were assessed upon evaluation of the steady-state level of mRNA coding for photosystem reaction center proteins. **Figure 7** shows hybridization analyses of total cellular RNA from low-light (L) and high-light (H) grown cells with random primed *psbA* and *psbD* probes (genes for the PSII reaction center protein D1 and D2, respectively), and with a *psaB* probe (gene for the PSI reaction center protein). Laser densitometry (LKB-Pharmacia) of the autoradiograms (**Fig. 7**) indicated higher levels (by a factor of about 2) of *psbA* gene transcripts in high-light than in low-light grown *D. salina*. There were no differences in the level of mRNA hybridizing to the *psbD* and *psaB* probes. The results suggest a greater rate of transcription and/or greater stability of message for the *psbA* gene transcripts under irradiance stress.

CONCLUSIONS

Suboptimal and adverse irradiance exert changes in the photosystem composition and gene expression in chloroplasts. In this work, suboptimal irradiance was defined as the light-quality that is absorbed preferentially by PSI (PSI-light) or PSII (PSII-light). Changes in the plant growth conditions from a PSI-light to PSII-light, and vice versa, bring about adjustments in the photosystem composition (PSII/PSI ratio) in the thylakoid membrane. These are manifested as parallel changes in the Q_A, D1 and D2 content (PSII) as well as in the P700 and *psaA*/*psaB* gene product content (PSI). The results show an orderly response of the photosynthetic apparatus to suboptimal light-qualities as manifested by the gradual change in the photosystem composition of thylakoid membranes.

Another dynamic response of the photosynthetic apparatus involves the capacity of chloroplasts to carry out the repair of damaged D1/32 kDa reaction center proteins. Under low-light conditions, the rate of damage to PSII is limited and a slow (half-time of 7 h) turnover of D1 is manifested. Under irradiance-stress conditions, the rate of damage is enhanced approximately in proportion to the light intensity. At the same time, the rate of D1 biosynthesis is enhanced to match the rate of damage. In this case, however, the results suggested an emergency response of the photosynthetic apparatus to the adverse irradiance conditions, manifested by the accumulation of a modified form of D1 in the thylakoid membrane (D1* is migrating to 33 kDa in lane 2 of Fig. 4), and by the formation of photosystem-II reaction center dimers which persist even under denaturing SDS-PAGE conditions (migrating to 160 kDa in lane 2 of Fig. 4).

Our results suggest that chloroplasts employ different mechanisms in the adjustment and optimization of function depending on the suboptimal or adverse irradiance conditions prevailing during growth.

REFERENCES

1 Ley AC, Mauzerall DC (1982) Biochim. Biophys. Acta 680, 95-106
2 Björkman O, Demmig B (1987) Planta 170, 489-504
3 Evans JR (1987) Aust J Plant Physiol 14, 69-79
4 Björkman O, Ludlow MM (1972) Carnegie Inst. Washington Yearbook 71, 85-94
5 Kirk JTO (1983) Light and Photosynthesis in Aquatic Ecosystems, Cambridge University Press, London
6 Terashima I, Saeki T (1983) Plant Cell Physiol. 24, 1493-1501
7 Melis A, Spangfort M, Andersson B (1987) Photochem. Photobiol. 45, 129-136
8 Murakami A, Fujita Y (1988) Plant Cell Physiol. 29, 305-311
9 Melis A, Mulineaux CW, Allen JF (1989) Z. Naturforsch. Teil C 44, 109-118
10 Chow WS, Melis A, Anderson JM (1990 Proc. Natl. Acad. Sci. U.S.A. 87, 7502-7506
11 Kawamura M, Mimuro M and Fujita Y (1979) Plant and Cell Physiol 20, 697-705
12 Myers J, Graham JR and Wang RT (1980) Plant Physiol 66, 1144-1149
13 Melis A, Harvey GW (1981) Biochim Biophys Acta 637, 138-145
14 Wilhelm C, Wild A (1984) J Plant Physiol 115, 125-135
15 Wilhelm C, Kramer P, Wild A (1985) Physiol Plantarum 64, 359-364
16 Glick RE, McCauley SW, Melis A (1985) Planta 164, 487-494
17 Glick RE, McCauley SW, Gruissem W Melis A (1986) Proc Natl Acad Sci USA 83, 4287-4291
18 Fujita Y, Murakami A, Ohki K (1987) Plant Cell Physiol 28, 283-292
19 Fujita Y, Murakami A, Ohki K (1987) Plant Cell Physiol 28, 283-292
20 Murakami A, Fujita Y (1988) Plant Cell Physiol 29, 305-311
21 Deng X-W, Tonkyn JC, Peter GF, Thornber JP, Gruissem W (1989) Plant Cell 1, 645-654
22 Cunningham FX, Dennenberg RJ, Jursinic PA, and Gantt E (1990) Plant Physiol 93, 888-895
23 Anderson JM (1986) Annu Rev Plant Physiol 37, 93-136
24 Glazer AN, Melis A (1987) Annu Rev Plant Physiol 38, 11-45
25 Melis A (1991) Biochim Biophys Acta 1058, 87-106
26 Björkman O, Boardman NK, Anderson JM, Thorne SW, Goodchild DJ, Pyliotis NA (1972) Carnegie Inst Washington Yearbook 71, 115-135
27 Lichtenthaler HK, Meier D (1984) In Chloroplast Biogenesis ed RJ Ellis, pp 245-258, Cambridge Univ
28 Leong TA, Anderson JM (1986) Biochim Biophys Acta 850, 57-83
29 Chow W-S, Hope AB, and Anderson JM (1989) Biochim Biophys Acta 973, 105-108
30 Powles SB (1984) Annu Rev Plant Physiol 35, 15-44
31 Kyle DJ, Ohad I, and Arntzen CJ (1984) Proc Natl Acad Sci USA 81, 4070-4074
32 Ohad I, Kyle DJ, and Arntzen CJ (1984) J Cell Biol 99, 481-485
33 Demeter S, Neale PJ, and Melis A (1987) FEBS Lett 214, 370-374
34 Callahan FE, Ghirardi ML, Sopory SK, Mehta AM, Edelman M, Mattoo A (1990) J Biol Chem 265, 15357-15360
35 Kettunen R, Tyystjärvi E, Aro E-M (1991) FEBS Lett 290, 153-156
36 Melis A (1991) In Regulation of Chloroplast Biogenesis" JH Argyroudi-Akoyunoglou Ed Plenum New York in press
37 Smith BM, Morrissey PJ, Guenther JE, Nemson JA, Harrison MA, Allen JF, and Melis A (1990) Plant Physiol 93, 1433-1440
38 Mattoo AK, Edelman M (1987) Proc Natl Acad Sci USA 84, 1497-1501

Blue and Red Light Irradiance Effects on Chloroplast Gene Expression in Arabidopsis and Sorghum.

Kenneth Eskins and Nancy Alexander, USDA, ARS, National Center for Agriculture Utilization Research, Phytoproducts Research Unit, Peoria, IL, 61604

INTRODUCTION

Red-blue light regulation of LHCP2 and psbA gene expression was studied at 50 and 130 umol m^{-2} s^{-1} in two different species, Arabidopsis and Sorghum, at different stages of development. Plasticity of gene expression during sequential application of blue and red light and switching effects of blue light in constant irradiance (50 umol m^{-2} s^{-1}) blue-red light mixtures are also presented.

MATERIALS and METHODS

Arabidopsis-Seeds of Arabidopsis thaliana (L.) Heynh, race Columbia were germinated at 20°C in white light, then transferred to growth chambers (20°C and 50 % humidity) which had different light qualities and irradiances (14hlight/10hdark). Plants were grown under red, blue or red + far-red light or were moved from one quality to another at suitable intervals. Sorghum-Seeds of sorghum bicolor, cv. Tx 623 B-line (Pioneer Hi-Bred Inc., Plainview, TX) were planted in top soil in 6 inch pots, well watered and allowed to emerge under the various light sources. Total leaf material was harvested for total RNA isolation after 11 days of growth.

Spectra and calculations -Spectral irradiances of Red1 (a), Red2 (c), Blue (b), and blue + red + Far-red (d) light sources are shown in Figure 1. Analysis of steady state mRNA-Total RNA was isolated from whole Arabidopsis plants (20-33 d old) and leaves of 11 day old sorghum plants and separated on formaldehyde-agarose gels, transferred to Magnagraph nylon (Fisher Biotechnology) and hydridized with two different clones. The clones are as follows: (1) psbA, reaction center for photosystem 2, (P. Westhoff, Univ. of Dusseldorf) (2) LHCP2, light harvesting for photosystem II, (L. Walling, Univ. of California, Riverside). Hybridizations were corrected for loading decrepancies using ribosomal RNA.

N. Murata (ed.), Research in Photosynthesis, Vol. IV, 325–328.

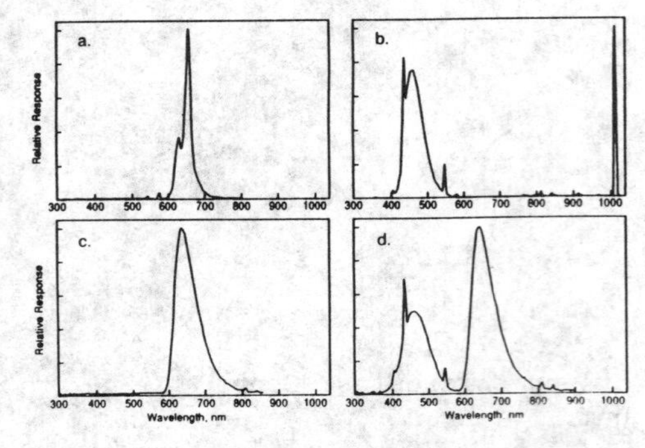

Fig. 1 Spectral irradiance curve. Wave length (nm) vs relative response. a, red light source. b, blue light source. c, red + far-red light source.

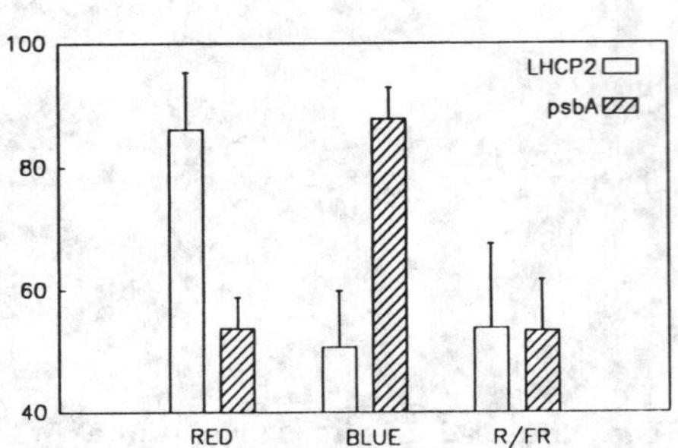

Fig. 2 Light-quality effects on gene expression. Relative amounts of mRNA in Arabidopsis plants grown for 20 days under 130 umol $m^{-2}s^{-1}$ of red, blue or red + far-red light.

RESULTS and DISCUSSION

Figure 2 showns that red light enhances the expression of LHCP2

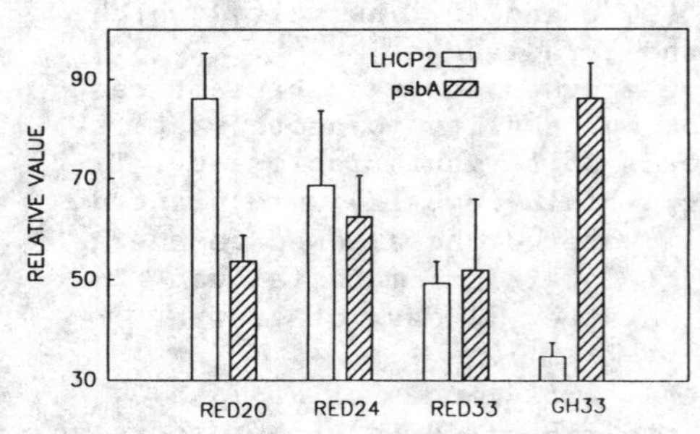

Fig. 3 Effects of plant age on expression of genes LHCP2 and psbA in Arabidopsis grown in 130 umol m^{-2} s^{-1} green-house light.

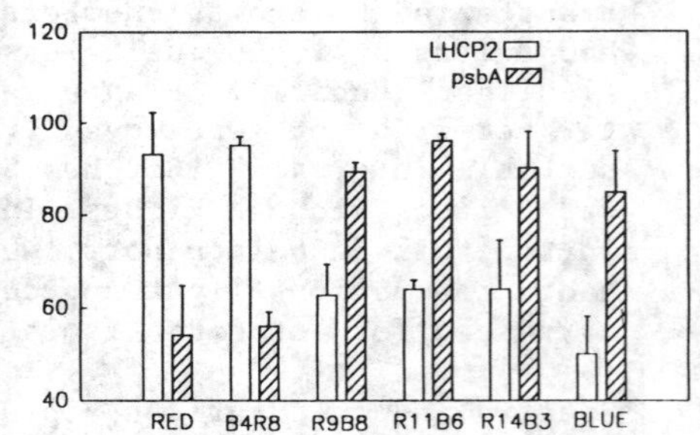

Fig. 4 Effects of sequential treatment by 130 umol m^{-2} s^{-1} of blue or red light quality on relative expression of mRNA.

and depresses the expression of psbA in Arabidopsis grown at 130 umol m^{-2} s^{-1} whereas blue light has the opposite effect. Red/far-red light which establishes a Pfr/Ptot similar to that of blue light also represses the expression of LHCP2 but does not enhance the expression of psbA. Figure 3 shows that enhancement of LHCP2 gene expression by red light is dependent on stage of development and decreases directly with plant age. Expression of psbA, however is essentially unchanged in young and mature red light grown Arabidopsis. In comparison, 33 day old Arabidopsis grown in the greenhouse has lower levels of LHCP2 and higher levels of psbA gene expression than red grown Arabidopsis.

Expression of LHCP2 and psbA genes in Arabidopsis grown under various sequential red and blue light regimes, is shown in figure 4. Plants grown for 4 days in blue light then for 8 days in red light have the same stationary state expression as red light, whereas, plants grown in red light for 9, 11, and 14 days then in blue light for 8, 6, and 3 days respectively, have the same pattern of expression as blue light. The sequential light quality experiments indicate that chloroplast genes,unlike flowering and morphology genes, are plastic and responsive to the immediate environment.

Expression of LHCP2 and psbA genes in plants grown under a constant irradiance level (50 umol m^{-2} s^{-1}) but different ratios of blue to red + far-red is shown for Arabidopsis in Figure 5 and Sorghum in Figure 6.

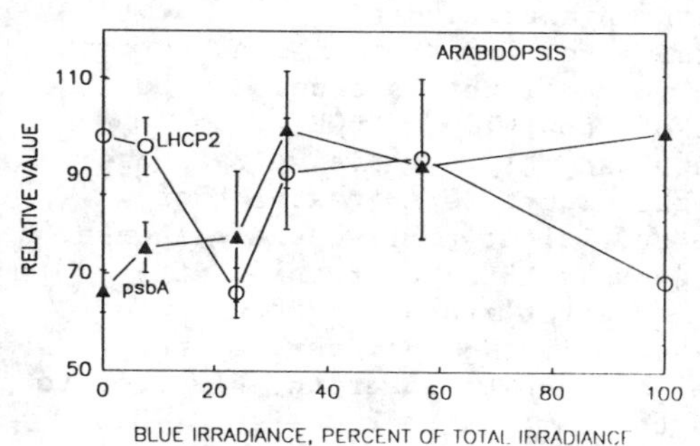

Fig. 5 Effect of blue light as a percentage of total irradiance on expression of mRNA in Arabidopsis plants grown under light mixtures.

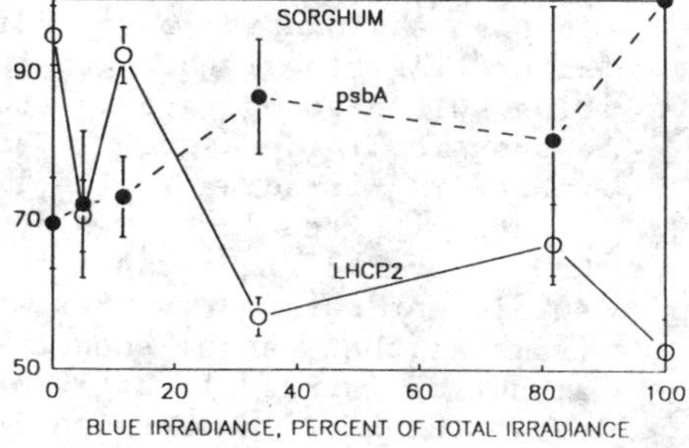

Fig. 6 Effect of blue light as a percentage of total irradiance on expression of mRNA in sorghum plants grown under light mixtures.

The red source used in these experiments (figure 1c) contains sufficient far-red light to establish a Pfr/Ptot ratio of 0.64 (Ref. 1). Addition of blue light to this red source does not significantly change the calculated Pfr/Ptot ratio (Ref. 2), but the expression of LHCP2 and psbA changes as a function of percent blue light. In both Arabidopsis and sorghum, increasing percentage of blue light increases the expression of the psbA gene. Expression of LHCP2 is more complex. In Arabidopsis (Figure 5), all mixtures of blue and red light give the same response as red light except the mixture containing approximately 20 percent blue light. In Sorghum (Figure 6), all mixtures except the 20 percent blue light mixture give the same response as blue light.

Previous work (Ref. 3), (Ref. 4) suggested that a light quality-irradiance switch may operate at 8-10 umol m^{-2} s^{-1} of blue light. Unlike our previous study with maize grown at 8 umol m^{-2} s^{-1} total irradiance, all mixtures of blue, red, and far-red light with a total irradiance of 50 umol $m^{-2}s^{-1}$ and a constant calculated-value of Pfr/Ptot, do not give the same response as pure blue light. Instead, a response is given only at 20 percent blue light. This 20 percent light mixture corresponds to the 8-10 umol m^{-2} s^{-1} of blue light previously reported in maize (Ref. 3) and in pea (Ref. 4) to be a node of switching for LHCP2. That work and the present combine to show that the blue light mediated switching is negative in maize and arabidopsis and positive in Sorghum and pea.

However, the negative and positive aspects of the switch with regard to light quality may also be a reflection of developmental differences in the plants studied.

In plants grown in low irradiance red light, then flashed with saturating blue light, growth in red light is necessary for the blue switch to operate in the off position. LHCP2 gene expression in dark grown plants had only a positive response to increasing irradiance blue light. Short term treatment of plants with red light was not sufficient to give the response. Red + far-red light can also depress LHCP2 expression if sufficient far-red is present to establish a Pfr/Ptot ~ 0.4 (same as that established by blue light). However, if the amount of far-red light is only enough to lower the Pfr/Ptot to 0.64, the LHCP2 expression is the same as in red light. Under these conditions (constant irradiance and constant Prf/Ptot), addition of blue to red + far-red light switches LHCP2 expression on and then off over a short irradiance range near 10 umol m^{-2} s^{-1} blue irradiance.

REFERENCES

1. Gardner, G. and Graceffo, M.A. (1982) Photochem. Photobiol. 36: 349-354.
2. Eskins, K. (1992) Plant Physiol. (In Press).
3. Eskins, K. and Beremand, P. (1990) Physiol. Plant. 78: 435-440.
4. Warpeha, K.M.F. and Kaufman, L.S. (1990) Planta 182: 553-558.

REGULATION OF PS I FORMATION INDUCED BY LIGHT QUALITY OBSERVED WITH SYNECHOCYSTIS PCC 6714

KATSUNORI AIZAWA AND YOSHIHIKO FUJITA
Department of Cell Biology, National Institute for Basic Biology, Okazaki, Aichi 444, JAPAN

1. INTRODUCTION

Thylakoids are dynamic membrane systems, in which the stoichiometry of the two photosystems is adjusted and optimized to ensure efficient utilization of light. When imbalance between PS I and PS II actions occurs, the ratio of PS I to PS II is adjusted so as to balance their actions under such a light regime. PS I / PS II ratio becomes higher under the light exciting preferentially PS II (PS II light), and is lowered under the light exciting mainly PS I (PS I light)(1,2). The experimental results on changes in photosytem abundance have indicated that changes in PS I/PS II ratio are due to the control of formation of PS I during cell growth (3-5). Adjustment of the ratio is a long-term but reversible response. The process of the adaptive response may involve selective regulation of biosynthesis, assembly or turnover of PS components in thylakoid membranes. In this study, we characterized the synthesis of psaA/B, psbA and psbC *in vivo* under PS I and PS II light.

2. MATERIAL AND METHODS

Synechocystis PCC 6714 was grown at 25°C in MDM under PS I or PS II light (cf. 6), but at double strength of K_2HPO_4 and with 30 mM glucose. Harvested cells were resuspended in culture medium, in which $MgSO_4$ had been replaced with $MgCl_2$ at equimolar concentration. After preillumination under PS I or PS II light, ^{35}S-methionine was added to the cell suspensions. Labeling time in most of pulse/chase studies was 24 min. Chase period was 96 min after addition of excess (2 mM) unlabeled methionine. Cells treated with pulse- or pulse/chase-labeling were washed with chilled 50 mM Tris-HCl (pH 7.6), 2 mM EDTA, 2 mM chloramphenicol, 4 mM methionine and protease inhibitors (0.01% PMSF, 1 mM 6-amino-1-caproic acid and 1 mM benzamidine-HCl)(Buffer A). Incorporation of ^{35}S into cells was counted with a portion of cell suspensions. Other portion was incubated in 1 N NaOH at 34°C for 30 min, and solubilized proteins were precipitated with chilled TCA. Incorporation of ^{35}S into total proteins was determined with the precipitates. Remaining cells were disrupted with glass beads and

N. Murata (ed.), Research in Photosynthesis, Vol. IV, 329–332.

washed with chilled Buffer A and with chilled 6 mM Tris-Maleate (pH 7) containing chloramphenicol and protease inhibitors (Buffer B) as described above. Membrane proteins were solubilized with Buffer B containing 0.2% LDS on ice for 30 min, and centrifuged at 10,000g for 6 min. For immuno-precipitation, supernatants were mixed with 2% BSA in phosphate buffer, followed by incubation with antibodies on ice for one hour. Protein-A Sepharose was used to absorb the antibody-antigen complex.

3. RESULTS AND DISCUSSION

Growth constants of the cells grown under PS I (0.78-0.82 d^{-1}) and PS II light (0.70-0.77 d^{-1}) were almost the same under our experimental conditions. Incorporation of ^{35}S-methionine into cells, total proteins, membrane proteins and psaA/B was linear against labeling time over a range from 3 to 24 min in both cells grown under PS I and PS II lights. Rates of synthesis of total and

TABLE 1. Incorporation of ^{35}S-methionine into various cellular fractions of <u>Synechocystis</u> PCC 6714 growing under PS I and PS II light

Light regime for growth	^{35}S incorporated into (CPM/10^3cells)					
	Cells	Total proteins	Membrane proteins	psaA/B	psbA	psbC
PS I	3.8±0.1	3.4±0.1	1.6±0.1	0.07±0.02	0.08±0.01	0.09±0.01
PS II	3.9±0.2	3.5±0.2	1.7±0.1	0.14±0.02	0.08±0.01	0.11±0.02

Pulse-labeling was made for 24 min with ^{35}S-methionine (2.5 μCi/ml). Light regimes were the same as those for cell growth. Values are means of three measurements.

membrane proteins were fairly constant in cells of the two types, when compared on a per cell basis. Rates of psbA and psbC synthesis in cells of the two types were also very similar to each other (Table 1). In contrast, rates of psaA/B synthesis in cells grown under PS II light were about twofold higher than those under PS I light (Table 1). Pulse/chase assay showed that only a small portion of newly synthesized psaA/B (2-14%), psbA (6-21%) and psbC (10-18%) was degraded and/or disassembled in cells of the two types during the chase period of 96 min. Results indicate that light quality-induced changes in the PS I/PS II ratio are mainly due to regulation of the rates of psaA/B synthesis, but not of PS II synthesis. Turnover of psbA (D_1) is as slow as other polypeptides of photosystem complexes, indicating that our experimental light regimes are safe from a selective damage of psbA.

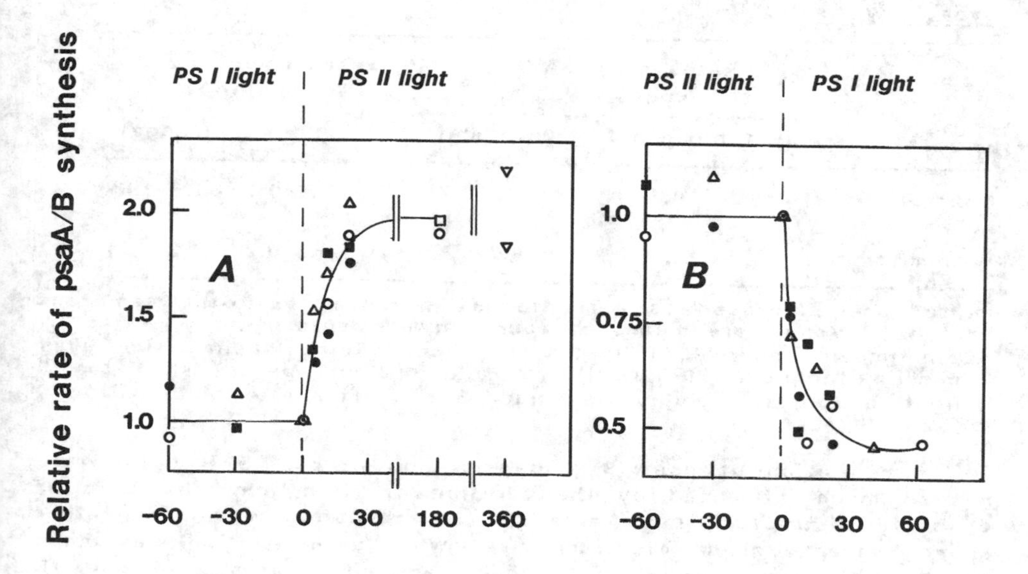

FIGURE 1. Effects of shift of light regime on the rates of psaA/B synthesis of Synechocystis PCC 6714. Light was shifted at time zero from PS I to PS II light (A) and from PS II to PS I light (B), respectively. Rates, on a per cell basis, of psaA/B synthesis relative to those at time zero were plotted against the time after and before shift of light. Pulse-labeling period was 3 min except for open circles (in A, 2 min). Symbols indicate difference in experiments.

Upon shift from PS I to PS II light, rates of psaA/B synthesis in cells grown under PS I light were accelerated; changes occurred with $T_{1/2}$ of around 10 min (Fig.1A). Increase in rates of psaA/B synthesis was found to correspond to stimulation of Chl a synthesis by PS II light (7). Chl a synthesis must be very closely related to the regulation of PS I synthesis. Shift from PS II to PS I light caused a rapid decrease in rates of psaA/B synthesis; the change (Fig.1B) seems to be faster than the enhancement induced by PS II light (Fig.1A). The time scales for changes in rates of psaA/B synthesis are similar to those for the state transition due to phosphorylation/dephosphorylation of LHC observed with pea chloroplasts (8). The shift of light regime did not change rates of ^{35}S incorporation into cells and of synthesis of total and membrane proteins (data not shown).

TABLE 2. Effect of rifampicin on the enhancement of psaA/B synthesis induced by shift from PS I to PS II light observed with Synechocystis PCC 6714

	Rates of psaA/B synthesis* (%)		Enhancement by PS II light	
	Without shift	With shift		(range)
Control	5.3±0.7	7.5±0.7	1.4±0.1	(1.3-1.6)
With rifampicin	5.2±1.0	6.7±0.5	1.3±0.2	(1.2-1.7)

*Rates are expressed as percentages of those for total membrane proteins. Values are means of four measurements.
Cells grown under PS I light were used. Pulse-labeling time was 3 min. Rifampicin (50 μg/ml) was added 2 min before shift to PS II light, and pulse-labeling was made 5 min after the shift.

Acceleration of psaA/B synthesis induced by PS II light was not so much influenced by the addition of rifampicin, the inhibitor of bacterial transcription (Table 2). Determination was made rather shortly after addition of rifampicin. When determination was made after prolonged incubation with rifampicin, rates of psaA/B synthesis became very low (data not shown) indicating that psaA/B products turn over. Results indicate that the regulation of PS I synthesis occurs at a step(s) after the transcription if the apoprotein synthesis itself is regulated.

ACKNOWLEDGEMENTS
This study was supported in part by Grants-in-Aid for Scientific Research from the Ministry of Education, Science and Culture. The authors are grateful to professor T. Hiyama for his generous gift of CP1 antibody, and also grateful to Drs. M. Ikeuchi and Y. Inoue for their generous gift of psbA and psbC antibodies.

REFERENCES
1 Fujita Y. (1990) Bot. Mag., Tokyo, Special Issue 2, 29-42
2 Melis A. (1991) Biochim. Biophys. Acta 1058, 87-106
3 Fujita Y. and Murakami A.(1987) Plant Cell Physiol. 28, 1547-1553
4 Fujita Y., Murakami A., Ohki K. and Hagiwara N. (1988) Plant Cell Physiol. 29, 557-564
5 Aizawa K., Shimizu T., Hiyama T., Satoh K., Nakamura Y. and Fujita Y. (1992) Photosyn. Res. 32, 131-138
6 Fujita Y., Ohki K. and Murakami A. (1985) Plant Cell Physiol. 26, 1541-1548
7 Fujita Y., Murakami A. and Aizawa K. (1993) This issue
8 Telfer A., Allen J.F., Barber J. and Bennett J. (1983) Biochim. Biophys. Acta 722, 176-181

VARIATION OF CHLOROPHYLL-PROTEIN COMPLEXES OF ORYZA PUNCTATA AND ORYZA EICHINGERI : ITS CONSEQUENCE FOR ADAPTATION IN HIGH AND LOW LIGHT ENVIRONMENTS

N. WATANABE, CH. FUJII, M. SHIROTA AND Y. FURUTA
FACULTY OF AGRICULTURE, GIFU UNIVERSITY, GIFU 501-11 JAPAN

1. INTRODUCTION

Oryza punctata is widely distributed in Africa and comprises of diploid (2n=24) and tetraploid (2n=48) forms, the genome of the diploid form in BB, while that of tetraploid form in BBCC.
The diploid form is often found in open habitats, while the tetraploid form favours shaded habitat. Therefore, the CC genome of *O. eichingeri* may carry genes controlling adaptation to shaded habitats while the B genome may carry genes for adaptation to open and more variable habitats (1). *O. sativa* leaves respond at several levels of organisation to light regime in which they grow. It is now recognised that there are differences among rice genotypes in these responses, some varieties being well adapted for low-light and other best adapted for high-light environments (2). These varieties also differed in their responsiveness to light at the level of the organisation of the thylakoid membranes (3).
In this paper we describe the difference of chlorophyll-protein complexes among diploid and tetraploid forms of *O. punctata* and diploid progenitor, *O. eichingeri*. We also discuss its consequences for adaptation within the habitats and its potential benefits in *O. sativa*.

2 MATERIALS AND METHODS

2.1 Plants: Two strains of *O. punctata*, the diploid form (W1582) and the tetraploid form (W1564), and one strain of the diploid species, *O. eichingeri* (W1521) were included in this study. W1564 and W1521 were collected from shaded habitats and W1582 from open habitat.

2.2 Cultivation of plants and isolation of thylakoids: After dormancy breaking of freshly harvested seeds by heat treatment (50° C for 3 days), young seedlings were grown under partial shade untill they have recovered from the trauma of transplanting. At there leaf stage, about 30 days from seeding, twelve plants per each countainer (30 cm x 30 cm x 8cm depth) were transplanted. Two batches were prepared for each strain. The plants were grown in an unheated glasshouse under natural day length. No supplementary lightning was given. Sixty days after sowing, plants of each starin were transferred either full sun light (high light) or placed under a close meshed net transmitting 20% of the incident light (low

N. Murata (ed.), Research in Photosynthesis, Vol. IV, 333–336.

light). It was expected that the shaded condition would favour the tetraploid form of O. punctata and O. eichingeri. At the tillering stage, fully expanded leaves from both sets of plants were harvested and thylakoids were isolated from them as described by (3). Two replications were done. Chlorophyll content and chlorophyll a:b ratio were also determined.

2.3 Separation of proteins: The membranes were resolved three times per extraction using Deriphat-PAGE gels (4).

2.4 Photosynthesis measurement: Light-saturated photosynthetic rates were measured as the steady-state rate of oxygen evolution on leaf sections of fully expanded leaves from comparable batches in a Hansatech leaf disc oxygen electrode. Measurement were made at a leaf temperature of 25°C in a saturating carbon-dioxide (ca. 1% of carbondioxide from a 1 mol carbonate/bicarbonate buffer solution at pH 9); (5). Measurements were done for five leaves per treatment.

3 RESULTS AND DISCUSSION

3.1 Chlrophyll a:b ratio and variation in chlorophyll-protein complexes within and between species.

O. eichingeri and O. punctata 4x grown in high light, had higher specific leaf weight (SLW), hence thicker leaves than ones grown in low light (Table 1). Chlorophyll a:b ratio also indicated the effect of light intensity. The membrane proteins were resolved into seven fractions, the free chlorophyll amounting to less than 4 % of total. For the present analysis the fractions were grouped on the basis of their apparent molecular weight and chlorophyll a:b ratio into three classes, photosystem I (PSI), the core complex of photosystem II (CCII) and the light-harvesting antenna chlorophyll

Table 1. Chlorophyll a:b ratio and the relative amounts of chlorophyll associated with chlorophyll-protein complexes and their ratios of leaves. NS: non-significant; **: significant at 1% level.

Genotype	Light intensity	SLW (mg/m^2)	Chl.a:b	CCII(%)	PSII/PSI	LHCII/CCII
O. eichingeri	HL	69	2.80	14.5	2.84	4.07
	LL	65	2.48	15.8	2.93	3.64
O. punctata 4x	HL	61	3.06	17.3	2.75	3.26
	LL	50	2.61	16.6	2.93	3.43
O. punctata 2x	HL	40	3.14	16.2	3.05	3.52
	LL	43	2.57	14.1	2.65	3.96
Significance of effect						
Light		**	**	NS	NS	NS
Genotype		NS	**	NS	NS	NS
Genotype x Light		NS	**	NS	NS	NS
S.E.		9.5	0.14	1.78	0.27	0.71

associated with photosystem II (LHCII). Relative amount of chlorophyll associated with each class was shown in Table 1.
The habitats which the strains were collected originally would indicate favourable light condition for each strain, high light for O. punctata 2x, and low light for O. eichingeri and O. punctata 4x. We could not found any statistically significant difference among strains. PSI(%) was very similar among strains grown in two light conditions. O. punctata 2x had 1.9% less CCII(%) and 0.4 less PSII/CCII than those grown under low light. LHCII/CCII was slightly affected by low light.

Table 2. Photosynthetic rates and distribution of chlorophyll in two photosystems in leaves. NS: non-significant; *,**: significant at 1% and 5% levels, respectively.

Genotype	Light intensity	Photosynthetic rates (μmol O_2/m^2/s)	Chlorophyll distribution Total	PSI (μmol/m^2)	CCII	LHCII
O. eichingeri	HL	14.6	168	45	25	98
	LL	10.8	318	88	51	179
O. punctata 4x	HL	13.3	153	40	28	86
	LL	8.9	235	58	41	135
O. punctata 2x	HL	12.5	188	45	32	111
	LL	7.3	233	67	34	132
Significance of effects						
Light		**	**	**	**	**
Genotype		*	**	**	**	**
Genotype x Light		NS	**	*	**	**
S.E.		1.37	4.7	5.4	3.6	3.2

3.2 Photosynthetic rates and distribution of chlorophyll in O. punctata and O. eichingeri.

Light-saturated photosynthetic rates per unit leaf area and distribution of chlorophyll associated with two photosystems were shown in Table 2. Amount of photosynthetic apparatus per unit leaf area can be estimated with distribution of chlorophyll content per unit area of leaf. Distribution of chlorophyll was estimated by multiplying relative amount of chlorophyll associated with each complex (%) by the chlorophyll content per unit area of leaf. In high light condition, photosynthetic rates per unit leaf area did not differ among strains. O. punctata 2x collected at open habitat most decreased the photosynthetic rate, when grown in low light. Ratio of photosynthetic rate of the shade-grown plants as compared to the sun-grown ones was 0.74 in O. eichingeri and 0.64 in O. punctata 4x, and lowest (0.58) in O. punctata 2x. Photosynthetic rates of the plants grown under low light were

highly dependent on chlorophyll amount per unit leaf area and the amount of chlorophyll associated with PSI, LHCII and CCII. We suggest that O. punctata 2x is unable to grow in low light conditions either by total amount of chlorophyll produced or in the partitioning of the thylakoid protein into CCII or LHCII. This contrasts with strains collected from shaded habitats.
O. eichingeri and O. punctata 4x are likely to possess much more genetic potential to adapt to shade than O. punctata 2x, and our results showed BB genome species have the genes which confer a capacity for adaptation to shade than CC genome species.

3.3 Stress or adaptive response to the shade environment ?

The effect of growth irradiance on chlorophyll a:b ratios of leaves is the most characteristic and easily observed feature of sun/shade response. However, relative distribution of chlorophyll associated with chlorophyll-protein complexes did not differ among strains statistically, regardless of whether the plants were growing in high and low light conditions.
While the wild strains of rice were originally adapted for shaded area, the cultivated rice had characteristics of sun plants (7). Cultivars of rice have only a limited potential to adapt to shade since they were derived from open habitats , where the capacity for adaptation to shade would not be a selection pressure. Consequently, when exposed to light levels less than those experienced in their natural environments, such plants may exhibit a stress rather than an adaptive response to shade environments.
It may be the case that O. punctata 2x, a sun plant, did not well adapt for shaded condition.

4 ADDENDUM

We are grateful to Dr. Y. Sano providing us the seed of wild rice species.

REFERENCES

1 Sano, Y. (1980) Bot. Mag. Tokyo 93,171-180.
2 Tu, Z.P., Lin, X.Z., Huang, Q.M., Cai, W.J., Feng, H.Y. and Ye, L.Y. (1988) Aust. J. Plant. Physiol. 15,277-286.
3 Watanabe, N., Austin, R.B. and Morgan, C.L. (1991) Rice Genetics II,775-777.
4 Peter, G.F. and Thornber, J.P. (1989) in Methods in Plant Biochemistry Vol. 2 : Amino Acids, Proteins and Nucleic Acid (Roger, L.J. ed.), pp. 194-212, Academic Press, San Diego.
5 Watanabe, N., Morgan, C.L., Mabuchi, Y., Kitaya, T., Nishikawa, K. and Austin R.B. (1992) Seiken Ziho (in press).
6 Chow,W.S. and Anderson, J.M. (1987) Aust. J. Plant Physiol. 14,9-19.
7 Li, M.Q., Lu, Z.R. and Deng, X.Q. (1984) Acta Phytophysiol. Sinica 10,333-338.

LIGHT-INDUCED D1 PROTEIN DEGRADATION AND PHOTOSYNTHESIS IN SUN AND SHADE LEAVES

A.J. Syme[1], H.R. Bolhàr-Nordenkampf[2], and C. Critchley[1]
Department of Botany, The University of Queensland[1], QLD 4072, Australia, and Institute of Plant Physiology[2], University of Vienna, Vienna Austria.

1. INTRODUCTION

The D1 protein has intrigued photosynthesis researchers for a number of years. Originally noted for its herbicide binding properties (1), and its unusually rapid synthesis and degradation (2), it has been at the centre of Photosystem II (PSII) research since about 1986, when it became clear that the D1 protein is an integral protein of the PSII reaction centre (3). This discovery created a dilemma in photosynthesis research. While most D1 protein studies investigated the molecular mechanism of D1 degradation in the context of its possible association with photoinhibition, the purpose of this study was to investigate the relationship between D1 degradation and leaf photosynthesis.

D1 degradation was measured *in vivo* in *Schefflera polybotrya* sun and shade leaves, at light intensities experienced by the plants *in situ.* As the upper and lower sides of bifacial leaves exhibit sun and shade characteristics, respectively, D1 degradation was also measured in the palisade parenchyma and spongy mesophyll tissues of *Schefflera polybotrya* leaves. Chlorophyll fluorescence of the upper and lower sides of the leaves was monitored to determine any changes in the photochemical capacity of the leaves. Little difference in degradation rates was observed between tissues, although they were seen between leaf types. The results do not support a correlation between photochemical capacity, or indeed photoinhibition, and D1 degradation. They also indicate that there may be different, and generally low, light saturation levels for D1 degradation in sun and shade leaves.

2. MATERIALS AND METHODS

D1 degradation was determined by radioactive pulse-chase labelling experiments. An outline of the experimental protocol is given in the flow diagram in Figure 1. The *Schefflera polybotrya* sun and shade leaves were obtained from a shrub in the University of Queensland grounds. Sun leaves grew in full sunlight, with a maximum irradiance of approximately 2200 μmol quanta m^{-2} s^{-1}, and shade leaves in shade conditions with a maximum irradiance of approximately 100 μmol quanta

N. Murata (ed.), Research in Photosynthesis, Vol. IV, 337–340.

m^{-2} s^{-1}. Pulse–chase labelling was conducted *in vivo*, by feeding whole leaves radioactive methionine through the petiole. These leaves were then placed under light intensities of 90, 300 and 1000 μmol quanta m^{-2} s^{-1}, and one leaf was hand sectioned into its palisade parenchyma and spongy mesophyll tissues every six hours for 24 hours. Chlorophyll fluorescence was measured concurrently on leaves undergoing identical treatment, with a Plant Stress Meter (PSM, Biomonitor, Umeå, Sweden). Thylakoid membrane isolations, gel electrophoresis, and radioactive protein quantification using an AMBIS scanner were conducted according to Critchley *et al.*, 1992 (4). Oxygen evolution rates illuminating the upper or lower surface of the leaves were measured in a closed system (Hansatech, England) in saturating CO_2 at 21°C (±1°C).

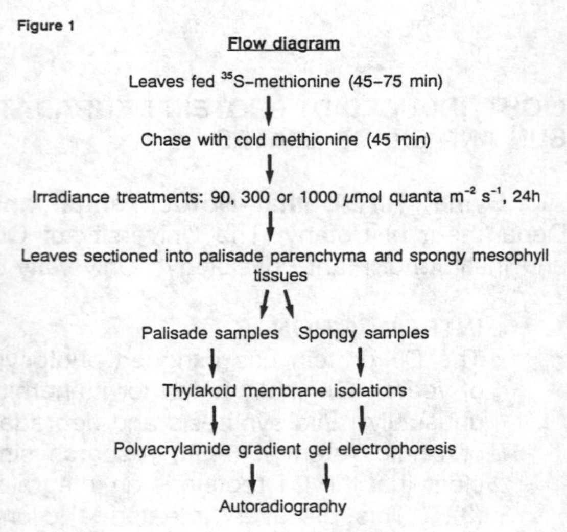

3. RESULTS AND DISCUSSION

The *Schefflera* sun and shade leaflets showed marked differences in oxygen evolution. Such differences were also seen when the leaf was illuminated either on the upper or the lower side, demonstrating the shade adapted nature of the chloroplasts in the spongy mesophyll cells of the leaf (Fig. 2). Similar results have been measured in a variety of species (5). Fluorescence data and electron microscopy (not shown) also indicated that a strong light gradient was present in the leaf, causing substantial increases in thylakoid membrane stacking in shaded chloroplasts as seen by Terashima (6), and lower $t_{1/2}$ and higher Fm values when chlorophyll fluorescence was measured from the lower side of the leaf.

Significant D1 degradation was observed after 24 hours of illumination in both leaf types and tissue types at all three light intensities (90, 300 and 1000 μmol quanta m^{-2} s^{-1}), except in shade leaves exposed to 90 μmol quanta m^{-2} s^{-1}. Figure 3 is a typical example of an autoradiograph, which shows clearly the loss of labelled D1 protein over 24 hours.

Figure 4 shows the degradation of D1 as quantified by the AMBIS

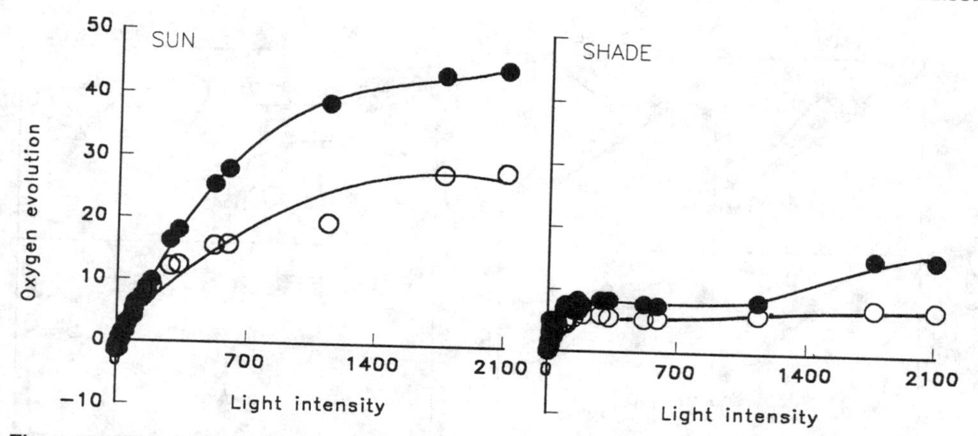

Figure 2. Rates of O_2 evolution ($\mu mol\ m^{-2}\ s^{-1}$) measured as a function of light intensity on the upper (●) or lower (○) sides of sun or shade leaves of Schefflera polybotrya

scanner (Fig. 4A), with concurrent changes in the chlorophyll fluorescence ratio Fv/Fm (Fig. 4B). Little difference was seen in the degradation rates between the two tissues. The Fv/Fm ratio data, however, showed the upper side of the leaf to be photoinhibited, but the lower side to be protected from photoinhibition. In sun leaves, the degradation rates were similar at all light intensities, indicating that rapid D1 degradation occurred at photoinhibitory and non-photoinhibitory light intensities. These results also suggest that there may be a D1 degradation light saturation level, which, in the case of *Schefflera polybotrya* sun leaves, is below 90 μmol quanta $m^{-2}\ s^{-1}$. In shade leaves, degradation of D1 followed more closely the changes in Fv/Fm

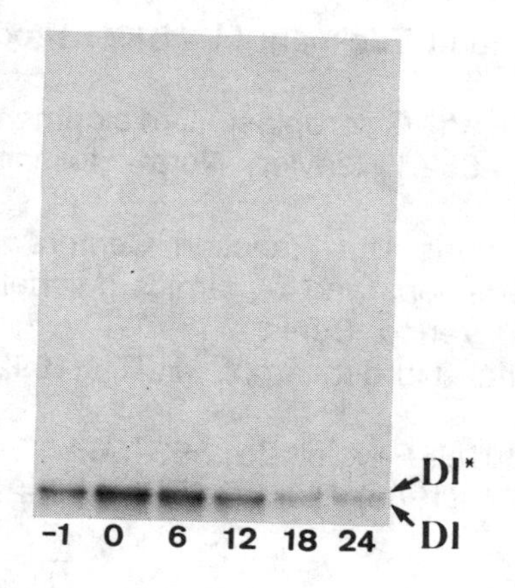

Figure 3. Autoradiograph of a typical D1 pulse-chase experiment, showing accumulation of label in D1 and D1* and degradation over 24 hours. Samples were taken every 6 hours.

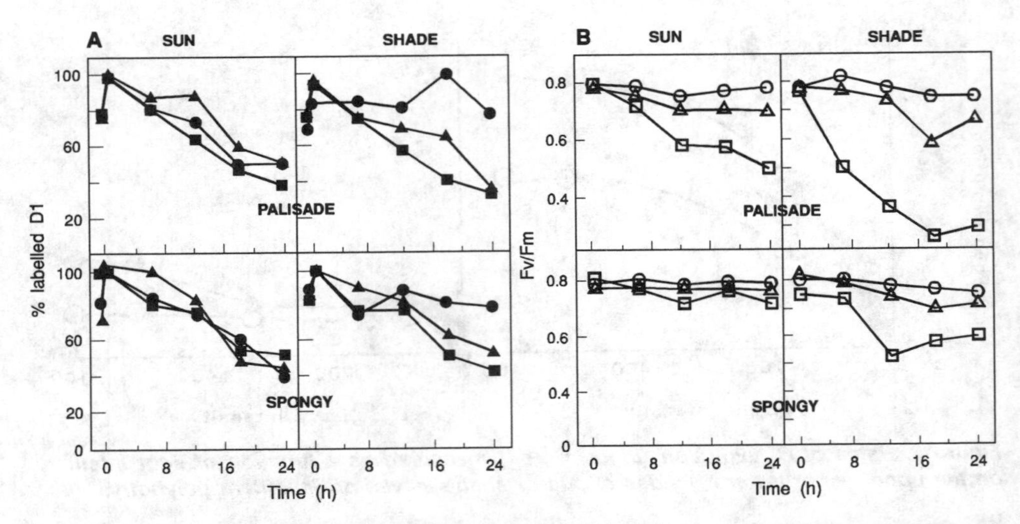

Figure 4. (A) Degradation of prelabelled D1 in palisade parenchyma or spongy mesophyll cells of sun and shade leaves of Schefflera polybotrya when exposed to limiting (●), saturating (▲) or excess (■) irradiances. (B) Corresponding changes in photochemical capacity of the leaves (F_V/F_M measured from the upper or lower side of the leaf).

data. At 90 μmol quanta m^{-2} s^{-1} little degradation was measured, while degradation was significant at the higher light intensities. This suggests that there is a higher D1 light saturation level in shade leaves. Further investigation into D1 light saturation levels, and the implications of sun and shade leaf type on D1 turnover is currently in progress.

4. REFERENCES

1 Mattoo, A.K., Pick, U., Hoffman-Falk, H. and Edelman, M. (1981) Proc. Natl. Acad. Sci. USA 78, 1572-1576

2 Edelman, M. and Reisfeld, A. (1978) in Chloroplast Development (Akoyunoglou, G. et al. eds.), pp. 641-652, Elsevier, North Holland, Biomedical Press, Amsterdam

3 Trebst A. and Depka B. (1985) in Antennas and Reaction Centers in Photosynthetic Bacteria - Structure, Interactions and Dynamics (Michel-Beyerle, M.E. ed.), pp.216-224, Springer Verlag, Berlin

4 Critchley, C., Russell, A.W. and Bolhàr-Nordenkampf, H.R. (1992) Photosynthetica 27, in press

5 Terashima, I. and Inoue, Y. (1984) Plant Cell Physiol. 25, 555-563

6 Terashima, I., Sakaguchi, S. and Hara, N. (1986) Plant Cell Physiol. 27, 1023-1031

Effects of light on degradation of chlorophyll and chloroplast proteins during senescence of rice leaves

Katsuhiko Okada and Sakae Katoh
Dept. Biol., Fac. Sci., Univ. Tokyo, Hongo 7-3-1, Bunkyo-Ku, Tokyo 113 (Japan)

1. Introduction

The photosynthetic activity of leaves gradually decreases, accompanied by loss of chlorophyll and chloroplast proteins, during senescence of leaves. When plants or leaves are placed in the dark, degradation of chlorophyll and proteins are greatly accelerated. Light is required to keep leaves green and involvement of phytochrome or a photosynthetic product in the light effect has been suggested (1,2,3). In the present study, we investigated effects of light on degradation of chlorophyll, chlorophyll-carrying proteins and ribulose 1,5-bisphosphate carboxylase/oxygenase (Rubisco) in rice leaves. The results show that breakdown of chlorophyll-carrying proteins and Rubisco are differently regulated by light.

2. Materials and Methods

Fully expanded third leaves of *Oryza sativa* L. cv. "Nipponbare" were used (4). Leaves or plants were kept in the dark or under different light conditions at 30°C for 3 to 4 days. Chlorophyll was determined spectorphotometrically (5) and proteins were analyzed by SDS-polyacrylamide gel electrophoresis (6).

3. Results and Discussion

3.1 Effect of light on degradation of chlorophyll

When leaves, either detached from or attached to plants, had been placed in the total darkness, rapid breakdown of chlorophyll occurred after an initial lag lasting one whole day and leaves became yellowish in the third or fourth days of the dark treatment (Fig. 1, trace a). Breakdown of chlorophyll was strongly retarded by continuous illumination with white light (trace b). Fig. 2 shows effect of different intensities of light on loss of chlorophyll in detached and attached leaves. Loss of chlorophyll was strongly suppressed by light at intensities below the compensation point of photosynthesis in rice leaves used here. This indicates that light serves as a signal but not as energy source. Involvement of phytochrome in the light effect was indicated by changing color of light. A brief illumination with weak red light once every eight h strongly retarded chlorophyll breakdown and the effect of red light was abolished by far red light. Fig. 2 also shows that the protecting effect of light disappeared above 30 µmol quanta m^{-2} s^{-1} in detached leaves but not leaves attached to plants. Similar observations were reported previously (7,8). Loss of chlorophyll at higher light intensities cannot be ascribed to photooxidative bleaching of the pigment because the amounts of chlorophyll degraded were apparently independent of light-intensity.

N. Murata (ed.), Research in Photosynthesis, Vol. IV, 341–344.

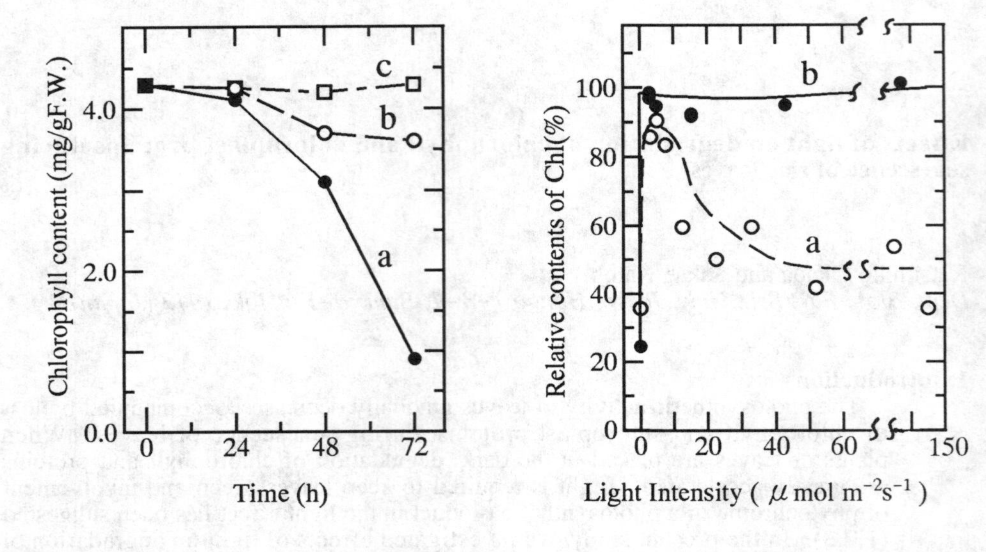

Fig. 1 (left) Time courses of changes in chlorophyll–contents of leaves in the dark or light. a, detached leaves were kept in the dark; b, detached leaves were continuously illuminated with white light of 5 μmol quanta m^{-2} s^{-1}; c, leaves attached to plants growing under natural conditions.

Fig. 2 (right) Effects of different intensities of white light on degradation of chlorophyll in detached (curve a) and attached leaves (curve b). Duration of experiments were four days. Chlorophyll content of leaves before experiments was taken as 100 %.

Thus, the loss of chlorophyll at high intensities of light appears to be an artifact introduced by detachment or wounding of leaves.

3.2 Effect of light on degradation of proteins

Insoluble proteins extracted from rice leaves mainly consisted of the thylakoid membrane proteins (Fig. 2, trace a). Chlorophyll–carrying proteins of the thylakoid membranes, LHCII and chlorophyll–proteins of PS I and PS II reaction center complexes, were largely degraded during four days in the dark (trace b). Breakdown of the membrane proteins was strongly suppressed under illumination with weak white light (5 μmol quanta m^{-2} s^{-1}) (trace c). Thus, loss of chlorophyll can be correlated with breakdown of LHC II and reaction center chlorophyll–binding proteins. Other membrane proteins containing no chlorophyll also disappeared in the dark but not in the light. It may be suggested, therefore, that a degradation system of the intrinsic membrane proteins is regulated by phytochrome.

Rubisco was also rapidly degraded in leaves placed in the dark, and light had a protecting effect on the enzyme protein. However, the effect of light on breakdown of Rubisco was markedly different from that on breakdown of chlorophyll or chlorophyll–binding proteins. As shown in Fig. 3, the full

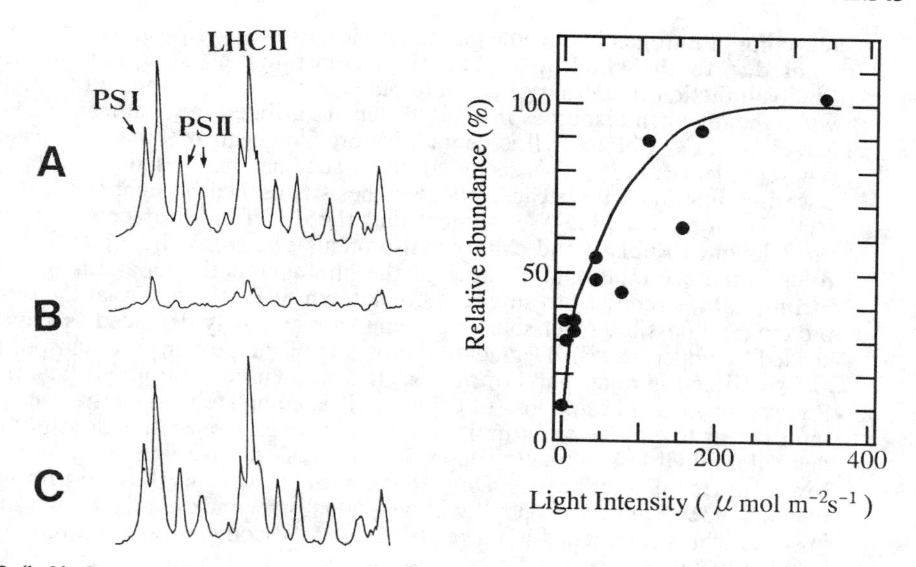

Fig. 3 (left) Compositions of insoluble proteins. A, untreated leaves; B, leaves kept in the dark; C, leaves kept under continuous illumination with white light of 5 μmol quanta m^{-2} s^{-1}.

Fig. 4 (right) Effects of different intensities of white light on degradation of the large subunit of Rubisco. Attached third leaves were exposed to white light of various intensities for 72 hours at 30°C. Relative contents of the large subunits were determined by measuring peak heights of the subunits resolved by SDS gel electrophoresis. The content of the large subunit in leaves.

protection of the enzyme protein was attained only at light intensities above 200 μmol quanta m^{-2} s^{-1}. This suggests that degradation of the enzyme protein is regulated by a mechanism related to photosynthesis. However, loss of Rubisco was also partially but significantly suppressed with very weak light of several μmol quanta m^{-2} s^{-1}. The effect of light (200 μmol quanta m^{-2} s^{-1}) was only partially reduced when photosynthesis had been completely inhibited by application of DCMU to both sides of leaf blades. These observations suggest that the effect of light on breakdown of the enzyme protein cannot be related to photosynthesis alone. Mechanisms underlying the protecting effect of light on the enzyme protein are under investigation.

Thus, breakdowns of chlorophyll-binding proteins of the thylakoid membranes and Rubisco are differently regulated by light. This suggests that the membrane proteins and the stroma enzyme are degraded by different systems. In this respect, of interest are the previous observation with a non-yellowing mutant of *Festuca pratensis* that degradation of chlorophyll-carrying membrane proteins and chlorophyll were inhibited by the mutation, while Rubisco and other soluble proteins were degraded as in normal leaves (2,9). This also indicates that degradation pathways of chlorophyll-carrying intrinsic membrane proteins are different from those of Rubisco and other soluble proteins.

Senescence of leaves is a normal physiological process from the viewpoint of recycling of nitrogen in a whole plant. Old leaves at lower positions receive less light due to the shading effect of younger leaves at upper positions. Photosynthetic production of a whole plant is, therefore, expected to increase when the nitrogen resources in aged leaves are utilized for synthesis of young leaves (10,11). Chlorophyll is degraded more slowly than Rubisco in naturally senescing leaves (12). This seems to be an acclimational response of leaves to lowering light intensity because photosynthesis is limited by light rather than by CO_2 fixation in shade. We suggest that the differential effects of light on breakdown of Rubisco and chlorophyll proteins discovered here play important roles in the acclimational changes of the photosynthetic apparatus of leaves. Strong light is required to suppress breakdown of Rubisco so that the enzyme protein (and possibly other soluble proteins) are gradually degraded as leaves are shaded by upper leaves. Degradation products of the proteins are transported to and reutilized in other parts of plants. Breakdown of chlorophyll lags that of Rubisco in shade became loss of chlorophyll is completely suppressed at a light intensity as low as several μmol quanta m^{-2} s^{-1}. However, this does not mean that chlorophyll loss is totally suppressed by weak diffuse light penetrating into lower parts of a canopy. Degradation of chlorophyll is regulated by phytochrome. Thus, chlorophyll will be gradually degraded in light environment in shade which is enriched in far red light due to selective absorption of red light by chlorophyll.

References

1, Thimann, K. V. (1980) *In* Senescence in Plants. Edited by Thimann, K. V., CRC Press, Florida, pp.85–115.

2, Stoddart, J. L. and Thomas, H. (1982) *In* Encyclopedia of Plant Physiology (New Series), Vol. 14A, Nucleic Acid and Proteins in Plants I. Edited by Boulter, D. and Pathier, B., Academic Press, New York, pp.592–636.

3, Biswal, U. C. and Biswal, B. (1984) Photochem. Photobiol. 39: 875–879.

4, Kura–Hotta, M., Satoh, K. and Katoh, S. (1987) Plant Cell Physiol. 28: 1321–1329.

5, Porra, R. J., Thompson, W. A. and Kriedemann, P. E.(1989) Biochim. Biophys. Acta. 975: 384–394.

6, Laemmli, U. K. (1970) Nature 227: 680–685.

7, Goldthwaite, J. J. and Laetsch, W. M. (1967) Plant Physiol. 42: 1757–1762.

8, Biswal, B. and Choudhury, N. K. (1986) Plant Cell Physiol. 27: 1439–1444.

9, Hilditch, P. I., Thomas, H. and Thomas, B. J. and Rogers, L. J. (1989) Planta 177: 265–272.

10, Hirose, T. and Werger, M. J. A. (1987) Oecologia. 72: 520–526.

11, Field, C. (1983) Oecologia. 56: 341–347.

12. Makino, A., Mae, T. and Ohira, K. (1984) Plant Cell Physiol. 25: 429–437.

PURIFICATION OF THE 15 kDa PHOSPHOPROTEIN OF *SYNECHOCOCCUS 6301*

B.F., Nore, M.A., Harrison[‡] and J.F., Allen[*]

Dept. of Biochemistry, Arrhenius Laboratories, Stockholm Univ., Sweden, [‡]Dept. of Biochem. and Mol. Biol., Univ. of Leeds, U.K., and [*]Plant Cell Biology, Univ. of Lund, Sweden.

1. INTRODUCTION

In photosynthetic membranes, protein phosphorylation is a regulatory mechanism responding to changes that would otherwise result in damage or reduced efficiency of photosynthetic energy conversion. One mechanism is readjustment of the relative distribution of excitation energy between the two photosystems [1,2,3].

In cyanobacteria the phosphorylation reaction and associated functional changes in energy distribution are under redox control [4], resembling the redox control of the thylakoid LHCII kinase in chloroplasts [5]. The first identification of light-dependent labelling of both membrane-bound and soluble proteins in *Synechococcus 6301* (*Anacystis nidulans*) was observed with cells grown in the presence of [^{32}P] P_i. The most obvious proteins labelled had apparent relative molecular masses 18.5, 15, 13 kDa [6]. The 18.5 kDa and 13 kDa proteins are predominantly in the soluble fraction and the 15 kDa is located exclusively in the thylakoid membrane fraction. From both fractions other labelled bands were seen but their phosphorylation did not appear to be light-dependent. The illumination that produced labelling of the 18.5 and 15 kDa proteins *in vivo* also gave a shift in chlorophyll fluorescence emission spectra, indicating induction of state 2 [7]. This result is consistent with redistribution of excitation energy distribution in favour of PSI at the expense of PSII [7]. In this work, we describe identification and purification procedures for the 15 kDa phophoprotein of the thylakoid membrane of *Synechococcus 6301*.

2. MATERIALS AND METHODS

2.1 Thylakoid Membrane preparation

Cells of *Synechococcus 6301* were grown at 30 °C in the medium BG 11 as described by Rippka et al. [8] and the thylakoid membranes were prepared as described in Ref. [9] with some modifications. Cell suspension, including a few milligrams of DNase and RNase, was disrupted using a bead beater, 20 cycles of 20 sec on 3 min intervals between each cycle, instead of lysozyme treatment. Finally the thylakoid membrane was resuspended to a chlorophyll concentration of 1 mg Chl a. ml^{-1} in 10% glycerol, 25 mM HEPES-NaOH pH 7.8, 10 mM $MgCl_2$ and 20 mM NaF.

2.2 *In vitro* radiolabelling

Thylakoid membranes (100 µg Chl.a) were incubated in Eppendorf tubes with 500 µl of a buffer containing 10% glycerol, 25 mM HEPES-NaOH pH 7.8, and 10 mM $MgCl_2$ in the dark for 5 min. (γ-^{32}P) ATP (4 µM ≈ 20 µCi) was added to the suspension to 40 µM ATP final concentration and then duroquinol (DQH_2) to 0.9 mM final

N. Murata (ed.), Research in Photosynthesis, Vol. IV, 345–348.

concentration. The mixture was transfered to orange light 2 (PS II light)[cinemoid 5] for 20 min. The reaction was stopped with EDTA to 20 mM. Radiolabelled-membranes were centrifuged at 13,000 rpm for 15 min. Samples were washed twice with 80% Acetone at -20 °C, dried under N_2, and resuspended with 100 µl sample buffer for gradient SDS-PAGE (12%-22.5%) analysis [10], on Coomassie blue stained gels.

For protein purification, suspensions of the thylakoid membranes (5 mg Chl. a) were preincubated in the dark for 15 min. (γ-^{32}P) ATP (≈1 mC_i) was added to the suspension to 20 µM final concentration and then duroquinol (DQH_2) to 0.9 mM final concentration. The mixture was incubated further in the dark for 5 min and then cold ATP was added to 35 µM final concentration. The mixture was transfered to orange light 2 for 20 min. The reaction was stopped with EDTA to 20 mM. The mixture was centrifuged at at 100,000 x g for 50 min. Membranes were washed once with 10% glycerol, 10 mM HEPES-NaOH pH 7.8, 20 mM EDTA and 20 mM NaF. Radiolabelled-membranes were pelleted by centrifugation.

2.3 Rotofor running conditions

The thylakoid pellet was solubilised as described earlier [11] in 30 mls of "extraction buffer" containing 10 mM HEPES, pH 7.8, 20 mM NaF, 10% glycerol, 2% Thesit®, 2% Triton X-100 and 0.2 % dodecyl-β-D-maltoside. The solubilised proteins "membrane extract" (≈ 150 mg total protein) was loaded on a Bio-Rad Rotofor (preparative IEF) system with addition of 5 mM dithiothreitol, 5 mM EDTA and 2 ml Bio-Lyte® ampholyte solution (pH range 3-10; 40% w/v). The Rotofor IEF chamber was filled with extraction buffer (total volume 55 ml). Focusing was carried out for 5 hours at 12 W constant power at 4°C. The initial conditions were 240 V and 50 mA. At equilibrium the values were 1020 V and 14 mA. Twenty fractions were collected, their pH values were measured. Aliquots of each fraction were analysed by SDS-PAGE [10], using Coomassie blue stain.

3. RESULTS AND DISCUSSIONS

3.1 Conditions for *in vitro* radiolabelling

A set of incubation conditions for *in vitro* phosphorylation of *Synechococcus 6301* thylakoid membranes were used and the corresponding autoradiographs of SDS-PAGE gels are shown in Fig. 1.

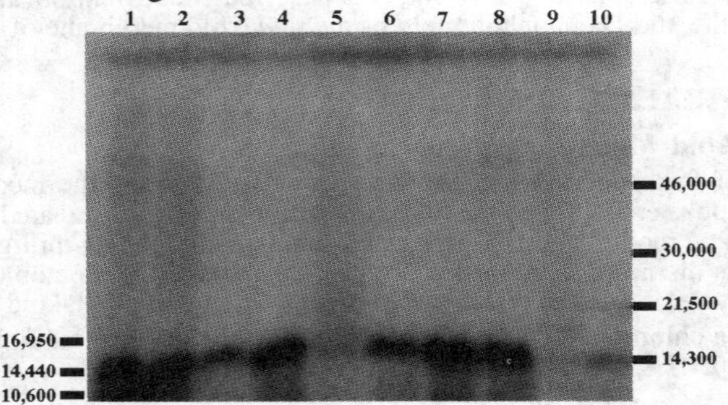

Fig. 1 Autoradiographs of SDS-PAGE analysis of [γ^{32}P]ATP-radiolabelled *Synechococcus 6301* thylakoid membranes under different conditions (for details see under Results and Discussions)

It is seen that the 15 kDa phosphoprotein is labelled specifically in this system and the degree of phosphorylation is affected by a number of reagents. The phosphorylation reaction shows light and NaF–dependence, consistent with the data from Harrison et al. [9]. The presence of 20 mM NaF with light 2 incubation (Lane 1) shows clearly a stimulation of the labelling in comparison to light 2 incubation without NaF (Lane 10). Light 2 incubation (Lane 1) also shows higher labelling than dark incubation (Lane 2) when NaF is present in both conditions. In the presence of 2 mM quinol and under light 2 (Lane 3 and 4) the phosphorylation is elevated, but labelling is much higher when NaF is present (Lane 4). Similar effects are observed when 0.8 mM duroquinol is present, with NaF (lane 7) and without NaF (lane 6). In the presence of 5 mM methyl viologen with 20 mM NaF, the phosphorylation reaction is also stimulated. For control experiments, 5% TCA (lane 5) and 15 mM EDTA (lane 9) final cencentration were added prior to phosphorylation reaction and it is shown that no proteins were labelled. Either quinol or duroquinol with NaF result in maximum labelling (lanes 4 and 7, respectively) compared to other conditions. For subsequent radiolabelling experiments, 0.8-0.9 mM duroquinol and 20 mM NaF under light 2 are used as a standard incubation condition.

3.2 Preparative IEF on the Rotofor System

In order to isolate the 15 kDa phosphoprotein several purification procedures were tested. Initial attempts to fractionate thylakoid membrane proteins with the Rotofor cell were unsuccessful due to protein precipitation at different compartments. These problems were minimised by using 10% glycerol, higher amount of detergents and pre-focussing of the pH gradient before loading the extracted proteins. Still some precipitation in the ends of the compartments was observed. In Fig. 2, a pH gradient of 3.2-12.8 was formed with almost a linear region at pH 3.2 to 10. It is also indicated (Fig. 2) the relative radiolabelling activity of the 15 kDa phosphoprotein. At both ends of the Rotofor compartments (fractions 1-3 and 20), the labelled 15 kDa protein is also observed (Fig. 2). This effect is due to precipitation of proteins at these sites. A single run (4-5 hours) of crude extract (≈150 mg protein) on the Rotofor system produces a good separation of the 15 kDa phosphoprotein (Fig.3). Further analysis of Rotofor fractions by SDS-PAGE (Fig. 3) and autoradiography (not shown) show a purified and radiolabelled 15 kDa band. The 15 kDa phosphoprotein is enriched among fractions 11-14. The fractions 13 and 14 have most purified protein but lower labelling while fractions 11 and 12 less pure protein with high labelling (Fig. 2 and 3).

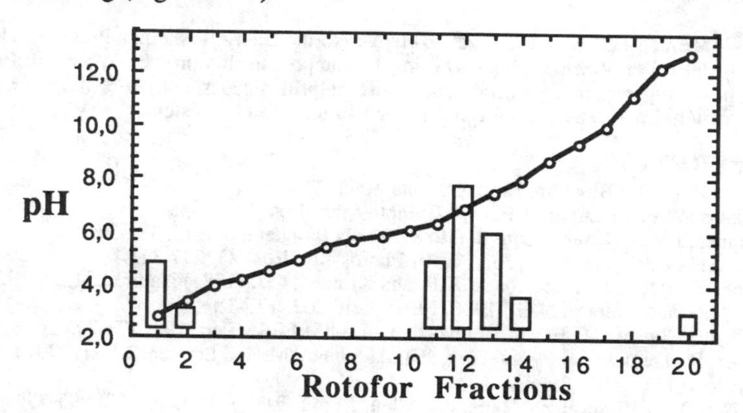

Fig. 2 Illustration of the pH profile of Rotofor separated fractions and relative radiolabelling activity (□) of the 15 kDa phosphoprotein.

This observations suggests that the isoelectric point (Ip) of the phosphorylated protein is shifted toward a lower pH, consistent with the predicted effect of phosphorylation. Therefore, this method can be used for separation between phosphorylated and non–phosphorylated protein forms. Also in these fractions a lower molecular weight protein (≈ 11-12 kDa) is co-purified (Fig. 3). This protein is also a membrane-bound phosphoprotein but it is labelled under different conditions (unpublished results).

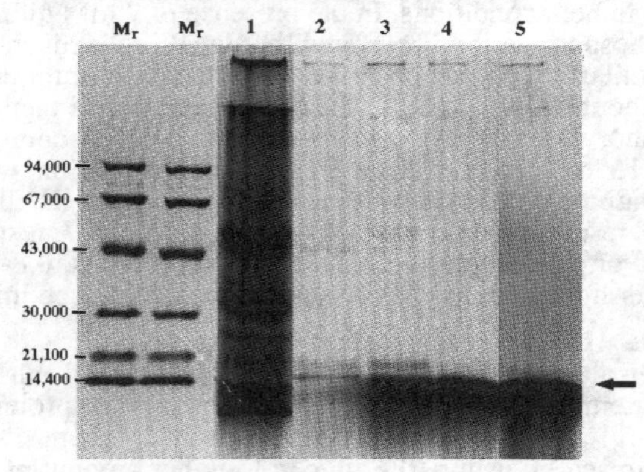

Fig. 3 SDS-PAGE analysis of the Rotofor fractions 11-14 (lane 2-5). Lane 1 is the crude extract of the solubilised thylakoid membrane. The arrow is indicated to the 15 kDa phosphoprotein. Each bands of protein standards (M_r) is equivalent to ≈1.2 μg protein.

4. SUMMARY

Partial purification of the 15 kDa phosphoprotein was achieved using the Rotofor system. This procedure predictes an isoelectric point between 7.0-8.0 for this protein. This technique is also effective for purification of other thylakoid membrane-bound proteins on a preparative scale. The next phase of this work will combine the use of Rotofor purification, SDS-preparative electrophoresis and sequence analysis to determine the identity of this protein.

ACKNOWLEDGEMENTS : BFN and JFA acknowledge Nordic Energiforsknings Program (NLVF) and Carl Tryggers Stiftelse För Vetenskaplig Forskning for support to this project. We thank Prof. Bertil Andersson for providing research facilities and many helpful discussions. BFN thanks Kemila AB (Sollentuna), especially Bo W. Hultgren, for loan of the Bio-Rad Rotofor system.

5. REFERENCES

1. Allen, J.F. (1992) Biochim. Biophys. Acta 1098, 275-335.
2. Williams, W.P. and Allen, J.F. (1987) Photosynth. Res. 13, 19-45.
3. Anderson, J.M. and Andersson, B. (1988) Trends Biochem. Sci. 13, 351-355.
4. Mullineaux,C.W. and Allen, J.F. (1990) Photosynth. Res. 23, 297-311.
5. Allen, J.F., Bennett, J., Steinback, K.E. and Arntzen, C.J. (1981) Nature 291, 25-29.
6. Allen, J.F. and Holmes, N.G. (1986) FEBS Lett. 202, 175-181.
7. Allen, J.F., Sanders, C.E. and Holmes, N.G. (1985) FEBS Lett. 193, 271-275.
8. Rippka, R., Deruelles, J., Waterburg, J.B., Herdman, M. and Stanier, R.Y. (1979) J. Gen. Microbiol. 111, 1-61.
9. Harrison, M.A., Tsinoremas, N.F. and Allen, J.F. (1991) FEBS Lett. 282, 295-299.
10. Laemmli, U.K. (1970) Nature 227, 680-685.
11. Nore, B.F., Harrison, M.A., Andersson, B.A. and Allen, J.F. (1991) First Nordic Congress on Photosynthesis, Copenhagen, pp. 11.

ROLE OF LIGHT-HARVESTING CHLOROPHYLL A/B PROTEIN COMPLEXES IN PHOTOSYNTHESIS UNDER LOW LIGHT AND HEAT STRESS

Yoshichika Kobayashi[1], **Takashi Yoshihira**[2], **Koichi Yamamoto**[1], **Etsuko Nishimoto**[1] **and Tatsuo Oku**[1], Forest. Dept., Kyushu Univ.[1], Fukuoka 812, Japan and Biol. Dept., Toyama Univ.[2], Toyama 930, Japan

1. INTRODUCTION

The treatment of thylakoid membranes and intact leaves at high temperatures leads to damage in membrane structure and photosynthetic activities. It has been shown that photosystem II (PSII) and photophosphorylation are the sensitive sites to be damaged by heat(1), but photosystem I(PSI)-mediated electron transport is stimulated after a short-time heat treatment of thylakoid membranes (2). Besides the heat damage on the photosynthetic activities, incubation of thylakoid membranes at high temperatures causes physical dissociation of the light-harvesting chlorophyll (Chl) *a/b* protein complex II(LHCII) from the PSII, and induces migration of the PSII core complex from grana into the PSI-containing lamellar region (3). These observations suggest that the organization of Chl-protein complex in PSII is particularly affected by heat. For the past few years, a portion of our work has focused on characterization of rice mutants that affect the pathway of Chl synthesis. In this study, we examined photosynthetic and thermal stability characteristics of rice mutants with alterations in the synthesis of Chl *b* and the hydrogenation of Chl-geranylgeraniol to Chl-phytol. It is shown that the heat stability of photosynthetic apparatus is greatly enhanced by the accumulation of Chl *b* and the full reduction of esterifying alcohol to phytol.

2. MATERIALS AND METHODS

The strains of Chl *b*-deficient and Chl *b*-less mutants derived from *Oryza sativa L. var.* Kinmaze were homozygous for known characters, and found to be mutant alleles of the nuclear gene *pgl* that shows pleiotropic effects on the level of Chl *b* accumulation. Phenotypes of two other strains, M134 and M249, segregated as different recessive nuclear mutations in genetic crosses. Seeds of wild type and mutants were germinated in tap-water moistened soil and

N. Murata (ed.), Research in Photosynthesis, Vol. IV, 349–352.

grown for 3 weeks in a growth chamber at 25°C, 70% RH, 12 h photoperiod and a PPFD of 85 umol/m^{2}s. Oxygen evolution was measured at 22°C using a Clark-type electrode. Rates of CO_2 exchange and transpiration of attached leaves were measured with an open gas exchange system under illumination with white light at 25°C. Heat treatment was performed in two different ways: 1) by changing growth temperature of seedlings from 25°C to 40°C and 2) by transitory exposing leaf segments at a certain temperature as heating occurs at 1°C/40 sec.

3. RESULTS AND DISCUSSION

Rate of CO_2 uptake in attached leaves calculated on the basis of total Chl was 2.5-fold higher for Chl *b*-less mutant than for wild type. When the rates were calculated on the basis of leaf area, there was no significant difference in the rates of these leaves. To estimate the antenna size in wild type and Chl *b*-less mutant, we examined the amount of CP43 in the thylakoid membranes by protein gel blot analysis using antibody specific for CP43, which is a component of PSII core complex. The amount of Chl calculated on the basis of CP43 was about 2.5-fold higher in wild type than in Chl *b*-less mutants. The small antenna size in the mutant is correlated with the loss of LHCII, of which amount was estimated to be about 6% of that in wild type on CP43 basis. We interpret these data that energy transfer in the PSII of Chl *b*-less mutant depleting LHCII occurs at similar rate to that of wild type even under extreme low light.

Schreiber and Berry found that the degree of heat damage of photosynthesis depends on light conditions during heating of leaves(4). However, the reason why light raises the heat tolerance of photosynthetic apparatus is still unknown. In Fig. 1, we compared the thermal inactivation characteristics between wild type (curves A and B), Chl *b*-deficient mutant (curves C and D) and Chl *b*-less mutant (curves E and F). In the experiments leaf segments were heated slowly at the rate of 1°C/40sec in the dark or in the light (36 W/m^{2}), and the sample was immediately cooled when leaf temperature reached at the indicated temperature. Heat damage in wild type occurred at temperatures higher than 43°C when the leaves were heated in the dark (curve A). When the leaves were heated in the light, damage caused at the temperature higher than 49°C. The critical temperature causing damage shifted obviously from 43°C to 49° (curve B). The results support the previous conclusion that light raises the heat tolerance of plants (4). In Chl *b*-deficient mutant which accumulated Chl *b* amounts to about 15% of total Chl, the critical temperature was 42°C in the dark (curve C) and 45°C in the light (curve D). In Chl *b*-less mutant the shift was small; heat inactivation occurred

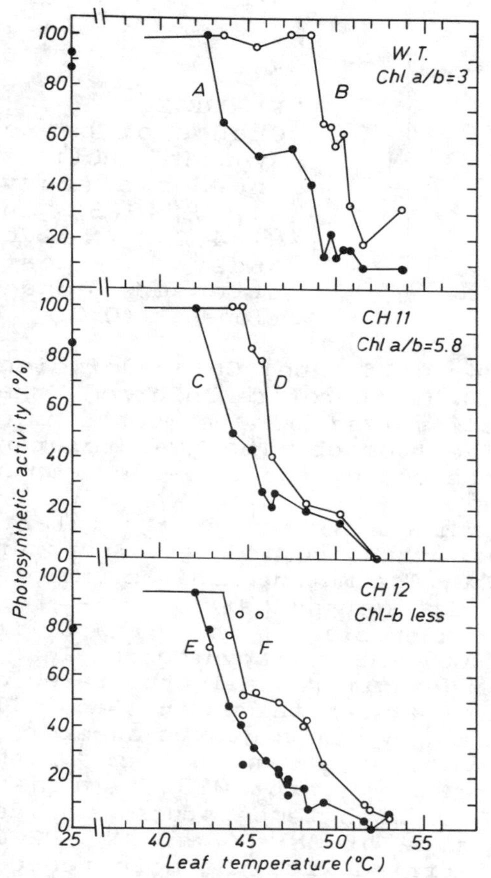

FIGURE 1. Effect of pretreatment temperature on photosynthetic activity in the leaves of wild type, Chl *b*-deficient (CH11) and Chl *b*-less mutant (CH12). Leaf temperature was elevated at the rate of 1°C/40 sec from 25°C to the indicated temperature in the dark (curves A, C and E) or in the light (curves B, D and F). The CO_2-dependent O_2-evolving activity in the preheated leaves was measured at 22°C.

at 42°C in the dark (curve E) and 42- 44°C in the light (curve F). In view of these results the extent of shift seems to be correlated with the amount of Chl *b* accumulated in the leaves. We confirmed that there is agood correlation between the ratio of Chl *b*/total Chl and the amount of LHCII determined by protein gel blot analysis. Gounaris *et al.* observed that heat treatment caused loss of grana stacking in the range 35-45°C, and induced vesiculation of thylakoid membranes at the temperatures higher than 45°C (2). The change of thylakoid membrane structureture was accompanied by dissociation of LHCII from PSII core complexe (3). From these data and our results one can suppose that the heat damage of photosynthesis is caused by a drastic change of membrane properties. It is important to note that the critical temperature causing heat damage in the dark was almost same in the normal and mutant leaves, but in the light the temperature was apparently different between these leaves (Fig. 1). The extent of temperature

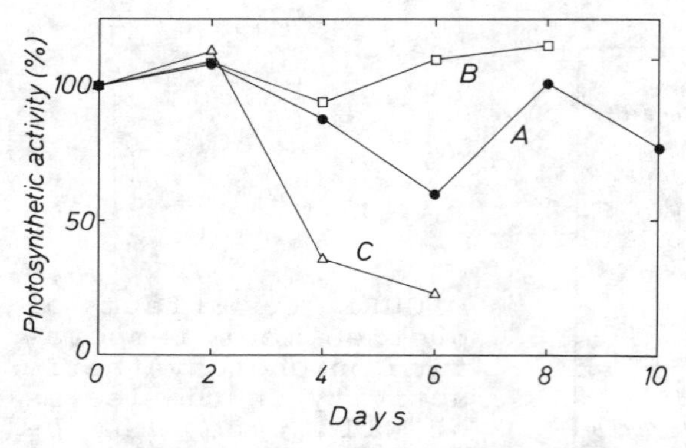

FIGURE 2. Change of photosynthetic activity in normal(curve A), M249(B) and M134(C) leaves under heat-stressed conditions at 40°C.

shift decreased in the order wild type, Chl *b*-deficient mutant, Chl *b*-less mutant. It is therefore inferred that a possible role of LHCII is involved in the mechanism of the light protection from heat dmage. The heat tolerant ability could be possibly enhanced by the increased amount of LHCII in wild type leaves.

The thermal stability characteristics of the mutants M134 and M249 were examined by changing growth temperature of seedlings from 25°C to 40°C. The mutant M134 accumulates preferentially Chl *a* and *b* with geranylgeraniol(GG), and the mutant M249 accumulates six species of Chl *a* and *b* with GG, dihydrogeranylgeraniol(DHGG) and tetrahydrogeranylgeraniol (THGG). There was no large difference in the rates of CO_2-dependent oxygen evolution between the mutants and wild type when the seedlings were grown in a growth chamber at 25°C under low light. However, as shown in Fig. 2, the photo synthetic activity of the mutant M134 decreased steeply after 2 days under the high temperature. The decrease was due to decomposition of Chl-GG and Chl-DHGG, because the Chl species esterified with the more reduced alcohols THGG and phytol were relatively stable under the stressed conditions. The activity of the mutant M249 which accumulated Chl *a* and Chl *b* with the incompletely reduced alcohol side chains GG, DHGG and THGG was also diminished by extending the heat treatment time, by decreasing of leaf Chl content, but the activity of wild type does not (data not shown). These results suggest that the heat stability of plant is improved by the reduction of alcohol side chain, indicating physiological significance of phytol.

REFERENCES

1 Berry, J. and Bjorkman, O. (1980) Annu. Rev. Plant Physiol.31, 491-543.
2 Gounaris, K, Brian, A. P. R., Quinn, O. J. and Williams, W. P. (1984) Biochim. Biophys. Acta 766, 198-208
3 Sundby, C., Melis, A, Maenpaa, P and Andersson, B. (1986) Biochim. Biophys. Acta 851, 457-483
4 Schreiber, U. and Berry, A. (1977) Planta 136, 233-238

EFFECTS OF DARK ADAPTATION ON PARAMETERS OF PROMPT AND DELAYED FLUORESCENCE OF CHLOROPHYLL IN *CHLORELLA*.

Ilya R. Vasil'ev[1], Ljudmila V. Shenderova[1], Yuri N. Konev[2], Yuri V. Kazimirko[2] and Pavel S. Venediktov[1]
[1]Department of Biophysics, Faculty of Biology, Moscow State University, Moscow 119899, Russia, [2]"Ecomonitor" Laboratory, Moscow Institute of Engineering Physics, Moscow 115522, Russia

INTRODUCTION

Transition of unicellular algae from light to darkness results in changes of efficiency of PS II reactions. In *Dunaliella* and *Chlamydomonas* this process was found to be associated with transformation of Q_B-reducing PS II centers (Q_B-centers) to Q_B-nonreducing ones (non-Q_B-centers) [1, 2]. Using prompt and delayed fluorescence methods we show that upon dark incubation of *Chlorella* cells the Q_B-centers are transformed to centers with altered Q_A properties.

MATERIALS AND METHODS

Chlorella vulgaris (green alga) was grown for 48 h at 37°C upon white light illumination (40 W m^{-2}). Dark-inactivated cells were obtained by 24-h incubation in darkness, light-reactivated cells by transferring for 1 h to 15 W m^{-2} white light illumination. The density of suspensions was 4×10^6 cells ml^{-1}.

Prompt fluorescence induction was measured with fluorometer upon excitation by a broad band green light (16 W m^{-2}). The cells were dark adapted for 3 min before measurement and DCMU was added, when mentioned, in the dark before this adaptation.

Induction curves and steady-state decay of delayed fluorescence (DF) were measured with a computer-controlled rotating-disc phosphoroscope upon red light excitation (up to 340 W m^{-2}). The excitation/dark period was 16/4 ms; DF was registrated within 3.2 ms starting 0.4 ms from the end of excitation. Seconds time domain DF decay was measured after turning the excitation off by a shutter.

Light saturation curves of DF were monitored with an electronic phosphoroscope upon red excitation from a battery of light-emitting diodes. Incident light intensity was varied by modulating the feeding current of the photodiods. The excitation/dark period was 4/1.8 s; DF was registrated within 0.7 s starting 1.1 s from the end of excitation. DF light curves were approximated by a sum of hyperbolas by nonlinear regression.

RESULTS AND DISCUSSION

As seen from Fig. 1, in dark-incubated *Chlorella* the fast O-I phase of fluorescence induction corresponding to reduction of non-Q_B-centers was retained. The amplitudes of this phase were nearly the

N. Murata (ed.), Research in Photosynthesis, Vol. IV, 353–356.

same in reactivated and 'dark' cells. The phase of rise to P maximum was suppressed in 'dark' cells, thus reflecting inactivation of Q_B-centers. If F_m is measured in the presence of DCMU near 1-2 s, the percentage of non-Q_B-centers as determined according to Guenther and Melis [1] is 60% in dark-incubated and 30% in reactivated cells. However, the seemingly attained steady-state fluorescence was followed by a slow rise phase in minutes time domain. This phase was the main in contribution to variable fluorescence of 'dark' cells, whereas light reactivation caused its elimination and enhancement of fast phases (Fig. 1). The slow phase of induction might correspond to a fraction of centers with a slow photoreduction of Q_A. Therefore the percentage of the non-Q_B-centers in 'dark' cells should be significantly lower, if all phases of induction are taken into consideration for measurement of F_m.

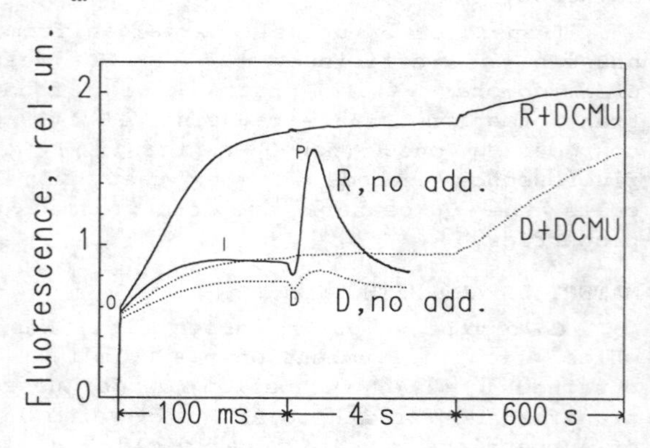

FIGURE 1. Induction curves of prompt fluorescence of dark-incubated (D) and reactivated (R) *Chlorella* cells with no additions and in the presence of 10 μM DCMU.

Induction kinetics of DF from 'dark' cells comprised all phases typical to reactivated cells, but the kinetics and amplitudes of initial phases were modified. However, in the presence of DCMU the minutes time domain DF induction kinetics of 'dark' *Chlorella* was almost identical to that of reactivated cells for excitation intensities close to that used in measurement of prompt fluorescence. In 'dark' cells the rate of DF decline from initial peak to intermediate minimum (at 340 W m^{-2}) was 5 times lower than in reactivated cells. This is probably related to a lower rate of reduction of electron transport components.

The decay kinetics of steady-state DF measured in the presence of 10 μM DCMU comprised components with τ = 500 μs, 300 ms and 2-4 s. The first component of 'dark' cells exceeded that of reactivated cells, while in normal, light grown *Chlorella* this component was almost undetectable. In the presence of DCMU, recombination is the only way of Q_A^- reoxidation. One of possible explanations for generation of 500-μs DF in this situation is that dark incubation causes impairment of normal donor to P_{680}^+ due to extraction of Mn in the dark [3] and recombination of Q_A^- with an P_{680}^+ gives rise to this DF.

Fig. 2 shows the results of decomposition of seconds time domain DF decay kinetics measured at different light intensities. Light dependency of 300-ms component had the same light saturation characteristic for both types of cells, but the intensity of this DF in reactivated *Chlorella* was 1.75 times higher than in the 'dark' cells. However, it is evident that there is a considerable difference in shapes of light dependencies of 2-4 s DF component between reactivated and 'dark' *Chlorella*. (Fig. 2, right).

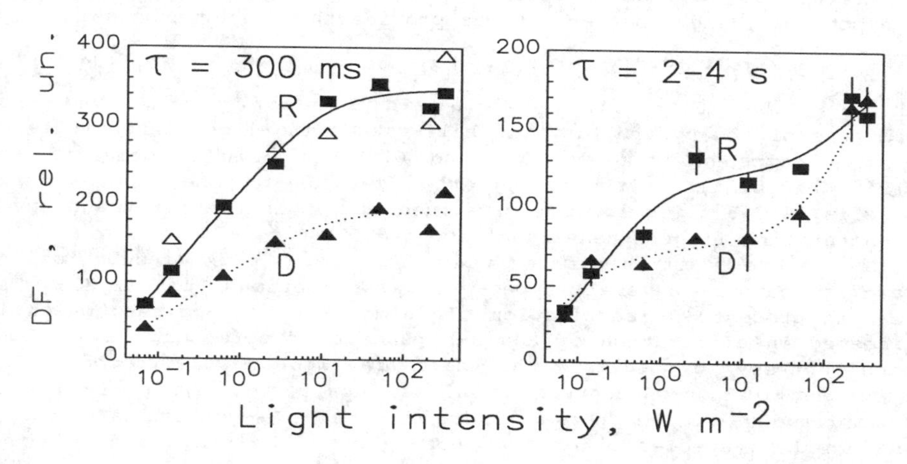

FIGURE 2. Dependencies of DF intensity (light sum calculated as a product of initial amplitude and life time) of DF components on excitation light intensity for 'dark' (triangles) and reactivated cells (squares). Left: component with τ = 300 ms; open triangles, the data are multiplied by 1.75. Right: component with τ = 2-4 s (10 μM DCMU added)

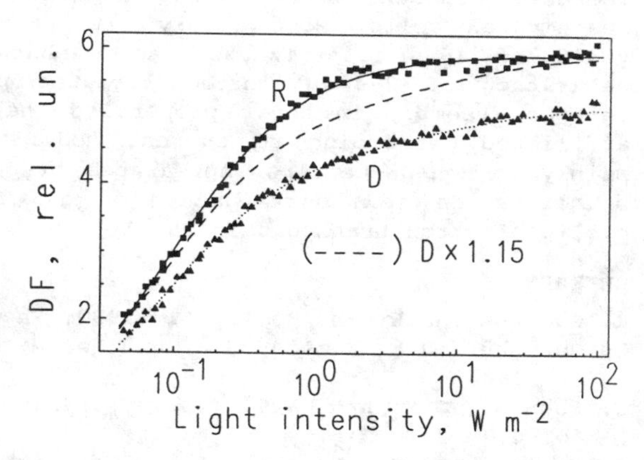

FIGURE 3. Light saturation curves of DF (component with τ = 2-4 s) of 'dark' (D) and reactivated (R) *Chlorella* (10 μM DCMU added). Continuous lines, the approximation curves according to Eq. (1) (R) and Eq. (2) (D). Dashed line, the approximation curve for 'dark' *Chlorella* multiplied by 1.15.

The shapes of light saturation curves were analyzed using data obtained with electronic phosphoroscope monitoring 2-4 s DF component

(Fig. 3). In the case of reactivated cells the dependence of DF intensity (L) on incident light intensity (I) was approximated by a single hyperbola of an order of n:

$$L = L_o/(J_o + I^n) \qquad \text{Eq. (1)}$$

with $n = 0.92$, $L_o = 5.92$ (maximal intensity of DF) and $J_o = 0.12$. Half-saturating light intensity, I_o, is related to J_o as: $I_o^n = J_o$.

In the case of 'dark' cells approximation by a single hyperbola had a poor fit, and a better fit was provided by two hyperbolas:

$$L = L_1/(J_1 + I^{0.92}) + L_2/(I_2 + I) \qquad \text{Eq. (2)}$$

with $L_1 = 4.55$, $J_1 = 0.1$, $L_2 = 0.6$ and $I_2 = 8.6$. As derived from parameters of the hyperbolas, the half-saturating light intensities of the main component make up 0.1 and 0.08 W m^{-2} in reactivated and 'dark' *Chlorella*, respectively; the second component of 'dark' *Chlorella* is 7.5 times lower in its intensity than the first and has a half-saturating light intensity of about 8.6 W m^{-2}.

The above data indicate that long-term dark incubation of *Chlorella* causes several types of modifications of PS II. The governing process is inactivation of (almost) all Q_B-centers which is manifested in elimination of the D-P phase of fluorescence induction. On the contrary to results with *Dunaliella* [1] and *Chlamydomonas* [2], the content of non-Q_B-centers is almost unaffected, as derived from the amplitudes of O-I phase. Therefore, the Q_B-centers are to be transformed to species other than non-Q_B ones. We propose that these species are in fact centers with low yield of Q_A^- reduction. The latter centers are manifested in slow phase of fluorescence rise in 'dark' cells in the presence of DCMU.

Another indication of inactive centers in 'dark' *Chlorella* is the poorly saturating DF component. However, this component does not correspond to the centers with low yield of Q_A^- reduction because of identity between minutes time domain DF induction of 'dark' and reactivated cells. More likely, it is related to centers with low yield of Q_A^- stabilization as characterized earlier by light saturation of 2-s DF in DCMU-treated pea chloroplasts [4]. These centers resemble in their properties the Q_2 acceptor which might be affiliated, according to current model of PS II heterogeneity [5], mainly to non-Q_B-centers. Appearance of centers with low yield of Q_A^- stabilization upon dark incubation can be related to activation of cyclic electron transport in PS II.

REFERENCES

1. Guenther, J.E. and Melis, A. (1990) Photosynth. Res. 23, 195-203
2. Guenther, J.E. Nemson, J.A. and Melis, A. (1990) Photosynth. Res. 24, 35-46
3. Cheniae, G.M. and Martin, I.F. (1973) Photochem. Photobiol. 17, 441-460
4. Vasil'ev, I.R., Komarov, A.I., Matorin, D.N., Verkhoturov, V.N. and Venediktov, P.S. (1990) Photosynth. Res. 26, 101-107
5. Govindjee (1990) Photosynth. Res. 25, 151-160

RESPONSES TO LIGHT IN THE GREEN ALGA *MESOTAENIUM CALDARIORUM*: A POSSIBLE ROLE FOR PHOTOSYNTHETIC ACTIVITY IN THE REGULATION OF PHYTOCHROME

LARRY ZEE MORAND AND J. CLARK LAGARIAS
DEPT BIOCHEMISTRY AND BIOPHYSICS, UNIVERSITY OF CALIFORNIA, DAVIS CA 95616

INTRODUCTION

The ability of photosynthetic organisms to sense light and to respond appropriately is essential for photosynthesis. Thus, these organisms have evolved many strategies to respond to both short and long term changes in the light quality and quantity in their environment (1,2,3,4). One such strategy is the phenomenon of chloroplast rotation displayed by some lower green plants. In the fern *Adiantum*, and the algae *Mougeotia* and *Mesotaenium*, the photoreceptor phytochrome regulates chloroplast orientation to maximize photon capture for optimal photosynthesis or to minimize photodamage under high light intensities (5,6).

Mesotaenium is an especially attractive system to study the mechanisms involved in the phytochrome-mediated chloroplast rotation. This alga is unicellular thereby avoiding the complications of different cell and tissue types. Indeed, each cell contains all of the components of the signal transduction pathway for phytochrome action. This alga also can be grown axenically in liquid culture under defined conditions. For these reasons, we initiated experiments to examine the phytochrome system in *Mesotaenium*.

The purification and preliminary characterization of *Mesotaenium* phytochrome has been accomplished (7). During the course of this work, spectrophotometrically detectable phytochrome was observed to increase when the algal cultures were placed in darkness for 3 to 8 days. The light/dark dependency of phytochrome levels in *Mesotaenium* cells was unexpected in view of the suggestion that this alga, like other lower green plants which exhibit the capacity to synthesize chlorophyll and to produce functional chloroplasts in the dark, would contain a light-stable phytochrome (5). This light/dark phenomenon was then examined in greater detail. Algal cultures were light-grown for 3 to 4 weeks after initial inoculations, some light-grown cultures were dark-adapted for 8 days, and some dark-adapted cultures were light-returned for 1 to 24 hours. Immunoblot experiments were performed on whole cell extracts from *Mesotaenium* cultures to analyze the effect of these light/dark transitions on the levels of phytochrome. Immunostained blots were quantitated by densitometry with a BioImage Analyzer.

RESULTS AND DISCUSSION

The results of the examination of phytochrome levels during the light/dark transitions is presented in Table 1. Phytochrome levels increased greater than 4-fold after light-grown (LG) cells were dark-adapted (DA) for 8 days. Phytochrome levels from light-returned (LR) cells decreased back to that for light-grown cells within 24 hours. Following 24 hours of continuous illumination, no further change in the

N. Murata (ed.), Research in Photosynthesis, Vol. IV, 357–359.

immunodetectable levels of phytochrome were observed up to 8 days of additional illumination. To address the possibility that the light-dependent loss of phytochrome is Pfr-dependent (8), 8 day dark-adapted cells were irradiated with 10 minutes of white, red, or far red light and then left in darkness. No significant change was observed in the level of phytochrome during a 12 to 72 hour period.

TABLE 1. Immunoblot analyses of whole cell protein extracts from *Mesotaenium* cells. All values are normalized to 1.00 for the dark-adapted sample. The mean value and standard error of 4 independent experiments is shown.

	phytochrome	SSU	FNR	cytochrome f
LG	0.24 ± 0.04	0.93 ± 0.05	0.91 ± 0.11	1.02 ± 0.12
DA	1.00	1.00	1.00	1.00
LR (12h)	0.57 ± 0.10	0.84 ± 0.08	0.97 ± 0.04	0.97 ± 0.09
LR (24h)	0.33 ± 0.03	0.90 ± 0.21	0.80 ± 0.08	0.85 ± 0.12

These results show that the regulation of this algal phytochrome is not simply Pfr-dependent; hence, continuous illumination appears to be required for the loss of phytochrome. This requirement for continuous illumination, along with the preliminary observation that the photosystem II inhibitor DCMU enhances the stability of phytochrome under continuous illumination, implicates the involvement of photosynthetic activity in this regulation.

The suggested involvement of photosynthetic activity regulating phytochrome levels in *Mesotaenium* lead us to examine the light regulation of photosynthetic polypeptides. The relative levels of the components of the photosynthetic apparatus have been reported to change in response to varying light quality and quantity, and dark-adaptation of light-grown tissue (2,3,4). Therefore, immunoblots were analyzed for ribulose bis-phosphate carboxylase/oxygenase small subunit (SSU), ferredoxin-$NADP^+$ oxidoreductase (FNR), and cytochrome f. These analyses revealed no significant changes in the levels of these proteins during the light/dark transitions as shown in Table 1.

An analysis of the effect of light/dark transitions on cytochrome f levels in *Chlamydomonas* produced different results (9). This study reported the total loss of immunodetectable cytochrome f during an 8 day dark-adaptation period which was restored to light-grown levels upon illumination within 8 hours. This discrepency with our data can be accounted for by the differential growth rates of the two green algae. *Chlamydomonas* cells went through 10 generations of growth during the dark period under conditions described in that study. By contrast, the *Mesotaenium* cells display a growth rate of less than 1 generation during 8 days dark-adaptation. It would be of interest to know if *Mesotaenium* cells would turnover cytochrome f and other photosynthetic proteins during a period of prolonged dark-adaptation.

Photosynthesis-dependent regulation of *Mesotaenium* phytochrome levels represents a reasonable adaptive strategy with regards to the phytochrome-mediated chloroplast rotation displayed by this alga. Under conditions of severe light limitation, an increased level of phytochrome would serve to enhance the photoreponsiveness of the cell thereby facilitating light capture for photosynthesis through chloroplast reorientation. Such a response predicts that a signal derived from photosynthetic activity (ATP, NADPH, Calvin-cycle intermediates/products?) influences the regulation of phytochrome levels. This hypothesis is supported by the observations that photosynthetic activity exerts positive feedback control on the long-term regulation of the levels of the photosynthetic apparatus in higher plants in order to maximize photosynthetic activity in response to changes in light quality and quantity (4). Thus, *Mesotaenium* may acclimate to changes in light conditions by 2 interconnected mechanisms: (1) through the phytochrome mediated chloroplast rotation and (2) through regulation of phytochrome levels by photosynthetic activity.

Funded by NSF (DCB87-04266) to JCL

REFERENCES

1. Rudiger W, Lopez-Figueroa (1992) Photochem Photobiol 55, 949-954.
2. Thompson W, White M (1991) Ann Rev Plant Physiol Plant Mol Biol 42, 423-466.
3. Mullet J (1988) Ann Rev Plant Physiol Plant Mol Biol 39, 475-502.
4. Anderson J (1986) Ann Rev Plant Physiol Plant Mol Biol 37, 93-136.
5. Wada M, Kadota A (1989) Ann Rev Plant Physiol Plant Mol Biol 40, 169-191.
6. Haupt W (1982) Ann Rev Plant Physiol 33, 205-233.
7. Kidd D, Lagarias J (1990) J Biol Chem 265, 7026-7035.
8. Shanklin J, Jabben M, Vierstra R (1987) Proc Natl Acad Sci USA 84, 359-363.
9. Matsumoto T, Matsuo M, Matsuda Y (1991) Plant Cell Physiol 32, 863-872.

SHORT-TERM TREATMENT OF PEA PLANTS WITH SUPPLEMENTARY ULTRAVIOLET-B RADIATION: RECOVERY TIME-COURSES OF SOME PHOTOSYNTHETIC FUNCTIONS AND COMPONENTS

Wah Soon Chow[1], Åke Strid[2] and Jan M. Anderson[1]

[1]CSIRO, Division of Plant Industry, GPO Box 1600, Canberra, Australia 2601, and
[2]Royal Institute of Technology, Stockholm, Sweden S100 44.

Introduction

The long-term effects of ultraviolet-B (UV-B) radiation on plants have been studied in some 300 species and cultivars, of which two-thirds appear to be sensitive to increased UV-B radiation [1]. However, despite investigations on a wide range of plant materials, little is known about the ability of plants to recover after supplementary UV-B irradiation. The time-course of recovery has an important bearing on the final outcome when plants are given daily doses of enhanced UV-B, for if recovery is incomplete by the beginning of the next exposure, plant function will progressively deteriorate.

Our previous medium-term treatment of pea plants with supplementary UV-B over one week showed that some photosynthetic components were decreased more than others [2]. The loss of photosynthetic components leads to decreased CO_2- and light-saturated photosynthetic capacity, and lower light-limited quantum efficiency. Even in the short term, within hours after commencement of supplementary UV-B treatment of pea plants, there is also a marked effect on mRNA levels. The nuclear-encoded *cab* [3] and *rbc*S [4] transcripts are decreased drastically, as are the chloroplast-encoded *rbc*L transcripts [4]; the subsequent recovery is very slow in all cases.

The present work extends the above studies with peas by elucidating the responses of (1) representative photosynthetic functions and components, and (2) the structural integrity of the thylakoid membrane, following short-term UV-B treatment.

Materials and Methods

Growth and treatment of plants

Pisum sativum L. (cv. Greenfeast) seedlings were grown under 150 μmol photons m^{-2} s^{-1} (PAR, 400-700 nm) as in [2]. At 17 days from sowing, pots of plants were transferred to another compartment in the growth room where the equal PAR was supplemented by 3 UV-B lamps (Philips TL 40W/12 UV, wrapped with cellulose acetate of thickness 0.13 mm). The levels of UV-B were 50 and 220 mW m^{-2} nm^{-1} at 297 nm and 313 nm, respectively. After 8 h of UV-B irradiation, the plants were retransferred into the control compartment, and allowed to recover. We monitored the time-courses of photosynthetic responses in the third pair of fully-expanded leaflets from the base during the onset and recovery phases, using methods described in [2].

Flash-induced electrochromic shift at 515 nm

The rapid flash-induced decrease in light transmission at 515 nm by leaves, and the subsequent relaxation of the signal after a single-turnover xenon flash, were measured using a laboratory-built spectrophotometer. Measuring light at 515 nm was selected by an interference filter (half-bandwidth, 4 nm). A detached leaf was pre-incubated in a humidified petri dish for 15 min in the dark. Immediately prior to measurement, it was sandwiched between a Corning 4-72 cut-off filter on the abaxial side, and a 1 mm air gap and a microscope cover slip on the adaxial side, with the Corning 4-72 filter placed adjacent to a photodiode detector. Flash illumination of the adaxial surface of a leaf was provided through a red cut-off filter (Corning 2-64).

N. Murata (ed.), Research in Photosynthesis, Vol. IV, 361–364.

Results

Chlorophyll content and composition

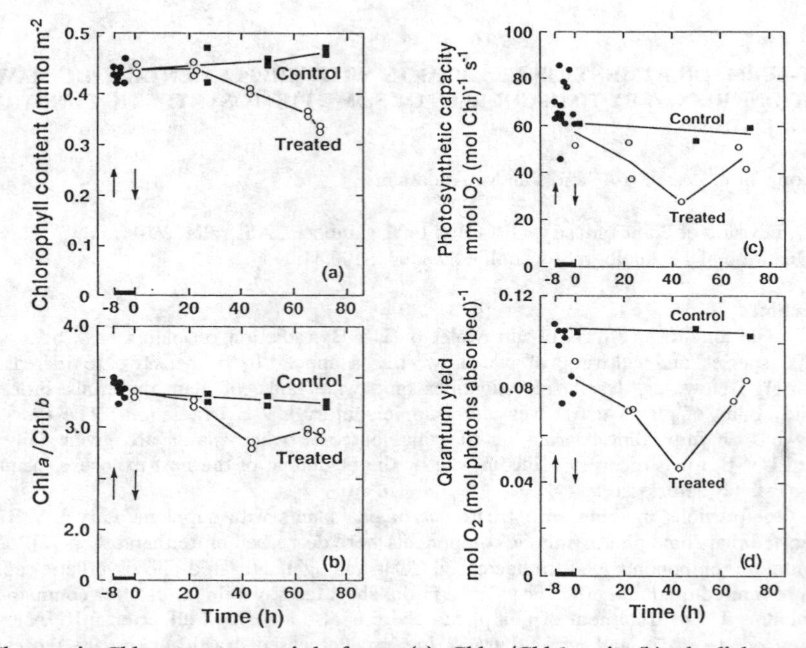

Fig. 1. Changes in Chl content per unit leaf area (a), Chl *a*/Chl *b* ratio (b), the light- and CO_2-saturated photosynthetic capacity (c), and the light-limited quantum yield of O_2 evolution (1% CO_2 in air) based on absorbed photons (d) of leaf discs during (●) and after (o) an 8-h supplementary UV-B treatment of pea plants. Upward and downward arrows indicate UV-B on (at the beginning of the photoperiod) and off, respectively. The PAR was 150 μmol photons m^{-2} s^{-1} throughout. Control leaves are denoted by (■).

During the 8 h of UV-B treatment, neither the chlorophyll content per unit leaf area (Fig. 1a) nor the Chl *a*/ Chl *b* ratio (Fig. 1b) was altered significantly. Within 40 h after the UV-B treatment, however, a decrease in both parameters was evident. Beyond 40 h, the chlorophyll content continued to decline, while the Chl *a*/ Chl *b* ratio increased slowly.

Maximum photosynthetic capacity and quantum yield of O_2 evolution

During supplementary UV-B irradiation, there was an initial, slight increase in the maximum rate of O_2 evolution (Fig. 1c). However, a net decline occurred within 20 h after the cessation of UV-B treatment, and the decline continued for another 20-h period before recovery was evident. The quantum yield of O_2 evolution (measured in limiting light) decreased slightly (by *ca.* 10%) during UV-B irradiation (Fig. 1d). It continued to decrease by a further 45% for a period of 40 h after the UV-B treatment; subsequently, however, there was considerable recovery.

Functionality of PS II

To investigate a possible cause of the decline in quantum yield, we assayed the functional PS II reaction centres in leaf discs as described in [5]. Fig. 2a shows that the number of functional PS II reaction centres declined by about 23% during the 8 h UV-B irradiation. There was a further 29% decrease for 40 h after the UV-B treatment, followed by some recovery.

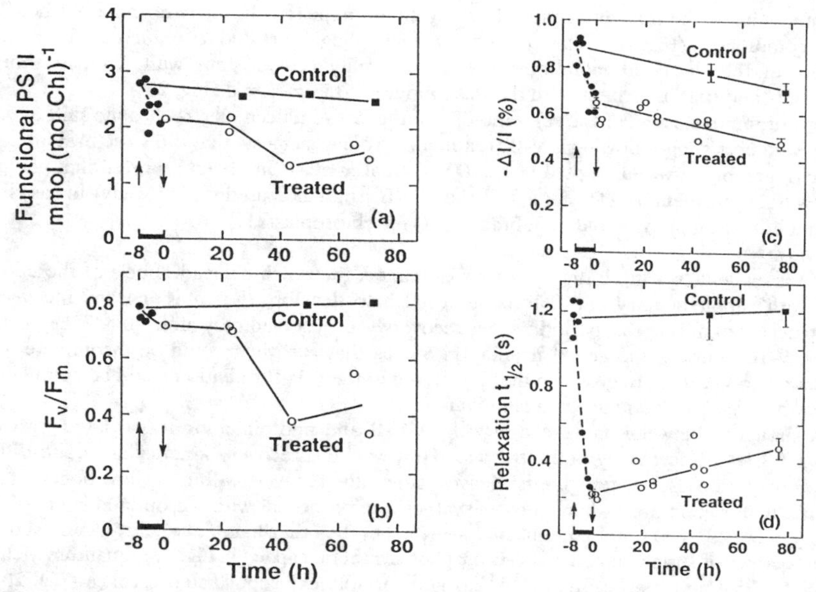

Fig. 2. Decreases in functional PS II reaction centres (a), the associated decline in quantum efficiency (F_v/F_m) of open PS II centres (b), the flash-induced electrochromic shift measured as the % decrease in the intensity, I, of transmitted light at 515 nm (c), and the half-time of post-flash relaxation of the signal (d) in pea leaves during (•) and after (o) an 8 h supplementary UV-B treatment of pea plants. Other conditions and symbols as in Fig. 1.

We also monitored the maximum efficiency of photochemistry in open PS II reaction centres, expressed as the ratio of variable (F_v) to maximal Chl fluorescence (F_m). The F_v/F_m ratio declined from 0.8 to 0.7 during the 8 h of supplementary UV-B treatment (Fig. 2b). In the 40-h recovery period, it further declined to 0.4, and then recovered slightly.

Electrochromic shift

Following flash-induced charge separation in functional PS II and PS I reaction centres, an electric field is generated across the thylakoid membrane, altering the absorbance of antenna pigments by an electrochromic shift at 515 nm [6]. The subsequent relaxation of the electric field occurs via ion movements across the membrane, with a half-time ($t_{1/2}$) dependent on the membrane permeability to ions. Fig. 2c shows that the maximal extent of the flash-induced electrochromic shift in a leaf was diminished during supplementary UV-B irradiation of pea plants. It continued to decline slowly after withdrawal of UV-B, suggesting that a decreased capacity for charge separation persisted for a considerable period after the UV-B irradiation. Most dramatic was $t_{1/2}$ for relaxation, which decreased from 1.2 s in the control to *ca.* 0.2 s after 8 h of UV-B irradiation (Fig. 2d). Even at 80 h after the UV-B treatment of pea plants, $t_{1/2}$ had recovered only slightly.

Discussion

Onset of supplementary UV-B effects during irradiation

Neither the chlorophyll content per unit leaf area nor the Chl *a*/ Chl *b* ratio was changed *during* the short-term treatment of pea plants with supplementary UV-B (Fig. 1a,b). In contrast, the flash-induced 515 nm signal in UV-B-treated leaves and particularly its relaxation kinetics were drastically altered (Fig. 2c,d). Other parameters such as quantum yield (Fig. 1d), functional PS II reaction centres and the F_v/F_m ratio (Fig. 2a,b) underwent intermediate extents of change.

Interestingly, the maximum rate of O_2 evolution appeared to *increase* initially when UV-B irradiation commenced (Fig. 1c). This could be an uncoupling effect due to an increase in the proton permeability of the thylakoid membrane. This possibility is consistent with a much shortened relaxation half-time ($t_{1/2}$) associated with the flash-induced 515 nm signal (Fig. 2d).

The dramatic decline of the relaxation $t_{1/2}$ of the flash-induced electrochromic shift at 515 nm induced by, and persisting following UV-B treatment, strongly suggests that the structural integrity of the thylakoid membrane was disrupted by the UV-B treatment. It has been reported that pea plants, irradiated with supplementary UV-B (at half the UV-B irradiance used in our study) for as short as 15 min, exhibit dilation of thylakoid membranes in some chloroplasts [7].

Recovery phase

It is evident that in all the responses examined, the much-delayed effects of the initial 8 h treatment with supplementary UV-B took some 40 h to develop, thus masking any recovery that might have occurred during this period. A net recovery was observed only after 40 h. The prolonged effects of UV-B following the actual irradiation means that recovery would be incomplete if short daily exposures to UV-B were given, so that injury due to the UV-B radiation could be cumulative.

Comparison between UV-B damage and photoinhibition

A similarity between damage caused by UV-B and photoinhibition associated with visible light is that PS II is affected by both stresses. However, the recovery kinetics are quite different. After photoinhibition for a few hours, leaves generally recover within a few hours at room temperature, under conditions where protein synthesis can proceed, with the optimal light conditions for recovery being 30 - 300 μmol photons m^{-2} s^{-1} [8]. On the other hand, our study clearly shows that the maximal effect of supplementary UV-B on photosynthetic capacity (Fig. 1c), quantum yield (Fig. 1d), functional PS II reaction centres (Fig. 2a) and variable chlorophyll fluorescence (Fig. 2b) took about 40 h to develop; only after this long lag period was net recovery evident.

Several reasons could explain why the recovery from UV-B is so slow (days) compared with that from photoinhibition (hours). Firstly, UV-B photons, being more energetic, are more likely to cause denigration of nucleic acids, enzymes, proteins and cellular membranes. Secondly, the structural integrity of thylakoid membranes was disrupted by UV-B, as indicated by the electrochromic shift (Fig. 2d), with the implication that ATP synthesis could have been partially uncoupled from electron transport. A limitation of ATP supply would have serious consequences for a system in need of repair, since the synthesis, translocation [9] and assembly of proteins [10] are ATP-dependent. Thirdly, a diversion of cellular activities towards the synthesis of enzymes and flavonoids for the defense against UV-B [11] must constitute significant competition for resources.

In conclusion, our study has demonstrated that the effects of short-term UV-B irradiation on photosynthetic functions and components of fully-expanded pea leaves continue to develop for many hours after the UV-B treatment, and that consequently recovery is very slow. Hence the effects of repeated daily UV-B exposures could have a compounding detrimental impact on the structure, composition and function of the photosynthetic apparatus of plants in the field.

References

[1] Caldwell MM, Teramura AH and Tevini M (1989). Trends Ecol Evol 4: 363-367
[2] Strid Å, Chow WS and Anderson JM (1990). Biochim Biophys Acta 1020: 260-268
[3] Jordan BR, Chow WS, Strid Å and Anderson JM (1991). FEBS Lett 284: 5-8
[4] Jordan BR, He J, Chow WS and Anderson JM (1992). Plant Cell Environ 15: 91-98
[5] Chow WS, Hope AB and Anderson JM (1991). Aust J Plant Physiol 18: 397-41
[6] Junge W and Witt HT (1968). Z Naturforsch 23b: 244-254
[7] Brandle JR, Campbell WF, Sisson WB and Caldwell MM (1977). Plant Physiol. 60: 165-169
[8] Skogen D, Chaturvedi R, Weidemann F, and Nilsen S (1986). J Plant Physiol 126: 195-205
[9] Lubben TH, Theg SM and Keegstra K (1988). Photosynth Res 17: 173-194
[10] Ellis J (1987). Nature 328: 378-379
[11] Chappell J and Hahlbrock K (1984). Nature 311: 76-78

Protein Turnover of Light-Harvesting Chlorophyll a/b Protein of Photosystem II in Rice (Oryza sativa L.) Leaves Aged under Different Irradiances from Full Expansion through Senescence

Jun Hidema, Amane Makino, Yasuko Kurita, Tadahiko Mae and Kunihiko Ojima

Department of Agricultural Chemistry, Faculty of Agriculture, Tohoku University, 1-1 Tsutsumidori-Amamiyamachi, Sendai 981, Japan

Introduction

When plants are grown under different irradiances, they show various acclimation of the photosynthetic system (1). It is, however, unclear whether the senescent leaves show the regulatory light acclimation.

We previously examined the photosynthetic characteristics of rice leaves aged under low irradiance after full expansion, and found that low irradiance strongly retarded the decline in Chl content (5). During this period, however, the Chl a/b ratio decreased with increasing relative amount of Chl b. Chl b is associated mostly with LHCII protein. Thus, the results suggested that low irradiance affects changes in the amounts of LHCII protein relative to other Chl proteins in the leaf during senescence. However, there is no data available on the effect of irradiance on the changes in the amounts of LHCII and other respective Chl components during senescence. In addition, the relationship between the amounts of LHCII protein and Chl bound to LHCII in senescent leaves is not known.

Protein level in a leaf is balanced by its synthesis and degradation. There are a few studies on the synthesis of LHCII protein during senescence (2, 10). These suggested that the capacity of LHCII synthesis declines during senescence. Recently, LaRoche et al. (6) observed that mRNA for LHCII accumulated in the photosynthetic alga, when it was transferred from high to low irradiance. However, it is unclear whether low irradiance affects the synthesis of LHCII in senescent leaves.

In this study, we first examined the effects of irradiances on the amounts of LHCII protein during senescence, and then analyzed the relationship between the Chl content and its a/b ratio, and LHCII content. Furthermore, we examined the turnover of LHCII during senescence, using ^{15}N as a tracer.

Materials and Methods

Plant Culture and ^{15}N-labeling: Rice (Oryza sativa L. cv Sasanishiki) plants were grown hydroponically to the ripening stage in a greenhouse as described previously (8). The 13th leaves on the main stems were used as samples throughout the experiments. From 5 days after the full expansion of the 13th leaves, the plants were grown under two different

N. Murata (ed.), Research in Photosynthesis, Vol. IV, 365–368.

light conditions; 100% and 20% natural sunlight.

^{15}N-labeling of the plants were done 4 times to different plants at 0, 15, 25, and 35 days after the full expansion of these leaves. When ^{15}N-labeling was carried out, the nutrient solution was given to one containing 0.5 mM ^{15}N-labeled ammonium sulfate (30.2 atom% excess) instead of 1 mM ammonium nitrate. Samples were collected at the 3rd day after the start of each ^{15}N-labeling.

Determination of Chl, and Total Leaf Nitrogen: Leaves were homogenized in 50 mM Li-phosphate buffer (pH 7.1) containing 5 mM dithiothreitol, 2 mM iodoacetic acid and 10% (v/v) glycerol at a ratio of leaves to buffer of 1:10 (g:ml). The Chl and total nitrogen contents were measured from part of this homogenate. The remaining homogenate was used for the determination of Rubisco, LHCII and ^{15}N-analysis of Rubisco.

Purification of LHCII and Determination by Western Blotting: Antisera against LHCII were raised in a rabbit with the purified LHCII. LHCII was purified from rice leaves according to the methods of Burke et al. (3) and Ryrie et al. (11) with some modifications. The final preparation was essentially pure by judging with SDS-PAGE. This procedure was also used for the isolation of LHCII for ^{15}N analysis.

The LHCII content was determined by Western Blotting. A part of the above leaf homogenate was treated with lithium dodecylsulfate solution, added to a final concentration of 2.0% (w/v), and then centrifuged to remove insoluble materials. After adding 2-mercaptoethanol (2% [v/v]), the supernatant was immediately heated at 100 C for 45 s. This preparation was used for determination of LHCII by SDS-PAGE, followed by immunoblotting.

Determination of Leaf Nitrogen and ^{15}N-analysis: Total leaf nitrogen content was determined with Nessler's reagent after Kjeldahl digestion. ^{15}N contents were determined with an emission spectrographic analysis system as described before (8).

Determination of Rubisco Content and Isolation of Rubisco for ^{15}N Analysis: Determination of Rubisco content was described elsewhere (9). For the ^{15}N analysis, the supernatant fraction of the leaf homogenate was subjected to polyethylene glycol-6000 fractionation between 12.5 and 17.5% solution in the presence of 100 mM NaCl, followed by a gel filtration on Sephacryl S-300.

Results and Discussion

Figure 1 shows the changes in Chl content and Chl a/b ratio during leaf senescence. Although the Chl content from the full sunlight treatment decreased appreciably, it from the shade treatment declined only a little during leaf senescence. The Chl a/b ratio from both treatments decreased, but the rate of decrease was faster from the shade treatment than that from the full sunlight treatment. These results agreed with those of our previous work (5).

The Chl a/b ratio of LHCII in higher plants is usually reported to be between 1.0 and 1.2 (1). However, in a photosynthetic alga, *Dunaliella tertiolecta*, a great difference in the a/b ratio of Chl bound to LHCII was found between low-light and high-light grown cells (12). To examine whether the a/b ratio of Chl bound to LHCII is affected by growth irradiance or leaf age, therefore we purified LHCII protein from each treatment. One main polypeptide at 29 kDa and two minor polypeptides at 26 and 25 kDa were detected from respective treatment by SDS-PAGE and immunoblotting (data not shown). The a/b ratio of Chl bound to LHCII remained fairly constant at 1.2 to 1.3, irrespective of irradiance treatment and leaf age (data not shown).

Changes in LHCII apoprotein content are shown in Figure 2. At the time of full expansion, LHCII accounted for about 4.5% of total leaf N. The LHCII content from the full sunlight treatment decreased steadily, whereas it from the shade treatment remained constant during senescence. These changes in LHCII were very similar to those of total Chl b content. Assuming that the a/b ratio of Chl bound to LHCII is 1.2 and all Chl b is associated with LHCII, the amounts of Chl bound to LHCII and other Chl-protein complexes were estimated (Figure 2). The amount of Chl bound to LHCII from the shade treatment also remained constant during leaf senescence, while the amount of Chl bound to other protein complexes from the shade treatment declined slightly. This means that decline in Chl a/b ratio from the shade treatment was caused by no apparent change in LHCII content and a slight decline of other Chl-protein complexes during leaf senescence.

Shade plants generally have relatively more Chl b and LHCII with a decline in PSII reaction center and core Chl (4, 7). Although we did not directly elucidate effects of irradiance on changes in the amounts of other Chl proteins, our results also suggest that changes in the respective Chl proteins similar to those of shade plants occur during senescence under shade conditions. Thus, leaf senescence under low irradiance has some of the regulatory characteristics of light acclimation.

Using ^{15}N as a tracer, we next deduced the changes in the amounts of LHCII synthesized under different irradiances during senescence. Incorporation of ^{15}N into LHCII declined markedly in both treatments after full expansion through senescence (Table 1). The ratio of labeled-N to total-N in LHCII fraction was lower than 1% in the senescent leaves from both treatments. In addition, the amount of LHCII synthesized from the shade treatment was more limited. These results indicate that no apparent change in LHCII content from the shade treatment was caused by little turnover of LHCII protein.

Rubisco synthesis was also very limited in the senescent leaves as previously observed (8).

Our previous studies showed that the rapid decrease in coupling factor 1 and cyt f contents occurred during senescence under shade conditions (5). However, in the present work, the amount of LHCII protein remained almost constant under shade conditions and this was caused by little turnover of LHCII. These results strongly suggest that there is a selective degradation mechanism(s) for each protein in the thylakoid. Light acclimation in senescent leaves may be mainly regulated by selective protein degradation in chloroplasts.

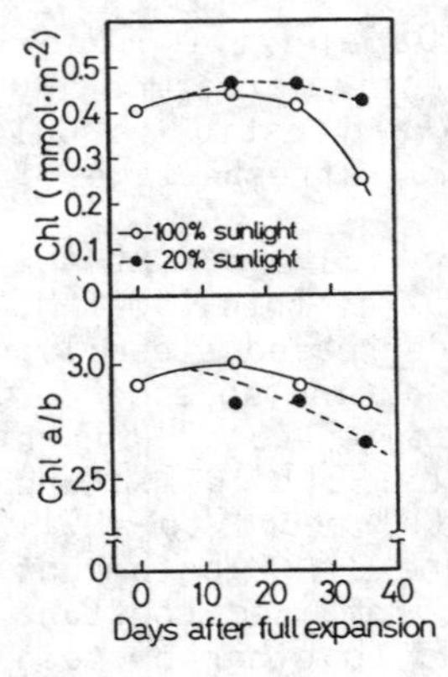

Fig. 1 (left) Changes in the Chl content and Chl a/b ratio in the 13th leaf aged under full sunlight and 20% sunlight conditions.

Fig. 2 (right) Changes in the amounts of LHCII protein, Chl bound to LHCII, and Chl bound to other Chl-proteins in the 13th leaf aged under full sunlight and 20% sunlight conditions.

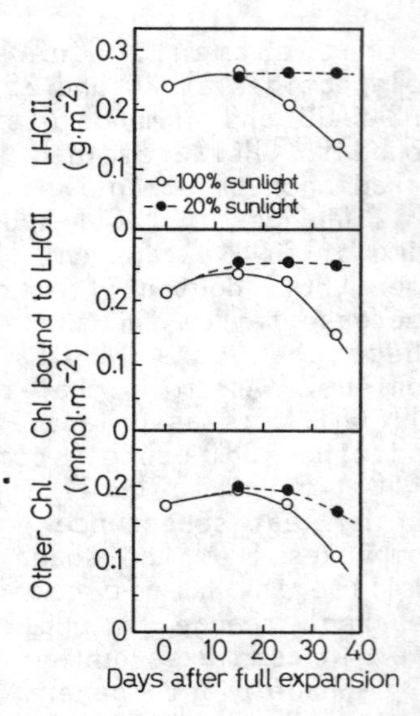

Table 1. Incorporation of ^{15}N into Total Leaf N, Rubisco and LHCII in the 13th leaves aged under full or 20% sunlight after ^{15}N-feeding to rice plants at different leaf ages.

Labeling time (Days after full expansion)		Labeled-N incorporated, mg/m^2 Total leaf N	LHCII	Rubisco
0		46.9 (4.0)	1.60 (3.3)	7.2 (3.0)
15	100% sunlight	24.4 (1.6)	0.63 (1.1)	4.0 (1.6)
	20% sunlight	9.1 (0.8)	0.30 (0.6)	0.3 (0.2)
25	100% sunlight	19.6 (1.8)	0.19 (0.5)	3.2 (1.8)
	20% sunlight	11.4 (1.2)	0.23 (0.5)	0.6 (0.4)
35	100% sunlight	13.4 (2.2)	0.20 (0.7)	1.6 (2.3)
	20% sunlight	1.9 (0.2)	0.06 (0.1)	ND

( ): Percentage of labeled-N to total each fraction N

References

(1) Anderson, J.M. (1986) Annu. Rev. Plant Physiol. 37: 93-136.
(2) Bate, N.J. et al. (1991) J. Exp. Bot. 42: 801-811.
(3) Burke, J.J. et al. (1978) Arch. Biochem, Biophys. 187: 252-263.
(4) Evans, J.R. (1987) Aust. J. Plant Physiol. 14: 157-170.
(5) Hidema, J. et al. (1991) Plant Physiol. 97: 1287-1293.
(6) LaRoche, J. et al. (1991) Plant Physiol. 97: 147-153.
(7) Leong, T. and Anderson, J.M. (1984) Photosyn. Res. 5: 105-115.
(8) Mae, T. et al. (1983) Plant Cell Physiol. 24: 1079-1086.
(9) Makino, A. et al. (1986) Agric. Biol. Chem. 50: 1911-1912.
(10) Roberts, D. R. et al. (1987) Plant Mol. Biol. 9: 343-353.
(11) Ryrie, I.J. et al. (1980) Eur. J. Biochem. 107: 345-354.
(12) Sukenik, A. et al. (1987) Nature 327: 704-707.

THE LIGHT RESPONSE CURVE OF THE CO_2 GAS EXCHANGE SEPARATED FOR THE ABAXIAL AND ADAXIAL LEAF SURFACE UNDER DIFFERENT LIGHT ENVIRONMENTS AND CO_2 CONCENTRATIONS.

W.F. POSTL and BOLHÁR-NORDENKAMPF, H.R., University of Vienna, Institute of Plant Physiology, Div. of Horticultural Plant Physiology, Althanstraße 14, A-1091 VIENNA, AUSTRIA.

1. INTRODUCTION

In natural habitats, dorsiventral leaves receive light on both surfaces. In diffuse light conditions the light intensity offered to the adaxial and abaxial surfaces may be equal depending on the reflexion properties of the soil surface and/or understory. In erectophile canopies leaves are submitted alternatively to full sunlight on both surfaces.
Since measurements of photosynthesis generally involve illumination of the upper (adaxial) surface only, This study was made to investigate any effects that an additional low intensity illumination of the abaxail leaf surface may have.

2. MATERIALS and METHODS

The leaves of 4 plant species with different leaf orientations and stomata densities on the ad- and abaxial surfaces, were investigated (Tab.1). *Eucalyptus globulus* was cultivated in the phytotronic unit of the Biocentre (Univ. of Vienna); *Canna indica*, *Ricinus comunis* and *Zea mays* were grown outside in the experimental garden of Institute. Light response curves were measured in 150, 350 and 650µl.l^{-1} CO_2 using an open system (Mark III-225, ADC, U.K.). A leaf section chamber (1) combined with electronically controlled solenoids permitted separate measurement of CO_2 gas exchange on the on the adaxial and abaxial leaf surface.
Three different light environments were simulated:
i) unilateral illumination of the adaxial surface,
ii) unilateral illumination of abaxial surface
iii) bilateral illumination; abaxial with a light intensity of 50µmol photons.m^{-2}.s^{-1}.

3. RESULTS and DISCUSSION

Additional low intensity illumination of the adaxial leaf surface was found to enhance CO_2 uptake in general. This effect was most pronounced in Canna, Mays and Eucalyptus although Eucalyptus leaves (juvenile-form) are orientated almost horizontally (Fig.1). In *Maize* intercellular systems in the upper and lower part of the mesophyll are well separated

N. Murata (ed.), Research in Photosynthesis, Vol. IV, 369–372.

from each other and the photosynthetic response of the upper and lower side of the leaf is different (2), (3). High photosynthetic rates performed by this C4-plant, are a result of gas exchange in independently responding mesophyll layers (2). With the exception of *Maize* (Fig 2), the contribution of the adaxial leaf surface to total gas fixation was found to be negligible (data not shown). When additional light was offered to the abaxial surface, an unexpected change in the 'apparent quantum requirement' was observed (Fig. 3). This indicates that besides photosynthesis, there may be one other target of stimulation. Due to the changes in stomatal conductance (Fig. 4), it was concluded that additional illumination of the abaxial surface induces a photoactive opening of stomatal pores, thus reducing the stomatal resistance for CO_2. An additional effect on dark respiration in lower layers of the mesophyll cannot be excluded. This would explain the shift of the compensation point to lower light intensities.

4. REFERENCES

1 HARRIS, G.C, J.K. CHEESBROUGH and WALKER, D.A. (1982). Plant Physiol. 71, 102- 107.

2 LONG, S.P., FARAGE, P.K., BOLHAR-NORDENKAMPF, H.R. and ROHRHOFER, U. (1989). Planta 177, 207-216.

3 POSTL, W.F. and BOLHAR-NORDENKAMPF, H.R. (1990). In: Current Research in Photosynthesis, Vol IV, 31-34.

Table 1: Stomata density and leaf orientation	Stomata per mm^2		Leaf posititon angle in degrees
	adaxial	abaxial	
Eucalyptus globulus	12 ± 1.7	90 ± 6.7	horizontal 0°
Canna indica	27 ± 3.3	60 ± 7.0	vertical 70°
Ricinus comunis	36 ± 5.0	78 ± 7.6	horizontal 0°
Zea mays	98 ± 10.3	108 ± 12.1	vertical 60°

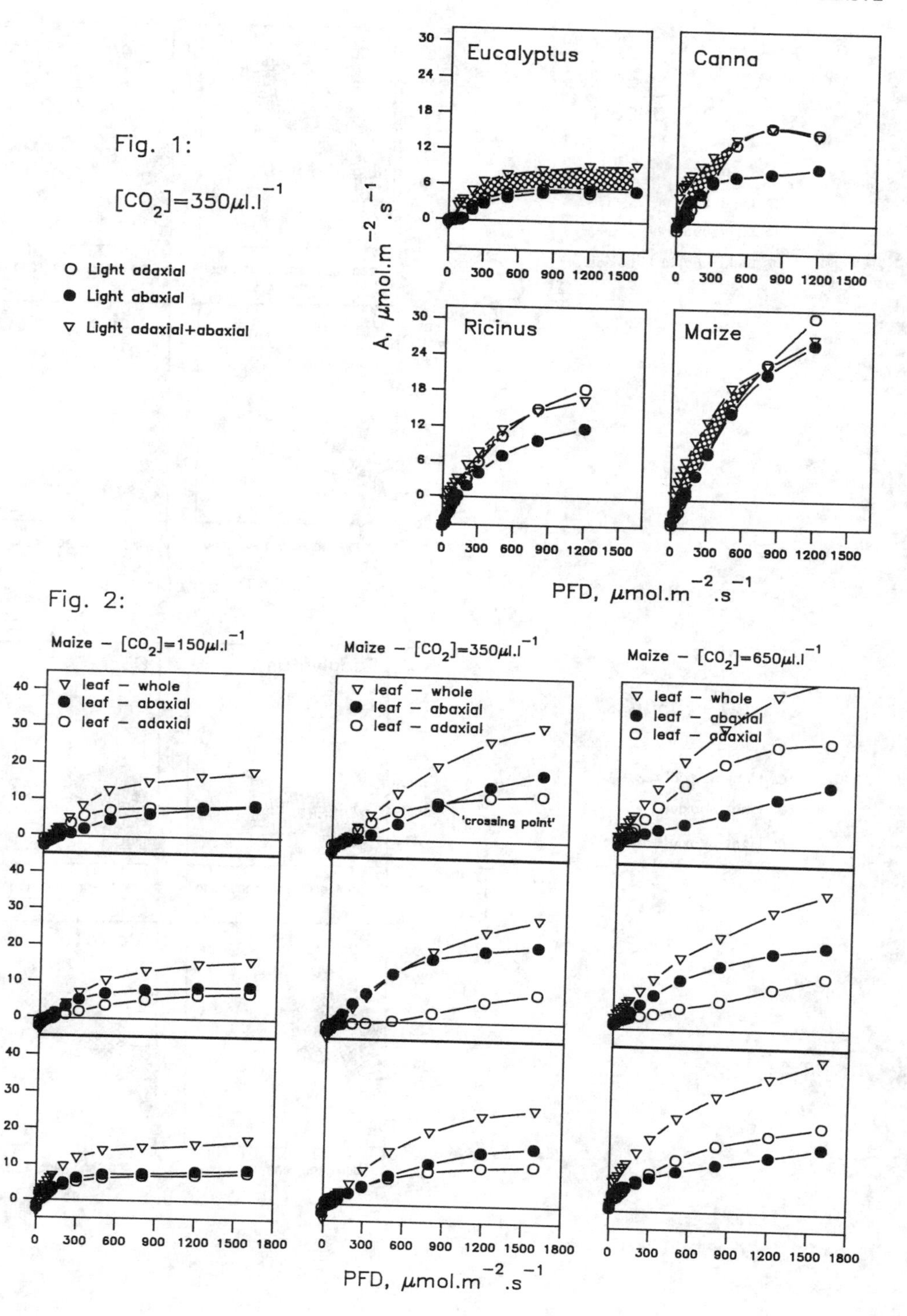
Fig. 1:
$[CO_2]=350\mu l.l^{-1}$
Light adaxial
Light abaxial
Light adaxial+abaxial
Eucalyptus
Canna
Ricinus
Maize
$A, \mu mol.m^{-2}.s^{-1}$
$PFD, \mu mol.m^{-2}.s^{-1}$
Fig. 2:
Maize – $[CO_2]=150\mu l.l^{-1}$
Maize – $[CO_2]=350\mu l.l^{-1}$
Maize – $[CO_2]=650\mu l.l^{-1}$
leaf – whole
leaf – abaxial
leaf – adaxial
'crossing point'
$A, \mu mol.m^{-2}.s^{-1}$
$PFD, \mu mol.m^{-2}.s^{-1}$

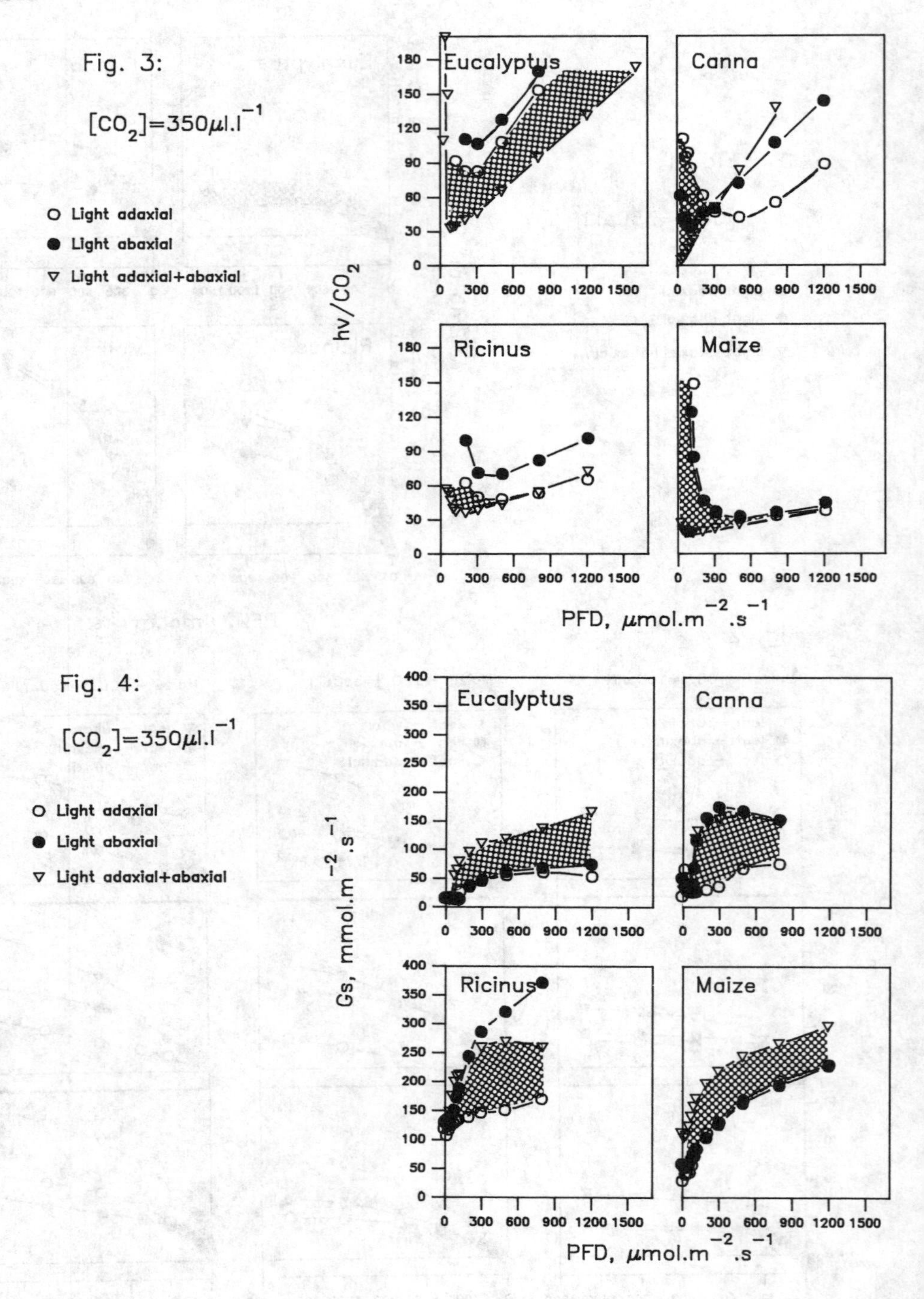
Fig. 3:
[CO2]=350µl.l −1
Light adaxial
Light abaxial
Light adaxial+abaxial
Eucalyptus
Canna
Ricinus
Maize
hν/CO2
PFD, µmol.m −2 .s −1
Fig. 4:
[CO2]=350µl.l −1
Light adaxial
Light abaxial
Light adaxial+abaxial
Eucalyptus
Canna
Ricinus
Maize
Gs, mmol.m −2 .s −1
PFD, µmol.m −2 .s −1

SUNFLECK ACCLIMATION IN RELATION TO PHOTOSYNTHETIC CO_2 ASSIMILATION IN *QUERCUS SERRATA* SEEDLINGS

YANHONG TANG[1], HIROSHI KOIZUMI[1], IZUMI WASHITANI[2] AND HIDEO IWAKI[2], NATL. INST. AGRO-ENVIRO. SCI., KANNONDAI 3-1-1, TSUKUBA 305, JAPAN[1] AND BIOL. DEPT., TSUKUBA UNIV. TSUKUBA 305, JAPAN[2]

1. INTRODUCTION

Leaves within canopies or in the understory experience long periods of diffuse light of low photon flux densities (PFD), separated by brief periods of sunflecks lasting from less than a second to several minutes (1, 2). Much knowledge of leaf photosynthetic responses to the rapid fluctuation in PFD by forest understory plants has accumulated recently due to the advances in gas exchange technology and the availability of computer-based data acquisition systems (3). The observed response of whole leaf photosynthesis to dynamic PFD is quite complex, with an induction period lasting from 10 min to an hour following an increase from low to high PFD and variations in the efficiency of utilization of lightflecks depending upon the previous irradiation history of a leaf. Pearcy *et al.* (4) suggested that photosynthetic induction response may well differ for plants adapting to different environments, but little has been known about the photosynthetic induction response of plants experiencing different light conditions.

Within the canopies of *Miscanthus sinensis* Anderss community, sunflecks contribute a great proportion to the daily and seasonal PFD (5,2). We have already addressed that the morphological plasticity, growth and survival in seedlings of *Quercus serrata* Thunb, which is one of the most common species invading the grassland, depend on the microsite light availability within the grass canopies (6). To further reveal the physiological mechanisms involved in such dependency, we investigated the induction responses of photosynthesis to lightflecks for the tree seedlings and compared the photosynthetic induction among the seedlings grown in the microsites differing in potential sunfleck PFD.

2. MATERIALS AND METHODS

2.1 *Plant materials and growth condition* In April, *Q. serrata* seedlings were transplanted to various locations within a *M. sinensis* grass canopy. Diffuse light PFDs were measured under overcast conditions for each seedling microsite at the height of 15 cm aboveground in May and October (See detail, 6). Potential microsite sunfleck PFDs were estimated from a regression model obtained for the same grass canopy (2). In October, the tree seedlings were carefully removed with surrounding soil to plastic packets and taken into laboratory for photosynthesis measurements.

2.2 *Gas exchange measurement* Photosynthesis was measured using a differential IR gas analyzer (IRGA URA-106, Shimadzu) in an open system. The entering air stream of

N. Murata (ed.), Research in Photosynthesis, Vol. IV, 373–376.

the chamber was first purified by a standard gas purifier (SGPU-51, STEC) and then mixed with O_2, CO_2, N_2 by a gas concentration regulator (AGRU-712, STEC). CO_2 concentration of the gas mixture was adjusted to 350 ppm. The air stream was humidified by bubbling through a gas washing bottle immersed in the water bath (Coolnit CL-19, Taiyo). Humidity of the air flow was controlled at about 70%. To increase the detecting speed of measurement system to a CO_2 concentration change within chamber, a small chamber (68 x 45 x 15 mm^3) was made for the photosynthesis measurement. An attached leaf was inserted into the chamber and leaf temperature kept between 24 to 26 °C. Light from a 1000W xenon-lamp (Toshiba) was filtered through 3 cm of water and then measured with a quantum sensor (LICOR model LI-190s). To measure the photosynthetic response to sudden increasing PFD, a high PFD level of 500 μmol m^{-2} s^{-1} was given to the leaf after 30 minutes at a low PFD of 50 μmol m^{-2} s^{-1}. The signals from the CO_2 analyzer, the thermocouples used for measuring leaf and air, and the monitoring quantum sensor were acquired at 1s intervals by a data logger (Model 5001A EDODENKI) connected to a personal computer (PC9801-F).

3. RESULTS AND DISCUSSION

3.1 *Photosynthetic induction response* When a leaf was exposed to a high PFD of 500 μmol m^{-2} s^{-1} following a period of 30 min in low PFD of 50 μmol m^{-2} s^{-1}, a short period of about 4 s was required for the computer to record the first signal of CO_2 assimilation. Assimilation then increased gradually and reached a maximum rate in about 12 minutes (Fig. 1). An induction period about 5 min after light increase was needed for the assimilation to reach 50% of the maximum rate. As CO_2 uptake reached a steady state, light was switched to the low PFD again. After a period of 5 min, light was then increased to 500 μmol m^{-2} s^{-1}. It took 7.6 min to reach the maximum rate of photosynthesis. In this case, two phases of CO_2 uptake were recognizable. The initial increase was very rapid and then there was a gradual increase as the maximum was approached. When the preceding period of low light become shorter, the increase in the first phase was prominently rapid, and the period of the following slow increase phase also become short.

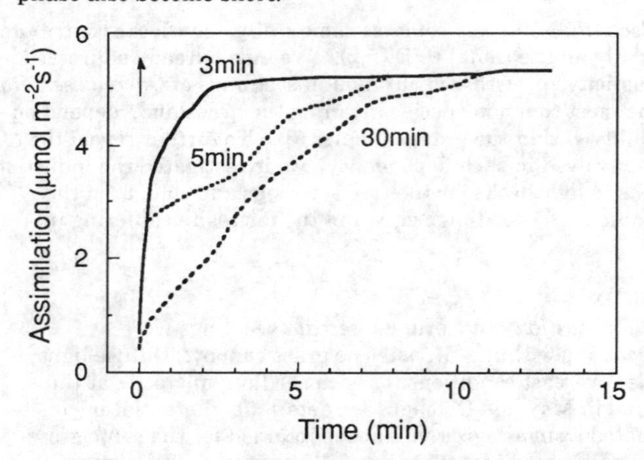

FIGURE 1. Time courses of assimilation in response to an increase of PFD from 50 to 500 μmol$m^{-2}s^{-1}$ following different periods of shade. Leaves were brought to steady-state assimilation rates in 500 μmol $m^{-2}s^{-1}$ before shading in 50 μmol $m^{-2}s^{-1}$ for 3, 5 and 30 minutes.

The intermittent shade between two sunflecks may have important ecological significance for *Q. serrata* seedlings to use sunflecks within *M. sinensis* canopies. In spring, sunflecks in the grass canopies are of a long duration (6) and such long sunflecks may increase water loss of young oak seedlings. Transpiration rates of understory plants are two or five times higher in sunflecks than in shade (7). The intermittent shade may thus favor a high water use efficiency of the young tree seedlings under relatively open grass canopies. This is because the plant water status can be significantly enhanced by exposure to intermittent shade. Such beneficial effects have been reported for the understory herbs that grow primarily beneath canopy gaps (8). However, if the intermittent shade lasts for too long, the induced state would diminish or disappear. Pfitsch and Pearcy (9) have reported that the initial photosynthetic response in a cluster of sunflecks preceded by only 5 min of diffuse light would be relatively independent of the induction state at the end of the preceding sunfleck. When the *M. sinensis* grass canopies become closed in summer, sunflecks become less and shorter but the duration of intermittent shade become longer. These longer intermittent shades may have negative effects on the sunfleck utilization of seedlings due to the independency of the induction state of each sunfleck.

3.2. *Relative photosynthetic induction efficiency* To facilitate the quantitative comparison of photosynthetic induction among the seedlings experiencing different light environments, a relative photosynthetic induction efficiency for a given sunfleck period was calculated from the percentage of integrated assimilation observed during the induction response to the integrated assimilation predicted from steady-state rates measured at the high and low PFD, assuming that there is an instantaneous increase of assimilation after the light increase (Fig. 2). The model is as follows:

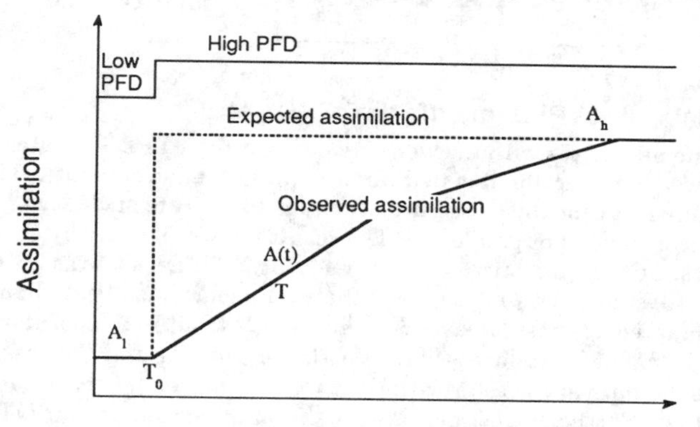

FIGURE 2. A diagram to illustrate the calculation of relative photosynthetic induction efficiency. A_l and A_h are the steady-state assimilations at low and high PFD. T_0 is the start time of the high PFD. A(t) is the assimilation as a function of time during the induction. (See text for detailed explanation).

$$RPIE_T = \frac{\int_{T_0}^{T} A(t)dt - A_l(T-T_0)}{(A_h - A_l)(T-T_0)} \times 100$$

Where, $RPIE_T$ is the relative photosynthetic induction efficiency (%) beginning from the increase of PFD to an interest time T during the lightfleck. A(t) is the observed assimilation as a function of time and can follow a sigmoidal or an exponential time course depending on previous PFD conditions. A_h and A_l are assimilation rates observed at the high (sunfleck) and the low PFD, respectively. The $RPIE_T$ was developed from the efficiency of sunfleck utilization used by Chazdon and Pearcy (10).

3.3 *Relative photosynthetic induction efficiency and the potential sunfleck PFD of microsites* To evaluate the effects of microsite light availability on photosynthetic induction response, CO_2 uptake of 12 individual seedlings, was measured under 500 $\mu mol\ m^{-2}\ s^{-1}$ following 30 min at 50 $\mu mol\ m^{-2}\ s^{-1}$. CO_2 assimilation in response to an increase of PFD for *Q. serrata* seedlings grown in microsites with a lower potential sunfleck PFD, increased more rapidly than those grown in microsites with a higher potential sunfleck PFD. As shown in Fig. 3, RPIEs were calculated for the durations of 10s and 60s after the light increase. During the early periods of induction relative sunfleck utilization efficiencies showed a highly negative relation with the potential sunfleck PFD of seedling microsites, but they tended to be less related to the microsite sunfleck PFD when assimilation reached a maximum.

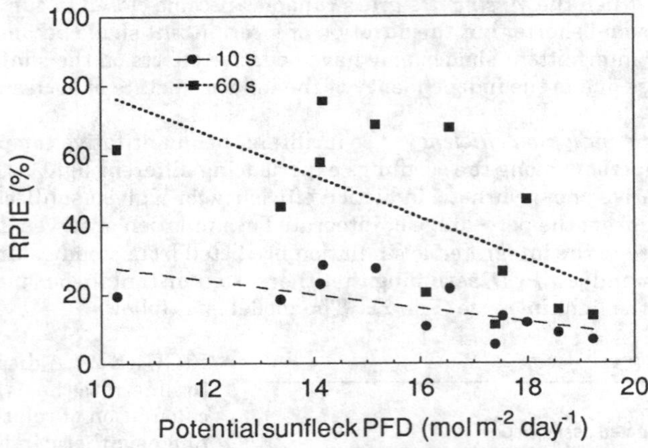

FIGURE 3. Dependence of the relative photosynthetic induction efficiency in 10 and 60 seconds after an increase of PFD for leaves of *Quercus serrata* seedlings on the potential microsite sunfleck PFD.

The higher RPIE in the microsites with a lower potential sunfleck PFD indicates that *Q. serrata* seedlings are able to acclimates to different sunfleck environments. The acclimation may be important for the *Q. serrata* seedlings to tolerate such environments, with deep shade but sunflecks. The result thus explains why *Q. serrata* seedlings can survive in the microsites with a relative PFD as low as 2% (6). Chazdon and Pearcy (10) suggested that photosynthetic efficiency may be higher for shade- than for sun-adapted species or leaves within a species, but in a laboratory experiment Gross and Chabot (11) addressed that both the time lag and time constant of leaf photosynthesis did not vary with growth light regime in *Fragaria virginiana* to sudden changes in PFD. Further investigations are therefore needed to clarify the photosynthetic induction responses to dynamic light environments

REFERENCES

1 Chazdon, R.L. (1988) Adv. Ecol. Res. 18,1-63
2 Tang Y., Washitani, I. and Iwaki, H. (1992) Ecol. Res. 7, 97-106
3 Pearcy , R. W. (1990) Annu. Rev. Plant Physiol. Plant Mol. Biol. 41, 421-53
4 Pearcy R.W., Osteryoung, K., Calkin, H. W. (1985) Plant Physiol. 79,896-902
5 Tang Y., Washitani, I., Tsuchiya, T., and Iwaki, H. (1988) Ecol. Res. 3, 253-266
6 Tang Y., Washitani, I. and Iwaki, H. (1992) Bot. Mag. 105, 281-288
7 Elias, P. (1983) Biol. Plant. 25, 68-74
8 Knapp, A.K., Smith, W.K. and Young, D. R. (1989). Funct. Ecol. 3, 375-58
9 Pfitsch, W.A., and Pearcy, R.W. (1989) Oecologia 80,465-70
10 Chazdon, R.L. and Pearcy R.W. (1986) Oecologia 69, 524-531
11 Gross, L. J. and Chabot, B.F. (1979) Plant Physiol. 63,1033-38

Photosynthetic Characteristics of Rice Leaves Aged under Different Irradiances from Full Expansion through Senescence

Jun Hidema, Amane Makino, Tadahiko Mae, and Kunihiko Ojima
Department of Agricultural Chemistry, Faculty of Agriculture, Tohoku University, Tsutsumidori-Amamiyamachi, Sendai 981, Japan

INTRODUCTION

Leaf photosynthesis declines during senescence. Several quantitative analyses indicated that decrease in photosynthesis under ambient air conditions can be predicted from changes in the amounts and kinetics of Rubisco (8). Electron transport activities and the reaction-center complexes also decreased during leaf senescence, and their positive correlations with photosynthesis have been frequently reported (5, 6). Thus, it can be expected that a decline in photosynthesis during senescence is mainly caused by a decrease in a functional unit of the photosynthetic system.

When plants are transferred to a different irradiance, they show acclimation of the photosynthetic system. The characteristics of plants acclimated to low irradiance have been reviewed in detail (1). These plants generally have relatively more Chl b, low capacities of electron transport per unit of Chl, and a reduction in soluble protein relative to Chl. However, the photosynthetic characteristics of leaves aged under low irradiance after full expansion are not known. In addition, it is unclear whether the senescent leaves show the regulatory light acclimation.

In this study (4), two irradiance treatments (100 and 20% sunlight) were imposed after the full expansion of the 13th leaf through senescence. We examined the effects of irradiance on the *in vivo* and *in vitro* photosynthetic characteristics of senescent leaves of rice. In addition, we characterized the photosynthetic system of the leaves aged under low irradiance in relation to acclimation of shade plants.

MATERIALS AND METHODS

Plant Culture---Rice (*Oryza sativa* L. cv Sasanishiki) plants were grown hydroponically to the ripening stage in a greenhouse under natural light conditions. The basal nutrient solution used was described in Makino *et al.* (8). The 13th leaves on the main stems were used as samples throughout the experiments. From 5 d after the full expansion of the 13th leaves, the plants were grown under two different light conditions: 100 and 20% natural sunlight. The average irradiances in both treatments were 2000 and 400 μmol quanta PAR m^{-2} s^{-1} at noon on a sunny day, respectively.

Photosynthetic Measurements---The rates of CO_2 exchange and transpira-

N. Murata (ed.), Research in Photosynthesis, Vol. IV, 377–380.

tion were measured with an open gas-exchange system using a temperature-controlled chamber equipped with two fans. This system was detailed in Makino et al. (8). Measurements were made at an irradiance of 1800 μmol quanta m^{-2} s^{-1} and a leaf temperature of 25°C.

Determinations of Chl, Rubisco, and Total Leaf-N--- These were determined as described elsewhere (7). The Chl and total leaf-N contents were measured from part of leaf homogenate. The remaining homogenate for the determination of Rubisco was centrifuged at 39,000g for 10 min at 0 to 4°C. The amount of Rubisco protein in the supernatant was determined by SDS-PAGE and densitometry.

Assay of NADP-G3P-DH---NADP-G3P-DH activity was measured at 25°C spectrophotometrically (340 nm) according to the method described by Makino et al. (7).

Determination of CF_1 and Cyt f by Western Blotting---The amounts of CF_1 and Cyt f were determined by Western-blotting using the respective monospecific antisera after SDS-PAGE.

RESULTS

In this report, we define the beginning of leaf senescence as the time when the photosynthetic rate begins to decrease. Because preliminary experiments showed that the photosynthetic rate begins to decrease about 5 d after full expansion, the plants were transferred to two different irradiances (100 and 20% sunlight) from 5 d after full expansion of the 13th leaves through senescence.

To deduce the effects of irradiance on the in vivo balance between capacities of Rubisco and other photosynthetic limiting factors in the leaves during senescence, we first examined the rate of CO_2 assimilation as a function of intercellular CO_2 pressure (C_i) according to the photosynthetic model of Farquhar and von Caemmerer (3). Fig. 1 shows the changes in the photosynthetic rates at ambient CO_2 air, at low CO_2 pressures ($Ci \leqq 200$ μbar) limited by Rubisco capacity, and at high CO_2 pressures ($C_i \approx 600$ μbar) limited by other factors such as electron transport capacity (2, 3). There was no difference in the rates at an ambient air and C_i = 200 μbar between the light treatments. The rate at C_i = 600 μbar, however, decreased faster in the 20% sunlight treatment than in the full sunlight treatment. This means that although there is no difference in the change in the Rubisco capacity between the treatments, the RuBP regeneration capacity from the shade treatment decreased at a faster rate than the full sunlight treatment during senescence.

Despite no difference in the photosynthetic rates at 200 μbar between the treatments, the Rubisco content from the full sunlight treatment decreased sooner, at the same rate than from the shade treatment during senescence (Fig. 2). The changes in the activity of NADP-G3P-DH was almost coordinated with that in Rubisco protein. In contrast, CF_1 and Cyt f contents decreased more rapidly from the shade treatment. These changes in CF_1 and Cyt f were very similar to those in the photosynthetic rate at 600 μbar with leaf age except in the late senescent leaves.

Changes in Chl content and Chl a/b ratio are shown in Figure 3. The Chl content from shade treatment decreased only a little until late senescence, although it from the full sunlight treatment decreased appreciably. The Chl a/b ratio from the full sunlight treatment remained relatively constant, but that from the shade treatment decreased with leaf age.

DISCUSSION

Rapid Decrease in CF_1 and Cyt f

The rapid decrease in CF_1 and Cyt f contents from the shade treatment during senescence is similar to one of the phenomena shown by the plants acclimated to low irradiance. It is well known that shade plants have lower electron transport capacities relative to Chl or total thylakoid nitrogen (1). This is mainly caused by a relative reduction in the amounts of electron transport components such as CF_1 (ATP-ase) and Cyt f (9). We also found that a rapid decrease in CF_1 and Cyt f contents from the shade treatment results in a similar reduction in the photosynthetic rate at high CO_2 pressure (Figs. 1 and 2).

Retardative Decrease in Rubisco

There was more Rubisco in shaded than in sunlight-illuminated leaves as a result of a retardative decrease (Fig. 2). The ratio of Rubisco to CF_1 or Cyt f contents from the shade treatment also increased, but the ratio to leaf nitrogen did not differ (data not shown) and ratio to Chl declined (Fig. 3). Shade plants generally have less Rubisco content for a given Chl or total leaf-nitrogen content. Concerning the ratio to electron transport, Terashima and Evans (9) reported that spinach plants adapted to low irradiance have reduced Rubisco content but that the decrease is less than that in electron transport activity. Thus, the effects of low irradiance on change in Rubisco content in senescing leaves differed from the characteristics of shade plants with the exception of the ratio to electron transport.

No Apparent Decline in Chl

Low irradiance strongly retarded the decline in the Chl content until late senescence (Fig. 3). In addition, the Chl a/b ratio from the shade treatment decreased during this period. A decline in Chl a/b ratio during senescence is mainly caused by a more rapid decrease in the reaction centers and core Chl than in the LHCII (6). No apparent change in the Chl content may be ascribed to changes in the relative amounts of several Chl proteins, especially a slight increase in LHCII. Shade plants have relatively more Chl b and LHC per PSII reaction center (1). Thus, it is possible that changes in the respective Chl components similar to those of shade plants occurred during leaf senescence under shade conditions, resulting in no apparent change in total Chl.

CONCLUSION

The photosynthetic characteristics of rice leaves aged under low irradiance were approximately similar to those of shade plants. This means that leaf senescence under light stress has some of the regulatory characteristics of acclimation, but with notable differences. One of the most interesting points is the greater content of Rubisco from the shade treatment. This was not reflected in the rate of photosynthesis. A plausible explanation is that *in vivo* Rubisco activity is coordinated with a reduction in electron transport components such as CF_1 and Cyt f.

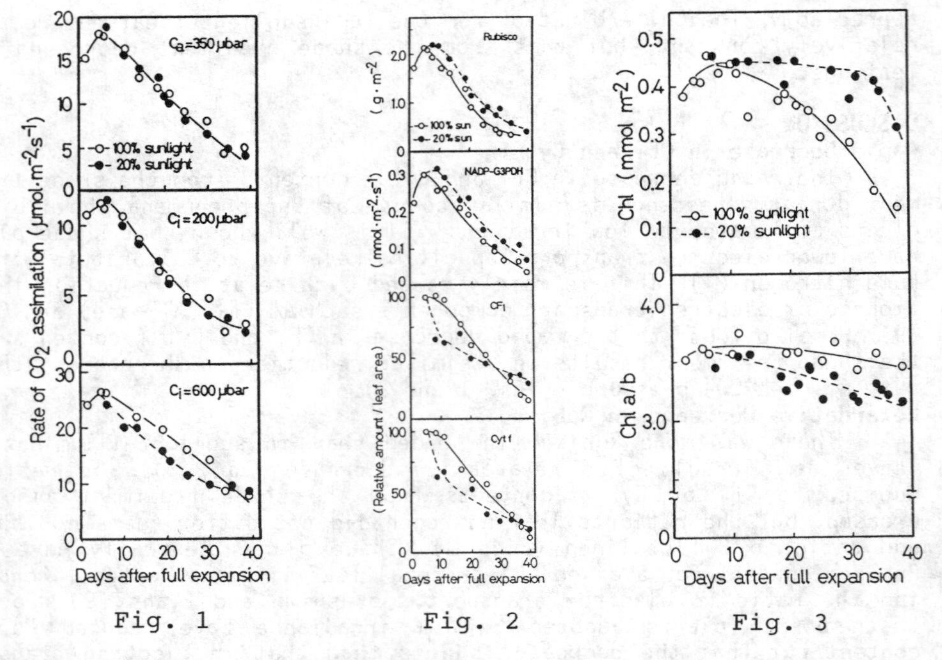

Fig. 1. Changes in the photosynthetic rates at an ambient CO_2 pressure (C_a) of 350 µbar, and at intercellular CO_2 pressures (C_i) of 200 and 600 µbar in the 13th leaves aged under full sunlight (○) and 20% sunlight (●) conditions.
Fig. 2. Changes in Rubisco content, NADP-G3P-DH activity, CF_1 and Cyt f contents. Symbols are the same in Fig. 1. The CF_1 and Cyt f contents were represented as relative content to those in the leaf on the 5th d after full expansion.
Fig. 3. Changes in the Chl content and Chl a/b ratio in the 13th leaf aged under full sunlight (○) and 20% sunlight (●) conditions.

REFERENCES

1. Anderson, J.M. (1986) Annu. Rev. Plant Physiol. 37, 93-136
2. Evans, J.R. and Terashima, I. (1988) Plant Cell Physiol. 29, 157-165
3. Farquhar, G.D., von Caemmerer, S. and Berry, J.A. (1980) Planta 149, 149, 78-90
4. Hidema, J., Makino, A., Mae, T. and Ojima, K. (1991) Plant Physiol. 97, 1287-1293
5. Holloway, P.J., Maclean, D.J. and Scott, K.J. (1983) Plant Physiol. 72, 795-801
6. Kura-Hotta, M., Satoh, K. and Katoh, S. (1987) Plant Cell Physiol. 28, 1321-1329
7. Makino, A., Mae, T. and Ohira, K. (1983) Plant Physiol. 73, 1002-1007
8. Makino, A., Mae, T. and Ohira, K. (1985) Planta 166, 414-420
9. Terashima, I. and Evans, J.R. (1988) Plant Cell Physiol. 29, 143-155

EFFECTS OF LIGHT, NUTRIENT AND AGE ON NITROGEN CONTENT AND PHOTOSYNTHESIS OF LEAVES.

Kouki Hikosaka, Ichiro Terashima and Sakae Katoh.
Dept. Biol., Fac. Sci., Univ. Tokyo, Hongo, Bunkyo-ku, Tokyo, 113, Japan.

Introduction

There is a correlation between the photosynthetic capacity and nitrogen content of leaves because a major fraction of leaf proteins is located in chloroplasts (1,2). Efficiency of nitrogen utilization of a leaf is expected to increase if more nitrogen is invested in the leaves which receive high photon flux density (PFD) than the leaves which receive low PFD (3). Carbon gain of a whole plant is, therefore, expected to be increased when nitrogen is distributed in such a way that upper leaves have higher nitrogen contents than leaves which are shaded by upper leaves (4). Hirose and co-workers (5,6,7) have shown that there is indeed a vertical gradient of nitrogen content of leaves along the gradient of PFD from the top of a leaf canopy of herbaceous plants downward. Based on the observation that the gradient of leaf nitrogen content was steeper in a dense stand of *Lysimachia vulgaris* than in a open stand, they suggested that light microenvironment of leaves is an important factor to determine distribution of nitrogen among leaves at different positions (6,7). On the other hand, there is also a vertical gradient of leaf age in the canopy, which is also considered as an important factor to determine distribution of nitrogen because younger leaves develop at upper positions (8). In the present study, attempts were made to distinguish between the effect of light environment and that of leaf age on the leaf nitrogen content. For this purpose, a vine, *Ipomoea tricolor* Cav. was grown horizontally so that all leaves developed and senesced under the same light conditions without mutual shading. Effects of shading and nitrogen nutrition on the distribution of nitrogen among leaves were studied.

Material and Methods

Ipomoea tricolor Cav. plants were grown hydroponically in a greenhouse and vines were allowed to extend only horizontally over a wire net so that all leaves received full sun light. Light environment of individual leaves was varied with small screen boxes. The hydroponic solution used was that of (9). Photosynthetic capacity of a leaf was measured at 1700 µmol quanta m^{-2} s^{-1} with an open gas exchange system. CO_2 concentration in the ambient air and leaf temperature were 350 µl l^{-1} and 25°C, respectively. Nitrogen contents of leaves, which had been dried for more than 3 days at 70°C, were measured with a NC-analyzer (NC-80, Sumitomo chemical).

N. Murata (ed.), Research in Photosynthesis, Vol. IV, 381–384.

Results and Discussion

First, plants were grown at four nitrate concentrations without any shading treatment. The photosynthetic capacities of leaves were well correlated with nitrogen contents of leaves irrespective of large differences in age of leaves analysed and in nitrate levels applied (Figure 1). Figure 2 shows nitrogen contents of leaves, which were sampled 43 days after planting. Generally, nitrogen content was the highest in newly developed leaves and decreased with advancing age of leaves. Note that the lower the nitrogen availability was, the steeper the gradient of nitrogen content. Because all the leaves have been exposed to full sun light throughout the course of plant growth, the result shows that a gradient of leaf nitrogen content is generated solely by effect of age of leaves at lower nitrogen availability.

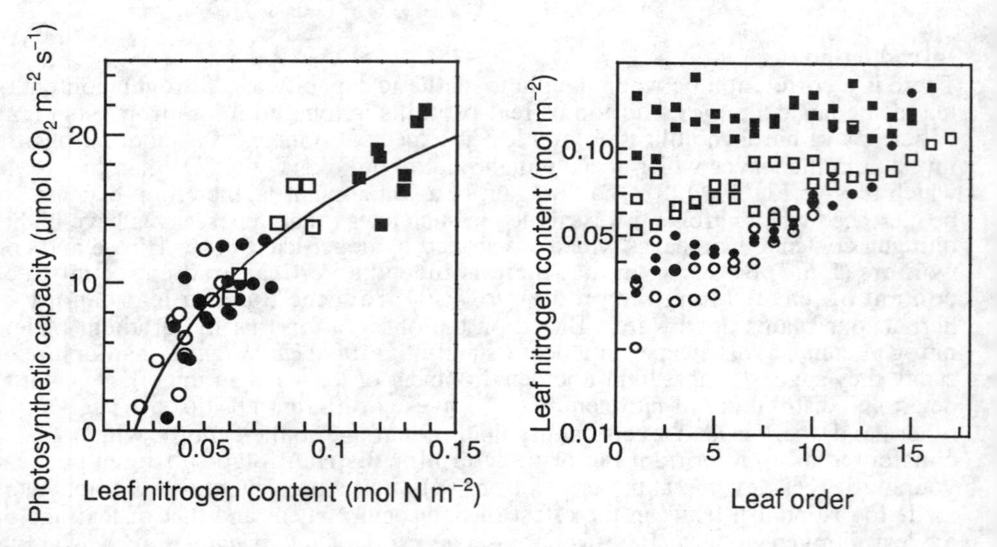

Figure 1. (left) The relationships between photosynthetic capacity and nitrogen content of 3rd leaves of plants grown under full sun light and at various nitrate concentrations of hydroponic solution. Each data point indicates a leaf of a plant grown at 0.04 (open circles), 0.24 (solid circles), 1.2 (open squares) or 12 (solid squares) mM NO_3^-. The 3rd leaves were sampled at 22, 29, 36, 43, 50, 57 days after transplanting of seedling to pots.

Figure 2. (right) Distribution of nitrogen among leaves of plants grown under full sun light and at various nitrate concentrations. The symbols are as in Figure 1. Two plants were grown at each nitrate level. Each data point indicates nitrogen content of a leaf. The number of leaves attached to a plants varied depending on nitrate concentration.

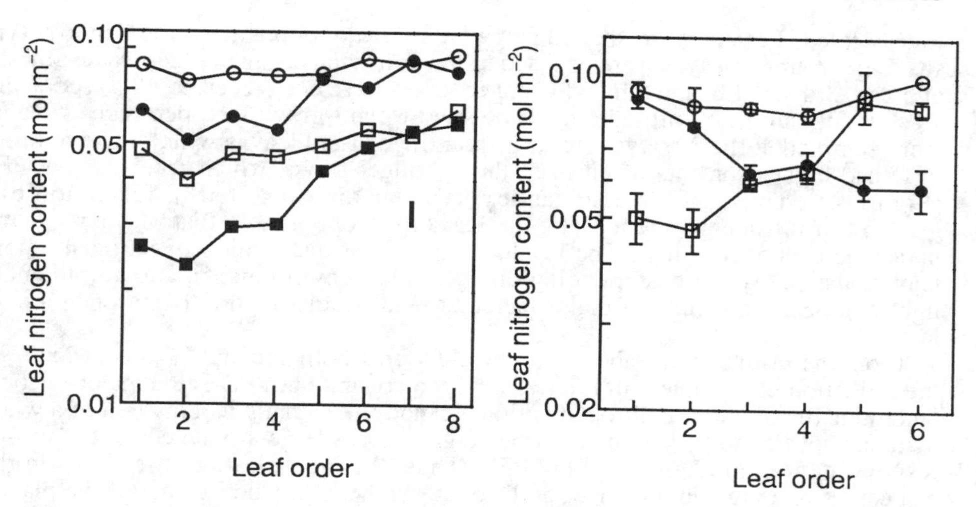

Figure 3. (left) Effects of "canopy-type shading" on distribution of nitrogen in leaves. Opened and solid symbols indicate leaves exposed to full sunlight and Leave to which "canopy shading was applied. Circles and squares indicate the plants grown at 12 and 0.12 mM NO_3^-, respectively. Each data point indicates the mean of 3 leaves. Bar indicates mean of S.D.

Figure 4. (right) Effects of "inverse canopy-type shading" on distribution of nitrogen in leaves. The concentration of nitrate was 12 mM. Open circles, all leaves were exposed to full sun light; open squares, canopy-type shading (the 1st and 2nd, 3rd and 4th, and 5th leaves were exposed to 14%, 35%, and 100% of full sunlight, respectively); solid circles, inverse canopy-type shading.

Next, we investigated effects of PFD on the leaf nitrogen content. In order to simulate the shading effect on a leaf which increases during development of a leaf canopy of erect herbaceous plants, leaves were shaded individually with shade boxes of different light transmittances in such a manner that PFD decreased with advancing age of a leaf. At the sampling time, 37 days after transplanting, the 1st and 2nd, 3rd and 4th, 5th and 6th, and 7th and younger leaves have been received 3.7%, 14%, 35% and 100% of full sun light, respectively, for 6 days. Figure 3 shows the results obtained with plants grown at two nitrogen availabilities. The "canopy-type shading" resulted in a steeper gradient of the leaf nitrogen content compared with the gradient formed without shading, at both levels of nitrogen nutrition applied. Thus, the gradient of light microenvironments of leaves in a leaf canopy is also an important factor to regulate distribution of nitrogen among leaves.

In the third experiment, effects of "inverse canopy-type shading" were investigated. Leaves were shaded stepwise in a way opposite to the canopy–type shading. Younger leaves were exposed to lower irradiances than older leaves; the 1st and 2nd, 3rd and 4th, and 5th and younger leaves have been received 100%, 35% and 14% of full sun light throughout the course of plant growth, respectively. Leaves were sampled at the 32 days after transplanting. Aged leaves which received high PFD had higher contents of nitrogen than younger leaves which received low PFD (Figure 4). Thus, the inverse canopy–type shading resulted in formation of a gradient of nitrogen content along the leaf order, opposite to that of plants grown under the canopy shading. The results indicate that distribution of nitrogen among leaves plastically varies depending on light microenvironments, and a gradient of light microenvironment is a major factor to regulate distribution of nitrogen among leaves.

From the results stated above, we conclude that both age and PFD contribute to the formation of a gradient of the leaf nitrogen content but PFD is the major factor to determine distribution of nitrogen within a canopy. The daily carbon gain of a whole plant is expected to be maximized when a gradient of leaf nitrogen content is formed responding to a gradient of PFD (4,5). Thus, the high plasticity of plants in this respecte is of a great importance for the photosynthetic production of a whole plant.

The whole carbon gain of a plant, of which all leaves receive the same PFD, is expected to be maximized when nitrogen is distributed uniformly among leaves (4). However, we observed that a gradient of leaf nitrogen content was formed in the plant grown under full sun light and at low nitrate concentrations (Figure 2). The result indicates distribution of leaf nitrogen content is not always optimized for the whole plant carbon gain if leaf age is a dominant factor.

References

1. Field C and Mooney HA (1986) in: On the Economy of Plant Form and Function. ed by Givnish TJ. pp.25–55 Cambridge Univ. Press, Cambridge.
2. Terashima I and Evans JR (1988) Plant Cell Physiol. 29:143–155
3. Mooney HA and Gulmon SL (1979) in: Topics in Plant Population Biology. eds by Solbrig OT, Jain S, Johnson GB, Raven PH. pp.316–337. Columbia Univ. Press, New York.
4. Field C (1983) Oecologia(Berlin). 56:341–347.
5. Hirose T and Werger MJA (1987) Oecologia(Berlin). 72:520–526
6. Hirose T, Werger MJA, Pons TL and van Rheenen JWA (1988) Oecolgia(Berlin) 77:145–150.
7. Hirose T, Werger MJA and van Rheenen JWA (1989) Ecology 70:1610–1618
8. Mooney HA, Field C, Gulmon SL and Bazzaz FA (1981) Oecologia(Berlin) 50:109–112
9. Hewitt EJ and Smith TA (1975) Plant Mineral Nutrition. P.298 The English Univ. Press, London.

TIME COURSE RESPONSES OF PHOTOSYNTHETIC ADAPTATION OF TWO FRESHWATER DIATOMS TO TEMPERATURE CHANGES AND ITS ECOLOGICAL INTERPRETATION

YOSHIHIRO SUZUKI AND MASAYUKI TAKAHASHI,
Botany Department, University of Tokyo, Hongo, Tokyo 113, JAPAN

1. INTRODUCTION

Most organisms are expected to adapt environmental changes through various ways (4). Adaptation which includes instantaneous responses and acclimation having phenotypic changes could contribute for the enhancement of activity (1) under a given environment. In algae as photoautotrophs such adaptation could depend upon photosynthetic processes (2,3), and possibly enhance photosynthesis and the resulted growth rate (6,8). Suzuki and Takahashi (in preparation) found actual improvements in the growth rates associated with rate changes in photosynthesis and dark respiration by temperature changes with diatom species in close association of chlorophyll a and RuBP carboxylase.

Some of the above mentioned responses may require responding time (3,2). It will then be important to evaluate time response of adaptation and associated processes for the understanding of life of organism under natural changing environments at various temporal scales (7). The present paper will deal with evaluations of time responses of observed adaptation processes by temperature changes and with making possible ecological interpretations. Cellular chlorophyll a and growth rate were both particularly focussed the attention because of their close relation to photosynthesis.

2. MATERIALS AND METHODS

Two unicellular freshwater diatoms, Asterionella formosa Hass. and Stephanodiscus sp. isolated by the author (Y.S.) were used. Stock cultures were preincubated in the modified Chu No.10 medium (5) under 200 $\mu E\ m^{-2}\ s^{-1}$ (14L/10D LD cycle) of day light type fluorescent tubes for one week. For the acclimation experiments, the preincubated cultures were inoculated into new media at the same preincubation temperature, and were periodically determined the changes of cell numbers by cell counting, of cellular volume by a particle counter, and of chlorophyll a by the fluorometry. For the time course experiments of acclimation, medium was adjusted to the preincubation temperature before the inoculation of preincubated algal cells. After confirming the exponential growth, the culture flask was then put under a new temperature at the beginning of light period.

3. RESULTS AND DISCUSSION

Fig. 1 represents the results of growth rates at the logarithmic growth phase and chlorophyll a contents of A. formosa and Stephanodiscus sp. acclimated at each temperature. A. formosa showed a gradual small increase in the growth rate from 0.87 doublings.day^{-1} at 10 °C to 1.55 doublings.day^{-1} at 25 °C. Previous experiments have shown that A. formosa had positive growth at 5 °C but no growth at 30 °C (unpublished). Stephanodiscus sp. showed a rapid and large increase in the growth rate from 0.12 doublings.day^{-1} at 10 °C to 1.94 doublings.day^{-1} at 25 °C. Stephanodiscus sp. was confirmed their no growth at 5 °C but positive rapid growth at 30 °C (unpublished). These results indicated that A. formosa adapted to lower temperatures than Stephanodiscus sp., and vice versa. The growth rate of A. formosa was

N. Murata (ed.), Research in Photosynthesis, Vol. IV, 385–388.

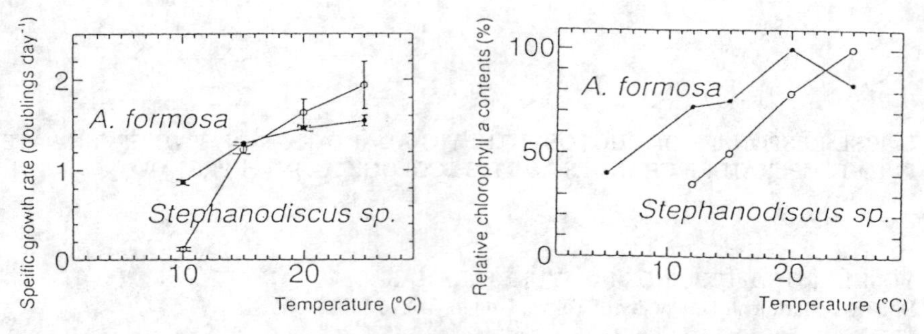

FIGURE 1. Temperature dependency of the specific growth rate and cellular chlorophyll a contents of A. formosa and Stephanodiscus sp. cultured at various temperatures. Short bars in the growth rate indicate standard errors.

much larger below ca 16 °C, and both species showed a consistent linear increase of cellular chlorophyll a at a similar rate (twice as much increase with a temperature increase of 15 °C) along with the increase of temperature although the relative chlorophyll a contents of A. formosa were much greater than those of Stephanodiscus sp. and showed an obvious decrease at 25 °C. It has then become clear that relative chlorophyll a contents of the two diatom species varied depending upon differences in the growth temperature in different response manner between species.

Time required for the observed changes after the alteration of temperature was then evaluated (Fig. 2). Each data point in the figure represents the average of duplicate cultures. Two temperatures of 25 °C and 10 °C within the active growth temperature ranges of the two species were chosen for comparison experiments. Almost immediate temperature change compared to seasonal temperature event under natural

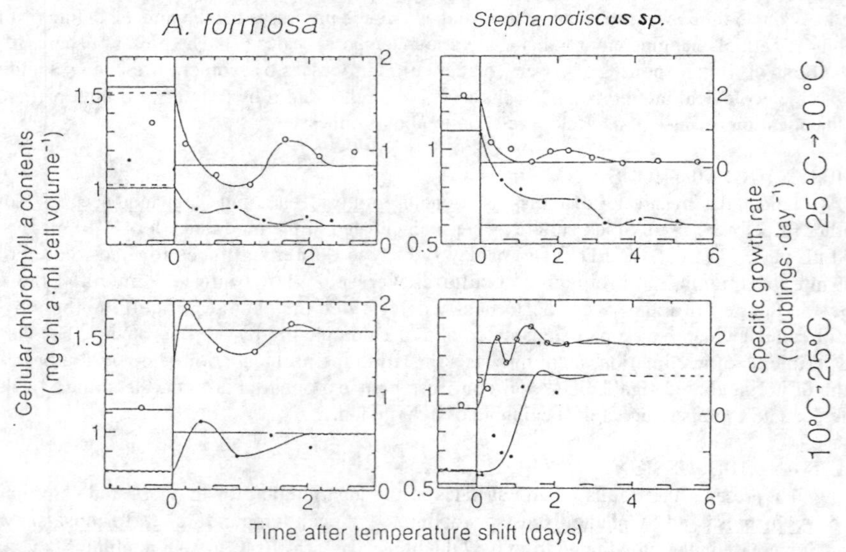

FIGURE 2. Time changes of the specific growth rate (open circle) and cellular chlorophyll a contents (solid circle) of A. formosa and Stephanodiscus sp. after changing growth temperature from 25 °C to 10 °C (upper figures) and vice versa (lower figures). Thin horizontal lines represent average steady levels for each given temperature. Horizontal short thick bars along the temperature axis indicate dark periods. Curves were drawn by visual inspection.

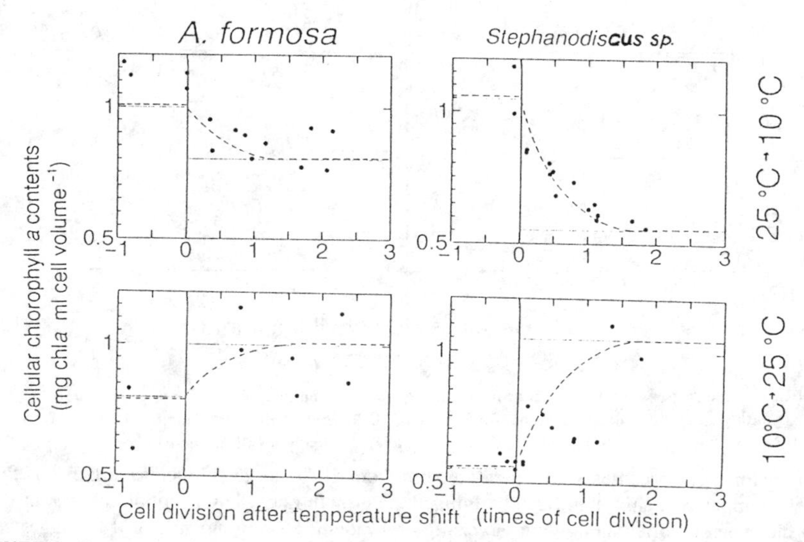

FIGURE 3. Changes of cellular chlorophyll a contents against cell division of A. formosa and Stephanodiscus sp. after changing growth temperature from 25 °C to 10 °C (upper figures) and vice versa (lower figures). Thin horizontal lines represent average steady levels for each given temperature. Dotted curves were drawn by visual inspection.

condition was taken for the experiment because it was assumed that cells acclimating to a fast temperature change can acclimate slow temperature changes. By transferring the cells into a new temperature, the cells gradually reached a new level or a new rate after some oscillations including an immediate overshooting. Oscillations were more obvious in the changes of growth rate than that of chlorophyll a contents. A. formosa required ca 2.0 days to settle down to a new level although low temperature shifts seem to take a little longer period of time. The observed changes were rapid initially followed by a gradual slowing down. On the other hands, Stephanodiscus sp. required much longer period of time for settlement into a new level such as ca 3.0 days from 10 °C to 25 °C, and ca 5.0 days from 25 °C to 10 °C in both changes of growth rate and chlorophyll a contents. Time response curves of Stephanodiscus sp. also showed similar changing patterns having rapid initial changes as the cases of A. formosa.

Fig. 3 represents the changes of cellular chlorophyll a contents against cell division. The same sets of data of Fig. 2 were applied for Fig. 3 although each data point of duplicate experiment was plotted separately. It seems that both A. formosa and Stephanodiscus sp. completed the changes within ca two cell divisions regardless the differences in growth temperature. This suggests that the slow acclimation observed at the low temperature in Fig. 2 was due to possible decrease in cellular metabolism accompanying with low temperature as suggested by Davison (1991).

For comparing response behaviors of two parameters of the two tested species, chlorophyll a contents vs. growth rates obtained from Fig. 2 were graphically compared in Fig. 4. A. formosa was characterized with rather small changes in which chlorophyll a contents and growth rates of cells acclimated at 10 °C and 25 °C behaved in a narrow area showing 0.3 and 0.4 times in chlorophyll a contents and growth rate, respectively, compared with those of Stephanodiscus sp., and small changes corresponded well with their rapid acclimation as observed in Fig. 2. There occurred a drop in the growth rate when temperature was changed from 25 °C to 10 °C although no such immediate changes was detected from 10 °C to 25 °C. Stephanodiscus sp. showed much greater changing ranges reaching 10 to 20 times in the growth rates and about two times in cellular chlorophyll a contents in the acclimation between 10 °C and 25 °C. Growth rate showed initial large changes in the both temperature changes followed by

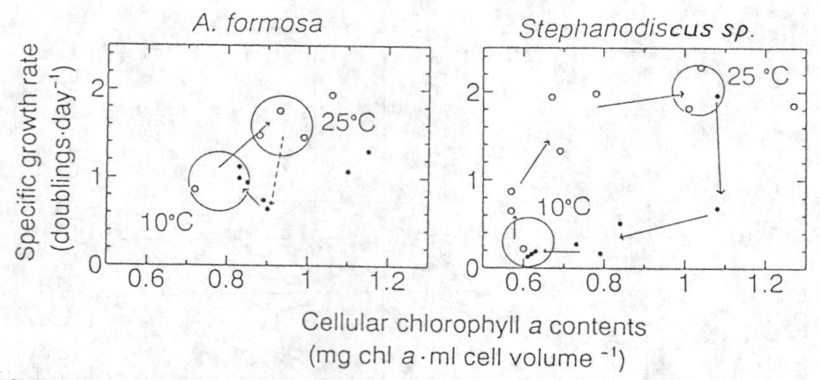

FIGURE 4. Time response relations between specific growth rate and cellular chlorophyll a contents of A. formosa and Stephanodiscus sp. cells acclimated at 10 °C to 25 °C (opencircle) and vice versa (closed circle). Arrows indicate time order, an circles represent average steady levels either 10°C or 25°C.

changes in chlorophyll a contents. Temperature shift from 10 °C to 25 °C increased the growth rate, but the opposite temperature shift significantly dropped the growth rate. Similar initial changes in the growth rate have also been reported along with the changes in radiation environment (7). It is suggested that the observed initial immediate changes in growth rate could be independent with the possible acclimation having phenotypic changes in photosynthetic processes. At least there could be two mechanisms, with or without phenotypic changes, involved in the observed growth rate changes responding to temperature shifts although each mechanism cannot be separated at this stage.

4. CONCLUSION

(1) Growth rate and cellular chlorophyll a contents increased with temperature increase in the active growth temperature range in the two tested diatom species (Fig.1), which represents that cells at a certain temperature have to change them accommodating to a new temperature if their surrounding temperature changes.

(2) By changing the surrounding temperature, the tested cells acclimated to a new temperature with rapid initial change followed by gradual change evaluated by growth rate and chlorophyll a contents (Figs. 2, 3). In the growth rate instantaneous change was also noticed almost immediately after temperature change (Fig. 4). All these responses will be important for the consideration of temperature acclimation of algae.

(3) The above mentioned changes equally occurred within 2 cell divisions regardless differences in species and temperature (Fig. 3). Apparent differences were possibly due to the effects of temperature on the processes within cells. Observed type of acclimation to temperature changes could be essential for algal cells to carry out their life under natural environment having temperature changes including seasonal events.

REFERENCES

1.Berry, J. and Bjorkman, B. (1980) Ann. Rev. Plant Physiol. 31,491–543
2.Davison, I. R. (1991) J. Phycol. 27,2–8
3.Falkowski, P. G. and Thomas, G. O. (1980) Plant Physiol. 66,441–461
4.Hochachka, P. W. and Somero, G.N. (1984) Biochemical adaptation. Princeton University Press
5.Kudo, S. and Takahashi, M. (1989) J. Plankton Res. 11,1001–1019
6.Li, W. K. W. (1980) In Primary productivity in the sea (P. G. Falkowski, ed.) Plenum Press, New York and London, pp. 259–278
7.Post, A. F., Dubinsky, Z., Wyman, K. and Falkowski, P. G. (1984) Mar. Biol. 83,239–246
8.Raven, J. A. and Geider, R. J. (1988) New Phytol. 110,441– 461

Adaptation of the photosynthetic apparatus of green algae to intensities and wavelengths of light

Horst Senger[1], Klaus Humbeck[2], Norman I. Bishop[3]

[1]Fachbereich Biologie/Botanik, Philipps-Universität Marburg, Karl-von-Frisch-Str., 3550 Marburg, Germany.
[2]Institut für Allgemeine Botanik, Universität Hamburg, Ohnhorststr. 18, 2000 Hamburg 52, Germany.
[3]Oregon State University, Dept. of Botany and Plant Pathology, Corvallis, OR, 97331-2902, USA.

The photosynthetic apparatus adapts to intensities and qualities of light to optimize the photosynthetic efficiency (1). Under low light intensities the respiration, the compensation point and the photosynthetic capacity are reduced, the chlorophyll concentration, however, is increased. This adaptation phenomenon is common for all organisms with oxygenic photosynthesis

In order to understand the mechanism of this adaptation phenomenon *Scenedesmus obliquus* (2,3) and other green algae (4,5) have been investigated. Under different intensities of white light the ratio of chlorophyll/P700, the distribution of pigment protein complexes, the size of PSII and the chlorophyll a/b ratio remained constant (2,3, Table I). We conclude that the pigment apparatus, including PSI and PSII multiplied under low light intensities, while the electron transport chains per cell mass remained constant (Fig. I).

In higher plants the light adaptation is mediated by the phytochrome system. In this case red light mimics the shade conditions. According to the different biotope, blue light mimics the shade conditions for green algae (6). This was confirmed by action spectroscopy (7).

Phenotypically green algae demonstrate the same adaptional phenomena under blue light as under low intensities of white light. However, the strategy of adaptation of the photosynthetic apparatus is different. The chlorophyll a/b ratio decreases while the chlorophyll/P700 ratio and the size of PSII increase under blue light in comparison to red light of the same intensity (8). We conclude that the blue light receptor system mediates an enhancement in chlorophyll b synthesis which in turn enlarges the light harvesting complex. This interpretation is confirmed by the distribution of LHCPs after PAGE separation (8).

N. Murata (ed.), Research in Photosynthesis, Vol. IV, 389–392.

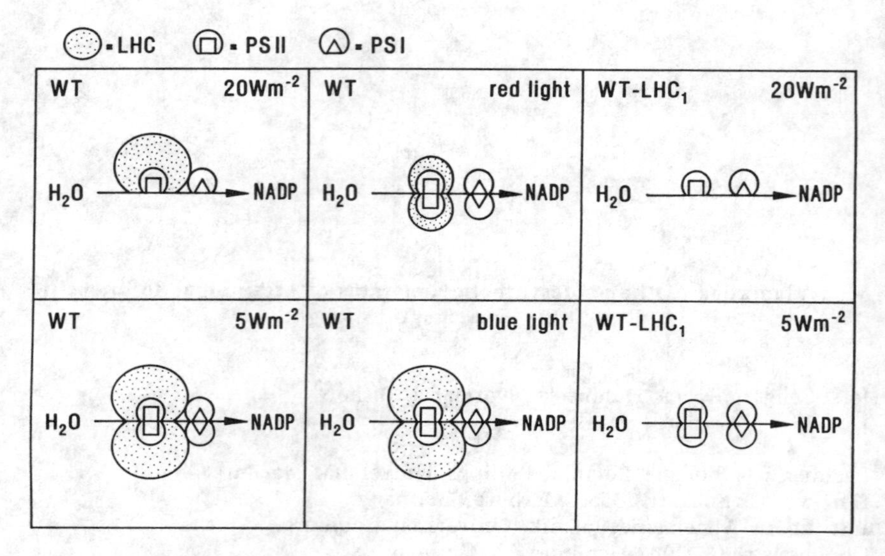

Fig. 1: Schematic diagram of the changes in molecular organization during adaptation of the photosynthetic apparatus of the wild type (WT) and the mutant lacking the light harvesting complex ($WT-LHC_1$) of *Scenedesmus obliquus*.

		Dark	5 W m^{-2}	20 W m^{-2}	Blue	Red
WT	Loro/Lut	0.80	0.32	0.03	0.13	0.05
	O_2/Chl	—	100	200	90	160
$WT-LHC_1$	Loro/Lut	0.99	0.16	0.04	0.06	0.03
	O_2/Chl	—	70	180	50	120

Table II: Comparison of photosynthetic capacity (O_2/Chl) and changes in xanthophyll pattern (loroxanthin/lutein) in the wild type (WT) and the mutant without light harvesting complex ($WT-LHC_1$) of *Scenedesmus obliquus*, adapted to various light conditions.

	Sample	µg Chl / µl PCV	Chl a / Chl b	Respiration ($\frac{\mu\ mol\ O_2}{h \times mg\ Chl}$)	max. PS-rate ($\frac{\mu\ mol\ O_2}{h \times mg\ Chl}$)	Comp. point ($W \times m^{-2}$)	$T_{1/2}$ (ms)
wild type	$20\ W \times m^{-2}$ white light	7.8	2.7	- 23.8	166.3	6.7	100
	$5\ W \times m^{-2}$ white light	12.8	2.5	- 9.5	88.8	3.2	105
	red light	9.3	5.6	- 23.2	91.9	7.0	138
	blue light	13.8	3.1	- 11.8	30.9	3.2	106
$WT - LHC_1$	$20\ W \times m^{-2}$ white light	4.62	∞	- 24.9	107.4	27	189
	$5\ W \times m^{-2}$ white light	6.05	∞	- 11.4	61.2	16	192

Table I: Comparison of several parameters during adaptation to various light conditions of the photosynthetic apparatus of the wild type (WT) and the mutant without light harvesting complex ($WT-LHC_1$) of *Scenedesmus obliquus*. For pigment determination, polarographical oxygen measurements and estimation of half rise time ($T_{1/2}$) during fluorescence induction see Reference 8.

Under these aspects it was of interest to apply to the adaptation studies a mutant of *Scenedesmus* without light harvesting complex ($WT\ -LHC_1$). This mutant adapts under high or low intensities of white light like the wild type cells (9, Table I) under low intensities of white light. Chlorophyll per cell mass increases without forming LHCPs, the size of PSII and the ratio of chlorophyll/P700 remains constant. Thus we have to conclude that the reaction centers with the core antennae multiply under low intensities (Fig. 1).

The investigations on green algae demonstrate the high flexibility of the photosynthetic apparatus to adapt to different light intensities and qualities in order to optimize the photosynthetic reactions.

During the adaptation studies we observed an interesting change in the pattern of caroteniods. The ratio of loroxanthin/lutein decreases with increasing light intensity and with increasing photosynthetic capacity (Table II). These ratios are reversible in the same way as the adaptation to changes in light conditions is. The question about the metabolic meaning of the change in the loroxanthin/lutein ratio and whether the oxydation of lutein to loroxanthin might be a reversable process is the topic of current investigations.

REFERENCES

1. Senger, H. and Bauer, B. (1987) The influence of light quality on adaptation and function of the photosynthetic apparatus. Photochem. Photobiol., 45, 939-946

2. Senger, H. and Fleischhacker, Ph. (1978) Adaptation of the photosynthetic apparatus of *Scenedesmus obliquus* to strong and weak light conditions. I. Differences in pigments, photosynthetic capacity, quantum yield and dark reactions. Physiol. Plant. 43, 35-42

3. Fleischhacker, Ph. and Senger, H. (1978) Adaptation of the photosynthetic apparatus of *Scenedesmus obliquus* to strong and weak light conditions. II. Differences in photochemical reactions, the photosynthetic electron transport and photosynthetic units. Physiol. Plant 43, 43-51

4. Senge, M. and Senger, H. (1990) Response of the photosynthetic apparatus during adaptation of *Chlorella and Ankistrodesmus* to irradiance changes. J. Plant Physiol. 136, 675-679

5. Senge, M. and Senger, H. (1990) Functional changes in the photosynthetic apparatus during light adaptation of the green alga *Chlorella fusca*. J. Photochem. Photobiol. B.8, 63-71

6. Humbeck, K. and Senger, H. (1984) The blue light factor in sun and shade plant adaptation. In Blue Light Effects in Biological Systems (Senger, H., ed.), pp 344-351, Springer-Verlag Berlin, Heidelberg, New York

7. Thielmann, J., Galland, P. and Senger, H. (1991) Action spectra for photosynthetic adaptation in *Scenedesmus obliquus*. I. Chlorophyll biosynthesis under autotrophic conditions. Planta 183, 334-339.

8. Humbeck, K., Hoffmann, B. and H. Senger (1988) Influence of energy flux and quality of light on the molecular organization of the photosynthetic apparatus in *Scenedesmus*. Planta 173, 205-212

9. Bishop, N.I., Humbeck, K., Römer, S. and Senger, H. (1989) The mode of adaptation of the photosynthetic apparatus of a pigment mutant of *Scenedesmus* without light harvesting complex to different light intensities. J. Plant Physiol. 135, 144-149

23. Photoinhibition

ON THE MOLECULAR MECHANISMS OF LIGHT-INDUCED D1 PROTEIN DEGRADATION

A. H. Salter[1], J. De Las Rivas[2], J. Barber[2] and B. Andersson[1]
[1]Department of Biochemistry, Arrhenius Laboratories, Stockholm University, S-106 91 Stockholm, Sweden and [2]AFRC Photosynthesis Research Group, Department of Biochemistry, Imperial College, London SW7 2AY, U.K.

1. PHOTOINHIBITION OF PHOTOSYSTEM II - A BACKGROUND

Excess light can deactivate and damage photosystem II (PSII), a phenomenon that is generally known as photoinhibition. The damage is mainly concentrated onto the D1 protein, which together with the D2 protein carries essentially all the redox components necessary for the water-plastoquinone oxido-reductase reaction (1). Initially, excess light leads to photoinactivation of electron flow. This in turn leads to irreversible damage to the reaction centre proteins which are then triggered for degradation and removed by a machinery that can discriminate between damaged and native protein (Fig. 1). The damaged and degraded protein has eventually to be replaced with a new copy in order to re-establish photosynthetic function, and the plant has therefore evolved a complex repair mechanism for dealing with damaged PSII (Fig. 1). Beyond the triggering and degradation, the repair phase of the cycle involves partial disassembly of PSII, lateral migration of non-degraded subunits, resynthesis *de novo* of a new copy of the damaged protein and reassembly (2). This is a physiologically important repair process, since photosynthetic capacity *in vivo* is adversely affected when the rate of inactivation and damage exceeds the rate of repair. Consequently, the D1 protein turns over rapidly at high light intensities *in vivo* (3,4).

Over the last few years, a number of studies have approached the problem of D1 protein damage and degradation *in vitro*. It has become clear that isolated thylakoid membranes contain the complete machinery necessary for the total hydrolysis of the D1 protein (1,2). The processes of triggering for degradation and primary cleavage are associated with the PSII complex itself, and these events can be observed *in vitro* even in isolated preparations of the PSII complex (2,5,6).

Two separate mechanisms can lead to photoinactivation and damage to the D1 protein (1-3,7). These two inactivation mechanisms, which both lead to irreversible oxidative damage around the P_{680} chlorophyll dimer (2), are mediated by either the acceptor (stromal) or donor (lumenal) sides of the complex. Strong illumination under 'acceptor' photoinhibitory conditions means that the particle retains an intact water oxidation system and is thus predisposed towards the production of stably-reduced abnormal quinone states that ultimately lead to the production of singlet

N. Murata (ed.), Research in Photosynthesis, Vol. IV, 395–402.

oxygen via chlorophyll triplets (8). 'Donor' photoinhibitory conditions imply that the water oxidation system is inefficient and hence that strongly oxidising radicals such as $P680^+$ and/or $Tyr_Z{}^+$can accumulate (2,9) with increased quantum yield. Both of the these mechanisms ultimately result in the production of irreversibly damaged D1 protein and the consequent need for repair.

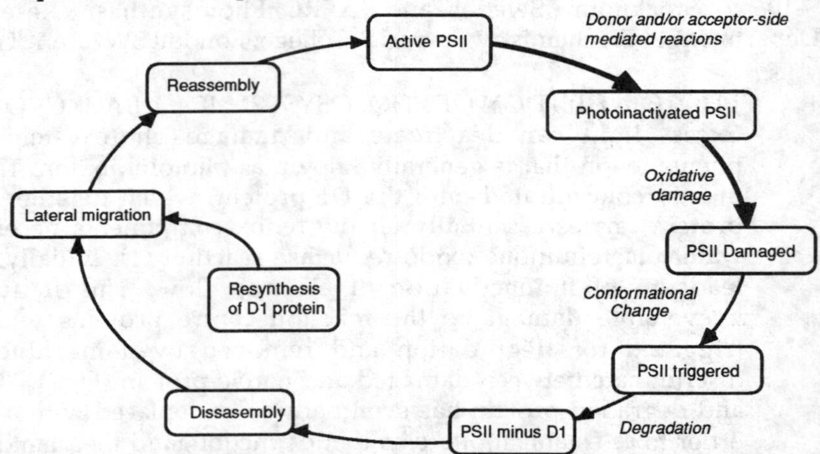

FIGURE 1. The sequential events of the pathway of D1 protein damage (bold arrows) and repair (single arrows) are shown in schematic form.

In this communication, we describe how photoinactivated and damaged D1 protein is converted into a proteolytic substrate via the triggering process (section 2). We further characterise the proteolytic fragments that are associated with the primary degradative process (section 3), and discuss the identity of the protease associated with the PSII complex (section 4).

2. TRIGGERING OF DAMAGED D1 PROTEIN FOR DEGRADATION.

The separation of the inactivation and degradative phases of the cycle shown in figure 1 has been clearly demonstrated (10). In this study, thylakoid membranes were illuminated at low temperature, during which photoinactivation of electron flow through PSII took place without D1 protein degradation. The membranes were subsequently incubated at room temperature in complete darkness whereupon D1 protein degradation occurred without further loss of electron transport capacity. This is indicative of a proteolytic mechanism existing in the thylakoid membrane that can recognize and remove photodamaged D1 protein in the dark. Some 'molecular memory' event thus occurs whereby the system can identify damaged subunits as such during the subsequent degradative stage. This process is referred to as triggering. By means of this triggering

process the damaged D1 protein is turned into a substrate for degradation. We here present data elucidating the nature of triggering by use of the herbicide 3-(3',4'-dichlorophenyl)-1,1-dimethylurea (DCMU). It has been observed previously that DCMU, which binds to the Q_B-site on the D1 protein, can protect against light-induced degradation of the protein during continuous illumination both in vivo (11) and in vitro (12).
We here demonstrate that the triggering event involves a change in the D1 protein that can be prevented by DCMU binding. The approach taken was to employ a modified version of the experiments described above (10). Cold-light (inactivation) and warm-dark (degradation) phases were separated by a cold dark period of 30 min (Fig. 2). DCMU was added from the beginning of the experiment and also both before and after the cold-dark intermediate phase.

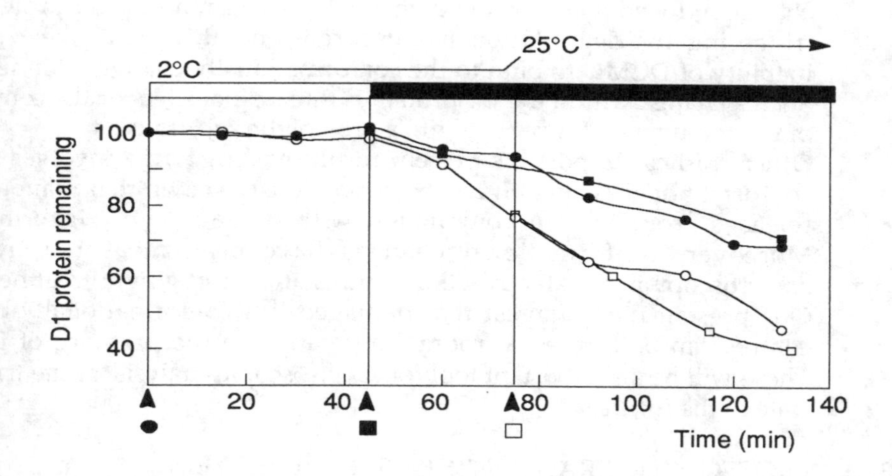

FIGURE 2. The stabilizing effect of DCMU upon the different phases of the D1 protein degradation process. 40 µM DCMU was added before (filled squares) or after (open squares) a cold-dark incubation phase of 30 min that was intermediate between a cold photoinactivation phase and a dark degradation phase. Data is also shown from conditions where was DCMU present throughout (added at time 0, filled circles) or never added (open circles). Spinach thylakoid membranes were illuminated at a concentration of 0.1 mg $chl.ml^{-1}$ and light intensity of 4000 $\mu E.m^{2}.s^{-1}$. The amount of D1 protein was determined by quantitative western blotting.

The data show that DCMU exerts an equivalent protective effect on the control degradation reaction (open circles) whether added at the start (leftmost arrow; filled circles) or at the end (middle arrow; filled squares) of the photoinactivation period. Hence, no protective effect via photoinactivation upon degradation could be ascribed to DCMU.

Most importantly, DCMU had no protective effect when added at the end of the intermediate phase (rightmost arrow; open squares). It can therefore be concluded that DCMU must be present during the cold intermediate phase, before triggering has occurred, for degradation to be inhibited. We thus demonstrate that DCMU, in the dark, specifically blocks temperature-dependant triggering of degradation following photoinactivation. This was confirmed by the observation of a linear relationship between cold-dark incubation time and the extent of degradation reaction inhibition (data not shown).

How can this result be explained, and how does this relate to the nature of the triggering event itself? DCMU is known to tightly occupy the Q_B binding site located between helices IV and V of the D1 protein (1,3,11). We suggest therefore that during triggering the mode of action of bound DCMU is steric hindrance of a temperature-dependant conformational change induced by oxidative damage. DCMU can no longer protect after triggering for degradation has occured, and this most likely reflects inability of DCMU to bind to the conformationally-changed binding site. Such a change within the D1 protein is thus responsible for the conversion of photodamaged D1 protein into a proteolytic substrate.

Other studies support the present result that triggering involves a gross conformational change. It has been previously shown that manganese is released from PSII in conjunction with damage and triggering (13). Moreover, conformational changes have been measured by FTIR spectroscopy in isolated reaction centres after strong light treatment (14). Our present data suggest that damaged but conformationally-blocked centres can be formed at room temperature in the presence of DCMU. These will be an important tool for spectroscopic analysis of the triggered state in the future.

3. PROTEOLYTIC FRAGMENTS OF THE D1 PROTEIN.

A number of light-induced proteolytic fragments of the D1 protein have been observed *in vitro* (1,2,5,6,10,15,16). Fragments of the D1 protein have been detected in thylakoid membranes (11), PSII-enriched membranes (1), PSII core particles (5) and reaction centre particles (6). The approach of increasing the level of purification has revealed increasing fragment levels and diversity. Interestingly, although the two mechanisms of photoinactivation discussed in section 1 both apparently lead to damage around the P680 chlorophyll dimer, they give rise to different sets of initial degradation products (15). PSII core particles (8,15) and reaction centre complexes (De Las Rivas et al, elsewhere in these proceedings) when illuminated under conditions of acceptor-side photoinhibition produce initial fragments of 23, 16, and 10 kDa (16, Fig. 3). Also detected are less abundant fragments of 14 and 13 kDa (5). Of these, the 23 kDa has been shown to contain the *N*-terminus of the mature protein while the 16 kDa and 10 kDa fragments contain the *C*-terminus (16). These fragments are likely to be associated with a major cleavage event on the stromal side of the protein between loops IV and V (5,15,16). In contrast, PSII core and reaction centres particles which are non-functional in water oxidation give rise to light-induced fragments of 24, 17 and 9 kDa when provided with an electron acceptor (6,15, Table 1). The 24 kDa fragment was shown to be derived from the *C*-terminus of the protein and the 9 kDa to contain the *N*-terminus (17). These fragments are associated with a cleavage in the lumenal loops between helices I and II. Some of the fragments found in the 15-17 kDa range under both types of conditions may be associated with an additional cleavage site between helices III and IV.

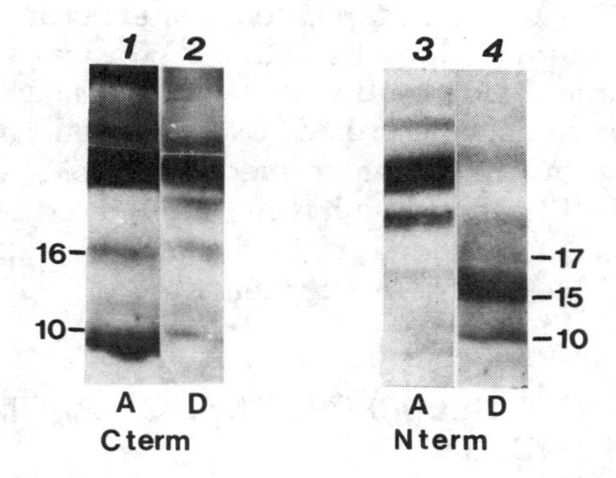

Figure 3. Light-induced D1 protein fragments. Lane 1 shows *C*-terminal fragments induced after an aerobic flush (20 min) of anaerobically-maintained (20 min) PSII core complexes under acceptor-side photoinhibition. Lane 2 shows *C*-terminal fragments detected in anaerobically-maintained PSII core complexes under donor-side photoinhibition (40 min). The right hand panel shows fragments induced by illumination under 'acceptor' conditions (lane 3, 45 min) followed by 'donor' conditions (lane 4, 45 min). Lanes 3 and 4 are labelled with *N*-terminal antisera.

We here present a summary of data identifying direct proteolytic fragments that are associated with D1 protein degradation in PSII core particles under different conditions. We thus present additional evidence related to the assignments presented in (15) and identify a number of less abundant fragments. The data of the present and cited studies from our two laboratories are shown in Table 1.

In addition to experiments involving direct aerobic photoinhibition under differing conditions, fragments clearly associated with acceptor-side induced photoinactivation were identified by flushing air into anaerobically illuminated PSII core complexes. This will identify fragments associated with oxygen quenching of chlorophyll triplets (8). By this method, we identified *C*-terminal fragments of 16 and 10 kDa fragments (Figure 3, lane 1) and also a *N*-terminal fragment of 23 kDa (not shown), as would be expected from previous studies (1,2,5,15,16). Comparable photoinhibition under donor-side mediated conditions in the absence of oxygen (18) identified *C*-terminal fragments of 24 and 16 kDa (Figure 3, lane 2) in agreement with (6,8,15,17) and a *N*-terminal 9 kDa fragment (7,15,17).

A further approach to fragment localisation was to illuminate particles under 'acceptor' photoinhibitory conditions for a short period and then transfer them to 'donor' photoinhibitory conditions by buffer manipulation. Such an experiment is shown in figure 3, lanes 3 and 4. It can be seen that the 23 kDa and 16 kDa acceptor fragments decay after transfer to donor conditions whilst the 9 kDa and a novel 15 kDa fragment are strongly induced. Complementary experiments with *C*-terminal specific antisera also show that the 15 kDa fragment strongly induced under these donor-side conditions is not the same as the 16 and 17 kDa fragments previously described. Experimentally, it is very difficult to resolve the various fragments formed in the 15-17 kDa range, hampering conclusive identification. We have also observed fragments of 14 and 13 kDa under 'acceptor 'conditions (5), the latter also appearing under 'donor' conditions (Table 1). These fragments are of low abundance and slow kinetics.

TABLE 1. LIGHT-INDUCED PROTEOLYTIC FRAGMENTS OF THE D1 PROTEIN - ORIGIN AND KINETICS.

Fragment kDa	*Origin within D1 protein*	*Acceptor -induced*		*Donor-induced*	
		Fast	*Slow*	*Fast*	*Slow*
24	*CT*		+	++++	
23	*NT*	+++++O_2			+
17	*CT*				++
16	*CT*	+++++O_2			
15	*N*			++++	
14	*?*		+++		
13	*CT*		+++		++
10	*CT*	+++O_2			+
9	*NT*			++	

The relative abundance, (+ signs), origin and kinetics of known light-induced D1 protein fragments is shown. NT : Contains N-terminal phosphothreonine (1516). CT : Contains C-terminus as determined by site-specific antibodies (1516,17). N : Detected with antisera against the N-terminal LysC fragment of wheat (15,17).O_2: Accumulates rapidly after oxygen flush of triggered particles (Figure 3).

Fragments that can be characterised as 'acceptor side-induced' are often found in prolonged 'donor-side' photoinhibition and vice versa. This is to be expected given the instability that must arise as a result of initial cleavage at any location and the necessity for the protein to be cleaved at both sides of the membrane. Interestingly, all of the light-induced fragments here described could conceivably arise as a result of cleavage events concentrated in three of the six non-bilayer domains within the D1 protein. These would be the regions between helices I-II, III-IV and IV-V The first two domains are extremely close to each other (1), and a single catalytic domain could easily affect both.
It is difficult at our current level of understanding to distinguish between cleavages of the native D1 protein and subsequent cleavages of the fragments themselves, particularly given the heterogeneity of fragment abundance, origin and kinetics discussed above. It is consequently difficult to unambiguously describe the sequence of cleavage events. However, it is clear that the primary cleavage events occur in specific domains of the protein as outlined above.

ENZYMOLOGY OF D1 PROTEIN DEGRADATION.
Since the reactions that lead to the production of the fragments discussed above take place in highly purified PSII particles *in vitro*, it is clear that the proteolytic activity involved in primary degradation is integral to or extremely tightly associated with the PSII complex itself. The reaction has been enzymatically characterised both directly (19,20) and in the separated inactivation-degradation system (16). The reaction has a pH optimum of 7.5-8.0 (16,20). The protease action has been shown to be stimulated by, but to be not dependant upon, Mg^{2+} ions (16). The reaction does not require ATP and phosphorylated D1 protein is a poor substrate for the degradation reaction *in vitro* (16,21).
The degradation reaction can be inhibited by externally added protease inhibitors (19,21). Particularly effective are those acting against serine-type enzymes (19,21). Inhibition of the reaction by the inhibitor diisopropylfluorophosphate (18) was used by in conjunction with affinity labelling to identify the chlorophyll *a*-binding protein CP43 as a candidate proteolytic subunit (16). However, the apparent absence of CP43 from the isolated reaction centre complex would tend to argue against this, and autoproteolysis may occur in this particle (6). The possibility of multiple protease activities within the PSII complex and the nature of their action on damaged D1 proteins remain a crucial topic for future molecular studies on the mechanism of photoinhibition.

ACKNOWLEDGEMENTS

This work was supported by the Swedish Natural Science Research Council, the Göran Gustaffson Foundation of Sweden, the UK Agricultural and Food Research Council and the Nordic Ministers of Energy. AHS and JDLR are post-doctoral fellows supported by the Wenner-Grenska Foundation and the Federation of European Biochemical Societies, respectively.

REFERENCES

1 Andersson, B. and Styring, S. (1991) Current Topics in Bioenergetics, (Lee, C.P., ed.), Vol. 16, pp. 1-81, Academic Press, San Diego.
2 Barber, J. and Andersson, B. (1992) Trends Biochem. Sci, 17, 61-66.
3 Prasil, O., Adir, N. and Ohad, I. (1992) in Current Topics in Photosynthesis, (Barber, J., ed.), Vol. 11, pp. 220-250, Elsevier, Amsterdam.
4 Greenberg, B. M., Gaba, V., Mattoo, A. K., and Edelman, M. (1987) EMBO J. 6, 2865-2869.
5 Virgin, I., Ghanotakis, D. F. and Andersson, B. (1990) FEBS Lett. 269, 45-48.
6 Shipton, C. A. and Barber, J. (1991) Proc. Natl. Acad. Sci., U.S.A. 88, 6691-6695.
7 Eckert, H.-J., Geiken, B., Bernading, J., Napiwotzki, A., Eichler, H.-J., and Renger, G. (1991) Photosynth. Res. 27, 97-108.
8 Vass, I., Styring, S., Hundal, T., Koivuniemi, A., Aro, E.-M. and Andersson, B. (1992) Proc. Natl. Acad. Sci. USA 89, 1408-1412.
9 Blubaugh, D. J. and Cheniae, G. M. (1990) Biochemistry 29, 5109-5118.
10 Aro, E.-M., Hundal, T., Carlberg, I. and Andersson, B. (1990) Biochim. Biophys. Acta 1019, 269-275.
11 Kyle, D.J., Ohad, I., and Arntzen, C.J. (1984) Proc. Natl. Acad. Sci., U.S.A. 81, 4070-4074.
12 Trebst, A. and Depka, B. (1990) Z. Naturforsch. 45c, 765-771.
13 van Wijk, K., Andersson, B. and Styring, S. (1992) Biochim. Biophys. Acta 1100, 207-215
14 He, W. Z., Newell, W. R., Harris, P. I., Chapman, D., and Barber, J. (1991) Biochemistry 30, 4552-4559.
15 de las Rivas, J., Andersson, B. and Barber, J. (1992) FEBS Lett. 391. 246-252.
16 Salter, A. H., Virgin I., Hagman, Å., and Andersson, B. (1992) Biochemistry 31, 3990-3998
17 Barbato, R., Shipton, C. A., Giacometti, M., and Barber, J. (1991) FEBS Lett. 290, 162-166.
18 Jegerschöld, C. and Styring, S. (1991)FEBS Lett., 280, 87-90
19 Virgin, I., Salter, A. H., Ghanotakis, D. F. and Andersson, B. (1991) FEBS Lett. 287, 125-128.
20 Shipton, C. A., and Barber, J. (1992) Biochim. Biophys. Acta, 1099, 85-90.
21 Kettunen, R., Tyystjärvi, E., and Aro, E.-M. (1991) FEBS Lett. 290, 153-156.

THE LIGHT-STRESS SYNDROME: PROTEIN TURNOVER AND POSSIBLE PROTECTIVE MECHANISMS

[1]I.Adamska, A.Gal, Y. Soroka, S.Tal, H.Zer,[2]N.Ohad,[2]J.Hirschberg, [1]K.Kloppstech and I.Ohad, Departments of Biological Chemistry and [2]Genetics, The Hebrew University, Jerusalem Israel and [1]Botanical Institute, University of Hannover, Germany

1. RESULTS AND DISCUSSION

Excess light-excitation of oxygen evolving photosynthetic membranes which can not be utilized for photochemical energy conversion has detrimental effects on the activity of photosystem II (PSII) and accelerates specific degradation of photosystem II-reaction center (RCII) proteins. Two major mechanisms for the PSII photoinactivation, damage and degradation of RCII-D1 protein have been proposed involving either inactivation of the acceptor or of the donor side of PSII (1,2). Inactivation of the acceptor side seems to be caused by a conformational change of the QB site (1,3) resulting in lowering QA^- to QB electron flow followed by double reduction of the QA quinone, its protonation and release from the QA site (4) leading to formation of triplet P_{680} which may react with O_2 and form harmful active oxygen species (1-4). Inactivation of the PSII donor side leads to increase in the life time of P_{680}^+ and Y_z^+ which could interact directly with the RCII proteins, specifically D1, or with O_2 generating O_2radicals which may interact with pigments or proteins of RCII (1). Evidence in support of two alternative inactivation mechanisms has been obtained mostly using <u>in vitro</u> experimental systems. Under certain conditions such as anaerobiosis (4), inactivation of the water splitting complex by low thylakoid lumenal pH, removal of Mn or mutations inducing defects in the acceptor or donor side of PSII (1) either one of these mechanisms may become preferentially operative. However it is not yet well understood what may initiate the photo-inactivation process(s) <u>in vivo</u> in a normal active unperturbed photosynthetic membrane. Degradation of D1 protein occurs at light intensities below those causing measurable los of activity as well as in light which does not support photosynthetic electron flow such as far-red UVA,or UVB light (5). Under such light conditions <u>in vivo</u> the acceptor side precedes donor side inactivation (1,3). Following loss of electron flow via PSII, activation of cyclic electron flow and generation of a significant δpH across the thylakoid membrane (6) may induce loss of Ca^{2+} from the water splitting complex (7) and thus result in donor side inactivation with the incumbent above mentioned consequences. This sequence of events may explain

N. Murata (ed.), Research in Photosynthesis, Vol. IV, 403–410.

the data obtained using in vivo experimental systems (1). It was proposed before that D1 is targeted for degradation by a covalent modification, possibly an internal crosslink between transmembrane loops II and III due to formation of bityrosine at positions Y161-Y112 (1,3). The site Y112 directed mutation D1-Y112L causes loss of PSII activity and 32kDa D1 protein band (Fig.1) while no such effects are obtained in the mutant Y112F (data not shown). Degradation of D1 at low light intensities may be explained if one

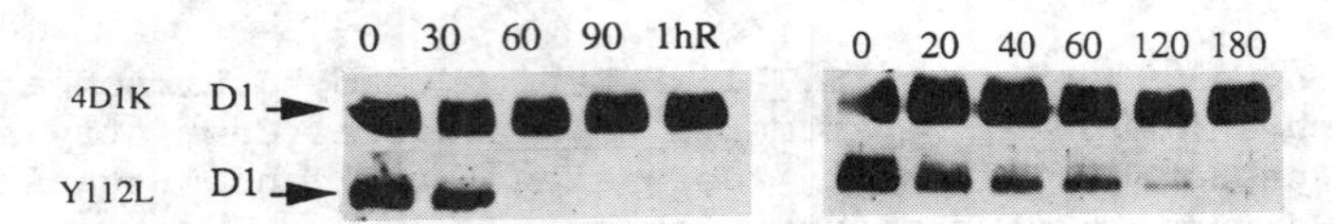

Figure 1. Loss of 32-KDa D1 in Synechocystis PCC6803 site directed mutant D1-Y112L exposed to 1,500 (left) or 1,000 $\mu E/m^2s$ white light (right) as compared to wt cells (4D1k).

considers that the membrane microenvironment conditions may accelerate photoinactivation even at low photon flux densities. However repair of the inactivated centers may be sufficiently high to replace the damaged D1, the the total loss of PSII activity remaining thus undetected. Heterogeneity of the thylakoids response to light stress within the same cell or chloroplast was recently demonstrated in Chlamydomonas cells (6). The UV-effect may be due to direct excitation of the acceptor QA /QB quinones, or the Y_z tyrosine on the donor site of RCII.
Factors enhancing the repair of PSII or protecting against damage are crucial in maintaining the overall photosynthetic capacity of the chloroplast. Such processes are the down regulation of PSII excitation (state transition), and of PSII electron flow activity by energy quenching or rise in δpH (7,8) as well as modulation of the redox state of the quinone pool and its turnover at the QB site (9). The state transition process is mediated by activation of the redox controlled LHCII kinase. The sensor of PQ/PQH_2 ratio appears to be the cytochrome b6/f complex which interacts with the LHCII kinase and modifies its specificity to LHCII (10). The effect of quinone analogs competing for the quinone binding site involved in the activation of LHCII kinase support the concept that modulation of the cyt.b6/f-kinase interaction regulate kinase activity. The most potent analogs are benzo-quinones halogenated at position 2,3 and possessing a small side chain at position 5. Increasing the bulk or hydrophobicity of the side chain or the number of benzene rings of the analog such as in naphthoquinone lowers the analog effectivity. The quinone analogs deactivate LHCII-kinase preactivated by electron-flow via PSII **(Table I)**. The kinetics of LHCII-kinase deactivation in the dark in absence of inhibitors is significantly slower than that of the reoxidation of the plastoquinone pool (**Fig.2**). Thus the kinase-cyt.b6/f interaction controls both the kinase activation and deactivation, their dissociation being the rate-limiting step in the deactivation process. Control of LHCII-kinase activity by

structural interactions is demonstrated also by studies of the kinase activation during chloroplast membrane development. During greening of etiolated spinach or dark grown Chlamydomonas y-1 cells (data not shown) the appearance of the 64 kDa kinase, the cytochrome b6/f complex the LHCII substrate (**Fig.3**) and activation of electron flow to NADP (data not shown) precedes the activation of LHCII kinase. Activation of the latent redox dependent LHCII-kinase coincides in time with the segregation of the thylakoid components into defined grana and stroma domains. In mature pea chloroplasts the kinase is specifically located in microdomains confined to grana edges (10). The above results support the concept that organization of the membrane complexes in microdomains may regulate the activation/deactivation process and

TABLE I Deactivation of LHCII-kinase in dark incubated Pea thylakoids by various quinone analogs

	LHCII KINASE (dark)	LHCII KINASE (light)	H_2O-DCIP (light)
	(% inhibition)		
1,4-benzoquinone	75	7	0
2,3-dichloro-5-6-butyl	95	73	70
2,3-dibromo-5-t-butyl	96	85	77
1,4-naphtoquinone	30	9	26
2,3-dimethyl	2	18	9
2,3-dichloro	88	59	33
2,3-diiodo	84	80	57

Pea thylakoids preactivated by 30 s illumination (20 µg Chl,ml^{-1}) were incubated in the absence or presence of 0.5µM quinone analogs. Same experimental conditions as in Fig.2.

the resulting modulation of energy transfer from the antennae complex to RCII. The interaction LHCII-kinase/cytochrome b6./f complex and state transition may be involved also in the changes in the cytochrome b6/f distribution between the grana and stroma domains and the activation of PSI cyclic electron flow (11). This may contribute to the process of downregulation of energy transfer to PSII as well as the down regulation of its electron transfer capacity by increasing the thylakoid δpH (6).

The redox state of the plastoquinone pool appears to play an important role not only in the downregulation of the energy transfer to PSII but also in the modulation of the light induced degradation of its reaction center, the D1 protein (1,9). This effect seems to be achieved not by the ratio PQ/PQH_2 but rather by the turnover of the quinone at the QB site. In Chlamydomonas mutants impaired in their ability to oxidize PQH_2 the light-dependent degradation of D1 is significantly slowed down (**Fig.4**). This phenomenon is explained as being due to conformational changes in the QB binding niche as a result of its occupancy by PQH_2 accumulating in such cells or unoccupancy by PQ (1,9).

In this case PSII is photoinactivated by strong light whyle D1 is not rapidly degraded. Recent results indicate that the D1 protein may be damaged in the mutants exposed to high light conditions while degradation is retarded (Prasil et al., this Proceedings).

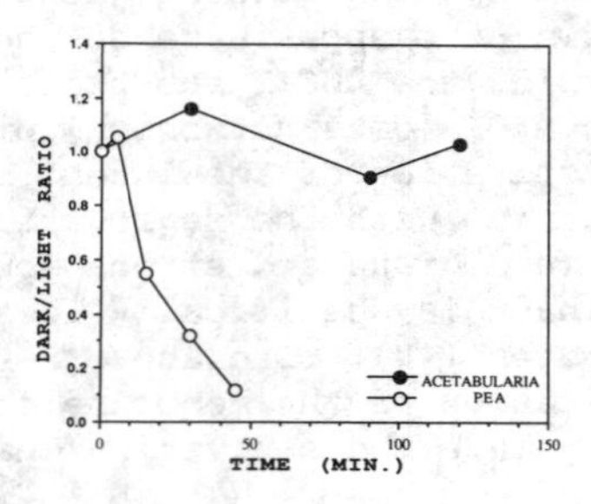

Figure 2. Deactivation of pea thylakoid LHCII kinase in the dark.

Thylakoids (20 µg Chl, ml^{-1}) were activated in the light for 30 s to activate the kinase and further stored in the dark in ice. LHCII was phosphorylated (10) in the dark or light for 10 min at 25 °C. A higher stability is exhibited under similar conditions by the Acetabularia LHCII kinase. The ratios of the dark to light activity is plotted. Light activity (100%) was 2,1 and 0,75 nmols ^{32}P,mg⁻27kDa LHCII protein band of pea and Acetabularia membranes.

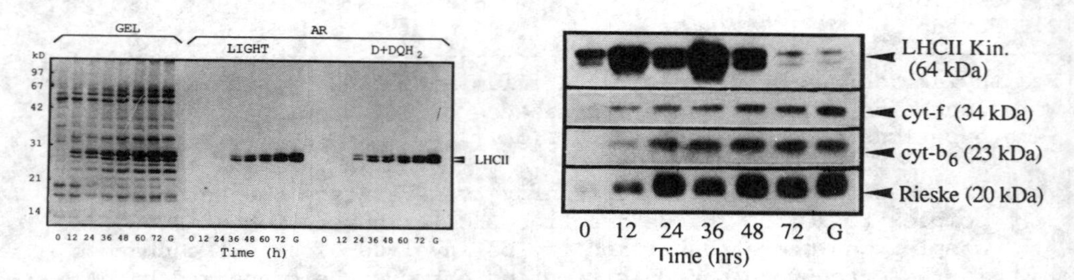

Figure 3. Development of redox-controlled LHCII-phosphorylation, cyt.b6/f and LHCII-kinase during greening of spinach seedlings. Left panel, thylakoids polypeptide content resolved by LDS-PAGE (GEL), phosphorylation pattern in the light or in the dark with addition of duroquinol (DQH_2) followed by autoradiography (AR); G, samples from control light grown spinach leaves; LHCII (arrows) indicate the 27 kDa and 25 kDa polypeptide components of the LHCII complex. Right panel, western blot.

One should consider that at ambient light intensities below those resulting in extensive photoinactivation a lowering the PQ/PQH_2 turnover at the QB site may have a similar effect and retard the degradation of D1. This down regulation of PQ turnover at the QB site may occur when the accessibility of CO_2 is limiting, and/or the rate of $NADPH_2$ oxidation is lowered.

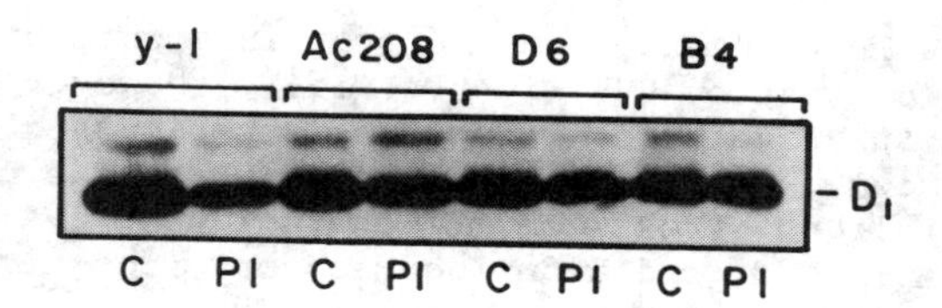

Figure 4. Light induced degradation of D1 in Chlamydomonas reinhardtii. Cells were exposed to photoinhibitory light and the loss of the D1 protein assayed by western blotting as described in (9). AC208, D6 and B4, cells impaired in plastocyanin, cytochrome b6/f and photosystem-I activity respectively.

Under such conditions PSI cyclic electron flow may be activated and the energy quenching due to rise in δpH may be established. Thus two protective mechanisms may be activated simultaneously by changes in the environmental conditions, down regulation of PSII electron flow and protection against the degradation of its reaction center protein D1.

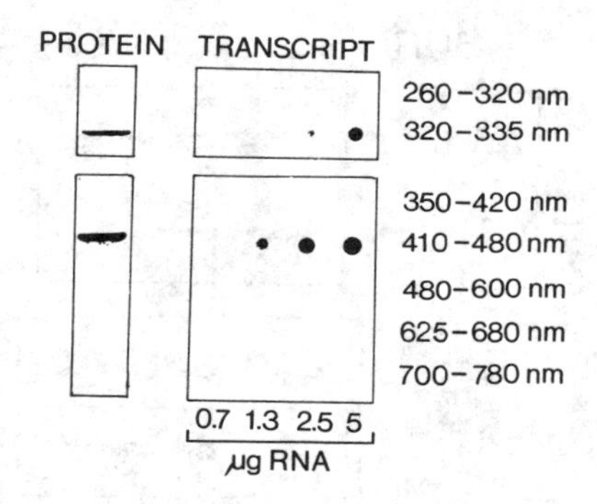

Figure 5. Induction of ELIP by light of different wavelenghts in pea. Leaves were exposed for 3 hours to UVB, UVA, ($44 \mu E/m^2 s$) or for two hours to visible light of various wavelenghts at 700 i$\mu E/m^2 s$. Poly(A+)-RNA was dot-blot hybridized with labeled ELIP insert of cDNA clone (right panel). The membrane polypeptide pattern was resolved by SDS-PAGE followed by western blotting with anti-ELIP antiserum (right panel).

Recently we have demonstrated that the early light inducible p rotein (ELIP) appearing during the greening process of etiolated plants is induced in mature plants as well in response to light stress (12). ELIPs are nuclear-encoded chloroplast proteins related to the cab gene family. ELIP transcription occurs in etiolated pea during the first 2-4 hours of the greening process. The protein can be detected in isolated etioplast membranes of pea within 4-6 hours of the transcription initiation (13). ELIP transcription in light grown pea exposed to light stress is specifically induced by blue (410-480 nm) but not by red or far-red light. ELIP transcription and protein accumulation are induced also by UVA but not by UVB light. (**Fig.5**). However UVB light does not prevent ELIP synthesis induced by superimposed white light (data not shown). ELIP mRNA is short lived. The protein is stable under light stress conditions including UVA and UVB light but it is rapidly degraded during recovery from light stress conditions (data not shown).

The nuclear-encoded ELIPs are translated on cytosolic ribosomes as precursor proteins and imported, processed and inserted into the thylakoid membranes (13). ELIPs are hydrophobic proteins possessing three transmembrane helices. Helices I and III of ELIP are homologous with those of the cab genes products (14) suggesting that ELIPs may function in pigment (chlorophyll or carotenoids) binding and/or translocation.

Accumulation of ELIP transcript is induced in plants exposed to light intensities above 500 µE/m²s and is maximal at about 1500 µE/m²s. The ELIP mRNA level increases in correlation with the degree of photoinhibition. The increase in ELIP level in the thylakoid membranes parallels the decrease in the amount of D1 protein of the photosystem II reaction center (**Fig.6**).

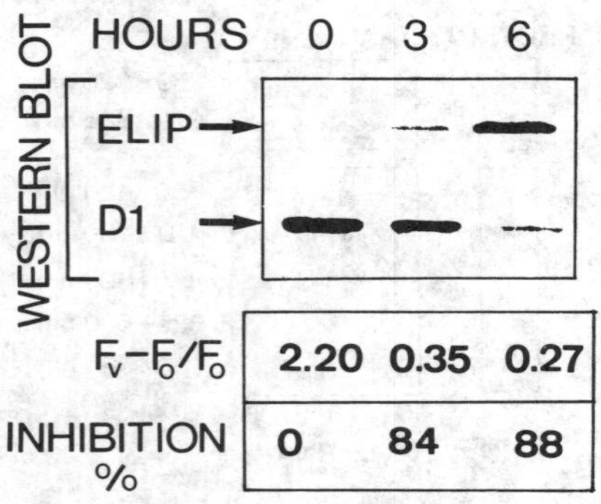

Figure 6. Accumulation of ELIP in thylakoids during light stress. Pea leaves were exposed to 2,500µE/m²s white light for up to 3 hours. Thylakoid were isolated and polypeptides were resolved by SDA-PAGE followed by western blotting using ELIP specific antibodies (upper panel). Loss of photosynthetic activity was measured by fluorescence kinetics (lower panel).

One postulated mechanism of protection against the photo-inactivation of PSII is provided by light induced changes in the carotenoid composition and amount in the photosynthetic membrane. The activation of the xanthophyll cycle resulting in the inter-conversion of ß-carotene to violaxanthin and zeaxanthin may alleviate the light stress effect by a twofold action: increase in the nonradiative energy dissipation by the antennae system of PSII and scavenging of free radicals or active oxygen species resulting from their interaction with oxygen. While the first mechanism is controversial the second seems to be generally accepted (reviewed in 1,15). The possibility that ELIP induction may be related to the light induced changes in the pigment content and composition was thus considered. Inhibition of phytoene desaturase and/or ß-carotene desaturase during light stress has no effect on the level of ELIP mRNA but drastically increase ELIP accumulation in mature but not in the etiolated plants (**Fig.7**). The results presented here and elsewhere (12) do not permit yet to establish a well defined function for ELIP. Induction of an ELIP like transcript was reported in the green alga Dunaliella salina exposed to light stress conditions, which is accompanied by a large increase in the

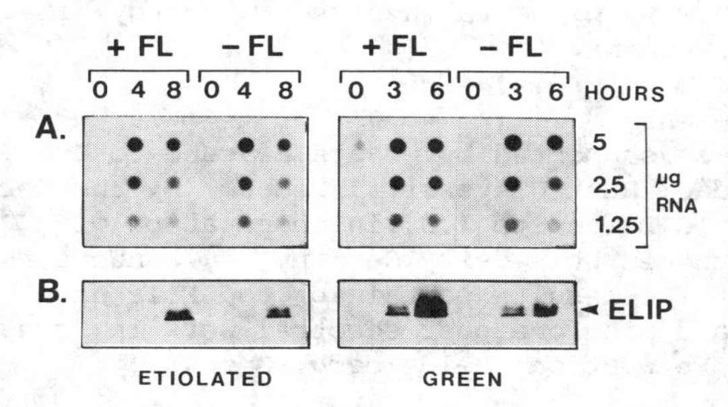

Figure 7. Accumulation of ELIP in presence of a carotenoids synthesis inhbitor in plants with normal or partially arested plastid developement. Six-day old pea plants grown in the dark (etiolated) or under low light/dark regime (green) with or without added fluridone (+/-Fl) were exposed to 40µE/m²s or 1,500µEm²s white light respectively for times as indicated; A), dot blot hybridization of isolated poly(A+)-RNA with nik-translated insert of ELIP clone; B), western blot of SDAS-PAGE-resolved membrane proteins.

chloroplast ß-carotene content (16). However it is possible that light stress conditions induce parallel cellular responses which may coincide in time and be elicited by the same stress conditions but have independent functions. Light stress results also in degradation of RCII proteins and pigment release. Free chlorophyll may be harmful to its environment when sensitized by light absorption. Thus it is possible that ELIP may function as a chlorophyll scavenger. This possibility should be considered in view of the report indicating that ELIP transported in vitro in chloroplasts exposed to high light can be cross-linked with the D1 protein (17) whose degradation is enhanced by such conditions (1). We thus propose that ELIP is related to the light stress syndrome possibly acting in a yet not defined protective mechanism of PSII.

2. Conclusions

Plants are exposed daily to different stresses among which light-stress may be one of the major factors. In natural conditions light stress does not necessarily imply extreme high light intensities. The degree of damage at any light intensity may be modulated by microenvironmental factors within the cell and/or the chloroplasts which may enhance or reduce the effect by activation of defense mechanisms. These include among others: Modulation of energy transfer to PSII regulated by the activation/deactivation of the LHCII-kinase; Modulation of the degradation of the D1 protein of RCII by regulation of the PQ/PQH_2 ratio and the plastoquinon turnover at the QB site; Modulation of the ratio linear/PSI cyclic electron flow thereby downregulating PSII activity and affecting excess energy dissipation; Synthesis transport and integration of nuclear-encoded proteins into the chloroplast membranes which may have protective roles possibly by interaction with pigments involved in energy dissipation and free radical scavenging.

3. Acknowledgements

This work was supported by grants awarded to I.O., in cooperation with D. Godde, Ruhr University, Bochum, by the German-Israel Foundation (GIF) and to I.O.,in cooperation with R.Herrmann and W. Rudiger, Munchen University,Germany, by Sonderforschungsbereiche (SFB 184). The results pertaining tho ELIP have been obtained by Dr. Adamska during one post docotral work in Jerusalem supported by MINERVA Foundation, Heidelberg, Germany.

References

1. Prasil,O.,Adir,N., & Ohad,I. (1992), in The Photosystems: Structure, Function and Molecular Biology (J.Barber ed.),(1992), pp295-348, Elsevier, Sci.Publishers
2. De Las Rivas, J.,Andersson,B.,& Barber,J.(1992), FEBS Lett. 301,246-252
3. Ohad,I., Adir,N., Koike,H.,Kyle, D.J., & Inoue,Y. (1990),J. Biol. Chem. 265, 1972-1979
4. Vass,I.,Styring,S., Hundal,T., Koivuniemi,A., Aro,E-M, & Andersson,B. (1992), Proc.Natl.Acad.Sci. USA, 89,1408-1412
5. Greenberg,B.M., Gaba,V., Canaani,O., Malkin,S., Mattoo,A.K., & Edelman,M. (1989), Proc.Natl.Acad.Sci USA 86, 6617-6620
6. Topf,J.Gong,H., Timberg,R., Mets,L.,& Ohad,I. (1992), Photosynth.Res. 32,59-69
7. Krieger,A., & Weiss, E. (1992), Photosynthetica, (in press).
8. Rees, D., & Horton P. (1990), Biochim. Biophys. Acta. 1016,219-227
9. Gong,H.& Ohad,I. (1991), J.Biol.Chem. 266,21293-21299
10. Gal,A., Hauska,G.,Herrmann,R., & Ohad,I. (1990), J.Biol.Chem. 265,19742-19749
11. Vallon, O., Bulte, L., Dainesse, P., Olive, J., Bassi, R., & Wollmann, F.-A. (1991), Proc. Natl.Acad. Sci. USA 88, 8262-8266.
12. Adamska,I., Ohad,I.& Kloppstech,K. (1992), Proc.Natl.Acad.Sci. USA 89,2610-2613
13. Meyer, G. & Kloppstech, K. (1984), Eur. J. Biochem., 138,201-207.
14. Grimm, B., Kruse, E. & Kloppstech, K. (1989), Plant Mol.Biol.,13, 583-593.
15. Demmig-Adams,B, & Adams, W.W. (1992), Ann.Rev.Plant Physiol. 43, 599-626
16. Lers,A., Levy,H. Zamir,A. (1991), J.Biol. Chem. 266, 13698-13705
17. Adamska,I.,Kloppstech,K.(1991), Plant Mol.biol. 16, 209-223

SEQUENTIAL REDUCTION AND PROTONATION OF THE FIRST QUINONE ACCEPTOR PROMOTES CHLOROPHYLL TRIPLET FORMATION IN PHOTOSYSTEM II DURING PHOTOINHIBITION

Imre Vass[1,2] and Stenbjörn Styring[1]

[1]Department of Biochemistry, Arrhenius Laboratories for Natural Sciences, University of Stockholm, S-106 91 Stockholm, Sweden, and [2] Institute of Plant Physiology, Biological Research Center of the Hungarian Academy of Sciences, H-6724 Szeged, P.O.Box 521, Hungary

1. INTRODUCTION

The reaction center in photosystem II (PSII) is composed of the D1 and D2 proteins that form a heterodimer (1) in close structural and functional homology to the reaction center complex of purple bacteria (for recent reviews see Refs. 2,3). The D1/D2 heterodimer binds the redox cofactors of light-induced electron transport: the primary electron donor chlorophyll(s), P_{680}; the pheophytin electron acceptor, Phe; the first, Q_A, and second, Q_B, quinone electron acceptors; and the redox active tyrosine residues, Tyr_Z on the D1 protein and Tyr_D on the D2 protein. The catalytic manganese cluster of the water-oxidation reaction is probably also bound to the D1/D2 heterodimer.

Exposure to high light intensities inhibits the photosynthetic electron transport. This phenomenon, denoted photoinhibition, is targeted to the reaction center of PSII and results in the subsequent degradation of the D1 protein (reviewed in Refs. 3,4). Strong illumination can impair electron transport both at donor and acceptor sides of PSII. Donor side photoinhibition most likely affects the functioning of Tyr-Z or P_{680} (5-7). Considering the acceptor side photoinhibition, the primary lesion in the electron transport was earlier thought to occur at Q_B (8-10) or at the primary charge separation step (11). However, recent spectroscopic studies have shown that the function of Q_A is impaired due to double reduction during the early phase of photoinhibition (12-14). Doubly reduced Q_A is an abnormal state that promotes the formation of $^3P_{680}$ with a high yield during illumination (14-16). $^3P_{680}$ in turn, interacts with molecular oxygen leading to the production of singlet oxygen. Singlet oxygen is highly reactive (17) and its damaging effects are very likely to trigger the degradation of the D1 protein (14).

High yield of $^3P_{680}$ formation in PSII can be facilitated by chemical double reduction (and presumed protonation) of Q_A (15) or by its absence from the binding site (18). However, we also observed high yield of $^3P_{680}$ formation in the earlier phases of anaerobic photoinhibition in centers which we proposed to contain singly reduced Q_A (14).

Here we have characterized in further detail the triplet producing PSII centers which are formed during strong anaerobic illumination. The results indicate that $^3P_{680}$ formation may indeed occur in the presence of singly reduced Q_A whose negative charge is neutralized by a protonation event.

2. MATERIALS AND METHODS

N. Murata (ed.), Research in Photosynthesis, Vol. IV, 411–418.

PSII enriched membranes from spinach thylakoids were prepared according to Ref. 22, and stored at -80 °C in 0.4 M sucrose, 15 mM NaCl, 5 mM $MgCl_2$, 20 mM Mes pH 6.3 at 3-4 mg Chl/ml.

For anaerobic photoinhibition, PSII membranes at a concentration of 1.5-2.5 mg Chl ml^{-1} were gently flushed in EPR tubes for 5 minutes with argon. The tubes were sealed and subsequently illuminated at room temperature with white light through a 5cm thick copper sulfate heat absorbing solution at 3000 µE $m^{-2}s^{-1}$ intensity, for different periods of time. After illumination, the samples were quickly frozen (in about 1-2 seconds if not otherwise indicated) and kept in liquid nitrogen until the EPR measurements.

To study the pH dependent formation of $^3P_{680}$ promoting centers, PSII membranes were washed with a medium of 0.4 M sucrose, 15 mM NaCl, 5 mM $MgCl_2$, 2 mM Mes pH 6.3, then suspended at different pHs in the above medium but with 40 mM L-glutamic acid (pH 4.5-5.0), 40 mM Mes (pH 5.0-7.0), 40 mM Hepes (pH 7.0-8.0) or 40 mM glycyl-glycine (pH 8.0-8.5) as buffering agents.

In experiments where the $Q_A^-Fe^{2+}$ signal was measured, the samples were incubated with 25mM formate for 10 min prior to the photoinhibitory illumination treatment to enhance the size of the signal. Illumination at 200 K (in solid CO_2/ethanol bath) was performed in an unsilvered dewar, using heat-filtered white light from a 1000 W projector. Chemical double reduction of Q_A was achieved by incubating PSII membranes with 40 mM dithionite and 30 µM benzyl viologen in the dark at room temperature for five hours as described by van Mieghem et al. (15).

X-band low-temperature EPR spectra were recorded at 9.234 GHz with a Bruker ESP 300 spectrometer equipped with an Oxford Instruments helium cryostat and temperature controller. Data acquisition and data handling were performed with the ESP 300 program of the EPR spectrometer. For light-induced generation at 4K of the spin polarized $^3P_{680}$ EPR signal, the samples were illuminated in the EPR cavity with a 1000 W tungsten projector through a 5 cm thick copper sulfate heat absorbing solution. The triplet spectra were obtained as the light minus dark difference spectra.

3. RESULTS

3.1. *Build-up of $^3P_{680}$ forming centers during anaerobic illumination.*

The functioning of Q_A can be directly monitored by EPR spectroscopy since the magnetic interaction between the singly reduced quinone, Q_A^- and the nearby acceptor side iron, Fe^{2+} gives rise to a well characterized EPR signal (for a recent review see Ref. 23). In contrast, the oxidized or double reduced states of Q_A are diamagnetic and thus, EPR silent. In the non-photoinhibited PSII membranes the $Q_A^-Fe^{2+}$ EPR signal is absent in the dark (Fig. 1A solid curve a), however, it can be induced by illumination at 200 K which traps Q_A in the singly reduced state (Fig. 1A dotted curve a). In the non-photoinhibited control sample Q_A^- is quickly reoxidized at room temperature (in a few seconds) probably by recombination with donor-side components.

Five minutes photoinhibitory illumination of the PSII membranes under anaerobic conditions at room temperature induced a large, almost quantitative, Q_A^- Fe^{2+} EPR signal (Fig. 1A, curve b). This signal was very stable in the dark at room

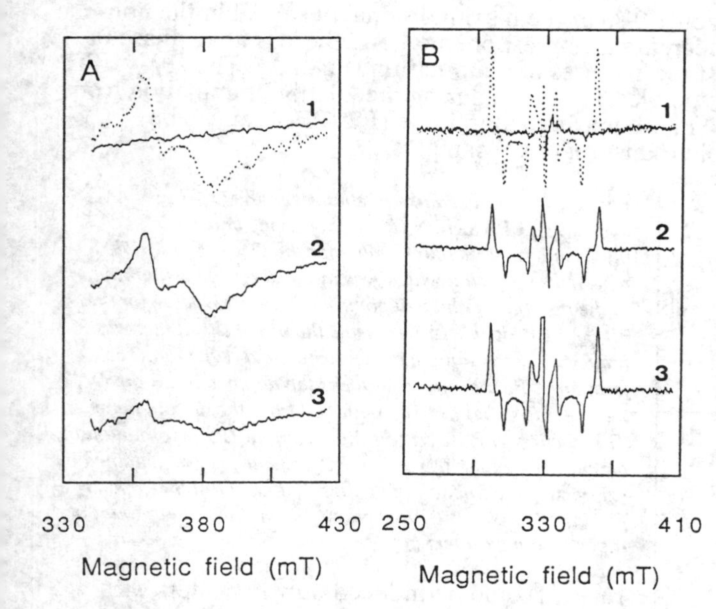

Figure 1. Effect of anaerobic photoinhibition on the $Q_A^-Fe^{2+}$ and $^3P_{680}$ EPR signals. A; The $Q_A^-Fe^{2+}$ signal was measured either in the dark (solid spectra) or after 20 min illumination at 200 K (dotted spectrum) on samples which had been photo-inhibited for 0 min (1), 5 min (2) and 20 min (3). (Temperature, 4K; microwave power, 32 mW; modulation amplitude, 3.2mT). B: The $^3P_{680}$ EPR signal after 0 min (1), 5 min (2) and 20 min (3) photoinhibition (solid spectra) or after 5 h additional dark incubation with 50 mM sodium dithionite/30 μM benzyl viologen to quantitatively double reduce Q_A (dotted spectrum). (Temperature, 4K; microwave power, 63 μW; modulation amplitude, 2.2 mT).

temperature and decayed with a half-time of several minutes (see below). Further illumination gradually decreased the $Q_A^-Fe^{2+}$ signal, and after 20 min illumination about 30 % of the maximal signal remained (Fig. 1A, curve c).

The light-induced decrease of the $Q_A^-Fe^{2+}$ EPR signal indicates that Q_A is either double reduced or lost (disconnected) from its binding site. Both of these conditions are known to facilitate the light-induced formation of $^3P_{680}$ (15,18) which gives rise to a spin-polarized chlorophyll triplet EPR signal at 4K. The fraction of $^3P_{680}$ forming PSII centers gradually increased during the course of the photoinhibitory illumination (Fig. 1B). This supports earlier suggestions that photoinhibition may lead to double reduction, and subsequently to disconnection of Q_A from its site (13-15).

However, the results presented in Fig. 1B indicate that $^3P_{680}$ formation not only occurs in PSII reaction centers with doubly reduced Q_A but to a large extent also in reaction centers containing Q_A^-. The amplitude of the $Q_A^-Fe^{2+}$ signal recorded in a sample after 5 min of anaerobic illumination suggests that it represents about 75 % of the PSII centers (Fig. 1A spectrum b). In the same sample the light-induced $^3P_{680}$ signal (Fig. 1B spectrum b) was about 60 % of the maximal signal size observed after chemical double reduction of Q_A (Fig. 1B spectrum a, dotted). Thus, it is reasonable to suggest, in accordance with our earlier hypothesis (14), that short anaerobic photoinhibition induces a substantial fraction of PSII centers in which a singly reduced Q_A species promotes the formation of $^3P_{680}$.

The formation of $^3P_{680}$ in the presence of what seems to be singly reduced Q_A is surprising and seemingly contradictory to the idea of electrostatic control of primary charge separation reaction (15,16,19-21). Therefore the time course for the induction of the $^3P_{680}$ and the $Q_A^-Fe^{2+}$ EPR signals was carefully measured during strong anaerobic illumination (Fig. 2A and B) to test whether these signals may indeed arise from the same PSII center. The $Q_A^-Fe^{2+}$ EPR signal decreased after 20 minutes photoinhibition to about 30 % of the maximal signal observed in the non-photoinhibited control. The decrease is non-exponential and there is a lag phase in the Q_A^--decline during the first few minutes of illumination (Fig. 2A). The $^3P_{680}$ EPR signal, measured in the same samples, increased during the 20 min illumination from less than 1-2 % to about 80 % of the maximal amplitude (Fig. 2B) that can be observed after chemical double reduction of the samples.

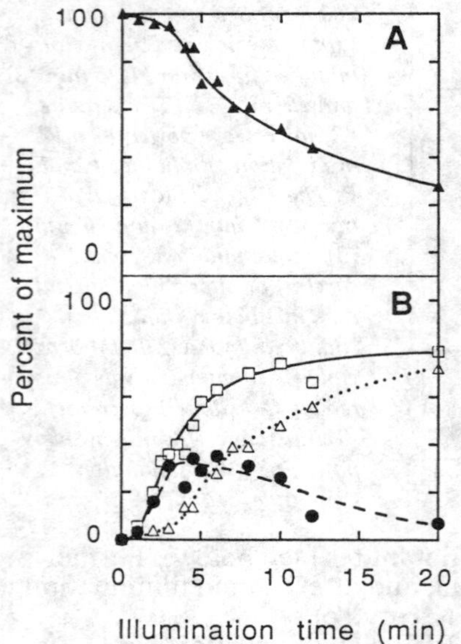

Figure 2. The time course of changes in the $Q_A^-Fe^{2+}$ (A) and $^3P_{680}$ EPR signals (B) during strong anaerobic illumination. The 100 % value for the $Q_A^-Fe^{2+}$ signal represents the signal which was induced by 200 K illumination in the non-photoinhibited control. The 100 % value for the $^3P_{680}$ EPR signal (□) represents the triplet signal that was induced in each sample by dark chemical reduction. The fraction of PSII centers that lacks the ability to form the $Q_A^-Fe^{2+}$ EPR signal (△) was obtained from the data in panel A. The fraction of PSII centers that promote $^3P_{680}$ formation in the presence of the $Q_A^-Fe^{2+}$ EPR signal (●) was obtained by subtracting the fraction of centers that have lost the capacity to form the $Q_A^-Fe^{2+}$ EPR signal (△) from the total amount of triplet forming centers (□).

If $^3P_{680}$ could be induced only in centers with double reduced or lost Q_A, the decrease of the $Q_A^-Fe^{2+}$ signal and the increase in the formation of $^3P_{680}$ should proceed in parallel during the course of the anaerobic photoinhibition.
However, this is not the case! Instead, the fraction of triplet forming centers is induced faster than the PSII centers with singly reduced Q_A are lost (Fig. 2B). The difference between the two curves (Fig. 2B, dashed curve) represents centers in which $^3P_{680}$ is formed in the presence of singly reduced Q_A. This population comprises the totally dominating fraction of $^3P_{680}$ forming centers in the very early phase of photoinhibition, and reaches a maximum at almost 35 % of the centers after approximately 4-5 min illumination (Fig. 2B, dashed curve). During the continued illumination the Q_A^- containing, $^3P_{680}$ promoting centers are converted to other populations of PSII centers which also promote $^3P_{680}$ formation but now in the absence of Q_A^-.

3.2. *pH dependent build-up of $^3P_{680}$ promoting PSII centers during photoinhibition*

The normally low yield of $^3P_{680}$ formation in the presence of singly reduced Q_A is thought to reflect the suppression of the primary radical pair formation in PSII due to electrostatic repulsion between Phe^- and Q_A^- (15, 19-21). The high triplet yield observed after double reduction of Q_A or in purified reaction center complexes which lack Q_A, was explained by charge neutralization by protonation or by the absence of Q_A, both of which would remove the electrostatic effect (15,16). The observation of high triplet yield in photoinhibited PSII centers which exhibit the $Q_A^-Fe^{2+}$ EPR signal (Fig. 2B) suggests that the charge on Q_A^- is neutralized in these centers. A likely mechanism that could result in charge neutralization is protonation

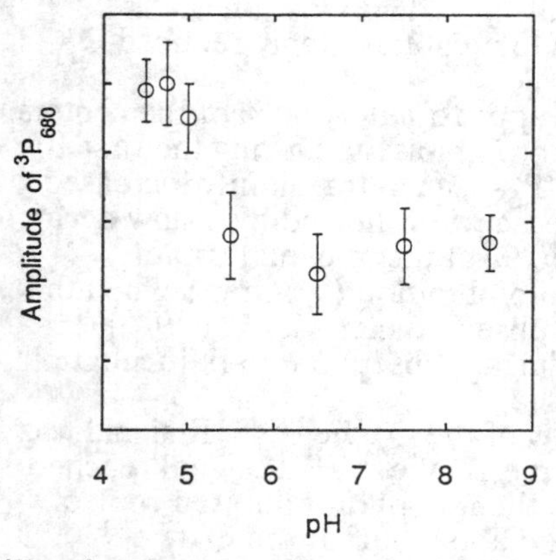

Figure 3. The pH dependent build-up of $^3P_{680}$ promoting PSII centers during strong anaerobic illumination. PSII membranes were suspended at different pHs and illuminated for 3 min. The relative amplitude of the light-induced $^3P_{680}$ EPR signal is plotted as a function of pH. The data represent the average of 4 experiments with the indicated standard deviation.

of Q_A^- or an amino acid residue in its close vicinity. In an attempt to test this hypothesis the build-up of $^3P_{680}$ forming PSII centers was measured in PSII membranes which were anaerobically illuminated at different pHs for a constant period of time. Based on the data in Fig. 2B, the duration of the strong illumination was chosen to 3 min to produce the maximal amount of triplet forming centers in which Q_A is singly reduced, with minimal interference from centers in which $^3P_{680}$ is formed in the absence of Q_A^-. The size of the $^3P_{680}$ EPR signal was practically constant above pH 6.0. However, the yield increased steeply between pH 6.0 and 4.5 (Fig. 3) supporting the hypothesis that protonation events are involved in the build-up of $^3P_{680}$ promoting centers.

3.3. *The decay of triplet forming PSII centers at room temperature*

The results described above demonstrate the existence of a heterogeneous population of PSII centers, with different degree of Q_A reduction, which promote

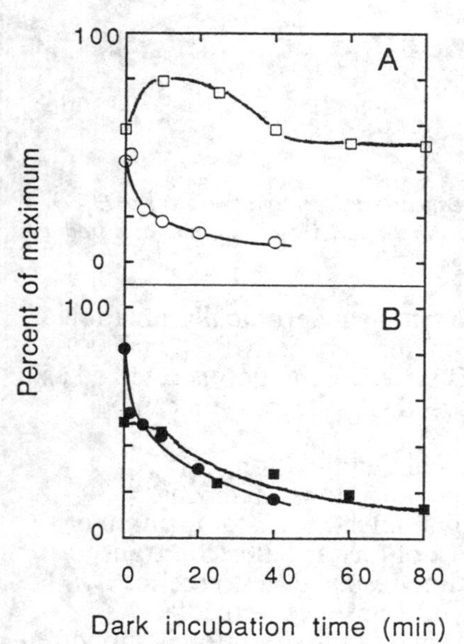

Figure 4. The room temperature stability of the $^3P_{680}$ promoting centers and the $Q_A^-Fe^{2+}$ EPR signal during dark incubation after strong anaerobic illumination. PSII membranes were photoinhibited as in Fig. 1 and the decrease of the light-inducible $^3P_{680}$ (□,○) (A) and of the dark-stable $Q_A^-Fe^{2+}$ EPR signals (■,●) (B) was monitored during room temperature dark storage of samples which were photoinhibited for 3 min (○,●) and 12 min (□,■), respectively.

$^3P_{680}$ formation in anaerobically photoinhibited PSII centers. Here we have used EPR spectroscopy to directly detect the decay of the different triplet promoting states during room-temperature incubation in the dark. After 3 minutes anaerobic illumination the amplitude of the triplet signal was 30-35 % of the maximal triplet size. During dark storage, subsequent to the photoinhibitory illumination, the ability of $^3P_{680}$ formation showed a biphasic decay, with half-decay times of about 2-3 and 30 minutes (Fig. 4A). About 70-80 % of the $^3P_{680}$ promoting centers, corresponding to about 30 % of the total PSII population, decayed with the short half-time. This fraction is approximately equal to the $^3P_{680}$ promoting centers that contain singly reduced Q_A (Fig. 2B, dashed).

In a sample that was illuminated for 12 min, approximately 60% of the centers promoted $^3P_{680}$ formation immediately after the photoinhibition. During the first 10 minutes of the dark incubation, the light-inducible $^3P_{680}$ signal transiently increased to about 80 % of the maximum. This transient increase was followed by a slow decay ($t_{1/2}$≈30 min) to a constant level at approximately 50 % of the maximal triplet amplitude. After extended periods of anaerobic photoinhibition (>30min), when the $Q_A^-Fe^{2+}$ signal had almost totally disappeared, we observed high yield of $^3P_{680}$ formation which remained completely unchanged during subsequent dark incubation (not shown).

In the same series of experiments the stability of the $Q_A^-Fe^{2+}$ EPR signal was also measured. After 3 min anaerobic illumination the $Q_A^-Fe^{2+}$ EPR signal reached about 80 % of the maximal amplitude, measured in the non-photoinhibited control. During the first minute of the dark adaptation period about half of the $Q_A^-Fe^{2+}$ signal was lost (Fig. 4B). The rest decayed slowly ($t_{1/2}$≈30 min). In the sample that was exposed to the anaerobic illumination for 12 min, the $Q_A^-Fe^{2+}$ EPR signal, which amounted only to 50% of the maximum amplitude, decayed monophasically ($t_{1/2}$≈35 min) after an apparent lag period of about 10 min (Fig. 4B).

4. DISCUSSION

In the following we will analyze our results in the framework of a model for the stepwise reduction and protonation of Q_A during the course of strong anaerobic illumination as summarized in Scheme I.

$$Q_A \overset{e^-}{\longleftrightarrow} Q^-_{A,norm} \longrightarrow Q^-_{A,stab} \overset{H^+}{\longleftrightarrow} Q^-_{A,stab}(H^+) \overset{e^-}{\longleftrightarrow} \left[Q_A^{=}(H^+)\right] \overset{H^+}{\longleftrightarrow} Q_A^{=}(H^+)_2 \longrightarrow \square$$

Triplet yield	low	low	high	low	high	high

Scheme I. Schematic representation of the proposed sequential reduction and protonation steps of Q_A occurring during anaerobic photoinhibition. The indicated stability of the various states is obtained from the measured decay kinetics of the $^3P_{680}$ and the $Q_A^-Fe^{2+}$ EPR signals.

Single reduction of Q_A. Shortly after the onset of the strong anaerobic illumination PSII centers containing singly reduced Q_A will dominate. Very early the $Q_A^-Fe^{2+}$ EPR signal decays rapidly (in few seconds), and this state in Scheme I is referred as $Q_A^-{}_{,norm}$. In centers with "normal Q_A^-" no light-induced $^3P_{680}$ formation can be observed.

Stabilization of Q_A^-. During the continued strong illumination, $Q_A^-{}_{,norm}$ becomes stabilized as revealed by the formation of a more slowly decaying population of the $Q_A^-Fe^{2+}$ EPR signal ($t_{1/2}$≈30-35 minutes). The stabilization of Q_A^- is most likely caused by two factors: (i) the block of forward electron transport from Q_A^- to Q_B, which has been demonstrated by time resolved fluorescence measurements in our previous work (14), and by (ii) the absence of oxidized recombination partners at the donor side of PSII. This latter assumption is supported by the absence of the S_2-state multiline signal under the conditions where stable Q_A^-

is present (not shown). The room temperature stability of this Q_A^- population is longer than that observed in the previous fluorescence study (2-3 min, Ref. 14). The reason for this difference might come from the much higher chlorophyll concentration (1.5-2.5 mg Chl/ml) in Ref. 14 as compared to that used in the present study (20 µg Chl/ml) and/or from the more complete exclusion of oxygen which is an important factor of Q_A^- reoxidation.

Protonation of stable Q_A^-. Initially, the centers with stabilized Q_A^- do not promote $^3P_{680}$ formation (Fig. 2) but later they are converted to $^3P_{680}$ forming centers (Scheme I). The amount of these centers increases fast during the early phase of photoinhibition, reaching transiently 30-35 % of all centers (Fig. 2B, dashed curve).

The absence (or very low yield) of $^3P_{680}$ formation which is usually observed when Q_A is singly reduced has been satisfactorily explained by the suppression of the primary radical pair formation due to electrostatic repulsion between Q_A^- and Phe^-. The electrostatic effect can be removed by the protonation of the reduced Q_A states or by the absence of Q_A (15,16,21), leading to high yield of light-induced $^3P_{680}$. Our observation of high triplet yield in PSII centers which possess stable singly reduced Q_A suggests that the charge on Q_A^- is neutralized. The formation of triplet promoting PSII centers is enhanced at low pH (Fig. 3), and we propose that this reflects a protonation event at or near Q_A^- ($Q_{A,stab}^-(H^+)$ state in Scheme I). This hypothesis is also supported by our previous fluorescence data showing a similar pH dependence of the increased F_o fluorescence which arises from the centers which have stable Q_A^- (14).

When PSII samples in which $^3P_{680}$ is formed in the presence of stable reduced Q_A are incubated in darkness, a small population of the $Q_A^-Fe^{2+}$ signal (reflecting PSII centers with the "normal" form of Q_A^-, Scheme I) is lost within 1 min, while the rest decays with approximately 30 min half-time (reflecting the "stable" Q_A^-, Scheme I). In the same samples most of the $^3P_{680}$ centers are lost within 2-3 min, while only a small fraction decays with about 30 min half-time. A likely explanation for this complex behavior is that the proton which neutralizes the negative charge on Q_A^- (or on a nearby base) is released faster in the dark (with $t_{1/2}$=2-3 min) than the reoxidation of stable Q_A^- occurs (with $t_{1/2}$ =30-35 min).

Second reduction and protonation of $Q_A^-(H^+)$. The protonated form of Q_A^- is not very stable in the dark. Instead the proton at or near Q_A^- seems to be stabilized via the light-driven arrival of the second electron to form the state $Q_A^=(H^+)$ (Scheme I). This species is diamagnetic and results in the loss of the $Q_A^-Fe^{2+}$ EPR signal. The concept of electrostatic control of primary charge separation predicts the suppression of light-induced $P_{680}^+Phe^-$, and consequently $^3P_{680}$ formation in the presence of $Q_A^=(H^+)$, similarly to the case of Q_A^- (21). However, the observation of very high $^3P_{680}$ yields shows that the second electron on Q_A is quickly neutralized, most likely by a second protonation (Scheme I). This results in the formation of reaction centers containing double reduced and double protonated Q_A, which is quite stable and characterized by a slowly decaying ($t_{1/2}$=20-30 min) $^3P_{680}$ yield and by the absence of the $Q_A^-Fe^{2+}$ EPR signal. The formation of $Q_A^=(H^+)$ before the $Q_A^=(H^+)_2$ state is also supported by the transient increase of $^3P_{680}$ formation observed during dark adaptation after 12 min photoinhibition (Fig. 4A) which process is likely to reflect the decay of the non triplet promoting $Q_A^=(H^+)$ to the triplet promoting $Q_A^-(H^+)$.

Release of $Q_A(H_2)$. In PSII centers where no $Q_A^-Fe^{2+}$ can be observed, part of the $^3P_{680}$ forming population does not decay at all. We propose that in these centers the double reduced and protonated Q_A has either left or been displaced from its proper binding site (Scheme I) similarly to what has been proposed to occur following chemical reduction of Q_A (15). This is supported by recent biochemical evidence published elsewhere in these proceedings (24).

Scheme I represent the summary of events that are likely to occur at the level of Q_A during anaerobic photoinhibition. An exact kinetic model of these events can not be formulated at present, and further experiments to improve the kinetic resolution of the protonation/deprotonation steps are in progress.

REFERENCES

1. Nanba, O. and Satoh, K. (1987) Proc. Natl. Acad. Sci. U.S.A. 84, 109-112
2. Hansson, Ö. and Wydrzynski, T. (1990) Photosynth. Res. 23, 131-162
3. Andersson, B. and Styring, S. (1991) in Current Topics in Bioenergetics (Lee, C. P., ed.) Vol. 16, pp. 1-81, Academic Press, San Diego
4. Prasil, O., Adir, N. and Ohad, I. (1992) in Current Topics in Photosynthesis (Barber, J, ed.) Vol. 11, pp. 220-250, Elsevier, Amsterdam
5. Callahan, F.E., Becker, D. W. and Cheniae, G.M. (1986) Plant Physiol. 82, 261-269
6. Jegerschöld, C., Virgin, I. and Styring, S. (1990) Biochemistry 29, 6179-6186
7. Eckert, H.-J., Geiken, B., Bernarding, J., Napiwotzki, A., Eichler, H.-J. and Renger, G. (1991) Photosynth. Res. 27, 97-108
8. Kyle, D. J., Ohad, I. and Arntzen, C. J. (1984) Proc. Natl. Acad. Sci. U.S.A. 81, 4070-4074
9. Ohad, I., Koike, H., Shochat, S. and Inoue, Y. (1988) Biochim. Biophys. Acta 933, 288-298
10. Kirilovsky, D., Vernotte, C., Astier, C. and Etienne, A. -L. (1988) Biochim. Biophys. Acta 933, 124-131
11. Cleland, R.E, Melis, A. and Neale, P. J. (1986) Photosynth. Res. 9, 79-88
12. Setlik, I., Allakhverdiev, S. I., Nedbal, L., Setlikova, N. and Klimov, V. V. (1990) Photosynth. Res. 23, 39-48
13. Styring, S., Virgin, I., Ehrenberg, A. and Andersson, B. (1990) Biochim. Biophys. Acta 1015, 269-278
14. Vass, I., Styring, S., Hundall, T., Koivuniemi, A., Aro, E. -M. and Andersson, B. (1992) Proc. Natl. Acad. Sci. U.S.A. 89, 1408-1412
15. van Mieghem, F. J. E., Nitschke, W., Mathis, P. and Rutherford, A. W. (1989) Biochim. Biophys. Acta 977, 207-214
16. van Mieghem, F. J. E., Searle, G.F.W., Rutherford, A. W. and Schaafsma, T.J. (1992) Biochim. Biophys. Acta 1100, 198-206
17. Asada, K. and Takahashi, M. (1987) in Topics in Photosynthesis Vol. 9 (Kyle, D. J., Osmond, C. B. and Arntzen, C. J. eds.) pp. 227-288, Elsevier, Amsterdam)
18. Okamura, M. Y., Satoh, K., Isaacson, R. A. and Feher, G. (1987) in Progress in Photosynthesis Research (Biggins, J., ed.), Vol. 1. pp. 379-381, Martinus Nijhoff, Dordrect, The Netherlands
19. Schatz, G. H., Brock, H. and Holzwarth, A. R. (1987) Proc. Natl. Acad. Sci. U.S.A. 84, 8414-8418
20. Schatz, G. H., Brock, H. and Holzwarth, A. R. (1988) Biophys. J. 54, 397-405
21. Vass, I. and Styring, S. (1992) Biochemistry, 31, 5957-5963
22. Ono, T. and Inoue, Y. (1985) Biochim. Biophys. Acta 806, 331-340
23. Miller, A. -F. and Brudvig, G. W. (1991) Biochim. Biophys. Acta 1056, 1-18
24. Koivuniemi, A., Swiezewska, E., Styring, S., Aro, E.-M. and Andersson. B. (1992) These proceedings

LIGHT-DEPENDENT TURNOVER RATE OF THE D1 POLYPEPTIDE IN NEW SITE-SPECIFIC *SYNECHOCYSTIS* PCC 6803 MUTANTS

TAINA KALLIO, EVA-MARI ARO, CHRISTER JANSSON* AND PIRKKO MÄENPÄÄ
DEPT. OF BIOLOGY, UNIV. OF TURKU, SF-20700 TURKU, FINLAND; *DEPT. OF BIOCHEMISTRY, ARRHENIUS LABORATORIES, UNIV. OF STOCKHOLM, S-10691 STOCKHOLM, SWEDEN

1. INTRODUCTION

The detailed mechanism of the light-induced turnover of the D1 polypeptide of PSII is still unknown. The primary cleavage area in the enzymatic degradation of the D1 polypeptide *in vivo* seems to be in the loop connecting transmembrane helices D and E, most probably between amino acids 238-248 (1). The QEEET motif (amino acids 241-245) has been supposed to be important for the enzymatic clevage of the D1 polypeptide. N-terminally from the cleavage area is a PEST-like-sequence rich in glutamate (E), serine (S) and threonine (T). PEST sequences are often found in proteins having a fast turnover rate (2) and it has been speculated that the PEST-like-sequence may have a role in the enzymatic degradation of the D1 polypeptide. We have created site-specific mutations in the PEST-like-area and in the QEEET motif. Mutations in both areas affect the light dependent turnover of the D1 polypeptide.

2. MATERIALS AND METHODS

Three new photosynthetically growing site-spesific mutants of *Synechocystis* 6803 were created (see Mäenpää et al., these proceedings). Two of them, E243K (glutamate 243 -> lysine) and CA1 (deletion of glutamates 242-244, glutamine 241 -> histidine), are targeted to the QEEET motif. E229D (glutamate 229 -> aspartate) has a mutation in the PEST-like-sequence. Antibiotic resistance control (AR) having similar DNA construction as the site-specific mutants without any site-specific mutations was also created.

In vivo pulse and chase experiments with ^{35}S-methionine were used to measure the degradation rate of the D1 polypeptide in growth PFD (50 μmol m^{-2}s^{-1}) and high light (1500 μmol m^{-2}s^{-1}). Pulse and chase were done at the same light intensity in BG11 medium (9μg chl/ml) at 32 °C. In growth light the duration of pulse was 30 min. and the chase

N. Murata (ed.), Research in Photosynthesis, Vol. IV, 419–422.

times were 0, 1 and 3 h. In high light, the cells were radiolabeled for 75 min. and the chase times were 0, 15, 30, 45 and 60 min.

Membranes were isolated at 4 °C. Cells were broken down by vortexing them with glass beads in STN buffer (10 mM Tris-HCl, pH 8.0, 0.4 M sucrose, 10 mM NaCl and 20 mM Na-EDTA) and cell debris was pelleted by centrifugation at 2500 rpm in a microfuge. The supernatant was collected and membranes were pelleted at 14000 rpm. The pellet was redissolved in STN buffer. Polypeptides were separated by SDS-PAGE using a 12 to 22.5 % acrylamide gradient. Each sample contained an equal amount of chlorophyll. Gels were fixed, treated with amplifier and dried before autoradiography. X-ray films were scanned and samples were normalized using the sum of three stable polypeptide bands as a reference.

Oxygen evolution was measured *in vivo* according to (3) in limiting and saturating lights. F_V/F_{MAX} was measured with a PAM fluorometer after 5 min. dark adaptation. Both measurements were done at 32 °C.

3. RESULTS AND DISCUSSION

Rate of oxygen evolution (H_2O -> dichlorobenzoquinone) in AR was 244 μmol O_2 h^{-1}/mg chl in saturating light, PSII activity in all mutants was 10-20% less than that of AR. In all mutants and AR both oxygen evolution and F_V/F_{MAX} were measured after 75 min. (= pulse) and 135 min. (= chase 60 min.) treatment at 1500 μmol photons $m^{-2}s^{-1}$. When PSII activity was measured at limiting light, all the strains had lost 50-60 % of PSII activity within 75 min. of high light treatment, and only a little more within 135 min. Slightly less inhibition was seen if oxygen evolution was measured in saturating light. The decrase in F_V/F_{MAX} was correlated with the loss of oxygen evolution.

Using immunoblot technique we have found out that the D1 polypeptide of both QEEET motif mutants has slightly faster electrophoretic mobility than that of the wild type D1 polypeptide (data not shown). We think that this difference is because of a modified conformation of the D1 polypeptide. The D1 polypeptide of E229D has the same electroforetic mobility as the wild type D1 polypeptide.

The PEST-like-region mutant E229D has two times slower degradation rate of the D1 polypeptide in high light than that of the wild type D1 polypeptide (Fig 1b). As far as we know this is the first time when a mutant having a slower degradation rate of the D1 polypeptide *in vivo* is reported. In growth light the D1 polypeptide of this mutant is degraded as the wild type D1 polypeptide (Fig 1a). At the moment we can't explain the relationship between the turnover rate of the D1 polypeptide (there may be changes in the synthesis of the D1 polypeptide as well) and the PSII activity. We conclude that the PEST-like sequence of the D1 polypeptide has an effect on the light dependent turnover of the D1 polypeptide.

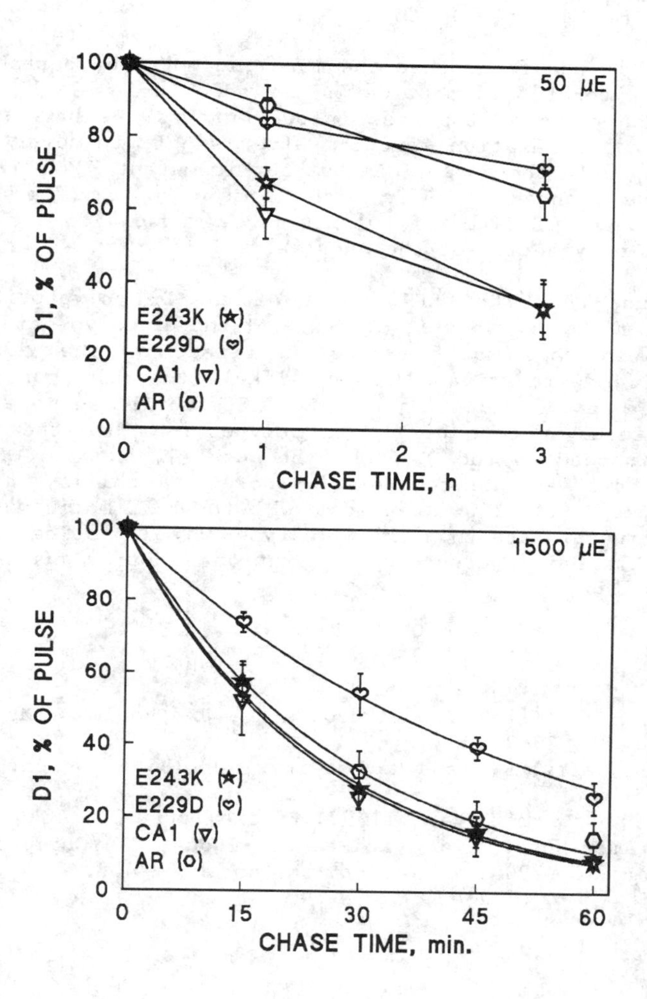

FIGURE 1. *In vivo* degradation rate of the D1 polypeptide in new site-specific *Synechocystis* 6803 mutants and antibiotic resistance control (AR) in growth light (50 μmol $m^{-2}s^{-1}$) and high light (1500 μmol $m^{-2}s^{-1}$). Both pulse and chase were done at the same light intensity. QEEET motif mutants are E243K (glutamate 243->lysine) and CA1 (deletion of glutamates 242-244, glutamine 241-> histidine), E229D (glutamate 229->aspartate) is the PEST-like-sequence mutant. AR is the control strain without site-specific mutations.

In growth light (50 μmol $m^{-2}s^{-1}$) both QEEET motif mutants (CA1, E243K) have faster degradation rate of the D1 polypeptide than AR (Fig 1a). In some herbicide resistant mutants in which the Q_B binding is affected, it was found that the more the mutation destabilizes Q_B^- the faster the D1 polypeptide is degraded in low light (4). That does not seem to be the case in our mutants. We have shown that fluorescence relaxation kinetics after single turnover flash has been changed in the mutant CA1 but not in mutant E243K (Mäenpää et al., these proceedings). In high light (1500 μmol $m^{-2}s^{-1}$) the D1 polypeptide of QEEET motif mutants is degraded with the same rate as the D1 polypeptide of the AR strain (Fig 1b).

We conclude that the QEEET motif of the D1 polypeptide is not crucial for the proteolytic cleavage of the D1 polypeptide *in vivo*. Nevertheless this motif exerts an effect on the rate of the polypeptide degradation. It seems likely that the conformational changes brought by mutations of the QEEET motif are more important for the turnover rate of the D1 polypeptide than the functional changes induced to the Q_B pocket because (i) both of QEEET motif mutants have an altered electrophoretic mobility of the D1 polypeptide, (ii) D1 polypeptides of both QEEET motif mutants have faster turnover rate than the wild type D1 polypeptide, (iii) only CA1 has altered fluorescence relaxation kinetics after a single turnover flash.

REFERENCES

1. Greenberg, B.M., Gaba, V., Mattoo, A.K., and Edelman, M. (1987) EMBO J. 6, 3865-2869.
2. Rogers, S., Wells; R., and Rechsteiner, M. (1986) Science 234, 364-368.
3. Tae, G.-S. and Cramer, W.A. (1992) Biochemistry 31, 4066-4074.
4. Ohad, N., Amir-Shapira, D., Koike, H., Inoue, Y., Ohad, I. and Hirschberg, J. (1990) Z. Naturforch. 45c, 402-408.

LIGHT-INDUCED TURNOVER OF THE D1 PROTEIN OF THE PHOTOSYSTEM II REACTION CENTRE AND PHOTOINHIBITION IN VIVO

B. SCHNETTGER[1], U.J. SANTORE[2], C. CRITCHLEY[3], J. LEITSCH[1] and G.H. KRAUSE[1], Institute of Plant Biochemistry[1], Institute of Developmental & Molecular Biology of Plants[2], Heinrich Heine University, D-4000 Düsseldorf, Germany, and Department of Botany[3], University of Queensland, Qld 4072, Australia

1. INTRODUCTION

Previous studies (1-3) on photoinhibition of photosystem (PS) II *in vitro* have shown that degradation of the D1 protein is not a primary event in the inactivation of the reaction centre. However, in inactive PS II centres, the D1 protein may become 'marked' for following degradation, possibly by action of singlet oxygen (4). *In vivo*, recovery from photoinhibition of such centres can occur only via the light-dependent turnover of the D1 protein. In the present study, we applied an inhibitor of protein synthesis in the chloroplasts, streptomycin (SM), to investigate the role of D1 protein turnover in photoinhibition and recovery in leaves of a higher plant *in vivo*. SM was preferred to chloramphenicol because of strong side effects of the latter (5, and own observations).

2. MATERIALS AND METHODS

Spinach plants (*Spinacia oleracea* L.) were grown in a greenhouse. Incubation with SM (3mM) occurred through the petioles of detached leaves for 4-6 h in light (30-50 µmol m^{-2} s^{-1}). Photoinhibition was induced by strong illumination of leaf disks either floating on water (20°C) in normal air or enclosed in a cuvette, exposed to a gas stream (20 l h^{-1}) of defined composition (18°C). After pretreatments and 5-10 min dark adaptation, the ratio Fv/Fm of fluorescence induction was determined. In part of the leaf disks, recovery was allowed to proceed in low light (10-30 µmol m^{-2} s^{-1}). Further sections were used to isolate thylakoids for measuring uncoupled PS II -driven electron transport (acceptor 1,4-benzoquinone, 1 mM) and for separation of polypeptides with SDS-PAGE. The relative D1 protein content was determined by Western blotting using a specific antibody. Blots were quantitated with a Laser densitometer. From certain leaf disks, sections were prepared for transmission electron microscopy.

3. RESULTS AND DISCUSSION

3.1 Effects of streptomycin on photoinhibition and D1 protein: In leaves incubated with SM, photoinhibition at 20°C is strongly enhanced, as seen from the decline in Fv/Fm ratios of leaf disks and decrease of PS

N. Murata (ed.), Research in Photosynthesis, Vol. IV, 423–426.

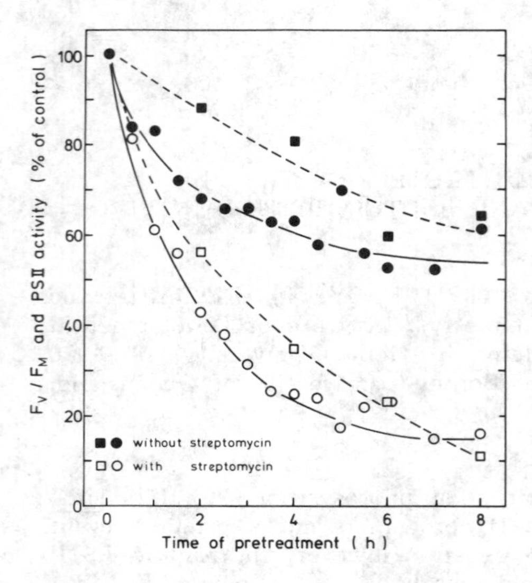

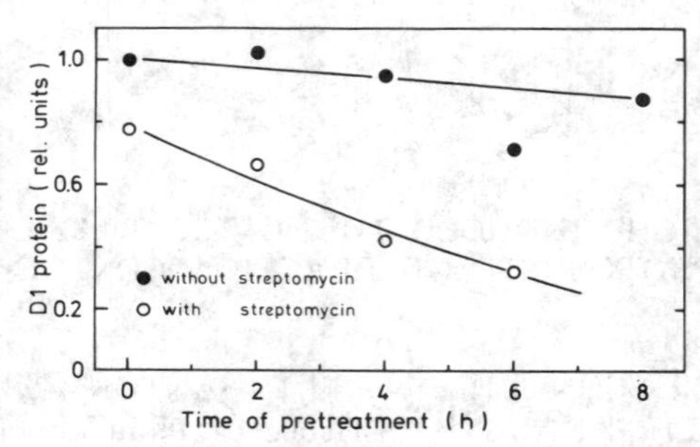

FIGURE 2. Effect of photoinhibition treatment of spinach leaf disks (as for Fig. 1) on relative D1 protein content of thylakoid membranes.

FIGURE 1. Photoinhibition of spinach leaf disks in normal air at 20 °C by exposure to 1.9 mmol m^{-2} s^{-1} white light, in the absence and presence of streptomycin (SM). Fv/Fm ratios (circles) and rates of PS II -driven electron transport in saturating red light (squares) are given in percent of untreated controls.

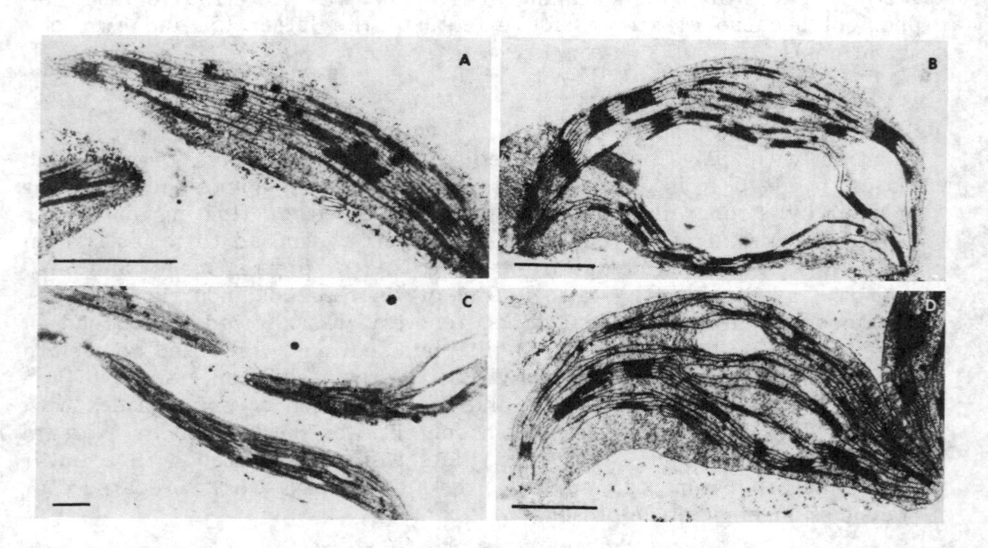

FIGURE 3. Ultrastructure of chloroplasts before and after photoinhibition treatments of leaf disks (as for Fig. 1). a) Control without SM; b) 4 h preillumination without SM; c) Control incubated with SM; d) 4 h preillumination with SM. Bars denote 1 µm.

II -driven electron transport rates of isolated thylakoids (Fig. 1). No significant net D1 degradation is observed in the absence of SM, even after long pretreatment periods (Fig. 2). This confirms (6, 7) that in intact systems (leaf tissue, isolated protoplasts) D1 degradation and resynthesis/replacement are closely synchronized. Photoinhibition then represents an accumulation of inactive PS II centres that still possess the D1 protein. These centres may exert a physiological function in dissipating excess absorbed light energy as heat. In the presence of SM, the tuning of D1 turnover is disturbed, and strong net degradation does occur (Fig. 2), as also observed with isolated protoplasts (7).

3.2 Ultrastructure of photoinhibited chloroplasts: Fig. 3 shows that the ultrastructure of the thylakoids is not significantly affected by the photoinhibition treatment of leaf disks in the absence and presence of SM. It is remarkable that the grana remain apparently unaltered, even when due to the presence of SM about 50% of the D1 protein has been degraded (cf. Fig. 2). If indeed the PS II units, which undergo D1 degradation, move to the stroma-exposed membrane regions and leave behind their peripheral light harvesting complexes (8), these detached antenna systems should be capable of maintaining the stacking of thylakoids.

3.3 Recovery in relation to D1 turnover: Recovery from photoinhibition in spinach leaves usually occurs in a fast (10-50 min) followed by a much slower phase (several h), as demonstrated in Fig. 4a for photoinhibition in an atmosphere containing 2.1% or 21% O_2. After pretreatment in low oxygen, the extent of the fast phase is considerably enlarged compared to photoinhibition at air level of O_2. It has been postulated (9) that

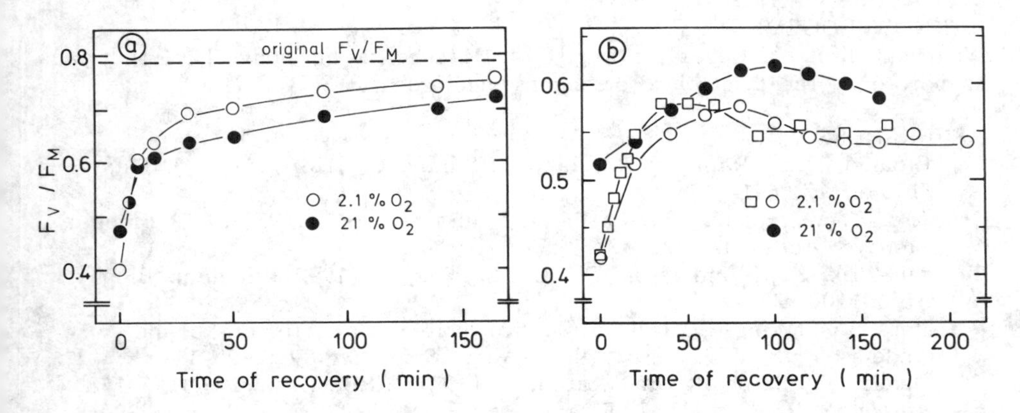

FIGURE 4. Recovery (in normal air, 18 °C) of the Fv/Fm ratio of leaf sections after illumination in a CO_2-free atmosphere containing 21% or 2.1% O_2. a) Absence of SM, preillumination 2 h, 2 mmol m^{-2} s^{-1} (mean of 8-10 experiments, S.D.: 0.03-0.05); b) leaves preincubated with SM, preillumination 30 min, 1 mmol m^{-2} s^{-1} (21% O_2: mean of 4 experiments, S.D.: 0.01-0.03; 2.1% O_2: 2 representative single experiments).

the fast recovery phase represents reactivation of PS II without D1 turnover, whereas the slow phase is based on 'repair' by replacement of D1. This hypothesis is supported by the effects of SM on recovery (Fig. 4b). After photoinhibition in 2.1% O_2, in the presence of SM, the large fast phase of recovery is retained, whereas the slow phase is fully inhibited. A similar effect is seen after photoinhibition in 21% O_2, although the rate of recovery is slowed down. Preliminary experiments indicate that the extent and kinetics of fast recovery, not blocked by SM, depend on the O_2 level present during photoinhibitory treatment and on the acclimation state of the leaves, but also on other, still unclarified experimental factors.

4. CONCLUSIONS

Our experiments indicate that, *in vivo*, photoinhibition proceeds in at least two principal steps. *First*, inactive centres accumulate, in which the D1 protein is still functional; fast reactivation is possible in low light without chloroplast protein synthesis. This step apparently is not identical with inhibition due to stabilized forms of reduced Q_A observed during irradiation under anaerobiosis (4), as usually little increase in initial fluorescence, Fo, is observed (not shown). *Second*, in the inactive centres, the D1 protein appears to be vulnerable to oxygen attack (or to active oxygen species such as singlet O_2), depending on O_2 concentration and other factors. From this second step, recovery is possible only via D1 turnover. PS II inactivation, D1 turnover, and even net D1 degradation (in the presence of SM) leave the grana structure basically untouched.

ACKNOWLEDGEMENTS
We thank Prof. P. Böger for a gift of D1-specific antibody. The study was supported by the Deutsche Forschungsgemeinschaft (SFB 189).

REFERENCES

1 Cleland, R.E., Ramage, R.T. and Critchley, C. (1990) Aust. J. Plant Physiol. 17, 641-651
2 Aro, E.-M., Hundal, T., Carlberg, I. and Andersson, B. (1990) Biochim. Biophys. Acta 1019, 269-275
3 van Wijk, K.J., Andersson, B., and Styring, S. (1992) Biochim. Biophys. Acta 1100, 207-215
4 Vass, I., Styring, S., Hundal, T., Koivuniemi, A., Aro, E.-M. and Andersson, B. (1992) Proc. Natl. Acad. Sci. USA 89, 1408-1412
5 Okada, K., Satoh, K. and Katoh, S. (1991) FEBS Lett. 295, 155-158
6 Kettunen, R., Tyystjärvi, E. and Aro, E.-M. (1991) FEBS Lett. 290, 153-156
7 Schnettger, B., Leitsch, J. and Krause, G.H. (1992) Photosynthetica, in press
8 Guenther, J.E. and Melis, A. (1990) Photosynth. Res. 23, 105-109
9 Krause, G.H. and Weis, E. (1991) Annu. Rev. Plant Physiol. Plant Mol. Biol. 42, 313-349

REVEALING TWO MECHANISMS OF D1 PROTEIN DEGRADATION USING ISOLATED PHOTOSYSTEM TWO COMPLEXES

J. DE LAS RIVAS, C. A. SHIPTON, M. PONTICOS and J. BARBER.
AFRC PHOTOSYNTHESIS GROUP, BIOCHEMISTRY DEPARTMENT, IMPERIAL COLLEGE OF SCIENCE, TECHNOLOGY & MEDICINE, LONDON SW7 2AY, UK

1. INTRODUCTION

Photosystem II (PSII) of higher plants is a multienzymatic complex composed of more than 22 polypeptides integrated within the thylakoid membrane. Many PSII preparations containing different numbers of polypeptides have been reported since the first isolation of the PSII reaction centre complex from higher plants [1]. In this investigation, two isolated PSII particles (reaction centres and core complexes) different in size yet both containing the special dimer D1/D2, have been studied in terms of their sensitivity to high-light treatment. A comparative study was carried out since they are different photochemically. Cores can carry out secondary electron transport reactions from water splitting to Q_A reduction whereas the reaction centres are only capable of primary charge separation without additions. We haved looked at and compared the pattern of light-induced degradation of D1 protein in these two complexes.

2. MATERIALS AND METHODS

The oxygen evolving PSII core complexes were isolated from wheat leaves as described previously [2]. PSII reaction centres from pea were prepared as described in [3]. The light treatments of the PS II complexes solutions were performed as indicated elsewhere [2, 4]. Absorption spectra were measured as in Telfer *et al.* [5]. PSII cores and reaction centres were illuminated after suspension in appropriate buffers to allow either donor side or acceptor side protection. In order to obtain a protected and active acceptor side, the particles were suspended in the buffer 50 mM Tris-Cl (pH 8.0) / 2 mM dodecylmaltoside (DM) / 0.2 mM sucrose and in the presence of 200 µM 2,5-dibromo-3-methyl-6-isopropyl-p-benzoquinone (DBMIB) as an electron acceptor. A protected and active donor side was achieved in core particles by suspending them in the buffer 50 mM MES (pH 6.0) / 2 mM DM / 0.2 mM sucrose, with 5 mM $CaCl_2$. Under these conditions, the core particles evolved oxygen at a rate of approx. 400 $\mu moles O_2 \cdot mgChl^{-1} \cdot h^{-1}$ when DCBQ was used as electron acceptor. For donor side protection, reaction centres samples were suspended in 50 mM MES (pH 6.0) / 2 mM DM / 0.2 mM sucrose.

Western blot analyses was carried out as in Marder *et al.* [6]. Three different anti-D1 polyclonal antisera were utilized: anti-D1T , raised against the product of *psb* A gene (Nixon *et al.*)[7]; anti-D1c, C-terminal specific antiserum, raised to the C-terminal region of the D1 protein molecule (kind gift of Dr. P. J. Nixon and Dr. B. Diner); anti-D1n, N-terminal specific antiserum, raised to the N-terminal portion of the D1 protein (kind gift of Dr. J. A. Mullet).

3. RESULTS AND DISCUSSION

Fig. 1 shows the absorption spectra of the two isolated PS II particles. The reaction centre (RC) contains the polypeptides D1, D2, cytochrome b-559 and *psb* I gene product, has a chlorophyll to pheophytin ratio of 6:2, and the maximum of the red peak at 676 nm (see Fig.1 and Table I). The core (CO) contains D1, D2, cyt b-559, *psb* I and *psb* H gene products, CP47 and CP43 chlorophyll *a*-binding proteins and the extrinsic 33 kDa protein (the latter was not present in stoichiometric amounts). Its chlorophyll to pheophytin ratio was determined to be about 38:2, and the red peak maximum was at 674 nm (Fig.1). The two particles were highly active in primary charge separation: > 0.95 $Pheo^-$ is photoaccumulated per reaction centre in the two preparations under reducing conditions (+ dithionite) (see Table I).

N. Murata (ed.), Research in Photosynthesis, Vol. IV, 427–430.

TABLE I

PSII preps.	Chla:Pheo Ratio	Red Peak λ_{max}	Relative Activity Pheo⁻ photoaccumulation (per2Pheo)	β-Car content (per2Pheo)	Car bleached * λ_{max}	ΔOD ($x10^{-2}$)
RC	6:2	676	0.98	1.8	485-86	5.0
CO	38:2	674	0.97	3.8	492-95	11.2

* Photoinduced bleaching in the presence of silicomolybdate as electron acceptor.

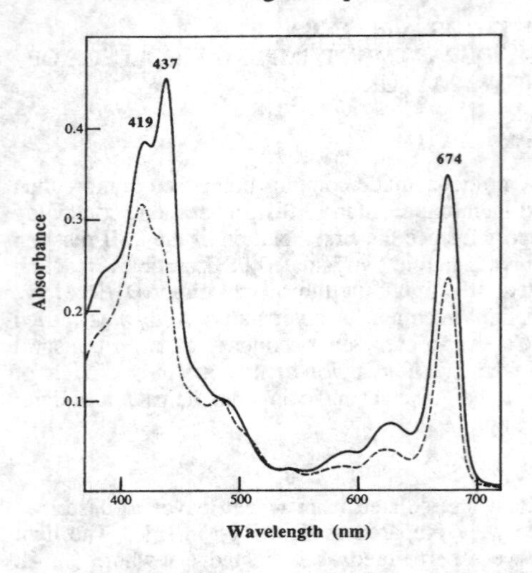

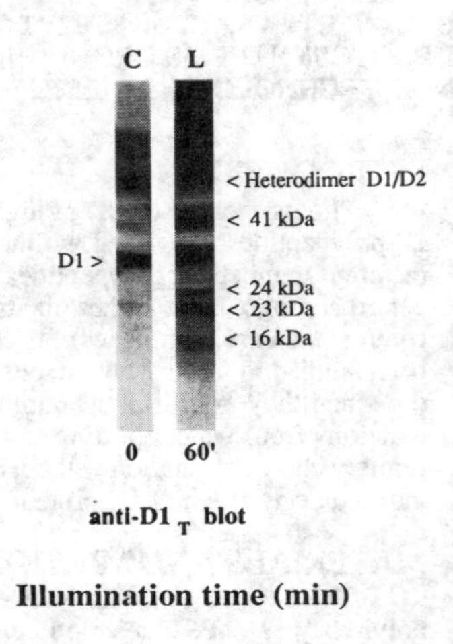

Fig. 1 Absorption spectra of the PSII cores (continuous line) compaired with the absorption spectra of PSII reaction centres (dotted line).

Fig. 2 Immunoblot of the isolated PSII core complexes, control and light-treated. The PSII particles were maintained in the darkness (C) or illuminated (L) for 60 min in 6,000 $\mu E \cdot m^{-2} \cdot s^{-1}$ of white light at 20°C at a chlorophyll concentration of 100 $\mu g \cdot ml^{-1}$. The antibody used was anti-$D1_T$. The PSII core complexes were suspended in the Tris-HCl (pH 8.0) buffer in the presence of 0.2mM DBMIB.

Fig. 2 shows the pattern of D1 protein breakdown fragments generated by illuminating the PS II core complexes for 1 h (Fig. 2, L), detected inmunologically with an antibody raised against the whole D1 (anti-$D1_T$). This experiment was performed at pH 8.0, without Ca^{2+}, in the presence of the electron acceptor DBMIB. Under these conditions three main D1 degradation fragments were detected in the PSII core: two large, of about 24 kDa and 23 kDa, and another smaller fragment of 16 kDa. This latter fragment has been observed after photoinhibitory treatments of several different PSII particles [8, 9]. A possible explanation for its origin is given in Ponticos *et al.* [10]. The other two fragments, 24 and 23 kDa, are primary products of D1 degradation that have been characterized in De Las Rivas *et al.* [2] and contain respectively the C-terminal or N-terminal regions of the D1 protein. In that work it was found that depending on the experimental conditions during photoinhibitory treatment of PSII core complexes, two different fragments of about 23-24 kDa can be generated that are the product of peptidic cleavage in two different sites of the D1 sequence. The identification and characterization of these two fragments in PSII cores gave experimental support to the existence of two mechanisms of photoinactivation of the electron transport reactions in PSII, one originating from acceptor-side damage and the other from donor-side damage [2].

Fig. 3 shows the production of these two major fragments in the isolated PSII reaction centres subjected to two different conditions: with addition of an electron acceptor and pH 8.0, a 24 kDa fragment is obtained (Fig.3a); without any addition and pH 6.0, a 23 kDa fragment is obtained (Fig. 3c). The production of each of the fragments correlates with a different and specific pattern of light-induced bleaching of the chromophores of the reaction centre (Fig. 3 b and d). The origin of the fragments is identified in Fig. 4 using two specific D1 antibodies, raised against the C-terminal and the N-terminal region of D1. In this way we show that the 23 kDa fragment is N-terminal and it is only produced when the main photochemical reaction in the reaction centre is primary charge separation and recombination [11]. The 24 kDa C-terminal fragment has been already characterized by Shipton *et al.* [4, 8, 12].

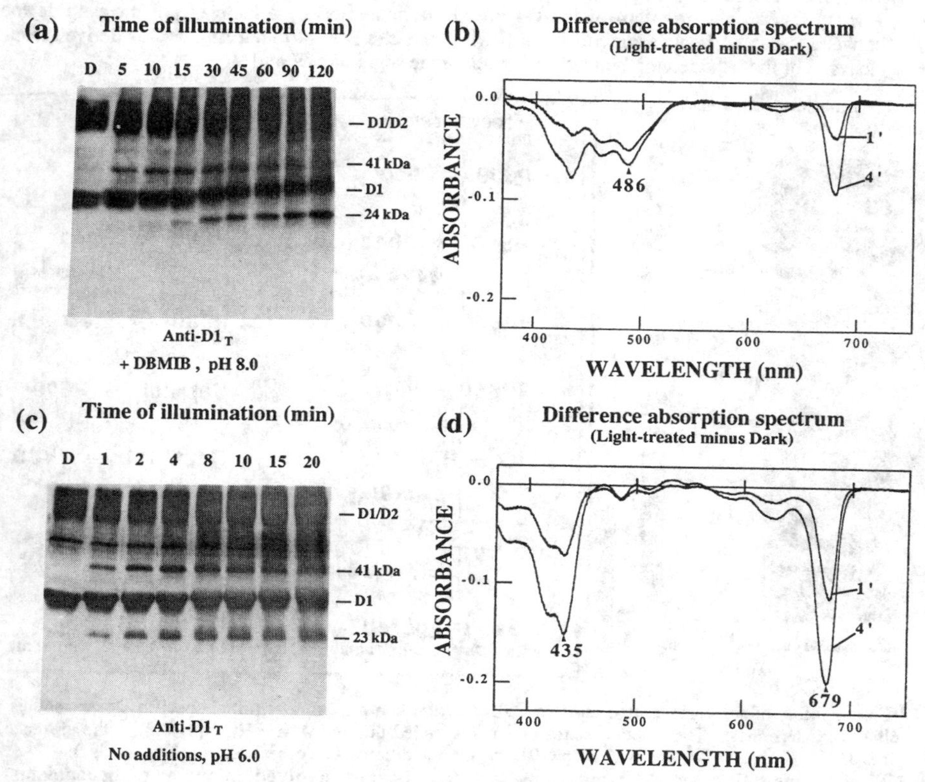

Fig. 3 Immunoblots (a, c) and difference absorption spectra (b, d) of the light-treated isolated PSII reaction centres. For the western blots the PSII particles were illuminated for different lengths of time with 6,000 μE$\cdot$m-2 $\cdot$s-1 of white light at 20°C at a chlorophyll concentration of 50 μg$\cdot$ml-1. The antibody used was anti-D1T. The reaction centres were suspended in the Tris-HCl (pH 8.0) buffer in the presence of 0.2mM DBMIB (a, b), or in the Mes-NaOH (pH 6.0) buffer without electron acceptors (c, d). The difference absorption spectra correspond to samples with a chlorophyll concentration of 4 μg$\cdot$ml-1 illuminated with approx. 500 μE$\cdot$m-2$\cdot$s-1 of white light at 10°C for 1 and 4 minutes.

4. CONCLUSIONS

We have carried out *in vitro* work on isolated PSII particles (described above) showing that the position of the initial cleavage of the D1 protein in response to photoinhibitory light depends on whether the secondary electron donors or acceptors are present and active. When primary charge separation and recombination occurs, high-light treatment produces a cleavage that generates a 23 kDa fragment containing the N-terminus of the D1 protein. When enough electron acceptors are present but donation is impaired, high-light treatment produces a cleavage located on the lumenal side of the reaction centre and generates a 24 kD C-terminal fragment. The 'donor' or 'acceptor' side degradation seems to be the consequence of two different photochemical processes involving either the formation of highly oxidised species on the donor side ($P680^+$) or the formation of species highly reactive with oxygen ($^3P680 + O_2 \rightarrow P680 + {}^1O_2$). In both cases P680 is at the root of the process, though different damaging mechanisms are provoked, since the latter is oxygen dependent while the other can occur under anaerobic conditions [11]. A model including the different steps and components involved in each mechanism is proposed in Fig. 5.

With respect to the specific location of the primary D1 fragmentation, we propose that the 24 kDa C-terminal fragment of the D1 protein is generated by a cleavage of the peptide loop between transmembrane segments I and II while the 23 kD N-terminal fragment is derived from a cleavage of the peptide loop between transmembrane segments IV and V.

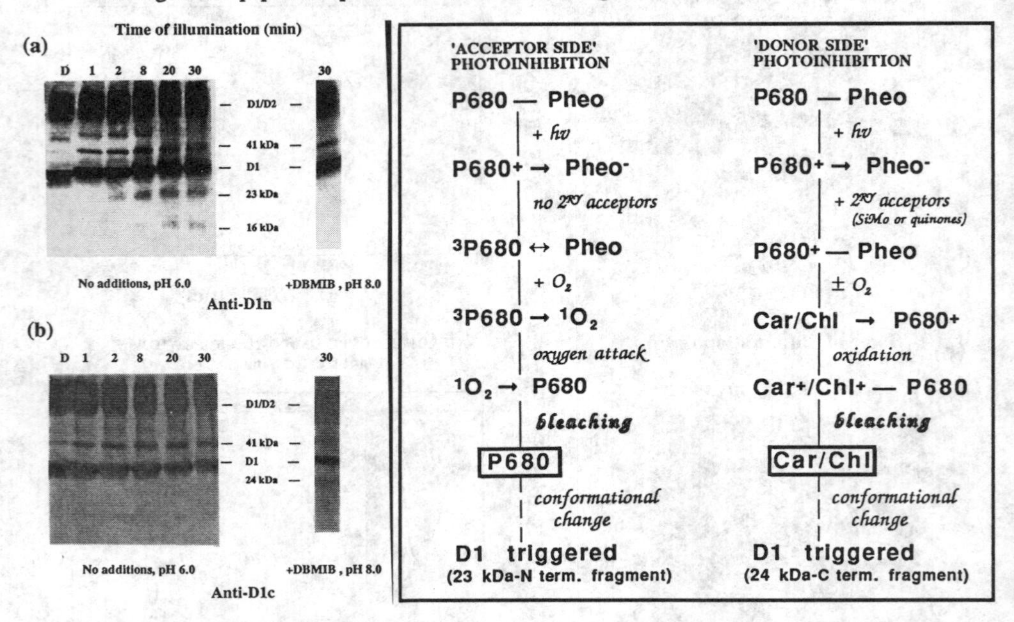

Fig. 4 Immunoblots of the light-treated isolated PSII reaction centres using terminal-specific D1 antibodies (a, N-terminal; b, C-terminal). The reaction centres were suspended in 50 mM Tris-HCl (pH 8.0) in the presence of 0.2 mM DBMIB, or in 50 mM Mes-NaOH (pH 6.0) with no additions. The other conditions as in Fig.3.

Fig. 5 Model illustrating the different steps and components involved in the two mechanisms of photoinhibition in PSII: acceptor side and donor side.

REFERENCES

1. Nanba, O. and Satoh, K. (1987) Proc. Natl. Acad. Sci. USA 84, 109-112
2. De Las Rivas, J., Andersson, B. and Barber, J. (1992) FEBS Lett. 301, 246-252
3. Chapman, D.J., Gounaris, K. and Barber, J. (1988) Biochim. Biophys. Acta 933, 423-431
4. Shipton, C.A. and Barber, J. (1991) Proc. Natl. Acad. Sci. U.S.A. 88, 6691-6695
5. Telfer, A., De Las Rivas, J. and Barber, J. (1991) Biochim. Biophys. Acta 1060, 106-114
6. Marder,J. B., Chapman,D.J., Telfer,A., Nixon,P.J. and Barber,J. (1987) Plant Mol. Biol. 9, 325-333
7. Nixon, P.J., Dyer, T.A., Barber, J. and Hunter, C.N. (1987) FEBS Lett. 209, 83-86
8. Barbato, R., Shipton, C.A., Giacometti, G.M. and Barber, J. (1991) FEBS Lett. 290, 162-166
9. Salter, A.H., Virgin, I., Hagman, Å. and Andersson, B. (1992) Biochemistry 31, 3990-3998
10. Ponticos, M., Shipton, C.A., De Las Rivas, J. and Barber, J. (1992) Photosynthetica. In press
11. Barber, J. and Andersson, B. (1992) Trends Biochem. Sci. 17, 61-66
12. Shipton, C.A. and Barber, J. (1992) Biochim. Biophys. Acta 1099, 85-90

TURNOVER OF D1 PROTEIN DURING PHOTOINHIBITION AND RECOVERY IN A MOSS *CERATODON PURPUREUS*

RINTAMÄKI, EEVI, SALO, RIITTA AND ARO, EVA-MARI, DEPT OF BIOLOGY, UNIV. OF TURKU, SF-20700 TURKU, FINLAND

1. INTRODUCTION

Photoinhibition induced decline of photosynthesis probably results both from induction of photoprotective mechanisms associated with the dissipation of excessive energy in photosynthetic apparatus as well as from the photodamage to Photosystem II (PSII) (1). The latter stage is often called irreversible photoinhibition, because the recovery from photodamage demands chloroplast protein synthesis emphasizing the turnover of PSII reaction center polypeptide, the D1 protein (2). Although individual processes of photoinhibition have been well characterized, timing and the relative contributions of the different components in photoinhibition are still under discussion. The aim of the present paper was to elucidate the role of the D1 protein turnover in the course of photoinhibition and subsequent recovery in a moss *Ceratodon purpureus*.

2. MATERIALS AND METHODS

Protonemata of moss, *Ceratodon purpureus* (Hedw.) Brid. were grown at 20°C at 70 μmol photons m^{-2} s^{-1}. Protonemata were incubated overnight in the dark before transferring to illumination of 1000 μmol photons m^{-2} s^{-1} for 4.5 h at 28°C. The recovery was followed under photon flux densities of 50 μmol m^{-2} s^{-1} for 20 h at 25°C. Chloroplast translation inhibitor, lincomycin (1 kg m^{-3}) and dithiothreitol (DTT) (2 mol m^{-3}) were added on the growth medium one hour before photoinhibitory treatment. Fluorescence induction of protonemata sample was measured with pulse amplitude modulated fluorometer (PAM 101; Heinz Walz, Germany) at room temperature after 15 min dark incubation. Rates of synthesis and degradation of the D1 protein were followed by pulse-chase techniques and immunoblot analysis.

3. RESULTS AND DISCUSSION

3.1 Association of the D1 protein turnover with the decline of photochemical efficiency of PSII during photoinhibtion: Illumination at high light for 4.5 h resulted in about 30 % inhibition of the ratio of variable fluorescence (F_v) to maximal fluorescence (F_{max}) (Fig. 1.a.). Although protonemata were grown at low PFD, they possessed

N. Murata (ed.), Research in Photosynthesis, Vol. IV, 431–434.

a high turnover rate of the D1 protein at high light. Half-life of the D1 protein was less than 30 min. Only slight net loss of the D1 protein occured during photoinhibition in the absence of lincomycin (Table 1.). Degradation of D1 protein occured without any transient phosphorylation detected in higher plant thylakoids during photoinhibition (3). Apparently the high capacity to repair damaged PSII centres protected protonemata against severe photoinhibition of PSII. Indeed, photoinhibition was clearly accelerated in the presence of chloroplast translation inhibitor. 60 % inhibition in F_v/F_{max} was observed in the samples incubated with lincomysin during 4.5 h with corresponding loss also in the D1 protein (Fig. 1.a. and Table 1.). Inhibition of the formation of zeaxanthin with DTT (4) further enhanced the decline of F_v/F_{max} indicating, that xanthophyll cycle has some protective role against photoinhibition in protonemata.

The decline of F_v/F_{max} was biphasic. The fast phase was characterized by strong decrease of F_{max} values (Fig.1.c.) and might be caused by induction of photoprotective mechanisms. The slow phase seemed to be associated with the damage to PSII reaction centres, since the decline in F_v/F_{max} was enhanced in the presence of lincomycin (Fig. 1.a.) with corresponding increase in initial fluorescence (F_o) (1) (Fig. 1.b.).

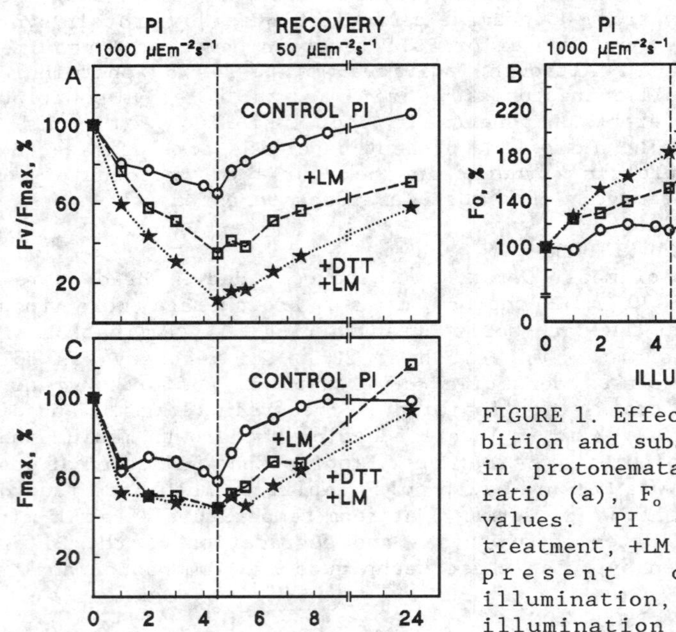

FIGURE 1. Effects of photoinhibition and subsequent recovery in protonemata on the F_v/F_{max} ratio (a), F_o (b) and F_{max} (c) values. PI =photoinhibition treatment, +LM = lincomycin was present during the illumination, +DTT+LM = illumination both with dithiothreitol and lincomycin. The means of three to five samples are presented as a percentage of the control value measured before onset of illumination.

Table 1. Relative amount of D1 protein in the samples after photoinhibition (PI) and after recovery of 20 h (REC) in the presence or absence of inhibitors. Abbreviations as in Fig. 1.

	Control PI	+LM	+DTT+LM
Control	100%	100%	100%
PI	85%	38%	25%
REC	106%	30%	27%

3.2 Restoration of F_o in recovery conditions is dependent on chloroplast protein synthesis: Recovery of photoinhibited control samples consisted both of an increase in F_{max} and decrease in F_o (Fig. 1.). In the presence of lincomycin some recovery of F_v/F_{max} was also detected (Fig. 1.a.). The rise resulted from full recovery of F_{max}, while F_o level even continued to increase during recovery (Fig 1.b. and c.). The results suggest that increase in F_o is connected to the accumulation of damaged and/or D1 depleted PSII centres and decrease in F_o to the repair of these centres. The conclusion was further supported by the experiment, where restoration of F_v/F_{max} was followed in the presence of lincomycin after high light treatments of 1, 2, 3 and 4.5 hours. The longer the duration of photoinhibition the higher F_o level after recovery (data not shown).

Dependence of the F_o level of fluorescence on the proportion of irreversibly damaged PSII was also seen, if the D1 protein synthesis was inhibited with lincomycin during recovery (Fig. 2.) or by

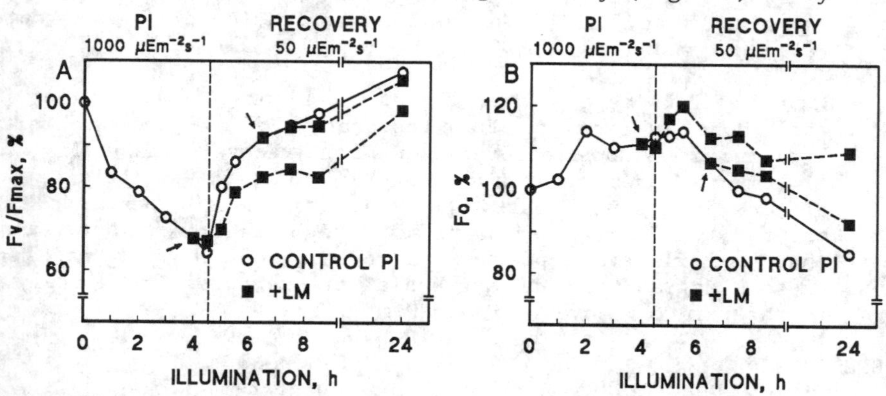

FIGURE 2. Effect of lincomycin on the restoration of F_v/F_{max} ratio (a) and F_o value (b) in photoinhibited C. purpureus. Addition time of lincomycin is indicated by arrows. The effects of lincomycin on the fluorescence parameters at recovery light in the samples without preceding high light treatment have been subtracted from the values presented in the figure. Abbreviations as in Fig. 1.

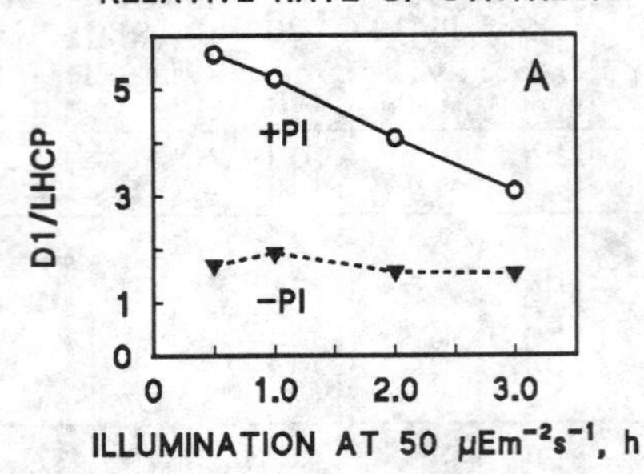

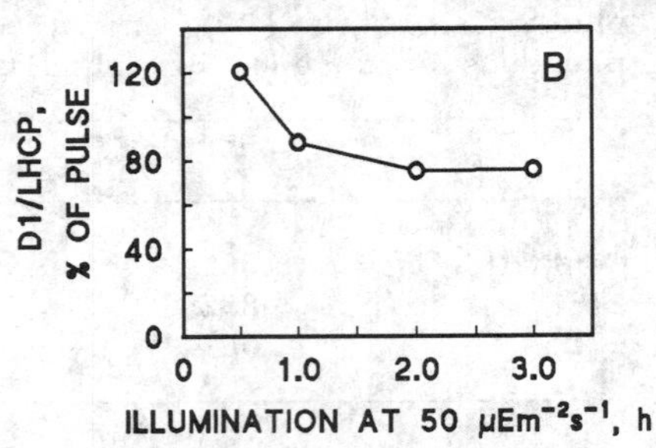

FIGURE 3. Relative rates of synthesis (a) and degradation (b) of D1 protein at recovery light after photoinhibition treatment. a) The rates of synthesis were estimated by following the incorboration of ^{35}S-methionine into D1 protein and light harvesting polypeptides (LHCP) in samples photoinhibited at high light (+PI) or in control samples without preceding photoinhibition treatment (-PI). The results are presented as a ratio of radioactivity in D1 protein to the that in LHCP. b) Samples were labelled with ^{35}S-methionine for three hours durig photoinhibition (=pulse), after that the samples were incubated at recovery light with cold methionine for indicated times (=chase). The loss of radioactivity from D1 protein was estimated as in a) and expressed as a percentage from pulse sample.

incubation in the dark after photoinhibition (data not shown). As mentioned above, some net loss of D1 protein occured at high light (Table 1). If the synthesis of D1 protein was inhibited during recovery, the level of F_o remained high (Fig. 2.a). Neither in these experiments any inhibition of the restoration of F_{max} was detected (data not shown).

3.3 Repair of PSII centres depleted of the D1 protein took place in the early hours of recovery: Full restoration of F_v/F_{max} was inhibited if lincomycin was added before onset of the recovery phase (Fig. 2.a.). Lincomycin added after two hours in recovery conditions, had no effect, indicating that D1 protein synthesis dependent recovery occured during the first hours after high light treatment. Pulse and chase experiments supported the conclusion. Highest rates of D1 protein degradation and synthesis were measured immediately after transfer into recovery light (Fig. 3.).

REFERENCES

1 Krause, G.H. (1988) Physiol. Plant. 74, 566-574
2 Schuster, G., Timberg, R. and Ohad, I. (1988) Eur. J. Biochem. 177, 403-410
3 Aro,E.-M. Kettunen,R. and Tyystjärvi,E.(1992) FEBS Lett. 297,29-33
4 Bilger, W., Björkman, O. and Thayer, S.S. (1989) Plant Physiol. 91, 542-551

STUDIES ON D1 PROTEIN DEGRADATION IN ISOLATED PHOTOSYSTEM II MEMBRANES FROM *SYNECHOCYSTIS* 6803.

Åsa Hagman, Fredrik Nilsson and Bertil Andersson
Department of Biochemistry, Arrhenius Laboratories for Natural Sciences, Stockholm University, S-106 91 Stockholm, Sweden

1. INTRODUCTION

Our knowledge on the mechanism of light-induced D1 protein degradation in plants has advanced through photoinhibition experiment performed on isolated PS II subfractions (1). It has been possible to identify proteolytic activites tightly associated with the PS II complex and several D1 protein fragments have been identified (1). In this study we have applied a preparation of highly active PS II membranes from *Synechocystis* 6803 (2) for studies on light-induced D1 protein degradation in cyanobacteria. The results suggest that the overall properties of the degradation process is the same in cyanobacteria and plants thereby giving credibility to use of site directed mutagenesis in *Synechocystis* for studies on the mechanism of D1 protein proteolysis.

2. MATERIALS AND METHODS

Thylakoids isolated from *Synechocystis* 6803 cells according to (2) were suspended in medium A, 50 mM Hepes (pH 6.5), 10 mM $MgCl_2$, 30 mM $CaCl_2$, 0.2 M sucrose, 25 % (v/v) glycerol, to a concentration of 3.0 mg chl/ml. (Fig. 1). Dodecyl-ß-maltoside was added to a final concentration of 0.01 % (w/v) and the suspension was gently agitated for 1 min. An equal volume of medium A containing 5 % (w/v) Triton X-100 was added to the thylakoid suspension and the mixture was gently stirred for 30 sec. Twice the initial volume of medium A containing 10 mM $LiClO_4$ was added and the suspension was centrifuged at 20 000 x g for 15 min. The supernatant was collected and centrifuged at 100 000 x g for 45 min (Fig. 1). All preparation steps were performed at 4°C and dimlight.

For studies on light-induced D1 protein degradation the final pellet of thylakoid membranes was diluted to 200 µg chl/ml in 50 mM MES (pH 6.0), 0.4 M sucrose, 20 mM $CaCl_2$ and 10 mM NaCl. The high light illumination was carried out aerobically at 20°C under white light using a projector lamp (5000 µE. $m^{-2}.s^{-1}$.) during

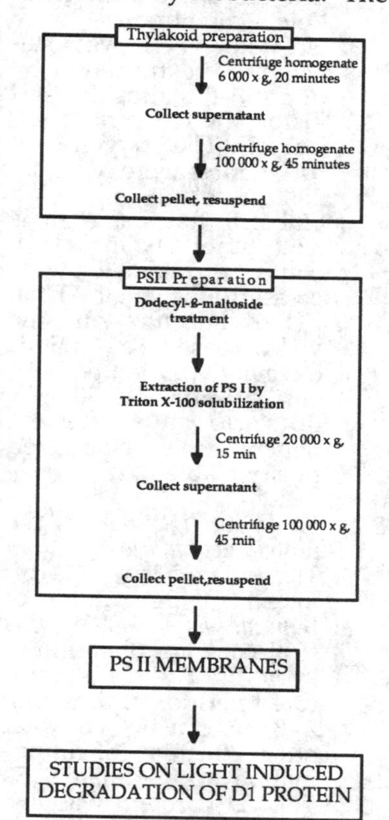

Fig. 1 Preparation scheme for PS II enriched thylakoid membranes from *Synechocystis* 6803.

N. Murata (ed.), Research in Photosynthesis, Vol. IV, 435–438.

0-60 minutes. In certain experiments the PS II mebranes were incubated with 0.1 mM diisopropyl fluorophosphate (DFP) at 4°C for 6 h in 50 mM phosphate buffer (pH 7.5) and 200 mM NaCl (3) prior to the photoinhibitory illumination. Polypeptides were separated by SDS-PAGE and immunoblotted according to standard procedures. Monospecific antibodies against D1 protein and its C-terminus were gifts from Drs. W. Vermaas and R.T. Sayre respectivily. Quantification of autoradiograms were performed by a scanning laser densiometer.

3. RESULTS

3.1. *Preparation of PSII enriched thylakoid membranes*

A highly active PS II subfraction can be isolated from *Synechocystis* 6803. The cells were broken in a glass-bead cell disrupter and thylakoid membranes were isolated. PS I was selectivily extracted by dodecyl-ß-maltoside and Triton X-100 treatment (Fig. 1). The oxygen evolution rates were typically 2800 µmol O_2/mg chl h (Table I). Rates as high as 3200 µmol O_2/mg chl h could be obtained by increasing the final Triton X-100 concentration. The yield, based on PS II oxygen evolution activity, varies from about 30-35 % down to a few percent depending on the desired purity (Table I).

TABLE 1. PROPERTIES AND YIELD OF PHOTOSYSTEM II MEMBRANES ISOLATED FROM *SYNECHOCYSTIS* 6803

	Yield (activity)	Oxygen evolution (µmol O_2/mg chlh)	Chl/P_{700}^+ (mol/mol)
Thylakoids	100	520	150
PS II membranes[a]	30	2800	890
PS II membranes[b]	4	3200	1080

The yield is based on PS II activity (%). a) values obtained from a high yield preparation b) values obtained from a high purity preparation.

3.2. *Studies on light-induced D1 protein degradation.*

The isolated oxygen evolving PS II preparation of *Synechocystis* 6803 was subjected to photoinhibitory light for the indicated periods of time (Fig 2 ,3). It can be seen that after 20 min. of illumination approximately 50 % of D1 protein was lost and after 60 min. there is virtually no D1 protein left. These results give

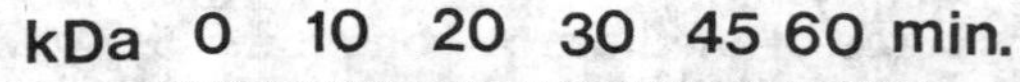

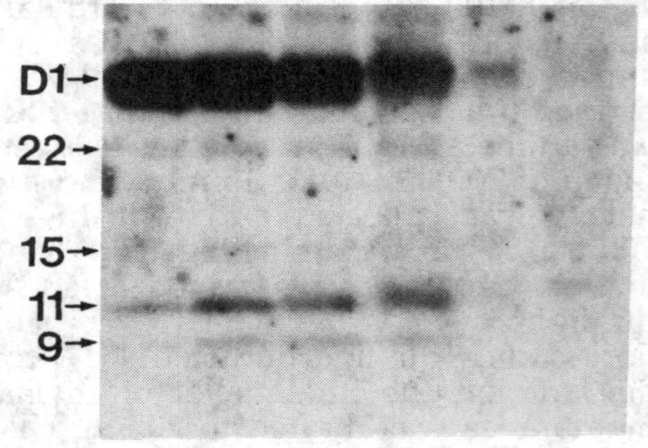

Fig. 2 Western blot analyses of D1 protein in PS II enriched cyanobacterial thylakoid membranes exposed to photoinhibitory light.

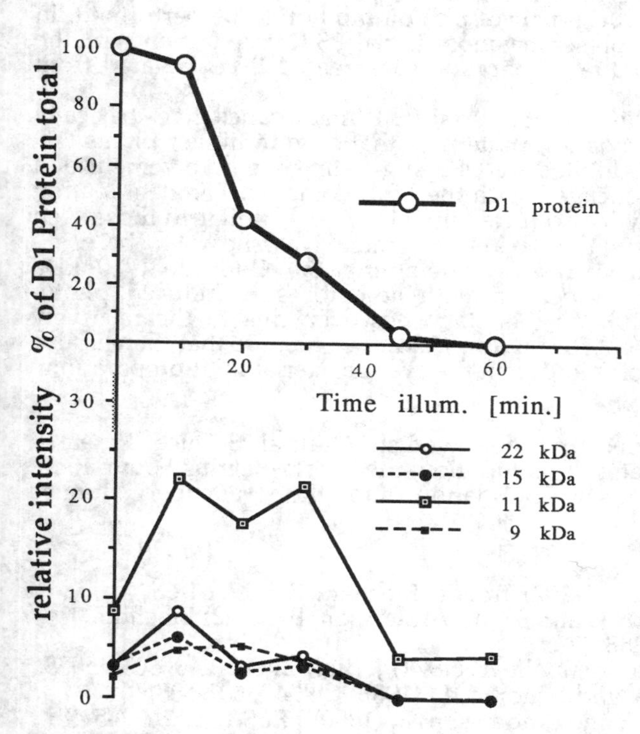

Fig. 3 Correlation between D1 protein degradation and the accumulation of 22, 15, 11 and 9 kDa proteolytic fragments.

evidence that light-induced degradation of D1 protein can occur in vitro in the cyanobacterial PS II membranes. This conclusion is further supported by the light dependant accumulation of four D1 protein fragments with apparent molecular weight of 22, 15, 11 and 9 kDa (Figs. 2, 3) during the course of the experiment. Surprisingly, small amounts of the fragments were present already in the dark control, an observation to which we presently have no direct explanation and which is not seen in a corresponding experiment using spinach PS II preparations (4). The amount of fragments was most pronounced after 10-20 minutes of the photoinhibitory illumination. The intensity of the two major immunoblotted bands, the 22 and 11 kDa fragments, increased about 2.5 times after 10 minutes of illumination. The fragments are almost completely degraded after 60 minutes, indicating the presence of secondary proteolytic activity in the preparation.

Using an antibody raised against a synthetic peptide representing the C-terminal of the D1 protein (5), it could be seen that the 11 kDa fragment is of C-terminal origin (not shown).

As has previously been shown for plant PS II, the D1 protein degradation can be blocked by the action of serine protease inhibitors (6, 7) such as diisopropyl fluorophosphate (DFP), which binds to the serine of the catalytic site. When DFP was added to the cyanobacterial PS II membranes partial inhibition of D1 protein was obtained. Thus after 30 minutes of strong illumination 43 % of the D1 protein remained in the presence of the protease inhibitor while 15 % was left in the control sample.

4. DISCUSSION

The major advantages with the PS II preparation from *Synechocystis* 6803 are that it is rapid, has a high yield and that the functional intactness (2) allows several studies such as the analysis of light-induced D1 protein degradation associated with repair of photoinhibition to be performed. In fact, one can compare the present cyanobacterial PS II preparation with the widely used PS II membrane preparation (designated BBY) isolated from plant thylakoids (8).

High light treatment of the cyanobacterial PS II membranes gives basically the same D1 protein degradation pattern as that seen in higher plants (1,9 ,10). The degradation is inhibited by DFP suggesting the involvement of a serine protease tightly associated with the PS II complex. The degradation gives rise to four proteolytic products with sizes very similar to those seen for the plant PS II (9, 10). The 11 kDa fragment was shown to be of C-terminal origin and thus probably resembling the C-terminal 10 kDa fragment reported to be associated with acceptor side induced photo-inhibition in plants (9, 10). At this stage however, due to the relatively complex pattern of fragment formation, we cannot exclude that there is also donor side induced photoinhibition in the cyanobacterial PS II preparation.

5. ACKNOWLEDGEMENT

This work was supported by the Swedish Natural Science Research Council, the Göran Gustafsson Foundation, the Hierta-Retzius Foundation, the Carl-Fredrik von Horn Foundation and the Wallenberg Jubilee Foundation.

REFERENCES

1. Barber, J. and Andersson, B. (1992) Trends. Biochem. Sci. 17, 61-66.
2. Nilsson, F., Gounaris, K., Styring, S. and Andersson, B. (1992) Biochim. Biophys. Acta 1100, 251-258.
3. Maroux, S., Baratti, J. and Desnuelle, P. (1971) J. Biol. Chem. 246, 5031-5038.
4. Sayre, R.T., Andersson, B. and Bogorad, L. (1986) Cell 47, 601-608.
5. Virgin, I., Ghanotakis, D.F. and Andersson, B. (1990) FEBS Lett. 269, 45-48.
6. Virgin, I., Salter, A.H., Ghanotakis, D.F. and Andersson, B. (1991) FEBS Lett. 287, 125-128.
7. Shipton, C. A., and Barber, J. (1992) Biochim. Biophys. Acta 1099, 85-90.
8. Berthold, D.A., Babcock, G.T. and Yocum, C.F. (1981) FEBS Lett. 134, 231-234.
9. De Las Rivas, J. Andersson, B. and Barber, J. (1992) FEBS Lett. 301, 246-252.
10. Salter, A.H., Virgin, I., Hagman, Å. and Andersson, B. (1992) Biochemistry. 31, 3990-3998

MULTI-STEP REACTION OF THE PHOTODAMAGE TO PHOTOSYSTEM II REACTION CENTER D1/D2/CYT B-559 COMPLEX

Chong-Qin Tang, Ting-Yun Kuang, Zhen-Bao Yu, Yong-He Lu,
De-Chuan Peng and Pei-Sung Tang

Laboratory of Photosynthesis, Institute of Botany,
Academia Sinica, Beijing 100044, P.R. China

1. INTRODUCTION

It has been proved that PS II reaction center D1/D2/cyt b-559 complex isolated from higher plants is very sensitive to strong illumination. Both pigments (Chl and β-carotene) and D1 protein can be damaged by light treatment in specific conditions [1,2,3]. In this paper, we discovered that in the abscence of the secondary acceptor (Q_A), the photodamage of D1/D2/cyt b-559 complex is likely a multi-step reaction, and some His residues are involved in the photodamage process.

2. MATERIALS AND METHODS

D1/D2/cyt b-559 complex was isolated from spinach as described by Nanba and Satoh [4] and Chapman et al.[5]. The purified D1/D2/cyt b-559 complex was deluted with a buffer of 50mM Tris-Cl (pH 7.2), containing 30 mM NaCl, 2 mM β-dodecyl maltoside, and then illuminated at 25 ℃ with heat-filtered white light from a 500W projector lamp delivering 330 Watts/m^2 onto the sample. Optical absorption spectra were measured with Shimadz UV-3000 spectrophotometer. Fluorescence emission spectra were obtained by a Hitachi MPF-4 fluorometer. Excitation was at 436 nm. Amino acid composition was measured by 835-50 Hitachi amino acid analyzer.

3. RESULTS AND DISCUSSION

3.1 Effect of illumination and the following incubation in the dark on the absorption and fluorescence spectra of D1/D2/cyt b-559 complex

As observed, the light treatment of D1/D2/cyt b-559 complex might lead to a decrease in red absorption peak, and concomitant blue-shift. During the incubation in the dark following illumination, the decrease of the absorbance and blue-shift continually proceeded. But, in control experiments, little changes in the absorption spectrum of the non-photodamaged sample were observed after 10 min incubation in the dark at 25 ℃ (data not shown). The results of a

N. Murata (ed.), Research in Photosynthesis, Vol. IV, 439–442.

similar experiment are presented as absorption difference spectra in Fig.1. The difference between the absorption spectrum measured immediately after 2 min illumination or 10 min incubation in the dark following the 2 min preillumination and the initial dark absorption spectrum shows a negative peak at 680 nm. Fig.2 shows the change of absorbance at 680 nm as a function of incubation time in the dark at 25 ℃ following preillumination. The rate and degree of the absorbance changes are highly influenced by preillumination time. Although the absorbance of the non-preilluminated D1/D2/cyt b-559 complex also changed during incubation in the dark, the change rate was much slower than that of the preilluminated sample.

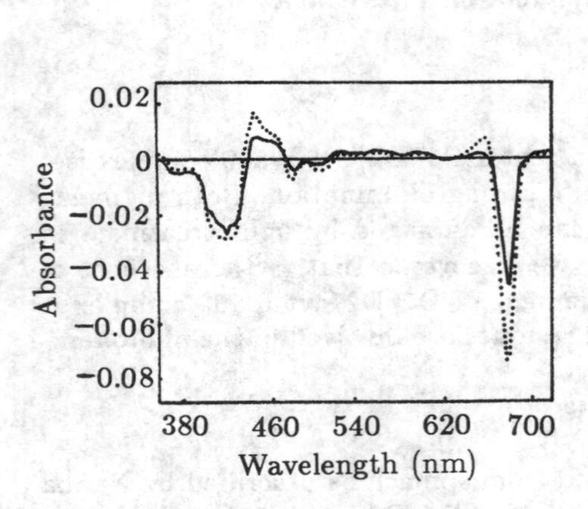

Fig.1 Difference between the absorption spectrum measured immediately after 2 min illumination (——) or 10 min incubation at 25 ℃ in the dark following the 2 min preillumination (- - - -) and the initial dark absorption spectum of D1/D2/cyt b-559 complex.

Fig.2 Effect of incubation in the dark at 25 ℃ after 0 (A), 1 (B), 5 (C) and 10 min (D) preillumination on the relative absorbance changes at 680 nm of D1/D2/cyt b-559 complex.

It was reported that the photodamage of D1/D2/cyt b-559 complex led to a large increase in fluorescence and a blue-shift of the maximum emission wavelength [6]. The decrease of fluorescence intensity could also be observed, if the fluorescence emission spectra were immediately measured following illumination (Fig.3). But, incubation in the dark at room temperature (25 ℃) after 2 min preillumination made the fluorescence intensity increase and emission maximum wavelength blue-shift. The changes of relative fluorescence intensity at 680 nm are shown in Fig.4, the data are similar to those shown in Fig.2 .

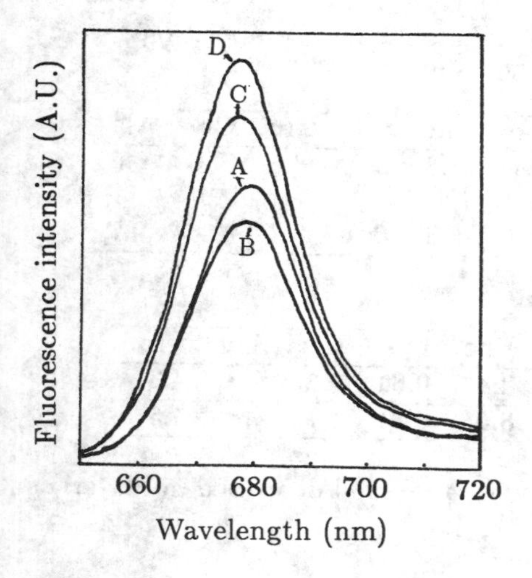

Fig.3 Fluorescence emission spectra of D1/D2/cyt b-559 complex without light treatment (A) and after incubation in the dark at 25 ℃ for 0.25 (B), 10 (C) and 20 min (D) following 2 min illumination.

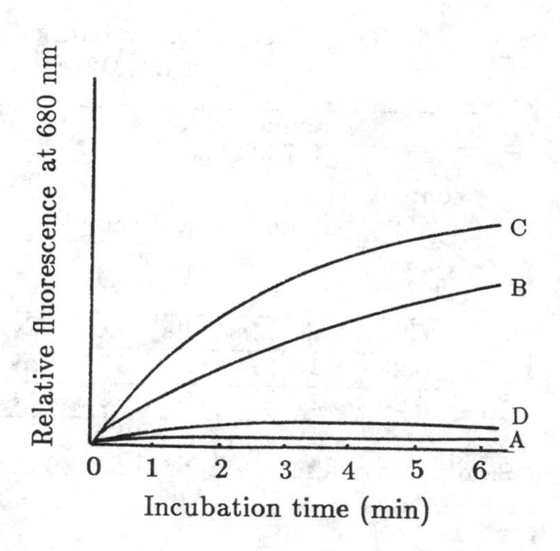

Fig.4 Effect of incubation in the dark at 25 ℃ after 0 (A), 2 (B), 5 (C) and 10 min (D) preillumination on the relative fluorescence emission at 680 nm of D1/D2/cyt b-559 complex.

3.2 Effect of photodamage on the amino acid composition of D1/D2/cyt b-559 complex

Amino acid composition of the control and photodamaged D1/D2/cyt b-559 complex is shown in Table 1. Except that His residue content decreased by about 28%, there were no obvious changes in the contents of other amino acid residues after illumination. The result suggests that some His residues were damaged by illumination. As reported by Durrant [7], singlet oxygen was generated during the charge separation and recombination in D1/D2/cyt b-559 complex. The former is likely toxic to some amino acid residues, such as His residue in this work. What's more, the His residue would be the most possible site binding with P680 as predicted by comparing D1/D2 with the photosynthetic reaction center of purple bacteria.

Telfer et al. demonstrated that, in the absence of the secondary acceptor, P680 was damaged by strong illumination[1]. We observed that the changes of absorption, CD (not shown in this paper) and fluorescence spectra were continuously occured during the incubation period following the preillumination, but these changes were not dramatic in the control sample, which were not preilluminated. These results suggest that a relative stable intermediate was likely generated by illumination, resulting in the further damage of the reaction center complex in the following dark incubation period.

Table 1. Effect of photodamage on the amino acid composition of D1/D2/cyt b-559 complex

	amino acids	Asp	Thr	Ser	Glu	Gly	Ala
content (%)	control sample	7.1	5.3	5.9	8.5	9.6	9.6
	photodamaged sample*	7.2	5.3	6.0	8.7	9.6	9.7

Cys	Val	Met	Ile	Leu	Tyr	Phe	Lys	His	Arg	Pro
0.23	5.2	2.3	5.2	10.5	2.9	8.4	0.84	2.3	5.9	4.3
0.24	5.2	2.2	5.2	10.5	2.8	8.5	0.84	1.7	5.8	4.5

* Samlpe was illuminated for about 30 min with a method described in Materials and Methods.

Our result also show that besides P680, some His residues were damaged by illumination, so the spectral changes of D1/D2/Cyt b-559 complex during the incubation after preillumination may result from the damage, which probably made the conformation of proteins, particularly in the P680-binding sites, become more labile. The spetral properties could be affected by the change of protein conformation.

It was noted that photodamage in the absence of acceptor Q_A resulted in an increase of apparent molecular mass of D1 polypeptide, but no breakdown fragments were observed in SDS/PAGE profile [3,6]. We think that the shift in apparent molecular mass of D1 polypeptide may be related to the abnormal behaviours of the damaged polypeptide.

REFERENCES

1. Telfer, A., He, W.-Z. and Barber, J. (1990) Biochim. Biophys. Acta 1017, 143-151
2. Telfer, A., De Las Rivas, J. and Barber, J. (1991) Biochim. Biophys. Acta 1060, 106-114
3. Shipton, C.A. and Barber, J. (1991) Proc. Natl. Acad. Sci. USA 88, 6691-6695
4. Nanba, D. and Satah, K. (1987) Proc. Natl. Acad. Sci. USA 84, 109-112
5. Chapman, D.J., Gounaris, K. and Barber, J. (1988) Biochim. Biophys. Acta 933, 423-431
6. Chapman, D.J., Gounaris, K. and Barber, J. (1989) Photosynthetica 23, 411-426
7. Durrant, J.R., Giorgi, L.B., Barber, J., Klug, D.R. and Porter, G. (1990) Biochim. Biophys. Acta 1017, 167-175

PHOTOSYSTEM II FUNCTION, PHOTOINHIBITION AND TURNOVER OF D1 PROTEIN AT DIFFERENT IRRADIANCES IN NORMAL AND ATRAZINE-RESISTANT PLANTS WITH AN ALTERED Q_B-BINDING SITE

Cecilia Sundby*, Stephanie McCaffery, Wah Soon Chow and Jan M. Anderson
CSIRO, Division of Plant Industry, GPO Box 1600, ACT 2601, Canberra, Australia

INTRODUCTION

The spontaneous mutation of D1 protein in the reaction centre of photosystem II (PSII), involving the substitution of serine-264 by glycine, has been detected in several weed species in response to extensive use of the PSII herbicide, atrazine [1]. This atrazine-resistance trait has been bred into crop plants such as *Brassica napus* for potential use in selective weed control. Ser-264 is involved in atrazine binding in the Q_B-binding niche of D1 protein [2]; its absence not only prevents binding of atrazine but also decreases the binding affinity for plastoquinone. The decreased affinity for plastoquinone retards electron transfer from Q_A^- to Q_B [3].

Our analyses of D1 Ser-264 mutants of *Brassica napus*, grown over a wide range of constant irradiances, show that (1) the altered Q_B-binding causes primary effects (observable at all growth irradiances) on PSII photochemistry which lower the light-limited photosynthetic efficiency and (2) the effects on PSII photochemistry in turn increase both the susceptibility to photoinhibition and the rate of D1 protein turnover.

Moreover, our studies show that the rate of D1 protein turnover is maximal at a light level corresponding to the growth irradiance. This unexpected finding probably reflects a down-regulation of PSII [4] when the growth irradiance is exceeded.

MATERIALS AND METHODS

Atrazine-susceptible wildtype (S) and atrazine-resistant mutant (R) of *Brassica napus* were grown at 50, 150, 350 or 600-700 μmol photons m^{-2} s^{-1} (μE m^{-2} s^{-1} for short) in a growth cabinet, as in [5]. Chlorophyll fluorescence yield was measured in intact leaves with a PAM fluorometer. Quantum yields in limiting light, CO_2- and light-saturated rates of oxygen evolution and oxygen yields per single-turnover flash were determined with a Hansatech leaf disc oxygen electrode. DCMU-binding sites per mol Chl were determined in isolated thylakoids as in [5]. Leaf discs (on water) were photoinhibited by exposure to 1500 μE m^{-2} s^{-1}. The rate of D1 protein turnover was determined in leaf discs by using ^{35}S-methionine and analysis of label in the D1 protein band after SDS-PAGE, either after chasing of prelabelled leaf discs (rate of D1 protein degradation) or by estimating the uptake of ^{35}S-methionine during 1 hour of illumination at different irradiances.

RESULTS AND DISCUSSION

1. The altered Q_B-binding site in atrazine-resistant biotypes: effects on PSII function

The fraction of open PSII centres is estimated by the chlorophyll fluorescence photochemical quenching parameter, q_P. Fig. 1A shows that q_P in leaves of plants grown at 350 μE m^{-2} s^{-1} decreased with increasing actinic light; R-biotypes differ from wildtypes in that q_P is some 25% lower at all actinic irradiances. Also when grown under very low light (50 μE m^{-2} s^{-1}) as shown in Fig. 1B, the R-biotype (R50) had a lower value of q_P than the wildtype (S50). Notably, both biotypes showed lower values of q_P when compared to the respective plants grown under 350 μE m^{-2} s^{-1}, indicating that the ability of the plants to maintain the acceptor side oxidised at a given irradiance is rather limited at very low growth irradiance. At low actinic irradiances, the more reduced state of Q_A in R-biotypes coincided with an increased probability for absorbed photons to be dissipated as heat, since the non-photochemical quenching coefficient, q_N, for R-biotypes was higher than for the wildtype (Fig. 1C). However, at higher actinic irradiances, the situation was reversed, with q_N being lower for R-biotypes than for the wildtype.

---

*Permanent address: Dept. of Biochemistry, University of Lund, PO Box 124, S-221 00 Lund, Sweden

N. Murata (ed.), Research in Photosynthesis, Vol. IV, 443–446.

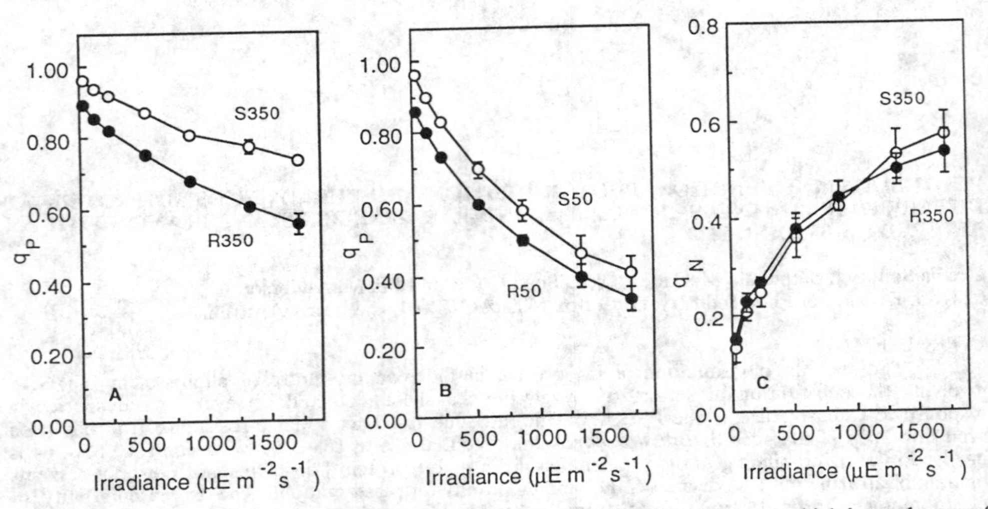

Fig. 1. Chlorophyll fluorescence quenching coefficients *vs* incident irradiance to which intact leaves of wildtype (S) and atrazine-resistant (R) biotypes were exposed. The photochemical quenching coefficient, q_p, (A,B) and the non-photochemical quenching parameter, q_N, (C) were determined for plants grown under 350 (A,C) or 50 μE m^{-2} s^{-1} (B).

The lower values of q_p for R- than S- biotypes (Fig. 1A, 1B), indicative of a more reduced state of Q_A, should decrease the quantum efficiency of R-biotypes. Quantum yields based on absorbed photons were measured for plants grown at different irradiances. While the quantum yield was close to 0.10 for the wildtype, irrespective of growth irradiance, it was lower for R-biotypes at all growth irradiances. These data strongly suggest that the lower quantum yields of R-biotypes are an inevitable consequence of a more reduced state of Q_A during illumination, and *not only* an indirect effect of photoinhibition [6,7] at higher growth irradiances. Another consequence of the slower rate of electron transfer from Q_A^- to Q_B in R-biotypes is reflected in the oxygen yield during repetitive flash illumination. Fig. 2B shows that the oxygen yield per flash is 25% lower for R-biotypes irrespective of growth irradiance. Therefore, the number of PSII centres calculated from this oxygen flash yield is under-estimated for R-biotypes. That the total number of PSII centres is the same for R-biotypes as for the wildtype is evident from the number of DCMU-binding sites per Chl (Fig. 2B). Thus, the lower oxygen flash yield is not due to fewer PSII centres on a chlorophyll basis in R-biotypes, but to the larger proportion of PSII centres with Q_A in the reduced form during repetitive flash illumination.

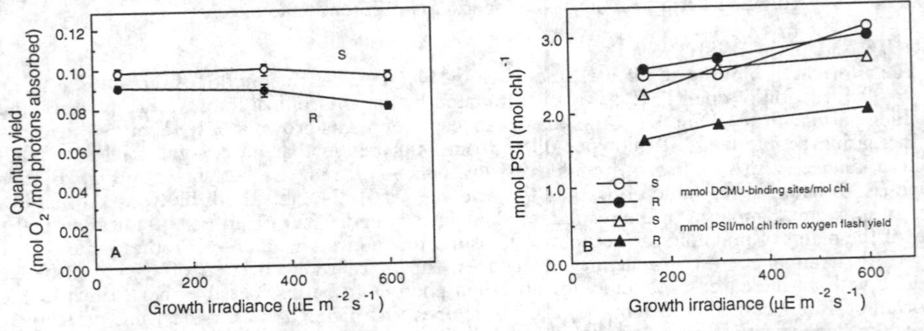

Fig. 2. (A) The light-limited quantum yield of O_2 evolution in air + 1% CO_2, based on absorbed light (B) The numbers of PSII reaction centres per Chl assayed from (1) leaf disc O_2 yield per flash and (2) DCMU-binding sites in isolated thylakoids for S- and R- biotypes grown at different irradiances.

Together these data suggest that the decreased binding of plastoquinone in the Q_B-binding niche of R-biotypes retards electron transfer from Q_A^- to Q_B, which in turn causes an intrinsic lowering of the photosynthetic efficiency of PSII, even at low irradiance. However, in spite of this defect, maximal photosynthetic rates of oxygen evolution under light saturation were *not* lower for R-biotypes compared to the wildtype with our plants [5]. This is consistent with *in vivo* electron transport through PSII not being rate limiting for photosynthesis. Nevertheless, the decreased PSII photochemical efficiency may decrease crop yield of atrazine-resistant plants, since non-saturating light conditions are not uncommon in temperate regions [8].

2. The altered Q_B-binding site in atrazine-resistant biotypes is associated with increased susceptibility to photoinhibition and higher rates of D1 protein turnover

Apart from direct effects on PSII photochemistry, which affects light-limited but not light-saturated photosynthesis rates in R-biotypes, the altered Q_B-binding site with decreased rates of electron transfer from Q_A^- to Q_B in turn causes secondary effects: upon exposure to high irradiances, the R-biotypes are more sensitive to photoinhibition [5,7 and Fig. 3 insert]. We therefore investigated the rate of D1 protein turnover after photoinhibition and found it to be higher in R-biotypes ($t_{1/2}$ = 1.3 hours) than in the wildtype ($t_{1/2}$ = 1.9 hours), as seen in Fig. 3. Moreover, further studies of rates of D1 protein turnover at different irradiances showed that D1 protein turnover was distinctly faster in the R-bioypes as in wildtypes, *not only after photoinhibition but during normal growth* (see Fig. 4 and below).

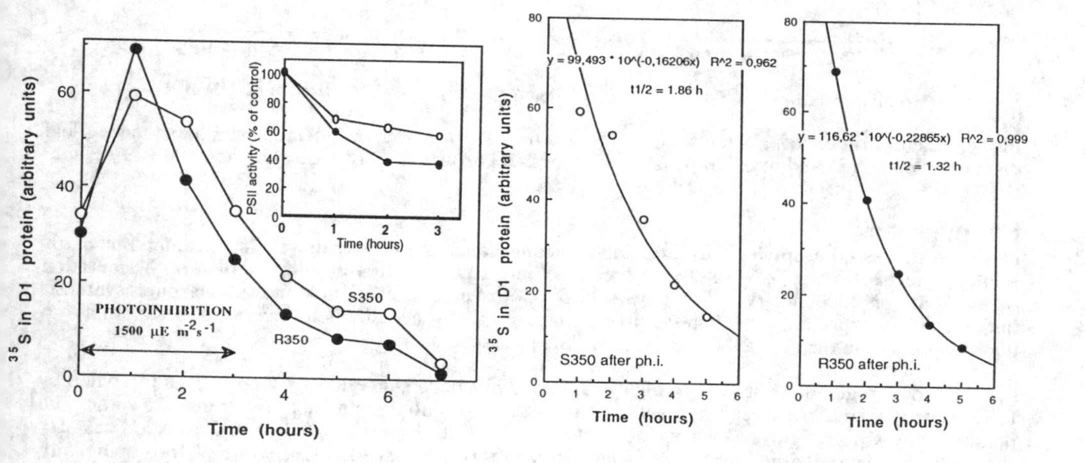

Fig. 3. Rates of D1 protein degradation for wildtype (S) and R-biotypes determined by chasing the label in D1 of leaf discs prelabelled with ^{35}S-methionine and then subjected to photoinhibition for 3 h. Insert shows the decrease in the relative number of functional PSII centres during the photoinhibitory illumination as determined by oxygen flash yield measurements. To the right is shown the fitting of first-order rate equations to the disappearance of label from D1 protein.

3. D1 protein turnover is maximal at a light level corresponding to the growth irradiance

The D1 protein turnover *in vivo* was determined as a function of incident light for plants grown under different irradiances. For each type of plant grown at 50, 350 or 600 μE m^{-2} s^{-1}, the rate was maximum at a light level corresponding to the growth irradiance (Fig. 4). Thus, at irradiances below the growth irradiance the incorporation of label into D1 protein *increased* with the incident irradiance, but at irradiances above the growth irradiance it *decreased* with increasing incident irradiance. These data are consistent with a "down-regulation" of PSII at high irradiances [4], as summarized below in (2).

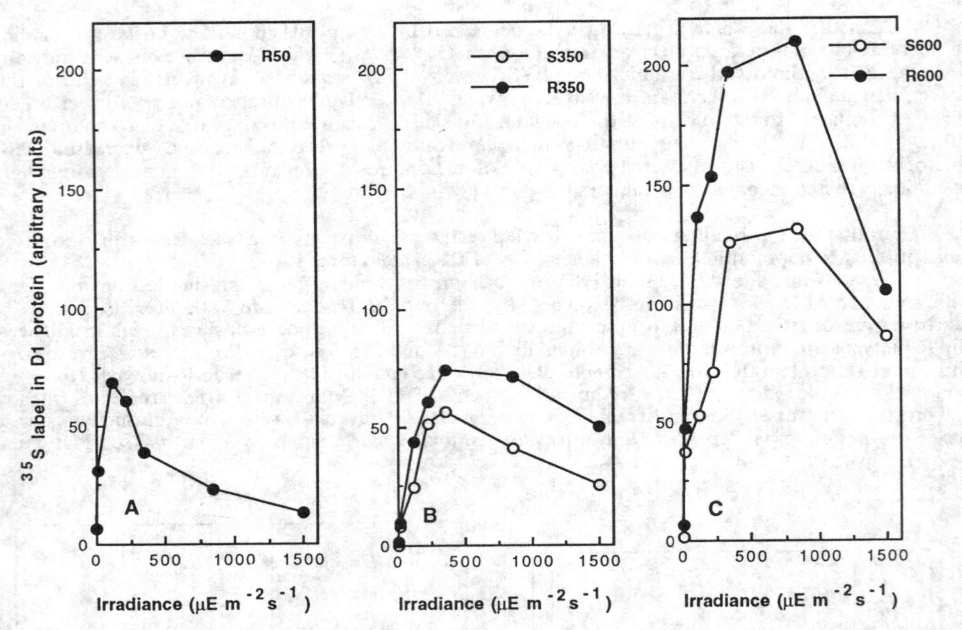

Fig. 4. Incorporation of ^{35}S-methionine (1 h) into D1 protein *vs* the incident irradiance, using leaf discs of wildtype (S) and atrazine-resistant biotypes (R) grown at 50 (A), 350 (B) and 600 (C) μE m^{-2} s^{-1}.

CONCLUSIONS

(1). The decreased crop yields for atrazine-resistant plants is probably due to two distinct, but partly related, effects of the Ser-264 to glycine exchange on D1 protein: firstly, a direct effect of the mutation on the PSII photochemistry which lowers PSII photosynthetic efficiency and affects photosynthesis under light-limiting but not light-saturating conditions; secondly, an increased suseptibility to photoinhibition, in turn caused by the altered PSII photochemistry.

(2). A "down-regulation" of PSII at high irradiances has been suggested by Öquist et al [4], whereby PSII centres which become non-functional in oxygen evolution and electron transport retain the possibility to absorb light and act as efficient quenchers of absorbed light energy, provided that D1 protein is *not* degraded and replaced. This has been termed a "shade plant strategy" for coping with photoinhibition [9], as opposed to a "sun plant strategy", where damaged centres are repaired by D1 protein turnover. We conclude that our data, showing a maximal rate of D1 protein turnover at a light level corresponding to growth irradiance, indicates that each plant uses both sun *and* shade plant strategies, the former at or below the growth irradiance, and the latter above the growth irradiance.

REFERENCES

1. Hirschberg J, Yehuda AB, Pecker I and Ohad I. 1987 In : Plant Molecular Biology (von Wettstein, D. and Chua, N.-H., eds.), Plenum Press, New York, pp 357-366.
2. Trebst A 1987 Z. Naturforsch. 42c, 742-750.
3. Bowes J, Crofts AR and Arntzen CJ 1980 Arch.Biochem.Biophys. 200, 303-308.
4. Öquist G, Chow WS and Anderson JM 1992 Planta 186, 450-460.
5. Sundby C, Chow WS and Anderson JM Biochim. Biophys. Acta (submitted).
6. Hart JJ and Stemler A 1990 Plant Physiol. 94, 1295-1300.
7. Hart JJ and Stemler A 1990 Plant Physiol. 94, 1301-1307.
8. Ort DR and Baker NR 1988 Plant Physiol. Biochem. 26, 555-565.
9. Öquist G, Anderson JM, McCaffery S and Chow WS 1992 Planta (in press).

Photoinhibition of Photosystem II in vivo: Does photoinhibition take place in the centers down-regulated by acidification of the lumen?

K.J. van Wijk and P.R. van Hasselt. Department of Plant Biology, University of Groningen, P.O. Box 14, 9750 AA Haren, The Netherlands

Introduction

Illumination of photosystem II (PS II) by excess light leads to a stepwise inactivation of PS II and results in degradation of the D_1-reaction center protein [e.g. 1]. In vitro photoinhibition of PS II can be caused by strong reduction ('overreduction') of the acceptor side [1,2] or by accumulation of oxidizing species on the donor side when PS II centers are inhibited in the water splitting complex prior to the photoinhibition treatment [3-7].

The prevailing mechanism of photoinhibition of PS II in vivo is unclear so far. The in vivo situation is complicated as closure of PS II (reduction of Q_A) is usually accompanied by light-induced acidification of the lumen resulting in down-regulation of PS II. This pH-dependent down-regulation was proposed to result from limitation of electron donation to P_{680} [8,9] keeping Q_A in its oxidized form.

In this study we were able to manipulate the 'energy'- and redox state of PS II quite independent of the photon flux density (PFD), by varying the metabolic demand for ATP and NADPH by temperature and $[CO_2]$ at different PFD's.

Material and Methods

Spinach was grown in soil in a controlled growth chamber (10 h light/14 h dark; 19°C/16°C (l/d); Rel. humidity 70/90% (l/d); PFD 220-250 μmol $^{-2}$ s^{-1}).
The photoinhibitory treatment of spinach leaf discs (d=17 mm) was carried out in a temperature-controlled cuvette by illumination of the upper side of the leaf discs, while monitoring chlorophyll a fluorescence using a PAM fluorometer (Walz). After dark adaptation at the specific temperature and gas mixture (for 30 minutes), basic (F_O) and maximum fluorescence (F_M) were measured. Subsequently, white inhibitory light was turned on, and saturating pulses were applied to allow separation of photochemical (q_P) and non-photochemical quenching (q_N). Basic fluorescence in the energized state (F_O') was measured after brief illumination (5 s) with far red light after the inhibitory light was turned off. Subsequent to the strong illumination treatment, the light was turned off and the leaf was dark adapted again for 30 minutes at 20°C after which F_O and F_M were measured again.

q_N and q_P were calculated as described by [10]. Photoinhibitory quenching (q_I), was calculated after 30 min dark adaptation at 20°C, following the photoinhibition treatment.

N. Murata (ed.), Research in Photosynthesis, Vol. IV, 447–450.

The energy-dependent quenching component (q_E) was calculated as $q_E=q_N-q_I$. This implies that q_E is calculated over the total population PS II centers, including the photoinhibited fraction (see Results and Discussion). A possible (small) contribution of quenching by state transitions (q_T) was neglected [see 10].

Results and Discussion

Spinach leaf discs were illuminated with strong light at different temperatures, while fluorescence was monitored continuously. A high [CO_2] was applied to prevent limitation of CO_2 by stomatal closure and to suppress photorespiration. Fig 1A shows the steady state values for q_P, q_N and q_E in the light (1.2 mmol m^{-2} s^{-1}), and q_I determined after the illumination treatment. With decreasing temperature, q_N shifted from q_E to q_I, while q_P decreased to zero (Fig 1A). Fig 1B shows q_I and q_E, as function of q_P, resulting from illumination with 0.6 and 1.2 mmol m^{-2} s^{-1}. q_N shifted from q_E to q_I while q_P decreased from 0.6 to zero. No effect of PFD on these relations was observed (Fig 1B).

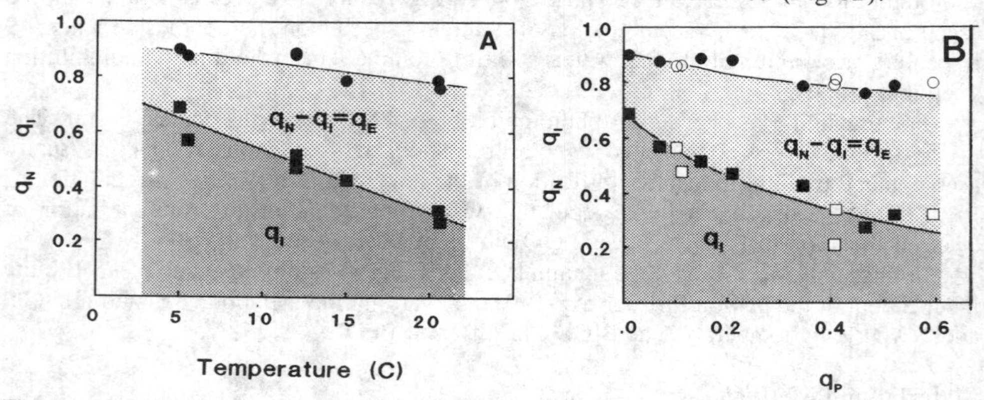

Fig. 1A,B. Effect of 100 min strong illumination of spinach leaf discs in 3% CO_2 and 21% O_2 at different temperatures. **A.** Temperature dependence of the quenching components, q_N (●) and q_P (■), measured in 1.2 mmol m^{-2} s^{-1} at the end of the illumination period and photoinhibition, calculated as q_I. **B.** Correlation between q_P and the quenching components q_N (●,○) and q_I (■,□) The leaf discs were illuminated in 0.6 (open symbols) or 1.2 closed symbols) mmol m^{-2} s^{-1} white light.

In a second set of experiments spinach leaf discs were illuminated at constant temperature. The metabolic demand for ATP and NADPH was influenced by manipulation of the [CO_2]. Large differences in q_P were induced at each PFD, depending on the [CO_2]. At the low [CO_2] (30 ppm), a high q_N (> 0.8) was established within 8 min of illumination (not shown) at all PFD's applied (Fig 2A). As can be seen in this figure, q_E was already maximal in 0.6 mmol m^{-2} s^{-1}, and is shifted to q_I with increasing light flux. At high [CO_2], q_N could be as low as 0.65 and increased to 0.9 in 3 mmol m^{-2} s^{-1} (Fig 2B).

As in Fig. 1B, an inverse correlation between q_P and photoinhibition (expressed as q_I or F_V) was found, but the low [CO_2] (30 ppm) shifted this correlation to lower q_P

values (Fig 2B). F_O was slightly increased after the photoinhibition treatment, with the highest increase when q_P was close to zero (not shown).

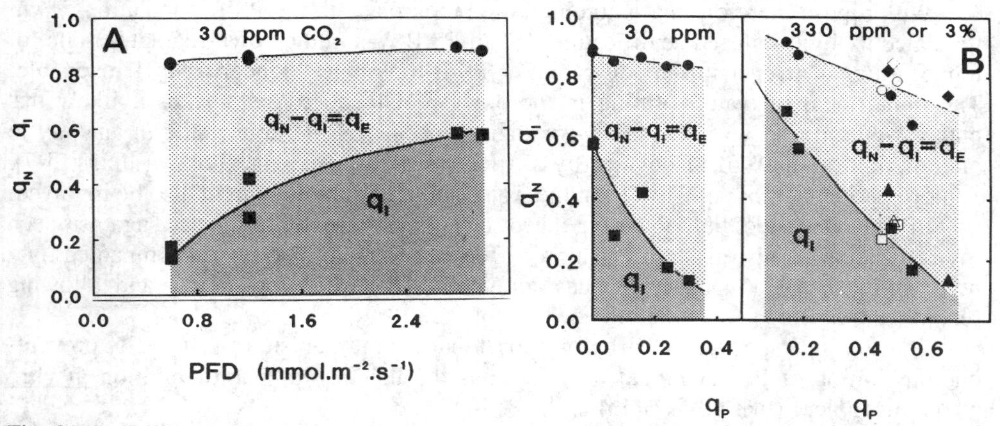

Fig. 2A,B. Effect of 100 min strong illumination of spinach leaf discs in the presence of different $[CO_2]$ and $[O_2]$ at 20-22°C. **A.** The quenching components q_N (●) and q_I (■) in 2 % O_2 and 30 ppm CO_2 as function of the PFD during the inhibition treatment. **B.** The quenching components q_N (●,○,◆,◇) and q_I (■,□,▲,△) as function of q_P. The photoinhibition was performed in 2% O_2 and 30 ppm CO_2 (left hand panel) or in 330 ppm (◆,◇,▲,△), 3% (●,○,■,□) CO_2 in either 2% O_2 (closed symbols) or 21% O_2 (open symbols).

The inhibition experiment at constant temperature (22°C) and varying $[CO_2]$ was repeated in a different setup, using detached V. unguiculata leaves while chloroplast-encoded translation was inhibited by streptomycin to prevent possible repair. Practically identical results as in the previous experiment with spinach were found (data not shown).

Mechanism of photoinhibition of PS II in vivo. Plotting the data from all experiments with spinach together in a single figure, shows an inverse relationship between q_I and q_E, independent of temperature, $[CO_2]$, $[O_2]$ and PFD (Fig 3A). Thus, when high values of q_E (mainly above 0.7) were reached, a further increase of the light intensity or a decrease of the metabolic demand for ATP and NADPH by decrease of temperature lead to a shift from q_E to q_I (Figs 1A, 2A). The same conclusion was reached when q_E was calculated using F_M obtained after the photoinhibitory treatment for normalisation (q_E denoted as q_E^*), implying that $(1-q_N) = (1-q_E^*) \cdot (1-q_I)$ [see 10] (Fig 3B).

Our data indicate that photoinhibition took place when 70-85% of the PS II population was down-regulated by light-induced acidification of the lumen. Strong evidence was recently presented that q_E was caused by impairment of the water splitting complex by a (reversible) release of Ca^{2+} [8]; the down-regulated centers kept Q_A in an oxidised form [9]. Therefore photoinhibition in such 'energized' centers is unlikely to result from overreduction of Q_A, as was shown to occur in absence of efficient acceptors and ΔpH in vitro [1,2]. It is hard to envisage that photoinhibition took place by overreduction of the small PS II population not affected by q_E (less than 30%) at such relatively low PFD's, as strongly reducing conditions and a high number of turnovers of P680 are needed to accomplish overreduction and subsequent photoinhibition through chlorophyll triplet formation [see 2].

We propose therefore that photoinhibition took place in the PS II population down-regulated by light-induced acidification; When PS II was in the down-regulated state for longer time, an irreversible modification of PS II took place, rendering q_N irreversible. The impairment of water-splitting in the down-regulated centers, makes it likely that photoinhibition in vivo is caused by oxidizing species on the donor side in analogy to photoinhibition of PS II inactivated by artificial pretreatment (e.g. Tris-washing) [3-7]. A more permanent loss of Ca^{2+} from the water splitting complex might also be involved.

In first instance the down-regulated centers should be protected against such 'overoxidation' as it was shown that the reversible Ca^{2+} release was accompanied by a redox shift of Q_A to positive values, preventing electron flow to Q_B and allowing recombination of Q_A^- with the oxidized donor side [8,9].

These results support the earlier proposal that the mechanism of q_E initially prevents photoinhibition of PS II [11,12], and explains the increase of photoinhibition in vitro when uncouplers (like gramicidin) are added [11].

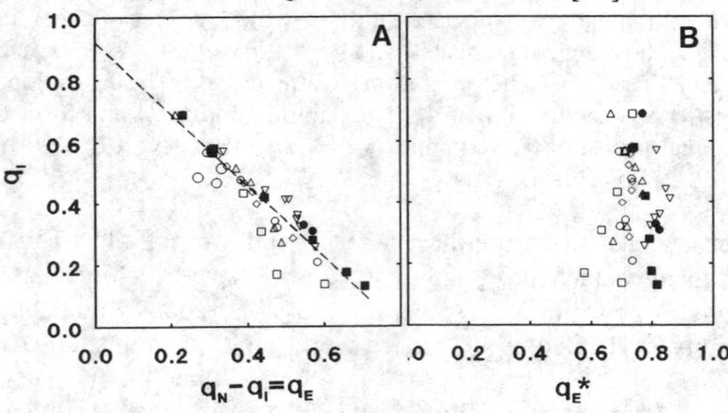

Fig. 3A,B. Correlation between q_E (**A**) or q_E^* (**B**) and q_I, using the data from Figs. 1 & 2. Different symbols are used for different environmental conditions.

Acknowledgements. This study was financially supported by BION, which is subsidized by the Netherlands Organization for the advancement of Pure Research (NWO).

References

1. Van Wijk, K.J., Andersson, B. and Styring, S. (1992) Biochim. Biophys. Acta 1100: 207-215
2. Vass, I., Styring, S., Hundal, T., Koivuniemi, A., Aro, E-M., Andersson, B. (1992) Proc. Nat. Acad. Sci. USA 89: 1408-1412
3. Callahan, F.E., Becker, D.W., Cheniae, G.M. (1986) Plant Physiol. 82: 261-269
4. Theg, S.M., Filar, L.J. and Dilley, R.A. (1986) Biochim. Biophys. Acta 849: 104-111
5. Blubaugh, D.J., Atamian, M., Babcock, G.T., Golbeck, J.H. and Cheniae, G.M. (1991) Biochem. 30: 7586-7597
6. Jegerschöld, C., Virgin, I. and Styring, S. (1990) Biochem. 29: 6179-6186
7. Eckert, H.J., Geiken, B., Bernarding, J., Napiwotzki, A., Eichler, H-J., Renger, G. (1991) Photosynth. Res. 27: 97-108
8. Krieger, A. and Weis, E. (1992) Photosynth. (in press)
9. Krieger, A., Moya, I. and Weis, E. (1992) Biochem. Biophys. Acta (in press)
10. Horton, P. and Hague, A. (1988) Biochim. Biophys. Acta 932: 107-115
11. Krause, G.H., Laasch, H. and Weis, E. (1988) Plant Physiol. Biochem. 26: 445-452
12. Horton, P., Oxborough, K., Rees, D. and Scholes, J.D. (1988) Plant Psyiol. Biochem. 26: 453-460

PHOTOINACTIVATION OF PS2 SECONDARY DONORS BY PS2 CATION RADICALS AND SUPEROXIDE RADICALS

G.-X. Chen[1], D.J. Blubaugh[2], J.H. Golbeck[3], and G.M. Cheniae[1], Univ. Kentucky[1], Utah State Univ.[2], and Univ. Nebraska[3], USA

1. INTRODUCTION

Illumination of Mn- and Cl-depleted PS2 causes rapid irreversible inactivation of specific redox-active components on the donor side of the PS2 Reaction Center (RC). Under aerobic conditions, weak light preillumination of NH_2OH-PS2 causes rapid loss of Y_Z^+-formation, $Y_Z \rightarrow P_{680}^+$, the A_T-band thermoluminescence emission, the Y_Z^+-dependent (Site 1) photooxidation of exogenous e^- donors, and the capability to photoligate Mn^{2+} into the water oxidizing enzyme (photoactivation), all without significantly affecting P_{680}^+/Q_A^- charge separation (1,2). In contrast, aerobic high light preillumination of Mn-depleted PS2 promotes very rapid and parallel loss of photoactivation and A_T-band emission capabilities significantly faster than loss of either Y_Z^+-formation or P_{680}^+/Q_A^- charge separation capabilities (2,3). These photodamages and those to Cl^--depleted thylakoids (4,5) generally are believed to be caused by reactions between the highly oxidizing cation radicals (P_{680}^+/Chl^+) and nearby amino acid residues of D_1>D_2. The reported promotion of the photodamages by e^- acceptors of Q_A^-/Q_B^- (3), their inhibition by e^- donors to Y_Z^+ (3,6,7), and their occurrence under strict anaerobic conditions (5) all tend to support the idea of direct damage by P_{680}^+/Chl^+. Our studies, however, lead us to conclude that the photodamages to the donor side components are caused minimally by two mechanisms: 1) a rapid mechanism requiring both superoxide and PS2 cation radicals; and 2) a slower mechanism driven by the PS2 cation radicals only.

2. PROCEDURES

NH_2OH/EDTA-PS2 membranes were prepared as described in Ref. 7 with the following exceptions: 1) 1 mM EDTA was included during the extraction with NH_2OH and the first wash; 2) all buffers were treated with Chelex-100; and 3) all labware used in the preparation and photoinhibition of membranes was presoaked either in 2N HNO_3 or 10 mM EDTA then rinsed with Milli-Q water just prior to use. Membranes were routinely photoinhibited with weak light under aerobic conditions (1,7). When used, strict anaerobic conditions ($\leq$2 μM O_2) were obtained essentially as described in Ref. 5. Following photoinhibition, membranes were pelleted and washed twice before assays. The procedures for measurements of $Y_Z^+/Y_D^+/Chl^+$ and the formation and decay of P_{680}^+ have been described (1) with the exception that here 40 μM benzidene (BZ) was used in the latter determinations.

N. Murata (ed.), Research in Photosynthesis, Vol. IV, 451–454.

DCIP photoreduction was measured at a light limiting condition in a mixture containing 2 μM Mn^{2+}, 3 mM H_2O_2, 50 μM DCIP and membranes equivalent to 20 μg Chl/ml.

3. RESULTS AND DISCUSSION

In the experiments of Fig. 1, NH_2OH/EDTA-PS2 were preincubated without any additions (open circles) or with 1 μM Mn^{2+} (K_m ~400 nM) to give ~1 Mn/RC (closed circles) and, additionally, 100 μM NH_2NH_2 (closed triangles); alternatively, Mn^{2+} was omitted and either 100 μM NH_2NH_2 (open triangles) or 50 μM BZ (closed squares) was added.

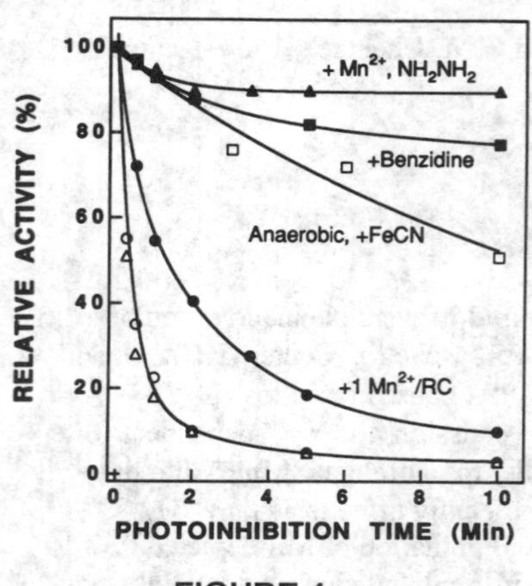

FIGURE 1

Following illumination with weak light for times shown, the capability of the membranes to photoreduce DCIP with e^-'s from Mn^{2+}/H_2O_2 was determined. As shown, e^- donation from BZ or Mn^{2+} bound with high affinity to only 1 site/RC greatly suppressed photoinhibition, particularly in the presence of NH_2NH_2 which, by itself, was ineffective. Such results support the idea that an accumulation of PS2 cation radicals cause damage to donor side components of Mn-depleted PS2. On the other hand, in the absence of PS2 e^- donors, photoinhibition also was greatly suppressed by strict anaerobiosis even with addition of HCO_3^- and e^- acceptors (FeCN, PBQ) to permit e^- flow through Q_A/Q_B (open squares, Fig. 1). Moreover, under aerobic conditions (Fig. 2), the rate of photoinhibition in the presence of 50 μM DCIP (closed diamonds) or 1 mM FeCN (closed squares) was much slower than in the absence of an added e^- acceptor (open circles). Additionally, 80 μM cyt.c (open triangles), a scavenger of superoxide, and 5 μg/ml superoxide dismutase (SOD) (open squares) suppressed photoinhibition. Similar protective effects from e^- acceptors and SOD were observed during photoinhibition of Tris- or NH_2OH-PS2 with strong light. This effect of e^- acceptors is opposite to that reported in Ref. 3.

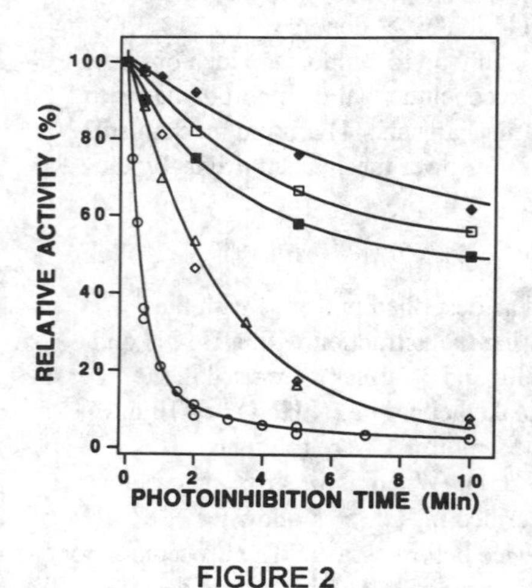

FIGURE 2

In the absence of e^- acceptors under conditions of aerobic weak light photoinhibition, an atrazine-sensitive low rate of superoxide formation (5 nmol/min) was measured using a conventional cyt.c-based assay procedure. Increase of this rate during illumination by additions of either xanthine/xanthine oxidase or $\leq$3 mM H_2O_2 ($K_m \approx$ 380 μM) (8) increased the rate of photoinhibition several fold. On the other hand, even $\geq$ 10 min strict dark preincubation of NH_2OH-PS2 with sufficient xanthine/xanthine oxidase to give 50 nmol superoxide/min caused no loss of PS2 photochemical activities. The effects of a saturating concentration (20 μg/ml) of SOD on the weak-light induced loss of the total amplitude of P_{680}^+ formation (open circles), the fast (~4 μs) phase of P_{680}^+ reduction by Y_Z^+ (closed circles), and the decrease in the quantum yield of DCIP photoreduction (open squares) are shown in Fig. 3. In the absence of SOD addition, the loss of the ~4 μs component of P_{680}^+ reduction and the decrease in the quantum yield of DCIP photoreduction occurred essentially in parallel via a double-exponential decay process with the major exponential process being quite rapid ($t_{1/2}$ ~ 18s). In the presence of SOD, the loss of each of these activities was essentially linear with time and about ~25-fold slower (extrapolated $t_{1/2}$ ~530s) than in the absence of SOD. The relative total amplitude of Δ820 (open circles), reflecting P_{680}^+/Q_A^- charge separation capability, was not significantly affected either in the presence/absence of SOD. The time-course of photodamage of the $Y_Z \rightarrow P_{680}^+$ reaction and its suppression by SOD also were seen from EPR analyses of Y_Z^+ formation capability following photoinhibition. This could be observed more directly by real time, *in situ* measurements (g=2.0104) of Y_Z^+ during illumination (16.4 mE/m^2•s) of membranes (Fig. 4). In the absence of SOD, the Y_Z^+/Y_D^+ amplitude decreased rapidly [$t_{1/2}$=6.6 s (81%); 63 s (19%)] to half of the original amplitude and to a level equivalent to the dark-stable Y_D^+ signal. In the presence of SOD, the loss of Y_Z^+/Y_D^+ amplitude, reflecting loss of Y_Z^+, was much slower [$t_{1/2}$=68 s (100%)].

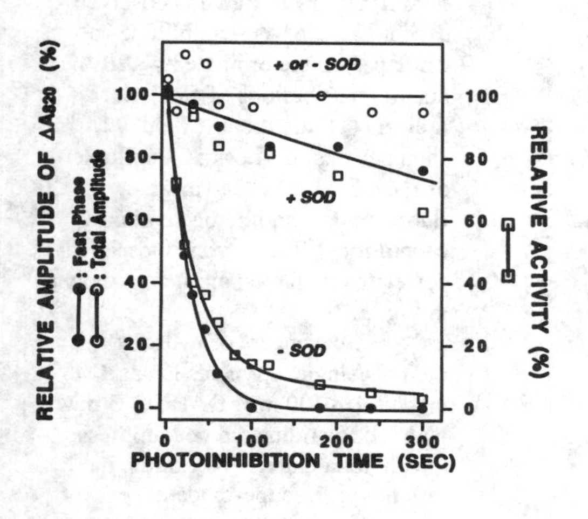

FIGURE 3

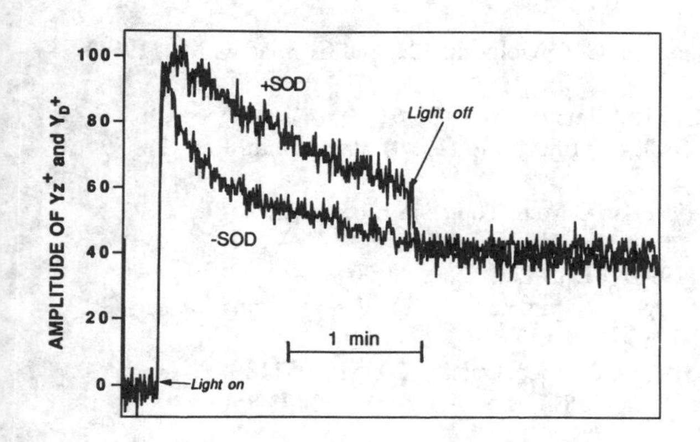

FIGURE 4

Fig. 5 records the decreases of "Y_Z^+" amplitude (g=2.0104) (closed circles) and the quantum yield of Mn^{2+}/H_2O_2 photooxidation (open squares) versus the decrease in the amplitude of the ~4 μs component of P_{680}^+ reduction caused by photoinhibition of

NH_2OH/EDTA-PS2 in the absence of SOD. As shown, excellent correlation between loss of quantum yield of Mn^{2+}/H_2O_2 photooxidation (open squares), decrease in the amplitude of $Y_Z \rightarrow P_{680}^+$, and decrease in amplitude of the "Y_Z" EPR signal is observed except that the "Y_Z" amplitude is displaced on the ordinate by ≤20% due to contributions of Chl^+/Car^+ radicals (1) into the low field shoulder region. Loss of amplitude of flash-induced Chl$\underline{a}$ variable fluorescence and photoactivation capability (1,7) also were closely correlated with the parameters shown in Fig. 5.

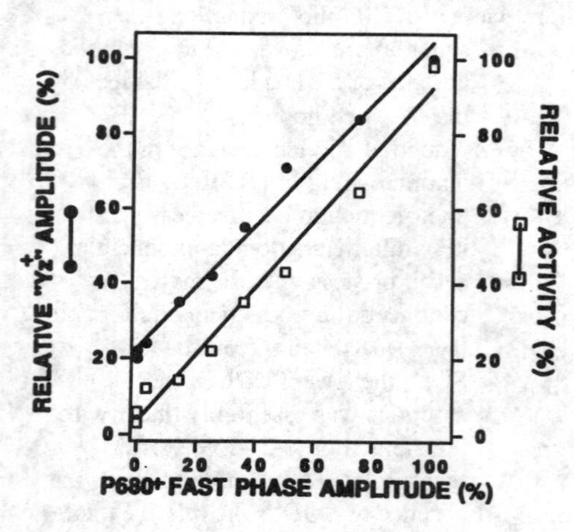

FIGURE 5

Scavengers of hydroxy radicals/singlet oxygen such as 1M mannitol, ≤300 mM DABCO, 5 mM NaN_3 or histidine did not suppress the photodamages. To explain the rapid oxygen-/superoxide-dependent photoinhibition process, we postulate that a bimolecular reaction between superoxide and the Y_Z^+ radical, resulting perhaps in the formation of a redox-inactive peroxy-derivative of Y_Z. The slower oxygen-/superoxide-independent photodamage process apparently reflects damages caused by the accumulation of PS2 cation radicals (P_{680}^+, Chl^+).

REFERENCES

1. Blubaugh, D.J., Atamian, M., Babcock, G.T., Golbeck, J.H. and Cheniae, G.M. (1991) Biochemistry 30, 7586-7597.
2. Ono, T.-A. and Inoue, Y. (1991) Biochemistry 30, 6183-6188.
3. Klimov, V.V., Shafiev, M.A. and Allakhverdiev, S.I. (1990) Photosynth. Res. 23, 59-65.
4. Andersson, B. and Styring, S. (1991) in Current Topics in Bioenergetics (Lee, C.P., ed.) Vol. 16, pp 1-81, Academic Press, New York.
5. Jegerschold, C. and Styring, S. (1990) FEBS Lett. 280, 87-90.
6. Eckert, H.-J., Geiken, B., Bernarding, J., Napiwotzki, A., Eichler, H.-J. and Renger, G. (1991) Photosynth. Res. 27, 97-108.
7. Blubaugh, D.J. and Cheniae, G.M. (1990) Biochemistry 29, 5109-5118.
8. Mano, J., Takahashi, M. an Asada, K. (1987) Biochemistry 26, 2495-2501.

ACKNOWLEDGMENT: This work was supported principally by the U.S. Department of Energy (Contract DE-FG05-86ER13533 to G.M.C.).

ON THE SUSCEPTIBILITY OF PHOTOSYNTHESIS TO PHOTOINHIBITION AT LOW TEMPERATURES.

Christina Ottander, Torill Hundal[1], Bertil Andersson[1], Norman P.A. Huner[2] and Gunnar Öquist. Dept of Plant Physiology, Univ of Umeå, S-901 87 Umeå, Sweden; [1]Dept of Biochemistry, Arrhenius laboratories, Univ of Stockholm, S-106 91 Stockholm, Sweden ; [2]Dept of Plant Sciences, Univ of Western Ontario, London, Ontario, N6A 5B7, Canada

INTRODUCTION

Low temperature is an important environmental stress which makes photosynthesis more sensitive to photoinhibition so that even low photon flux densities may cause photoinhibition (1, 2). Two hypotheses to explain why plants become much more sensitive to photoinhibition at low temperatures are; 1) Low temperatures reduce the capacity of photosynthesis and thereby increase the probability for excessive excitation of photosystem II (PS II). 2) The ability for repair of PS II is reduced at low temperatures. Degradation and synthesis of the D1-protein in the reaction centre appears to be slowed down by low temperatures (3, 4). Also, the rates of migration, protein assembly and ligation of co-factors are slowed down at low temperatures (5). The aim of this work was to determine whether this increased susceptibility to photoinhibition at low temperature was an effect of a decreased capacity of the PS II repair cycle alone, or whether a temperature inhibition of photosynthesis causing increased excitation pressure of the reaction centre of PS II also was involved.

MATERIAL AND METHODS

The photochemical efficiency of PS II was measured as the Fv/Fm ratio of dark adapted leaves. Modulated fluorescence was used to monitor the reduction state of Q_A (6). The reduction state of Q_A was used as an approximation of the excitation pressure on PS II (7). To assay effects on the PS II repair cycle, leaves were painted with 300 $\mu g\ ml^{-1}$ CAP (D-threochloramphenicol) in 1 % (v/v) Tween 20. Measurements of D1-content was determined by Western blotting (8), using antibodies against the D1-protein and the nuclear encoded 22 kDa protein and by ^{14}C-atrazine binding to the D1-protein (9).

RESULTS AND DISCUSSION

The light and temperature dependence of the reduction state of Q_A showed that Q_A was more sensitive to irradiance at 5 than at 20 °C (Fig. 1A and B). The relative susceptibility to photoinhibition at 5 and 20 °C were examined by adjusting the light so that similar values of the reduction state of Q_A were maintained at the two temperatures. Photon flux densities causing a 60 % steady state reduction of Q_A (i.e.300 and 1200 $\mu mol\ m^{-2}\ s^{-1}$ at 5 and 20 °C, respectively, fig. 1A, B),

N. Murata (ed.), Research in Photosynthesis, Vol. IV, 455–458.

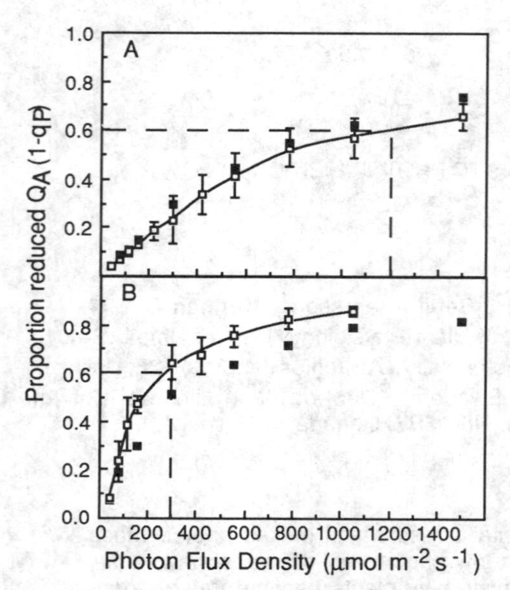

Figure 1. Light response curves of the reduction state of the primary electron acceptor QA before (open) and after (filled) 6 h of photoinhibition at 20 (A) and 5 °C (B). Measurements were done in an O2-electrode flushed with water saturated air to simulate the conditions used during photoinhibition. Bars show the standard deviation, n=5-15.

resulted in initially identical kinetics of the decrease in the photochemical efficiency of PS II (Fv/Fm) (Fig 2). After 6 h under conditions of <u>equivalent</u> initial reduction state of Q_A, Fv/Fm was inhibited 30 % at both 5 and 20 °C and a steady state level of photoinhibition was reached at 20 °C (Fig. 2). Fv/Fm continued to decrease at 5 °C and reached steady state after 10 h with Fv/Fm inhibited to 55 % of control (Fig 2). Thus, the increased excitation pressure on PS II at 5 °C, accounts for a significant part of the increased sensitivity to photoinhibition at this temperature. In accordance, winter rye at different state of cold hardiness and at different temperatures, showed that the susceptibility of photosynthesis to photoinhibition was fully controlled by the redox state of PS II(10). To further evaluate the significance of the reduction state of Q_A in determining the susceptibility to photoinhibition, we compared the level of inhibition of Fv/Fm after light treatment at different reduction state of Q_A, both with and without blocking repair of the D1-protein. At 5 and 20 °C, with repair of PS II going on, the level of photoinhibition was similarly controlled by the reduction state of Q_A (Fig 3). Blocking repair of the D1-protein resulted in a severe inhibition of Fv/Fm at 20 °C, but at 5 °C, almost no increase in sensitivity occurred (Fig. 3, 11). This indicates that the repair cycle is largely inactivated at 5 °C and thus has a very limited protective role at low temperatures.

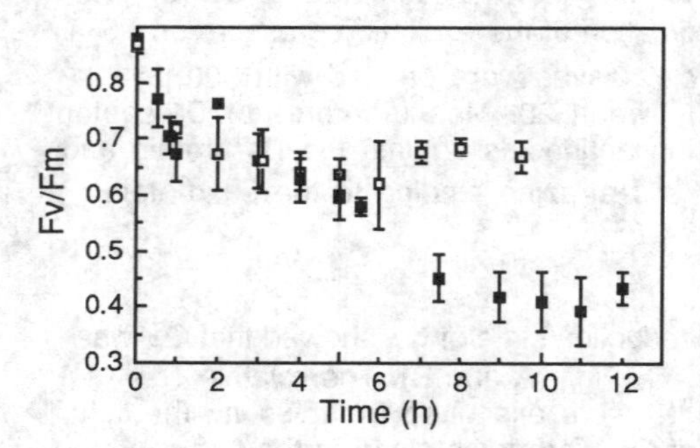

Figure 2. Photoinhibition of Fv/Fm in intact barley leaves at light intensities initially giving 60 % of Q_A in a reduced state, i.e. 300 $\mu mol\ m^{-2}\ s^{-1}$ at 5 °C (filled) and 1200 $\mu mol\ m^{-2}\ s^{-1}$ at 20 °C (open). Bars show the standard deviation, n = 5-15.

The decrease in Fv/Fm showed the same kinetics at both temperatures the first 6 h, but subsequently differed (Fig. 2). Therefore it was of interest to see if the reduction state of Q_A changed during photoinhibition or if the difference was due to a temperature effect on the repair cycle. There was no change in the light response of the proportion of reduced Q_A after photoinhibition at 20 °C (Fig. 1A). However, after photoinhibition at 5 °C, the proportion of reduced Q_A was 10-20 % lower than before photoinhibition (Fig. 1B). To test whether inhibition of the replacement of inhibited D1-protein in the reaction centre of PS II is responsible for the increased sensitivity to photoinhibition at low temperature, changes in D1 content during photoinhibition at 5 and 20 °C, with and without addition of CAP,were measured by immunoblotting and by capacity to bind labelled atrazine. The activity and structural integrity of the reaction centre of PS II are closely related during photoinhibition at 20 °C since the decrease in D1-content was closely correlated to the inhibition of the photochemical efficiency of PS II (Fig. 4A). Both degradation and synthesis was rapid at 20 °C and during the 6.5 hours treatment almost all D1-protein in the reaction centres was exchanged for newly synthesized D1-protein (Fig. 4A). These results support the model that, at 20 °C, net photoinhibition is the difference between inactivation and repair of PS II. At 5 °C, the decrease in photochemical efficiency of PS II was more severe than the decrease in D1-protein (Fig. 4B). The amount of D1-protein measured by immunoblotting and by atrazine binding was closely correlated (Fig. 4B). Clearly, loss of PS II photochemical function and changes in the structural integrity occur separately (Fig. 4B, 12, 4). Almost no turnover of D1-protein had occurred at 5 °C (Fig. 4B).

There are now several lines of evidence suggesting that more than one reaction centre of PS II may share a common pool of antenna molecules (e.g. 13). Theoretically, if some reaction centres are inhibited and do not become quenchers of excitation energy, the effective antenna size would increase for the remaining PS II, and thus the rate of photoinhibition would increase. However, even though the photochemical efficiency of PS II was inhibitied 30 % after photoinhibition at 20 °C (Fig.2), which implies that approximately 30 % of D1-protein was lost (cf. Fig.4A), no difference in the light response of the proportion of closed reaction centres was seen (Fig. 1A). The relatively limited degradation of PS II reaction centres at 5 °C (Fig. 4B), in comparison with loss of photochemical efficiency, suggest that a large proportion of the photoinhibited reaction centres remain physically intact. These inactive reaction centres may be able to protect the remaining photochemically active reaction centres
by quenching excess excitation energy through non-radiative heat dissipation. In fact, the decrease in the reduction state of Q_A following low temperature photoinhibition implies that less excitation energy reaches the remaining photochemically active reaction centres.

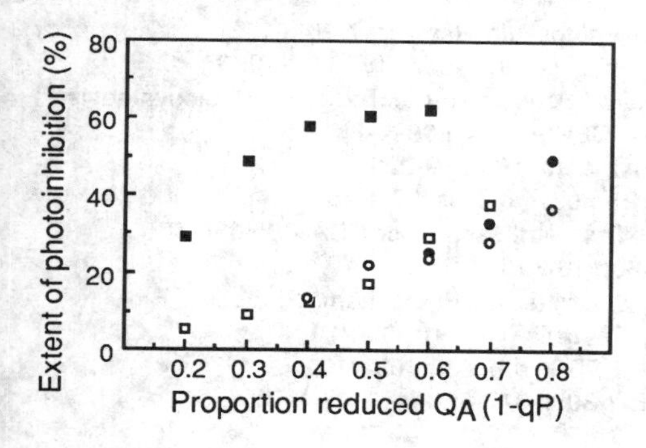

Figure 3. The relationship between the reduction state of the primary electron acceptor Q_A (1-qP) at steady state photosynthesis and the extent of inhibition of the photochemical efficiency of PS II (expressed as Fv/Fm). The extent of photoinhibition after 2.5 hours treatment at 20 (□) and 5 °C (○), without (open) and with (filled) addition of chloramphenicol.

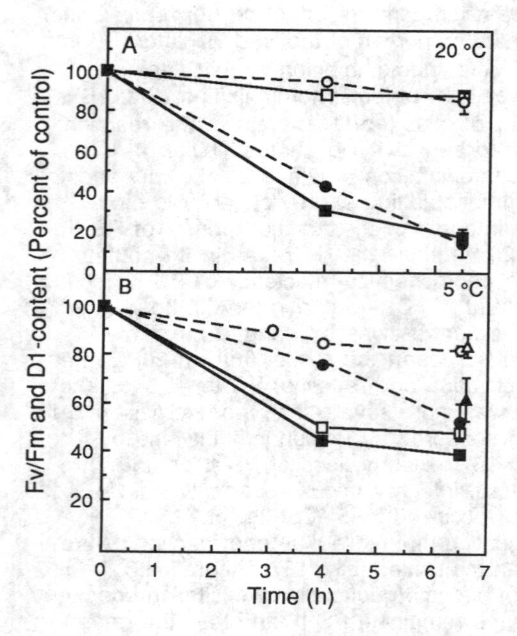

Figure 4. Relative changes in D1-content (---) and Fv/Fm (——) during photoinhibition at 800 µmol m^{-2} s^{-1} and 20 (A) and at 5 °C (B), with (filled) and without (open) chloramphenicol. □ represents D1 measured by immunoblotting and △ represents D1 measured by atrazine binding. Each D1-value represents the average of 3-6 separate replicates. Bars show the standard deviation.

In conclusion, the PS II repair cycle is important in protecting barley from photoinhibition at higher temperatures (Figs. 3 and 4A). The increased susceptibility to photoinhibition at low temperature in barley must be explained both by an increased excitation pressure on PS II at low temperatures and by an inhibited repair cycle of PS II. However, the suggested effect exerted by the temperature on the PS II repair cycle, appears to become significant only after prolonged (> 6 h) light exposure at low temperatures. We propose that photochemically inactive reaction centres, which accumulate during photoinhibitory exposures at low temperatures (Fig. 4B, 11, 3), are not degraded but act as potential quenchers of excitation energy. Thus, they may confer protection of remaining photochemically active centres.

REFERENCES:

1 Öquist G, Greer DH and Ögren E (1987) In: Kyle, Osmond and Arntzen, (eds). Topics in Photosynthesis, Vol 9, pp. 67-87, Elsevier, Amsterdam. ISBN 0-444-808990-6
2 Öquist G and Huner NPA (1991) Func Ecol 5:91-100
3 Chow WS, Osmond CB and Huang LK (1989) Photosynth Res 21:17-26
4 Aro E-M, Hundal T, Carlberg I and Andersson B (1990). BBA 1019:269-275
5 Kyle DJ (1987) In: DJ Kyle, CB Osmond and CJ Arntzen, (eds) Topics in Photosynthesis, Vol. 9, pp. 197-226. Elsevier, Amsterdam, ISBN 0-444-80890-6
6 Dietz K-J, Schreiber U and Heber U (1985) Planta 166:219-226
7 Havaux M, Strasser RJ, Greppin H (1991) Photosynth Res 27:41-55
8 Towbin H, Staehelin T and Cordon J (1979) Proc Natl Acad Sci USA 76:4350-4353
9 Tischer W and Strotmann H (1977) BBA 460:113-125
10 Öquist G, Hurry VM and Huner NPA (1992). Submitted to Photochem. Photobiol. Biol.
11 Greer DH, Ottander C and Öquist G (1991) Physiol Plant 81:203-210
12 Virgin I, Styring S and Andersson B (1988) FEBS lett. 233:408-412
13 Joliot P, Bennoun P and Joliot A (1973) BBA 305: 317-328

SIMULTANEOUS DETERMINATION OF *IN VIVO* ACTIVITIES OF PSI AND PSII FOLLOWING HIGH-LIGHT STRESS.

Marc Charland[1,2], Konka Veeranjaneyulu[1] and Roger M. Leblanc[1]; [1] Centre de recherche en photobiophysique, Université du Québec à Trois-Rivières, C.P. 500, Trois-Rivières, Québec, G9A 5H7, Canada; [2] Present address: H.J.F. Forestry Center, Forestry Canada, Maritimes Region, Regent Street South, P.O. Box 4000, Fredericton, New Brunswick, E3B 5P7, Canada.

1. INTRODUCTION

Light energy drives photosynthesis, but excessive light intensity might damage the photosynthetic apparatus, a phenomenon termed as photoinhibition (1,2). As shown by numerous fluorescence and electron transport studies, the primary site of photoinhibitory injury is located in PSII complex, even if there is still controversy on its exact site (2,3).

Besides PSII inactivation, little is known about high-light effects on higher plants' PSI. Some studies, particularly done on chloroplasts isolated from high-light treated leaves showed some damages to PSI, but to a lower extent than to PSII (1,4,5). Moreover, PSI-resistance was demonstrated by measuring cyclic electron transport in *Chlamydomonas* (6) and in pea leaves (7).

Photoacoustic (PA) methodology has been successfully applied to photosynthesis research by allowing the determination of O_2 evolution and photosynthetic energy storage ((ES) 8). Recently, we have shown the feasibility to use it to record simultaneously PSI and PSII activities, by measuring their relative contribution to ES (9). Here, we have used this methodology to study PSI and PSII activities following high-light stress.

2. MATERIALS AND METHODS

Three months old seedlings of sugar maple (*Acer saccharum* Marsh.), maintained in a growth room were used as experimental material.

In the present study, an 18 mm-diameter disk was punched from one half of the leaf and was used as control. The leaf, still attached to the plant, was then perpendicularly exposed to the strong white light from a projector lamp (through a 10 cm-layer of water), which constitutes the high-light treatement (420 W m^{-2}, 1h, otherwise stated).

PA measurements were conducted with the experimental set-up described elsewhere (9). We used 100 Hz as modulation frequency, which is high enough to avoid O_2-evolution PA signal from sugar maple leaves (9). Energy storage of both photosystems (ES_T) was determined by recording the PA signal at 650 nm modulated light in the presence and the absence of saturating white light (6,8). ES

N. Murata (ed.), Research in Photosynthesis, Vol. IV, 459–462.

of PSI (ES_{PSI}) was measured by following variations of PA signal at 650 nm with and without saturating far-red light ($\lambda > 715$ nm) (9). ES of PSII (ES_{PSII}) is calculated from the difference between ES_T and ES_{PSI} (9). By using 710 nm modulated light and saturating white light, ES related to cyclic electron transport around PSI ($ES_{PSI\text{-}cy}$) was determined (6,7). We also used the difference in 710 nm PA signal following saturating blue-green light (obtained with a Corning 4-96 filter) illumination as PSII-dependent PSI activity (li-ES_{PSI}).

3. RESULTS AND DISCUSSION

Light energy inhibits photosynthesis when its intensity exceeds the optimum level. This is shown in Figure 1, where ES_T decreased gradually during high-light treatment. This is due to the inactivation of PSII, as seen by the lessening of ES_{PSII}. We also observed a parallel decrease of PA O_2-evolution signal in course of time (results not shown). The specific inhibition of PSII by high-light treatment has already been reported by numerous workers (1,2). In contrast to this, ES_{PSI} increased during the treatment, by about 60% (Table 1).

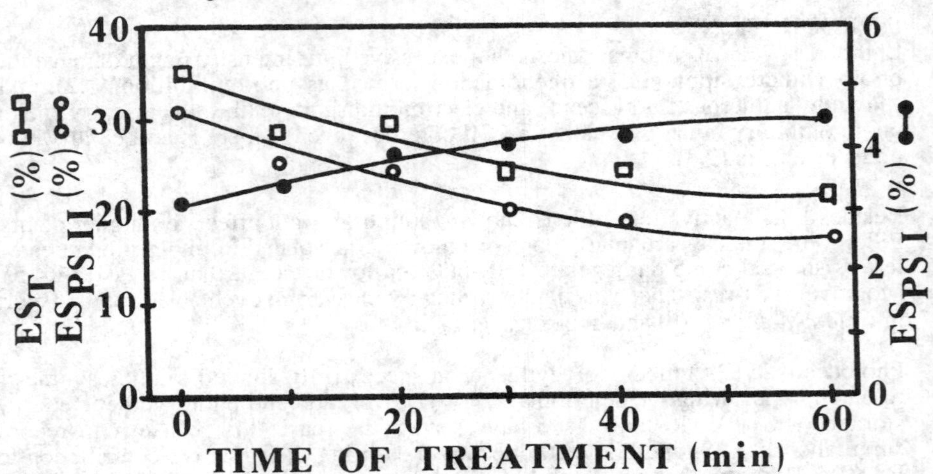

FIGURE 1. Changes in ES_T, ES_{PSI} and ES_{PSII} in course of time during high-light treatment (420 W m^{-2}) of sugar maple leaves.

We observed some variation in the response of leaves with age to high-light stress. The photoinhibitory effect is more important on ES_T and ES_{PSII} in young leaves than in mature leaves (Table 1). Moreover, the increase in ES_{PSI} is less evident in young leaves than in mature leaves (Table 1). In order to understand the PSI activity, we measured ES with 705 nm modulated light, which is preferentially absorbed by PSI. $ES_{PSI\text{-}cy}$ increased by about 20% over control (Table 1). Previous results showed that cyclic electron transport around PSI was resistant to photoinhibition in *Chlamydomonas* (6) and transitorily increased in pea leaves (7). The PSII-dependent PSI activity (li-ES_{PSI}) indicated the energy stored in chemical intermediates, both upstream and downstream of PSI. Interestingly, it increased during high-light treatment, despite a noticeable decrease of PSII activity (Table 1). From this, it appears that PSII electron flow is not limiting to PSI in high-light treated leaves. This might be due to a larger PSII population than that of PSI *in vivo*.

The increase in PSI activity may be an adaptative process against high-light stress. For one, the physiological significance of cyclic electron transport around PSI in C_3 plants is not clearly understood. There are evidences that cyclic electron flow around PSI is required to prevent photodamage to chloroplasts (10). Thus the enhanced cyclic flow around PSI can dissipate PSI excitation and can generate ATP molecules necessary during repair processes (6). It can also produce a large trans-thylakoid proton gradient that can induce the xanthophyll cycle, which is reported to be involved in heat dissipation during high-light stress (11).

TABLE 1. High-light treatment effect on ES_T, ES_{PSII}, ES_{PSI}, $ES_{PSI\text{-}cy}$ and li-ES_{PSI} of intact sugar maple leaves.

	Control	Treated	% Effect
Mature leaves (n=6)			
ES_T	32.2 ± 4.3	23.6 ± 3.9	-25
ES_{PSII}	28.7 ± 4.4	18.0 ± 5.1	-40
ES_{PSI}	3.5 ± 0.7	5.6 ± 1.8	+60
$ES_{PSI\text{-}cy}$	5.4 ± 2.0	6.6 ± 1.3	+22
li-ES_{PSI}	7.1 ± 2.5	8.5 ± 2.5	+19
Young leaves (n=5)			
ES_T	33.6 ± 5.2	8.2 ± 1.9	-75
ES_{PSII}	31.4 ± 5.7	5.6 ± 2.0	-80
ES_{PSI}	2.2 ± 0.5	2.6 ± 0.8	+18
Mature leaves pre-adapted to state 1			
ES_T	32.6 ± 6.3	25.9 ± 40	-21
ES_{PSII}	29.5 ± 7.0	20.9 ± 3.8	-30
ES_{PSI}	3.1 ± 1.3	5.0 ± 1.4	+61

High-light intensity effect during 1 h treatment was studied on leaves (Figure 2). At 650 W m^{-2}, ES_{PSI} decreased by about 20%, which is much less that the strong lowerings of ES_T and ES_{PSII}. A further increase of light intensity to 950 W m^{-2} caused a significant diminution of activities of both photosystems. We observed that PSI inhibition may occur at a stage when PSII is inhibited at an extent larger than 40% in many samples. This may suggest the existence of an internal physiological threshold, at which PSI inhibition may occur. However, this needs more experimental data to draw a definite conclusion.

The influence of LHCII association with PSII during high-light stress was studied by driving the leaf to state 1 conditions before photoinhibitory treatment. We observed that, despite the association of LHCII with PSII, the decrease is comparable to that observed in earlier experiments. Thus LHCII association with PSII may not induce any additional damage to PSII. It may be stated that during high-light treatment, LHCII migrates towards PSI, increasing its absorption cross-section, and its activity. We still have to study this phenomenon.

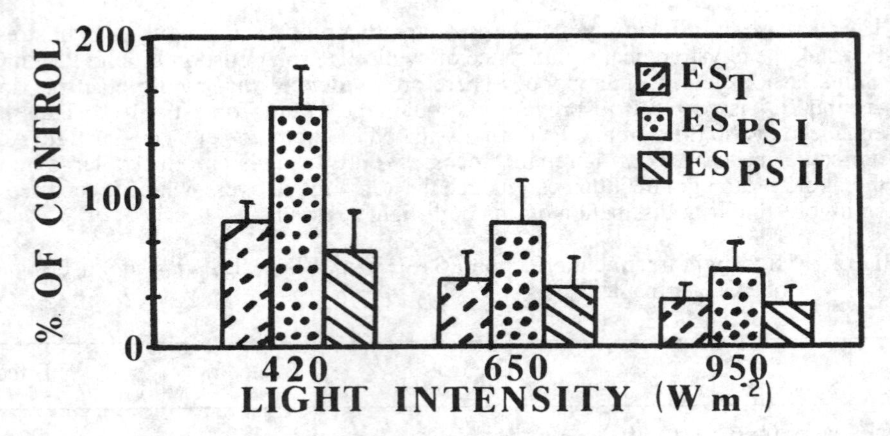

FIGURE 2. Effect of different light intensities on ES_T, ES_{PSI} and ES_{PSII} following 1 h high-light treatment.

4. CONCLUSIONS

From the present study, it can be stated that PSII is specifically inhibited and PSI activity increases during moderate high-light treatment (420 W m^{-2}, 1h) of sugar maple leaves. This enhancement is observed both in cyclic and PSII-dependent electron transport around PSI. At higher light intensities (650, 960 W m^{-2}) both PSII and PSI are inhibited, but the later at a lower extent. The increase of PSI activity may be an adaptative process to high-light stress.

ACKNOWLEDGMENTS: This work was financially supported by the NSERC of Canada and Le Fonds FCAR of Québec. MC thanks NSERCC for a post-graduate fellowship.

REFERENCES

1 Powles, S.B. (1984) Annu. Rev. Plant Physiol. 35, 15-44
2 Critchley, C. (1988) Aust. J. Plant Physiol. 15, 27-41
3 Eckert, H.J., Geiken, B., Bernarding, J., Napiwotzki, A., Eichler, H.J. and Renger, G. (1991) Photosynth. Res. 27, 97-108
4 Tyystarvi, E., Ovaska, J., Karunen, P. and Aro, E.-M. (1989) Plant Physiol. 91, 1069-1074
5 Inoue, K., Sakurai, H. and Hiyama, T. (1986) Plant Cell Physiol. 27, 961-968
6 Canaani, O., Schuster, G. and Ohad, I. (1989) Photosynth. Res. 129-146
7 Havaux, M. and Eyletters, M. (1992) Z. Naturforsch. 46C, 1038-1044
8 Poulet, P., Cahen, D. and Malkin, S. (1983) Biochim. Biophys. Acta 724, 433-446
9 Veeranjaneyulu, K., Charland, M., Charlebois, D. and Leblanc, R.M. (1991) Plant Physiol. 97, 330-334
10 Ridley, S.M. and Horton, P. (1984) Z. Naturforsch. 39C, 351-353
11 Demmig-Adams, B. and Adams, W.W. (1992) Annu. Rev. Plant Physiol. Plant Molec. Biol. 43, 599-626

INVESTIGATION OF THE ROLE OF THE ACCESSORY CHROMOPHORES OF ISOLATED PHOTOSYSTEM TWO REACTION CENTRES

Alison Telfer, Javier De Las Rivas and James Barber
AFRC Photosynthesis Research Group, Department of Biochemistry, Imperial College of Science, Technology and Medicine, London SW7 2AY, U.K.

1. INTRODUCTION

The chromophore composition of isolated PSII reaction centres indicates that despite the strong homology between the binding sites of the major chromophores involved in electron transfer in PSII and the reaction centre (RC) of purple photosynthetic bacteria, there are a number of striking differences. In particular the two RCs seem to differ in the number of their chromophores. PSII RCs bind two extra chlorophyll molecules and an extra carotenoid molecule as well as the haem of cytochrome b559. Previously we have suggested that these 'accessory' chromophores can function in a protective role as well as acting as light harvesting pigments [2]. In this paper we have further investigated the role of the extra chlorophyll and carotenoid on PSII structure and function and discuss our results in relation to the 'acceptor-side' and 'donor-side' photoinhibition mechanisms proposed by Barber and Andersson [3].

2. MATERIALS AND METHODS

PSII reaction centres, with the normal chromophore stoichiometry (NRC), were isolated from pea thylakoids as before [1]. Washed reaction centres (WRC) were isolated essentially as the NRC preparation except that the first column was washed with 5x the normal volume of buffer (50mM Tris-Cl, pH 7.2, 30mM NaCl and 0.2% Triton X-100). Steady-state and flash induced transient absorption, electron transport, and HPLC measurements were carried as previously described [2]. 2,5-dibromo-3-methyl-6-isopropyl-*p*-benzoquinone (DBMIB) was a gift from Dr W. Oettmeier.

3. RESULTS

Fig.1 shows irreversible light-induced changes in absorption spectra, rate of bleaching at 486 nm and ability to carry out electron transfer in normally isolated PSII reaction centres (NRC) which have 6Chl: 2β-Car: 2Pheo. In the absence of added electron acceptor, electron transfer is rapidly inhibited and chlorophyll bleaching centred at 680 nm indicates specific loss of P680 (Fig.1a,c). This effect requires oxygen. Under aerobic conditions $P680^{+}Pheo^{-}$ recombines forming some $^{3}P680$ and consequently singlet oxygen (which we have detected by its phosphorescence at 1270nm, ref. 4). This toxic species causes preferential bleaching of P680 and inactivation of the RCs.

When silicomolybdate (SiMo) is present, during the light treatment, electron transfer activity is substantially protected but there is irreversible loss of β-carotene (bleach maxima at 460, 486 and 510 nm) and Chl670 (bleach maximum at 670 nm) with very little loss of P680 (Fig.1b,d). Essentially all the β-carotene present but less than one Chl670 was bleached per RC before there is significant loss of electron transfer activity or P680. SiMo-dependent pigment loss is oxygen independent (Fig.1b,d and Fig.2). Fig.2b shows that the 670nm component ($\Delta A_{670-680}$) of chlorophyll bleaching has approx. the same kinetics as those of β-carotene (ΔA_{486}).

N. Murata (ed.), Research in Photosynthesis, Vol. IV, 463–466.

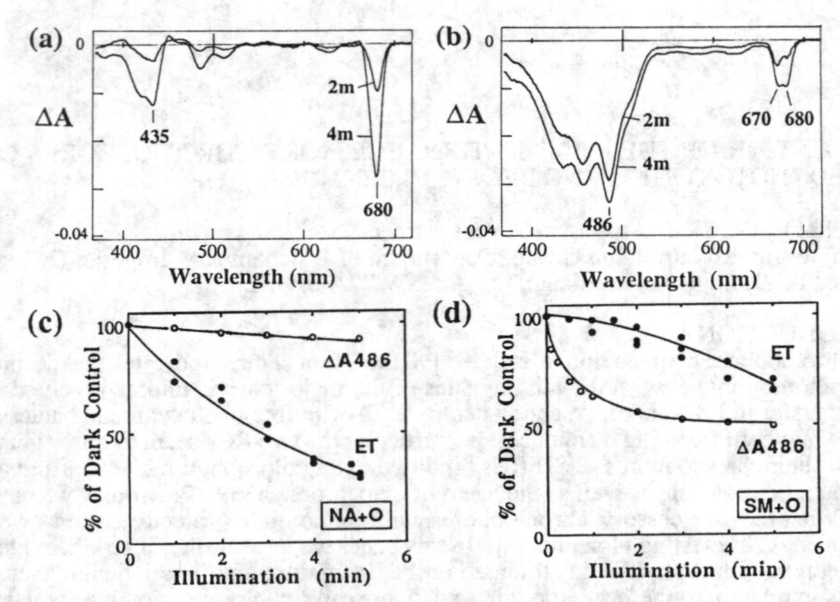

Fig.1 Light-treated minus dark control absorption difference spectra (a,b) and rate of bleaching at 486nm and Mn^{2+} to SiMo electron transport (ET) activity as a function of illumination time (c,d) in NRC plus and minus 0.1mM SiMo. Aerobic conditions. Red light, 600μE m^{-2} s^{-1}. 4 μg ml^{-1} Chl.

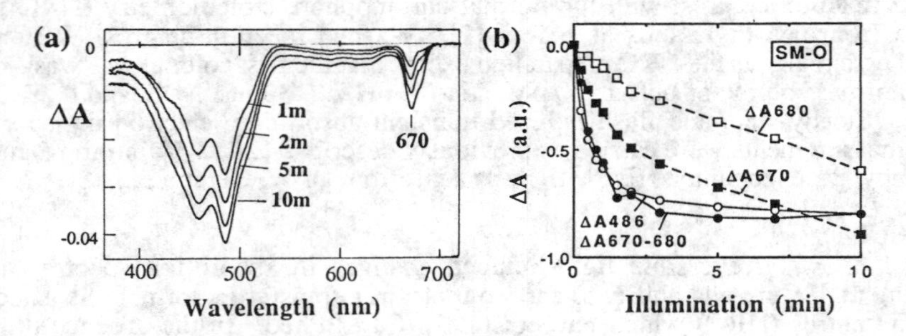

Fig.2 (a) As Fig.1b, anaerobic conditions. (b) Rate of bleaching at 486, 670 and 680nm and $\Delta A_{670-680}$ as a function of illumination. 0.45mM SiMo and 3μg ml^{-1} Chl.

Flash induced transient absorption changes indicate that β-carotene is oxidised prior to its irreversible bleaching. Fig.3 shows Car^+ formation (ΔA_{950}) in PSII reaction centres with added SiMo, confirming our previous demonstration of electron acceptor (DBMIB) dependent Car oxidation in PSII RCs [2]. Comparison of the SiMo-dependent increase in at 950 nm with the multiphasic decay seen at 680 nm shows there is a long lived component in the A680 decay that correlates with Car oxidation. Under steady state illumination the Car bleaching is irreversible indicating that Car^+ is rather unstable. Because of this instability it is difficult to resolve the absorption changes spectrally in the red region, but we assume that Chl670 is also oxidised prior to its irreversible bleaching.

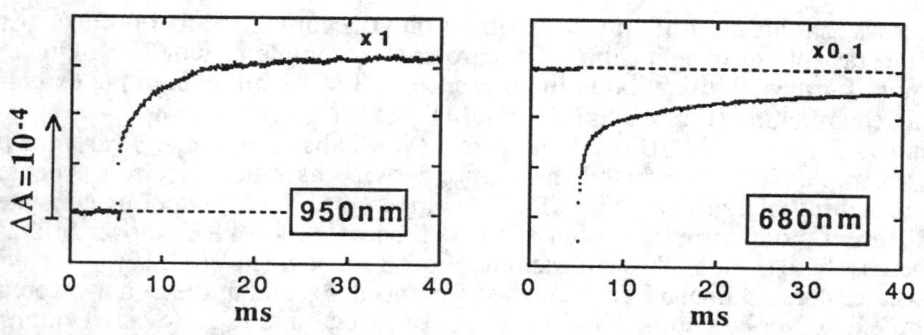

Fig.3 Transient absorption changes at 950 and 680nm of NRC (5 μg ml^{-1} Chl) with 0.1mM SiMo under anaerobic conditions. Flash frequency 1 Hz.

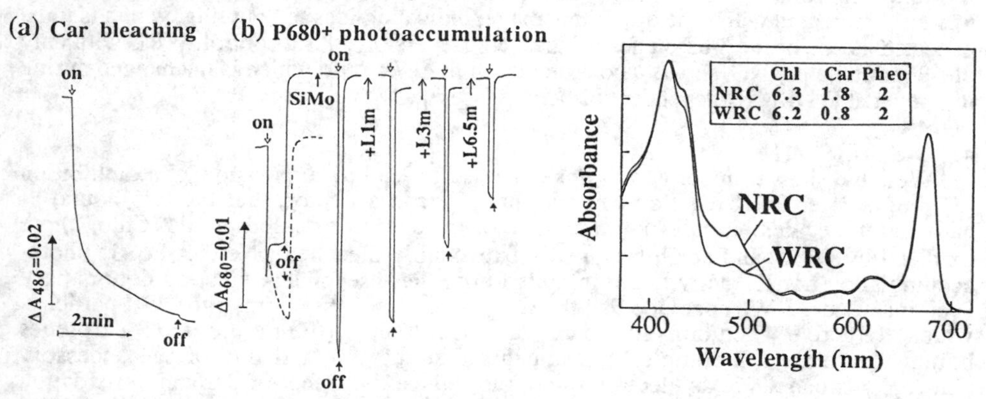

Fig.4 Comparison of the time course of Car bleaching at 486nm (a) and $P680^+$ photoaccumulation (b) in NRC with 0.2mM SiMo in the absence (——) and presence of oxygen (------). Extra SiMo was added and white light treatment given (5000 μE m^{-2} s^{-1}) as indicated. 2μg ml^{-1} Chl.

Fig.5 Absorption spectra of NRC and WRC with HPLC data for the stoichiometry of chromophores per two pheophytin molecules.

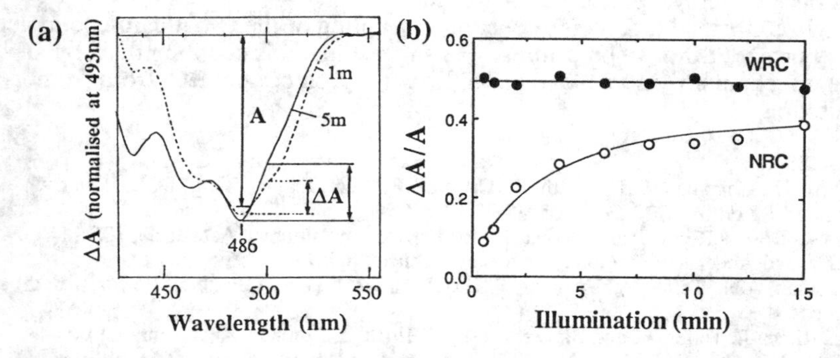

Fig.6 (a) DBMIB-dependent light-treated minus dark control absorption difference spectra of NRC under aerobic conditions. Measurement of A and ΔA for estimation of β-carotene 'coupling' indicated. (b) Changes in ΔA/A (β-carotene 'coupling' ratio) for NRC (o) and WRC (•) as a function of illumination time.

Fig.4 shows that all the P680 present can be photoaccumulated as $P680^+$ (1 per 6 Chl) after the fast phase of bleaching of β-carotene is complete, whether oxygen is present or not. Further illumination in the presence of SiMo inhibits both the extent of $P680^+$ photoaccumulation (Fig.4) and ET from Mn^{2+} to SiMo (not shown).

Fig.5 shows that washed PSII reaction centres (WRC) have only one β-carotene per 2 pheophytin molecules. We found that approx. twice as much electron acceptor-dependent bleaching of Car occurs in NRC as compared to WRC, which is consistent with the different stoichiometry. Bleaching of β-carotene in NRC shows biphasic kinetics whereas there is monophasic bleaching of the β-carotene in WRC [5].

Previous circular and linear dichroic measurements suggest that the two β-carotenes of NRCs are excitonically coupled and we have confirmed this as follows. 'Coupling' of the two β-carotenes results in spectral broadening and a low $\Delta A/A$ ratio (measured as in Fig.6a and ref.5). Fig.6b shows, using DBMIB as electron acceptor, that with NRC this ratio increases with time of photodamage, indicating loss of coupling, which is to be expected as one of the β-carotenes is bleached irreversibly. As a control, WRC with only one β-carotene per RC, shows a consistently high $\Delta A/A$ ratio which is unchanged during its irreversible DBMIB-dependent bleaching [see 5].

4. DISCUSSION

We have shown, under conditions expected to lead to 'donor-side' photoinhibition [3], i.e. isolated PSII reaction centres plus electron acceptor, that the two bound β-carotene molecules but not more than one of the accessory chlorophylls (Chl670) are oxidised by $P680^+$ and are subsequently irreversibly bleached. Neither $P680^+$ photoaccumulation nor ET activity are inhibited until these secondary electron donors have been inactivated. We conclude that the Car donor(s), identified in larger PSII particles, which are active when donation from water is inhibited [6], are the two β-carotenes bound to the D1/D2 complex. It appears that the Car and one of the accessory chlorophylls can serve as electron donors to reduce the effect of damaging oxidation reactions by $P680^+$. The fact that only one chlorophyll molecule is oxidised by $P680^+$, before it is destroyed itself, has implications for the relative binding distances of the accessory chlorophylls to the D1- and D2-proteins. As yet, a link between pigment degradation [5] and D1-protein cleavage [7] has not been defined. However, the former could possibly be the first signal that the D1-protein receives to initiate its structural modification and ultimate proteolytic degradation.

We have confirmed that there is excitonic coupling of the two β-carotene molecules present in normal PSII reaction centres. We suggest that this coupling may, by an as yet unknown mechanism, increase their ability to protect the RC from 'donor-side' photoinhibition.

REFERENCES

1. Gounaris, K., Chapman, D.J., Booth, P., Crystall, B., Giorgi, L.B., Klug, D.R., Porter, G. and Barber, J. (1990) FEBS Lett. 265, 88-92
2. Telfer, A., De Las Rivas, J. and Barber, J. (1991) Biochim. Biophys. Acta 1060, 106-114
3. Barber, J. and Andersson, B. (1992) Trends in Biochem. Sci. 17, 61-66
4. Macpherson, A.N., Telfer, A., Truscott, T.G. and Barber, J. (1992) Biochim. Biophys. Acta, submitted
5. De Las Rivas, J., Telfer, A. and Barber, J. (1992) Biochim. Biophys. Acta, submitted
6. Blubaugh, D.J., Atamian, M., Babcock, G.T., Golbeck, J.H. and Cheniae, G.M. (1991) Biochemistry 30, 7586-7597
7. Shipton, C.A. and Barber, J. (1991) Proc. Natl. Acad. Sci. USA 88, 6691-6695

Funded by the AFRC and a Spanish Government Fellowship to JDLR

EFFECTS OF MINERAL DEFICIENCIES ON PS II ACTIVITY AND ON THE TURNOVER OF THE D1 REACTION CENTER PROTEIN

D. Godde and M. Hefer, Department of Plant Biochemistry, Ruhr-University Bochum, Germany

1. Introduction

Disorders in the supply with mineral nutrients play an important role in stress induced photodamage of plants. Plants suffering under a deficient supply with Mg, Zn or K are characterized by a light enhanced chlorosis (1). Light dependent bleaching indicates chronic photoinhibition of PS II. On a molecular level photoinactivation is known to induce the degradation of the D1 reaction center protein (2). We like to present evidence that plants grown under permanent stress conditions like low pH, Mg deficiency alone and combined with S deficiency become susceptible towards photoinhibition. Chlorophyll fluorescence measurements indicated a loss of PS II quantum efficiency. Pulse-chase experiments with ^{14}C-leucine could show that the degradation of the D1 protein, which is induced by overexitation and photoinactivation of PS II, was significantly stimulated under stress conditions. However, also the synthesis of the D1 protein was changed in the deficient plants. The actual level of photoinhibition seems to be determined by the equilibrium between synthesis and degradation of the D1 protein.

2. Materials and Methods

Spinach plants were kept for 8-12 weeks on either full or deficient medium. Damage by acidic pH was induced by adjusting the pH of the growth medium to pH 3.0 with H_2SO_4 once a weak. Mg deficiency was induced by replacement of $MgSO_4$ with K_2SO_4. $MgCl_2$ was omitted. To induce S and Mg deficiency $MgSO_4$ and $MgCl_2$ was omitted from the growth medium. The plants were grown at a PFD of 400 μmol $m^{-2}s^{-1}$ for 9 h alternating with a dark phase of 15 h. Pulse modulated chlorophyll fluorescence was measured according to Schreiber (3). Immunological determination and pulse labelling of the D1 protein was performed as previously reported (4).

N. Murata (ed.), Research in Photosynthesis, Vol. IV, 467–470.

3. Results and Discussion

3.1 *Photosystem II Activity*

Photosystem II activity was followed by pulse modulated Kautsky chlorophyll fluorescence measurements.15 h dark adapted control plants, grown on a full medium, had a F_v/F_m ratio of 0.84, which indicated maximum quantum efficiency of photosystem II (Fig. 1).

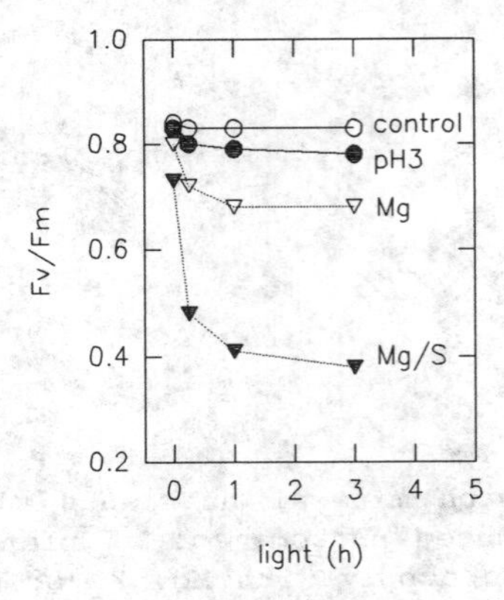

Fig. 1 Changes of PS II Activity During Illumination of Nutrient Deficient Spinach

During illumination with a PFD of 400 µmoles m^{-2} s^{-1} F_v/F_m stayed stable around 0.83. Also plants kept at pH 3.0 did not show a significant loss of PS II activity. However, in plants suffering under Mg deficiency PS II became susceptible towards photoinhibition and F_v/F_m dropped down below 0.7 after 3 h illumination. In the 15 h dark period recovery of PS II activity was possible and F_v/F_m raised up to 0.80. Photoinhibition was even increased in plants where Mg deficiency was combined with a low S supply. Here F_v/F_m dropped down to 0.36 in the light. In these plants PS II activity could not be fully restored during the 15 h dark period and the F_v/F_m ratio was with 0.73 significantly lower as in the control.

3.2 *Content of D1 Protein*

Photoinactivation of PS II is known to induce the degradation of the D1 reaction center polypeptide. In systems without protein synthesis this can be seen as a decrease in D1 protein content. No loss of D1 protein per chlorophyll could be detected illuminated non-photoinhibited control leaves when compared to dark adapted leaves (data not shown). The pH 3 grown plants, also not photoinhibited, had the same D1 protein content as the control leaves, both in the light and in the dark. In Mg deficient plants, which showed a significant loss of PS II activity, the D1 protein content was diminished to 63% in the light adapted leaves as determined by laser-densitometrical evaluation of the Western-blots. Dark adapted leaves had almost the same content (84%) of D1 protein as the control. In these plants PS II activity was almost completly restored in the subsequent dark phase. Plants grown without Mg and S, which were easily photoinhibited, also showed a loss of 40% of the D1 protein in their light adapted leaves. However, an increase in the D1 content in the dark as has been found in the Mg deficient plants could not be observed. This might explain, why dark recovery of PS II activity was low in Mg/S deficient plants. Obviously, in the photoinhibited plants the synthesis of the D1 protein could not keep up with its degradation. Also the content of the D2 protein was diminished indicating a loss of whole PS II reaction center (data not shown).

3.3 *Degradation and Synthesis of D1 Protein*

The higher D1 protein degradation in the stressed plants could be confirmed by pulse-chase experiments where leaves were labelled for 1 h in the light (4000 μmol m^{-2} s^{-1}) with the radioactive aminoacid. After adding CAP, to inhibit protein synthesis, the samples were illuminated for another 4 h and the decrease in radioactivity located in the D1 protein was determined by autoradiography. The laserdensitometrical evaluation of the autoradiogram is shown in Fig. 2.

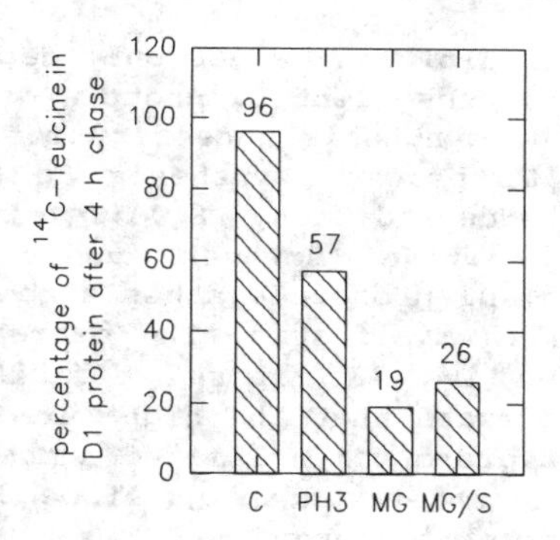

Fig. 2 Light induced D1 protein degradation in nutrient deficient spinach

In the control the D1 protein was relatively stable and still 96% of the radioactivity could be detected in the D1 protein after the chase period. The high proportion of radioactivity found in D1 protein might be due to the fact, that CAP did not inhibit D1 protein synthesis immediately. In the photoinhibited Mg and Mg/S deficient plants the degradation of D1 protein was significantly accelerated. 80% of the D1 protein was degraded after 4 h chase period. Since the D1 content in these plants was lower, at least in light adapted leaves, we assume that the D1 protein synthesis rate was not high enough to keep up with the degradation. This could be confirmed by short term pulse labelling experiment. In light adapted Mg/S deficient plants incorporation of ^{14}C leucine into the D1 protein after a 15 min light pulse was 20% lower as in the control plants. In this experiment the D1 protein content in the stressed leaves has decreased by 60%. However, in plants grown at pH 3, which were not photoinhibited, degradation of D1 protein was also found to be stimulated when compared to the control. After 4 h more than 40% of the D1 protein was degraded. Since the content of D1 protein remained stable (3.2). D1 protein synthesis should also be stimulated to keep up with the enhanced degradation. Short term pulse-labelling experiments revealed that in pH 3 grown plants D1 protein synthesis was more than 2 fold higher than in control leaves. So the increase in the turnover of the D1 protein occurred before any loss of PS II function was detectable.

Our results show that mineral deficiencies lead to an increase in the degradation of D1 protein known to be induced by overexitation of PS II. It seems very likely that in our system overexitation is caused by disturbancies in the export of photosynthates. We could find an increasing amount of starch accumu-lating in dark adapted deficient plants. In Mg/S deficient leaves the starch content was more than 20 fold higher than in the corresponding control leaves. The increase in starch content should consequently reduce the demand for NADPH and ATP and overexitation of PS II is induced by an increase in the reduction state of plastoquinone pool.

The actual level of photoinhibition is not only determined by overexitation of PS II and subsequent D1 protein degradation, but also by the rate of D1 synthesis necessary for PS II repair. When the rate of D1 protein synthesis is still high enough to keep up with its degradation, PS II can be repaired and remains functionally active. However, under severe or chronic stress conditions, D1 protein synthesis becomes limiting and photoinhibition is manifested. The decrease in the chlorophyll content found in all mineral deficient plants (data not shown) might indicate that the high turnover of the D1 protein can only be afforded for a limited number of PS II reaction center. This is understandable, since D1 protein synthesis is costly in terms of energy.

References

1 Marschner, H. and Cakmak, I. (1989) J.Plant Physiol. 134, 308-315

2 Prasil, O., Adir, N. and Ohad, I. (1992) in The photosystems: Structure, function and molecular biology (Barber, J., ed.), pp. 295-348, Elsevier, Amsterdam

3 Schreiber, U., Schliwa, U. and Bilger,W. (1986) Photosynthesis Res., 51, 51-62

4 Godde, D., Schmitz, H. and Weidner, M. (1991) Z.Naturforsch. 46c, 245-251

THE INFLUENCE OF PHOTOINHIBITION ON α- AND ß-CENTRES OF PHOTOSYSTEM II

ALOYSIUS WILD, MICHAEL RICHTER, AND BIRGIT BÖTHIN,
INSTITUTE OF GENERAL BOTANY, JOHANNES GUTENBERG-UNIVERSITY,
SAARSTR. 21, 6500 MAINZ, GER

INTRODUCTION

Our former studies on the photoinhibition of isolated spinach thylakoids focussed on the mechanisms leading to decreased electron transport capacity and the degradation of the D1 protein of Photosystem II. From the protective effect of an antioxidant mixture against photodamage to PS II we got information about the involvement of activated oxygen species in the mechanism of photoinhibition (1). In the present investigation we used the same antioxidant mixture to study the photoinhibitory changes in α- and ß-centres which occur before the D1 protein is degraded and the electron transport capacity is lost to a large extent. These changes are difficult to resolve with normally photoinhibited thylakoids due to the overlap with D1 degradation and the associated photochemical loss. On the other hand the more intact test systems like whole leaves are often not accessible to special methodical approaches like the analysis of the area growth over the fluorescence induction curve.

MATERIALS AND METHODS

All experiments were performed with isolated spinach thylakoids. The isolation procedure has been described in (2). Thylakoids were photoinhibited by 30 min exposure to 100 W m^{-2} photosynthetically active radiation provided by an Osram HQI-T 400 W lamp, heat filtered through a 7 cm layer of water. The suspensions were exposed in dishes to give a maximal layer of 2-3 mm at a chlorophyll content of 100 $\mu g\ ml^{-1}$. The incubation medium consisted of 0.33 M sorbitol, 5 mM $MgCl_2$, 10 mM NaCl, 40 mM HEPES/NaOH pH 7.6. The temperature was 20°C. The antioxidant mixture applied to the spinach thylakoids during the photoinhibitory treatment consisted of glutathione (10 mM), ascorbate (5 mM), SOD (100 U ml^{-1}), and catalase (2000 U ml^{-1}). The respective final concentrations in the thylakoid suspensions are given in brackets. Controls were kept in the dark otherwise under the same conditions. Prior to measurements of electron transport, fluorescence and atrazine binding sites, the antioxidants were removed from the thylakoid suspensions. In the following the term antioxidants always denotes the above described combination of protective enzymes and reducing agents.

The measurement of electron transport from water to ferricyanide (FeCy) was performed in an oxygen electrode. The reaction medium consisted of 0.33 M sorbitol, 10 mM NaCl, 5 mM $MgCl_2$, 40 mM HEPES/NaOH pH 7.6, 1 mM FeCy and 5 mM of the uncoupling reagent NH_4Cl. The chlorophyll content in the electrode chamber was 10 $\mu g\ ml^{-1}$. Relative values for the yield of oxygen evolution, Φ_{O_2}, were estimated from the slopes of the linear part of light response curves (including 4 values in the range up to 20 W m^{-2}).

The content of atrazine binding sites of thylakoids was determined according to (3) except that the incubation temperature was lowered to 0°C and the ethanol content was

N. Murata (ed.), Research in Photosynthesis, Vol. IV, 471–474.

reduced to 0.5 %. The applied ^{14}C-atrazine concentrations (25 - 400 nM) reached equilibrium within 15 minutes. Following centrifugation an aliquot of the supernatant was taken for liquid scintillation counting. The chlorophyll content in the binding assay was 50 $\mu g\ ml^{-1}$.
The room temperature fluorescence induction was measured with a laboratory built fluorometer. 20 μM DCMU and 2 mM diphenylcarbazide were present in the fluorescence probes. The intensity of the green actinic light was 10 W m^{-2}. The shutter was built in the laboratory and reached full opening in less than 200 μs. The sampling rates were 0.2 and 10 ms per datapoint for correct determination of the initial (F_0) and the maximal fluorescence (F_m), respectively. The thylakoids were kept three minutes in the dark before fluorescence measurement.
The relative proportions of PS IIα and PS IIß were determined by the analysis of the area growth over the fluorescence induction curve (4). Changes in the content of α- and ß- centres can be caused either by alterations in the relative proportions of both PS II populations or by a decrease of the area over the fluorescence induction curve due to a loss of total fluorescent PS II. Both possibilities are included through calculation of PS IIα and PS IIß from the products (α·area) and (ß·area), respectively (5).

RESULTS AND DISCUSSION

Photoinhibition of isolated spinach thylakoids without the addition of antioxidants causes damage to the reaction centre of PS II as indicated by the loss of atrazine binding sites to 57 % of dark controls. The electron transport capacity and Φ_{O_2} declines to 31 % and 27 %, respectively (Tab. 1). These results have been shown earlier (6). PS IIα as determined by the product (α·area) decreases to 16 % of dark controls while 35 % of PS IIß remain following photoinhibition. The decline of PS IIα-centres predominantly results from the loss of the area over the fluorescence induction curve (Tab. 1) and is less determined by the slight decrease in their relative proportion (Tab. 2). The increase in the relative proportion of the ß-centres is small compared to the decline of the area. The result is a net loss of PS IIß. The PS IIα are a little more affected as PS IIß. However, the difference in sensitivity to photoinhibition is not as extrem as obtained in (5) where no decrease of the ß-centres was found in thylakoids isolated from photoinhibited leaves. A possible explanation for the apparent discrepancy could be a de novo synthesis of ß-centres during the photoinhibitory treatment in whole leaves. This could be expected from the operation of the socalled PS II repair cycle which does, however, not work in isolated thylakoids (7).
When the antioxidants are present during photoinhibition the thylakoids show no decline of atrazine binding sites and retain 79 % of the control electron transport capacity. This indicates that no D1 protein degradation occurs and the most part of PS II remains in a photochemically active state. However, the same thylakoids show a marked loss of the quantum yield of oxygen evolution, Φ_{O_2} (Tab. 1).
Despite the presence of the antioxidants both the α- and ß-centres strongly decrease during photoinhibition, with the α-fraction again only little more affected than the ß-fraction (Tab. 1). The decrease is mainly caused by the area loss while there are only minor changes in the relative proportions of both fractions (Tab. 2).
When the photochemical activity of photoinhibited thylakoids is related to changes in PS II heterogeneity the main interest will concern the behaviour of the PS IIα-centres. These are thought to be responsible for the most part of the Q_B-reducing activity in spinach (7). With 31 % the remaining α-centres do not match up to the 79 % electron transport capacity obtained following photoinhibition in the presence of the antioxidants. It seems that a special PS II-population participates in electron transport which is neither of α- nor of ß-type. The strong decrease of Φ_{O_2} to 46 % of dark

TABLE 1. The decline of atrazine binding sites (D1), electron transport capacity from water to ferricyanide (ETC), quantum yield of oxygen evolution (Φ_{O_2}), variable fluorescence F_v, area over the fluorescence induction curve, the content of PS IIα (α·area) and PS IIß (ß·area), and the rate constant K_α during photoinhibition of spinach thylakoids. The presence and the missing of the antioxidants is indicated by (+) and (-), respectively. All values represent the mean of 3 - 6 independent measurements and are given in % of dark controls. The atrazine binding sites of dark controls ranged from 2.6 to 3.3 nmol mg^{-1} Chl, the electron transport capacity (H_2O to FeCy) was 170 -190 μmol mg^{-1} Chl h^{-1}, the ratio F_v/F_m was 0.77 - 0.80.

	D1	ETC	Φ_{O2}	F_V	area	α·area	ß·area	K_α
-	57±5	31±3	27±5	19±3	20±2	16±2	35±11	92±7
+	97±2	79±4	46±5	33±6	33±6	31±8	42±14	93±11

TABLE 2. Changes in the relative area proportions attributable to PS IIα and PS IIß, respectively, during photoinhibition of spinach thylakoids in the presence (+) and without antioxidants (-). The values represent the mean of 4 - 5 measurements and are given in % of total area over the fluorescence induction curve.

	dark control		photoinhibited	
	PS IIα	PS IIß	PS IIα	PS IIß
-	82	18	67	33
+	84	16	75	25

controls in relation to the still high electron transport capacity indicates that a large quantity of the whole photochemically active PS II operates at a low quantum yield of oxygen evolution. Interestingly the rate constants K_α of photoinhibited thylakoids are rather the same as found with control thylakoids whether antioxidants are present during the photoinhibitory treatment or not (Tab. 1). Since K_α represents the rate constant for the closure of open PS IIα in the light we conclude from our results that the quantum yield of the α-centres is not significantly affected by photoinhibition. Following photoinhibition in the presence of antioxidants the remaining α-centres should therefore contribute 31 % to both the measured Φ_{O_2} (if for simplification the slight decrease of K_α is neglected) and the electron transport capacity. A PS II of non-α-type must then contribute the rest of the measured activity which is 15 % for Φ_{O_2} and 48 % for the electron transport capacity. If we assume that the relative values for the electron transport capacity reflect the proportion of remaining photochemically active PS II then the calculated quantum yield of oxygen evolution (Φ_{O_2}) of the non-α-PS II would be as low as 32 % of dark controls. It appears that the non-α-PS II is not only less efficient in photochemistry but has also a very low fluorescence yield. Following photoinhibition in the presence of the antioxidants the variable fluorescence F_v decreased to 33 % of dark controls. This corresponds well to the remaining α- and ß-centres keeping in mind that the proportion of variable fluorescence attributable to the ß-centres is small in relation to the contribution of α-centres. An influence of a PS II donor side limitation on the shape of the fluorescence induction curve can be excluded from the presence of diphenylcarbazide in the fluorescence probes.

At present we do not know the mechanism underlying the observed changes in photochemical and fluorescence properties during the photoinhibition of thylakoids in the presence of the antioxidants. As the antioxidant mixture included 5 mM ascorbate we cannot exclude an influence from the operation of the xanthophyll cycle (8). Indeed preliminary results of spectroscopic analysis for zeaxanthin from the absorbance change at 505 nm indicate that small amounts of zeaxanthin are generated under the applied conditions (data not shown). This is at present confirmed by HPLC-determinations. The missing of zeaxanthin due to the lack of ascorbate could be one reason why we did not observe such striking differences between PS IIα and Φ_{O_2} on the one hand and the electron transport capacity on the other in the normally photoinhibited thylakoids. In addition we have to take in account the above mentioned problems arising from the overlap between changes of Φ_{O_2} and fluorescence in intact PS II with the respective changes due to the extensive destruction of the PS II reaction centre in the normally photoinhibited thylakoids.

Our results can be summarized as follows. When isolated spinach thylakoids are photoinhibited in the presence of the above mentioned antioxidants the damage to the reaction centre of Photosystem II is largely suppressed. However, part of the high fluorescent PS IIα seems to convert to a special form of fluorescence quencher which is photochemically active, though at a comparatively low quantum yield. These centres are not identical to the α-quenchers described in (9) as the latter should not have any photochemical activity.

REFERENCES

1 Richter, M., Rühle, W., and Wild, A. (1990) Photosynth. Res. 24, 237-243
2 Richter, M., Rühle, W., and Wild, A. (1990) Photosynth. Res. 24, 229-235
3 Tischer, W. and Strotmann H. (1977) Biochim. Biophys. Acta 460, 113-125
4 Melis, A. and Homann P. (1976) Photochem. Photobiol. 23, 343-350
5 Krause, G.H., Somersalo, S., Zumbusch, E., Weyers, B., and Laasch H. (1990) J. Plant Physiol. 136, 472-479
6 Richter, M., Böthin, B., and Wild, A. (1992) J. Plant Physiol. 140, 244-246
7 Guenther, J.E. and Melis A. (1990) Photosynth. Res. 23, 105-109
8 Demmig-Adams, B. (1990) Biochim. Biophys. Acta 1020, 1-24
9 Krause, G.H. and Weiß, E. (1991) Annu. Rev. Plant Physiol. Plant Mol. Biol. 42, 313-49

ANALYSIS OF THE INDUCTION KINETICS OF CHLOROPHYLL FLUORESCENCE AND OXYGEN EVOLUTION OBTAINED BY SIMULTANEOUS MEASUREMENT OF THE FLUORESCENCE AND PHOTOACOUSTIC SIGNAL: EFFECT OF A PHOTOINHIBITORY TREATMENT

Gert Schansker, Jan F.H. Snel and Jack J.S. van Rensen
Dept. Plant Physiological Research, Wageningen Agricultural University, Gen. Foulkesweg 72, NL-6703 BW Wageningen, The Netherlands.

1. INTRODUCTION

There are several ways to study "inactive centers". Vredenberg *et al.* (1) measured simultaneously the induction of oxygen evolution (the photobaric component of the photoacoustic signal) and fluorescence. Plotting of the oxygen evolution against fluorescence gives plots like those in Fig. 3. After keeping the spinach plants for more than twelve hours in the dark, Vredenberg *et al.* found that oxygen evolution, after an initial rise, declined linearly with the increase of fluorescence. After 8 hours daylight the initial rise of the oxygen evolution had decreased somewhat and the decline of the oxygen evolution was no longer linear. Vredenberg et al. ascribed this deviation from linearity to PS II centers with a lower oxygen yield. They calculated that 20-30% of the PS II centers had a lower oxygen yield after 8 hours irradiation with daylight.

The goal of this research was to study the effect of a short term photoinhibitory (PI) treatment on the form of the above mentioned plot and on the amount of PS II centers with a lower oxygen yield. This report gives a characterisation of the leaf material used and preliminary data on the effect of a PI treatment on the induction of oxygen evolution and fluorescence.

2. MATERIAL and METHODS

Pea plants (*Pisum sativum* var. Finale) were grown in continuous light of 90 - 140 µE for 14 h day^{-1} at 20 °C. For the experiments leaves of 10 - 15 days old plants were used. Measurements of the photosynthetic capacity of the pea leaves were performed as described in (2) with slight modifications. This analysis is based on the method of Genty (3). Maximum electron transport was calculated by fitting the irradiance response curves to an equation derived by Leverenz (4). Relaxation of non-photochemical quenching was analysed as described in (5). Dark adaptation time between the saturating flashes was 100 s. Induction curves of fluorescence and oxygen evolution were measured as described in (1). A saturating flash was given 1.3 s after turning on the actinic light. The measurements were done with leaf discs (12 mm). Trace a (Fig. 3) was normalised as described in (8). Trace b and c were normalised to trace a. The leaf discs were punctured with a sharp needle to minimise the effect of the opening state of the stomata on the diffusion of O_2. A PI treatment was given by removing a pea plant from the growth chamber and

N. Murata (ed.), Research in Photosynthesis, Vol. IV, 475–478.

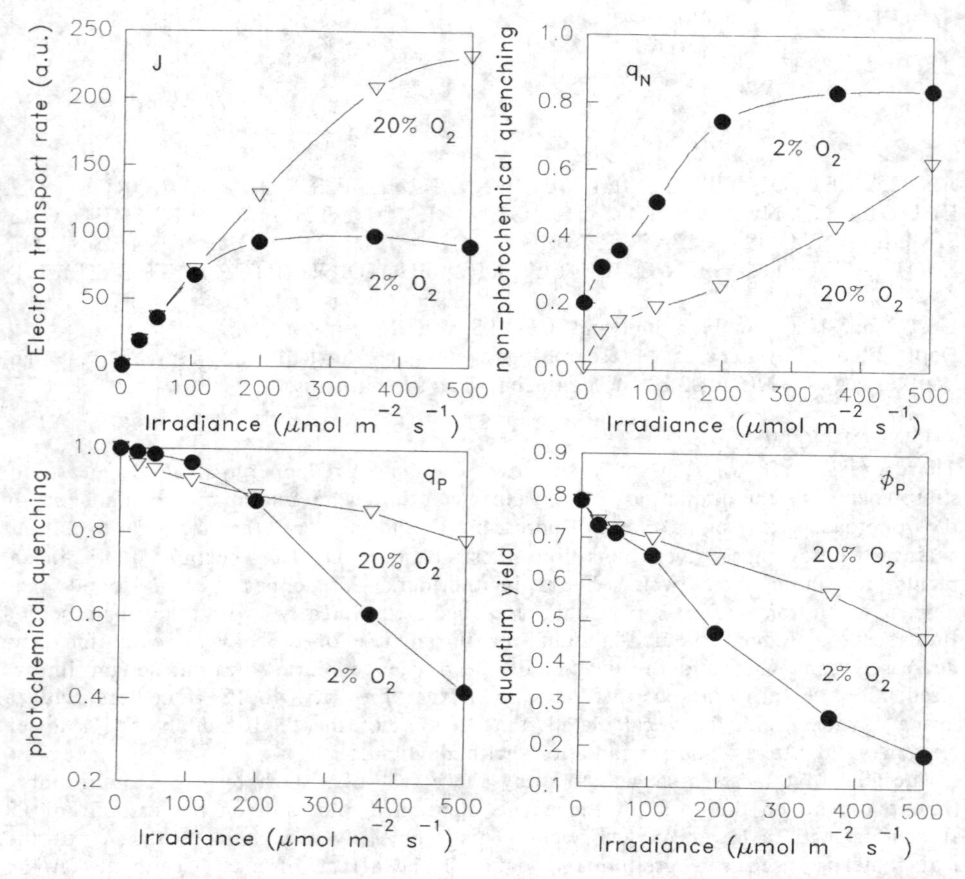

Fig. 1. Irradiance response curves of electron transport (J), non-photochemical quenching (q_N), photochemical quenching (q_P) and the quantum yield of PS II (ϕ_P). Every serie of measurements was performed on the same leaf, starting at the highest irradiance used.

irradiating one of its leaves with light from a slide projector (3000 - 3500 μE). The light was filtered through a water filter. The Fv/Fm value measured as part of the measurements of the induction curves was used to assess the severity of the treatment.

3. RESULTS and DISCUSSION

Before starting the photoinhibition experiments we wanted to have some information on the photosynthetic capacity of the pea leaves that were to be used. For this purpose irradiance response curves of electron transport (J), non-photochemical quenching (q_N), photochemical quenching (q_P) and the quantum yield of PS II (ϕ_P) were made (Fig. 1). The role of photorespiration was assessed by

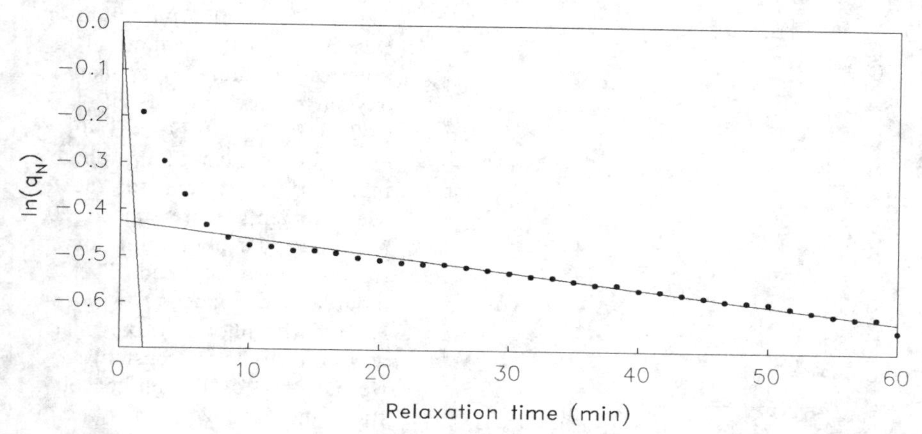

Fig. 2. Relaxation of non-photochemical quenching. The curve was deconvoluted as described in (5). The photoinhibitory treatment (45 min) preceding the measurement was carried out under 2% O_2 and the leaf was irradiated with 2570 µE light provided by the actinic light source of the PAM (Kl1500). At the end of the photoinhibitory treatment the atmosphere was changed from 2% to 20% O_2. The interval between the saturating flashes was 100 s.

measuring at 2% and 20% oxygen. Allowing photorespiration (20% O_2) caused an increase of electron transport by a factor 2.5 (from 101 to 255) and the saturation irradiance shifted from 200 µE to more than 500 µE (Fig. 1). Photorespiration also strongly delayed the induction of q_N (Fig. 1). In contrast to measurements done under 20% O_2, the qN did not relax totally under 2% O_2, indicating that dark adaptation under 2% O_2 takes more time than under 20% O_2. Under 20% O_2 maximum induction of the q_N occurred around 2500 µE (not shown). Photorespiration also inhibited the decreases of q_P and ϕ_P (Fig. 1).

A PI treatment causes a decline of F_m. This decline is caused by several processes, like energetisation of the membrane, changes induced by the formation of zeaxanthin and inactivation of PS II. (Phosphorylation of LHC II is claimed not to occur under photoinhibitory conditions (6)). A collective term for the effects of these processes on F_m is non-photochemical quenching (7). After the PI treatment is stopped, F_m increases again or, to put it differently, the q_N relaxes. Relaxation of q_N was monitored (Fig. 2). The experiment was repeated four times. Every time two phases were found, a fast phase with a $t_{½} = 2.69 \pm 0.48$ min and a slow phase with a $t_{½} = 218.3 \pm 28.1$ min. From Fig. 2 it can be concluded that as far as the fluorescence measurements are concerned the dark adaptation time of photoinhibited leaves makes little difference as long as the dark adaptation time is more than 10 min.

In Fig. 3 the relationship between induction of oxygen evolution and chlorophyll fluorescence before (a) and after (b and c) a PI treatment is plotted. Only the first 1.75 s of induction are presented. The PI treatment caused on average a 12% increase of F_o. However there was no correlation between F_o and F_v/F_m. (n=17; Spearman correlation test). This makes it doubtful that the

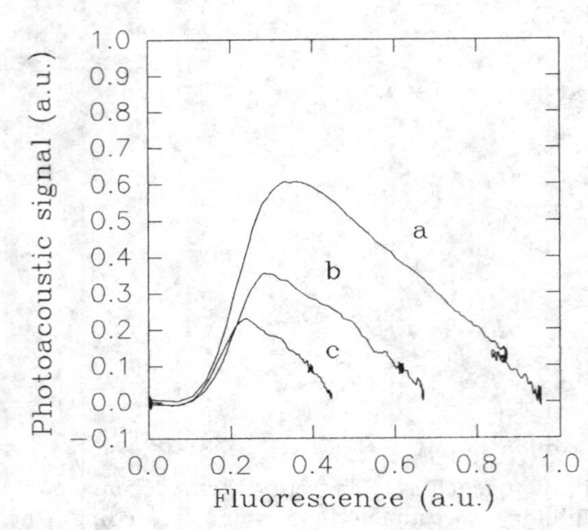

Fig. 3. Effect of a photoinhitory treatment on the induction kinetics of fluorescence and oxygen evolution. a. F_v/F_m = 0.87; b. F_v/F_m = 0.77; c. F_v/F_m =0.70. For details of the photoinhibitory treatment see the text Measurements were started 20 min after the photoinhibitory treatment was stopped. The modulation frequency was 144.5 Hz and the photon flux density was 200 μE. Time constants were 10 ms for the photoacoustic signal and 24 ms for the fluorescence signal.

increase of F_o was caused by photoinhibition. The preliminary data in Fig. 3 indicate that the relation between the rate of oxygen evolution and fluorescence yield is still linear after a PI treatment. However, in trace c this part of the curve was reduced to less than 0.05 fluorescence units and the inactive centers as interpreted in (1,8) formed the largest part of the trace (almost 0.2 fluorescence units). This increase is, however relative and caused completely by the loss of active centers. Compared to trace b the amount of inactive centers had even declined a little. Fig. 3 indicates that the inactive centers are considerably less sensitive to the PI treatment than the active centers. More experiments have to be done to determine where the inactive centers came from.

4. ACKNOWLEDGEMENTS

We would like to thank dr. W.F. Buurmeijer for his help in using the photoacoustic equipment. This research was supported in part by the Netherlands Foundation for Chemical Research (SON), financed by the Netherlands Organisation for Scientific Research (NWO).

5. REFERENCES

1 Vredenberg, W.J., Snel, J.F.H., Buurmeijer, W.F. and Boumans, H. (1992) Photosynthetica, in press.
2 Van Kooten, O., Van Hove, L.W.A. and Vredenberg, W.J. (1990) In Curr. Res. Photosynth. IV, 611-614.
3 Genty, B., Briantais, J.-M.and Baker, N.R. (1989) Biochim. Biophys. Acta 990, 87-92.
4 Leverenz, J.W. (1987) Physiol. Plant. 71, 20-29.
5 Walters, R.G. and Horton, P. (1991) Photosynth Res. 27, 121-133.
6 Schuster, G., Dewit, M., Staehelin, L.A. and Ohad, I. (1986) J. Cell Biol. 103, 71-80.
7 Demmig, B. and Winter, K. (1988) Aust. J. Plant Physiol. 15, 163-177.
8 Snel, J.F.H., Boumans, H. and Vredenberg, W.F. (1992) these proceedings.

BIOCHEMICAL EVIDENCE FOR LOSS OF Q_A FROM PHOTOSYSTEM II REACTION CENTRES DURING PHOTOINHIBITION

A. Koivuniemi[1,2], E. Swiezewska[1,3], S. Styring[1], E.-M. Aro[2] and B. Andersson[1]

[1]Department of Biochemistry, Stockholm University,Sweden, [2]Department of Biology, University of Turku, Finland and [3]Institute of Biochemistry and Biophysics, Polish Academy of Sciences, Warsaw, Poland

1. INTRODUCTION

There is now compelling evidence that photoinactivation of PSII can be induced by reactions occuring both at the acceptor- and donor-side of P_{680} (1). A mechanism for the acceptor-side inactivation has recently been proposed, based upon EPR and fluorescence analysis of thylakoid membranes subjected to strong illumination under anaerobic conditions (2). Three reversible intermediate steps (fast, semi-stable and stable) were identified in addition to a fourth irreversible step (non-decaying). The four photoinactivation intermediates are formed in a sequential manner and the two first ones are characterized by long-lived Q_A^--species. The third intermediate (stable) is proposed to contain doubly-reduced and protonated Q_A. The final, non-decaying state was proposed to represent centres where Q_AH_2 has left its binding site on the D_2-protein. The creation of empty Q_A-sites has previously been suggested to occur after chemical reduction (3) or photoinhibition of PSII under aerobic conditions (4).

In this study we have made a direct HPLC-analysis of the plastoquinone (PQ) content in PSII core complexes purified from thylakoid membranes subjected to photoinhibitory illumination under anaerobic conditions.

2. MATERIALS and METHODS

Spinach "BBY-type" of PSII membranes were isolated according to (5) and suspended in 50 mM Mes, pH 6,0, 10 mM NaCl, 5 mM $CaCl_2$ and 400 mM sucrose to a concentration of 200 µg chl/ml. The sample was photoinactivated by white light at an intensity of 5500 µE m-2 s-1 in anaerobic glass vials as in (6). PSII core complexes were prepared essentially according to Ghanotakis et al. (7) on ice.

The PQ content of the isolated PSII core complexes was determined as described by Kalén et al. (8) with slight modifications. Diethylether (25%)

N. Murata (ed.), Research in Photosynthesis, Vol. IV, 479–482.

in hexane was used instead of chloroform for extraction and purification of lipids. The dried eluate was dissolved in 20 µl of ethanol. HPLC analyses were performed on a Schimazu-CR4A system fitted with a C 18 reverse phase column. For elution, a combination of linear gradients from the initial methanol: water (9:1) in pump A to methanol: 2-propanol (8:2) in pump B was operated for 35 min at a flow rate of 1.5 ml/min. The absorbance of the eluate was monitored at 210 nm. Chlorophyll was estimated according to (9). Western blot analyses were performed according to standard procedures. PSII electron transport was measured polarographically in the presence of 0.4 mM phenyl-p-benzoquinone.

3. RESULTS

When isolated PSII membranes (5) were subjected to the strong illumination photoinhibition caused decrease of oxygen evolving activity. Typically, the inactivation half-time was approximately 30 min. After 80 min of strong illumination only 15% of the activity remained and the majority of the centres were trapped in the non-decaying state (2) previously suggested to lack Q_A. Despite the pronounced inactivation of PSII electron transport there was virtually no degradation of the D_1- and D_2-protein due to the anaerobic conditions during the illumination(6). Prior to the analysis of the quinone content PSII core complexes were isolated from the thylakoid membrane, thereby eliminating contribution from the PQ pool. In addition, isolated PSII core complexes contain empty Q_B-sites (7) thereby allowing a direct estimation of PQ bound to the Q_A-site.
After extraction with organic solvents and HPLC analyses of the isolated PSII core complexes one peak representing PQ was seen (not shown). There was no plastoquinol present since the preparation procedure converts all quinone molecules into the oxidized form.

Table I Loss of Q_A from photoinhibited PSII centres

Photoinhibitory illumination of "BBY"-membranes was performed for 80 min under anaerobic conditions. PSII core complexes were then isolated and their PQ content was analyzed by HPLC.

sample	*PQ/chl*
PSII core, dark control	*1/128**
PSII core, strong illum. 80 min.	*1/423*

** The low PQ/Chl ratio in the control sample is partly due to contaminating chlorophyll a/b -proteins.*

In the PSII core complexes isolated from BBY-membranes kept in the dark there was one PQ per 128 molecules of chlorophyll (Table I). This somewhat low plastoquinone/chlorophyll ratio can partially be explained by contamination of chlorophyll a/b-proteins. Significantly, in the PSII core complexes isolated from the photoinhibited thylakoid material there was only 1 PQ per 423 chlorophyll molecules. This means that the PSII core complexes isolated after strong illumination only contain 30% of Q_A compared to those obtained from the dark control material.

4. DISCUSSION

The present results give direct biochemical evidence that the primary quinone acceptor Q_A can be released from PSII reaction centres during photoinhibition. As illustrated in Fig. 1 after prolonged photoinhibitory illumination in the absence of oxygen as much as 70% of the PSII reaction centres are lacking their Q_A. In approximately 10% of the PSII complexes electron transfer is impaired but the Q_A is still occupied. It is likely that these centres are trapped in the semi-stable and stable inactivation states, represented by stable singly- and doubly-reduced Q_A respectively, and therefore able to recover into functional units (2). After shorter periods of strong illumination the fraction of centres containing inactive Q_A increases while that containing empty Q_A-sites decreases (not shown).

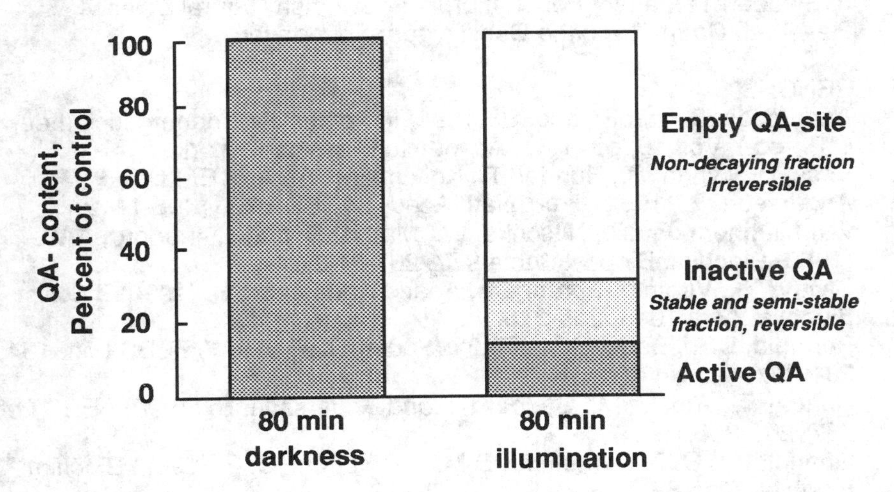

FIGURE 1 State of the Q_A-sites in PSII after photoinhibitory illumination of BBY-membranes for 80 min under anaerobic conditions

It can be concluded that the present data strongly corroborates previous spectroscopic measurements (2-4) suggesting that Q_A upon double reduction leaves the reaction centre. They also support the model for acceptor-side induced photoinactivation involving sequential accumulation of stably-reduced QA-species and that the ultimate consequence of strong illumination under anaerobic conditions is an empty Q_A-site. In the presence of oxygen, however this final stage may not be reached very frequently since the preceding inactivation intermediates will be quenched. This is because they produce chlorophyll triplets and mediate formation of reactive singlet oxygen (2).
Two populations of photoinactivated PSII centres containing doubly-reduced Q_A can be discriminated. On one hand there are centres where the Q_A to Q_B electron transfer can be reestablished by oxidation and on the other hand those where the Q_AH_2 leaves its binding site. It is presently not known if the double reduction of Q_A in itself is the cause of its release or if some structural alteration in the reaction centre induced by the photoinhibitory treatment also is required. In favour of the latter possibility is that recovery of PSII activity in centres containing doubly-reduced Q_A requires a conformational change (2).

5. ACKNOWLEDGEMENTS

This project was supported by the Nordic Ministers of Energy, the Bank of Sweden Tercenary Foundation, the Swedish Natural Science Research Council and the Carl Trygger Foundation.

REFERENCES

1 Andersson, B. and Styring, S. (1991) in Topics of Bioenergetics (Lee, C.P., ed.), Vol. 16, pp. 1-81, Academic Press, New York.
2 Vass, I., Styring, S., Hundal, T., Koivuniemi, A., Aro, E.-M. and Andersson, B. (1992) Proc. Natl. Acad. Sci. USA 89, 1408-1412.
3 van Mieghem, F.J.E., Nitschke, W., Mathis, P. and Rutherford, A.W. (1989) Biochim. Biophys. Acta 977, 207-214.
4 Styring, S., Virgin, I. Ehrenberg, A. and Andersson, B. (1990) Biochim. Biophys. Acta 1015, 269-278.
5 Berthold, D.A., Babcock, G.T. and Yocum, C.F. (1981) FEBS Lett. 134, 231-234.
6 Hundal, T., Aro, E.-M., Carlberg, I. and Andersson, B. (1990) FEBS Lett. 267, 203-206.
7 Ghanotakis, D.F., Demetriou, D.M. and Yocum, C. F. (1987) Biochim. Biophys. Acta 891, 15-21.
8 Kalén, A., Appelkvist, E.-L., Chojnacki, T. and Dallner, G. (1990) J. Biol. Chem. 265, 1158-1164.
9 Lichtenthaler, H. (1987) Methods Enzymol. 148, 350-382.

RESPONSE OF SITE-SPECIFIC *psbA* MUTANTS OF *SYNECHOCYSTIS* 6803 TO PHOTOINHIBITORY ILLUMINATION

PIRKKO MÄENPÄÄ, TAINA KALLIO, PAULA MULO, GAZA SALIH*, EVA-MARI ARO, ESA TYYSTJÄRVI AND CHRISTER JANSSON*.
Dept of Biology, Univ. of Turku, SF-20700 Turku, Finland, *Dept of Biochemistry, Arrhenius laboratories, Univ. of Stockholm, S-10691 Stockholm, Sweden

1. INTRODUCTION

Photoinhibition of photosystem II (PS II) takes place under high light. Primary photodamage leads to light-induced turnover of the reaction center polypeptide D1. In the proteolytical breakdown of the polypeptide the stromal loop connecting transmembrane α-helices D and E has been suggested to play a crucial role for several reasons: Firstly, it contains a PEST-like area. Secondly, it includes the possible primary cleavage area (1) during acceptor-side photoinhibition (2). Thirdly, it is part of the Q_B binding site. In addition, it is in close proximity to the Q_A binding area of the D2 polypeptide (3).

We have created three new site-specific mutations in the loop between helices D and E. Two mutations (mutants CA1 and E243K) are close to the possible cleavage site of the D1 polypeptide and were directed to three consecutive glutamates (242-244). In the mutant CA1 all three glutamates were removed and Q241 was changed to H. In the mutant E243K the middle one of the negative charges was changed to a positive one. The mutation E229D was aimed at diluting the possible PEST-property of the area.

2. MATERIALS AND METHODS

Site-specific mutagenesis of the *psbA2* gene of *S*. 6803 was performed according to (4). The mutated area of *psbA2* was transferred to pGS1 (Salih et al.,these proceedings) which was used to transform the A2 strain (5) of *S*. 6803. In A2, both *psbA1* and *psbA3* are inactivated, *psbA2* being the only functional *psbA* gene. An antibiotic control strain (AR) with the same DNA construction as in the mutants but with no site-specific mutation was created to be used as a physiological control. Transformant colonies were selected according to antibiotic resistance. The PS II inhibitor DCMU was present during the isolation of pure mutant lines to prevent any selective advantage for functional wild type PS II. During cultivations for the physiological experiments no DCMU was used. The mutations were confirmed by sequencing. In order to confirm that the transformants preserved the desired DNA structure, the genomic DNA was isolated

N. Murata (ed.), Research in Photosynthesis, Vol. IV, 483–486.

and analyzed by Southern blot hybridization using the *psbA2* coding sequence as a probe.

The cells were photoinhibited for one hour at 700 μmol photons $m^{-2}s^{-1}$ at 32°C (20 μg chl/ml) and their F_V/F_M was registrated with a PAM fluorometer. For the studies of recovery from photoinhibition, the control cells and the mutants were photoinhibited to the same level and subsequently the recovery was followed at 20 μmol photons $m^{-2}s^{-1}$ for one hour. Fluorescence relaxation after a single turnover flash was monitored with the PAM fluorometer.

3. RESULTS AND DISCUSSION

The control cells (wildtype and AR) behaved similarly during strong illumination (Figs.1.and 2.): Quenching of F_V/F_M started from the onset of the treatment and in 10 min. the F_V/F_M ratio was inhibited 42% in the wildtype and 33% in the AR cells. During the entire photoinhibitory period of one hour, F_V/F_M of the wildtype cells reduced 55% and that of the AR cells 51%.

F_V/F_M of all the site-specific mutants decreased only about 10% during the first 10 min. of photoinhibitory illumination (Fig.1.). During prolonged illumination (Fig.2.) the mutant CA1 became more severely inhibited than the other mutants reaching the inhibition level of control strains during one hour. F_V/F_M of mutants E229D and E243K were less severely inhibited during an one hour treatment: 35% and 40%, respectively.

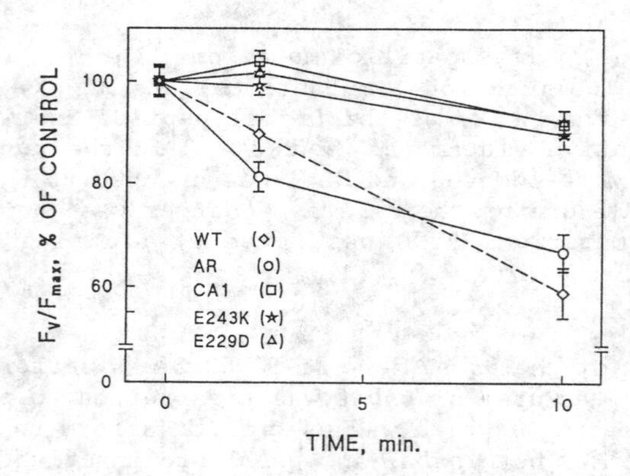

Fig.1. Changes in F_V/F_M in vivo during short-term illumination (PPFD 700 μmol $m^{-2}s^{-1}$) of wild type (wt) cells, antibiotic resistance control (AR) cells and the site-specific mutants CA1, E243K and E229D. For the photoinhibitory conditions see Materials and Methods.

To follow the recovery from photoinhibition at dim light (Fig.3.), all strains were first photoinhibited to the same level. In control cells, substantial recovery of F_V/F_M after a high light treatment took place also in the presence of the protein synthesis inhibitor streptomycin. We interpret this to indicate an intermediate, reversible phase of photoinhibition (6). Possibly, this phase involves a conformational change in the D1 protein. For the mutants, *de novo* synthesis of the D1 polypeptide was an absolute requirement to recover from photoinhibition. The protein synthesis independent recovery in F_V/F_M represents a relaxation of the conformational change in D1 protein. The mutants seem to be resistant to this less severe type of photoinhibition. It is possible as well, that the mutants proceed to a subsequent irreversible phase of photoinhibition so fast that the irreversible phase cannot be seen. Our results suggest a crucial role for the mutated amino acids in the conformational modification of the D1 polypeptide during illumination. The decrease in F_V/F_M that recovers in the presence of streptomycin might also be partially due to non-photoinhibitory downregulation of PS II.

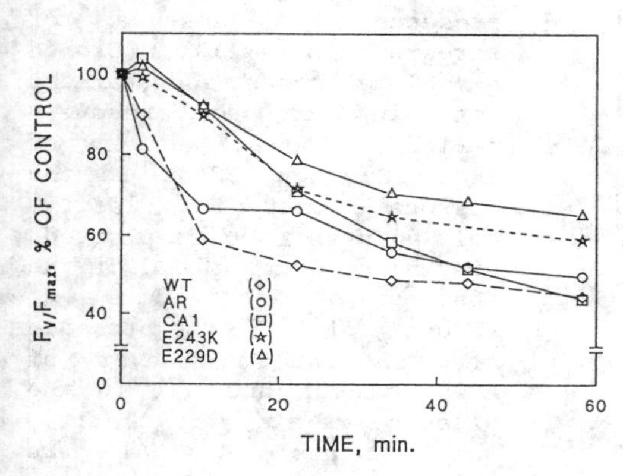

Fig.2. Changes in F_V/F_M *in vivo* during long-term illumination (PPFD 700 μmol $m^{-2}s^{-1}$) of wt, AR, CA1, E243K and E229D. For the inhibitory conditions, see Materials and Methods.

Mutant	$t_{1/2}$(μs)	A (%)	$t_{1/2}$(μs)	A (%)	$t_{1/2}$ (ms)	A(%)
Control	130±12.2	33.6±3.4	589±47.7	49.8±2.5	3.8±0.4	15.7±1.2
E243K	165±22.5	33.5±6.1	620±73.0	49.4±4.6	3.9±0.2	12.0±1.5
E229D	154±18.8	37.2±1.8	660±25.8	48.6±2.1	4.2±0.4	14.2±1.4
CA1	216±9.3	24.0±2.0	801±37.4	39.7±2.4	9.3±0.3	35.6±1.2
Reaction	$Q_A^- \rightarrow Q_B$		$Q_A^- \rightarrow Q_B^-$		$Q_BH_2 \leftrightarrow Q_B$	

Table I. Half-times ($t_{1/2}$) and amplitudes (A) of fluorescence relaxation kinetics after single turnover flashes in *Synechocystis* 6803 control cells and the three mutants. Averages of 60 fluorescence relaxations were fitted, and the sample points were weighed according to their individual standard errors.

All three phases of fluorescence relaxation after a single turnover flash (Table I) were markedly slower in CA1 than in AR. We think that the mutation of CA1 probably affects the conformation of the Q_B binding site and the contact to area of the D2 protein binding Q_A. Also the function of the non heme iron may be affected in CA1. To understand the molecular mechanisms underlying the photoinhibitory behaviour of the site-specific mutants demands more detailed biochemical studies which are presently going on.

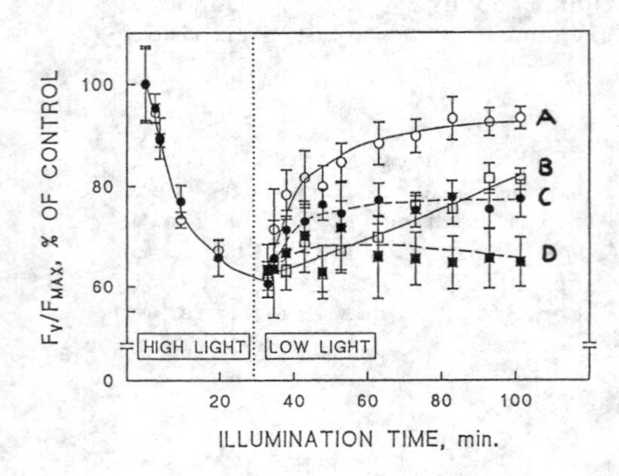

Fig.3. Photoinhibition and recovery of F_V/F_M in AR, CA1, E243K and E229D in the presence or absence of streptomycin (str). (Closed symbols with str, added at the beginning of the recovery period). Line A: recovery of AR, E229D and E243K in the absence of str. For clarity, only points of AR are plotted. Line B: recovery of CA1 in the absence of str. Line C: recovery of AR in the presence of str. Line D: recovery of E229D, E243K and CA1 in the presence of str. For clarity, only points of CA1 are plotted.

REFERENCES

1. Greenberg, B. M., Gaba, V., Mattoo, A. K. and Edelman, M. (1987) EMBO J. 6, 2865-2869
2. De Las Rivas, J., Andersson, B. and Barber, J. (1992) FEBS Lett. 301, 246-252
3. Trebst, A. (1991) Z. Naturforsch. 46c, 557-562
4. Kunkel, T. A., Roberts, J. D. and Zakour, R. A. (1987) Methods Enzymol. 154, 367-382
5. Jansson, C., Debus, R. J., Osiewacz, H. D., Gurevitz, M. and McIntosh, L. (1987) Plant Physiol. 85, 1021-1025
6. Ohad, I., Adir, N., Koike, H., Kyle, D.J. and Inoue, Y. (1990) J. Biol. Chem. 265, 1972-1979.

Characterization of Paraquat resistant mutants of *Chlamydomonas reinhardtii*

Kaoru Kitayama and Robert K. Togasaki
Dept. Biology, Indiana University, Bloomington, IN 47405, U.S.A.

1. Introduction

Plant cells have a defense mechanism against oxygen toxicity, which is pronounced during active photosynthesis and many stress conditions (1). Superoxide dismutase (SOD), the key enzyme involved in this defense mechanism, is generally acknowledged to play an important role in the resistance against the herbicide paraquat, through the reduction of the superoxide anion level. We are interested in the regulation of this defense mechanism, and because the same mechanism seems to be responsible to the resistance against paraquat, we focus on the regulation of SOD levels in paraquat resistant cells.

2. Materials and Methods

2.1 Strains and culture conditions: Paraquat resistant mutants were isolated by UV-mutagenesis of the wild-type strain 137c (+) followed by liquid selection. Cells were grown heterotrophically in TAP medium in white light (4000lux) unless otherwise specified.

2.2 SOD assay: Cells were sonicated and soluble fractions were assayed for SOD activity (2).

2.3 Subcellular localization: Chloroplast and mitochondria were fractionated with Percoll gradients (3, 4).Soluble fractions were analyzed on non-denaturing gels and stained for SOD activity as described previously (5). The contamination of mitochondria in chloroplast fractions was checked by cytochrome-c oxidase assays (6)

2.4 Recombinant DNA techniques: The cDNA library (generously supplied by Dr. S.Merchant) was screened by plaque hybridization with an oligonucleotide probe using standard techniques (7). DNA sequencing was carried out by the dideoxy chain termination method using Sequenase v. 2.0 (U. S. Biochem.).

3. Results and discussion

3.1 SOD levels in Paraquat resistant mutants

Paraquat resistant mutants were selected in minimal medium containing paraquat (0.1mM) with a short period of saturated light illumination (10,000 lux, 40sec.). allowing only those cells that are resistant to paraquat and photosynthetically competent to survive. All the paraquat resistant mutants tested showed about two-fold higher SOD levels than that of the wild type cells in tandard culture conditions without paraquat (Table 1). The SOD activity was induced by four-fold in the wild type cells when grown in the presence of paraquat (0.3 μM) (Fig.1). One mutant (par19-5) showing the greatest resistance of all was further studied and the SOD level was also induced by paraquat in this mutant to the same level as in the wild-type cells. This result indicates that the constitutively high SOD activity in the mutant cells might confer resistance to paraquat.

N. Murata (ed.), Research in Photosynthesis, Vol. IV, 487–490.

Table 1. SOD activity and paraquat resistance level in wt and resistant mutants

Strain	[SOD] in cell (U/10-7cells)	Resistance [paraquat] in medium (μM)
137c (+), wild-type	5.5	0.3
par1	9.0	1.0
par5	11.5	1.0
par19-5	12.0	1.0+

Figure.1. SOD induction in Wt cell and par19-5.

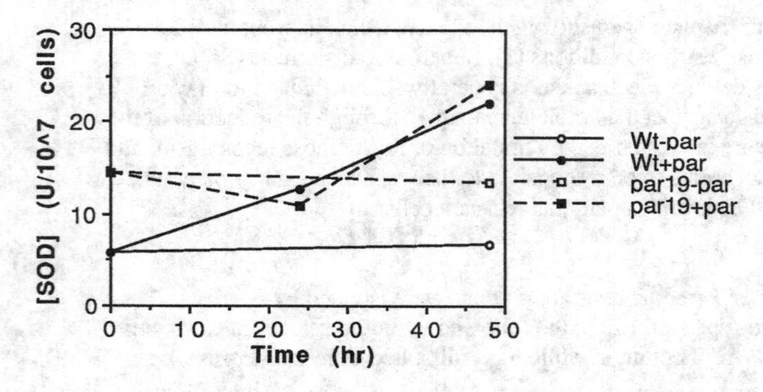

3.2 Localization of SOD isozymes

In order to determine which isozyme of SOD is responsible for the acquisition of paraquat resistance, whole cell extract was subjected to non-denaturing gel electrophoresis followed by the SOD activity stain. At least two distinct bands were detected on the gel (data not shown). By inhibition studies with H_2O_2 and KCN, it was demonstrated that the upper band was a FeSOD (resistant to KCN and sensitive to H_2O_2), and the lower band was a MnSOD (resistant to both KCN and H_2O_2). Occasionally, some other bands were detected in various conditions. These may be other isozymes or hybrid molecules between two different isozymes. Subcellular localization of isozymes were studied in the isolated mitochondrial and chloroplast fractions (Fig.2). Only the MnSOD was detected in the mitochondrial fraction, indicating that this MnSOD is located to the mitochondria. When the soluble stromal fraction prepared from isolated chloroplast was analyzed, however, both FeSOD and MnSOD bands were detected. Subsequent enzyme assays for cytochrome-c oxidase in the mitochondrial and chloroplast fractions showed that the chloroplast fraction was contaminated with mitochondria. Thus, it is most likely that FeSOD is located in the chloroplast. When both wild-type and paraquat resistant cells were compared for the SOD profiles on the activity stained gel, however, obvious differences were not detected. The activity stain used might not be sensitive enough to detect two-fold differences.

Figure 2. Profile of SOD enzymes in *C. reinhardtii*. Soluble proteins of whole cell extract and organellar fractions were separated on non-denaturing gel and stained for SOD activity.

lane 1-3 whole cell extract (100μg, 50μg, 25μg protein)
4 mitochondrial fraction (50μg protein)
5 stromal fraction 50μg protein)

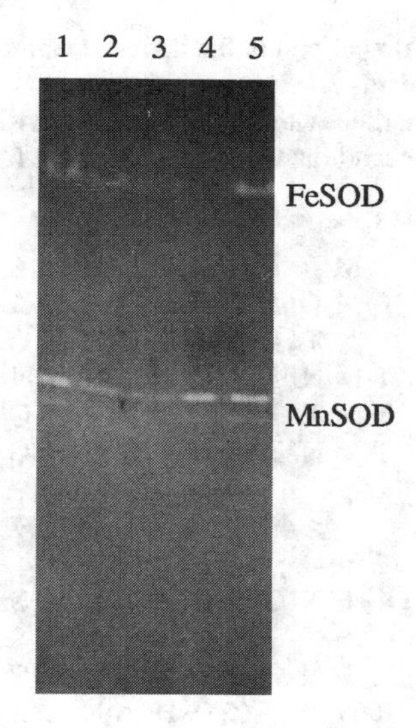

3.3 Cloning of cDNA encoding MnSOD

To study the regulation of the SOD expression in the wild-type and paraquat resistant cells at the transcriptional and translational levels, we made an effort to isolate cDNA clone(s) encoding SOD. An oligonucleotide probe was derived from the amino-acid sequence which is highly conserved among MnSODs and FeSODs from various species (8), aiming to obtain cDNA clones corresponding both to MnSOD and to FeSOD. Three clones which hybridized to the oligonucleotide were isolated with the DNA inserts sizing 1.0-1.5 kb. DNA sequencing of the cDNA inserts revealed that those three clones were identical but different from each other at 5' and 3' ends of the cDNAs. The deduced amino-acid sequence had regions of significant homology to other MnSODs (9). The largest clone (sod2, 1.5kd) covered the entire coding region. Fig.3 shows some of the conserved sequences nearby the metal ligand residues (marked with asterisks). All four ligands are conserved in sod2. There are several other residues which have been pointed out for distinguishing between MnSOD and FeSOD (marked with dots, 10). These residues in sod2 correspond well to those of MnSODs. The results of amino-acid sequence comparisons indicate that sod2 encodes the MnSOD. The MnSOD from *C. reinhardtii* shows a higher overall homology with bacterial MnSODs (48-55%) than eukaryotic MnSOD (37-43%).

3.4 Conclusions

Although the significant differences could not be detected between the wild-type and resistant cells at the SOD activity levels (two-fold differences), it will be interesting to study the regulation of the SOD expression in the cell at the transcriptional and translational levels. Isolation of the SOD genes is the first step in understanding the gene regulation and expression of the SODs. We can determine how SOD levels are regulated under various oxidative stress conditions and through what mechanism paraquat resistance is conferred.

Figure 3. Comparison of the deduced amino-acid sequences for MnSOD of *C.reinhardtii* and other organisms

Residues marked with asterisks are ligands to the metal cofactor. Residues marked by dots are the primary candidates for distinguishing MnSOD from FeSOD (by Parker and Blake, 10)

	22					*															42
1. maize	I	M	R	L	H	H	Q	K	H	H	A	T	Y	V	A	N	Y	N	K	A	L
2. human	I	M	Q	L	H	H	S	K	H	H	A	A	Y	V	N	N	L	N	V	T	E
3. yeast	I	N	E	L	H	Y	T	K	H	H	Q	T	Y	V	N	G	F	N	T	A	V
4. Bacillus	T	M	N	I	H	H	T	K	H	H	N	T	Y	V	T	N	L	N	A	A	L
5. E.coli	T	M	E	I	H	H	T	K	H	H	Q	T	Y	V	N	N	A	N	A	A	L
6. Chlamy	T	M	N	I	H	H	T	K	H	H	Q	T	Y	V	N	N	L	N	A	A	L

	72								*									90
1	K	F	N	G	G	G	H	V	N	H	S	I	F	W	K	N	L	K	P
2	K	F	N	G	G	G	H	I	N	H	S	I	F	W	T	N	L	S	P
3	K	F	H	G	G	G	F	T	N	H	C	L	F	W	E	N	L	A	P
4	R	N	N	G	G	G	H	A	N	H	S	L	F	W	T	I	L	S	P
5	R	N	N	A	G	G	H	A	H	N	S	L	F	W	K	G	L	K	K
6	R	N	N	G	G	G	H	Y	N	H	S	F	F	W	K	V	M	T	N
					•	•		•					•			•			

	171					*				*												192
1	P	L	L	G	I	D	V	W	E	H	A	Y	Y	L	Q	Y	K	N	V	R	P	D	Y
2	P	L	L	G	I	D	V	W	E	H	A	Y	Y	L	Q	Y	K	N	V	R	P	D	Y
3	P	L	V	A	I	D	A	W	E	H	A	Y	Y	L	Q	Y	Q	N	K	K	A	D	Y
4	P	I	L	G	L	D	V	W	E	H	A	Y	Y	L	K	Y	Q	N	R	R	P	E	Y
5	P	I	L	G	L	D	V	W	E	H	A	Y	Y	L	K	F	Q	N	R	R	P	D	Y
6	P	L	L	G	L	D	V	W	E	H	A	Y	Y	L	K	Y	Q	N	R	R	P	E	Y
				•											•		•						

References

1 Van Montague, M.V. and Inze, D. (1992) Ann. Rev. Plant Physiol. Plant Mol. Biol. **43**, 83-116.

2 McCord, J. M. and Fridovich, I. (1969) J. Biol. Chem. 244, 6049-6055.

3 Belknap, W.R. (1983) Plant Physiol. **72**, 1130-1132.

4 Ryan, R, Grant, D., Chiang, K-S. and Swift, H. (1978) Proc. Natl. Acad. Sci. USA 75, 3268-3272.

5 Beauchamp, C and Fridovich, I. (1971) Anal. Biochem. 44, 276-287.

6 Tolbert, N.E., Kisaki, T., Hageman, R.H. and Yamazaki, R.K. (1968) J. Biol. Chem. **243**, 5179-5184.

7 Maniatis, T., Fritsch, E.F. and Sambrook, J. (1982) Molecular Cloning, A Labolatory Manual. Cold Spring Harbor Laboratory, Cold Spring Harbor,N. Y.

8 Van Camp, W. Bowler, C., Villarroel, R., Tsang, Ed W.T., Van Montague, M. and Inze, D. (1990) Proc. Natl. Acad. Sci. USA 87, 9903-9907.

9 White, J. A. and Scandalios, J. G. (1988) Biochim. Biophys. Acta, 951, 61-70.

10 Parker, M. W. and Blake, C. C. F. (1988) FEBS lett. 229, 377-382.

PHOTOINHIBITION STUDIED IN A MUTANT OF *CHLAMYDOMONAS REINHARDTII* LACKING THE 23 kDa EXTRINSIC SUBUNIT OF PHOTOSYSTEM II.

Per-Olof. Fredriksson[1], Lars-Gunnar Franzén and Stenbjörn Styring
Department of Biochemistry, Arrheniuslaboratories for Natural Sciences, Stockholm University, S-106 91 Stockholm, Sweden
[1]Department of Chemistry, University of Karlstad, Box 9501, S-650 09 Karlstad, Sweden

1. INTRODUCTION

Photosystem II (PSII) is a large multisubunit enzyme in the thylakoid membrane that catalyzes the reduction of plastoquinone. The electrons come from water which is oxidized to molecular oxygen by a series of oxidizing redox components including the primary electron donor, P680, a tyrosine residue, Tyr_Z (Tyr_{161} on the D1 protein) and a cluster containing 4 Mn ions. Water oxidation also depends on the functional binding of the cofactors Cl^- and Ca^{2+} (for recent reviews of PSII see [1,2]). The reaction center of PSII is composed of heterodimer of two hydrophobic proteins denoted D1 and D2 which carries most of the redox components [1,2]. The D1 protein has been found to be degraded and eliminated from the reaction center in a process called photoinhibition. This may be caused by two, principally different mechanisms denoted acceptor-side and donor-side induced photoinhibiton (for reviews see [1,3,4]). Donor-side induced photoinhibition is due to the oxidizing chemistry on the electron donor-side of PSII, and is likely to involve the strongly oxidizing radicals $P680^+$ and/or Tyr_Z^+ [5,6], which may accumulate during illumination of PSII when O_2 evolution is inhibited. Such conditions have been much studied in purified PSII membranes with inactivated Mn cluster [5,6,7].

The Mn cluster in PSII is stabilized by three extrinsic subunits of 16, 23 and 33 kDa, which influence the Cl^- binding to the Mn cluster [1,2,8,9]. In the absence of the 23 or 33 kDa proteins, the Mn cluster is functional only in presence of elevated concentrations of Cl^- while it is unable to oxidize water at normal Cl^--concentrations although the remaining photochemistry of PSII remains functional. There exists a set of natural mutants lacking the 23 and 33kDa subunits in the green algae *Chlamydomonas reinhardtii* [10,11]. These mutants have been partially characterized with respect to presence and function of PSII and the existing evidence suggest that they still contain PSII reaction centers, although at decreased levels, but that PSII is partially or not at all active in oxygen evolution [10,11]. We hypothesize that the lower PSII content reflect that PSII in the mutants is rapidly turned over due to donor-side photoinhibition.

We have recently initiated studies of photoinhibition in two mutants of *C. reinhardtii* that lack the extrinsic PSII subunits of 23 kDa (the mutant FUD39) or 33kDa (the FUD44 mutant). The idea behind the experiments is to study photoinhibition in an eukaryotic system where it is possible to manipulate PSII by molecular genetical methods. Here we present the first results from these experiments in the mutant of that lacks the 23 kDa subunit.

2. MATERIALS and METHODS

Chlamydomonas reinhardtii, wild type and the mutant FUD39, was grown in Tris-acetate-phosphate medium at pH 7.0. The mutant was grown in dim light to avoid photoinhibition. The cells were harvested during exponential growth, washed once in 25 mM HEPES, pH 7.0, and 50 mM NaCl and

N. Murata (ed.), Research in Photosynthesis, Vol. IV, 491–494.

resuspended in the same buffer. Thylakoid membranes were prepared by sonication for 3 x10 s. Whole cells were removed by centrifugation and the membranes were collected by centrifugation at 16 000 g for 3 min. The pellet was washed once with 25 mM HEPES, pH 7.0, with varying concentrations of NaCl (0-50 mM). All procedures were performed in dim light at 0-4 °C. Oxygen evolution was measured with an oxygen electrode in saturating white light at 25 °C in 25 mM HEPES, pH 7.0, 400 mM sucrose, 6µg/ml gramicidin and 0.5 mM phenyl-*p*-benzoquinone in presence of varying amounts of NaCl (0-50 mM). The oxygen evolving activities of the wild-type and the mutant FUD39 at saturating Cl^- were 270 and 90 µmol O2/mg Chl per h, respectively.

3. RESULTS and DISCUSSION

3.1. Cl^- dependence of O_2 evolution in the absence of the 23 kDa protein. The extrinsic 23 kDa protein is involved in the binding of Cl^- to the oxygen-evolving complex of PSII. This has been well characterized when the protein has been removed by salt washings [1,2,5,9]. We have investigated a natural mutant in *C. reinhardtii*, FUD39, which lacks the 23 kDa protein. Earlier studies in cells of a similar mutant have indicated that although the content of PSII is quite high the oxygen evolving capacity is low [10]. We have studied the Cl^- dependence of the oxygen evolution in thylakoid membranes from this mutant and found that the O_2 evolution is strictly dependent on the presence of Cl^- in the assay medium (Figs. 1A; 2, The oxygen evolution is very low in the absence of added Cl^- but is much enhanced in the presence of high Cl^- (Fig. 1A). The dissociation constant of Cl^- is approximately 5 mM (Fig. 2). These results explain the earlier observation of low O_2 evolution in whole cells where the concentration of Cl^- is not sufficient to allow maximal O_2 evolution [10]. In the wild-type, the O_2 evolution showed very little Cl^- dependence (not shown), indicative of a high affinity for Cl^- (dissociation constant <1 mM). Our results from the mutant FUD39, indicating that Cl^- binds with an approximate binding constant of 5mM in the absence of the 23 kDa subunit, are in good agreement with earlier studies of salt-washed PSII preparations [5,9].

3.2. Cl^- dependence of photoinhibition of O_2 evolution in the absence of the 23 kDa protein. During the measurements we observed that the O_2 evolution in the thylakoids from FUD39 was not only much lower in the absence of Cl^-, it was also more unstable and decreased during the measurement to become almost completely inhibited after 30s (Fig. 1A). At saturating Cl^-

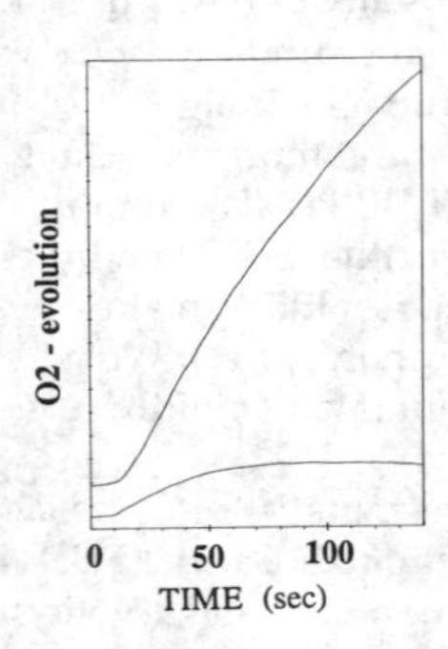

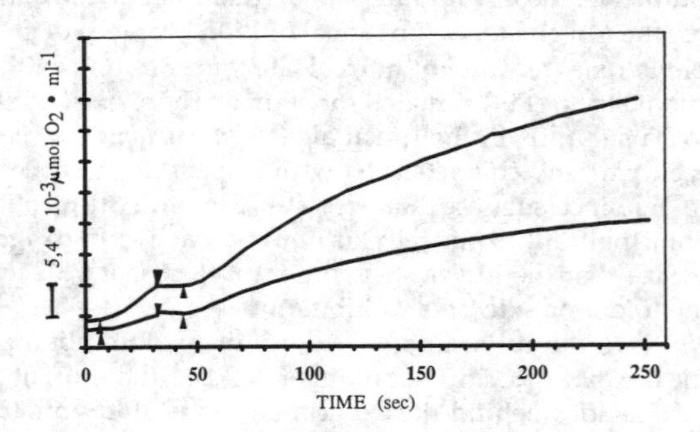

Figure 1. A (left). Oxygen evolution at 2mM Cl- (lower trace) or 50mM Cl- (upper trace) in thylakoid membranes from the mutant lacking the 23kDa extrinsic subunit (FUD39 mutant).
***B (right)**. Irreversibility of the inhibition of the oxygen evolution. Lower trace: Thylakoid membranes at 2 mM Cl^- were illuminated for 25 s, then 50 mM Cl^- was added and the sample was again illuminated (arrow-heads pointing up and down = light on and off, respectively). Upper trace: A control trace containing 50 mM Cl^- from start.*

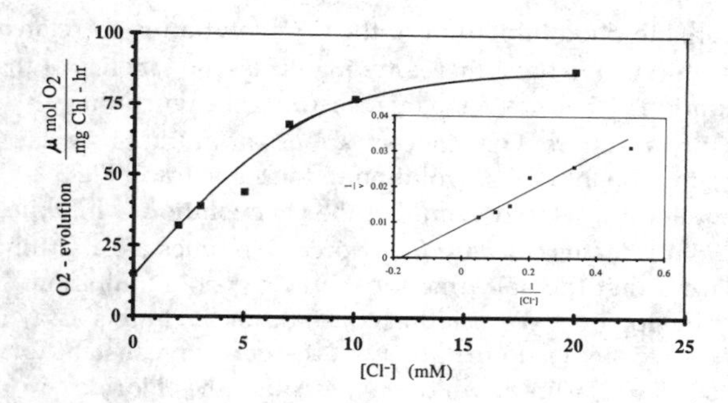

Figure 2. Chloride dependence of the initial O_2 evolution in thylakoid membranes FUD39 measured as in Fig. 1. The inset shows an inverse replot of the data showing that Cl^- activates the oxygen evolution with a $K_d \approx 5mM$.

concentration, the oxygen evolution was high and remained fairly constant for more than 60 s (Fig. 1A). The inactivation of the O_2 evolution at low Cl^- was largely irreversible, since readdition of Cl^- did not restore the lost activity (Fig. 1B). Contrary to this, preliminary measurements of the electron transfer to DCIP from DPC (diphenylcarbazid, an electron donor to Tyr_Z) under the same conditions (not shown) indicate that the remaining photochemistry through the PSII reaction centre is not inhibited although the O_2 evolution is irreversibly lost. Our interpretation of these results is that the illumination during the O_2 assay results in an irreversible photoinhibition of the O_2-evolving site. Initially this occurs without affecting the remaining photochemistry in PSII quite similar to what has been observed in normal PSII that has been depleted of chloride [12].

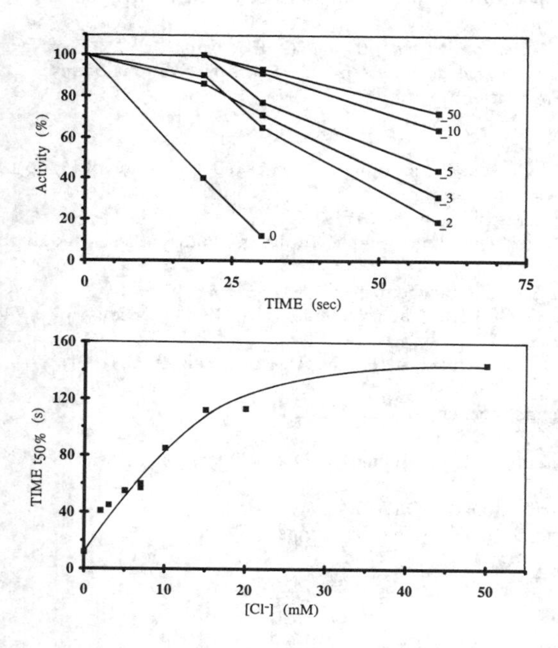

Figure 3. A (upper). Time course of photoinhibition of the oxygen evolution in FUD39 thylakoids at varying Cl^- concentrations measured as in Fig. 1. Samples containing various Cl^- concentrations were illuminated in the oxygen electrode and the rate of O_2 evolution was determined after 0, 20, 30 and 60 s of illumination. For all samples (Cl^- concentrations) the initial activity at 0 s was defined as 100 %.

Figure 3. B (lower). Time to obtain 50 % inhibition of O_2 evolution in each sample versus Cl^- concentration.

Our hypothesis is that the irreversible photoinhibition of the O_2 evolution is correlated to the lack of Cl^- from the Mn cluster of PSII. We have therefore quantified the kinetics of the photoinhibition at various Cl^- concentrations. This was done by measuring the remaining O_2 evolution after various times of the assay at different Cl^- concentrations (from traces similar to the ones in Fig. 1A) and comparing it to the initial O_2 evolution in the same trace. Fig 3 shows the results from this experiment and it is clearly seen that the O_2 evolution is inhibited faster at lower Cl^- concentrations while it remains constant for appreciable times at saturating Cl^- (>10mM). A replot of the data shows that the half-time for the irreversible inhibition increases with the Cl^- concentration. The apparent dissociation constant for Cl^- in this assay is approximately 8 mM (Fig. 3B). This is quite similar to the apparent dissociation constant for the Cl^- dependence of oxygen evolution (Fig. 2, ≈5mM) which suggests that the chloride dependence of the O_2 evolution and the photoinhibition have the same origin.

4. CONCLUSIONS

Our initial experiments in the FUD39 mutant of *C. reinhardtii* that lacks the 23 kDa extrinsic subunit indicate that the oxygen evolution is inhibited in a similar manner as in Cl^--depleted PSII enriched membranes. This would explain the earlier observed low O_2 evolution in whole cells of a similar mutant [10] since it is unlikely that there is enough Cl^- in cells to saturate the O_2 evolution. The observation in natural mutants of the photoinhibitory reactions that earlier have been studied in purified systems is useful and will provide an ideal system to investigate donor-side photoinhibition using mutagenesis techniques. Experiments with the mutant FUD44 [11] that lacks the 33kDa extrinsic protein are in progress. This mutant has been reported to lack oxygen evolution and to show a very low amount of reaction centers. Our hypothesis is that this is due to the even lower affinity for Cl^- leading to an even higher sensitivity for illumination in the absence of the 33 kDa subunit.

We thank P. Bennoun for strains of C. reinhardtii mutants and G. Håkansson and M. Rova for skilful technical assistance. This work was supported by grants from the Swedish Natural Science Research Council and the Carl Trygger Foundation.

REFERENCES

1. Andersson, B. and Styring, S. (1990) in Current Topics in Bioenergetics (ed. C.P. Lee) vol 16, pp 1-81.
2. Debus, R. (1992) Biochim. Biophys. Acta in press.
3. Barber, J. and Andersson, B. (1992) Trends Biochem. Sci. 17, 61-66.
4. Prasil, O., Adir, N. and Ohad, I. (1992) in "The Photosystems, Topics in Photosynthesis" (ed. Barber, J.) vol. 11, pp 220-250, Elsevier, Amsterdam.
5. Jegerschöld, C., Virgin, I. and Styring, S. (1990) Biochemistry 29, 6179-6186.
6. Blubaugh, D., Atamian, M., Babcock, G. Golbeck, J. and Cheniae, G.M. (1991) Biocemistry 30, 7486-7497.
7. Eckert, H.-J., Geiken, B., Bernarding, J., Napiwotski, A., Eichler, H.-J. and Renger, G. (1991) Photosynth. Res. 27, 97-108.
8. Murata, N. and Miyao, M. (1985) Trends Biochem. Sci. 10, 122-124.
9. Coleman, W.J. (1990) Photosynth. Res. 23, 1-27.
10. Mayfield, S.P., Rahire, M., Frank, G., Zuber, H. and Rochaix, J.-D. (1987) Proc. Natl. Acad. Sci. USA 84, 749-753.
11. Mayfield, S.P., Bennoun, P. and Rochaix, J.-D. (1987) EMBO J. 6, 313-318.
12. Jegerschöld, C., Ågren, H. and Styring, S. (1993) these proccedings.

DEFENCE MECHANISMS AGAINST PHOTOOXIDATIVE DAMAGE IN PARAQUAT-ATRAZINE CO-RESISTANT *CONYZA (ERIGERON) CANADENSIS*

VÁRADI, GY. and PÖLÖS, E., RESEARCH INSTITUTE FOR VITICULTURE and ENOLOGY, P.O.Box 25, KECSKEMÉT, H-6001, HUNGARY

1. INTRODUCTION

Paraquat has been used for many years as a broad-spectrum nonselective herbicide. Resistance to paraquat has developed but the exact mechanism of resistance is still unclear (3). Paraquat accepts electrons from PS I possibly at ferredoxin. Several hypotheses for mechanisms of paraquat resistance have been proposed. These include adsorption of paraquat to lignified structures; lack of penetration due to increased epicuticular wax; binding of paraquat to cell walls; restriction of paraquat movement into the chloroplast; an alteration in the redox potential of the PS I primary electron acceptor; detoxification of the superoxide dismutase, ascorbate peroxidase, and glutathione reductase; or that resistant plants must are able to prevent paraquat from entering the symplast (3).
Transient characteristics of the initial effects of paraquat on horseweed (8) suggests that paraquat enters the chloroplasts of both the resistant and susceptible biotypes, Our aim was to further investigate the transient effects of paraquat action on susceptible and resistant plants with respect to the role of light.
Jansen et al. (6) have reported an enhanced tolerance to photoinhibition of the paraquat-resistant *C. bonariensis* but recently this was disputed (11). To further study this area we compared the xanthophyll cycle in biotypes of *C. canadensis* susceptible and resistant to paraquat.

2. MATERIALS and METHODS

2.1 Whole plants were treated with 1 kg/ha paraquat (active ingredient) as 1 % (v/v) tap-water solution of Gramoxone^{R} (250 g/l dichloride salt) in sunlight 1300 $\mu Em^{-2}s$. For violaxanthin measurements excised leaves of both biotypes were floated on 10^{-5} M paraquat solution for 24 hr under similar light conditions.
Inhibition of photosynthetic O_2 evolution and

N. Murata (ed.), Research in Photosynthesis, Vol. IV, 495–499.

variable fluorescence (F_v) were monitored in a continuous daylight treatment. Fluorescence induction kinetics were recorded according to Szigeti et al. (15), and O_2 evolution was measured according to Walker and Osmond (19) with a Hansatech LD2 leaf disc electrode.

2.2 For the xanthophyll measurements field grown resistant and susceptible horseweed plants in the well developed rosette stage were sampled at different sunlight (PAR) levels. Samples were immediately dipped in liquid N_2 and then acetone (80 % v/v) extracts were HPLC analyzed using a special gradient elution optimized for a satisfactory separation of zeaxanthin from lutein (17).
Light intensities were measured by Li-190SA quantum sensor.

3. RESULTS AND DISCUSSION

Paraquat treatment of susceptible plants completely inhibited photosynthetic activity (Fig.1). In addition paraquat treatment of resistant horseweed showed a large initial inhibition of both the photosynthetic O_2 evolution and fluorescence induction. The effects of paraquat on photosynthetic CO_2 fixation showed a similar trend (8).

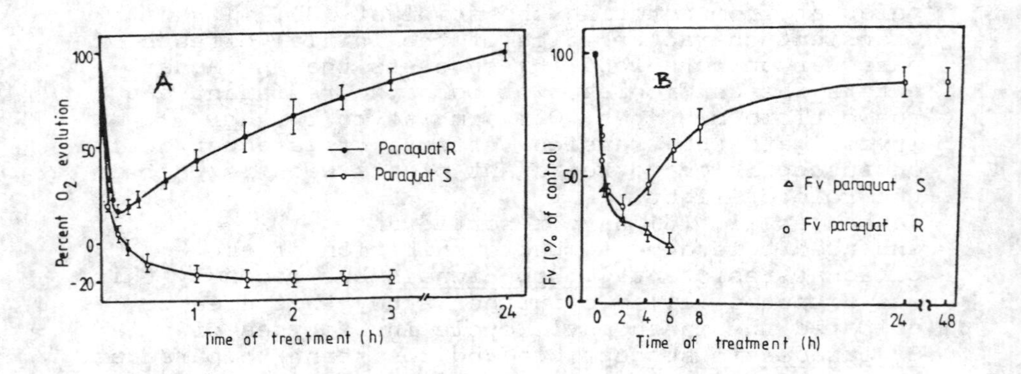

Figure 1. Time dependence of photosynthetic O_2 evolution (1A) and variable fluorescence (1B) in horseweed treated with paraquat in continuous daylight

Continuation of the dark paraquat treatment for several hours results in a steady-state level of about 40 % fluorescence quenching (Lehoczki, unpublished data) instead of a transient inhibition. This suggests a role of light in the initial processes. In paraquat treatments with different sunlight plus dark combinations there was no recovery in the dark period after 1 or 2 hr light treatments, i.e. the F_v remained nearly constant at 30-40 %, but after 3 hr of sunlight a pronounced increase in F_v occured in the dark (up to 55 % of control) in the resistant plants suggesting a key role for light in the initiation of recovery processes in the paraquat-resistant horseweed (5).

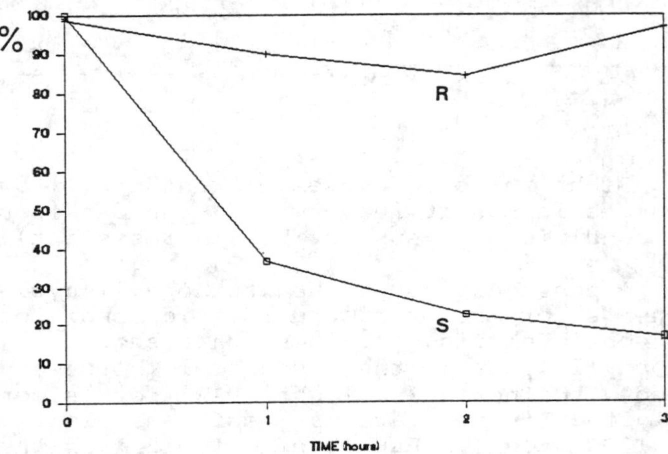

Fig. 2 Time response curves of violaxanthin during 10^{-5} M paraquat treatment in leaves of C. canadensis biotypes (S=susceptible, R=resistant)

Different patterns of violaxanthin were observed during paraquat treatments (Fig. 2) and this needed further examination because violaxanthin is known as one of the three components of the xanthophyll cycle (20). Violaxanthin showed a dramatic decrease in the leaves of the susceptible biotype floated on 10^{-5} M paraquat but violaxanthin in the leaves of the resistant biotype remained just unaffected. This phenomenon was then studied more detailed especially because of the possible correlation between the resistance to paraquat and a higher tolerance to photoinhibition (6). Violaxanthin is de-epoxized to zeaxanthin (via antheraxanthin) when the absorbed light energy has become excessive in the chloroplasts. Zeaxanthin has been reported to play an important role in radiationless energy dissipation of excess light energy possibly interacting with different excited chlorophyll forms in chloroplast antennae (2).

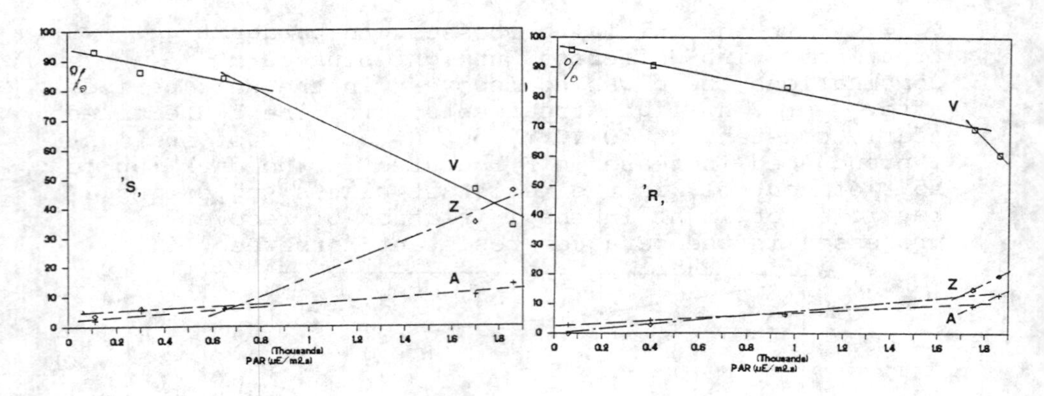

Fig. 3 Light response curves of xanthophyll cycle components in sunlit leaves of C. canadensis under field conditions (S=susceptible, R=resistant)

Light response curves of the xanthophyll cycle components were recorded under field conditions using HPLC technique (Fig. 3). These data show that the xanthophyll cycle in the susceptible horseweed responded to increasing light (PAR) levels more readily than in the paraquat-resistant plants. At about 1700 $\mu E.m^{-2}.s$ PAR level only 15 % of the pool was in the form of zeaxanthin in the leaves of the paraquat-resistant horseweed while this value was nearly 40 % in the case of the susceptible biotype. Both biotypes had the same size of xanthophyll pool and β-carotene (data not shown here). Indeed, there can be observed characteristic break-points in the shape of the curves at about 700-800 $\mu E.m^{-2}.s$ and 1700-1800 $\mu E.m^{-2}.s$ PAR levels in the susceptible and in the resistant plants, respectively. These values may correspond to the saturating light levels of the CO_2 fixation in these biotypes as it was found e.g. in the case of Vitis vinifera (not published). Although, Preston et al. (11) disputed the correlation between resistance to paraquat and tolerance to photoinhibition in some weed species, but it cannot be excluded because their plants used in photoinhibitory treatments were adapted to a rather low light intensity (3oo $\mu E.m^{-2}.s$).
Our results seem to be supporting the hypothesis of this correlation of the paraquat resistance and the tolerance to photoinhibition. To explain this behavioural alteration of the xanthophyll cycle in the

two biotypes we can suppose even that the resistant biotype should have a more effective photochemistry or it has a less efficient light harvesting or it may have further dissipative pathways other than xanthophyll cycle for protection against excess light.

REFERENCES

1. Bishop, T., Powles, S.B., and Cornic, G. (1987) Aust.J.Plant Physiol., 14: 539-547.
2. Demmig-Adams, B. (1990) Biochim. Biophys. Acta, 1020: 1-24.
3. Fuerst, E.P., and Vaughn, K.C. (1990) Weed Technol., 4: 150-156.
4. Fuerst, E.P., Nakatani, H.Y., Dodge, A.D., Penner,D., and Arntzen, C.J. (1985) Plant Physiol., 77: 984-989.
5. Itoh, K., and Matsunaka, S. (1989) Proc. of the 4th International Symposium of Plant Biosystematics, Kyoto - Japan.
6. Jansen, M.A.K., Shaaltiel, Y., Kazzes, D., Canaani, O., Malkin, S., and Gressel, J. (1989) Plant Physiol., 91: 1174-1178.
7. Powles, S.B., and Cornic, G. (1987) Aust.J.Plant Physiol., 14: 81-89.
8. Pölös, E., Mikulás, J., Szigeti, Z., Matkovics, B., Hai, D.Q., Párducz, Á., and Lehoczki, E. (1988) Pestic.Biochem. Physiol., 30: 142-154.
9. Pölös, E., Szigeti, Z., Laskay, G., and Lehoczki, E. (1988) Abstracts of the Conference of the Federation of European Societies of Plant Physiology, Split - Yugoslavia.
10. Pölös, E., Szigeti, Z., Váradi, Gy., and Lehoczki, E. (1989) Proc. Herbicide Resistance in Weeds and Crops Conference, Bristol - England, (in press).
11. Preston, C., Holtum, J.A.M., and Powles, S.B. (1991) Plant Physiol., 96: 314-318.
12. Shaaltiel, Y., and Gressel, J. (1986) Pestic. Biochem. Physiol., 26: 22-28.
13. Shaaltiel, Y., and Gressel, J. (1987) Plant Physiol., 85: 869-871.
14. Shaaltiel, Y., Glazer, A., Bocion, P.F., and Gressel, J. (1988) Pestic. Biochem. Physiol., 31: 13-23.
15. Szigeti, Z., Pölös, E., and Lehoczki, E. (1988) in: Applications of Chlorophyll Fluorescence (Lichtenthaler, H.K., ed.), Kluwer Acad. Publ., pp. 1o9-114.
16. Váradi, Gy., Lehoczki, E., Szigeti, Z., and Pölös. E. (1990) Proc. 9t h Australian Weeds Conference, Adelaide, pp. 257-259.
17. Váradi, Gy., Botos-Bálo, B., Pölös, E. (1991) Proc. 4t h International Symp. on Grapevine Physiology, San Michele All'Adige - Torino (Italy) (in press)

ROLE OF THE PSII ACCEPTOR SITE IN THE LIGHT INDUCED DEGRADATION OF D1

Ondrej Prasil[1,2], Hagit Zer[1], Doris Godde[3] and Itzhak Ohad[1]
Dept. of Biological Chemistry, The Hebrew University of Jerusalem, 91904 Jerusalem (Israel)[1], Institute of Microbiology CSAV, 37981 Trebon (Czechoslovakia)[2] and Dept. of Plant Biochemistry, Ruhr University Bochum D-4630 Bochum 1, (Germany)[3]

1. INTRODUCTION

Photoinactivation (PI) of photosystem II (PSII) results in the degradation of the reaction center II polypeptides D1 and D2. While progress has been made toward understanding of PI mechanism *in vitro* a satisfactory explanation of the PI process and subsequent D1 protein degradation *in vivo* is still lacking (reviewed recently in (1)).

Previous results with green alga *Chlamydomonas reinhardtii* and its mutants indicated that the redox state and turnover of plastoquinone (PQ) at the Q_B site regulates the D1 degradation (2). Cooperative events connecting conformational changes on the acceptor side with impairment of the donor side were proposed to explain PI phenomemenon *in vivo* (1).

The PI process was further investigated in *C.reinhardtii* WT and mutants which can not oxidize PQH_2. The results indicate that in photoinhibited mutants D1 protein is damaged but not degraded. However D1 is rapidly degraded in these mutants when exposed to UV light. The previously reported shift in the TL B band temperature (3) appears to be related to the formation of a proton gradient across the thylakoid membrane in photoinhibited cells.

2. MATERIALS AND METHODS

C.reinhardtii y-1 (WT) and mutants D6, Ac208, B4 defective in cyt b6/f, plastocyanin and Photosystem I, respectively were grown on acetate containing medium. Photoinhibition, fluorescence induction measurments and quantification of D1 protein were carried out as described in (2,3). UV-B illumination of cell suspensions was in open Petri dishes by RFR-3000A Rayonet lamps. TL signals were measured using home made apparatus. The cells (15 μg chl/sample) were dark adapted (1 min) before excitation by a given number of single turnover Xe flashes. When indicated, 5 μM DCMU was added before dark adaptation. Fluorescence yield decay after a single turnover flash was recorded by PAM fluorometer (Walz, Germany) and its kinetics was deconvoluted into monoexponential components.

3. RESULTS AND DISCUSSION

3.1. THERMOLUMINESCENCE CHARACTERIZATION OF MUTANTS, ROLE OF AMMONIA

The TL glow curves are complex and different for WT and each mutant. The peak temperatures of B1,B2 and Q bands, which arise from recombination of $S_3Q_B^-$, $S_2Q_B^-$ and $S_2Q_A^-$, resp., are given in Tab.1. Contrary to the mutants (and other algae investigated), the position of the B2 band is in the WT at higher temperatures than the B1 band. This holds only in the presence of ammonia (3.7 mM NH_4NO_3) in the medium; when ammonia is omitted the B2 band peaks at 25 °C. The ammonia in low concentrations is known to modify the function of OEC by decreasing the redox potential of S_2 (4). The absence of the effect in the mutants indicates that only in the WT the ammonia is transported into the lumenal space. The oscillation patterns (i.e. dependence of TL band amplitude on the number of exciting flashes) of the B band are

N. Murata (ed.), Research in Photosynthesis, Vol. IV, 501–504.

similar in WT and mutant cells (maxima on 2nd and 6th flashes, data not shown). The data from TL measurments indicate that the PSII of the mutants is functional in terms of charge separation and S states formation. The analysis of fluorescence yield decay after a single turnover flash (see Tab.1) shows significant increase in the slow component (ascribed to the recombination of Q_A^- with the S states) in the mutants. This indicates increased proportion of PSII centers which can not reduce PQ and is possibly due to the high ratio of PQH_2/PQ generated even by the weak measuring beam. These results indicate that the electron flow from Q_A to Q_B is limited by slow reoxidation of PQH_2.

TAB.1 Characterization of mutants by TL and fluorescence decay.
The mutants with impaired reoxidation of PQH_2 require longer (min. 5 min) dark relaxation in order to get reproducible TL glow curves. Decay of fl. yield was deconvoluted into three monoexponential components with halftimes 300-600 µsec (fast), 2-10 msec (middle) and 0.5-1sec (slow).

	TL (Peak position,°C)			FL. DECAY (Rel.Amplitudes, %)		
	B1 ($S_3Q_B^-$)	B2 ($S_2Q_B^-$)	Q ($S_2Q_A^-$)	Fast	Middle	Slow
WT	26	34	5	59	24	17
Ac208	24	24	11	49	14	37
B4	24	23	10	37	16	47
D6	23	24	12	47	16	37

3.2. LIGHT INDUCED CHANGES IN TL CHARACTERISTICS

The overall activity of PSII, measured as Fv/Fm or H_2O-DCPIP electron transport (data not shown) declines with the same kinetics in both WT and mutant cells. A significant rise of the Fo level (up to 160%) is observed during the first 50 min of the photoinhibition of the WT cells, while practically no rise is observed in the mutants. Parallel to the loss of Fv/Fm, a decline in the amplitudes of the B and Q bands is observed (Fig.1). In the mutants both bands decline approximately with the same kinetics as Fv/Fm. In the WT the amplitude of the B band declines faster than of the Q band. Moreover, loss of the TL band amplitudes in the WT is accompanied by shifts in the peak temperatures (Fig.2). First, the B2 band shifts from its unusual position at 32 °C to the position of the B1 band (25 °C). This indicates that at light levels above saturation the NH_3 present in the lumen is protonated and the modifying effect on S states is relieved.

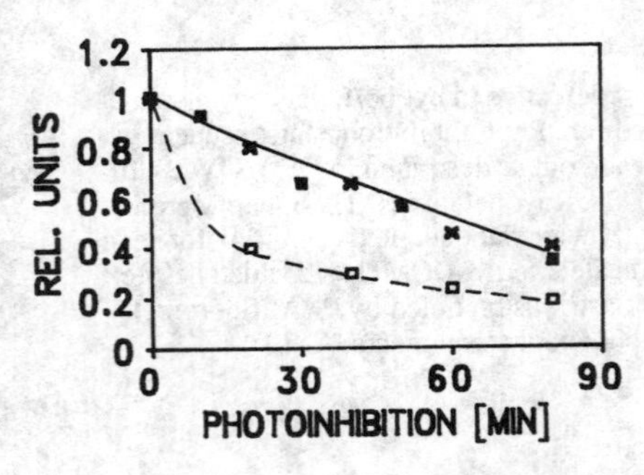

Fig.1 Decline in the amplitudes of TL bands during photoinhibition (600 µmol. $m^{-2}.s^{-1}$) in C. reinh. WT (X Q band, ❑ B band) and mutant lacking cyt b6/f complex (Q band same as WT, ■ B band). The Fv/Fm declined like Q bands in both strains.

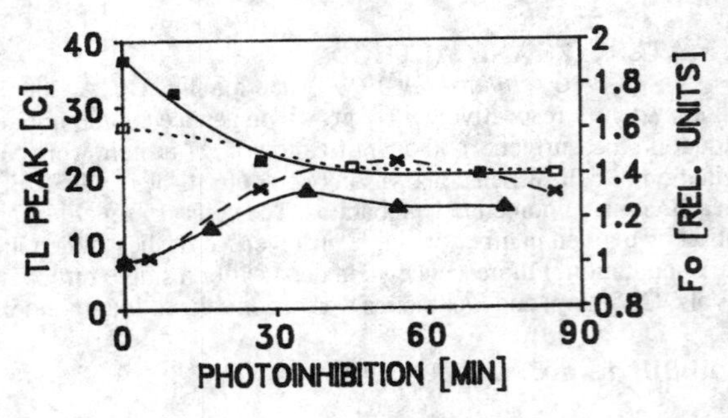

Fig.2 Time course of Fo rise (X) and changes in peak positions of TL bands (▲Q, ❑B1, ■ B2) during photoinactivation (600 µmol. $m^{-2}.s^{-1}$) of C. reinh. WT. 3.7 mM NH_4NO_3 was present in the medium.

The amplitude of the resulting B band at 25 °C oscillates with period of four and decreases gradually with the progress of PI; in the terminal stages of PI the B band gradually shifts to lower temperatures (15 °C), The behavior of the Q band ($S_2Q_A^-$) in the WT is antiparallel to the B band: the position of its maximum shifts gradually from 5 °C to 15 °C. Interestingly in the WT, also Fo rises with the similar kinetics as shifts in the TL bands. No significant changes in the peak positions of the TL bands, neither Fo rise are observed in the mutants.

We conclude that the changes of TL characteristics have at least two causes: First, the decline of the amplitudes of the peaks indicates the gradual decrease in the number of functional RCs. Second, the reduced activity of the PSII RCs entails a change in the membrane (e.g. in its degree of energization), leading to conformational changes of RC complexes. These changes modify the equilibrium constants for electron transitions between various carriers in PSII and thus cause the observed shifts in TL bands. The mutants, even with fully active PSII are all unable to maintain a high energization of the membrane. Consequently no significant change in the pH gradient occurs in the course of photoinhibition and no shifts of TL bands are observed.

As to the rise of Fo, it reflects similar changes caused by the progressive increase in the fraction of inactive RC. The latter evidently represents less efficient (more shallow) traps for excitons and this, according to the model of Holzwarth (5) increases the lifetimes of excitons in the PSII antenna.

3.3. DEGRADATION OF THE D1 PROTEIN.

While the rates of photoinactivation are in the WT and mutants comparable, the rate of light induced degradation is in the mutants markedly slowed down (Fig.3 and ref.2).

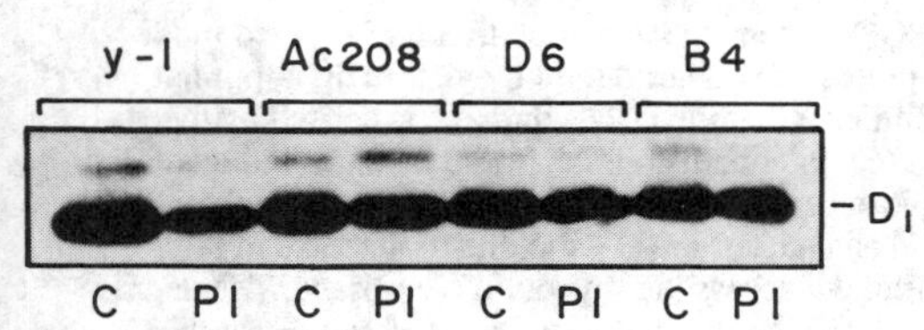

Fig.3 Light induced degradation of D1 protein is slowed down in C. reinhardii Ac208, D6 and B4 mutants as compared to WT (y-1). Cells were exposed to photoinhibitory light (3000 µmol.m-2.sec-1) for 180 min (PI). D1 protein content was estimated by Western blotting. The control cells (C) were kept at growth conditions (50 µmol.m-2.sec-1).

We have suggested that the nature of ligand occupying Q_B niche may play an important role in D1 degradation (2). In the WT, the presence and turnover of plastoquinone modifies the conformation of the Q_B region and exposes D1 to the proteolysis, while in the mutants the plastoquinol generated by the PSII activity is only slowly reoxidized and PQH_2 might be the predominant form present in the Q_B pocket. An alternative explanation is that the slow degradation of D1 in the mutants is due to the overall decrease of the electron transport rate past the Q_B site, which as a result prevents formation of harmful cation radicals ($P680^+$ or Y_Z^+). However, it has been argued that electron flow past Q_A is not required for the degradation of D1, since certain phenolic herbicides such as bromonitrothymol (BNT) which block electron flow via PSII by binding at the Q_B site, do not prevent D1 degradation (M.Jensen, B.Depka, A.Trebst and M.Edelman, in preparation). In experiments, in which we tested the effects of Diuron and BNT (2-10 µM concentrations) on light induced degradation of D1 in *C.reinhardtii* both herbicides ascribed protection against D1 degradation in WT as well as mutant cells (Fig.4).

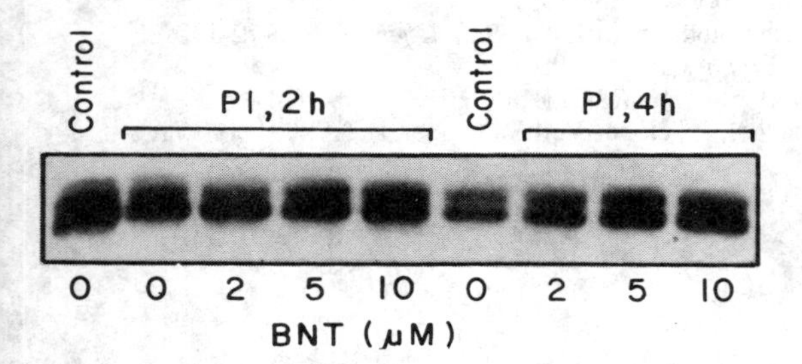

Fig.4 Light induced degradation of D1 protein in C.reinhardii cells is partially protected by bromonitrothymol (BNT). The cells were exposed to white light (3000 µmol.m^{-2}.s^{-1}) for 2 and 4 hours in the presence of BNT at indicated concentrations.

The protective effect of BNT against D1 degradation in these cells requires a more detailed analysis of its concentration dependency. If the degradation of D1 is prevented in the mutants due to the lack of the PQ at the Q_B site or its occupancy by PQH_2 in high light exposed cells, one would expect that UV light should induce D1 degradation, since UV light does not cause extensive reduction of the PQ pool but induces photoinactivation and D1 degradation (1). The site of damage of UV-B on PSII is still under dispute. UV-B light induces D1 degradation to the same extent in the WT and mutant cells. The combination of visible and UV-B light enhances significantly the degradation of D1 in the WT cells, but not in the mutants which can not oxidize PQH_2 (Fig.5).

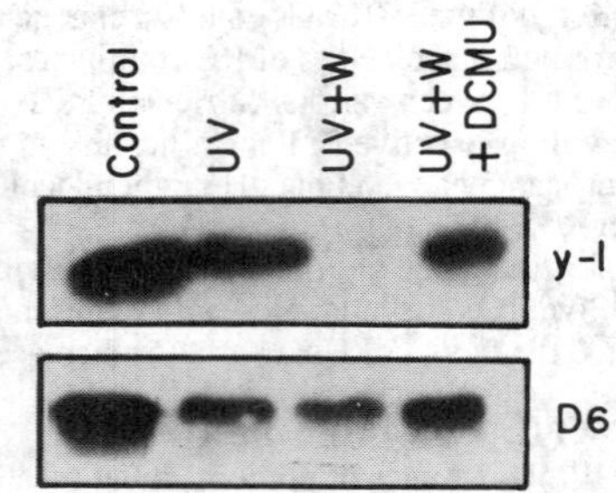

Fig.5 UV-B light (40 μmol. $m^{-2}.s^{-1}$) induces D1 degradation to the similar extent in WT (y-1) and mutants (D6). In the combination of visible (1500 μmol. $m^{-2}.s^{-1}$) and UV-B light the D1 degradation is enhanced in WT, but not in mutants. DCMU (5 μM) protects against D1 degradation by visible light.

This indicates that the presence of PQ/PQH_2 at the Q_B site is not directly involved in the mechanism of D1 degradation by UV-B light. Diuron protects D1 degradation by visible light, but not by UV-B in both the WT and mutant cells. These results indicate that the UV-B damage is caused by mechanism including a direct photodamage on the donor side (6). In conclusion, the initial changes induced in *C.reinhardtii* cells by photoinhibitory light appear in the acceptor side of PSII and may be related to changes in the Q_A/Q_B electron flow and conformational changes of the Q_B site due to increase in the membrane energization and/or formation of a proton gradient across the thylakoid membrane. The degradation of D1 induced by strong visible light is modulated by the ratio and turnover of PQ/PQH_2 at the Q_B site. The UV-B light induced degradation of D1 *in vivo* is due to different mechanism, which possibly directly effects PSII donor side as well.

ACKNOWLEDGMENTS

This work was supported by a grant awarded by the German-Israeli Foundation (GIF) to D.G. and I.O. We thank Drs.M.Jansen and M.Edelman, The Weizmann Inst.of Science, Israel, for using the UV-illumination system.

REFERENCES

1. Prasil, O., Adir, N., and Ohad, I. (1992) in: The photosystems: Structure, function and molecular biology (Barber, J.,ed.) p. 295-348.
2. Gong, H. and Ohad, I. (1991) J. *Biol. Chem.* 266, 21293-21299.
3. Ohad, I., Adir, N., Koike, H., Kyle, D.J., and Inoue, Y. (1990) J. *Biol. Chem.* 265, 1972-1979.
4. Ono, T.; Inoue,Y. (1988) A*rch. Biochem. Biophys.* 264, 82-92
5. Schatz, G.H. and Holzwarth, A.R. (1986) P*hotosynth. Res. 1*0, 309-18
6. Renger, G.; Volker, M.; Eckert, H.J.; Fromme, R.; Hohm-Veit,S.; Graber, P. (1989) P*hotochem. Photobiol. 49(1)*, 97-105

PHOTOSYSTEM II DEGRADATION PATHWAYS AFTER PHOTOINHIBITION OF ISOLATED THYLAKOIDS

G.M. Giacometti, R. Barbato, G. Friso, A. Frizzo, F. Rigoni

Department of Biology, University of Padova, Italy

INTRODUCTION

Coupling two photosystems to better utilize sunlight in producing chemical free-energy has represented the most important evolutionary achievement in the vegetable kingdom as it allowed water to be used as the electron source for the photosynthetic reduction of NADP. However, the realization of a water splitting system in PSII required the intervention of strongly oxidizing species, such as P680+ and Tyr+, whose presence proved dangerous to the integrity of the reaction centre (RC) itself. As a result, besides being a very complex machine, PSII is also fragile and its activity and structural integrity can be severely impaired when excessive excitation energy is conveyed to the RC. The evidence that too much light brings about significant reduction of the efficency of photosynthesis was already clear at the beginning of the century (1) and yet, it is only in the last decads that the molecular mechanisms underlying photoinhibition have started to be unravelled (2). We know now that the RC of PSII is composed, among others, of two polypeptides (D1 and D2) which form a heterodimer similar to the L and M proteins of the RC or purple bacteria (3,4). Most of the research on photoinhibition has been focused on the rapid and light dependent turnover of the 32 KDa D1-protein (5). The loss of PSII activity under photoinhibitory conditions has been attributed to an increased degradation of the D1-protein over its rate of biosynthesis (6). Accordingly, recovery from photoinhibition is thought to depend on the substitution of damaged D1-protein with newly sinthesized (7). The D1-protein is encoded by the plastidial psbA gene, translated on the 70S ribosomes attached to the stroma-exposed surface of the thylakoid membrane and therein inserted in the form of a precursor. After a number of post-translational modifications, the D1-protein migrate to its final destination to form a functional PSII RC in the grana compartment of the membrane (8). However, the migration of the newly sinthesized D1-protein from the stroma lamellae to the grana partitions does not occur as a free polypeptide

N. Murata (ed.), Research in Photosynthesis, Vol. IV, 505–508.

but already associated with other chlorophyll-proteins of PSII (9). Based on these observations a repair cycle has been hypotesized for PSII in which photoinhibited PSII centres, initially located in the grana, migrate to the stroma lamellae where, after removal of the damaged D1-protein, they acts as receptors for the newly synthesized polypeptides and once repaired, migrate back to the grana partitions (10,11).
In this paper we will summarize some recent results on the degradation of the reaction centre proteins and the succession of events involved in their repair cycle.

DEGRADATION OF THE RC PROTEINS
Photoinactivation of PSII brings about the degradation of the D1-protein. Recent evidence suggests that this process may proceed along different pathways depending on whether the damage is induced at the acceptor or at the donor side (12). Acceptor side mechanism involves over-reduction of the quinone acceptors, depends on the presence of oxygen and leads to production of a 23.5 KDa N-terminal proteolytic fragments of the protein (13). Donor side mechanism depends on the accumulation of higly oxidizing radicals, is independent of the presence of oxygen and produce at least two C-terminal fragments of 24 (14) and 16 KDa (15). Interestingly, while the latter fragment is observed, after donor side photoinhibition, independently of the antenna size of the PSII preparation, from isolated RCs to whole PSII membranes, the 24 KDa C-terminus appears only in PSII preparations in which the internal antenna CP43 is disconnected. Both these fragments are photoaccumulated during illumination. A 22 KDa fragment of N-terminal origine has been observed by De Las Rivas et al.(16) after acceptor side photoinhibition of PSII cores. However, the same fragment is also observed when donor side photoinhibition is performed on isolated RCs. Actually this fragment, which probably coincides whith that observed in (13), is the first fragment to appear in the blot being already detected after 5 min. illumination, but at variance with the other fragments it does not accumulate under these conditions and disappears from the blot after approx. 30 min. This finding indicates that photoinhibition of isolated RC starts with an acceptor side mechanism even when illumination is performed under conditions expected to induce donor side phenomena.
Besides D1, also D2 is degraded during high light illumination. Among others, two C-terminal fragments have been identified of 28 and 18 KDa. As for D1 these two fragments are produced by a cleavage at the hydrophylic loops connecting respectively the 1st and 2nd and the 3rd and 4th transmembrane segments (17).

THE REPAIR CYCLE

We have recently shown that after photoinhibition of isolated thylakoids, the degradation products of D1 are preferentially localized in the stroma lamellae, confirming that damaged D1-protein migrates from grana to stroma-exposed regions (18). In a more recent investigation (19), the succession of events which starts the repair cycle by which damaged PSII centres are brought back to full activity has been identified. As schematically depicted in fig.1, these involve in the order: i) lowering the oligomerization state of the PSII core (probably a transition from dimer to monomer); ii) clevage of D1 at specific sites; iii) dissociation of the CP43 internal antenna from the PSII core; iv) independent migration of the latter complex and of the remaining part of the core to the stroma-exposed region of the membrane where the fragments of the D1-protein are released and further metabolized. The insertion of newly sinthesized D1, riassociation of CP43 and back migration to the grana are supposed to complete the cycle.

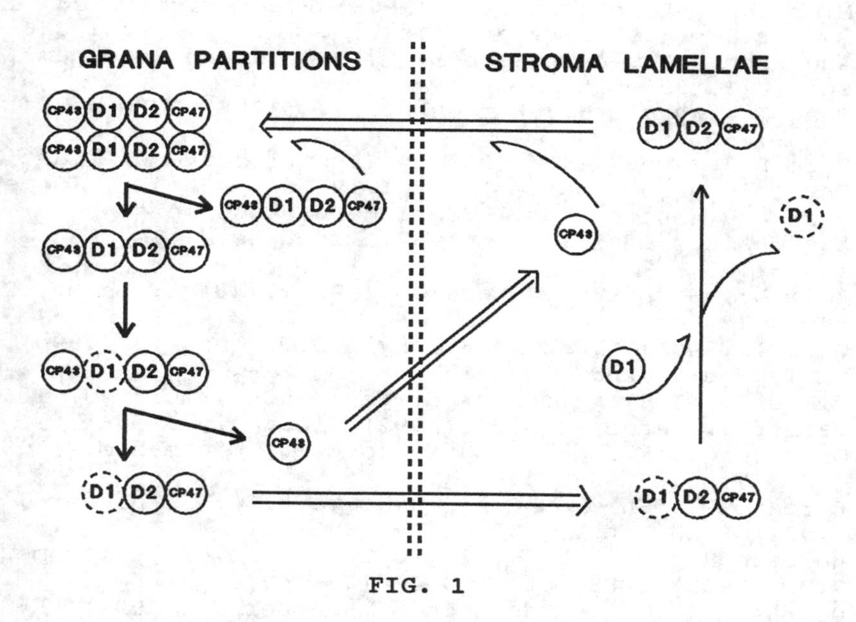

FIG. 1

Hypotetic scheme for the succession of events involved in the repair cycle of D1 after donor side photoinhibition.
Double arrows represent protein migration; the dotted circles represent the D1-protein after photoinduced cleavage.

In conclusion we may observe that the internal antenna CP43 seems to play an important role in the complex series of events related to photoinhibition. It is plausible that breaking of D1 may cause CP43 dissociation an this in turn may create the conditions for the migration to the stroma lamellae. This is in agreement with the finding that the D1-CP43 interaction prevents the cleavage of D1 at the site at which the C-terminal 24KDa fragment is generated. Which particular proteolytic mechanism is responsible for the photoinduced degradation of the RC proteins remains to be explained. A protease activity has been hypotesized and CP43 has been indicated as a possible candidate. In the light of the most recent results, a sort of auto-protelytic activity seems more likly, in which is the substrate itself to create the conditions for cleavage.

REFERENCES

1. Ewart A.J. (1896) J. Linn. Soc., 31, 364-461
2. Powles S.B. (1984) Annu. Rev. Plant Physiol., 35, 14-44
3. Michel H., Deisenhofer J. (1988) Biochemistry, 27, 1-7
4. Barber J. (1987) Trendfs Biochem. Sci., 12, 321-326
5. Anderson J.M., Andersson B., (1988) Trends Biochem. Sci., 13, 351-355
6. Ohad I., Kyle D.J., Hirschberg J. (1985) EMBO J., 4, 1655-1659
7. Kyle D.J., Ohad I. (1990) in "Encyclopedia of Plant Physiology (new series)", Vol.19, pp. 468-476, (Staehelin and Arntzen eds.), Springer, Heidelberg
8. Matoo A.K., Edelman M. (1987) Proc. Acad. Sci USA, 84, 1497-1501
9. Adir N., Sochat S., Ohad I. (1990) J. Biol. Chem., 265, 12563-12568
10. Ohad I., Adir N.,Koike H., Kyle D.J. Inou Y. (1990), J. Biol. Chem., 265, 1972-1979
11. Melis A. (1991) Biochim. Biophys. Acta, 1058, 87-106
12. Barber J., Andersson B. (1992) TIBS, 17, 61-66
13. Greenberg B.M., Gaba V., Matoo A.K., Edelman M. (1987) EMBO J., 6, 2865-2869
14. Barbato R., Shipton C.A., Giacometti G.M., Barber J. (1991) FEBS Lett., 290, 162-166
15. Barbato R., Frizzo A., Friso G., Rigoni F., Giacometti G.M. (1992) FEBS Lett., 304, 136-140
16. De Las Rivas J., Andersson B., Barber J. (1992) FEBS Lett., 301, 246-252
17. Barbato R., Friso G., Polverino de Laureto P., Frizzo A., Rigoni F., Giacometti G.M. (1992) FEBS Lett. in press
18. Barbato R., Friso G., Giardi M.T., Rigoni F., Giacometti G.M. (1991) Biochemistry, 30, 10220-10226
19. Barbato R., Friso G., Rigoni F., Dalla Vecchia F., Giacometti G.M. (1992) J. Cell Biol., in press

ASSAY OF PROTEASE ACTIVITY IN ISOLATED REACTION CENTER COMPLEX OF PHOTOSYSTEM II

MITSUE MIYAO-TOKUTOMI, Laboratory of Photosynthesis, National Institute of Agrobiological Resources (NIAR), Kannondai, Tsukuba 305, Japan

1. INTRODUCTION

The D1 protein of the reaction center of photosystem II (PSII) turns over at a higher rate than any of other subunit of PSII under illumination. Recently, it has been demonstrated that the light-induced degradation of D1 protein occurs in isolated PSII reaction center as *in vivo*, and suggested that the degradation is catalyzed by a serine-type protease in the reaction center [1]. The presence of protease in isolated reaction center was also demonstrated by assay of protease activity using a synthetic substrate, Ile-Glu-Gly-Arg-NA [2].

Use of synthetic substrates for assay of the protease activity could be powerful technique to characterize the tentative protease in the PSII reaction center in detail. In this study, protease activities of isolated PSII reaction center were examined using various synthetic substrates, 4-nitroaniline derivatives.

2. MATERIALS AND METHODS

Preparation of PSII Reaction Center and Photoinhibitory Treatment

Rice plants were grown in a green house for 3-4 weeks and then illuminated with white light at 400 $\mu E \cdot m^{-2} s^{-1}$ for 14 h. PSII reaction centers were isolated from the rice plants by a procedure based on that of Nanba and Satoh [3] according to Chapman et al. [4]. Chlorophyll was determined according to Arnon [5].

Photoinhibitory light treatment was performed in a stirred glass cuvette at 25°C. The reaction centers were suspended in 2 mM dodecyl maltoside (DM)/0.2 mM DBMIB/50 mM Tris-HCl (pH 8.0) at 50 μg $Chl \cdot ml^{-1}$ and illuminated with heat-filtered yellow light (4 $mE \cdot m^{-2} s^{-1}$) for 30 min.

Assay of Protease Activity

The reaction center and/or TPCK-treated trypsin was incubated at 25°C for 10 min in 2 mM DM/10 mM $CaCl_2$/50 mM Tris-HCl (pH 8.2). Then, 50 mM substrate solution prepared in dimethyl sulfoxide was added to the suspension to give a final concentration of 1 mM except for Ile-

---

Abbreviations:

Arg-NA	N^{α}-benzoyl-D,L-arginine-4-nitroanilide
Lys-NA	N^{α}-benzoyl-D,L-lysine-4-nitroanilide
Phe-NA	N-glutaryl-L-phenylalanine-4-nitroanilide
Ile-Glu-Gly-Arg-NA	N^{α}-benzoyl-L-isoleucyl-L-glutamyl-L-glycyl-L-arginine-4-nitroanilide

N. Murata (ed.), Research in Photosynthesis, Vol. IV, 509–512.

Glu-Gly-Arg-NA, which was dissolved in water at 1 mM and of which final concentration was 0.1 mM. After further incubation at 25°C for 30 min, the reaction was stopped by adding 1/6 vol. of 30% (v/v) acetic acid and incubating at 60°C for 10 min. The amount of 4-nitroaniline released was monitored by the increase in absorbance at 405 nm.

3. RESULTS AND DISCUSSION

Hydrolysis by proteases of the 4-nitroaniline derivatives releases 4-nitroaniline and can be monitored by the increase in absorbance at 400-410 nm [6]. When Arg-NA, a very commonly used substrate for trypsin, was added to the PSII reaction center, absorbance at 405 nm rose up rapidly and then increased gradually (Fig. 1). Depletion of Ca^{2+} from the reaction mixture reduced the absorbance increase to about 20% (not shown). This absorbance increase, however, did not reflect hydrolysis of the substrate, since similar absorbance increase was observed at 560 nm at which wavelength either the substrate or 4-nitroaniline has no absorption (Fig. 1). Rather, it is likely that the absorbance increase reflects turbidity increase of the reaction mixture, since absorbance increased more largely at shorter wavelengths (Fig. 2). Turbidity increase was also observed with Lys-NA, and in some reaction center preparations with Ile-Glu-Gly-Arg-NA though to a much lesser extent (c.a. 0.01 $\Delta A405$/15 min).

In order to correctly assay the hydrolysis activity of the PSII reaction center, the turbidity of reaction mixture must be canceled out on absorbance measurement. It was found that the turbid reaction mixture became clear by adding acetic acid (Fig. 2). Acetic acid is commonly used to stop protease reaction by shifting pH of a reaction mixture to around 5. Probably, the turbidity of reaction mixture was caused by aggregation of the PSII reaction centers and substrates by electrostatic interaction, and acetic acid eliminates the aggregates by changing charges of both reaction center and substrate. Heating at 60°C with acetic acid was employed to convert all chlorophylls to

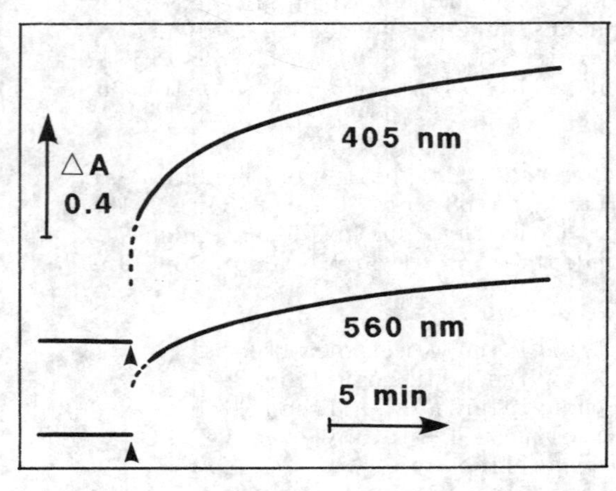

FIGURE 1. Changes in Absorbance of Reaction Mixture by Addition of Arg-NA. One mM Arg-NA was added to the reaction mixture containing 2 mM DM/10 mM Ca^{2+} and 10 μg Chl· ml^{-1} of PSII reaction center. Arrowheads indicate the time when Arg-NA was added.

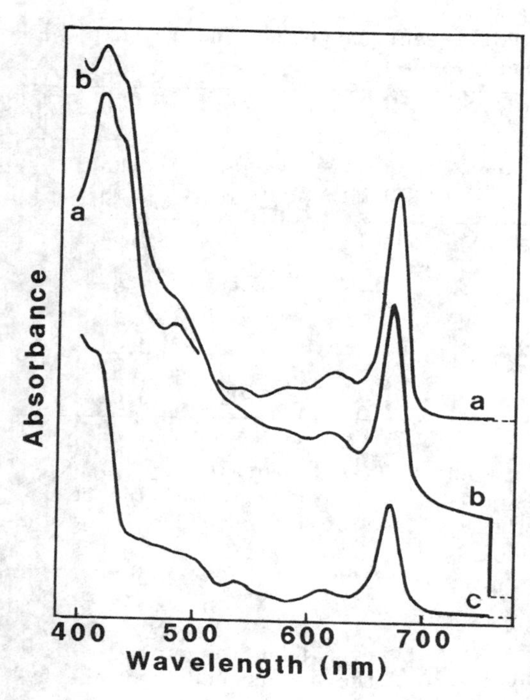

FIGURE 2. Effects of Arg-NA and Acetic Acid on Absorption Spectrum of Reaction Mixture. (a), before addition of Arg-NA; (b), after 15-min incubation with 1 mM Arg-NA; (c), after addition of acetic acid and heating at 60°C for 10 min.

pheophytins so that absorbance at 405 nm by the PSII reaction center reaches constant level (Fig. 2).

Protease activities measured using the acetate method were presented in Table 1. Calcium ion at 10 mM was included in the reaction mixture, since Ca^{2+} was reported to stimulate protease activity in the PSII reaction center [2]. With all substrates tested, incubation of the PSII reaction center increased absorbance at 405 nm without showing any substrate dependence. Photoinhibitory treatment of the PSII reaction center enhanced the absorbance increase slightly. Also in this case substrate dependence was not observed. In contrast, trypsin exhibited large absorbance increase with Ile-Glu-Gly-Arg-NA, a sensitive substrate for trypsin, but only small increase with other substrates. The small absorbance increase by trypsin with Arg-NA, a commonly used substrate for trypsin, can be ascribed to a low trypsin concentration in the reaction mixture of 2 nM, which was designed to optimize hydrolysis activity with Ile-Glu-Gly-Arg-NA.

When trypsin was incubated with substrates in the presence of the PSII reaction center, the resultant absorbance increases were almost the same as those by trypsin alone (Table 1). This indicates that the presence of the PSII reaction center does not disturb the trypsin action under the assay conditions employed in this study.

The absorbance increase with Ile-Glu-Gly-Arg-NA by the PSII reaction center was about 4% of that by trypsin. This corresponds to

TABLE 1. Protease Activities of PSII Reaction Center and Trypsin with Synthetic Substrates

Sample[a]	ΔA405/30 min[b]			
Substrate	Ile-Glu-Gly-Arg-NA (0.1 mM)	Arg-NA (1.0 mM)	Lys-NA (1.0 mM)	Phe-NA (1.0 mM)
Reaction center	0.04 (4%)	0.01	0.04	0.04
Photoinhibited reaction center	0.05 (5%)	----	0.06	0.04
Reaction center and trypsin	0.91 (99%)	0.01	0.02	0.01
Trypsin	0.92 (100%)	0.01	0.02	0.01

[a] Sample concentrations were 10 μg Chl·ml^{-1} for the PSII reaction center (c.a. 1 μM reaction center) and 0.05 μg protein·ml^{-1} (2 nM) for trypsin. [b] One ΔA405 corresponds to 0.1 mM 4-nitroaniline released. Measurement error with the PSII reaction center due to deviation of the sample amount was ± 0.01.

about 0.01% of the hydrolysis activity of trypsin on the molar basis. Taking into account the measurement error, the absorbance increase by the PSII reaction center was too low to demonstrate the presence of protease activity. Using Ile-Glu-Gly-Arg-NA as a substrate, Misra et al. [2] reported the protease activity in the PSII reaction center as high as 0.2% of the trypsin activity. Judging from their assay protocol, it is likely that the reported activity merely reflects turbidity increase by the substrate.

It is concluded that the PSII reaction center does not have significant protease activity as far as synthetic substrates, 4-nitroaniline derivatives, were used. However, it is noted that this does not stand against the presence of protease in the PSII reaction center, since the observed low hydrolysis activity might result from low specificity of the tentative protease to the used substrates.

REFERENCES

1 Barber, J. and Andersson, B. (1992) Trends Biochem. Sci. 17, 61-66
2 Misra, A.N., Hall, S.G. and Barber, J. (1991) Biochim. Biophys. Acta 1059, 239-242
3 Nanba, O. and Satoh, K. (1987) Proc. Natl. Acad. Sci. USA 84, 109-112
4 Chapman, D.J., Gounaris, K. and Barber, J. (1988) Biochim. Biophys. Acta 933, 423-431
5 Arnon, D.I. (1949) Plant Physiol. 24, 1-15
6 Erlanger, B.F., Kokowsky, N. and Cohen, W. (1961) Arch. Biochem. Biophys. 95, 271-278

DEGRADATION OF CP43 AND CP47 BY TRIS-TREATMENT OF PS II MEMBRANE IN WEAK LIGHT

Hiroki Mori and Yasusi Yamamoto

Department of Biology, Faculty of Science, Okayama University, Okayama 700, Japan

1. INTRODUCTION

Photo-inhibition of photosynthesis is a phenomenon which is observed in PS II, but not in PS I and photosynthetic bacteria. It is thought that PS II is susceptible to photoinhibition because a highly oxidizing molecule $P680^+$ is formed at the reaction center. Photo-inhibition leads to inactivation of electron transport in PS II and degradation of D1 protein. The damage leading to D1 degradation seems to occur at the acceptor or donor side in PS II (1). The damaged D1 protein is cleaved by a protease activity within the reaction center-binding proteins (2) or antenna Chl a-binding protein CP43 (3). The molecular mechanism of light-induced inactivation of PS II and D1 degradation is one of the central topics in the current research of photosynthesis.

Treatment of PS II membrane with alkaline Tris induces release of extrinsic 33-, 24-, 18-kDa proteins and Mn atoms from the membrane. The Tris-treated PS II membrane completely loses the ability to oxidize water. In the present study, we show that degradation of CP43 and CP47 occurs, in addition to that of the reaction center-binding proteins, by Tris-treatment of PS II membranes in weak light.

2. MATERIALS AND METHODS

PS II membranes were prepared from spinach thylakoid with Triton X-100 according to Kuwabara and Murata (4). For Tris-treatment, the PS II membranes were suspended in 0.8 M Tris-HCl to give a final Chl concentration of 0.5 mg ml^{-1} and incubated on ice for 30 min either in the dark or light. The pH of Tris-HCl was varied from 7.0 to 10.0. For illumination, white fluorescent light was used and the incident intensity was 20 $\mu E\ m^{-2}\ s^{-1}$ above the suspension of the PS II membranes. In the experiment where Tris-treated PS II membranes were illuminated at different pH conditions, the PS II membranes treated with 0.8 M Tris-HCl (pH 9.0) in the dark were washed twice with solution A (0.4 M sucrose, 40 mM MES-NaOH, 10 mM NaCl, pH 6.5), and resuspended in solution A containing the following buffers instead of MES; HEPES (pH 7.0), TAPS (pH 8.0), CHES (pH 9.0), CAPS (pH 10.0), Na/K phosphate (pH 11.0). The Tris-treated PS II membranes (0.5 mg Chl ml^{-1}) were illuminated as described above. Anaerobic condition was obtained by the addition of 10 mM glucose, 0.2 mg ml^{-1} glucose oxidase, 0.2 mg ml^{-1} catalase to the cuvette containing the suspension of PS II membranes.

N. Murata (ed.), Research in Photosynthesis, Vol. IV, 513–516.

3. RESULTS AND DISCUSSION

Tris-treatment (pH 7.0-10.0) of PS II membranes was performed under illumination at 20 μE m^{-2} s^{-1} and the proteins in the PS II membranes were analyzed by SDS/urea-polyacrylamide gel electrophoresis (PAGE) (Fig. 1A). With increase of pH from 7.0 to 10.0, three extrinsic proteins were released from PS II membranes, and above pH 8.0 all of them were completely removed. We found that the amount of the apoproteins of CP43 and 47 also decreased with increase of pH in the Tris-treatment (Fig 1A, B). With D1 protein, decrease in the amount was confirmed by Western blotting (Fig. 1B). In non-denaturing LDS-PAGE of PS II membranes solubilized with n-octyl β-D-glucopyranoside, decrease in green bands corresponding to the holo-complexes of CP43 and CP47 was detected (data not shown). Other major protein components in PS II membranes, such as LHC II and cyt b559, were not affected at all under the same conditions (Fig. 1A).

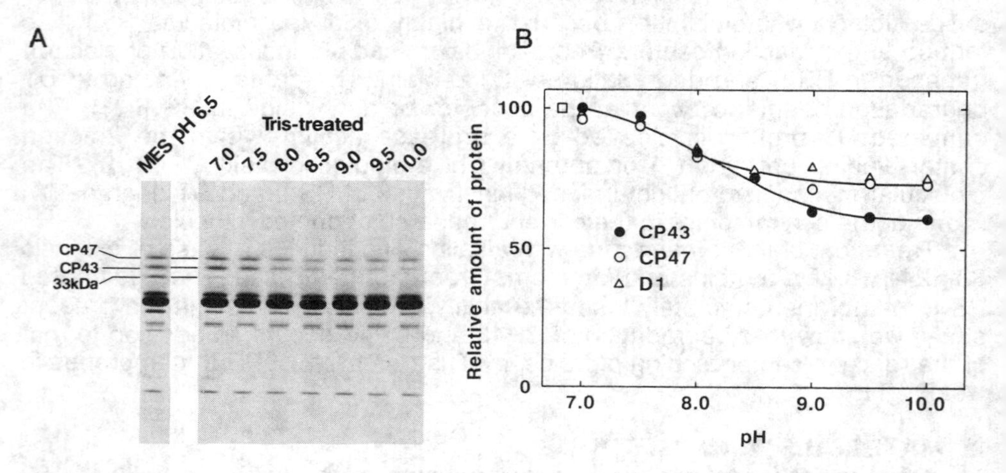

Figure 1 The effects of Tris-treatment in weak light on the proteins of PS II. (A) a SDS/urea-PAGE gel showing the degradation of PS II proteins. (B) dependency of the protein degradation on pH of the Tris-treatment.

Tris-treatment of PS II membrane released extrinsic 33-, 24-, 18-kDa proteins and Mn atoms involved in water oxidation. Considering the synergistic effects of alkaline-Tris and illumination with weak light on the degradation of CP43, it is probable that excitation of PS II induces accumulation of oxidant at the donor side of PS II where Mn is effectively removed. To examine this possibility, we studied the effect of reductants and an electron transport inhibitor, 3-(3,4-dichlorophenyl)-1,1-dimethylurea (DCMU) on the amount of CP43 during Tris-treatment in the light. The addition of the reductants and DCMU significantly suppressed the degradation of CP43 (data not shown).

These results suggest that the donor side of PS II is responsible for the degradation of CP43 .

The photo-degradation of CP43 was also observed when the PS II membranes were treated by Tris in the dark and illuminated at alkaline condition (Fig. 2). No significant degradation of CP43 was detected when the PS II membrane pre-treated by Tris in the dark was illuminated at neutral pH. In this experiment, we detected degradation of a 10 kDa protein, probably corresponds to *psb* R gene product at alkaline pH. The pH dependency of degradation of CP43 observed here is different from that of D1 which showed an optimum pH of degradation at 7.5-8.0 (2,3).

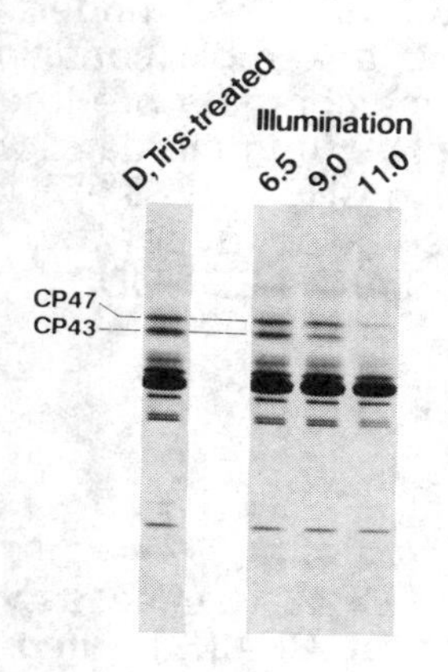

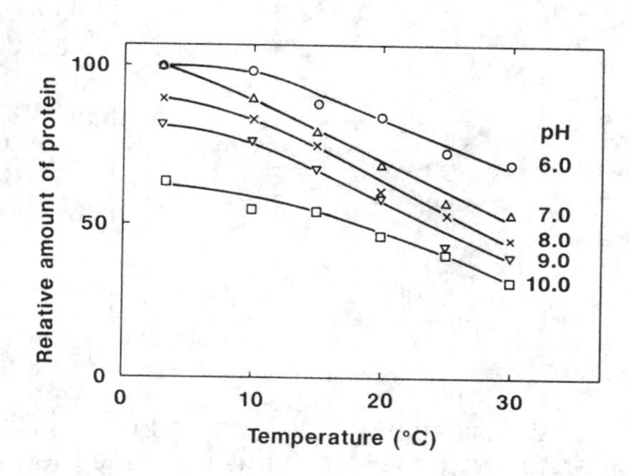

Figure 2 (left) Photo-degradation of CP43 in Tris-treated PS II membranes at alkaline pH. The experimental procedure is shown in MATERIALS AND METHODS.

Figure 3 (right) Dependency of the photo-degradation of CP43 on temperature and pH.

The degradation of CP43 was dependent on the temperature during illumination (Fig. 3), which suggests that a protease activity is involved in the degradation of CP43 at alkaline pH. We studied effects of protease inhibitors in photodegradation of CP43 in alkaline pH with Tris-treated PS II membranes, but so far an effective protease inhibitor was not found. Possibly the effect of protease inhibitors appears depending on the PS II membrane preparations used. With the degradation of D1, a serine-type protease inhibitor, phenylmethylsulphonyl fluoride (PMSF), was shown to be effective in the PS II core complex and the PS II reaction center complex (2, 3), but not in thylakoid membranes (5). It is possible that the same protease that cleaves the D1 protein is responsible for the degradation of CP43.

Generally, toxic oxygen species damage proteins. We examined the effects of aerobic and anaerobic conditions on the degradation of CP43 (Fig. 4). Under the anaerobic condition, the degradation of CP43 was retarded compared with that under the aerobic condition, and the extent of inhibition of CP43 degradation was small under the anaerobic condition. In the degradation of D1 proteins, it was shown that singlet oxygen, which is generated when the acceptor side of PS II is blocked, damages D1 protein (6). As the donor side of PS II is inhibited by Tris-treatment in our case, a different mechanism of action of toxic oxygen on the protein should be considered.

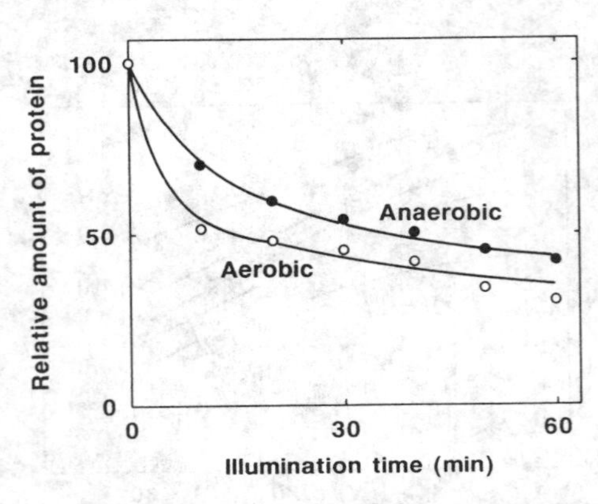

Figure 4 Time course of the degradation of CP43 under the aerobic and anaerobic conditions. the PS II membranes, pre-treated with Tris (pH 9.0) in the dark, were suspended in CHES (pH 9.0). Other conditions are described in MATERIALS AND METHODS.

Identification of the degradation products of CP43 is necessary for understanding the mechanism of the degradation of CP43. To find the degradation products, we treated PS II core particles as well as PS II membrane with Tris in the light in the presence of various electron acceptors. However, these trials are not successful so far. To find definite degradation products, we have to use more suitable experimental conditions.

4. ACKNOWLEDGMENT

The present work was supported by grants from the Ministry of Education, Science and Culture of Japan and from the Biox General Pathology Lab., Shimonoseki, Japan.

REFERENCES

1 Barber, J. & Andersson, B. (1992) TIBS 17, 61-66
2 Shipton, C.A. & Barber, J. (1992) Biochim. Biophys. Acta 1099, 85-90
3 Salter, A. H., Virgin, I., Hagman, A. & Andersson, B. (1992) Biochem. 31, 3990-3998
4 Kuwabara, T. & Murata, N. (1982) Plant Cell Physiol. 23, 533-539
5 Ohad, I., Kyle, D.J. & Hirschberg, J. (1985) EMBO J. 4, 1655-1659
6 Vass, I., Styring, S., Hundal, T., Koivuniemi, A., Aro, E.-M. & Andersson, B. (1992) Proc. Natl. Acad. Sci. USA 89, 1408-1412

STUDIES ON THE PHOTOPROTECTIVE FUNCTION OF ZEAXANTHIN AT HIGH-LIGHT CONDITIONS

HARTMUT K. LICHTENTHALER and CHRISTIANE SCHINDLER,
Botanisches Institut, University of Karlsruhe,
Kaiserstr. 12, D-7500 KARLSRUHE, GERMANY

1. INTRODUCTION

The operation of the high-light induced xanthophyll/zeaxanthin cycle in the chloroplasts of higher plants, as detected by Sapozhnikov (1), has long been established by several research groups (1, 2, 3, 4). At a high irradiance the photosynthetic apparatus de-epoxidizes the xanthophyll violaxanthin **v** (2 hydroxy, 2 epoxy groups) via antheraxanthin **a** (2 hydroxy, 1 epoxy group) to zeaxanthin **z** (2 hydroxy groups), whereas in darkness or low light the back reaction (z $\longrightarrow$ a $\longrightarrow$ v) takes place. The de-epoxidation requires reducing conditions (NADPH, reduced ascorbate) and a pH in the thylakoid lumen of about 5 which activates the de-epoxidase (2, 4). The back-reaction, in turn, proceeds at pH 7.5 and consumes NADPH and oxygen. Hitherto the exact physiological role of the plants' xanthophyll cycle is not yet known. Most authors assume a photoprotective function of zeaxanthin for the photosynthetic pigment apparatus. More recently a role of zeaxanthin in the non-radiative energy dissipation was proposed (5, 6), which would cause a decline in the variable fluorescence Fv. A direct correlation between zeaxanthin formation and the decline in the Fv and Fv/Fm was anticipated (5). Kinetic studies with maple leaves (7) and tobacco leaves described here, however, demonstrate that zeaxanthin accumulation and the decline in Fv under high irradiance do not proceed in a correlative way. A new hypothesis that zeaxanthin and the xanthophyll cycle function at high-light conditions in the destruction of highly reactive oxygen species is established.

2. MATERIALS and METHODS

2.1 **Growth of plants**: Tobacco plants (Nicotiana tabacum L, aurea form Su/su) were grown in a phytochamber at 24°C, 60% rel. humidity and 400 μmol $\cdot$ m^{-2} $\cdot$ s^{-1}. Three year old maple trees (Acer platanoides L.) were cultivated in 10 l pots in the Botanical Garden. Before high-light treatment the plants were kept for two hours in the laboratory at 50 μmol $\cdot$ m^{-2} $\cdot$ s^{-1}. High-light was provided by two 500W HQIE lamps applying a 8 cm water filter and an IR absorption filter (KG3 Schott, Mainz) to exclude heat.

2.2 **Photosynthetic pigments**: Chlorophylls and total carotenoids were extracted from leave disks (9 mm diameter) with 100% acetone and determined spectrophotometrically applying the redetermined absorption coefficients (8) which allow the parallel determination of chlorophylls a and b and total carotenoids in the same extract solution. The individual carotenoids and chlorophylls were quantified by reversed phase HPLC within 20 min (7, 9).

2.3 **Chlorophyll fluorescence measurements**: Several chlorophyll parameters (Fv, Fo, Fm) and ratios (Fv/Fm, Fv/Fo and the vitality index ratio Rfd730) were

N. Murata (ed.), Research in Photosynthesis, Vol. IV, 517–520.

determined in predarkened (10 min) leaves (leaf disks of 9 mm diameter) using a PAM fluorometer as described in (10).

3. RESULTS AND DISCUSSION

Leaves of the dominant tobacco aurea mutant Su/su exhibited a light saturation of photosynthesis at 600 μmol • m^{-2} • s^{-1}, P_N-rates of 5.8 μmol CO_2 • m^{-2} • s^{-1} and were much less sensitive to photoinhibition than the normal green variety su/su which exhibited the same light saturation point but P_N-rates of only 3.0 μmol CO_2 • m^{-2} • s^{-1}. After a longer exposure of 40 min to 5 h to excess high-light of 2200 μmol • m^{-2} • s^{-1} the variable fluorescence ratios Fv/Fm and Rfd 730 decreased in the aurea mutant only by 25% and 33% respectively, whereas in the green tobacco the variable fluorescence was almost fully lost.

Within 2 to 5 min of high-light exposure of the aurea tobacco leaves ca. 85 to 90% of the violaxanthin was deepoxidized to zeaxanthin (Fig. 1A and B). During the early phase of high-light exposure up to 20 min there occurred only very small changes in the chlorophyll fluorescence parameters as seen in a decrease of ca. 3% (in Rfd730 and Fv/Fm) and 6 to 8% (in Fv and Fv/Fo). Thereafter, from 20 via 40 to 60 min of high-light exposure the variable fluorescence decreased, however, without changes in the zeaxanthin content or percentage (of v + a + z) (Fig. 1) indicating that zeaxanthin formation and decrease in variable fluorescence parameters proceed independent of each other. Between 1 to 5 h of high irradiance the content of zeaxanthin (μg • 10 cm^{-2} leaf area) doubled by *de novo* biosynthesis, whereas the variable chlorophyll fluorescence (Fv, Fm, Rfd730, Fv/Fm) was little affected indicating that no further photoinhibition occurred. The level of chlorophylls and the other carotenoids did not change during the high-light treatment.

These results demonstrate that zeaxanthin accumulation at high-light conditions is a biphasic process: 1) a fast transformation of violaxanthin into zeaxanthin within minutes, followed 2) by a continuous increase of the zeaxanthin level by *de novo* biosynthesis throughout the high-light exposure. There was no correlation between zeaxanthin accumulation and decrease in variable fluorescence. Both processes are high-light induced, but seem to proceed independent of each other.

When leaves were returned to darkness or low light conditions zeaxanthin was epoxidized to violaxanthin. After a short high-light exposure of 5 to 15 min the back-reaction z - v was completed within 20 to 30 min. At longer high-light exposures this back-reaction was increasingly retarded and took many hours for completion. Also the back-reaction in the dark was a two-step mechanism, the major one proceeded fast with little changes in Fv or Fv/Fm, whereas only the second slower step paralleled in part the restoration of the ratio Fv and Fv/Fm.

In green maple leaves similar results were obtained: zeaxanthin formation proceeded within 2 to 5 minutes with little changes in the variable fluorescence, whereas thereafter a continuous decrease in the variable chlorophyll fluorescence occured (Fv/Fm -25% and Fv/Fo -55% after 1 h) without any changes in the zeaxanthin level and percentage of v + a + z.

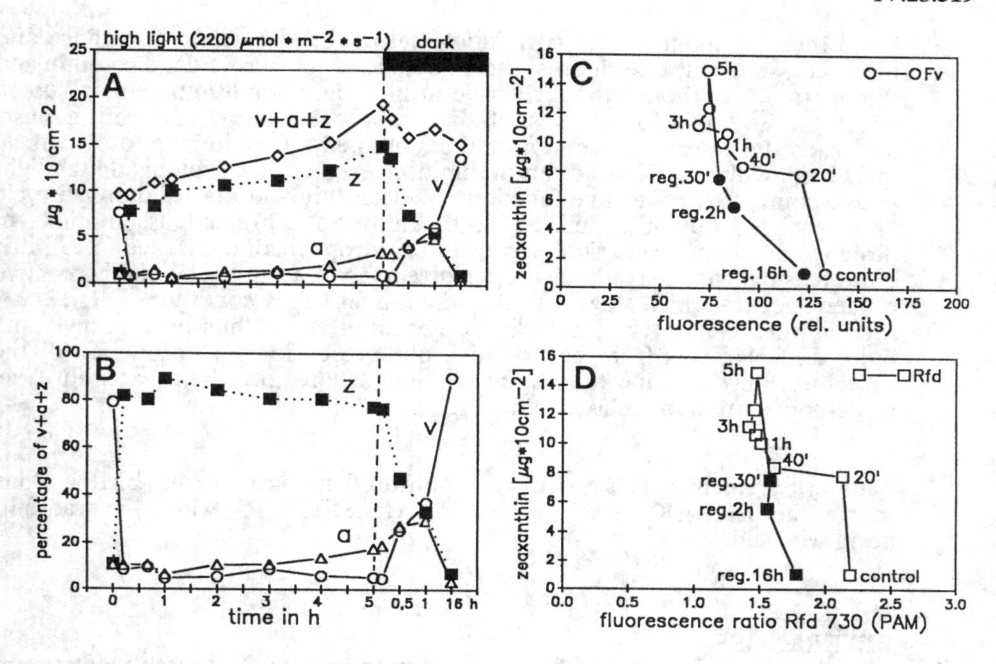

Fig. 1. A and B. Changes in the level ($\mu g \cdot 10\ cm^{-2}$) and percentage of zeaxanthin and total xanthophyll cycle carotenoids (v + a + z) in an aurea mutant of tobacco during a 5 h high-light exposure (2200 $\mu mol \cdot m^{-2} \cdot s^{-1}$) and a subsequent dark phase.
C and D. Attempts to correlate the decrease in Fv and the ratio Rfd730 with the zeaxanthin accumulation and regeneration of Fv and Rfd730 with the disappearance of zeaxanthin in the dark phase.
Mean of 3 (A, B) and 6 determinations (C, D), SD 6% or less.

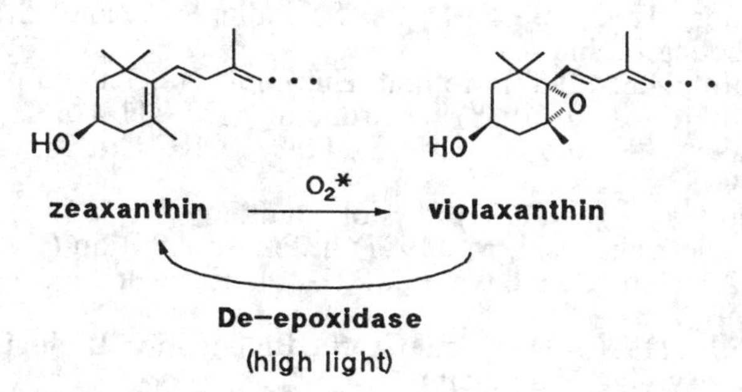

Fig. 2. Possible function of zeaxanthin and the xanthophyll cycle under high-light conditions in the destruction of highly reactive oxygen species O_2*, such as singlet oxygen $^1O_2$, superoxide radical anion $O_2^{\bullet -}$, hydroxyl radical $OH^{\bullet}$, hydrogen superoxide H_2O_2.

Since there exists no causal correlation between zeaxanthin appearance and the decrease in variable fluorescence, the physiological role of zeaxanthin and the operation of the xanthophyll cycle at high-light conditions remains open. From the fact that the leaves of the tobacco aurea mutant continuously increased the zeaxanthin content and maintained a functional photochemical machinery with only 30% of photoinhibition, even after a prolonged high-light stress, points to a protective function of zeaxanthin and the xanthophyll cycle against high irradiance. Instead of the hitherto expressed assumptions of directly quenching excitation energy and chlorophyll fluorescence (5, 6), it is quite feasible that zeaxanthin is epoxidized to violaxanthin by highly reactive oxygen species, which show up under high-light stress conditions (11, 12, 13) such as $^1O_2$, $O_2^{\bullet -}$, $OH^{\bullet}$ and H_2O_2. Zeaxanthin could thus protect thylakoid lipids and pigments from peroxidative photooxidations. The function of the xanthophyll cycle would then be to continuously restore the zeaxanthin level by de-epoxidation of violaxanthin (Fig. 2).

Acknowledgements: This work was sponsored in part by the BMFT Bonn within the EUREKA Project No. 380 (LASFLEUR) which is gratefully acknowledged.

REFERENCES

1 Sapozhnikov, D.J. (1969) in Progress in Photosynthesis Research (Metzner H. ed) Vol. 2, pp. 694-700, H. Laupp, Tübingen
2 Hager, A. (1975) Ber. Dtsch. Bot. Ges. 88, 27-44
3 Yamamoto, H.Y. (1979) Pure Appl. Chem. 51. 639-648
4 Siefermann-Harms, D. (1977) in Lipids and Lipid Polymers in Higher Plants (Tevini, M. and Lichtenthaler H.K. eds) pp. 218-230, Springer Verlag, Berlin
5 Demmig, B., Winter K., Krüger, A. and Czygan, F.-C. (1987) Plant Physiol. 84, 218-224
6 Demmig-Adams, B. and Adams, W.W.III. (1992) Ann. Rev. Plant Physiol. Plant Mol. Biol. 43, 599-626
7 Lichtenthaler, H.K., Burkart, S., Schindler, C. and Stober, F. (1992) Photosynthetica 26, in press.
8 Lichtenthaler, H.K. (1987) Methods Enzymol. 148, 350-382
9 Siefermann-Harms, D. (1988) J. Chromatogr. 20, 411-416
10 Lichtenthaler, H.K. and Rinderle, U. (1988) CRC Crit. Rev. Anal. Chem. 19, Suppl I, S85-S85
11 Siefermann-Harms, D. (1987) Physiol. Plant. 69, 561-568
12 Asada, K. and Takahashi, M. (1987) in Photoinhibition (Kyle, D.J., Osmond, C.B. and Arntzen, C.J., eds.), pp. 227-284, Elsevier Science Publishers BV, Amsterdam
13 Elstner, E.F. (1990) Der Sauerstoff (Biochemie, Biologie, Medizin), BI-Wissenschaftsverlag, Mannheim

RAPID LOSS OF THE PROTON GRADIENT ACROSS THE THYLAKOID MEMBRANE DURING PHOTOINHIBITORY ILLUMINATION

Staffan E. Tjus and Bertil Andersson
Department of Biochemistry, Arrhenius Laboratories for Natural Sciences, Stockholm University, S-106 91 Stockholm, SWEDEN

1. INTRODUCTION

Studies on photoinhibition of photosynthesis are focused on damaging events associated with PS II (1). It is well established that high light intensities lead to inactivation of PS II electron transport and degradation of damaged D1-protein (1, 2). PS I is however much more resistant to light stress and only at very extreme light conditions inactivation have been observed, involving impairment of Fe-S clusters (3) and direct photobleaching.

In this study we present evidence that under the early phase of photoinhibition there is an increase of PS I electron transport that is connected to a very rapid loss of both the trans-thylakoid Δ-pH and the cyclic photophosphorylation.

2. MATERIALS and METHODS

Intact chloroplasts, isolated according to (4), were suspended to a concentration of 0.1 mg chlorophyll/ml in a buffer containing 50 mM Hepes (pH 8.0), 5 mM $MgCl_2$, 1 mM $MnCl_2$, 2 mM EDTA, 1.2 mM ascorbate and 350 mM sorbitol at a volume of 20 ml
Thylakoid membranes, isolated as in (5), were suspended to a concentration of 0.1 mg chlorophyll/ml in a buffer containing 5 mM Tricine (pH 7.4), 6 mM $MgCl_2$,and 300 mM sucrose at a volume of 20 ml.
Photoinhibitory illumination was performed using white light at 3500-7000 $\mu E/m^2s$ as detailed in figure legends.
PS I electron transport was measured from ascorbate/DCIP to methylviologen and *PS II electron transport* was measured from H_2O to PpBQ using an oxygen electrode.
PMS-mediated proton translocation during cyclic electron transport was measured with a pH electrode in a medium composed of; 3.3 mM PMS, 0.7 mM DCMU, 75 mM KCl, 5 mM $MgCl_2$,, 150 mM sucrose and 25-50 µg chlorophyll in a total volume of 1.5 ml. The samples were irradiated by red-filtered light of saturating light intensity and the pH translocation was followed to steady-state level.
Cyclic photophosphorylation was measured by the luciferin-luciferase method (6).
Quantitative immunoblotting of the D1 protein was performed according to (7).

3. RESULTS

When illuminating isolated thylakoids with strong light there was the expected loss of PS II electron transport and the subsequent degradation of the D1 reaction centre protein (Fig.1). On the contrary, under identical conditions, there was a pronounced initial increase of the PS I electron transport (Fig.1). Thus, after 15 minutes of strong illumination the rate had increased to 150 % compared to the dark control. Only after prolonged illumination was there a detectable impairment of PS I in accordance with (3). When adding the uncoupler NH_4Cl the initial rates were higher and there was no

N. Murata (ed.), Research in Photosynthesis, Vol. IV, 521–524.

initial increase of the PS I activity during the photoinhibitory illumination (not shown).

In order to investigate if the initial rise of the PS I activity was associated with an uncoupling event, we measured light-induced proton uptake in the presence of PMS and DCMU. As shown in Fig. 1 a pronounced and rapid loss of Δ-pH during PMS mediated cyclic PS I electron transport was observed. Strikingly, the collapse of the proton gradient was even faster than the loss of PS II electron transport normally considered as the initial and major target for light stress.

To study if this light induced loss of the proton gradient also occured in a more native system, intact chloroplasts were subjected to the photoinhibitory illumination. The same results as observed with thylakoids were obtained, i.e.; a rapid loss of Δ-pH which preceded the inactivation of the PS II activity (Fig. 2).

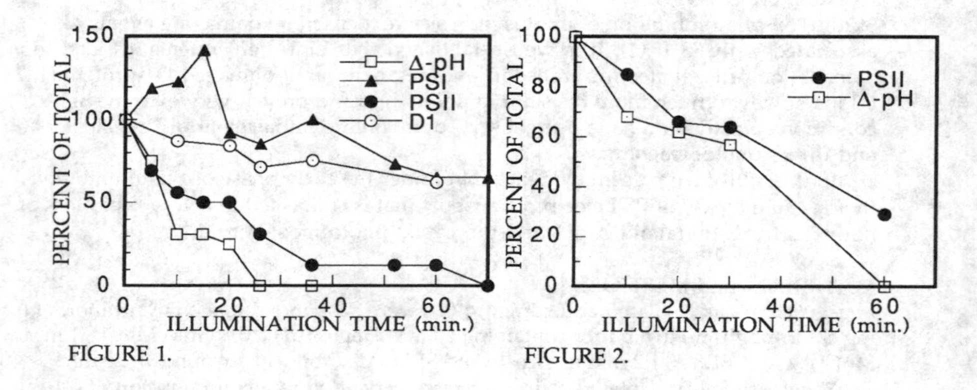

FIGURE 1.

FIGURE 2.

FIGURE 1. Thylakoids subjected to strong illumination (3500 μE/m2s) and analyzed for PMS-mediated steady-state proton-uptake (Δ-pH), PS I and PS II electron transport and amount of D1-protein.

FIGURE 2. Intact chloroplasts subjected to strong illumination (7000 μE/m2s) and analyzed for PMS-mediated steady-state proton-uptake (Δ-pH) and PS II electron transport

To find out whether the proton leakiness of the thylakoid membrane was connected to the degradation of D1 protein, we performed the strong illumination in the absence of oxygen. Under anaerobic conditions the D1-protein does not degrade despite severe photoinactivation of PS II (8). The reduction of the trans-thylakoid proton gradient was still occuring under anaerobiosis (not shown) strongly suggesting that it is not a direct effect of the D1-protein degradation process.

The loss of the proton gradient was less pronounced when the photoinhibitory illumination was performed in the cold (not shown). Low temperature is known to slow down the rate of D1-protein degradation but it also has a general stabilizing effect on the thylakoid membrane.

As shown in Fig. 3, loss of the Δ-pH showed the same light dependency as the impairment of PS II electron transport. Loss of proton-uptake was seen even at moderate photoinhibitory light intensities such as 250-500 μE/m2s and is therefore not only associated with extreme light conditions.

We also investigated if the rapid loss of Δ-pH was connected to changes in the CF_1-CF_0 complex. As expected, the light induced loss of the Δ-pH was accompanied by a rapid deactivation of photophosphorylation (Fig.4) in accordance with very recent work (9). The lost proton gradient could not be restored by addition of DCCD and no changes in the polypeptide composition of CF1 could be observed (not shown).

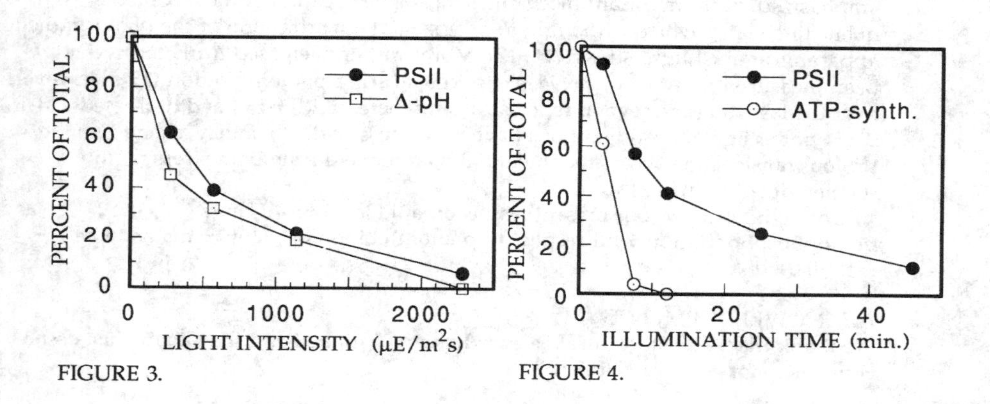

FIGURE 3. FIGURE 4.

FIGURE 3. Thylakoids subjected to photoinhibitory illumunation for 35 minutes at different light intensities and analyzed for PMS-mediated steady-state proton-uptake (Δ-pH) and PS II electron transport.

FIGURE 4. Thylakoids subjected to strong light (5500 μE/m2s) and analyzed for cyclic photophosphorylation (measured as ATP-synthesis) and PS II electron transport.

4. DISCUSSION

The present data provide information of a very rapid collapse of the trans-thylakoid proton gradient during photoinhibitory illumination. In fact the loss of the PS I mediated proton translocation was even faster than the loss of PS II electron transport normally considered as the major reason for photoinhibition of photosynthesis. The present study has been carried out at the in vitro level, using thylakoid membranes and intact chloroplasts, but preliminary observations indicate that loss of the proton gradient across the thylakoid membrane may also occur after strong illumination of intact leaves.

The mechanism behind the loss of the proton build-up is not known at present. It is not associated with damages to the membrane induced by the D1-protein degradation and it has not been possible to link it to any light induced changes of the ATP-

synthase. A general membrane damage induced by high light can not be excluded as the reason for the proton leakiness. However, the loss of the Δ-pH occured very rapidly even at moderate light intensities and general membrane damages such as lipid peroxidation are known to be late events during light stress of chloroplasts (10). Experiments are in progress to determine the quality of light giving rise to the loss of the trans-thylakoid proton gradient.

The build-up of a Δ-pH across the thylakoid membrane has recently been emphasized as an important mechanistic factor for creation of the so called qE-quenching state, which is thought to be essential for protection of the photosynthetic apparatus against light stress. (11, 12). Moreover, an increased Δ-pH has recently been measured in intact *Chlamydomonas* cells during photoinhibition (13). However, over the last 15 years, several reports on both increased(11-13) and decreased (14-16) Δ-pH under light stress conditions have been presented. Obviously, changes in the proton translocation across the thylakoid membrane during light stress require further detailed analyses.

The significance of our present results of rapid loss of Δ-pH and photophosphorylation with respect to photoinhibition of plants remains to be established.

5. ACKNOWLEDGEMENTS

We thank the Swedish Natural Science Research Council and the Göran Gustafsson Foundation for generous support.

REFERENCES

1 Prasil, O., Adir, N. and Ohad, I. (1992) in Topics in Photosynthesis (Barber, J., ed.), Vol 11, pp. 220-250, Elsevier, Amsterdam

2 Barber, J. and Andersson B. (1992) Trends Biochem. Sci. 17, 61-66

3 Inoue, K., Sakurai, H. and Hiyama, T. (1986) Plant Cell Physiol. 27, 961-968.

4 Bartlett, S.G., Grossman, A.R. and Chua, N.-H. (1982) in Methods in Chloroplast Molecular Biology (Edelman, M., Hallick, R.B. and Chua, N.H., Eds.) pp. 1081-1092, Elsevier, Amsterdam.

5 Andersson, B., Åkerlund, H.-E. and Albertsson, P.-Å. (1976) Biochim Biophys Acta 423, 122-132

6 Lundin, A., Thore, A. and Baltscheffsky, M. (1977) FEBS Lett. 79, 73-76

7 Towbin, H., Staehlin, T. and Gordon J. (1979) Proc. Natl. Acad. Sci. USA 76, 4350-4353

8 Arntz, B. and Trebst, A. (1986) FEBS Lett. 194, 43-49

9 Curviel, V.B. and Van Rensen, J.J.S. (1992) Abstracts FESPP Workshop on the Environmental Factors Affecting Photosystem II, p 46, Szeged, Hungary

10 Hundal, T., Forsmark, P., Ernster, L. and Andersson, B. (1992) Abstracts FESPP Workshop on the Environmental Factors Affecting Photosystem II, p 38, Szeged, Hungary

11 Krause, G.H. and Behrend, U. (1986) FEBS Lett. 200, 298-302

12 Oxborough, K. and Horton P. (1988) Biochim. Biophys. Acta 934, 135-143

13 Topf, J., Gong,H., Timberg,R., Metz, L. and Ohad, I. (1992) Photosynth. Res. 32, 59-69

14 Garber, P.J. (1977) Plant Physiol. 59, 981-985

15 Stark, B.C. and Uribe, E.G. (1981) Arch. Biochem. Biophys. 209, 471-479

16 Wu, J., Neimanis, S. and Heber, U. (1991) Bot. Acta 104, 283-291

MEASUREMENTS OF PHOTOSYNTHETIC EFFICIENCY AND PHOTOINHIBITION OF PHYTOPLANKTON BY FLUORESCENCE MEASUREMENTS USING THE SATURATING PULSE METHOD

C. GEEL[1], J.F.H. SNEL[1], J.W. HOFSTRAAT[2] AND J.H.C. PEETERS[2]. DEPARTMENT OF PLANT PHYSIOLOGICAL RESEARCH, WAGENINGEN AGRICULTURAL UNIVERSITY, GEN. FOULKESWEG 72, WAGENINGEN, THE NETHERLANDS[1], TIDAL WATERS DIVISION, PUBLIC WORKS DEPARTMENT, P.O. BOX 20907, NL 2500 EX THE HAGUE, THE NETHERLANDS[2].

1. INTRODUCTION

Fluorescence has proved to be an important tool in phytoplankton research. It has been used for rough taxa identification as algae contain several pigments most of which have a function in photosynthesis (1). Chlorophyll fluorescence has also been used for the estimation of phytoplankton biomass although the correlation between fluorescence yield and chlorophyll concentrations is not always good (2). The photosynthetic apparatus can respond rapidly to changes in the environmental circumstances. These adaptations influence the fluorescence yield.

Photochemical quenching of chlorophyll fluorescence gives information on the redox state of photosystem II. The maximal efficiency of PS2 $(F_V/F_M)=(F_M-F_0)/F_M$ can be determined by measuring the fluorescence yield in the dark adapted state (F_0) and during a short saturating light pulse (F_M). The actual efficiency of photosystem II (Φ_P) is determined *in situ* by measuring the fluorescence in the light adapted state (F) and during a short saturating light pulse $(F_{M'})$: $\Phi_P=(F_{M'}-F)/F_{M'}$ (3). This method has proved to be valuable with higher plants and might be applied to phytoplankton research as well. Important differences are the multiple species within a single field sample, the presence of varying pigments and usually very low chlorofyll concentration (< 0.1 μg/ml).

2. MATERIALS and METHODS

The chlorophyte *Dunaliella tertiolecta* was grown at 15 °C in a f/2 medium under a 14 h light/ 10 h dark cycle (4). The algae were grown in 6 batch cultures at different light intensities (42.1, 66.0, 92.3, 107.4, 137.3 and 214.3 μmol m^{-2} s^{-1}). The growth rate was determined with a custom-built flow cytometer measuring the concentration of particles emitting red fluorescence (>670 nm) upon 528 nm excitation with an Ar-ion laser (5).

Fluorescence was measured with a PAM fluorometer using the MKS-101 cuvette (H. Walz, Effeltrich, FRG.). Fluorescence could not be measured from the beginning of the experiment as the detection limit of our set-up was about 10^6 cells ml^{-1}. From day 3 on thin samples were concentrated by centrifuging for 5 min at 4500 rpm and from day 8-10 samples were measured without concentration. Measurements were done daily, starting 3 hours after the light in the incubator had been switched on. We chose this time to allow cells to adapt to the light. Fluorescence was measured at a pho-

N. Murata (ed.), Research in Photosynthesis, Vol. IV, 525–528.

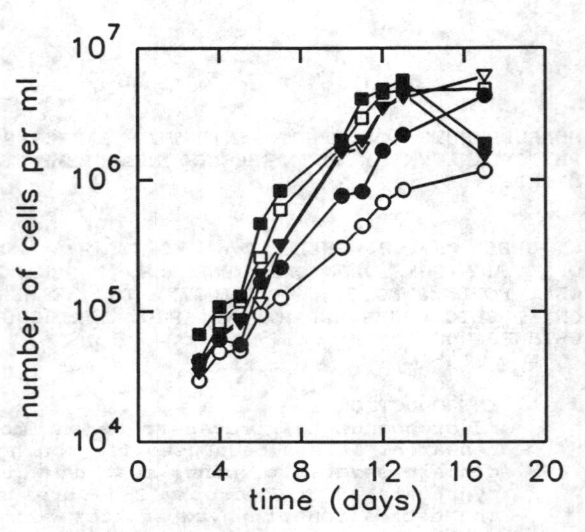

FIGURE 1. Growth of *Dunaliella tertiolecta* in batch culture as a function of incubation time. Photon flux density during growth: 42.1 (○), 66.0 (●), 92.3 (▿), 107.4 (▾), 137.3 (□) and 214.3 (■) μmol m^{-2} s^{-1}.

ton flux density which was identical to the light conditions in the incubator. F_0 and F_M were determined after 15 minutes dark adaptation. An error was introduced as the cultures were grown at white light and the fluorescence measurement was based upon absorption at 650 nm. However for *Dunaliella tertiolecta* this error is not large as the 650 nm excitation light coincides with the absorption maximum of the main photosynthetic pigment (chlorophyll a) in this alga.

3. RESULTS and DISCUSSION

In fig. 1 the number of cells is given as a function of the incubation time. The cells grow exponentially and the growth rate is dependent on the light intensity. The lowest growth rate is observed at the lowest light intensity. At the highest light intensity the stationary state is reached somewhere around day 10, probably because nutrients become limiting. Because of the detection limit of 10^6 cells/ml the efficiency of photosystem II electron transport could only be measured from day 8-10 depending on the incubation light intensity (see fig. 1). In fig. 2a Φ_P of various cultures is given as a function of the photon flux density at day 11, 12, 13 and 17. It can be seen that Φ_P is high (0,6-0,7) at day 11, when all cultures are in a more or less exponential phase. At days 12, 13 and 17 Φ_P is decreasing. Especially for the higher light intensities this effect is large. Comparing fig. 2a with fig. 1 it can be seen that a low value of Φ_P is only observed when the culture is in the steady state or in a decline phase.

In fig. 2b F_V/F_M which is said to be correlated with photoinhibition is given as a function of the light intensity for the same days as in fig. 2a. At day 11 F_V/F_M is high in all cultures indicating that no photoinhibition occured in this photon flux density range from 40 to 200 μmol m^{-2} s^{-1}. However as the exponential growth of the cultures stops, F_V/F_M is decreasing. At the

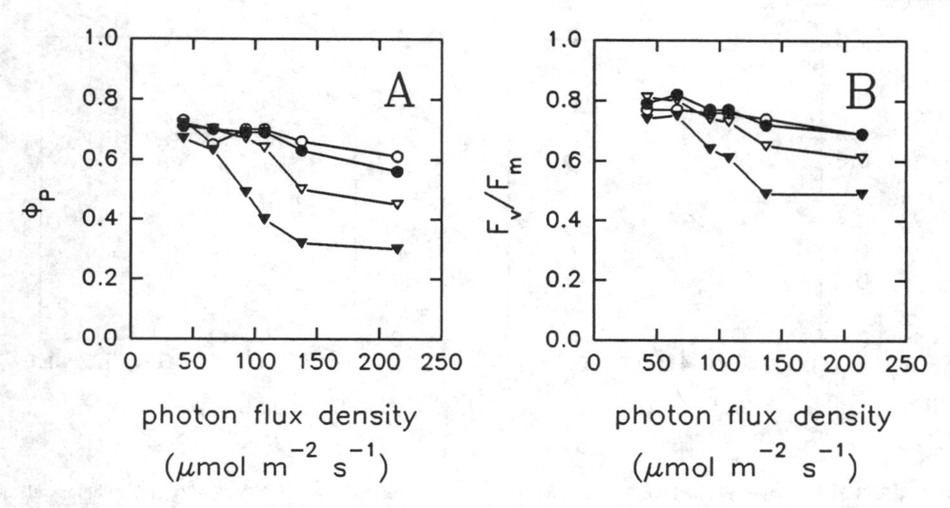

FIGURE 2. Photosynthetic efficiency Φ_P (A) and F_V/F_M (B) as a function of the irradiance of the culture measured at days 11 (○), 12 (●), 13 (▿) and 17 (▾).

highest light intensity F_V/F_M is decreasing from 0.69 at day 11 to 0.49 at day 17. It is not clear why this photoinhibitory effect is only observed in the stationairy phase. May be it does occur in the exponential phase but is the damage continuously repaired. However for F_V/F_M we can not exclude the effect of chlororespiration. Chlororespiration is shown to increase drastically in *Chlamydomonas reinhardtii* as they are nitrogen limited (6). Chlororespiration influences the redox state of the PQ pool and so it could have increased F_0 in the dark.

As can been seen in figs. 2a en b, Φ_P and F_V/F_M seem to be correlated. This relationship is checked in fig. 3. The efficiency of photosystem II at *in situ* light conditions is always lower than the efficiency of photosystem II in the dark adapted state due to photochemical and non-photochemical quenching.

Figure 4 shows the relation between Φ_P and the growth rate of the cultures. At the lowest light intensity the efficincy Φ_P and the growthrate show only little variation. At the higher light intensities there is little variation in efficiency Φ_P and more in the growthrate but the two do not seem te be correlated.

Although Φ_P and F_V/F_M seem to be related to the physiological state of the algae (combining fig. 1 with fig. 2a) we were not able to find a clear correlation with the growthrate of the culture (fig. 4). The fact that Φ_P is high at all photon flux densities in the exponentially growing cultures suggests that *Dunaliella tertiolecta* is able to adaptate its photosynthetic apparatus in this range of photon flux densities to obtain a maximal efficiency. This adaptation is probably realised for one part by decreasing the number of LHCII complexes (an increase in the chlorophyll a/b ratio of 6 % was found, unpublished results) and decreasing the absorption cross-section (a decrease in chlorophyll content per cell of a factor 2 was found from 40 to 200 $\mu mol\ m^{-2}\ s^{-1}$, unpublished results). However as nutrients become limiting the efficiency is reducing as a consequence of a changed

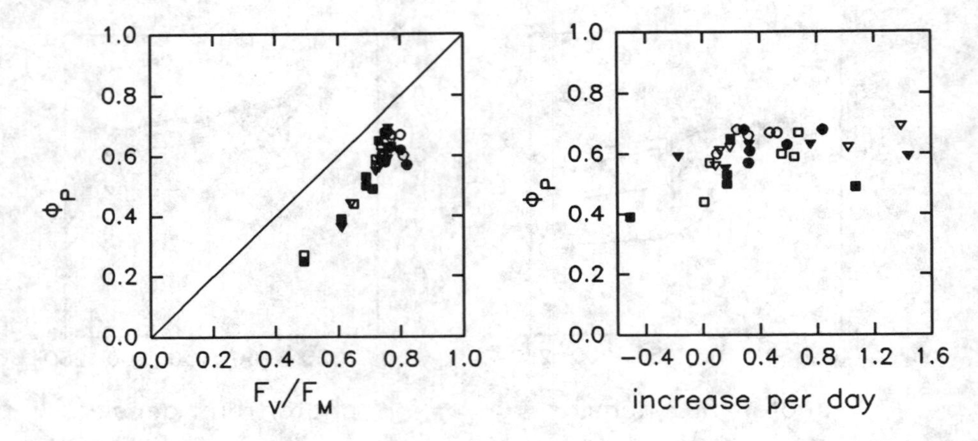

FIGURE 3 (left). Photosynthetic efficiency Φ_P as a function of F_V/F_M. **FIGURE 4** (right). Photosynthetic efficiency Φ_P of the cultures as a function of the growthrate defined as $(N_{x+1}-N_x)/N_x$. N_x is the number of cells per ml at day x. The symbols correspond with the symbols for the cultures as in figure 1. This are the data of all the different light intensities on all measured days.

metabolism in which other processes (for example chlororespiration) may become important.

REFERENCES

1 Hilton, J., Rigg, E. and Jaworski, G. (1989), J. Plankton Res. 11, 65-74

2 Falkowski, P. and Kiefer, D.A. (1985), J. Plankton Res. 7, 715-731

3 Genty, B., Briantais, J.-M. and Baker, N.R. (1989), Biochim. Biophys. Acta 990, 87-92

4 Hofstraat, J.W. van Zeijl, W.J.M., Peeters, J.H.C., Peperzak, L. and Dubelaar, G.B.J. (1990) In: Environment and Pollution Measurement Sensors and Systems (H.O. Nielsen, ed), SPIE Proceedings 1269, 116-133

5 Hofstraat, J.W., Peeters, J.H.C., Snel, J.F.H. and Geel, C. J.Phycology (submitted)

6 Peltier, G. and Schmidt, G.W. (1991) Proc. Natl. Sci. vol 88, 4791-4795

SEPARATE ASSAYS OF ASCORBATE PEROXIDASE AND GUAIACOL PEROXIDASE AND OF CHLOROPLASTIC AND CYTOSOLIC ISOZYMES OF ASCORBATE PEROXIDASE

Katsumi Amako and Kozi Asada, The Research Institute for Food Science, Kyoto University, Uji, Kyoto 611, Japan

1. INTRODUCTION

AsA peroxidase (APX) plays a role in scavenging of hydrogen peroxide in chloroplasts and the other compartments (1). Guaiacol peroxidase (GPX) participates in a great array of physiological processes such as lignin biosynthesis and development and organogenesis through the degradation of IAA or biosynthesis of ethylene. Because APX and GPX can oxidize both AsA and pyrogallol, the assays of two peroxidases by the respective electron donors doesn't give a reliable value. In addition, APX has three isozymes localized in thylakoid membrane (tAPX), stroma (sAPX) and cytosol (cAPX) (2) (3). To understand the physiological functions of APX and GPX and of APX isozymes their separate assays is essential. We show simple methods for separate assays of APX and GPX and of soluble (sAPX and cAPX) with their different sensitivities to a thiol modifying reagent and to the inactivation in the AsA-depleted medium, and surveyed about their distribution plant tissues.

2. MATERIALS AND METHODS

Tea leaves (Camellia sinesis cv. Yabukita) were kindly supplied by the Tea Research Institute of Kyoto Prefecture. Spinach was purchased from a local market. Other plants were grown in vermiculite for 2 weeks in a growth chamber at 20 °C under fluorescence lamps (5,000 lx). Isozymes I and II of APX purified from tea leaves (2) are referred to as cAPX and sAPX, respectively. The tissues (2 g in fresh weight) were homogenized in cooled mortar and pestle with 5 ml of the homogenizing medium (1 mM ascorbic acid (AsA)/1 mM EDTA/50 mM potassium phosphate, pH 7.0) filtered through a cheesecloth and centrifuged at 10,000 x g for 10 min. Sorbitol was added to the supernatant to 20% (w/v) for stabilization of APX. The supernatant (2 ml) was gel-filtrated through a column of Sephadex G-25 (1.5 x 5.0 cm) with 0.1 mM AsA/1 mM EDTA/20% (w/v) sorbitol /50 mM potassium phosphate (pH 7.0) and eluted by the same medium and a high molecular weight fraction (3.5 ml) was used as the extract. The peroxidase activity with either AsA or pyrogallol as the electron donors was determined using a reaction mixture that contained 50 mM potassium phosphate (pH 7.0)/0.5 mM hydrogen peroxide/1 mM AsA or 20 mM pyrogallol/enzyme. The enzyme should be added to the reaction mixture which contains AsA or pyrogallol, otherwise APX is

N. Murata (ed.), Research in Photosynthesis, Vol. IV, 529–532.

inactivated in absence of the electron donors. The reaction was started by the addition of hydrogen peroxide, and the oxidation rate of AsA was determined according to (2).

3. RESULTS AND DISCUSSIONS

3.1 Interference of low molecular weight components in the homogenate on the oxidation rate of AsA: Effects of low molecular weight components in the homogenate on peroxidase assay were tested (Table 1). The oxidation rate of AsA after the gel-filtration (AF).

Table 1 Interference of low molecular compounds contained in the extract from tea leaves on the oxidation rate of AsA. Where indicated, the extract was gel-filtered as described in MATERIALS AND METHODS. GPX (160 μg), the extract (protein 60 μg) or their mixture was assayed under the APX-assay conditions.

Protein	Gel-filtration	Oxidation rate of AsA (n=3) (nmol AsA oxidized min^{-1} ±s.d.)	Change by mixing
(1) GPX		30.0 ± 0.7	
(2) Extract	−	56.0 ± 2.1	
(3) GPX + Extract	−	164.4 ± 5.7	(1)+(2)−(3) = −78.4
(4) Extract	+	61.0 ± 2.5	
(5) GPX + Extract	+	90.7 ± 0.7	(1)+(4)−(5) = − 0.3

was a little higher than that before gel-filtration (BF) in the same amount of protein. By addition of GPX as external standard, BF was amplified but AF was equal to the sum of the oxidation rate of GPX and the extract. These phenomena were not seen using pyrogallol instead of AsA. These results show that gel-filtration is indespensable for the assay of peroxidases.

3.2 Separate assay of APX and GPX: tAPX from spinach, sAPX and cAPX from tea leaves are inactivated by pCMB, whereas GPX is little affected by it (2)(3). Horseradish peroxidase isozyme (C-I, C-II, type-IV) and the peroxidase from the fungus <u>Coprinus cinereus</u> also weren't affected by pCMB. GPX so far sequenced have the conserved eight half-cystines which forms four disulfides and the insensitivity to pCMB is expected (4). In contrast to GPX, cAPX and sAPX so far sequenced have no half-cystine residue corresponding to the conserved positions of GPX (5)(6)(7). In these results, the difference in inhibitory effect of pCMB between APX and GPX has been guaranteed by their amino acid sequences. Validity of the separate assay by pCMB was supported by APX-specific inactivation by both the antibody against sAPX from tea leaves and suicide inhibitor of APX, hydroxylamine (8).

3.3 Recommended procedure for separate assay of APX and GPX: The extract was assayed for the oxidation rate of AsA (A). Then, the oxidation rates of AsA (B) and pyrogallol (C) of the extract were assayed 10 min after its incubation with 0.2 mM pCMB. The pCMB-sensitive rate of AsA oxidation ((A)−(B)) and the pCMB-insensitive rate of pyrogallol oxidation (C) represent the activities of APX and GPX, respectively.

This procedure was applied to leaf and root tissues of several plants (Table 2). APX is the major peroxidase in leaf tissues. GPX activities were high in roots compared with those in leaf tissues,

Table 2 The content of APX isozymes and GPX. The molecular weights and specific activities of guaiacol peroxidase and AsA peoxidase of 34800 and 1460 μmol pyrogallol oxidizing mg protein^{-1} (9), 34000 and 580 μmol AsA oxidizing mg protein^{-1} (2), respectively.

		GPX (nmol mg protein^{-1})	APX (nmol mg protein^{-1})	Molar ratio (GPX/APX)	APX content cAPX (%)	APX content sAPX (%)	tAPX activity (+/-)
Cucumber	leaves	6.8	10.6	0.64	70	30	n. d.
	roots	33.8	28.4	1.19	90	10	
Pea	leaves	12.4	7.1	1.76	60	40	n. d.
	roots	51.7	17.8	2.90	95	5	
Spinach	chloroplasts	n. d.	n. d.	n. d.	0	100	+
	leaves	1.9	5.0	0.38	35	65	+
	roots	8.8	13.7	0.64	15	85	
Tea	leaves	8.8	24.9	0.35	25	75	+
Rice	leaves	n. d.	n. d.	n. d.	65	35	+
	roots	n. d.	n. d.	n. d.	95	5	
Maize	leaves	n. d.	n. d.	n. d.	80	20	+
	roots	n. d.	n. d.	n. d.	85	15	
Equisetum arvense		n. d.	n. d.	n. d.	80	20	+
Euglena gracilis		0.6	3.1	0.19	100	0	n. d.
Chlamydomonas reinhardtii		n. d.	n. d.	n. d.	100	0	–

n. d. :not determined

though at least 80% of AsA oxidation and 25% of pyrogallol oxidation were accounted for by APX.

3.4 Separate assays of sAPX and cAPX: When the concentration of AsA is below 20 μM, sAPX and cAPX are inactivated, but GPX is not. Half inactivation of sAPX and cAPX from tea leaves require 40 s and 40 min, respectively (2). These properties enable the separate assay of sAPX and cAPX. The extracts from intact chloroplasts, leaves and roots from spinach showed different kinetics of inactivation of APX (Fig. 1).

Fig. 1 The time course of oxidation rate of AsA by intact chloroplasts, matured leaves and roots from spinach in AsA-depleted medium. The incubation was started to 50-fold dilute the enzyme extract containing 0.1 mM AsA/50 mM potassium phosphate (pH 7.0). The inactivation in AsA-depleted medium was stopped by addition of AsA to 1 mM in each periods.

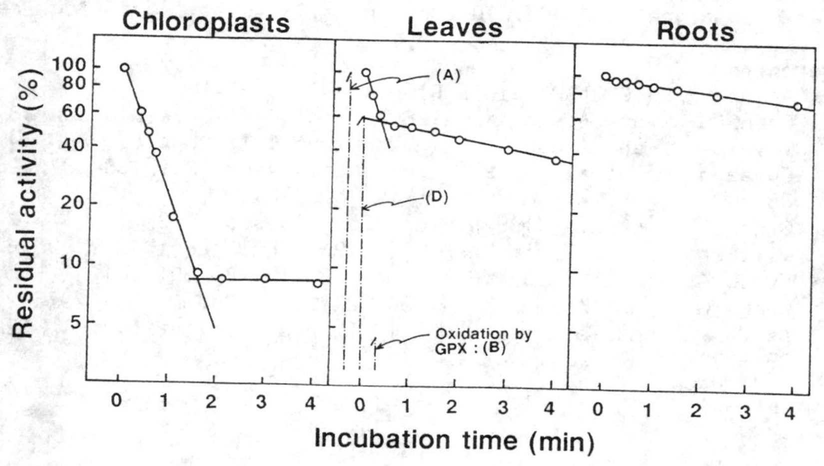

By dilution of AsA in the extract to 2 μM, APX was inactivated with pseudo-first order kinetics. The inactivation could be stopped by adding AsA to 1 mM, and the activity of APX was stable at least 15 min after the addition of AsA. In intact chloroplasts a single, rapid phase, in roots a single, slow phase, and in leaves two phases of inactivation of APX was observed. Because the residual activity in intact chloroplasts 2 min after the dilution was heat-stable, it seemed to be non-enzymatic oxidation. The half times of fast and slow phases in leaves were corresponded to those of chloroplasts and roots, respectively, which suggests that the fast phase represents sAPX, and the slow phase cAPX.

3.5 Recommended procedure of separate assay of sAPX and cAPX: First, the oxidation rates of AsA in the absence (A) and presence (B) of pCMB are determined as described above. The extracts (100 μl) are diluted 50-fold by 50 mM potassiu,m phosphate (pH 7.0) to lower the concentration of AsA to 2 μM. At 2, 3 and 4 min after the dilution, 940 μl of diluted extract is added to 50 μl of 20 mM AsA/50 mM potassium phosphate (pH 7.0) to terminate the inactivation. Residual oxidizing activity of AsA are assayed by adding 10 μl of 50 mM hydrogen peroxide/50 mM potassium phosphate (pH 7.0), and plotted as in Fig. 1. The value of the intercept of the vertical axis (D) is estimated. ((D)-(B)) is regarded as cAPX, and ((A)-(D)) sAPX.

The extracts from other plant tissues were tested using the above procedure (Table 2). In all plants, more chloroplastic APX was in leaves than in roots. 5-15% of sAPX was monitored in roots of each plant, which suggested that sAPX-like isozymes was localized in the other organella than chloroplast, for example, plastids and mithocondoria.

The eukariotic algae, <u>Euglena gracilis</u> and <u>Chlamydomonas reinhardtii</u>, showed over 95% of cAPX though they have chloroplasts. <u>C. reihardtii</u> had no tAPX activity, while leaves in higer plants examined had tAPX. cAPX may be at first acquired within the stage of eukariotic algae in the evolution, and sAPX is at second acquired.

References

1. Asada, K. (1992) Physiol. Plant. 85, 235-241
2. Chen, G-X. and Asada, K. (1989) Plant Cell Physiol. 30, 987-998
3. Miyake, C. and Asada, K. (1992) Plant Cell Physiol. 33, 541-553
4. Bufaard, D. et al. (1990) Proc. Natl. Acad. Sci. USA 87, 8874-8878
5. Chen, G-X. et al. (1992) Plant Cell Physiol. 33, 109-116
6. Mittler, R. and Zilinskas, BA. (1991) FEBS Lett. 289, 257-259
7. Kubo, A. et al. (1992) Plant Mol. Biol. 18, 691-701
8. Chen, G-X. and Asada, K. (1990) J. Biol. Chem. 265, 2775-2781
9. Asada, K. and Takahashi, M. (1971) Plant Cell. Physiol. 12, 361-375

MOLECULAR PROPERTIES OF MONODEHYDROASCORBATE REDUCTASE

Satoshi Sano and Kozi Asada, The Reserach Insutitute for Food Science, Kyoto University, Uji, Kyoto 611, Japan

1. INTRODUCTION

Monodehydroascorbate (MDA) reductase (EC 1.6.5.4) catalyzes the reduction of MDA using NAD(P)H. MDA reductase, occurring in chloroplast stroma, regenerates ascorbate from MDA radical, produced by ascorbate peroxidase and thus plays a key role in the scavenging system for hydrogen peroxide [1,2] MDA reductase is the first enzyme whose substrate is an organic radical.

Cucumber MDA reductase is a soluble monomeric enzyme of Mr 47,000, which contains 1 mol of FAD/mol. In addition to MDA, the enzyme catalyzes the reduction of ferricyanide and dichlorophenolindophenol but shows little reactivity with cytochromes $\underline{b}_5$ and $\underline{c}$ [3]. The activity of MDA reductase has been shown to be inhibited by thiol reagents, suggesting that the cysteine residue(s) participates in the reaction as elucidated in other flavin-containing oxidoreductase. [4]

Comparison of MDA reductase with other flavin-containing oxidoreductase will provide the useful information to clarify the reaction mechanism of MDA reductase. For this reason we intended to isolatea cDNA encoding MDA reductase to determine the primary structure of MDA reductase.

2. MATERIALS AND METHODS

Highly purified MDA reductase was obtained from 100 kg of cucumber (Cucumis sativus) fruits as described previouly [3] with an additional affinity chromatography as follows; the active fractions obtained after the Blue Sepharose step were pooled and concentrated by ultrafiltration through a PM 10 membrane (Amicon) and desalted by passing through a PD-10 Column (Pharmacia LKB). This solution was loaded on a column of 5' AMP-Sepharose 4B (Pharmacia LKB) equilibrated with 10 mM potassium phosphate, pH 7.0, containing 10 mM 2-mercaptoethanol and 0.1 mM EDTA. The enzyme was eluted from the column by linear concentration gradient of NADH (0-2 mM) in the above buffer. Active fractions were pooled and concentrated by ultrafiltration. The MDA reductase purified to homogeneity was digested with Achromobacter lysyl endopeptidase (Wako chemicals). The peptide fragments were separated and sequenced as described previously. [5]

N. Murata (ed.), Research in Photosynthesis, Vol. IV, 533–536.

A cDNA libraly made from cucumber seedling mRNA in the expression vector, λ22A, was a gift from Dr. Keinji Matsui (Yamaguchi University). The library was immunoscreened according to Mierendorf et al. [6]. Antisera of immunized rabbit against cucumber MDA reductase was used as the primary antibody. The isolated cDNA inserts of the λ phage clones were analysed by Southern blotting. A mixture of the 12 possible oligonucleotides (probe 1) consisting of 5'-TTDATCCARTAIGTICCRAA-3' and a mixture of 19 possible oligonucleotides (probe 2) consisting of 5'-TTRTCICCRTARAAYTGCCA-3' (D= G, A or T; R= G or A; and Y= C or T) were synthesized. Probes 1 and 2 represent DNA sequences complementary to all possible coding sequences for two regions of MDA reductase; FGTYWIK (peptide 18-4) and WQFYGDN (a part of peptide 37). Probes were labelled and hybridyzed membranes were detected using 3' ECL oligilabelling and detection system (Amersham). The cDNA inserts of the λ phage clones were subcloned into the plasmid pBluescript (Stratagene). The double stranded DNA templates were sequenced by the dideoxy chain-termination method on an ABI Model 370A sequencer (Applied Biosystems) with Taq DNA polymerase and dye primers. Sequences were analyzed using DNASIS computer software (Hitachi Software Engineering).

A search was made for proteins that were homologous to the peptides and the amino acid sequence deduced cDNA of MDA reductase on a FACOM M/10 computer using the program IDEAS (Institute for Chemical Research, Kyoto University).

3. RESULTS and DISCUSSION

3.1. Amino acid sequence of cucumber MDA reductase

The amino acid sequences were determined for 9 peptide fragments of MDA reductase obtained by digestion with lysyl endopeptidase. Sequences containing a total of 164 residues were determined (Fig. 1), which represented 37% of total 442 residues of MDA reductase, as deduced from the molecular weight and amino acid composition of the enzyme. [2] The amino terminal residue of MDA reductase could not be determined on the protein sequencer, which indicates the modification of the amino terminus of this enzyme.

The amino acid sequences of peptides 21 and 30 of MDA reductase showed a high degree of homology to other flavin-containing oxioreductase (Fig. 2) [7-19]. Peptide 21 aligned well with one of the two segments in human glutathione reductase which has been shown to make contacts with FAD [7]. The same arrangement of FAD binding domains has been found in other flavin-containing oxidoreductase.

Peptide number	
10	EAVAP YERPA LSK
15	LYNEL RRVEH VDHAR LK
18-4	FGTYW IK
18-5	VARVQ PPVES LDQLA K
18-6	VVGVF LEGGT PDEY
21	TSIPD VYAGD VATYP LK
30	LKDGR TLDAD IVVVG VGGRP LVSLF K
33	NIFYL REIAD ADQLV EAK
37	SIEEY DYLPY FYSRT FNLAW QFYGD NVGET VLFPD N

Fig. 1 Amino Acid Sequences of peptides derived from MDA reductase of cucumber.

Peptide 21	**TSIPDVYAVGDVATYPLK**	
Human GSH reductase (321-339)	TNVKGI**YAVGDV**CGKA**L**L	[6]
E.coli GSH reductase (293-311)	**T**N**I**EGI**YAVGD**NTGAVEL	[7]
Trypanothione reductase (318-336)	**T**NVPNI**YA**I**GDV**TGRIML	[8]
Human dihydrolipoamide DH (345-363)	**T**KIPNI**YA**I**GDV**VAG**P**ML	[9]
E.coli dihydrolipoamide DH (302-320)	**T**NV**P**HIF**A**I**GD**IVGQ**P**ML	[10]
P.putida toluene reductase (265-283)	**T**LAKG**V**F**AVGDVA**SW**PL**R	[11]
E.coli NADH DH (305-326)	**T**DD**PD**I**YA**I**GD**C**A**SCPRP	[12]
Pea lipoamide DH (348-366)	**T**NVSG**V**V**A**I**GDV**IPG**P**ML	[13]
Peptide 30	**LKDGRTLDADIVVVGVGGRPLVSLFK**	
P.putida GSH reductase (245-271)	**LKDGR**VLE**AD**C**V**FYAT**G**R**RP**MLDDLG	[14]
E.coli GSH reductase (124-150)	EVN**G**E**T**IT**AD**HILIAT**GGRP**SHPDIP	[7]
Pea GSH reductase (213-239)	D**V**D**G**KLYS**A**KHIL**V**S**VGGRP**FIPDIP	[15]
Trypanothione reductase (270-296)	FES**GKTLD**V**D**V**V**MMAI**G**RL**P**RTGYLQ	[8]
E.coli dihydrolipoamide DH (273-299)	VPN**G**KN**LDA**G**V**E**V**DDR**G**FIRVDKQLR	[10]
P.putida toluene reductase (92-118)	LD**DG**TT**L**S**AD**AI**V**IAT**G**S**R**ARTMALP	[11]
Putidaredoxin reductase (95-121)	LS**DGR**A**LD**Y**D**RL**V**LAT**GGRP**RPLPVA	[16]
P.vulgaris fumarate reductase (1-22)	----Q**T**FN**ADI**AII**G**A**GG**AG**L**RAAIA	[17]
E.coli nitrate reductase (226-252)	FA**DG**SE**L**EV**D**FI**V**FST**G**I**RP**RDKLAT	[18]

Fig. 2 Comparison of Amino Acid Sequences between Peptide 21 and 30 from MDA Reductase and flavin-containing oxidoreductase: Residues matched with residues of peptides of MDA reductase are bold.

The amino acid sequences of peptides 30 and 37 showed a homology to the subunit 5 of mitochondrial NADH dehydrogenase of Chlamydomonas reinhardtii [20], but not to the subunit 5 of chloroplastic NADH dehydrogenase of higher plants [21, 22]. NADH dehydrogenase contains one FMN and several Fe-S clusters, consisting of about 30 subunits, but the subunit 5 is unlikely responsible for the binding of flavin or Fe-S [23]. This homologous region is expected to participate in making the NAD(P)H binding region.

3.2. cDNA cloning of MDA reductase

About 6 x 10^5 recombinant λ phage plaques from a cucumber cDNA library were primarily screened with antisera, and 7 positive clones were isolated. These clones were subjected to Southern blot analysis, and three clones were hybridized with both probes 1 and 2.

The inserts of three individual clones were subcloned into the pBluescript, giving pCMR11, pCMR31 and pCMR91. The insert of pCMR11 was sequenced completely, and the 3'-terminal portions of inserts of pCMR31 and pCMR91 were sequenced. These three cDNAs had poly(A) track, and the common polyadenylation/processing signal, 5'-AATAAA-3', was located 18-nt upstream in pCMR11 and pCMR91 and 29-nt upstream in pCMR31 from the poly(A) track. No sequence difference was observed on pCMR11 and the 3'-terminal portion of pCMR31 and pCMR91, except the additional sequence of upstream from the poly(A) track of pCMR31. Thus, they were derived from the mRNA species transcribed on the same locus of cucumber genome.

The nucleotide sequence determined contained an reading frame of the carboxy terminus of MDA reductase. The amino acid sequence deduced from nucleotide sequence of reading frame, aligned with the amino acid sequences of 4 peptide fragments of MDA reductase, the peptide 18-4, 18-5, 18-3 and 37, but did not agree completely (Fig. 3). Eighteen residues of 73 amino acid residues of the peptide fragments aer different from the deduced amino acid sequence. These discrepancies are probably ascribed to the occurrence of isozymes of MDA reductase in cucumber [3]

The predicted amino acid sequence from the nucleotide sequence of the inserts pCMR11 and 3' portion of pCMR 31 and 91 did not show homology to any other proteins searched.

```
                         10                  20                  30                  40
        R G K A I E E Y D Y L P Y F Y S R S F D L S W Q F Y G D N V G D A V L F G D N S
                : : : : : : : : : : : : :   :   :   : : : : : : : : :     : : :   : :
           37)S I E E Y D Y L P Y F Y S R T F N L A W Q F Y G D N V G E T V L F P D N

                         50                  60                  70                  80
        P D S A T H K F G S Y W I K D G K V V G A F L E S G S P E E N K A I A K V A R I
                      : :   : : : :       : : :   : : :   :   :   :               : :
                 18-4)F G T Y W I K  18-6)V V G V F L E G G T P D E Y      18-5)V A R V

                         90                 100
        Q P S V E S S D L L L K E G I S F A S K V
        : :   : : :   :   :   :
        Q P P V E S L D Q L A K
```

Fig. 3 Alignment of amino acid sequences deduced from cDNA and derived from peptides of MDA reductase from cucumber: Upper rows, amino acid sequence deduced from cDNA of MDA reductase; lower rows, amino acid sequence derived from peptides of MDA reductase

REFERENCES

[1] Hossain, M. A. et al. (1984) Plant Cell Physiol. 25, 385-395

[2] Nakano, Y. & Asada, K (1981) Plant Cell Physiol. 22, 867-880

[3] Hossain, M. A. & Asada, K. (1985) J. Biol. Chem. 25, 12920-12926

[4] Schirmer, R. H. & Schulz, G. E. (1987) in Coenzymes and Cofactors, Vol. 2B: Pyridine Nucleotide Coenzymes: Chemical, Biochemical and Medical Aspects (Dalphin, D., Poulson, R., & Avramovic, O., eds) pp. 333-379, John Wiley & Sons, New York

[5] Chen, G.-X. et al. (1992) Plant Cell Physiol. 33, 109-116

[6] Mierendorf, R. C. et al. (1987) Methods in Enzymol., 152

[7] Krauth-Siegal, R. L. et al. (1982) Eur. J. Biochem. 121, 259-267

[8] Greer, S. & Perham, R. N. (1986) Biochemistry 25, 2736-2742

[9] Shames, S. L. et al. (1988) Biochemistry 27, 5014-5019

[10] Otulakowski, G. & Robinson, B. H. (1987) J. Biol. Chem. 262, 17313-17318

[11] Stephens, P. E. et al. (1983) Eur. J. Biochem. 135, 519-527

[12] Zylstra, G. J. & Gibson, D. T. (1989) J. Biol. Chem. 264, 14940-14946

[13] Young, I. G. et al. (1981) Eur. J. Biochem. 116, 165-170

[14] Turner, S. R. st al. submitted to the EMBL Data Library, Nov. 1991

[15] Perry, A. C. F. et al. (1991) Mol. Miclobiol. 5, 163-171

[16] Creissen, G. submitted to the EMBL Data Library, Aug. 1991

[17] Koga, H et al. (1989) J. Biochem. 106, 831-836

[18] Cole, S. T. (1987) Eur. J. Biochem. 167, 481-488

[19] Bell, A. I. et al. (1989) Nucleic Acids Res. 17, 3865-3874

[20] Boer, P. H. & Gray, M., W. (1986) EMBO J. 5, 21-28

[21] Kohchi, K. et al. (1988) J. Mol. Biol. 203, 353-372

[22] Matsubayashi, T. et al. (1987) Mol. Gen. Genet. 210, 385-393

[23] Weiss, H. et al. (1991) Eur. J. Biochem. 197, 563-576

PEROXIDE REMOVAL IN CYANOBACTERIA.

Anat Rozen, Sigal Lechno, Ron Mittler and Elisha Tel-Or
Agricultural Botany, The Hebrew University of Jerusalem, Faculty of Agriculture, P.O.Box 12, Rehovot 76100 ISRAEL.

INTRODUCTION

Recent results on enzymes and substrates involved in the removal of H_2O_2 in the unicellular cyanopbacterium *Synechococcus* R-2 (PCC 7942) are presented. Cyanobacteria were reported to photoproduce H_2O_2 (1) under conditions of low CO_2, high light and low temperatures. Hydroperoxide removal in *Nostoc moscorum* was shown to involve enzymes and substrates of the ascorbate - glutathione pathway (2). Ascorbate content in the chloroplast is 1000 fold higher than in the cyanobacteria (3).

We have investigated peroxide removal in Synechococcus R-2 cells, grown under extreme oxidative conditions. Their growth was followed by short term responses of the components involved in H_2O_2 removal: ascorbate peroxidase, catalase and ascorbate.

RESULTS AND DISCUSSION

1. Ascorbate peroxidase and catalase

Synechococcus R-2 cells grown in batch cultures were found to tolerate and adapt to 5 mM H_2O_2 added to the medium. Ascorbate peroxidase and catalae were shown to remove H_2O_2 in *Nostoc moscorum* (1) and *Synechococcus* R-2 (4). We selected extreme oxidative conditions of 1000μE x m^{-2} x sec^{-1} (twenty fold higher than the regular light growth intensity), H_2O_2 at 20 mM and cummene hydroperoxide at 20 mM which are lethal to the cells.

As shown in table 1, ascorbate peroxidase activity was increased in all three treatments, reaching 3-6 fold increase within 3 hrs. Catalase activity was enhanced by high light intensity and cummene hydroperoxide treatment, but was severely inhibited by H_2O_2. Chloramphenicol inhibited the activity of these enzymes, suggesting overproduction of the enzymes in response to the oxidative stress. *Synechococcus* R-2 cell failed to survive under extreme oxidative shock of 20 mM H_2O_2 and cummene hydroperoxide.

N. Murata (ed.), Research in Photosynthesis, Vol. IV, 537–540.

Table 1

Induction of ascorbate peroxidase and catalase in *Synechococcus* .

Treatment	Ascorbate peroxidase[1]	Catalase[2]
control cells ($50\mu E \times m^{-2} \times sec^{-1}$)	1.4	1.5
high light, 1hr ($1000\mu E\ m^{-2} \times sec^{-1}$)	9	2.9
H_2O_2 20 mM, 1hr	8.5	0.2
Cummene hydroperoxide 20 mM, 1hr	4.8	2.9

100 ml cell cultures were grown on a shaker under light conditions. After 1 hr treatment cells were sonicated and the supernatent was assayed as previously described (2).

[1] μmol asc x mg protein^{-1} x min^{-1}. [2] μmol O_2 x mg protein^{-1} x min^{-1}.

2. Ascorbate content in peroxide stressed cells.

Ascorbate is a substrate of ascorbate peroxidase known to protect and stabilize the plant enzyme (5). Ascorbate may be regenerated from the oxidized form of dehydroascorbate and monodehydroascorbate by specific GSH and NADPH dependent reductases, respectively. Recent survey of the reductases in *Synechococcus* R-2 showed lower activity of ascorbate regenaration as compared to ascorbate oxidation by ascorbate peroxidase (4). Moreover, short term stress experiment with *Synechococcus* cells, incubated with 20 mM H_2O_2 for 1 hr, resulted in the deplition of intracellular ascorbate as determined by the colorimetric assay of Omaya (6), in cell homogenates prepared by sonication in buffer. We have further investigated the status of ascorbate in *Synechococcus* R-2 extracted in metaphosphoric acid protecting ascorbate from cell free oxidation, and cell homogenates were analyzed by HPLC against ascorbate standards (7).

Intracellular ascorbate concentration in cells, grown in batch cultures, was 5-50 μM, which is extremely low compared to the chloroplast content (3).

Peroxide stressed cells of *Synechococcus* R-2 treated for 3 hrs with 5 and 10 mM H_2O_2 in the light showed a two fold increase in ascorbate content, but the changes in the dark were limited (Fig. 1). A much greater increase in ascorbate content was observed in cells treated with H_2O_2 for 24 hrs in the light.

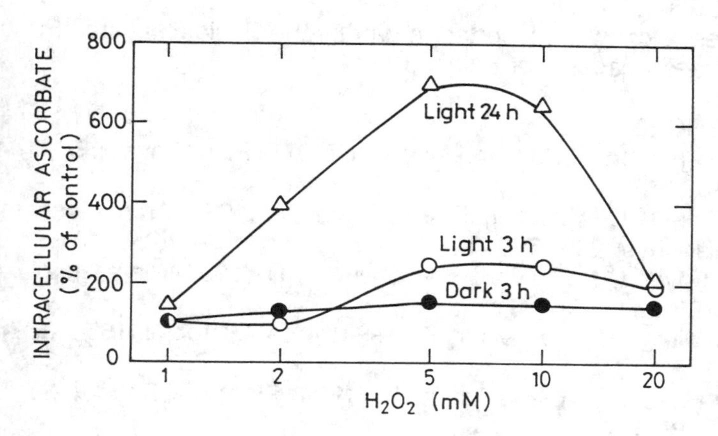

Fig. 1. Effect of H_2O_2 on intracellular ascorbate content in *Synechococcus* R-2.

It is likely that the increase in ascorbate content is due to induction of biosynthesis rather than to regeneration of oxidized ascorbate. The higher concentration of ascorbate in the peroxide stressed cells served as substrate and protectant of ascorbate peroxidase, and may explain cell survival at concentrations below 20 mM H_2O_2.

3. Ascorbate peroxidase active component (APAC).

The induced activity of ascorbate peroxidase led us to purify and characterize the cyanobacterial enzyme in peroxide treated cells. Ascorbate peroxidase activity was eluted from the DEAE-cellulose anion exchanger by low ionic strength. Active fractions were filtered through Amicon 3000 dalton filters and retained their activity. APAC activity was not lost throughout boiling (100°C) for 30 minutes, acidification at pH 2 for 10 min and by proteolytic enzymes treatment. APAC contained iron in all active fractions, and its E.S.R spectrum showed a resonance line at g=4.3 in the oxidized form. HPLC separation provided a major fraction of active component on a reverse phase C-18 column and was found to contain an oligopeptid conisting of glutamic acid: glycine and cysteine at 2:1:1

ratio. These findings led us to the conclusion that APAC is very different from the plant chloroplastic or cytosolic enzymes (8). This novel APAC component, formed under peroxide stress may provide the cyanobacterial cell with a simple mean for H_2O_2 removal, with high affinity to H_2O_2 (Km=0.38 mM) and to ascorbate (Km=0.2mM).

AKNOWLEDGEMENT

This research was supported in part by the Basic Research Fund of The Israeli Academy of Science.

REFERENCES

1 Patterson, C.O.P. and Myers, J. (1973) Plant Physiol. 51, 104-109.

2 Tel-Or, E., Huflejt, M.E. and Packer, L. (1986) Arch. Biochem. Biophys. 246, 396-402.

3 Foyer, C.H., Rowell, J. and Walker, D. (1983) Planta 157, 239-244.

4 Mittler, R. and Tel-Or, E. (1991) Arch. Microbiol. 155, 125-130.

5 Hossin, M.A. and Asada, K. (1984) Plant Cell Physiol. 25, 1285-1295.

6 Omaya, S.T., Turnbull, J.D. and Sauberlich, H.E. (1979) Meth. Enzymol. 62, 7-8.

7 Behens, W.A. and Madere, R. (1987) Analytical Biochem. 165, 102-107.

8 Cheng, G.X. and Asada, K. (1989) Plant Cell Physiol. 30, 987-998.

INTERACTIVE EFFECTS OF STRONG LIGHT AND HEAT STRESS ON PHOTOSYNTHETIC APPARATUS OF WHEAT

GAURI S. SINGHAL AND RANJIT K. MISHRA, SCHOOL OF LIFE SCIENCES, JAWAHARLAL NEHRU UNIVERSITY, NEW DELHI-110067 (INDIA)

1. INTRODUCTION

Photoinhibition of photosynthesis occurs when chloroplasts receive light in excess to that which can be dissipated by photochemical and non-photochemical processes associated with photosynthesis(1). It results in a damage to PSII complex by photodegradation of D_1 protein(2). High light stress is also known to interact with high temperature-stress at the level of thylakoid membranes and intensity needed to cause a given degree of injury falls as the other accompanying stress increases(3,4). Although the mechanism of photoinhibition remains a matter of debate, but there is growing evidence on the involvement of active oxygen species in the process(5,6). The abundance of polyunsaturated fatty acyl residues in the thylakoid make the thylakoid membrane fluid, which may be required for optimal functioning, but it also makes the membrane susceptible to oxidative degradation(7). As lipids are one of the factors in maintaining the optimal confirmational and functional integrity of thylakoid pigment-protein complexes it seems reasonable to analyze the effects of environmental stress on these structural counterparts and relate them with photosynthetic activity. We have attempted to examine the effects of these stresses independently and in combination and also the relationship between photosynthetic activity and peroxidation of thylakoid lipids.

2. MATERIALS AND METHODS

Wheat (*Triticum aestivum* L. var. HD 2329, IARI, New Delhi, India) seeds were grown in a plant growth chamber at 25°C under a photoperiod of 14h. Chloroplasts were isolated from 8-10 day old leaves as described earlier(8).

Photoinhibition of chloroplasts (10 ug Chl/ml) was performed in a jacketed glass container maintained at 25°C as described earlier(9). Photoinhibitory light was provided by a slide projector, equipped with a 24V/250W projection lamp which illumi-

N. Murata (ed.), Research in Photosynthesis, Vol. IV, 541–544.

nated the sample chamber at 1750 Wm^{-2}. The intensity of photoinhibitory light was varied by using neutral density filters.

Heat treatments were given to chloroplasts (10 µg Chl/ml) mixing appropriate amount of chloroplasts with buffer maintained at a desired temperature and keeping them in a water bath in dark. Heat treatments were terminated by bringing the vials back to ice. The effects of combination of heat (40,45 and 50°C) and high light (590, 1200 and 1750 Wm^{-2}) stresses in isolated chloroplasts were studied in a sequential and simultaneous manner subjecting the chloroplasts to various levels of the two types of stresses, as described earlier. The order of the two stresses was changed to examine the changes in the extent of damage to the photosynthetic apparatus. Fluorescence induction kinetics of chloroplasts at room temperature and peroxidation of thylakoid lipids were measured as described earlier(7).

3. RESULTS AND DISCUSSION

Electron transport activity of chloroplasts from water to DCIP decreased with increase in temperature (Fig.1). Activity measured in the presence of DPC was comparitavely less perturbed.

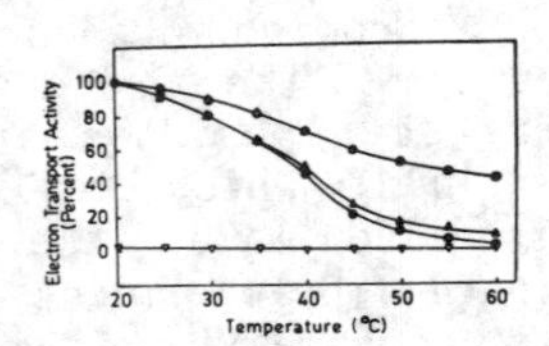

Fig.1: Partial electron transport activity of chloroplasts after heat treatment for 1 min. in dark (●) H_2O to DCIP, (O) DPC to DCIP, (▲) NH_2OH to DCIP, (Δ) DPC to DCIP after inactivation of OEC, (▽) H_2O to DCIP after inactivation of OEC.

As DPC donates electrons to tyr_z, the primary donor to $P680^+$, the target of heat induced damage plausibly is localized on the donor side of PSII. The reduction in DPC to DCIP electron transport, however, might indicate inhibition of primary charge separation due to heat denaturation of PSII polypeptides at relatively higher temperature(10). Electron transport activity from 20mM NH_2OH to DCIP followed a pattern similar to that from water to DCIP indicating that the site of electron donation by NH_2OH may be prior to tyr_z in the electron transport chain and the primary locus of heat-induced damage may lie between the sites of electron donation by DPC and 20mM NH_2OH. The reduction in electron transport activity on exposure of chloroplasts to strong light at 25°C (Fig.2) could be due to photoinhibition, which is known to result in the impairment of primary photochemistry and photodegradation of D_1 protein.

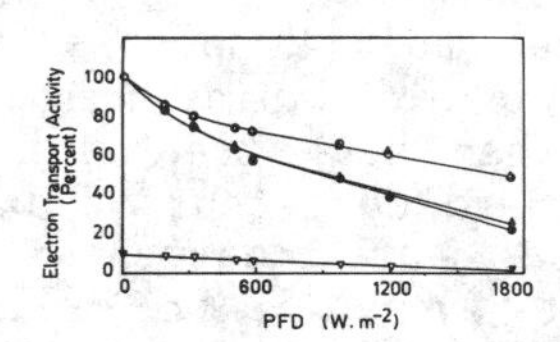

Fig.2: Partial electron transport activity of chloroplasts exposed to different PFD at 25°C for 1 min (●) H_2O to DCIP, (o) DPC to DCIP, (▲) NH_2OH to DCIP, (△) DPC to DCIP after inactivation of OEC, (▽) H_2O to DCIP after inactivation of OEC.

In vivo Chl fluorescence induction was used as the second parameter to investigate the stress induced damage to primary photochemistry of PSII in chloroplasts. The F_v/F_m ratio of chloroplasts followed a similar pattern to that as electron transport activity after heat and high light treatment (data not shown).

Fig.3 shows that at all the three temperatures and light intensities under the study, the inhibition of electron transport activity was more when photoinhibition preceded high temperature treatment. Chl fluorescence parameter F_v/F_m, which is directly related to PSII photochemistry also showed a similar pattern.

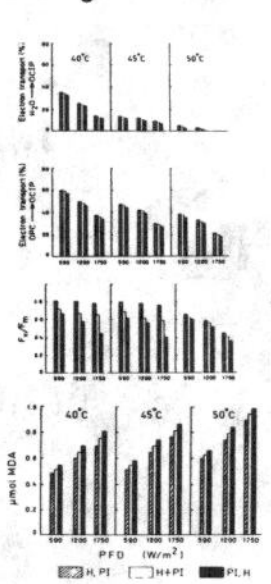

Fig.3: Interactive effects of high temperature (40,45 & 45°C, panel a,b and c respectively) and strong visible light on electron transport activity, F_v/F_m ratio and lipid peroxidation in isolated wheat chloroplasts.

Peroxidation of thylakoid lipids was also more when chloroplasts were photoinhibited before subjecting to high temperature stress (Fig.3). This suggests that plausibly enhanced generation of active oxygen species could be a reason for greater inhibition of photosynthetic activity and lipid peroxidation when high light was exposed before the heat stress. The reason for differential damage to chloroplasts on changing the sequence of heat and light stress could be that PSII centers which are partially damaged by photoinhibition, become more susceptible to heat stress as compared to the native PSII centers. The involvement of free radical species may not be ruled out as peroxidation of thylakoid lipids which may be a free radical--mediated process. When heat treatment was given before photo-inhibition, only a limited extent of oxygen evolution activation is expected because heat treatments were given in the dark, when oxygen didnot evolve from PSII. The functionality of reaction center is also substantiated by lower extent of damage to DPC to DCIP electron transport activity. Hence, the PSII centers are less perturbed when heat stress was imposed, prior to photoinhibition.

4. ACKNOWLEDGEMENT

The financial help of CSIR project grant no. 38(811)/91-EMRII is gratefully acknowledged.

REFERENCES

1 Baker, N.R. (1991) Physiol. Plant. 81, 563-570
2 Barber, J. and Anderson, B. (1992) TIBS 17, 61-66.
3 Al-Khatib, K. AND Paulsen, G.M. (1989) Plant Physiol. 90, 1041-1048
4 Greer, D.H. and Laing, W.A. (1990) in Current Research in Photo-synthesis (Baltscheffsky, M., ed.), Vol.II, pp.365-372, Kluwer Academic Publishers, The Netherlands.
5 Asada, K. and Takahashi, M. (1987) in Photoinhibition (Kyle, D.J., Osmond, C.B. and Arntzen, C.J. eds.), Vol.9, pp.227-287, Elsevier Science Publishers, The Netherland
6 Richter, M., Wild, A. and Ruhle, W. (1990) Photosynth. Res. 24, 237-243
7 Murphy, D.J. (1986) Biochim. Biophys. Acta 864, 33-94
8 Mishra, R.K. and Singhal, G.S. (1992) Plant PHysiol. 98, 1-6
9 Mishra, R.K., Chauhan, N.P. and Singhal, G.S. (1991) J. Plant Physiol. 138, 602-607
10 Thompson, L.K., Blaylock, R., Sturtevant, J.M. and Brudvig, G.W. (1989) Biochemistry 28, 6686-6695
11 Powles, S.B. (1984) Annu. Rev. Plant Physiol. 35, 15-44.

GENE REGULATION OF RICE SUPEROXIDE DISMUTASES IN RESPONSE TO OXIDATIVE STRESS

ATSUSHI SAKAMOTO AND KUNISUKE TANAKA, DEPARTMENT OF BIOCHEMISTRY, COLLEGE OF AGRICULTURE, KYOTO PREFECTURAL UNIVERSITY, SHIMOGAMO, KYOTO 606, JAPAN

1. INTRODUCTION

Superoxide dismutase (SOD; superoxide:superoxide oxidoreductase, EC 1.15.1.1), found in almost all living organisms, is a divergent class of metalloenzyme responsible for catalyzing the first step in the detoxification system of reactive oxygen species. Therefore, it has become the object of considerable attention in physiology, biochemistry, and molecular and cellular biology of plants. Higher plant SOD exists as different isozymes in subcellular compartments (1). Copper/zinc-SOD (Cu/Zn-SOD), the most prominent isozyme, is localized in both the cytosol and plastids, whereas manganese-SOD (Mn-SOD) usually occurs within the mitochondrial matrix. Several plant species have iron-SOD (Fe-SOD) in their plastids. Accumulating evidences strongly indicate that in plant system SOD plays a critical role in tolerance to stress arisen from numerous environmental cues (*i.e.*, exposure to air pollutants, treatment with reactive oxygen-generating agents, circumstantial factors leading to photoinhibition and so on) (2). One of our aims is to elucidate the organization and regulation of SOD gene families in rice plants (*Oryza sativa* L.) (3,4). Rice contains two Mn-isozymes and four Cu/Zn-isozymes (one for plastid while others for cytosol), but lacks detectable Fe-isozyme activity (5). The present paper characterizes the structure of rice Cu/Zn-SOD genes and investigates the expression of these genes in response to oxidative stress.

2. MATERIALS AND METHODS

2.1. *Isolation of cDNA and genomic clones*

Rice Cu/Zn-SOD cDNA clones were isolated by plaque hybridization for the λ gt11 cDNA library of developing rice (*Oryza sativa* L. cv. Nipponbare) seeds with the corresponding spinach cDNA (6). One of the purified rice Cu/Zn-SOD clones, RSODB (4), was then used as a probe to screen a rice genomic library.

2.2. *Construction of* sodB*-GUS fusion genes and introduction into rice protoplasts*

A genomic DNA fragment (ca. 2.2 kbp), which covers the 5' upstream sequence, 5' non-coding exon, 5' non-coding intron and a part of the first protein-coding exon from a rice Cu/Zn-SOD gene (*sodB*), was translationally fused to the coding region for the bacterial β-glucuronidase (GUS) gene (7) cloned in pUC19 (see Fig. 3: the resulting plasmid termed psodB-GUS1). An another construct, p35S-INTB, is a derivative of psodB-GUS1 containing the cauliflower mosaic virus (CaMV) 35S promoter in place of the *sodB* 5' upstream sequence (ca. 1.5 kbp). Chimeric constructs were introduced into rice protoplasts prepared from suspension-cultured cells via

N. Murata (ed.), Research in Photosynthesis, Vol. IV, 545–548.

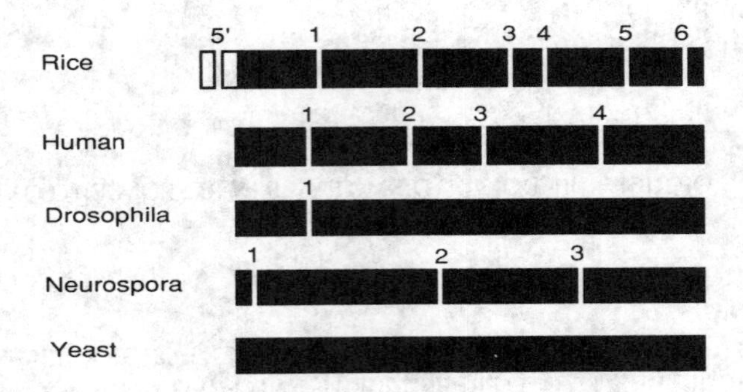

Fig. 1. Comparison of exon/intron organization of Cu/Zn-SOD genes. Closed boxes refer to protein-coding exons which are arranged for maximum matching. Introns are not shown but numbered above exon/exon junctions. Open boxes in the rice gene indicate the 5' non-coding sequence interrupted by insertion of the 5' non-coding intron (marked above as 5'). The yeast gene has no introns.

polyethyleneglycol method. After 48 hr incubation under illumination with or without the superoxide-generating agent paraquat (PQ) (10 μ M), transient GUS activities were measured by means of modified fluorometric assays (8).

3. RESULTS AND DISCUSSION

3.1. *Characterization of SOD genes*

Using the corresponding spinach cDNA as the heterologous probe, two cDNA clones (RSODA and RSODB) coding for distinct Cu/Zn-SODs were obtained from rice seeds (4). Each cDNA encodes 152 amino acid residues showing the characteristic sequence of cytosolic Cu/Zn-SOD. Corresponding nuclear genes (*sodA* for RSODA cDNA and *sodB* for RSODB cDNA) were subsequently isolated and the structural analyses revealed that both genes display identical exon/intron organization, consisting of 8 exons and 7 introns with the coding sequence beginning in the 2nd and ending in the 8th (3). Genomic Southern blot analysis indicated that cytosolic Cu/Zn-SOD is coded for by small multigene family in the rice genome (probably 2 to

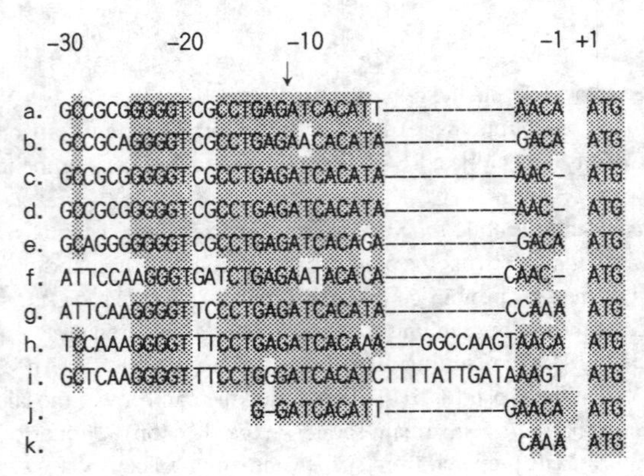

Fig. 2. Comparison of 5' non-coding sequences of cytosolic Cu/Zn-SOD cDNAs from plants. Sources are as follows: lines a, rice RSODA (4); b, rice RSODB (4); c, maize SOD4 (13); d, maize SOD4A (13); e, maize SOD2 (14); f, spinach (6); g, tobacco (15); h, *Arabidopsis* (16); i, scots pine (17); j, pea (18); k, tomato (19). Starts of translation are defined as +1 relative to the rice RSODA sequence. Identical residues are shaded and splice junctions in the rice sequences are indicated by an arrow.

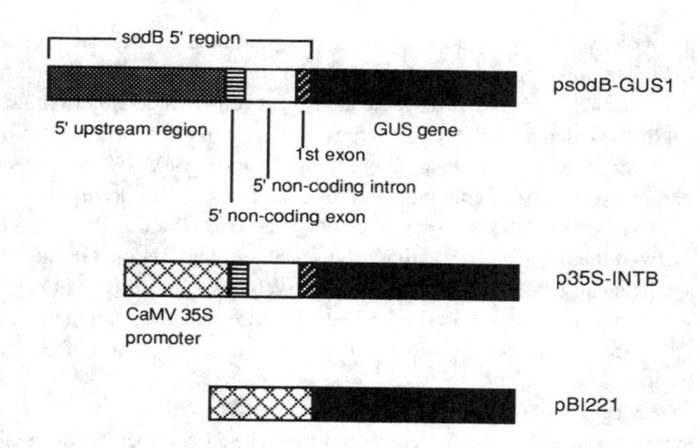

Fig. 3. Chimeric *sodB*-GUS constructs and pBI221 used for introduction into rice protoplasts.

3 copy-number) (3). We also isolated several cDNA and genomic clones for Mn-SODs. Preliminary characterization of the Mn-SOD clones suggested that the rice nuclear genome contains two genes for Mn-SOD, and that each structural region is separated by several introns (A. Sakamoto *et al.*, unpublished).

As the first information on the genomic sequence for plant SOD, we compared the gene structure of rice Cu/Zn-SOD with those from a broad range of eukaryotes [human (9), *Drosophila melanogaster* (10), *Neurospora crassa* (11) and yeast (12)]. It appeared that the exon/intron organization for plant Cu/Zn-SOD genes differs from those found in other sources, especially in terms of intron numbers and inserted positions (Fig. 1) (3). A unique feature observed in plant Cu/Zn-SOD genes is the occurrence of an intron (5' non-coding intron) in the 5' transcribed but untranslated region. This resulted in the creation of an upstream exon (5' non-coding exon) lacking any protein-coding informations. We found that 5' non-coding sequences of cytosolic Cu/Zn-SOD cDNAs are significantly conserved among different species (Fig. 2) (4). This is a rare case where high degree of sequence similarity is observed in untranslated regions of genes encoding the same protein from different species, implying functional significance of the conserved regions on the SOD-gene regulation (presumably intron-mediated regulation considering that rice genes carry an intron in this region).

Table 1. Response of the *sodB* 5' region to PQ-mediated oxidative stress

Construct	Relative GUS activity		Fold
	-PQ	+PQ	(+PQ/-PQ)
pBI221	100	176	1.76
psodB-GUS1	7	99	14.1
p35S-INTB	960	647	0.67

3.2. *Response of the* sodB *5' region to oxidative stress*

It has been observed that activities of plant SOD increase in response to a wide variety of environmental and chemical stress (2). Because the damage accelerated by the stress is considered to be mediated, at least in part, by the generation of reactive oxygen species, it is very interesting to know whether plant SOD promoters respond to oxidative stress which is caused by high reactivity of oxyradical species. To examine this point, the reporter GUS gene under the control of the *sodB* 5' region (Fig. 3) was introduced into rice protoplasts and expression of *sodB*-GUS constructs was measured by fluorometric assays for cells treated either with or without PQ (Table 1). In the absence of PQ, GUS expression directed by the *sodB* 5' region (construct psodB-GUS1) was very low when compared with those by the CaMV 35S promoter (pBI221). However, approximately 14-fold induction of GUS activity was occurred by PQ treatment. The chimeric CaMV 35S-GUS construct containing the *sodB* 5' non-coding exon/intron unit (p35S-INTB) showed the highest GUS activity, but the expression seemed not to be stimulated by PQ. These results mean that the *sodB* 5' region positively responds to oxidative stress and responsive *cis*-acting elements reside within the 1.5 kbp upstream sequence. On the other hand, the *sodB* 5' non-coding exon/intron sequence contributes quantitative expression of GUS activity.

ACKNOWLEDGEMENTS

A. Sakamoto is the recipient of a fellowship from the Japan Society for the Promotion of Science for Japanese Junior Scientists.

REFERENCES

1 Asada, K., Kanematsu, S., Okada, S. and Hayakawa, T. (1980) in Chemical and Biochemical Aspects of Superoxide and Superoxide Dismutase (Bannister, J.V. and Hill, H.A.O., eds.), pp. 136-153, Elsevier, Amsterdam

2 Bowler, C., Van Montagu, M. and Inze, D. (1992) Annu. Rev. Plant Physiol. Plant Mol. Biol. 43, 83-116

3 Sakamoto, A., Okumura, T., Ohsuga, H. and Tanaka, K. (1992) FEBS Lett. 301, 185-189

4 Sakamoto, A., Ohsuga, H. and Tanaka, K. (1992) Plant Mol. Biol. 19, 323-327

5 Kanematsu, S. and Asada, K. (1989) Plant Cell Physiol. 30, 381-391

6 Sakamoto, A., Ohsuga, H., Wakaura, M., Mitsukawa, N., Hibino, T., Masumura, T., Sasaki, Y. and Tanaka, K. (1990) Nucleic Acids Res. 18, 4923

7 Jefferson, R.A., Burgess, S.M. and Hirsh, D. (1986) Proc. Natl. Acad. Sci. USA 83, 8447-8451

8 Kosugi, S., Ohashi, Y., Nakajima, K. and Arai, Y. (1990) Plant Sci. 70, 133-140

9 Levanon, D., Lieman-Hurwitz, J., Dafni, N., Wigderson, M., Sherman, L., Bernstein, Y., Laver-Rudich, Z., Danciger, E., Stein, O. and Groner, Y. (1985) EMBO J. 4, 77-84

10 Seto, N.O.L., Hayashi, S. and Tener, G.M. (1987) Nucleic Acids Res. 15, 10601.

11 Chary, P., Hallewell, R.A. and Natvig, D.O. (1990) J. Biol. Chem. 265, 18961-18967

12 Bermingham-McDonogh, O., Gralla E.B. and Valentine, J.S. (1988) Proc. Natl. Acad. Sci. USA 85, 4789-4793

13 Cannon, R.E. and Scandalios, J.G. (1989) Mol. Gen. Genet. 219, 1-8

14 Cannon, R.E., White, J.A. and Scandalios, J.G. (1987) Proc. Natl. Acad. Sci. USA 84, 179-183

15 Tsang, E.W.T., Bowler, C., Herouart, D., Van Camp, W., Villarroel, R., Genetello, C., Van Montagu, M. and Inze, D. (1991) Plant Cell 3, 783-792

16 Hindges, R. and Slusarenko, A. (1992) Plant Mol. Biol. 18, 123-125

17 Karpinski, S., Wingsle, G., Olsson, O. and Hallgren, J.-E. (1992) Plant Mol. Biol. 18, 545-555

18 White, D.A. and Zilinskas, B.A. (1991) Plant Physiol. 96, 1391-1392

19 Perl-Treves, R., Nacmias, B., Aviv, D., Zeelon, E.P. and Galun, E. (1988) Plant Mol. Biol. 11, 609-623

PHOTODAMAGE INVOLVES MULTIPLE SITES AND IS DISTINGUISHABLE FROM PHOTOINACTIVATION

Huashi Gong, Stein Nilsen and John F. Allen*, *Dept. of Biology, Box 1045, University of Oslo, Blindern, 0316 Oslo 3, Norway and *Plant Cell Biology, University of Lund, Box 7007, S-220 07 Lund, Sweden*

Introduction

Photoinhibition of photosynthesis consists of photoinactivation of RCII and breakdown of the D1 protein (1). Photoinhibition can be strongly affected by O_2 and CO_2 (2). It is alleviated by the presence of CO_2 *in vivo* (2) or by addition of bicarbonate *in vitro* (3).

We find that multiple sites are involved in a photodamage process under CO_2- and O_2-free conditions, which are similar to the anaerobic conditions reported earlier (2-4).

Materials and methods

Axenic cultures of *Lemna gibba* L. G3 were grown as described (5). Photoinhibitory treatment and measurement of CO_2 uptake were carried out as before (5).

Chloroplasts were prepared (6) immediately after the photoinhibitory treatments. Thylakoid membranes were obtained by suspending the chloroplasts with Tricine buffer (50 mM K-Tricine, 10 mM NaCl, 5 mM $MgCl_2$, 2 mM EDTA, pH 7.6).

Photosynthetic electron transport was measured by DCIP reduction (7) or O_2 uptake (8).

For the room temperature fluorescence measurements, a PAM system (Waltz, Effeltrich, FRG) with standard accessories and computer analysis was used. The fluorescence decay after a single turnover flash (given by XST-103, Waltz) was recorded in order to detect reoxidation of Q_A^- (9). *Lemna* plants floated on the growth medium in a home-made aluminium cuvette in which light, temperature and gas compositions were controlled. The plants were dark adapted for 10 min before the flash. 77K fluorescence emission was measured using a Perkin-Elmer LS-5 luminescence spectrometer as described (10).

Pulse-chase experiments with ^{35}S methionine were performed as before (5). Thylakoid membrane and RC II-D1 polypeptides were separated by LDS-electrophoresis and autoradiography (5). D1 was quantified densitometrically.

Results and discussion

When *Lemna* plants were illuminated by high PFDs, CO_2 uptake was photoinhibited to a much higher degree in the absence than presence of CO_2 (Fig.1). In pure N_2 the degree of photoinhibition was the highest, and it recovered very slowly (2,5). We describe the high degree of photoinhibition in N_2 as photodamage. In N_2, PSII-dependent electron transport ($H_2O \rightarrow DCIP$) was inhibited by 43% which was also the highest among the other gas conditions (Table 1). This indicates that the photodamage locates at PSII. A similar degree of inhibition of DCIP reduction was obtained using DPC as an electron donor, showing that the water-splitting complex remained unimpaired. During photodamage, inhibition of CO_2 uptake was greater than that of PSII electron transport. The difference may be due to to inhibition of PSI, since in N_2 the rate of PSI electron transport, especially the light-limited, significantly decreased (Table 1).

To probe additional effects on PSI and PSII, we measured 77K fluorescence emission before and after photoinhibition (Table 2). Two emission maxima, at 692nm and 737nm, were observed in all cases. The fluorescence emission at 692 nm, which may reflect the state of the PSII and RCII (11), showed a pattern of changes (Table 2) consistent with those in electron transport (Table 1). Fluorescence emission at 737 nm, which may be ascribed to LHCI and the PSI core (12), decreased by 42% after photoinhibitory treatment in N_2 (Table

N. Murata (ed.), Research in Photosynthesis, Vol. IV, 549–552.

2). This again suggests that PSI may be inactivated during the photodamage process. The size of the PSI antenna may have decreased. This is supported by the decreased 77K fluorescence emission at 737 nm (Table 2) as well as by the inhibited PSI light-limited electron transport (Table 1).

Table 1 Inhibition of electron transport. Thylakoids were prepared from plants photoinhibited for 90 min under PFD of 2800 μmol m^{-2} s^{-1} in the gas phases indicated. The "Control" was at PFD 250 μmol m^{-2} s^{-1} in air. The rates of electron transport are expressed as a percentage of the control rate. The control rate was 268±40 μmol DCIP mg^{-1} chlorophyll hr^{-1} for the PSII reactions, and 167±15 μmol O_2 mg^{-1} chlorophyll hr^{-1} for PSI. HL: measured under saturated light; LL: measured under unsaturated light (PFD of 300 μmol m^{-2} s^{-1}).

		PSII		PSI	
		$H_2O \rightarrow$DCIP	DPC→DCIP	Asc→MV	
		HL	HL	HL	LL
Control		100	100	100	100
Photoinhibition	air	86.7	86.0	101	100
	air minus O_2	88.5	90.6	97.6	99.0
	air minus CO_2	67.9	70.2	92.2	86.7
	N_2	56.8	57.2	91.4	73.0

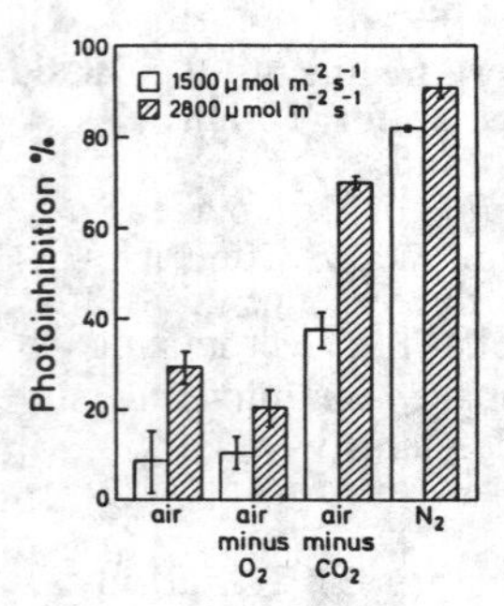

Fig.1 Loss of CO_2 uptake after photoinhibitory treatment. Plants were illuminated for 90 min under the PFD and atmospheric conditions as indicated. Vertical bars represent S.D.

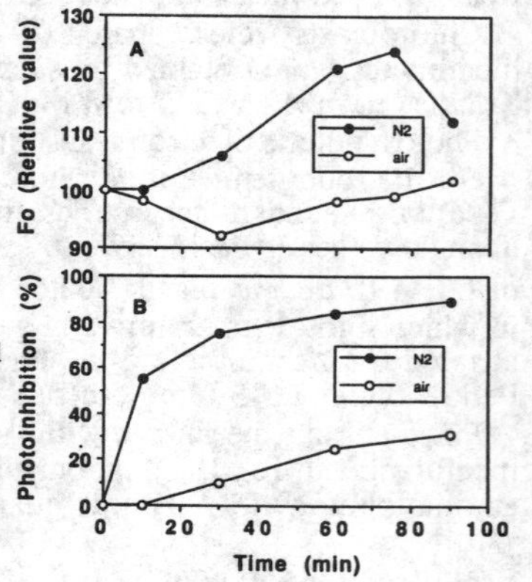

Fig.2 Photodamage occurred earlier than the rise in initial fluorescence (Fo). Plants were illuminated under a PFD of 2800 μmol m^{-2} s^{-1} in air or pure N_2. Fo (A) and CO_2 uptake (B) were measured at the times indicated and are expressed as percentages of photoinhibition (B).

To locate the site of inhibition within RCII during photoinhibition, kinetics of fluorescence decay were examined after giving intact plants a single turnover flash. The fluorescence decay during 40 msec showed three exponential components. The first component reflects the forward electron flow from Q_A^- to Q_B (13). The $t_{1/2}$ of this phase was increased by increasing PFDs (Table 3). Under 2800 mmol m^{-2} s^{-1}, the increase of $t_{1/2}$ of the fast phase was 20% greater in the presence than absence of O_2, and 19% greater in the absence than presence of CO_2 (Table 3). Photoinhibition in pure

Table 2 77K fluorescence emission during photoinhibition. *Lemna* plants were photoinhibited as that in Table 1. Fluorescence spectra were obtained for thylakoid extracts at equal chlorophyll concentration (7 μg ml^{-1}), and were normalised to fluorescence at 550 nm from 1μM fluorescein. The normalised values for total fluorescence emission are given in arbitrary units ±S.D. The "Control" condition was the same as that in Table 1.

		PSII (F_{692})	PSI (F_{737})
Control		0.47±0.03	0.66±0.06
Photoinhibition	air	0.38±0.04	0.58±0.07
	air minus O_2	0.43±0.01	0.62±0.03
	air minus CO_2	0.30±0.02	0.49±0.00
	N_2	0.24±0.04	0.38±0.09

N_2 resulted in a similar degree of inhibition of electron flow from Q_A^- to Q_B as that occurred in air (Table 3). In contrast, the inhibition of CO_2 uptake (Fig.1) and of PSII electron flow (Table 1) was much higher in N_2 than those in air. The higher inhibition of PSII electron transport in N_2 could be due to inhibition of RCII components from P680 to Q_A, since the water splitting component as a donor to PSII seems to have been unimpaired (Table 1).

Table 3 Kinetics of fluorescence decay and D1 degradation after photoinhibition. Intact plants were given a single turnover flash before (Control) and after photoinhibition in the conditions indicated. "Control" condition was the same as that in Table 1.Ymax was the maximal fluorescence following one flash. Fo and Ymax values after photoinhibitory treatment are expressed as percentages of the values before photoinhibitory treatment. The 100% values for Fo and for Ymax were the averages from the controls of each experiment. +CAP: in presence of 500 $\mu g\ ml^{-1}$ chloramphenicol.

PFD	Atmosphere	$t_{1/2}$ (µs) of fast phase			Fo±S.D. (%)	Ymax (%)	Degradation of D1 (%)
($\mu mol\ m^{-2}\ s^{-1}$)		Control	Photoin-hibited	Increase in $t_{1/2}$ (%)	Photoin-hibited	Photoin-hibited	Photoin-hibited
1500	air	486	547	13±5	96±2	76	43
	air minus O_2	493	496	1±2	93±7	75	25
	air minus CO_2	459	700	53±8	102±2	77	48
	N_2	508	545	7±15	98±6	78	33
	air (+CAP)	509	587	15	102	61	
2800	air	478	646	35±7	102±5	65	
	air minus O_2	529	563	6±11	102±4	76	
	air minus CO_2	512	937	83±14	107±2	63	
	N_2	460	616	34±2	112±2	74	

After photoinhibitory treatment, intrinsic fluorescence, Fo, increased in N_2 and, to a lesser extent, in air minus CO_2. Fo did not increase in the other gas phases (Table 3). The increased Fo can be due to RCII inactivation by trapping of Q_A^- or by Q_B^- destabilization (1). Fo did not rise in air *in vivo*, although the Q_A reoxidation was inhibited (Fig.2; Table 3). The kinetic studies show that, during photoinhibition in N_2, the rise of Fo occurs later than the inhibition of net photosynthesis (Fig.2). This suggests that the rise in Fo is a secondary event arising as a consequence of photodamage. Moreover, the rise in Fo during photodamage may indicate that PSII charge separation is inactivated. This is supported by the decrease in 77K fluorescence emission at 692 nm (Table 2), which is thought to be fluorescence from the photoactive pheophytin *a* that functions as an electron acceptor in RCII (11).

To test whether the lowered photosynthetic rate (Fig.1) and PSII-electron transport (Table 1) in N_2 result from impaired energy transfer from the antenna to the reaction centre of PSII, we measured PSII electron transport under the actinic light intensities below and above saturation. The results show that inhibition of electron transport could not be improved even if the measuring light intensity was increased by five times (data not shown). This indicates that energy transfer to RCII is unlikely to have impaired in these experiments.

Under high PFD in the atmospheres containing CO_2, photoinactivation (see Introduction), but not photodamage, occurred. The rate of CO_2 fixation (Fig.1) and PSII activity (Table 1 and 2) decreased by a lesser degree during photoinactivation than during photodamage. Kinetics of Fluorescence decay showed that the rate of electron flow from Q_A^- to Q_B was inhibited by 26% as represented by the $t_{1/2}$ after the plants were illuminated under PFD of 2800 $mmol\ m^{-2}\ s^{-1}$ in air (Table 3). The inhibition of reoxidation of Q_A^- fitted well with the inhibition of CO_2 uptake and that of PSII electron transport, and was largely prevented in air minus O_2 (Table 3). These results indicate that the photoinactivation is O_2 dependent and largely due to the inactivation of Q_B-site of the D1 protein. Pulse-chase experiments showed that the RCII-D1 protein degraded more rapidly than inhibition of Q_A reoxidation and was accelerated by presence of O_2 and absence of CO_2 (Table 3). D1 degradation without loss of Q_B reduction could result from efficient D1 synthesis and processing, since loss of Q_B reduction was increased by chloramphenicol, an inhibitor of protein synthesis (Table 3).

The above results indicate that multiple sites are involved in a photodamage process induced by CO_2- and O_2-free conditions. The inactivated sites include the RC II components from P680 to Q_A, the Q_B site, and a RC component of PSI. The donor side of PSII and excitation energy transfer within PSII seem to be unimpaired. We suggest that the photodamage results from the over-reducing conditions and depletion of bicarbonate. Bicarbonate is essential for keeping RCII functional (14). The CO_2- and O_2-free conditions may have caused partial removal of bicarbonate from its D1 binding site, since in *Lemna* the thylakoid has a relatively low pH under physiological condition, and this favours the dissociation of HCO_3^- to CO_2 (14). High light may promote the removal of bicarbonate, since high light drives CO_2 consumption by its assimilation. The removal of bicarbonate results in inactivation of quinone reactions (14), and may lead to inactivation of another component, as indicated in the present work, located between P680 and Q_A. The effect of bicarbonate-depletion is clearly reflected by the rapid degradation of D1 (Table 3), otherwise D1 degradation is largely decreased by O_2-free (1) and by a high ratio of PQH_2/PQ (15) during photoinhibition *in vivo*.

We suggest to distinguish between photodamage and photoinactivation. Photoinactivation occurs in air and the site is within PSII (1). At an early stage *in vivo*, high light drives RCII charge separation in a high rate, resulting in over-reduction of the PQ pool due to rate limitation of NADPH oxidation. When the PSII is gradually photoinactivated, the PQ pool become more oxidized due to a rate limitation of PSII electron flow (1). A high turnover and high ratio of PQ/PQH_2 favour the break down of D1 and thereby promote a degree of inactivation at this stage (15). In contrast, photodamage results from extreme reducing conditions and lack of bicarbonate in the reaction centres. The PQ pool is kept in a fully reduced state consistently. Fo rises during photodamage but not during photoinactivation (Table 3; Fig.2). The rise in Fo reflects over-reduction during photodamage. During photoinactivation such reducing condition may be transient and followed by gradual reoxidation of the PQ pool, and thus not sufficient to cause a rise in Fo. Photoinactivation is strongly temperature-dependent and is enhanced at low temperatures (1,5). In contrast, photodamage is relatively temperature-independent but the following recovery strongly depends on the temperature used during photodamage (5). Higher temperature induced photodamage inhibits subsequent recovery (5). Moreover, oxygen alleviates photodamage but aggravates photoinactivation (Fig.1, Table 1 and 3).

The mechanisms of inactivation of PSI (especially light limited, Table 1 and 2) during photodamage requires further investigation.

1. Prasil, O, Adir, N. and Ohad, I. (1992) in Topics in Photosynthesis (Barber, J. ed.) Vol. 11, pp. 220-250, Elsevier, Amsterdam.
2. Krause, G.H., Koster, S. and Wong, S.C. (1985) Planta 165, 430-438.
3. Sundby, C. (1990) FEBS Lett. 274, 77-81.
4. Arntz, B. and Trebst, A. (1986) FEBS Lett. 194, 43-49.
5. Gong, H. and Nilsen, S. (1989) J. Plant Physiol. 135, 9-14.
6. Mills, W.R. and Joy, K.W. (1980) Planta 148, 75-83.
7. Gershoni, J.M., Shochat, S., Malkin, S. and Ohad, I. (1982) Plant Physiol. 70, 637-644.
8. Allen, J.F. and Holmes, N.G. (1986) in Photosynthesis Energy Transduction (Hipkins, M.F. and Baker, N.R. eds.) pp. 103-142, IRL Press, Oxford and Washington D.C.
9. Schreiber, U. (1986) Photosynth. Res. 9, 261-272.
10. Allen, J.F., Sanders, C.E. and Holmes, N.G. (1985) FEBS Lett. 193, 271-275.
11. van Dorssen, R.J., Plijter, J.J., Dekker, J.P., den Ouden, A., Amesz, J. and van Gorkom, H.J. (1987) Biochim. Biophys. Acta 890, 134-143.
12. Ikegami, I. and Ke, B. (1984) Biochim. Biophys. Acta 764, 70-79.
13. Crofts, A.R. and Wraight, C.A. (1983) Biochim. Biophys. Acta 726, 149-185.
14. Blubaugh, D.J. and Govindjee (1988) Photosynth. Res. 19, 85-128.
15. Gong, H. and Ohad, I. (1991) J. Biol. Chem. 266, 21293-21299.

SHOCK PROTEIN SYNTHESIS BY NEAR-UV IRRADIATION IN ANCYSTIS NIDULANS R-2

HITOSHI SHIBATA and KATSUYA BABA
Applied Biological Science, Faculty of Agriculture, Shimane University, Matsue-Shi, Shimane 690, Japan

1. INTRODUCTION

Irradiation by near-UV light (295-390 nm) at an intensity that resulted in 30-40% survival, induced the preferential synthesis of sixteen proteins in Anacystis nidulans R-2 (Synechococcus sp. strain PCC 7942) (Shibata et al. 1991). Those near-UV induced proteins were designated UV-shock proteins. Several UV-shock proteins were also induced by heat shock. From these results, it seemed likely that near-UV irradiation of cyanobacterial cells resulted in a shift in the metabolic activities of the cells as they make use of a mechanism that limit UV-induced damage, by synthesizing a set of UV-shock proteins. In this study, we have shown that one major UV-shock protein is groEL, the heat-inducible product involving binding to and assisting in the renaturation of thermally denatured cytoplasmic proteins (Rhothman 1989). On the other hand, a suggested mechanism involves the absorption of near-UV light by chromohore(s) that results in their excitation, in a subsequent reaction with molecular oxygen to generate active species of oxygen (Kramer et al. 1988). Exopsure to near-UV light is also known to produce hydrogen peroxide (Kramer and Ames 1987). There is growing evidence that some overlap exists between cellular responses to heat-shock and responses to oxidative stress caused by active oxygens, and mechanisms have been proposed to explain an increase in active oxygen flux upon exposure to heat (Courgeon et al. 1988). Morgan et al. (1986) reported that H_2O_2-inducible proteins overlap with heat-shock and other stress proteins. From the above observations, it seems possible that production of active oxygens as a result of near-UV irradiation may elicit the synthesis of UV-shock proteins. We observed that superoxide anion radical was produced by the intact cyanobacterial cells and also by a water-soluble fraction from the cells.

2. MATERIALS AND METHODS

The cyanobacterilas cells were grown in Pyrex glass vessels with shaking at 25℃ and illumination at 1,500 lux by filtering through a combination of vinyl film (no transmission below 295 nm) and UV-cut film (no transmission below 390 nm) to exclude UV-light. In some cases, cells were grown under near-UV conditions, illuminated also by Toshiba-FL20SG lumps without UV-cut film. Near-UV irradiation to induce UV-shock proteins and to examine the production of superoxide anion radicals by monitoring Cyt c reduction, was obtained as described previously (Shibata et al. 1991).

N. Murata (ed.), Research in Photosynthesis, Vol. IV, 553–556.

3. RESULTS AND DISCUSSION

Synthesis of GroEL heat-inducible protein by near-UV irradiation. The near-UV irradiation induced the preferential synthesis of sixteen proteins, as compared with that of control (without irradiation). Almost all UV-shock proteins was not detected under irradiation by filtering through Y-50 filter that cut off light below 500 nm. But six UV-shock proteins were synthesized by treatment with methyl viologen (Shibata et al. 1991). Several UV-shock proteins were also induced by heat.

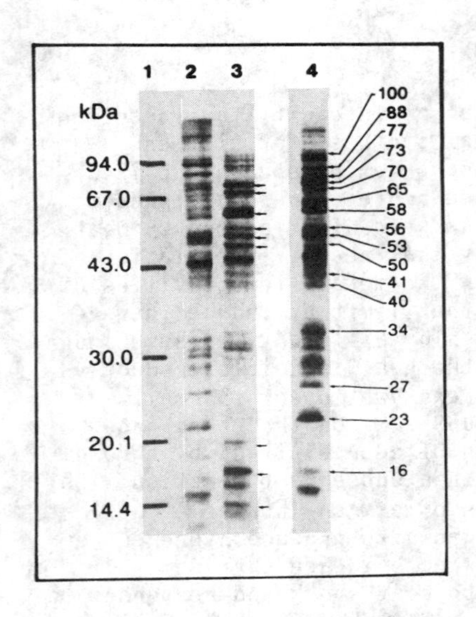

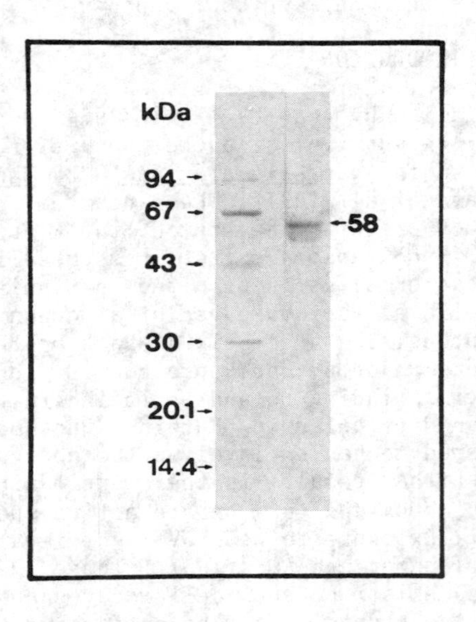

FIGURE 1. (left) Synthesis of shock proteins in Anacystis nidulas R-2. Cells were labeled with a mixture of ^{14}C-amino acids (0.25 MBq ml^{-1}) and proteins were analyzed by SDS-polyacrylamide gel electrophoresis (on a 10-15% linear-gradient gel, SDS-PAGE). Lane 1, molecular-mass markers; lane 2, control, without near-UV irradiation, 25 ℃, labeled from 0-3 hr ; lane 3, heat-shock, without irradiation at 42 ℃, labeled from 0-3 hr; lane 4, near-UV irradiation, 2.2 mW cm^{-2}, 25 ℃, labeled for 1 hr from 2 hr after the start of irradiation. Shock proteins are indicated by arrows, and the estimated molecular mass (kDa) of each UV-shock proteins is indicated in lane 4. FIGURE 2. (right) Purified 58kDa UV-shock protein. Cells were irradiated for 3 hr at 25 ℃ without ^{14}C-amino acid. Cellular proteins were extracted and subjected to electrophoresis, with ^{14}C-labeled UV-shock proteins which were co-electrophoresed separately in both side of the gel. The position of the 58 kDa UV-shock protein was cut from the gel, and poly peptide was eluted electrophoretically. The purified 58 kDa UV-shock protein was applied SDS-PAGE, blotted onto PVDF membrane, the Coomassie-stained protein was shown.

One major UV-shock protein, 58 kDa which was also induced by heat, was purified electrophoretically (FIGURE 2). The protein was cut out and sequenced. The amino terminal amino acid sequence of the excised 58 kDa UV-shock protein determined by Edman degradation was shown in TABLE 1.

TABLE 1 N-TERMINAL SEQUENCE OF 58 kDa UV-SHOCK PROTEIN

NH_2-Ala-Lys-Arg-Ile-Ile-Tyr-Asn-Glu-Asn-Ala-Arg- Arg-Ala-Leu-Glu-Lys-Gly-Ile-Asp-Ile-Leu-Ala-

The sequence is the same as that deduced from the nucleotide sequence of the <u>Cynechococcus</u> sp. strain PCC 7942 groEL gene (Webb et al. 1990). It was concluded that the 58 kDa heat-inducible cyanobacterial groEL, a member of chaperonin family, is also inducible by near-UV irradiation.

<u>Superoxide anion radical formation in vivo by near-UV irradiation</u> To examine the production of active oxygen under near-UV irradiation in the cyanobacterial cells, whole cells suspended in buffer containing Cyt <u>c</u> were irradiated by near-UV light (2.2 mW cm^{-2}), under which UV-shock protein was induced.

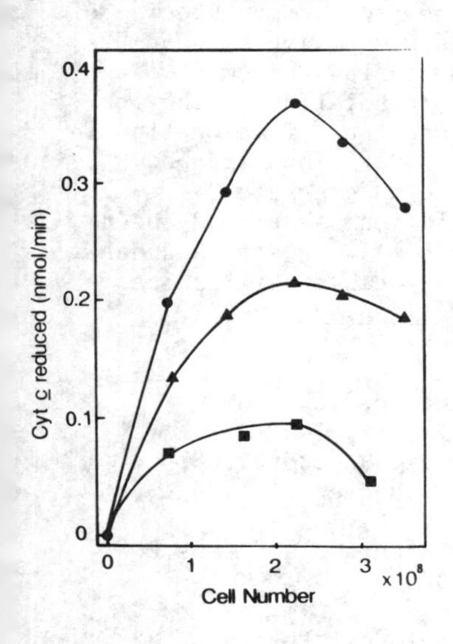

FIGURE 3 Near-UV induced Cyt <u>c</u> reduction by whole cyanobacterial cells grown under three different near-UV conditions. <u>A. nidulans</u> cells were grown under irradiation with three different intensities of near-UV light described in MATERIALS and MEHTODS. Cells were collected from cultures at logarithmic phase. The reaction mixture (1 ml) contained 50 mM potassium phosphate, pH 7.2, 10 mM NaCl, 0.1 mM EDTA, 1.2 mg Cyt <u>c</u> and the indicated cell density of cyanobacterial cells. During near-UV (2.2 mW cm^{-2}) irradiation the reduction of Cyt <u>c</u> by monitoring the increase in absorbance at 550 nm was followed every 1 min intervals. Cells were grown under UV-cut (●); near-UV 77 (▲), or 144 μW cm^{-2} (■)

FIGURE 3 shows the Cyt <u>c</u> reduction by three cyanobacterial cells grown under different near-UV conditions (UV-cut, near-UV, 77 μW cm^{-2} or 144 μW cm^{-2}). The intensities caused a neglegible inhibition of growth. Cyt <u>c</u> reduction which was inhibited by superoxide dismutase, was observed by near-UV irradiation, indicating the production of superoxide anion radical (O_2^-). Neglegible amount of Cyt <u>c</u> was reduced in the absence of cells. Up to the 2 x 10^8 cells in the reaction mixture, the amount of the O_2^- produced was approximately parallele to the cell number, however it was then decreased in the presence of more than 2 x 10^8 cells, suggesting the lowering near-UV irradiance by a high density of cells. Cyanobacterial cells grown under UV-cut condition produced effectively O_2^-. Non-lethal dose of near-UV irradiation to the cells during growth decreased the efficiency of O_2^- production. This may be interpreted by the results shown in TABLE 2.

TABLE 2 EFFECT OF NON-LETHAL DOSES OF NEAR-UV IRRADIATION DURING GROWTH OF ANACYSTIS NIDULANS R-2

Growth under near-UV (μW cm^{-2})	Superoxide dismutase units mg $protein^{-1}$	Catalase μmol min^{-1} mg $protein^{-1}$
0 (UV-cut)	1.72	10.9
77	3.98	14.6
144	7.54	18.0

Lower, non-lethal intensity of near-UV irradiated during the growth of the cells induced the activities of superoxide dismutase and catalase. These results, the induction of scavenging enzymes for active species of oxygen, may indicate the production of O_2^- and H_2O_2 in vivo by near-UV light depending on the fluence rate, at least up to 144 μW cm^{-2}. We reported the O_2^- production in vitro by near-UV irradiation to the low-molecular-weight fraction which showed a broad spectrum of absorption in the near-UV region (300-400 nm) (Shibata et al. 1991). The compound(s) may function as a near-UV-photosensitizer in vivo to generate O_2^-. Production of H_2O_2 as a result of near-UV irradiation has already been demonstrated (Kramer and Ames 1987, Tyrrell, 1985). The stress under near-UV irradiation that generates O_2^-, H_2O_2 and the hydroxyl radical elicits shock proteins including groEL in Anacystis nidulans R-2.

4. REFERENCES

Courgeon,A.-M., Rollet,E., Becker,J.,Maisonheute,J.C. and Best-Belpomme,M. (1988) Eur.J.Biochem. 171, 163-170.

Kramer,G.F. and Ames,B.N. (1987) J.Bacteriol. 169, 2259-2266.

Kramer,G.F., Baker,J.C. and Ames,B.N.(1988) J.Bacteriol. 170, 2344-2351.

Morgan,R.W., Christman,M.F., Jakobson,F.S., Stroz,G. and Ames,B.N. (1986) Proc.Natl.Acad.Sci.USA, 83, 8059-8063.

Rothman,J.E. (1989) Cell, 59, 591-601.

Shibata,H., Baba,K. and Ochiai,H. (1991) Plant Cell Physiol., 32, 771-776.

Tyrrell,R.M. (1985) Mutat, Res. 145, 129-136.

Webb,R., Reddy,K.J. and Sherman,L.A. (1990) J.Bacteriol. 172, 5079-5088

5. ACKNOWLEDGEMENTS

This study was performed partly through Special Coodination Funds of the Science and Technology Agency of the Japanese Government.

PHOTOINHIBITION IN TRANSGENIC SULPHUR TOBACCO CONTAINING SENSE AND ANTISENSE SUPEROXIDE-DISMUTASE GENES FROM TOMATO, ASSAYED BY THE PHOTOACOUSTIC METHOD

Dvora Aviv*, Alexandra R.J. Driesenaar**, Shmuel Malkin** and Esra Galun*.
*Plant Genetics and **Biochemistry Departments. The Weizmann Institute of Science. Rehovot. 76100 Israel.

INTRODUCTION

Photoinhibition is a complex process, probably occuring via several mechanisms. One of them may be the generation of oxygen radical anion (superoxide - O_2^-) which has non-specific destruction effects on various tissue constituents. This radical could be produced through a one-electron reduction step of triplet or singlet oxygen - in the last case it may be formed by sensitization at a closed reaction centers. Also, this radical might be produced as a side reaction in the oxygen evolving mechanism.
A protection mechanism against superoxide in plants involves several detoxifying enzymes working in tandem to reduce O_2^- to the level of H_2O (cf. [1]). The first one in this series is superoxide dismutase (SOD) which disproportionate O_2^- to the level of H_2O_2 and O_2 ($O_2^- + 2H^+ \rightarrow H_2O_2 + O_2$).

Looking in more depth into these possible processes and attempting to provide protection in sensitive plants, gene transfer experiments were performed to see if elevated or reduced levels of SOD will indeed change the performance of plants at elevated light intensities.

In the following experiments we attempted to see indications for possible correlation between photoinhibitory damage and the presence of various forms of the transferred gene. As a sensitive plant we chose the aurea mutant of *Nicotiana tabacum* Su/+ [2]. Photosynthetic performance was conveniently assayed by photoacoustics [3], allowing an immediate short measurement after each photoinhibitory treatment.

MATERIALS AND METHODS

Plant Material: The cDNAs of tomato cytosolic (Cyt) and chloroplastic (Chl) Cu/Zn SOD were cloned and sequenced [4]. The clones were transfered into an expression vector [5] in a sense orientation (p31A and pT_1) and in an anti-sense orientation (p31B). Employing *Agrobacterium*-mediated transformation, transgenic *N.*

N. Murata (ed.), Research in Photosynthesis, Vol. IV, 557–560.

tabacum plants were obtained carrying either the tomato chl-SOD in a sense orientation or the tomato cyt-SOD in sense and anti-sense orientation. Southern hybridization was employed to verify the integration of the tomato genes in the tobacco transformants. self-pollination and planting of seeds on kanamycin selective medium for at least two generations enabled us to establish several lines homozygotes for the alien gene. Thus line X31A7-1 harbors the tomato cyt-SOD in the sense orientation. Line X31B12-1 harbors the cyt-SOD in an anti-sense orientation and line $XT_1$5-1 harbors the tomato chl-SOD in a sense orientation.

Su is a nuclear encoded, semi dominant aurea mutation of *N. tabacum* [2], 1964). The heterozygote (Su/+) is light green and is easily distinguishable from either the green wild type (+/+) or the yellow, lethal homozygote (Su/Su). The heterozygote is very sensitive to light. Under high light intensity it is yellow-green while under low light it is pale green. Molecular analysis of the heterozygote [6] revealed a drastic reduction in the light harvesting chlorophyll a/b binding protein (LHCP).

To test whether modulation of SOD level could affect the response to photoinhibition we transferred the transgenic tomato genes into the aurea background by crossing the heterozygote (Su/+) with each one of the transgenic lines and selecting, among the seedlings, the light green heterozygotes, thus creating the following lines which served for the photoinhibition studies: Lines A, B: Su/+, harboring the tomato cyt-SOD in sense orientation. Line C: Su/+, harboring the tomato chl-SOD in sense orientation. Line D: Su/+, harboring the tomato cyt-SOD in an anti-sense orientation. Line E - control Su/+, not harboring any transgenic SOD. The above plants were sensitive to high light and hence were grown under low light conditions. In the comparison between the different plants we attempted to use plants at similar stages of the development. For each plant several repeating experiments were done in different leaves.

Photoacoustic measurements and photoinhibitory treatment: A description of the photoacoustic method was given in [3] and [7]. Usually, small discs cut from leaves are used and placed inside a small transparent enclosure, which communicates with a microphone. Absorption of periodically modulated light in a leaf disc causes the release of modulated heat and modulated oxygen evolution, which generate an acoustic wave (sound) in the leaf's inner air-phase. The sound propagates into the outside of the leaf and is sensed by the microphone. In the present experiments the microphone signal was processed by a lock-in amplifier (SR 530, Stanford Research Systems). Signals arising from heat evolution (photothermal) and from oxygen evolution (photobaric) were separated into their vectorial components, as described in [7]. Light was provided from two d.c. projectors and directed into the sample using a multi-branched light guide. Modulation at 20 Hz was obtained by passing light from one of the projectors through a mechanical chopper (Laser Precision). This modulated light passed further through a 650nm band interference filter (Ditric Optics) and had an intensity of 35 μEinsteins m^{-2} s^{-1} . The irradiation from the second projector (2500 μEinsteins m^{-2} s^{-1} of white light) served both to saturate the photoacoustic signal and for the photoinhibitory treatment.

In our experiments we used leaf discs, about 1cm in diameter, cut from the expanded leaves of the tobacco plants. After placing the discs in the photoacoustic cell, the initial thermal and oxygen evolution signals were determined. The photoinhibitory treatment was given at room temperature, in situ, as described by Jansen et al [2]. After a certain exposure to the strong light, during which the saturated photoacoustic signal was also recorded, the strong light was switched off for 1.5 minute and the photoacoustic oxygen evolution signal was determined. It was checked that the illumination by the strong light did not increase the temperature of the sample by more than about 1 ^{o}C.

RESULTS AND DISCUSSION

It has been shown [2] that the estimation of photoinhibition measured by photoacoustics in situ gives similar results as that measured outside the photoacoustic cell by CO_2 fixation. The photoacoustic determination *in situ* has the advantage that the relative results have very little scatter, so that even small changes in the photoacoustic signal are significant. The results are presented in Table I and give indications for the expected correlation. Two controls are present: the *N. tabacum* wild type, which was not sensitive to the photoinhibitory treatment and the Su/+ (E), whose activity declined to about 73% after 30 min. The trend of the other lines is generally similar throughout the treatment time. However, as the treatment progresses many other irrelevant and uncontrolled protecting mechanisms may come into play. Therefore one should consider the earlier times, although the occuring differences were relatively small.

TABLE I. Relative values of the photoacoustic oxygen evolution signal after photoinhibition

Photoinhibition time (min)	0	10	20	30
Relative oxygen evolution:				
Wild type	100	99.5	98.5	89.0
Line E	100	86.0	80.0	73.0
Line D	100	79.0	66.5	65.5
Line C	100	90.0	82.5	77.0
Line A	100	84.5	75.0	65.5
Line B	100	85.0	78.0	77.0

It seems, from Table I, that relative to the sensitive control (E), Su/+ with elevated chloroplastic SOD (C) was somewhat less affected, while Su/+ with an antisense cytosolic SOD (D) was more significantly affected. The effect of the antisense gene is to provide the complementary RNA strand which will bind to the active strand and thus reduce the basal level of SOD. The effect of photoinhibition on Su/+ with one of the elevated cytosolic SOD (A) was higher. With the other (B) it was close or even less than that on the control (E). However, cytosolic SOD is not expected to provide protection against the superoxide anion in the chloroplast.

Although the antisense construct was expected to reduce the endogenous mRNA of the cytosolic SOD of line D, hence reducing the relevant isoenzyme, it turned out that the endogenous chloroplast SOD isoenzyme of line D was also reduced, as judged by activity gel (not shown) The reduction in both endogenous SOD isoenzymes may explain the sensitivity of line D to photoinhibition. The dual reduction in both isoenzymes was probably due to the high similarity in their mRNA sequences.

Considering the complexity and the intervention of uncontrolled other mechanisms, we obtain a coarse picture. However, these results were repeated several times and therefore serve as a preliminary indications that the superoxide anion plays a partial role in photoinhibition. They also mark a strategy to provide a partial protection against photoinhibition. Further experiments are in progress.

ACKNOWLEDGEMENT

This research was partly supported by the MINERVA fund.

REFERENCES

1 Jansen, M.A.K., Shaaltiel, Y., Kazzes, D., Canaani, O., Malkin, S. and Gressel J. (1989). Plant Physiol. 91, 1174-1178

2 Burk, L.G. and Menser, H.A.(1964). Tobacco Sci. 18, 101-104.

3 Bults, G., Horwitz, B.A., Malkin, S. and Cahen, D. (1982) Biochim. Biophys. Acta 679, 452-465

4 Perl-Treves, R., Nachmias, B., Aviv, D., Zeelon, E.P. and Galun, E. (1988). Plant Mol. Biol. 11, 609-623.

5 Perl-Treves, R., (1990). Ph.D. thesis, submitted to the Feinberg Graduate School - The Weizmann Institute of Science.

6 Kawata, E.E. and Cheung, A.Y., (1990). EMBO J. 9, 4197-4203.

7 Poulet, P., Malkin, S. and Cahen, D., (1983). Biochim. Biophys. Acta 724, 433-446.

PHOTOINHIBITION IN FIELD GROWN KIWIFRUIT VINES

D.H. Greer and W.A. Laing, Hort Research, Batchelar Research Centre, Private Bag 11 030, Palmerston North, New Zealand.

INTRODUCTION

Kiwifruit (*Actinidia deliciosa*) vines growing outdoors in pots are susceptible to photoinhibition of photosynthesis, especially during spring and autumn (1). These results are comparable to studies of other species, including willow (2) and *Eucalyptus* (3), showing that photoinhibition occurs under natural conditions. However, given the attenuation of light through the canopy and the diurnal and seasonal variation in interception at the different leaf positions, it is likely that susceptibility to photoinhibition of kiwifruit leaves will vary over the vine. In this study, photosynthesis, fluorescence, and carotenoid pigments of leaves in different positions on orchard-grown kiwifruit vines were, therefore, followed through the growing season to assess their susceptibility to photoinhibition.

MATERIALS AND METHODS

Three mature kiwifruit (*Actinidia deliciosa*) vines growing in rows on a T-bar structure at the Massey University Research Orchard in Palmerston North were selected for study. The rows were orientated approximately southeast-northwest. Bud break occurred in September (spring) and the full canopy was achieved in December. At intervals, from October to May, leaf disks were collected off each of two leaves in six positions in the canopy. Small (10 mm diam.) disks were placed immediately in darkened cuvettes on moist filter paper, transferred to the laboratory and fluorescence at 77K measured (4). Larger disks (35 mm diam.) were immediately frozen in liquid nitrogen and, at a later stage, carotenoid and chlorophyll pigments extracted (5) and measured by HPLC (6). At similar times, net photosynthesis was measured *in situ* on 2-3 intact leaves at each position using an LCA2 portable IRGA. In midsummer, two young (30 mm diameter) and two mature fully exposed leaves were covered in 35% shade cloth and left for 7-8 days after which the shade cloth was removed. At daily intervals for 7 days leaf disks were removed as above and fluorescence measured and carotenoid pigments assayed.

RESULTS AND DISCUSSION

Canopy position effects

There were significant differences in the fluorescence ratio (Fv/Fm) at 77K, averaged over the growing season, at the 6 canopy positions on the vine (Fig. 1). The highest ratio of 0.864 was in leaves underneath the canopy in a well shaded position. These were characteristically shade leaves in photosynthetic response (not shown) and had a high photochemical efficiency. By

N. Murata (ed.), Research in Photosynthesis, Vol. IV, 561–564.

contrast, leaves in the upper, fully exposed, canopy were characteristically sun leaves and had the lowest Fv/Fm ratio of 0.702, 81% of that in shade leaves. The sun leaves thus experienced photoinhibitory reductions in photochemical efficiency in this position. The Fv/Fm ratios in leaves exposed predominantly to morning sun were 84% of that in the shade leaves with no difference between the lower and upper positions. Similarly, leaves exposed to the afternoon sun were as photoinhibited as the full sun leaves but lower in the canopy the leaves had a significantly higher Fv/Fm ratio than those in a higher position of the canopy. Similar differences in Fv/Fm in sun and shade leaves of pot-grown kiwifruit have been reported (1).

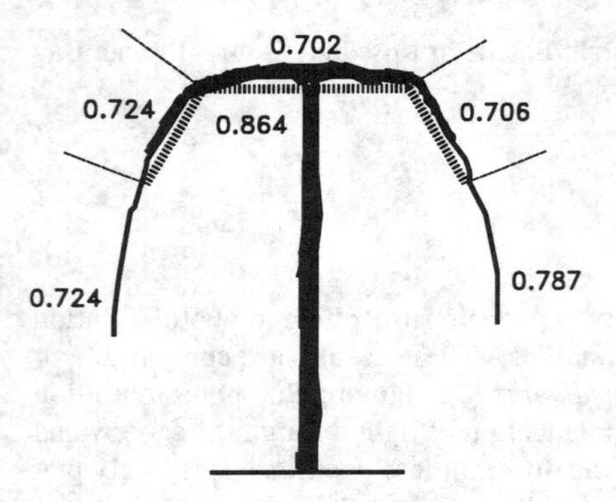

Figure 1. Cross section of a kiwifruit vine showing position effects on Fv/Fm, averaged over the growing season. Morning sun was predominant to the left (East).

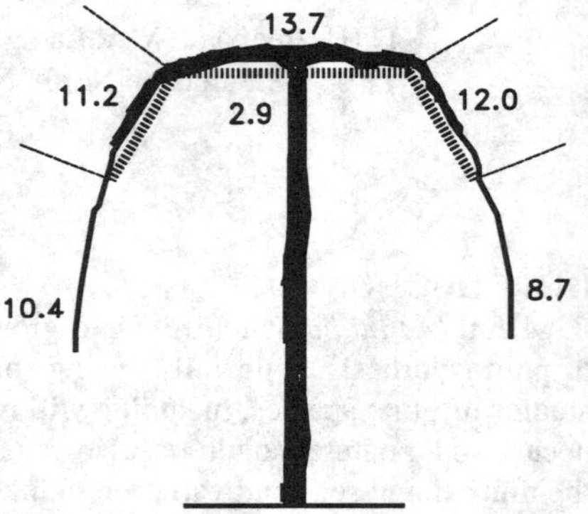

Figure 2. Vine position differences in photosynthesis ($\mu mol.m^{-2}.s^{-1}$) measured under ambient conditions, and averaged over the growing season.

There were also marked differences in photosynthesis at the different canopy positions (Fig. 2) with an extreme contrast from leaves underneath the canopy with the lowest rate of 3 $\mu mol.m^{-2}.s^{-1}$ to those at the top-most position with the highest rate at about 14 $\mu mol.m^{-2}.s^{-1}$, a 5-fold increase. In leaves in the two shoulder positions in the canopy, there was a 12-20% reduction in photosynthesis relative to the fully exposed leaves. Leaves further down on the vines had even lower rates of photosynthesis, averaging 65-75% of that at the top of the vine, with the lower rate in leaves on the west side.

There was a significant inverse linear relationship between the rates of photosynthesis and the Fv/Fm ratio (r^2=0.95) in leaves in the different positions on the vine. Thus for each 1 $\mu mol.m^{-2}.s^{-1}$ increase in photosynthesis there was an average 1.6% decline in the Fv/Fm ratio in these kiwifruit leaves. The photosynthetic rates around the vine reflect the average daily light interception at each position, with higher interception associated with higher rates of photosynthesis. In turn, the higher the light interception the lower is the Fv/Fm ratio and, therefore, the greater is the extent of photoinhibition in these leaves.

The amount of zeaxanthin relative to violaxanthin and antheraxanthin was very low in shade leaves [Z/(Z+A+V) = 0.09 ± 0.02] throughout the growing season whereas full sun leaves had a significant proportion (Z/(Z+A+V) = 0.31 ± 0.03]. This shows the sun leaves were stressed by high irradiance and required the production of zeaxanthin for some photoprotection from photoinhibition.

Seasonality of Fv/Fm

Kiwifruit leaves in the fully shaded position on the vine had a relatively constant and high Fv/Fm ratio throughout the growing season (Fig. 3) and thus experienced no photoinhibition.

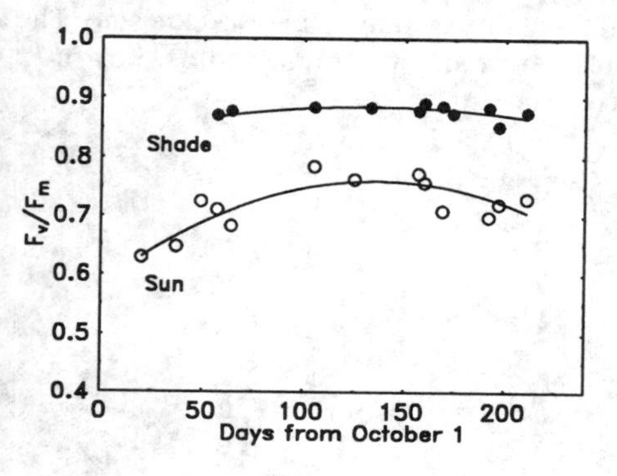

Figure 3. Seasonal changes in Fv/Fm at the top of the kiwifruit vine canopy (sun) and in shade leaves underneath the vine. Each point is the mean of 2-3 duplicate measurements.

Leaves at the top of the canopy, in contrast, had a ratio of 0.6 in spring, a maximum of 0.75 in midsummer and a lower ratio again in autumn. Thus these well exposed leaves were photoinhibited in spring and autumn and to a lesser extent in midsummer, as had previously been shown in pot-grown vines (1). At other positions on the vine (not shown) the seasonal changes in Fv/Fm were intermediate to these two positions.

Induced photoinhibition in sun leaves

Young kiwifruit leaves expanded in 65% of full sun had fluorescence characteristics approaching that of shade leaves (Fig. 4a). Immediately they were exposed to full sun, however, there were marked changes in fluorescence with both Fv and Fv/Fm declining over the next 4 days by 70 and 20% respectively, and Fo also declining after an initial rise, indicating severe photoinhibition occurred. Subsequently there was some adjustment as the leaves reacclimated to full sun. Comparable results were obtained with mature leaves.

Concomitant to the removal of the shade cloth, the carotenoid pigment ratio increased from about 0.1 to 0.45 within the first day and remained steady, indicative of a shift from violaxanthin to zeaxanthin (Fig. 4b). At the same time there was little change in the pool size, though over the next 3 days there was an increase in the total pigment pool size to a level consistent with that in sun leaves.

These data indicate that the leaves invoked the production of zeaxanthin rapidly to reduce the photoinhibitory stress imposed on their exposure to full sun but additional synthesis of carotenoids was required to provide further protection over the longer time. However, it is clear that the capacity for protection from photoinhibition in the sun leaves was insufficient since the Fv/Fm ratio remained significantly depressed, relative to leaves in the shade.

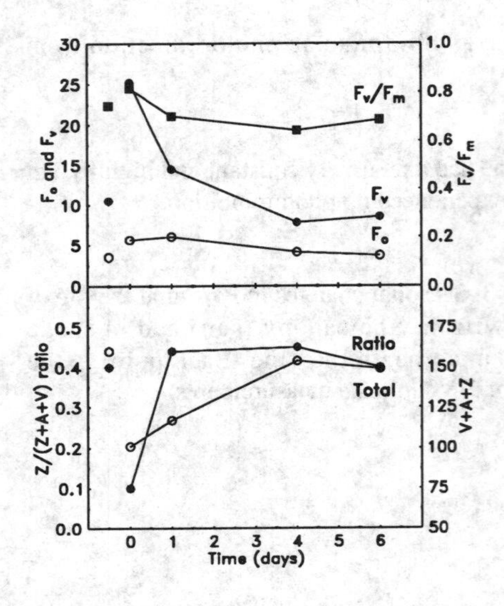

Figure 4a, b. Changes in fluorescence characteristics (a) and the zeaxanthin to violaxanthin ratio and total pigment content (b) in kiwifruit leaves initially shaded for 7 days before the leaf was re-exposed to full sun at day 0. The photon flux density during the exposure averaged 1800 $\mu mol.m^{-2}.s^{-1}$ throughout the exposure. The values before day 0 represent those for fully exposed sun leaves.

CONCLUSIONS

Leaves of kiwifruit vines growing in orchard conditions suffer from naturally-induced photoinhibition, in spite of an inherent capacity to dissipate excess excitation energy through the zeaxanthin-mediated pathway. However, there is marked variation around the vine in the extent of photoinhibition that is clearly dependent on the amount of light intercepted by the leaves. It remains to assess the 'cost' of this photoinhibition to the productivity of the leaves in carbon acquisition.

REFERENCES

1 Greer, D.H. and Laing, W.A. (1992) Planta 186, 418-425
2 Ögren, E. (1988) Planta 175, 229-236
3 Ögren, E. and Evans, J.R. (1992) Aust. J. Plant Physiol. 19, 223-232
4 Greer, D.H., Laing, W.A. and Kipnis, T. (1988) Planta 174, 152-158
5 Thayer, S.S. and Björkman O. (1990) Photosyn. Res. 23, 331-343
6 Gilmore, A.M. and Yamamoto, H.Y. (1991) J. Chromat. 543, 137-145

PHOTOINHIBITION OF INDICA AND JAPONICA RICE AND THEIR RECIPROCAL F_1 HYBRIDS

JIAO DEMAO, JI BENHUA, LI CHUANGUO, TONG HONGYU, Jiangsu Academy of Agricultural Sciences, Nanjing 210014, China

1. INTRODUCTION

Illumination of plants with photon flux density in excess of that required to saturate photosynthetic reaction will result in photoinhibition (1). Generally Photoinhibition was interpreted as the result of damage to the reaction center of photosystem II(2). During photoinhibition, D_1 protein was primarily damaged by high irradiation and high rate of turnover of this protein occured, The primary sites of photoinhibition had been suggested to be located within the D_1 protein to which the PSII reaction center was bound (3). The proposed mechanisms for damage to the D_1 protein was supposed to be via the quinone anion radical generated by hight light or the oxygen radical generated by the interaction of molecular oxygen with quinone anion (4). The enzymatic protective defenses were capable of scavenging oxygen radicals and oxy intermediates, Among which superoxide dismutase had been shown to play a major role in protecting photosynthetic apparatus from such oxidative damage (5). In recent years, It was found that difference in response to photoinhibition did exist in rice subspecies (O. Sativa l) indica and japonica (6). This work was taken to study the photoinhibitory differences among indica、japonica and their reciprocal F_1 hybrids in terms of photosynthetic rate. PSII activity、D_1 protein、SOD activity so as to develope a effective approach for indica—japonica hybrid rice breeding program.

2. MATERIALS AND METHODS

Japonica cultivars 02428、029 known for wide compatibility, Indica Cultivars 3037、Palghar and their reciprocal F_1 hybrids were grown in the field. Detached leaves were photoinhibited upon exposure to high light of 1250 $\mu mol\ m^{-2}s^{-1}$, CO_2 60ppm, O_2 2.5%, 30℃ for 4h. Photosynthetic rate was determined with Clark electrode, Photoinhibition was calculated as difference befor and after photoinhibitory treatment. Suspension of chloroplasts were isolated from rice leaves and photoinhibited under hight light of 1250 $\mu mol\ m^{-2}s^{-1}$, 30℃ for 25min. PSII activity of thylakoids was measured by the method of Shyam (7). ^{14}C—atrazine binding analysis to estimate the amount of D_1 protein was made by the method of Chow (8) SOD activity was assayed by the method of Giannopolitis (9).

3. RESULTS AND DISCUSSION

3.1 Photoinhibition of photosynthesis and PSII activity.

Photoinhibition in terms of photosynthesis and PSII activity with japonica cultivars 02428、029 and indica cultivars 3037.palghar were presented in

N. Murata (ed.), Research in Photosynthesis, Vol. IV, 565–568.

table 1. Results demonstrated that japonica usually showed a less photoinhibition than indica, While reciprocal F_1 hybrids were closer to their maternal parent respectively. It indicated that reciprocal crosses showed different response to photoinhibitory treatment depending upon the female used. F_1 hybrids with indica cultivar as the female were more susceptible to photoinhibition. Such tendency was also found in the PSII activity under inducing photoinhibitory condition.

TABLE 1. Photosynthetic rates of leves and PSII activities of thylakoids in indica and japonica and their reciprocal F_1 hybrids

Parents and F_1 hybrids	Photosynthetic rates ($\mu mol O_2/m^2 \cdot s$) Control (A) 0 hour	Treatment (B) 4 hour	$\frac{A-B}{A}$ Photoinhibition %	PSII activities ($\mu mol O_2/mgChl \cdot h$) Control (A) 0 min	Treatment (B) 25 min	$\frac{A-B}{A}$ Photoinhibition %
3037(indica)	10.48±1.26	4.52±0.45	56.87	54.43±1.81	27.62±2.13	49.26
3037/02428F_1	13.71±1.19	9.35±1.02	31.80	64.78±2.36	42.20±1.71	34.86
02428/3037F_1	12.66±0.61	9.76±0.28	22.91	67.27±1.43	53.02±1.12	21.18
02428(japonica)	12.10±0.81	9.99±0.58	17.44	75.40±1.32	59.88±1.23	20.58
02428/pal.F_1	12.77±0.46	8.95±0.48	29.91	70.76±2.22	54.63±2.53	22.80
Pal/02428F_1	12.07±0.38	7.96±0.28	34.05	69.55±1.21	46.96±1.81	32.48
Palghar(indica)	10.48±0.56	5.08±0.39	51.53	55.10±1.18	29.23±0.88	46.95
Palghar/029F_1	14.52±0.98	9.11±0.37	37.26	65.59±1.13	41.13±1.01	37.29
029/PalgharF_1	13.47±0.53	8.95±0.21	33.56	78.62±2.84	53.42±1.44	32.05
029(japonica)	12.18±0.53	9.27±0.40	23.89	78.76±2.82	55.24±1.65	29.86

Means±SD(n=3)

3.2 Analysis of ^{14}C-atrazine binding to D_1 protein

To elucidate physiological genetics of photoinhibition, The capacity of ^{14}C-atrazine binding to thylakoids in indica 3037 and japonica 02428 and their reciprocal F_1 hybrids were analyzed before and after photoinhibiton as shown in Fig1 and table2. The K_b represented D_1 protein binding affinity with atrazine. A higher K_b often gave less atrazine binding capacity to D_1 protein which might be related to higher tolerance to photoinhibition. Generally, The K_b in japonica was higher than that in indica. The K_b of indica/japonica F_1 and japonica/indica F_1 were egual to those of their maternal, respectively. It was interesting that the K_b value were not affected by photoinhibitory treatment, indicating D_1 protein was maternally inherited. The concentration of D_1 protein in indica 3037 and japonica 02428 were decreased by 47.62% and 17.43% respetfively as shown in table 2 after photoinhibition. It was certain that the maintaining capacity of D_1 protein in japonica/indica F_1 was nearly as much as that in maternal japonica; Meanwhile, the maintaining capacity of D_1 protein in indica/japonica F_1 is higher than that in meternal indica. It seemed that there was a mechanism in indica/japonica F_1 to protect D_1 protein against degradation from male japonica.

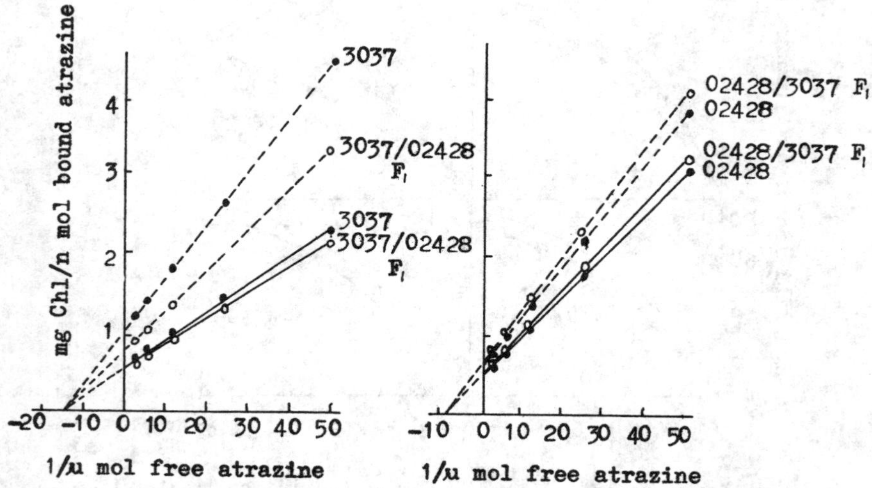

Solid lines: Control; Dotted lines: Photoinhibition treatment

Solid lines: Control; Dotted lines: Photoinhibition treatment

FIG 1. Double reciprocal plots for ^{14}C—atrazine bound to thylakoids against free atrazine in indica 3037 and japonica 02428 and their reciprocal F_1 hybrids.

TABLE 2. Kinetic parameters of ^{14}c—atrazine to thylakoids isolated from 3037. 02428 and their reciprocal F_1 hybrids (data derived from Fig1)

Parents and F_1 hybrids	k_d(μmol/L) Control	k_d(μmol/L) Treatment	Bound atrazine (n mol/mg chl) Control (A)	Bound atrazine (n mol/mg chl) Treatment (B)	$\frac{A-B}{A}\times 100\%$
3037	0.067	0.069	1.829	0.958	47.62
3037/02428F_1	0.068	0.067	1.916	1.300	32.15
02428/3037F_1	0.112	0.114	1.899	1.558	16.38
02428	0.113	0.116	1.968	1.625	17.43

3.3 Change of SOD activity induced during photoinhibition

SOD played some role in reducing photooxidative damage to D_1 protein. The changes of SOD activity in indica 3037 and japonica 02428 and their reciprocal F_1 hybrids were shown in Fig2. The relative activities of SOD in 3037, 3037/02428 F_1, 02428/3037 F_1, 02428 after photoinhibition were 74.01%, 112.88%, 118.32%, 156.50% of the controls, respectively. The intermediacy and no apparent difference of SOD activity induced between two F_1 hybrids was substantiated. It was concluded that SOD activities induced by photoinhibition in F_1 hybrids were not affected by reciprocal crossing between both parents.

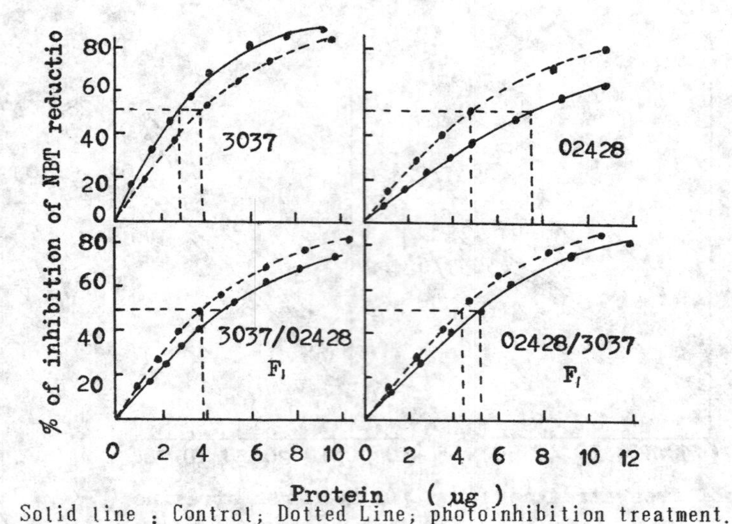

Solid line : Control; Dotted Line; photoinhibition treatment.

FIG 2. Changes of SOD activity in indica 3037 and japonica 02428 and their reciprocal F_1 hybrids during photoinhibition.

4. CONCLUSSION

We have shown that there was a significant difference between tolerant and susceptible rice subspecies in the responses to photoinhibition stress. Making a comparision among indica and japonica and reciprocal F_1 hybrids, The differential sensitivities to photoinhibition seemed to be related to D_1 protein encoded by chloroplast gene and SOD encoded by nuclear gene. The results suggested that photoinhibitory response in rice subspecies F_1 hybrids generally varied depending mainly upon the female cultivars used.

REFERENCES

1. Kyle, D.J., Ohad, I and Arntzen, C.J.(1985) Cellular and Molecular Biology of plant stress. 51－69
2. Krause, G·H.(1988) physiologia plantarum. 74, 566－574
3. Krupa, Z., Öquist, G., Gustafsson, P. and Golden, S.S.(1990)in Current Research in photosynthesis(Baltscheffsky, M., ed.), Vol. 2, PP. 431－434, kluwer Academic Publishers, Dordrecht
4. Gong, H. and Nilsen, S.(1990) in Current Research in Photosynthesis (Baltscheffsky, M., ed.), Vol. 2, PP. 397－400, Kluwer Academic publishers, Dordrecht
5. Scandalios, J.G.(1990) Advances in genetics. Vol. 28, 1－41
6. Jiao, D.M. Gu, X.Y. Ji, B.H. Zhang, C.L.(1991) Chinese J of Rice Sciences. Vol. 5 (3), 133－136
7. Shyam, R. and Sane, P. V.(1990) in Current Research in photosynthesis (Baltscheffsky, M., ed.), Vol. 2, PP. 447-450. kluwer Academic publisher, Dordrecht
8. Chow, W.S. Hope, A.B. and Anderson, J.M.(1989) Biochem. Biophys. Acta. 973, 105－108
9. Giannopolitis, C.N. and Ries, S.K.(1977) plant physiol. 59, 309－314

PHOTOSYNTHETIC ACTIVITY AND TRANSPIRATION RATE OF AZOLLA UNDER DECLINING PHOTOSYNTHETIC PHOTON FLUX DENSITY

Department of Agronomy, University of the Philippines at Los Baños, College, Laguna, Philippines.

Joveno S. Lales and Mario A. Lapitan

1. INTRODUCTION

Azolla, a small aquatic fern, was introduced to the Philippines because of its potential as green manure and its nutritive value as feed supplement for poultry and herbivorous fresh water fish. Biomass production varies widely because of seasonal fluctuation of climatic factors. Climatic influences on growth and nitrogenase activity[1,2,3,4,5] have been studied in recent years but the physiological basis of high productivity received little attention.

Recent investigations on the photosynthetic activity of azolla[6] focused on the interactive effects of temperature, relative humidity and solar radiation. No attempt, however, was initiated to investigate the effect of shade, a typical micro-environmental condition in rice canopies at different stages of development, on net photosynthesis. Stomatogenesis and stomatal development in *A. pinnata*[7] was studied but the stomatal behavior of the species under shade remains to be evaluated.

The study was conducted to determine the photosynthetic activity, transpiration rate and stomatal conductance of azolla when exposed to declining photosynthetic photon flux density (PPFD).

2. MATERIALS AND METHODS

Sporophytes of azolla, UPLB Hybrid 7, were grown under full sunlight. Three (3) fully-grown plants were randomly collected from the propagation pond, washed thoroughly then suspended on distilled water in petri dishes. After excising the roots, the size of individual plants was determined with a portable leaf area meter (Licor 3000A). The sample plants were then blot-dried before insertion into the one-fourth-liter chamber of a portable CO_2 analyzer (Licor 6200) for photosynthetic activity measurement under declining PPFD. To attain the desired PPFD, different layers of white single-wove nylon screen were placed on top of the chamber and quantum sensor (Licor LI-190SA). Plant surface temperature was determined with a fine-wire thermocouple attached to the chamber of the CO_2 analyzer. The change in CO_2 for each measurement was set at 3 ppm. This also set the duration of each measurement within 45 seconds. After each measurement, the samples were suspended on distilled water for about 2 minutes to allow them to recover before the next measurement. Gas exchange

N. Murata (ed.), Research in Photosynthesis, Vol. IV, 569–572.

measurements were undertaken between 1045 and 1215 h.

3. RESULTS AND DISCUSSION

Net photosynthesis declined sharply when PPFD was reduced by 15% (Fig. 1). The photosynthetic activity of the hybrid under

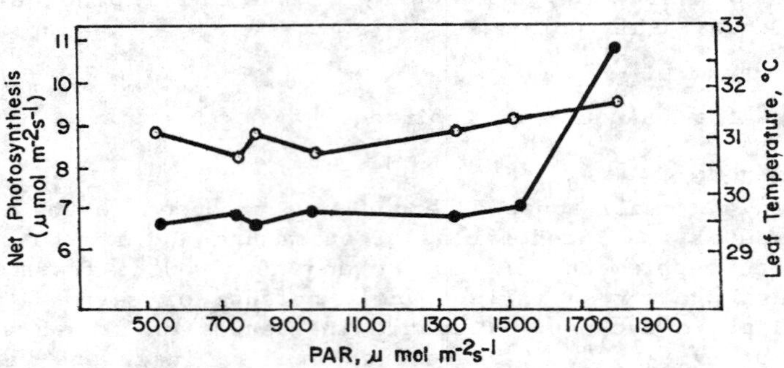

Fig. I. Net plant photosynthesis (o) and leaf temperature (•) at different levels of photosynthetically active radiation.

full sunlight was 10.59 umol $m^{-2}s^{-1}$ which is distinctly close to those obtained from *A. pinnata* through a simple CO_2 depletion technique for monitoring photosynthesis[6]. Within the full range of PPFD under shaded conditions, net photosynthesis fluctuated very slightly. The fluctuation was closely associated with the surface temperature of the plant, thus obscuring the plant's re sponse to diminishing PPFD. The rise in plant surface temperature when PPFD was reduced to the the range from 561 to 950 umol m^{-2} s^{-1} suggests local advection of heat that also influenced net photosynthesis. Similar adverse effect of temperature on the oxygen evolution in *A. pinnata* was observed particularly at temperatures greater than $30^{o}C$[8].

The low but relatively stable photosynthetic activity of the azolla hybrid under shaded conditions indicates the ability of the aquatic fern to grow concurrently with wetland rice at different stages of canopy development. Individual plants, however, tend to grow thin and small as the rice canopy develops and intercepts more solar radiation[9]. Since a sharp increase in PPFD occurs shortly after the rice crop is harvested, then the ability of the aquatic fern to adapt quickly to the new micro-environment is an equally important feature to consider in developing new hybrids for high dry matter production in wetland areas. Unfortunately, this was not evaluated in the study.

Transpiration rate (E) decreased slightly within the PPFD range from 561 to 800 umol m^{-2} s^{-1} (Table 1). Mean transpirational water loss under shade was 0.0238 mol m^{-2} s^{-1} and 0.0254 mol m^{-2} s^{-1} under full sunlight. The slight change in E is probably associated with a unique stomatal structure which influenced the sensitivity of the aquatic fern to decreasing PPFD. Other plant species generally respond quickly to brief exposure to low solar

Table 1. Transpiration rate and stomatal conductance of azolla c.v UPL Hybrid 7 under various levels of photon flux density.

PPFD ($uEm^{-2}s^{-1}$)	TRANSPIRATION RATE ($mmol\ m^{-2}s^{-1}$)	STOMATAL CONDUCTANCE ($mol\ m^{-2}s^{-1}$)
1,796 (Full)	25.4	3.53
1,524	25.9	2.28
1,348	25.6	2.32
972	25.4	2.75
799	21.1	1.76
769	23.2	1.76
561	21.9	2.87

radiation by restricting stomatal opening thus reducing transpiration rate. In contrast, the aquatic fern maintained relatively high transpiration rate even as PPFD was reduced by about 70%. A striking stomatal behavior observed was the tendency of the stomates to re-open at low PPFD (561 umol m^{-2} s^{-1}) while photosynthetic activity and transpiration rate did not increase.

Transpiration rate appeared to be overestimated. This is attributed to the inherent feature of the chamber which represents an artificial micro-environment. The boundary layer resistance of the plant which is expected to be small was virtually eliminated because of the turbulence caused by the fan assembly inside the chamber. Stomatal conductance (g_s) under full sunlight was almost two-fold greater than the maximum recorded previously for different groups of plants. Similar to E, g_s was overestimated because of the fan-mediated elimination of boundary layer resistance which is typically small considering the size of the fern. The relationship between g_s and PPFD was not clear. Similarly, the relationship between g_s with photosynthetic activity and transpiration rate was not clearly understood.

It is worthy to note that photosynthetic activity measured in the study did not only reflect the photosynthetic activity of the aquatic fern but also that of the endophyte (a blue-green alga). Indeed, the endophyte has been found photosynthetically competent but it is extremely difficult to quantify its contribution to the system's CO_2 fixation[10].

Independent measurements of stomatal conductance, transpiration and photosynthesis under varying photon flux density and controlled temperature are deemed necessary in future attempts to understand the role of stomates in controlling gas exchange in azolla.

REFERENCES

1 Ashton, P. J. (1974). In The Orange River Program Report, pp.123-138, Inst. Environ. Sci. Uni. O.F.S Bioenfortein, S.T.
2 Holst, R. W and Yapp, J. H. (1979). Am. Fern J. 69,12-25.
3 Watanabe, I. and Berja, N. S. (1982). Aquatic Bot. 15,175-185.
4 Lumpkin, T. A and Bartholomew, D. P. (1986). Crop Sci. 26,107-111.
5 Harro, W., Sang, W. F., and Vu, V. V. (1987). Plant and Soil 99,219-230.
6 Allen, S. G., Idso, S. B. , and Kimball, B. A. (1988). Agric. For. Agric. Meteor. 42,209-217.
7 Sen, U. (1983). Ann. Bot. 52,201-204.
8 Vu, V. V., Sang, H. W. W. F., Kijne, J. W., Planque, K.,and Kraay-enhof, R. (1986). Photosythetica 20(1),67-73.
9 Alcantara, N. P. and Lales, J. S. (1992). Phil. Agric. In Press.
10 Ray, T. B., Mayne, B. C., Toia, R. E., Jr., and Peters, G. A. (1979). Plant physiol. 64,791-795.

THE GRADIENTS OF CARBON FIXATION, RIBULOSE-BISPHOSPHATE CARBOXYLASE/OXYGENASE CONTENT, AND PHOTOSYNTHETIC PIGMENTS ACROSS "SUN" AND "SHADE" LEAVES OF SPINACH (*SPINACIA OLERACEA*)

JOHN N. NISHIO and **JINDONG SUN**
Department of Botany, University of Wyoming, Laramie, WY 82071, USA

INTRODUCTION

We are investigating the interactions among light, leaf anatomy, and photosynthesis. Leaf anatomy and photosynthetic characteristics are known to be dependent upon growth conditions (*e.g.*, 1,2,3). Some photosynthetic parameters across leaves have been measured (see review, 4), and there is evidence that shade-type "chloroplasts" exist in the abaxial portion of sun leaves. Such variation in photosynthetic characteristic is due in part to light environments within leaves that are also variable (5). In spinach red and blue light are rapidly attenuated by the upper portion of the palisade mesophyll (PM). Ninety percent attenuation occurs within 140 μm of the adaxial leaf surface, and the spongy mesophyll (SM) is exposed to very low quantities of blue and red light (6).

Carbon fixation measurements within leaf tissues has been limited to *in vitro* studies (*e.g.*, 7). Electron transport measurements in different leaf tissue has also been reported (*e.g.*, 8). We report here carbon fixation rates in 40 μm paradermal leaf sections of spinach sun and shade leaves labeled *in vivo*. Various combinations of treatments and assay conditions were tested. Additionally photosynthetic pigments have been quantified, as well as the rubisco (RuBPc) content.

MATERIALS AND METHODS

Plant Growth Conditions. Spinach (*Spinacia oleracea*) was cultured hydroponically. The plants were grown in controlled environment growth chambers. Lighting was provided by metal arc lamps plus incandescent lamps; PAR of sun condition was 800 $\mu mol \cdot m^{-2} \cdot s^{-1}$; PAR of shade condition was 200 $\mu mol \cdot m^{-2} \cdot s^{-1}$ obtained with 3M NR20SMARL film (Minneapolis MN). The film reduces the R:FR ratio to about 0.25, which is equivalent to deep shade. Five to six week old plants were sampled.

$^{14}CO_2$ Fixation. After 1 h illumination, a leaf was clamped in a small leaf chamber and illuminated by a quartz-halogen light directed with a fiber optic cable. $^{14}CO_2$(g) was injected to the abaxial surface of the leaf for 10 s. The total volume injected was 2.5 ml containing 1000 ppm CO_2 and $^{[14]}$-CO_2 with a total activity of 0.8 μCi. Immediately after labeling, a leaf disc (0.5 cm^2) was acquired with a precooled (N_2(*l*)) paper punch. A single leaf disc was then frozen onto the stage of a microtome and cut paradermally into 40 μm-thick sections. Each section was immediately put into 1 ml 95% ethanol in a liquid scintillation vial and kept at -20° C until counting.

Rubisco Determination. A leaf disc was sampled and microsectioned as described in "$^{14}CO_2$ Fixation" section above. Each section was extracted and soluble proteins were separated by PAGE.

Chlorophyll and Carotenoid Determination. Four leaf discs were sectioned paradermally into 40 μm-thick layers; corresponding layers were pooled in a small vial containing 1 ml 95% ethanol plus a little sodium ascorbate powder. Samples were kept

N. Murata (ed.), Research in Photosynthesis, Vol. IV, 573–576.

in dark until analysis. Chlorophyll a and b and carotenoids were determined by measuring absorbance at 470, 648.6, 664.2 nm minus absorbance at 730 nm using the extinction coefficients determined by Lichtenthaler (1987).

RESULTS AND DISCUSSION

Carbon fixation across leaves appears to occur independently of the light microenvironment within leaves. About 60% of the carbon fixation across a leaf occurs in the palisade mesophyll (the upper 40% of the leaf). On a relative basis (% of total carbon fixed), more fixation occurs in the PM of a shade leaf than in the PM of a sun leaf (Table I). Light gradients from spinach plants grown under our conditions are similar to those previously reported (6). In contrast to the light gradients, carbon fixation was maximal at a depth of 100-250 μm in sun leaves and 80-120 μm in shade leaves (Fig. 1). At the point where about 90% of the blue and red light are attenuated, photosynthetic carbon fixation rates were maximal.

Table I. Distribution of CO_2 Fixation in Palisade Mesophyll and Spongy Mesophyll of Sun and Shade Leaves.

GROWTH CONDITION*	TREATMENT AND ASSAY CONDITIONS (μmols PAR·m^{-2}·s^{-1})	% TOTAL CO_2 FIXATION PM	SM	DIFFERENCE
SUN	800-1h; 800	57	43	14
SUN	2000-2h; 800	56	44	12
SUN	800-1h; 2000	52	48	4
SHADE	200-1h; 200	64	36	28
SHADE	2000-2h; 200	60	40	20
SHADE	200-1h; 2000	57	43	14

Carbon reduction in sun plants measured at 800 and 2,000 μmols PAR·m^{-2}·s^{-1} were virtually identical, whereas there was a large increase in fixation when shade plants were assayed at 2,000 μmols PAR·m^{-2}·s^{-1} compared to the growth conditions of 200 μmols PAR·m^{-2}·s^{-1} (Fig. 1). Even though the assay light was increased 10-fold, there was only a 60% increase in total carbon reduction (Table I). The adaxial layers increased by about 30%, whereas the abaxial layers (SM) exhibited a doubling of rates (Fig 1). In sun leaves a 2.5-fold increase in assay light did not significantly increase the

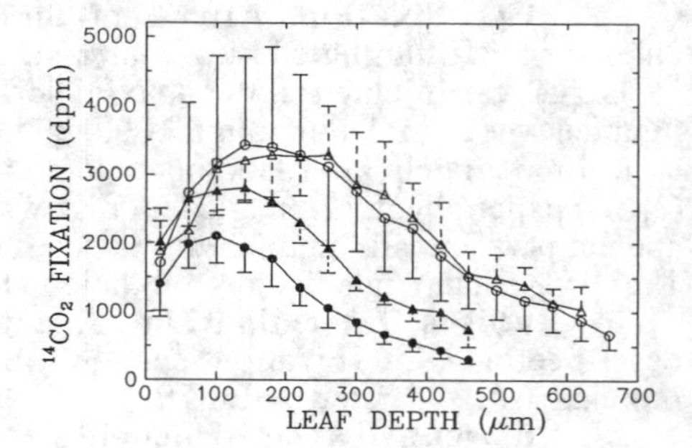

Figure 1. **CO_2 fixation across sun and shade leaves of spinach.** Sun plants were pretreated at growth condition of 800 μmols PAR·m^{-2}·s^{-1} for 1 h, and assayed at 800 μmols PAR (O), n=10 and 2,000 μmols PAR (Δ), n=6. Shade plants were pretreated at growth condition of 200 μmols PAR for 1 h, then assayed at 200 μmols PAR (●), n=22 and 2,000 μmols PAR (▲), n=5. Each point represents average dpm ± SD.

rate of fixation, although more fixation occurred in the SM (Fig. 1). The "sun" leaf is likely operating closer to saturation than a shade leaf. When viewed on a relative basis, increased light clearly shifted some of the fixation to the abaxial layers (Fig. 2).

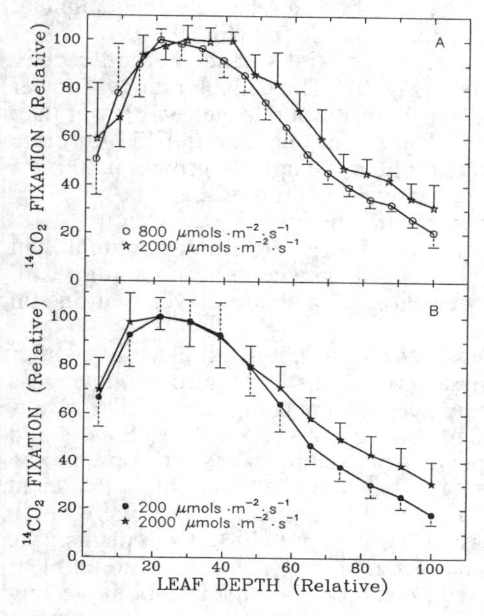

Figure 2. **CO_2 fixation in sun and shade leaves of spinach** normalized at 100 for maximum dpm/leaf section. **A.** Sun leaves assayed at 800 μmols PAR·m^{-2}·s^{-1} (O), n=10 and 2,000 μmols PAR (☆), n=6. **B.** Shade leaves measured at 200 μmols PAR (●), n=22 and 2,000 μmols PAR (★), n=5.

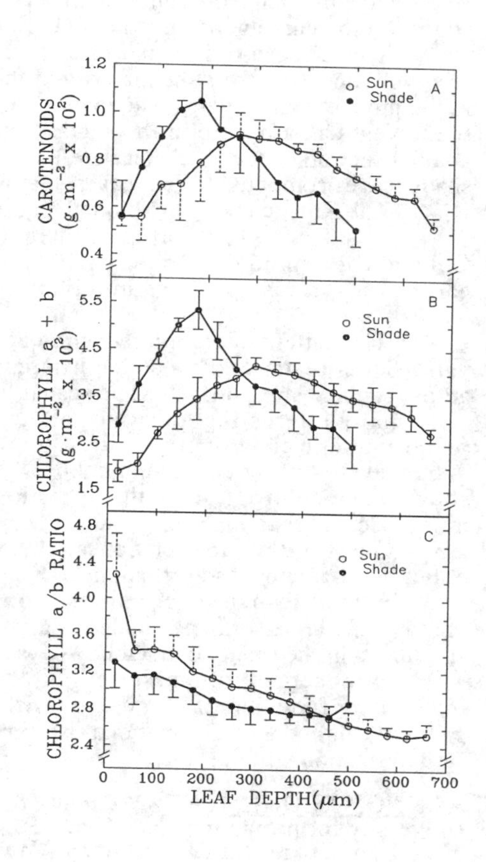

Figure 3. **Pigment composition.** Sun-- carotenoids (n=6), Chl a+b (n=7), Chl a/b (n=9); Shade--Chl a+b (n=7), carotenoids (n=8) Chl a/b (n=10).

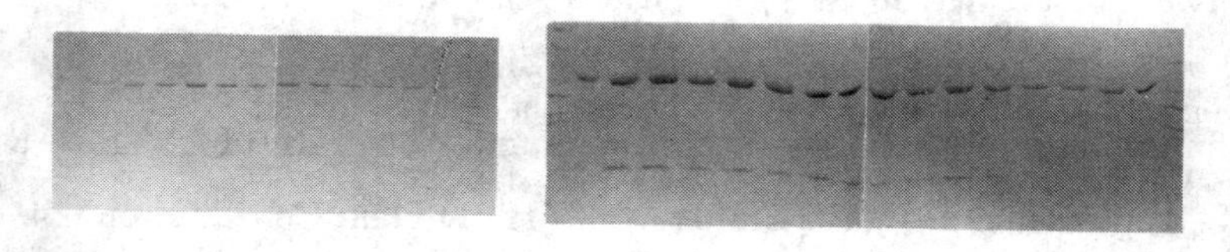

Figure 4. **Rubisco content across sun and shade leaves.** Left) Shade; Right) Sun. The large band represents LSU, and the distinct lower band represents SSU.

The carotenoid content correlated well with Chl a + b (Fig. 3). Carotenoid and Chl concentrations were higher in the PM of shade plants than in sun leaves. Pigment concentrations were maximal at a leaf depth between about 250-450 μm in sun leaves, whereas the pigment concentration in shade plants exhibited a relatively steep pigment concentration curve with a maximum between about 150-200 μm (Fig. 3).

The Chl a/b ratio was quite elevated at the adaxial surface and decreased relatively linearly across the majority of the leaf (Fig. 3). The Chl a/b ratio was lower in the most abaxial layers. The lowest Chl a/b ratio of the sun leaves was lower than the lowest Chl a/b ratio in the shade leaves. The slight increase in Chl a/b in the abaxial section of the shade leaf are likely due to the more upright growth pattern of shade leaves compared to sun leaves, that were relatively flat rosettes.

The RuBPc content exhibited a good correlation between CO_2 fixation.

Carbon reduction correlated more with RuBPc content than Chl and carotenoid content, especially in sun leaves. The correlation among Chl, carotenoids, rubisco, and carbon fixation were higher in shade leaves than in sun leaves.

The pattern of carbon reduction across leaves is strikingly similar. Even after various pre-treatments and under different assay conditions, carbon fixation patterns across sun and shade leaves when scaled for leaf depth were comparable. The results raise many interesting questions about the relation between light in leaves and photosynthetic electron transport. Chloroplasts from shade leaves are known to be vulnerable to long bouts of high light. Other data collected after a high light treatment showed that chloroplasts in the upper layers of the PM of shade plants were much more susceptible to high light than chloroplasts from the upper PM of sun plants. We now can test further, the relationship between leaf anatomy (possibly related to leaf optics and transport and diffusional considerations) and metabolism (light harvesting and electron transport considerations, for example) that leads to optimum photosynthetic performance under saturating conditions in the sun and non-saturating conditions in the shade or on cloudy days.

The method for measuring CO_2 fixation across leaves provides a method to investigate fundamental processes within leaves. The lack of correlation among pigments, light, and CO_2 fixation raises interesting questions about photosynthesis and carbon fixation within leaves.

ACKNOWLEDGEMENTS. Thanks to Dr. David W. Lee (Florida International University) for providing shade film. Research supported a CSCR USDA grant (91-37100-6672) and the University of Wyoming Research Office, Arts & Science College, and Department of Botany.

CITATIONS

1. Anderson, J.M. (1986) Ann. Rev. Plant Physiol. 37, 93-136
2. Baker, N.R. and Mckiernan, M. (1988) Biol J Linn Soc 34: 193-203
3. Boardman, N.K. (1977) Ann. Rev. Plant Physiol. 28, 355-377
4. Outlaw, W.H., JR (1987) In Progress in Photosynthesis Research (Biggins J., ed.) vol. 4, pp. 265-272, Martinus Nijhoff, Dordrecht, The Netherlands
5. Vogelmann, T.C., Bornman, J.F., and Josserand, S. (1989) Phil Trans R Soc Lond B 323: 411-421
6. Cui, M., Vogelmann, T.C., and Smith, W.K. (1991) Plant Cell Environ. 14, 493-500
7. Nishio J.N., and Ting, I.P (1987) Plant Physiol. 84, 600-604
8. Terashima I. and Inoue, Y. (1985) Plant Cell Physiol. 26, 781-785

PHOSPHORYLATION AND DISASSEMBLY OF PSII CORE DURING PHOTOINHIBITION

MARIA TERESA GIARDI

IREV-CNR, Via Salaria Km 29, 00016 Monterotondo Scalo, Italy
FAX: 39 6 9064492

1. INTRODUCTION

The photosynthetic membranes of green plants contain more than ten phosphoproteins. The most conspicuous are components of the light-harvesting chl a/b complex (LHCII). Their phosphorylation is thought to control the distribution of excitation energy between photosystems I and II as part of a mechanism to maximize the efficiency of photon utilization. Four other phosphosproteins, CP43, D2, D1 and the *psb*H plastidial gene product, are associated with photosystem II (PSII) itself and together with CP47 and cytb-559 build up the PSII core, but the significance of their phosphorylation is still unclear (1, 2).

It has recently been shown that differently phosphorylated PSII core populations are present in grana membranes, in an partial equilibrium regulated by light conditions. It has also been demonstrated that these PSII cores have different ability to bind photosynthetic herbicides as well as quinones. Thus, it has been suggested that the phosphorylation process of PSII core polypeptides induces heterogeneity of Q-B pocket activity and that possibly can be involved in the heterogeneity of PSII observed *in vivo* in the presence of herbicide inhibitors (3-6). In the present work, the effect of photoinhibitory conditions on the distribution of phosphorylated PSII core populations is studied. The results indicate that the sensitivity of the PSII core to strong illumination depends on phosphorylation of its polypeptides. Evidence of damage at the level between the internal antennae (CP47 and CP43) and the PSII reaction centre is observed to occur at an early stage of photoinhibition and probably to precede D1 protein degradation.

2. MATERIALS AND METHODS

Phosphorylation of spinach (*Spinacia oleracea* L.) thylakoids was performed as previously described (7). Photoinhibition was performed as reported in reference (3).

N. Murata (ed.), Research in Photosynthesis, Vol. IV, 577–580.

PSII enriched particles isolated from control and photoinhibited thylakoids were solubilized in 0.5 ml of 1% n-dodecyl ß-D-maltoside, and then applied to the cathode region of a flat-bed of granulated gel. Four chlorophyll bands were identified and isolated. These were applied on a linear gradient of sucrose (0 to 1M) made up in the above extraction buffer, and centrifuged at 60000 x g for 12 h under which conditions some distinct, differently phosphorylated PSII populations were separated (4-6).
Grana and stroma-exposed membranes, both from dark adapted and photoinhibited thylakoids were obtained by the digitonin-based method and by differential centrifugation as reported by Kyle et al. (8). Analysis of polypeptide content in grana and stroma lamellae was performed by sodium dodecyl sulfate polyacrylamide gel electrophoresis and immunoblot. Radiolabelled polypeptides were visualized by autoradiography of SDS-polyacrylamide gradient gels using hyperfilm TM MP (Amersham). Densitometric analysis of Coomassie-stained gels and corresponding autoradiography were carried out using a Shimadzu CS 9000.

3. RESULTS AND DISCUSSION

Four differently phosphorylated PSII core populations were previously obtained by isoelectrofocusing of PSII particles isolated from light adapted plants and referred to as complexes ***a***, ***b***, ***c***, and ***d*** in increasing order of their total phosphorylation level on PSII core polypeptides. The 9 kDa phosphoprotein (*psb*H plastidial gene product) was present in these PSII core populations at different levels, being detached from the PSII core when the extent of phosphorylation on D1 and D2 proteins increased, as in PSII core populations ***c*** and ***d*** (4-6). The relative distribution of the four PSII core populations was partially regulated by light conditions, besides partial interconversion of one population into another isoform was observed in the light. At least two differently phosphorylated PSII core populations were always detected from dark adapted thylakoids.
When thylakoids, prior to extraction, were subjected to illumination with strong light for 10 minutes, the distribution of isolated PSII core populations dramatically changed. The most phosphorylated PSII cores (***c*** and ***d***) were absent while new complexes (***c**** and ***d****), lacking the internal antennae CP43 and CP47, were observed (Fig 1). The finding that PSII complexes ***c**** and ***d**** directly derived from PSII core complexes ***c*** and ***d*** was confirmed by isolation of photoinhibited PSII complexes from thylakoids radiolabelled with ^{32}P-ATP (Fig. 1B). When thylakoids were exposed to illumination for a longer period (20 min) isolation of PSII particles led to a very low yield and, among the PSII core populations, only PSII core population ***a*** was observed to survive strong light treatment. No other PSII complexes were isolated in these conditions, suggesting almost complete disassembly of the PSII core within 20 min illumination (data not shown).
Grana and stroma lamellae of photoinhibited particles were obtained by the digitonin-based method. After photoinhibition, an increased content of

LHCII in stroma-exposed regions was observed probably due to the phosphorylation process, as suggested in a previous report on the movement of a "mobile" fraction of phosphorylated LHCII (8). Increased levels of the polypeptides attributed to CP47 and CP43 (about 24%) were also observed in stroma lamellae isolated from photoinhibited membranes, suggesting that lateral movement of these proteins is an early stage of photoinhibition.

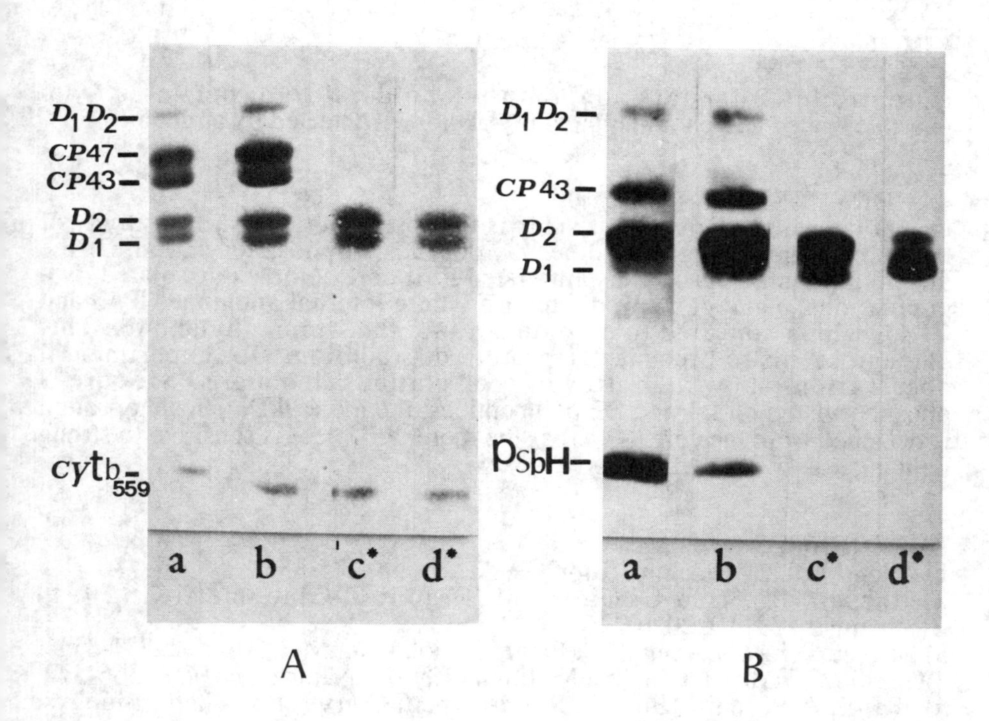

Figure 1. A: SDS-PAGE analysis of PSII complexes obtained by IEF and sucrose gradient ultracentrifugation from photoinhibited thylakoids; **B**: Autoradiography of the PSII complexes isolated from photoinhibited thylakoids treated with ^{32}P-ATP.

Table 1. Distribution of some proteins in grana and stroma lamellae fractions from dark adapted and photoinhibited thylakoids.

Component	Grana Fraction		Stroma Lamellae	
	D	P-Pho	D	P-Pho
CF	1.0	1.0	28.0	29.0
CP47	15.7	13.4	1.0	1.9
CP43	16.0	12.8	0.9	2.6
D2	14.0	13.9	1.9	2.0
D1	14.6	15.3	2.1	2.2
cyt b-559	13.1	12.0	2.3	2.4
psbH	d	d	d	d
LHCII	13.3	9.0	3.6	7.1

D: particles from dark adapted thylakoids; P-Pho: particles from phosphorylated and photoinhibited thylakoids; d: detected by antibodies

4. CONCLUSIONS

One of the main results of this study is the observation that the sensitivity of PSII core to strong light in some way depends on phosphorylation. Of the different populations of phosphorylated PSII core complexes isolated, two populations, ***c*** and ***d***, showed a release of the internal antennae CP43 and CP47, which appeared to migrate out into the stroma thylakoids. This damage seems to precede D1 protein degradation. Our experimental observations show the following correlations: the more PSII core is phosphorylated on D1 and D2 polypeptides, the more 9kDa phosphoprotein is detached from the core as well as the more PSII core is sensitive to strong light and easily disassembled.

REFERENCES

1) Allen J (1992) Biochim. Biophys. Acta **1098**, 275-335
2) Barbato R, Friso G, Giardi M, Rigoni F, Giacometti G (1991) Biochemistry **30**, 10220-10226
3) Bennett J (1991) Annu. Rev. Plant Physiol. Plant Mol. Biol. **42**, 281-311
4)Giardi M, Barber J, Giardina M, Bassi (1990) Z.Naturforsch. **45c**, 366-372
5) Giardi M, Rigoni F, Barbato R, Giacometti G (1991) Biochem. Biophys. Res. Com. **176**, 1298-1305
6) Giardi M, Rigoni F, and Barbato R Plant Physiology (in press)
7) Horton P and Lee P (1985) Planta, **165**, 37-42
8) Kyle D, Kuang T, Watson J, Arntzen C (1984) Biochim. Biophys. Acta **765**, 89-96

PHOTOINHIBITION AND ZEAXANTHIN FORMATION IN THE BROWN ALGAE *Laminaria saccharina* AND *Pelvetia canaliculata*.

J.C. Duval[1], M. Harker[2], B. Rousseau[1], A.J. Young[2], G. Britton[3] and Y. Lemoine[4].
[1].Laboratoire des Biomembranes, Ecole Normale Superieure, Paris France [2].School of Biological and Earth Sciences, Liverpool John Moores University, Liverpool U.K. [3].Department of Biochemistry, University of Liverpool, Liverpool U.K. [4]. Laboratoire de Cryptophysiologie Vegetale et Phycologie, Université des Sciences et Technologies de Lille, France

1.INTRODUCTION

The existence of cyclic interconversions of carotenoids (the xanthophyll cycle) in higher plants and algae has been known for a number of years[1]. In plants and in the green and brown algae this involves the de-epoxidation of violaxanthin into zeaxanthin *via* antheraxanthin when photosynthetic tissues are exposed to high light. The subsequent epoxidation reactions occur in low light or in the dark. Some other algae, notably the diatoms, posses a one-step reaction involving diatoxanthin and diadinoxanthin. Recent work[2,3] has pointed to a function for these interconversions and, more specifically, for zeaxanthin in protecting chloroplasts from photoinhibitory damage. Whilst the precise molecular mechanism for this protective process has not been elucidated, it is clear that zeaxanthin, formed either *de novo* or through the de-epoxidation of violaxanthin, is involved in the dissipation of excess excitation energy as determined by the quenching of chlorophyll fluorescence.
Whilst the role of zeaxanthin has been examined in higher plants[2], little attention has been paid to its possible role in macroalgae. In this study, we have examined the effect of photoinhibitory conditions on the pigment content and composition of two common marine algae, *Laminaria saccharina* and *Pelvetia canaliculata*. The former of these is subtidal, whereas the latter grows high on the shore where it is regularly exposed to severe stress conditions.

2.MATERIALS AND METHODS

Fresh algal material were obtained from sites near Roscoff, France and in North Wales, U.K. and maintained in the laboratory for no more than 4 days following collection. Experiments were performed on fully hydrated thalli.

N. Murata (ed.), Research in Photosynthesis, Vol. IV, 581–584.

O_2 evolution was measured using a DW1 Hansatech electrode which was modified to simultaneously record steady state fluorescence A detector beam, modulated at 1000Hz was provided by a light-emitting diode (Stanley HPG 5566X) at a light intensity of 0.3mW. A continuous actinic beam, filtered by anticaloric and interference blue-green filters (480 ± 50 nm, Balzers) was generated by two 250W quartz iodine lamps, which gave a uniform intensity on the whole electrode vial. The modulated signal was detected with a photomultiplier R928 (Hamamatsu) protected by a red interference filter (680 ± 10 nm) and integrated with a lock-in amplifier TE9700 (Tekelec Airtronic). O_2 and fluorescence signals were recorded simultaneously on a microcomputer through a two-channel analogic-digital interface (Botens III, Jagot and Lèon).
The pigment composition of both algae was determined by reversed-phase HPLC following conventional solvent extraction of small pieces of thalli immediately following treatment. Carotenoids and chlorophylls were resolved on a 5μ Spherisorb ODS2 column (25 x 0.46 cm) using a solvent gradient of 0-100% ethyl-acetate in acetonitrile/water (9/1 v/v, containing 0.5% triethylamine for resolution of chl.*c*) over 25 min at 1.0 ml/min. A HP1040 diode-array detector was used to monitor spectra and integrate at the λmax of the individual pigments.

3. RESULTS AND DISCUSSION

The pigment profile of *P. canaliculata* maintained under conditions of low light as determined by HPLC is shown in Fig. 1. The major carotenoid in this algae and in *L. saccharina* is the acetylenic compound, fucoxanthin but they also contain high levels of violaxanthin and ß-carotene. Extracts from *L. saccharina* were similar to that shown in Fig.1 but the ratio of total carotenoid:chlorophyll was much higher, largely as a result of high levels of fucoxanthin. Extracts from *Laminaria* were also found to contain small amounts of diadinoxanthin (probably present as a result of diatom contamination of the thallus, and completely absent from extracts of *Pelvetia*). In control thalli of both algae, the zeaxanthin content was negligible (Table 1).
In *L. saccharina*, photoinhibition was achieved following treatment with light ($30 Wm^{-2}$) for 90 min, whereas in *Pelvetia*, a much longer treatment under identical conditions (240 min) was required to achieve photoinhibition. The most notable effect of exposure to high light conditions in both *L. saccharina* and *P. canaliculata* was the de-epoxidation of violaxanthin into zeaxanthin (Fig.1, Table 1). The formation of zeaxanthin accompanied a decrease in chlorophyll fluorescence (F_v/F_m). As with the majority of higher plants, levels of the intermediate in this reaction, antheraxanthin, do not increase greatly during de-epoxidation. The epoxidation state ([V+0.5A] / [V+A+Z]) is commonly used to

express the extent of zeaxanthin formation and at its maximum was 0.60 for *Pelvetia* and 0.18 for *Laminaria*. It is interesting to note that diatoxanthin was also formed by the de-epoxidation of diadinoxanthin in the diatoms associated with *L. saccharina*.

Recovery from photoinhibition took place on return to low light with the fluorescence and carotenoid composition returning to values comparable with the control thalli, i.e. the epoxidation of zeaxanthin into violaxanthin. Prolonged treatment resulted in irreversible photoinhibition and selective photobleaching of pigments, notably ß-carotene and chl. *a*.

TABLE 1. Pigment composition of *P.canaliculata* (P) and *L. saccharina* (L). The data are expressed relative to 100 Chl.*a*.(--- not detected) and are the means of at least 3 samples.

	Control		Photoinhibited		Recovery	
Pigment	P	L	P	L	P	L
Fucoxanthin	39.83	71.72	27.38	75.25	40.48	71.16
Violaxanthin	9.95	8.27	1.83	4.23	7.00	8.28
Antheraxanthin	0.72	0.27	1.12	1.40	0.67	0.43
Zeaxanthin	0.29	---	6.45	2.53	0.43	0.32
ß-Carotene	5.10	8.11	3.66	8.15	5.41	8.34
Diadinoxanthin	---	1.03	---	0.36	---	0.95
Diatoxanthin	---	---	---	0.17	---	0.08
Chl.*c*	13.40	16.54	14.08	17.43	12.39	15.84
Phaeo.*a*	---	0.49	1.03	6.68	---	0.46

The xanthophyll cycle has been shown to be of considerable significance in tolerance to sun/shade conditions in higher plants[1]. Of particular importance is the size of the xanthophyll cycle pool [V+A+Z] which, at least in part, may determine the amount of zeaxanthin formed. Expressed per unit Chl.*a*, there are no significant differences in pool size between *Pelvetia* and *Laminaria*. However, the pool forms a much larger proportion of total carotenoid in *P. canaliculata*, which has relatively reduced levels of fucoxanthin and ß-carotene.

4. CONCLUSIONS

Pelvetia exhibits a much higher resistance to photoinhibition than *Laminaria*. There are differences between these two algae in terms of the xanthophyll cycle pool size and the ability to synthesise zeaxanthin in response to high light, suggesting that carotenoids could be involved in determining the zonation of marine algae.

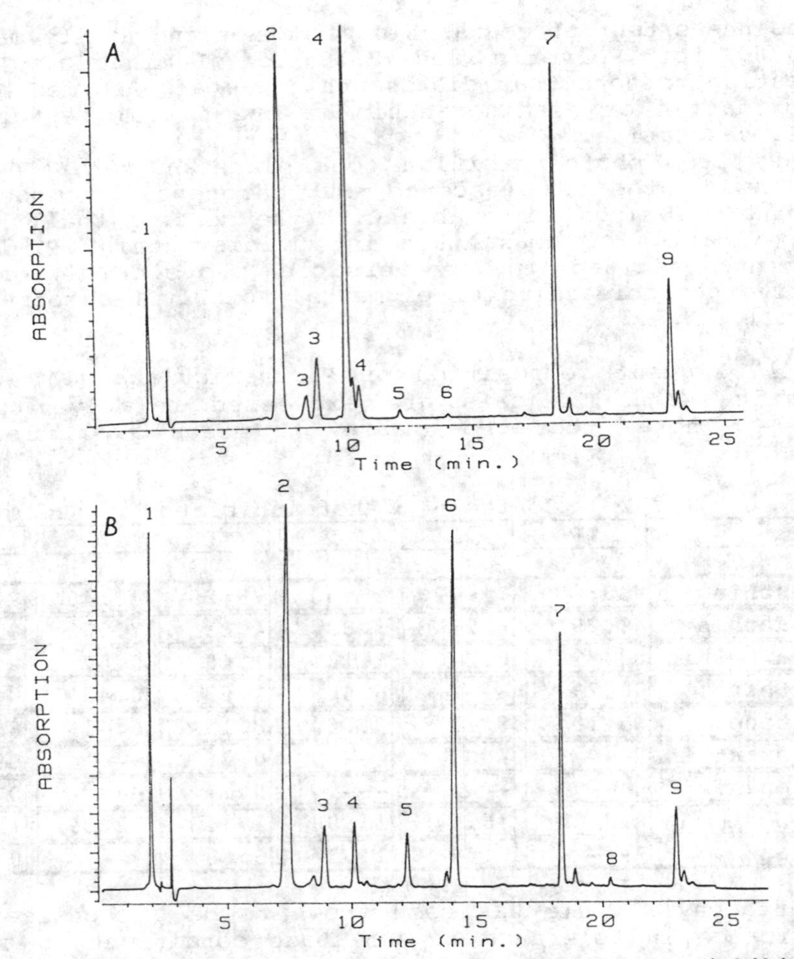

Figure 1. Pigments of (A) control, and (B) photoinhibited *P. canaliculata* as determined by Reversed-phase HPLC (at 447nm). Peak identifications: 1. Chlorophyll *c*; 2. Fucoxanthin; 3. *Cis*-isomers of fucoxanthin; 4. Violaxanthin; 5. Antheraxanthin; 6. Zeaxanthin; 7. Chlorophyll *a*; 8. Phaeophytin *a*; 9. ß-Carotene

5. ACKNOWLEDGEMENTS

This work was funded by the British Council Alliance programme.

6. REFERENCES

1.Goodwin, T.W. (1980) Biochemistry of Carotenoids, Vol. 1 Plants. Academic Press, London. 2.Demmig-Adams, B. (1990) Biochim. Biophys. Acta, 1020,1-24. 3.Horton, P., Ruban, A.V., Rees, D., Pascal, A.A., Noctor, G. and Young, A.J. (1991) FEBS Lett., 292, 1-4.

24. Photosynthesis in Intact Leaf

From leaf photosynthesis to crop productivity

L.T. Evans, CSIRO Division of Plant Industry, GPO Box 1600, Canberra, ACT 2601, Australia.

Introduction

I shall begin with a paradox and then spend the rest of my time trying to elucidate it and the implications for the improvement of crop productivity. But before that I need to make clear that most of my discussion of photosynthetic rates will be in terms of net CO_2 exchange rate per unit leaf area (designated CER), while productivity refers to the yield of either biomass (for forage plants) or harvested products (e.g. seeds, tubers, roots) per unit ground area per crop.

The paradox is this. There is often a strong positive relation between productivity and CER as determined by environmental conditions such as irradiance, CO_2 level or N fertilizer applications, but although there is plenty of heritable variation in CER within most crop species, there has been no rise in maximum CER as yield potential has increased and selection for high CER has been counterproductive in several crops, such as maize, peas and lucerne. Nor has there been any improvement in the quantum yield for absorbed radiation (1), but varietal comparisons of radiation use efficiency have not been nearly as extensive as those of CER. Nevertheless, the yield potential of many crops continues to increase by modification of processes later in the sequence between leaf photosynthesis and yield determination.

For example, the major factor contributing to the 40-100% or more rise in yield potential of many crops over the last 40-50 years has been the increase in the proportion of biomass partitioned to the harvested organs, i.e. in the harvest index. In many cases this has occurred without any increase in biomass, e.g. among winter wheat varieties in the UK (2), and where there has been an increase in biomass, it is commonly associated with a changed balance or duration in the life cycle, not with an enhanced maximum rate of photosynthesis or growth.

Murata (3) illustrated a fairly strong relation *across* species between maximum CER and the maximum recorded crop growth rate (CGR) for each species, but in many cases these were taken from different sources. Differences in CGR between cultivars of a crop can sometimes be significantly related to those in CER, especially during grain filling but not usually during early stages in the life cycle, as in wheat (4).

With forage and pasture plants, in which productivity is directly related to above-ground growth, there has been far less improvement in yield - at most a few % over many years - and that little has come mainly from greater leaf size, often at the expense of CER.

The canopy apparent (= net) photosynthesis rate (CAP) may be quite closely related to yield, e.g. in the comparison by Wells *et al.* (5) across soybean cultivars in four

N. Murata (ed.), Research in Photosynthesis, Vol. IV, 587–594.

maturity groups for the whole period of grain growth (r = + 0.64), but even CAP is not closely related to CER, mainly because it is highly dependent on the leaf area index and there is often a negative relation between CER and leaf area, as discussed below. Among the 16 soybean cultivars whose CER was measured by Bhagsari *et al.* (6) and CAP by Wells *et al.* (5), the correlation coefficients between CER and CAP over two intervals were only + 0.30 and + 0.15, an indication of how poor a determinant leaf CER is of canopy CER, let alone of yield.

Canopy CER would be a better guide to yield than is CER, but it is, less convenient to measure and is highly subject to varietal differences in leaf area index, stand structure, extinction coefficient and respiratory losses, all of which display varietal differences which make comparisons of CAP difficult to interpret.

Clearly, the importance of later processes, and of leaf area, for yield determination means that the correlation between CER and productivity will be at best tenuous, or even negative.

Complications to varietal comparisons of CER

The photosynthetic rate of a leaf depends on the immediate conditions of irradiance, temperature, CO_2 and water supply, but also on preceding conditions through their influence on growth and adaptation of the plant. Such preconditioning can have powerful effects on the relative CERs of genotypes. For example, growth under much higher irradiance had little effect on the light-saturated CER of bread wheat cultivars but greatly increased that of the wild diploid progenitor *T. boeoticum* (7). Growth at cool temperatures greatly reduced the CER of *Echinochloa* millets and reversed the CER rankings of Japanese millet and rice compared with their Indian counterparts (8). Thus, cultivar rankings for CER can vary not only with the conditions in which the leaves are measured but also with conditions during their growth as well as with leaf age and ontogenetic rank.

Daylength as well as irradiance during growth also affects the trade-off between CER and leaf area in many plants. In a high-latitude cultivar of *Poa pratensis*, for example, as daylength increased from 10 to 24 h, the CER was halved but leaf length more than doubled, with the result that photosynthesis per leaf increased (9). Such trade-offs between leaf size and CER, sometimes referred to as 'the dilution hypothesis', have strong adaptive implications, as have the cross-overs in performance like those for Japanese and Indian millets and rices with temperature.

In many crop simulation models, photosynthesis - which has been well simulated at many levels - drives growth. However, experiments by Ewart almost 100 years ago showed that CER also depends on growth and the demand for photosynthetic products. This has been confirmed in many cereal, pulse, root and other crops by a variety of manipulations ranging from the removal, shading or cooling of leaves, tubers, inflorescences or grains to grafting, physical restraints and treatment with hormones or inhibitors of photosynthesis. Removal of the major sink organ usually leads to a fall in CER, except when alternative sinks are available, while the shading or inhibition of other photosynthetic sources can lead to a rise in the CER measured in constant conditions. It has been suggested that such drastic treatments are irrelevant to field conditions and that such responses are not of significance in field crops, but several kinds of evidence suggest that feed-back control of CER does occur in the field (10, 11).

This phenomenon is of considerable significance in the comparison of CERs across old and new cultivars. In many grain crops, varietal differences in CER do not correlate with yield until the grain growth stage is reached, as in soybeans (12), *Vigna radiata* (13), wheat (4), sorghum hybrids (14) and U.S., Indian and Japanese cultivars of rice (15, 16, 17, 18). In these and many other cases the higher yielding cultivars are characterized by a slower decline in CER during grain growth, with the result that CERs measured during grain growth do correlate with yield. However, their maximum CER is no higher than in older cultivars, which raises the question whether their higher CER after flowering causes or is caused by their greater grain growth. Greater demand slows the post-anthesis decline in CER in wheat (19). With rice, Lafitte & Travis (15) concluded that the higher CER of higher-yielding cultivars was in response to greater sink: source ratios, but more erect leaves and higher leaf N as a result of more prolonged root activity have also been suggested as causes. It remains an open question, therefore, whether the positive correlation between yield and CER during grain growth is due to an inherently greater duration of photosynthetic activity or simply reflects the greater demands for grain growth in higher yielding cultivars.

A comparable question bedevils the most persuasive example of a positive correlation between CER and grain yield, among 22 parental and inbred lines of sorghum in both well-watered and water-limited conditions (20). In this case the correlation was for CERs measured before anthesis, not in decline, and not reflecting the demands of grain growth. However, CER and yield were more highly correlated during the development of panicles than at their initiation or exsertion, which could indicate an effect of demand.

Assessment

Clearly there are many hazards in relating CER to yield, associated with pre-conditioning and adaptation, leaf area X CER trade-offs and, not least, the problems of causality. From a survey of the literature, too comprehensive to be presented here (11), I concluded that there is no evidence that the improvement of yield potential has resulted from any increase in photosynthetic efficiency, and that significant positive correlations between maximum CER and yield among the cultivars of many crops are the exception rather than the rule. The photosynthetic rate has been increased agronomically, with N fertilizers and irrigation, rather than by selection, and there have been other routes to higher yield potential available, such as the rise in harvest index. These are not yet exhausted but there may soon be a need to raise CER by selection, as the following evolutionary perspective suggests.

Steps in the evolution of agriculture - implications for photosynthesis

1. Natural communities and wild relatives

In most plant communities natural selection is likely to favour genotypes with high rates of growth because such plants have more resources for competition and reproduction. For example, the relative growth rates of individuals of white clover from a population in permanent grassland revealed a considerable range but were clustered nearer to the upper extreme (21). The processes of photosynthesis have probably been under intense selection pressure throughout evolution, and are likely to have been optimized (22). Although some may regard photosynthesis, and especially its principal enzyme rubisco, as inefficient we have yet to demonstrate that either selection or re-engineering can improve photosynthetic performance. The large subunit of rubisco is inferred to have been around for 3.5 billion years and its amino acid sequence has changed by only 1% per 100 million years (23), so a little molecular modesty may be in order. A slow rate of evolution is to be expected for the kinetic characteristics determined by the large sub-unit of rubisco through cytoplasmic inheritance, so it is notable that the K_m and V_{max} of the enzyme from C_3 and C_4 plants have diverged in directions which enhance the performance of each photosynthetic pathway (24, 25, 26).

In many natural plant communities, N is the nutrient most limiting to growth and the allocation of N between and within organs is subject to adaptive optimization (27). Were N supply the only constraint, optimization would involve the partitioning of N to result in the maximum rate of C fixation per unit N. However, water is also often in short supply, so the fixation of C per unit of water must also be optimized, influencing the balance between root and shoot growth as well as the trade-offs between leaf area and CER, rubisco and carbonic anhydrase contents etc. (28). Besides these partitioning processes, stomatal mechanisms operate to maintain intercellular CO_2 concentration at the optimum value for water use efficiency (29).

Many of the wild progenitors of our major crop plants came from at least seasonally arid environments and are characterized by relatively small leaves with a high maximum CER, often of short duration due to the early mobilization of N from them. For quite a few crops, including wheat, rice, sorghum, pearl millet, soybean, sugar cane, cotton, cassava, *Brassica* and sunflower, the highest CERs recorded are for the wild relatives (11). For at least three of these - namely wheat, rice and *Brassica* - there is a strong negative correlation between CER and leaf area, the cultivars having larger leaves with less N and fewer chloroplasts dm^{-2} and a lower specific leaf weight (30, 31, 32, 33). The trade-off is such that photosynthesis per leaf is greater with the larger leaves, except perhaps at very high irradiance. Photosynthesis per unit N is also greater in the larger leaves with less N per unit area (31).

2. Traditional agriculture

Following domestication our crop plants were unconsciously selected for (1) rapid establishment on cultivated, bare ground; (2) performance in more or less pure stands; and (3) adaptation to different conditions as agriculture spread. Rapid early growth to compete with weeds and maximize light interception put a premium on greater leaf expansion and probably on larger leaves than in the wild relatives, so CER may well have fallen, but photosynthesis per leaf and per unit N risen. The negative correlation between CER and leaf area is consistently high among the cultivars of many crops, even in the absence of wild relatives from the comparisons (34).

However, cultivars of both *indica* and *japonica* rice, from primitive to advanced, are distributed right across the curve relating leaf area ratio to specific leaf weight (32), presumably reflecting adaptation to different environments. Differences between crops, and also between cultivars, in their investment in rubisco presumably also reflect different adaptive optima (35). For example, the higher proportion of rubisco in rice may be associated with the generally higher conductance of rice leaves grown in flooded conditions.

As crops spread they often had to adapt to a wider range of conditions than at the cradle of domestication. Among millets and rices, for example, the CERs of cultivars adapted to Japan are less inhibited by low temperatures than are those of India (8). A similar cross-over in ranking for CER occurs in cultivars of the common bean adapted to different altitudes in the Andes (36). Improvements in photosynthetic adaptation to adverse conditions continue, e.g. in the tolerance of maize hybrids to cool nights (37).

3. High input agriculture

The advent of cheaper N fertilizers 30 or so years ago and their widespread use have influenced crop photosynthesis in many ways:

(a) CER can be raised substantially, N fertilizers thereby acting as a surrogate for genetic improvement. Beyond a certain level of N in the leaf, however, further gains in CER are slight but area per leaf continues to increase, and total leaf area to even higher supplies of N. The trade-off between leaf area and CER can be broken, which may be why it was not apparent in some of the cases analysed by Bhagsari & Brown (34).

(b) The optimization of N use *vis-a-vis* that for other resources such as water or radiation can be relaxed.

(c) The need to mobilize N from the leaves to support grain growth is reduced and deferred, thereby increasing the duration of photosynthesis and slowing the fall in CER. In traditional N-limited agriculture, available soil N reached very low levels by flowering. Two consequences of this were, first, that the remobilization of N from leaves began soon after the grains strarted growing, putting a stop to further photosynthesis and, secondly, that the plants had to build up carbohydrate reserves before flowering to support grain growth after it. When those constraints are relieved by N fertilizer use, reliance on pre-anthesis reserves is diminished and they can be used to support the growth of a larger inflorescence. Photosynthesis after anthesis can continue at a faster rate and for longer, and selection to enhance that ability has occurred, as in rice, wheat and maize, evident in the longer 'stay green' of more recent hybrids.

(d) Larger leaves and faster growth result in earlier closure of the canopy and full interception of sunlight. In turn, this means that flower initiation and flowering can be advanced, and can occur after fewer leaves are formed, giving scope for further increase in the harvest index. Earlier flowering also allows additional time for grain growth, requiring selection for parallel increases in leaf longevity and grain growth duration. Whereas it is the leaf area X CER relation which has been important in the past, any trade-off there may be between maximum CER and leaf longevity might be more important in the future.

(e) With N fertilization there has been a need for shorter stature, to avoid lodging. The crops are also denser, leading in some cases to selection for more upright leaves at the top of the canopy. The consequent fall in the extinction coefficient for light within the canopy may contribute to more prolonged photosynthesis by lower leaves, as in modern Japanese rice cultivars (38).

Along with greater N fertilization and herbicide and pesticide use, there has also been greater use of both full and supplemental irrigation, which may also have changed selection pressures on photosynthetic characteristics. Among Pima cottons selected for irrigation in hot environments, stomatal conduction and CER have been raised, at certain times of day. The control of water use has been relaxed, with the consequence that transpirational cooling and heat tolerance have increased (39). As with the use of N fertilizers, empirical selection under irrigation has led to complex and sometimes counter-intuitive shifts in the photosynthetic processes.

4. Post-modern agriculture

Further intensification of agriculture is bound to occur, relaxing some of the constraints on photosynthesis still further. The possibilities include:

(a) Heavier and later applications of N fertilizers, raising leaf N content still further. Leaf area could continue to increase, but CER may soon approach the point where ribulose bisphosphate regeneration is more limiting than its carboxylation by rubisco, as in wheat (40).

(b) Further increase in leaf size and total leaf area with additional N may be helpful in increasing light interception in the early stages of the crop, but not desirable in already dense crops at anthesis. Many crops already display a shift from larger, more horizontal early leaves to smaller, more upright ones at flowering, and it may be possible to accentuate such ontogenetic changes by selection;

(c) With N fertilization later in the life cycle the need to mobilize rubisco and other photosynthetic enzymes out of the leaves could be deferred or even abolished. The high proportion of soluble N tied up by rubisco, often seen as one of its faults, may not in fact have been disadvantageous because it was efficiently mobilized into the grain. That still occurs, but more slowly, and it might soon be possible to dispense with such mobilization altogether, maintaining full photosynthetic activity until either environmental conditions or genetic limits to leaf longevity bring it to an end. The N remaining in the leaves would enhance their value as feed or mulch. But we need to know far more about what controls both photosynthetic longevity and the duration of grain growth before this scenario can be approached;

(d) At least with irrigated crops it may be feasible to raise CER by selecting for higher intercellular CO_2 concentration, which may have occurred already in cotton (39). This is likely to reduce water use efficiency, which may be maladaptive when irrigation is unreliable, or unwanted if the cost of irrigation water rises, as is likely.

(e) As the atmospheric CO_2 concentration rises, the kinetic properties of rubisco in C_3 crops may, under empirical selection, shift in the direction of a lower affinity for CO_2 but a higher V_{max}, becoming more like rubisco in C_4 plants (24, 25, 26).

Conclusions

(1) Although it is natural for participants in an international congress on photosynthesis to focus on the process itself, its relation to crop productivity requires that it be considered in the contexts of the whole plant and the crop. Its requirements for N, water and other resources, the price of carbon gain, are only part of the overall optimization processes subject to modification during empirical selection for higher yield.

(2) Although photosynthesis feeds forward to growth, and eventually to yield, it is also subject to feed-back control of its rate by the capacity of the plant to utilize its products. One consequence of this is that rankings for CER, especially after grain growth begins, may reflect as much as determine rankings for yield.

(3) Although photosynthesis can be modelled well at many levels, and is therefore used to drive crop simulations, explanatory models of important later steps to yield, such as the partitioning of assimilates, are lacking, making the analysis of yield determination a hazardous activity.

(4) As atmospheric CO_2 concentration and the use of N fertilizers continue to rise, the limitations on CER by rubisco will become less significant and more attention should be given to other components of the photosynthetic process.

(5) Adaptation to stress, ontogenetic shifts in leaf size and presentation, and the duration of photosynthetic activity in leaves are likely to be fruitful areas of investigation. In particular, I would single out determination of the longevity of leaf photosynthesis as an increasingly important determinant of crop productivity.

References

1. Osborne, B.A., Garrett, M.K. (1983) Plant, Cell & Environ. 6, 135-144.
2. Austin, R.B., Ford, M.A., Morgan, C.L. (1989) J. Agric. Sci. (Camb.) 112, 295-301.
3. Murata, Y. (1981) Jap. J. Crop. Sci. 50, 223-232.
4. Fischer, R.A., Bidinger, F., Syme, J.R., Wall, P.C. (1981) Crop Sci. 21, 367-373.
5. Wells, R., Schulze, L.L., Ashley, D.A., Boerma, H.R., Brown, R.H. (1982) Crop Sci. 22, 886-890.
6. Bhagsari, A.S., Ashley, D.A., Brown, R.H., Boerma, H.R. (1977) Crop Sci. 17, 929-932.
7. Dunstone, R.L., Gifford, R.M., Evans, L.T. (1973) Aust. J. Biol. Sci. 26, 295-307.
8. Evans, L.T., Bush, M.G. (1985) Field Crops Res. 12, 295-317.
9. Heide, O.M., Bush, M.G., Evans, L.T. (1985) Physiol. Plantar. 65, 135-145.
10. Sage, R.F., Sharkey, T.D. (1987) Plant Physiol. 84, 658-664.
11. Evans, L.T. (1992) Crop Evolution, Adaptation and Yield. Cambridge Univ. Press, Cambridge.
12. Buttery, B.R., Buzzell, R.I., Findlay, W.I. (1981) Can. J. Plant Sci. 61, 191-198.
13. Srinivasan, P.S., Chandrababu, R., Natarajaratnam, N., Rangaswamy, S.R.S. (1985) Trop. Agric. 62, 222-224.
14. Khanna-Chopra, R. (1982) Photosynth. Res. 3, 113-122.
15. Lafitte, H.R., Travis, R.L. (1984) Crop Sci. 24, 447-452.
16. Arjunan, A., Natarajaratnam, N., Nagarajan, M., Sadasiram, R., Balakrishnan, K. (1990) Photosynthetica 24, 273-275.
17. Kuroda, E., Kumura, A. (1990) Jap. J. Crop Sci. 59, 283-292.
18. Sasaki, H., Ishii, R. (1992) Photosynth. Res. 32, 139-146.
19. Atsmon, D., Bush, M.G., Evans, L.T. (1986) Aust. J. Plant Physiol., 13, 365-379.
20. Peng, S., Krieg, D.R., Girma, F.S. (1991) Photosynth. Res. 28, 1-7.
21. Burdon, J.J., Harper, J.L. (1980) J. Ecol. 68, 953-957.
22. Gifford, R.M. (1987) pp. IV. 7, 377-384 *in* Progress in Photosynthesis Research. (*ed*) J. Biggens, Martinus Nijhoff, Dordrecht.
23. Runnegar, B. (1991) Phil. Trans. Roy. Soc. Lond. B333, 391-397.
24. Yeoh, H-H., Badger, M.R., Watson, L. (1981) Plant Physiol. 67, 1151-1155.
25. Seemann, J.R., Badger, M.R., Berry, J.A. (1984) Plant Physiol. 74, 791-794.
26. Hudson, G.S., Mahon, J.D., Anderson, P.A., Gibbs, M.J., Badger, M.R., Andrews, T.J., Whitfeld, P.R. (1990) J. Biol. Chem. 265, 808-814.
27. Field, C., Mooney, H.A. (1986) pp. 25-55 *in* 'On the Economy of Plant Form and Function' (*ed*). T.J. Givnish'. Cambridge Univ. Press, Cambridge.
28. Cowan, I. (1986) Ibid pp. 133-170.
29. Cowan, I., Farquhar, G.D. (1977) pp. 471-505 *in* Integration of Activity in the Higher Plant. (*ed*). D.H. Jennings. Cambridge Univ. Press, Cambridge.
30. Evans, L.T., Dunstone, R.L. (1970) Aust. J. Biol. Sci. 23, 725-741.
31. Khan, M.A., Tsunoda, S. (1970) Jap. J. Breed. 20, 133-140.
32. Cook, M.G., Evans, L.T. (1983) Field Crops Res. 6, 219-238.
33. Kariya, K., Tsunoda, S. (1972) Tokohu J. Agric. Res. 23, 1-14.
34. Bhagsari, A.S., Brown, R.H. (1986) Crop Sci. 26, 127-132.
35. Evans, J.R. (1989) Oecologia 78, 9-19.
36. Laing, D.R., Jones, P.G., Davis, J.H.C. (1984) pp. 305-351 *in* The Physiology of Tropical Field Crops. *eds*. P.R. Goldsworthy, N.M. Fisher. John Wiley, New York.
37. Dwyer, L.M., Tollenaar, M. (1989) Can. J. Plant Sci. 69, 81-91.
38. Saitoh, H., Shimoda, H., Ishihara, K. (1990) Jap. J. Crop Sci. 59, 130-139.
39. Cornish, K., Radin, J.W., Turcotte, E.L., Lu, Z., Zeiger, E. (1991) Plant Physiol. 97, 484-489.
40. Evans, J.R. (1983) Plant Physiol. 72, 297-302.

PHOTOSYNTHESIS IN TRANSGENIC TOBACCO PLANTS WITH REDUCED RUBISCO CONTENTS

Susanne von Caemmerer, John R. Evans, Graham S. Hudson, Yvonne B.C. Arvidsson, Barbara A. Setchell, T. John Andrews, Research School of Biological Sciences, Australian National University, GPO Box 475, Canberra, ACT 2601, Australia

INTRODUCTION

CO_2 assimilation in leaves of C_3 plants is primarily dependent on stomatal conductance and the capacity of the mesophyll to fix CO_2. The mesophyll capacity is dependent on the amount and activity of Rubisco enzyme (EC 4.1.1.39) as well as the chloroplast's electron transport and enzymatic capacity for ribulose bisphosphate (RuBP) regeneration. Differences in CO_2 assimilation rates between leaves can occur because of differences in leaf age, plant nutrition or light conditions during growth. These differences can be correlated with the amount of Rubisco present in leaves (1), however the correlation is complicated by the observation that other Calvin cycle enzymes and chloroplast electron transport components often vary in parallel (2,3). Furthermore other leaf properties such as stomatal conductance also vary in parallel with photosynthetic capacity and Rubisco activity (4).

The advent of antisense RNA technology has made it possible to reduce the amounts of specific proteins. Rodermel et al. (5) demonstrated that an antisense RNA gene directed against the mRNA of the Rubisco small subunit (SSu) can reduce the amount of Rubisco in leaves of transformed tobacco plants. Using the same technique we have shown that in contrast to the effects of environmental factors or leaf age, anti-SSu RNA reduces the amount of Rubisco and the CO_2 assimilation of leaves with little perturbation to other chloroplast properties and stomatal conductance (6). Similar effects of antisense RNA have been reported by Quick et al. (7) and Stitt et al. (8).

MATERIALS and METHODS

An *rbc*S cDNA coding for the SSu of Rubisco was isolated from *Nicotiana tabacum* leaf RNA and fused in the antisense orientation to the CaMV 35S promoter in the binary vector pBIN19. The T-DNA of this recombinant plasmid was introduced into tobacco by *Agrobacterium*-mediated transformation of leaf discs. Control plants were transformed with the T-DNA of plasmid pBI121. Transformed cells were selected on kanamycin-containing medium, regenerated into plantlets and then transferred into pots of vermiculite. The primary transformants were grown in an air-conditioned glasshouse

N. Murata (ed.), Research in Photosynthesis, Vol. IV, 595–602.

during a Canberra summer and were given a complete nutrient solution. Leaves of the primary transformants were analysed by gas exchange measurements, carbon isotope analysis of leaf dry matter and biochemical assays on extracts of leaf punches (6).

R1 plants were produced by self-fertilization of selected antisense plants and were grown in a growth chamber under high irradiance (1000 μmol quanta $m^{-2}s^{-1}$) with 12 hour light, day and night temperatures of 25°C and 18°C respectively and an air humidity of 60%. A complete nutrient solution was given three times a week. Gas exchange analysis and biochemical analysis were as described (6). The amount of Rubisco and the activation state of Rubisco were measured by carboxyarabinitol bisphosphate binding (9). Measurements of carbon isotope discrimination were made concurrently with gas exchange measurements (10). Measurements were made at an irradiance of 1000 μmol quanta $m^{-2}s^{-1}$, a leaf temperature of 25°C, leaf to air vapour pressure difference of 10 mbar, a CO_2 partial pressure of 340 μbar and at 2% oxygen. The CO_2 transfer conductance, g_w, from the intercellular air spaces to the chloroplast was calculated (11) with a discrimination value for Rubisco of 30‰.

RESULTS AND DISCUSSION

We previously showed that the insertion of an antisense gene directed against *rbc*S mRNA resulted in a mean reduction of 82% in the amount of Rubisco holoenzyme in the primary transformants (6). This reduction was accompanied by a equally large reduction in carbon assimilation rate and a small reduction in soluble protein, but had little apparent effect on other chloroplast proteins and on stomatal conductance.

Three anti-SSu plants with a mean Rubisco content of 30% of control plants were selected for further study. The flowers were allowed to self fertilize and seed was collected. When germinated and grown in soil, the R1 progeny for each plant segregated into three groups at an approximate 1:2:1 ratio of plants with similar photosynthetic traits. These presumably corresponded to the zero (null or wild-type), one copy (hemizygous) and two copy (homozygous) plants with respect to the antisense T-DNA. Little variation was found within each group of plants such that the results of individuals were combined. The amount of Rubisco of the single-dose plants was 34% of the controls and in the double-dose plants it was 15% of that in the controls (Fig. 1). In the single-dose plants the loss in soluble protein matched the loss of Rubisco protein, as illustrated in Fig.1. In the double-dose plants, however, the loss in soluble protein was greater than the loss of Rubisco protein alone, showing that other leaf proteins had also decreased. The same was true for the amount of leaf nitrogen. There was little difference between the single-dose and control plants, but leaf nitrogen was reduced in the double-dose plants (Fig. 1). The chlorophyll content in the single-dose plants was slightly greater than in the control plants (0.6 compared to 0.53 mmol m^{-2}). The double-dose plants had only 70% of the chlorophyll of the control plants. The carbonic anhydrase activity was 87% of the control activity in the double-dose plants and 30% greater in the single-dose plants compared to the control plants. This was different to our observations in the primary transformants where carbonic anhydrase had been reduced significantly in the antisense plants (6). In summary, the single-dose R1 plants showed a reduction in Rubisco content with little decrease in other proteins whereas in the double-dose plants, where the reduction in Rubisco was severe, other chloroplast properties had also been affected. It is interesting to speculate on what may cause the decline in other proteins in the homozygous plants. Quick et al. (7) hyphothesized that other enzymes declined in the antisense plants once Rubisco became rate limiting to photosynthesis. As we discuss later, our results provide no evidence for such a link. In the case of Quick et al. (7), it may have been a coincidence of circumstances since they grew their plants at low irradiances, in which case Rubisco content is in excess of the level required for photosynthesis.

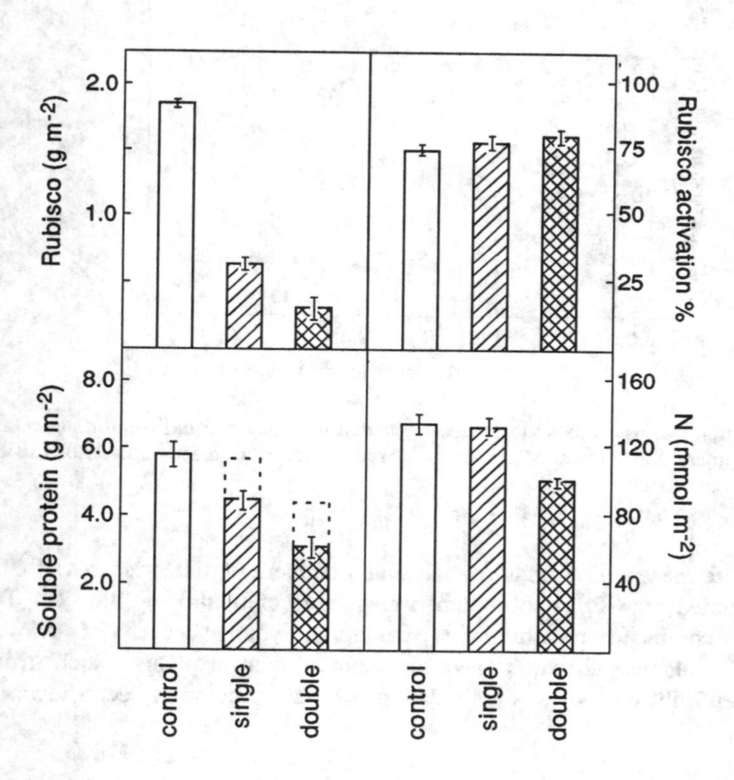

Fig.1 Rubisco content and activation state, soluble protein and total leaf nitrogen in leaves of control (n=7), single-dose (n=7), and double-dose (n=5) R1 plants. The dashed lines give the amount of soluble protein if no Rubisco had been lost. Bars give standard errors.

No significant differences in activation state of Rubisco occurred between control, single- and double-dose plants (Fig. 1). The activation state was approximately 75% which is consistent with previous observations at an irradiance of 1000 μmol quanta $m^{-2}s^{-1}$ (12). There was a small but insignificant increase in activation state in the double-dose plants. Quick et al. (7) found an increase in the activation state from 60% in the control plants to 90% in those antisense plants, with a severe reduction in Rubisco protein, when measurements were made at low irradiances.

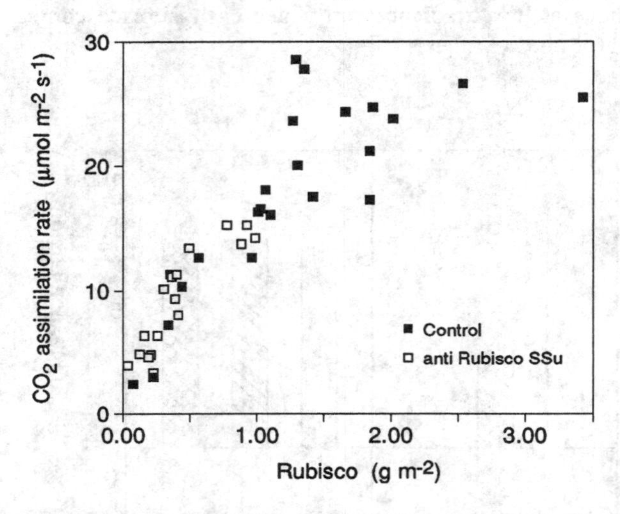

Fig. 2. CO_2 assimilation rate as a function of Rubisco content in young and old control leaves, and young leaves of the primary and R1 anti SSu plants. Measurements were made as described in the methods but at 21% oxygen.

CO_2 assimilation, rate measured at high irradiance and ambient partial pressures of CO_2 , was strongly correlated with Rubisco content irrespective of treatment (Fig. 2). The figure shows the combined measurements made on young leaves of primary transformants and R1 plants and leaves of various ages of control plants. Such strong relationships between Rubisco and CO_2 assimilation rate have previously been shown for other species (1, 2).

These anti-SSu plants have also given us the opportunity to reexamine models of leaf photosynthesis based on the kinetics of Rubisco (13). For example it was proposed that CO_2 assimilation is limited by the activity of Rubisco at high irradiance and/or low partial pressures of CO_2, or by the rate of RuBP supply at high CO_2 and/or low irradiances. In Fig. 3 the CO_2 assimilation rate of a control leaf and a leaf of an anti-SSu plant is shown at varying partial pressures of CO_2. The lines give the CO_2 assimilation rates predicted from the photosynthesis model assuming a Rubisco limitation alone. At high CO_2 partial pressures the rate of the control leaf clearly falls below that predicted by the Rubisco kinetics. We interpret this as indicative of a limit to RuBP regeneration at high CO_2 partial pressures. In the leaf of the anti SSu plant, however, the CO_2 assimilation rate follows the Rubisco kinetics even at very high CO_2 partial pressures. This provides *in vivo* evidence that the reduction in Rubisco engineered by the antisense gene has led to an imbalance between Rubisco activity and the capacity for RuBP regeneration.

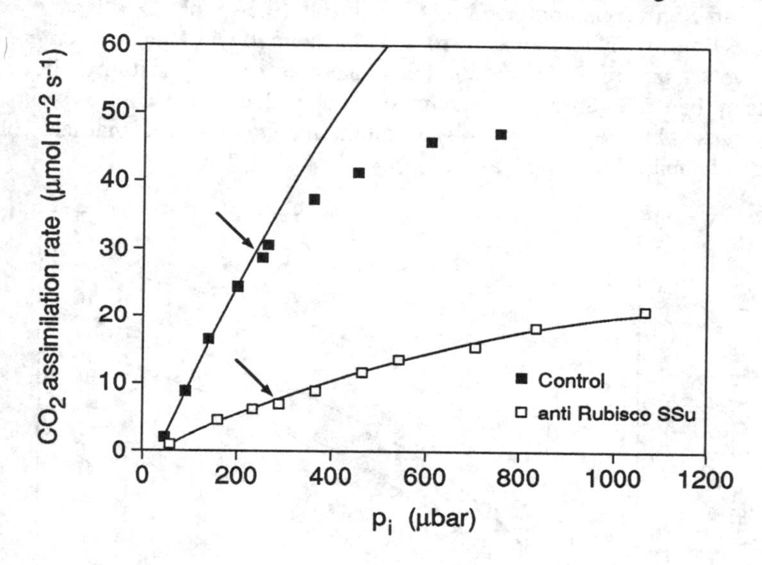

Fig. 3. The response of CO_2 assimilation to intercellular partial pressure of CO_2, p_i, for a control leaf and an anti SSu leaf. Irradiance was 1000 µmol quanta m^{-2} s^{-1}, leaf temperature was 25°C and oxygen concentration was 21%. Solid lines are calculated Rubisco limited rates (6).

In the absence of a rate limitation by RuBP regeneration, the anti-SSu plants provide a way of measuring Rubisco kinetics *in vivo*. Previously it was necessary to confine such analysis to CO_2 partial pressures near the compensation point. Fig. 4 shows measurements of CO_2 assimilation rate of an anti-SSu leaf at varying CO_2 and oxygen partial pressures. No other limits to rates are observed in these anti-SSu plants even at high CO_2 and low oxygen concentrations. Deviations from the predicted assimilation rate are frequently observed in other plants and result from a limit in the rate of triose phosphate utilization (14). The curves in Fig. 4 can be readily fitted with Michaelis-Menten curves and they confirm the well-known competitive inhibition of Rubisco carboxylase by oxygen.

To make accurate estimates of Rubisco kinetics, the CO_2 partial pressure at the site of carboxylation needs to be known. It has recently been shown that a considerable drop in CO_2 partial pressure can occur between intercellular airspaces and the chloroplasts (10). A good correlation between the CO_2 transfer conductance, g_w, and the photosynthetic capacity of leaves has also been demonstrated (10, 15). We have used measurements of carbon isotope discrimination made concurrently with measurements of gas exchange to estimate g_w in the single-dose R1 plants and the control plants. The g_w was reduced by 25% in the anti-SSu plants compared to the controls (0.34 mol m^{-2} s^{-1} bar^{-1} compared to 0.46 respectively). This compares to a 66% reduction in Rubisco content in these plants relative to the controls. Preliminary analyses of leaf anatomy show that the chloroplasts in the single-dose plants are much thinner than in the control plants. This is presumably caused by the loss of Rubisco protein and starch, given that leaf chlorophyll content is not decreased in these leaves.

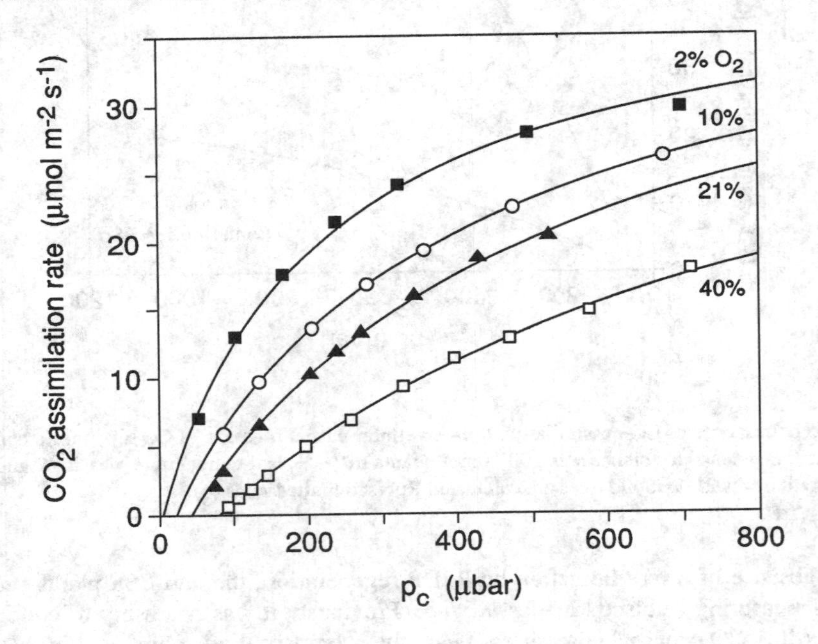

Fig. 4. CO_2 assimilation rate as function of CO_2 partial pressure at the sites of carboxylation, p_c, at four oxygen concentrations. For other conditions see Fig. 3. Solid lines are calculated Rubisco-limited rates (6).

The reduction in Rubisco content by antisense RNA to the Rubisco SSu has not only created an imbalance in the biochemical capacities but also resulted in an imbalance of leaf gas exchange properties (6). The reduction in Rubisco had no effect on stomatal conductance in the single-dose R1 plants and a small reduction in the double-dose plants despite the large reduction in CO_2 assimilation rate. The lack of stomatal response in the anti-SSu plants led to an increase in intercellular CO_2 partial pressure and to an increase in the ratio of intercellular to ambient CO_2 partial pressure, p_i/p_a. This increase in p_i/p_a was reflected by an increase in carbon isotope discrimination measured during CO_2 uptake in the single-dose and double-dose plants compared to control plants (Fig. 5.). However we find that stomata continue to respond to CO_2 (6) and irradiance (data not shown) and thus we conclude that stomatal conductance is independent of leaf Rubisco activity.

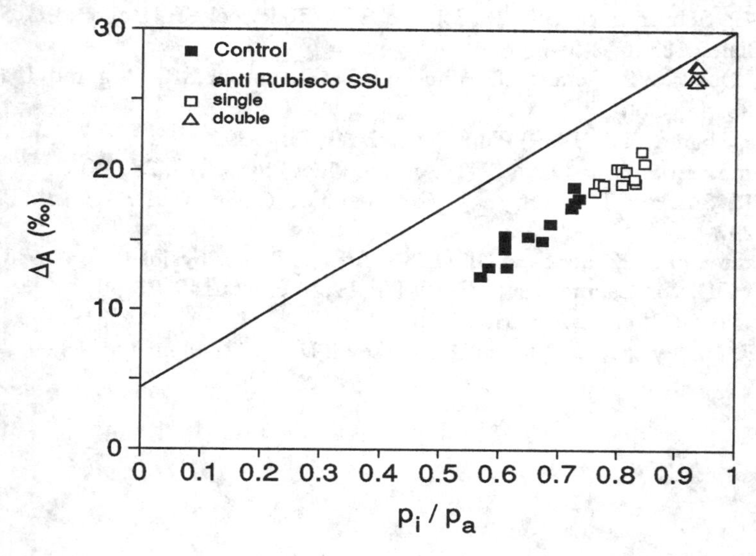

Fig. 5. Carbon isotope discrimination measured concurrently with CO_2 assimilation in leaves of a control plants, and single- and double-dose R1 plants Conditions are described in the methods.

ACKNOWLEDGMENTS

S.v.C. is supported by a Queen Elizabeth II Fellowship and a grant from the Australian Research Council. T.J.A. and G.S.H. are members of the Plant Science Cooperative Research Centre and Y.B.C.A. is supported by the Centre for Molecular Structure and Function, Australian National University.

REFERENCES

1. Björkman O (1981) In Physiological Plant Ecology I, (OL Lange, PS Nobel, CB Osmond, H Ziegler, ed), Vol 12A pp 57-107, Springer Verlag Berlin
2. Makino A, Mae T, Ohira K (1983) Plant Physiol. 73: 1002-1007
3. von Caemmerer S, Farquhar GD (1981) Planta 153: 276-387
4. Wong SC, Cowan IR, Farquhar GD (1979) Nature 282: 424-426
5. Rodermel SR, Abbott MS, Bogorad L (1988) Cell 55: 673-681
6. Hudson GS, Evans JR, von Caemmerer S, Arvidsson YBC, Andrews TJ (1992) Plant Physiol. 98: 294-302
7. Quick WP, Schurr U, Scheibe R, Schulze E-D, Rodermel SR, Bogorad L, Stitt M (1991) Planta 183: 542-554
8. Stitt M, Quick WP, Schurr U, Schulze E-D, Rodermel SR, Bogorad L (1991) Planta 183: 555-566
9. Butz ND, Sharkey TD (1989) Plant Physiol. 89: 735-739
10. von Caemmerer S, Evans JR, (1991) Aust. J. Plant Physiol.18: 287-305
11. Evans JR, Sharkey TD, Berry JA, Farquhar GD (1986) Aust. J Plant. Physiol. 13:281-292
12. von Caemmerer S, Edmondson DL (1986) Aust. J. Plant Physiol.13: 669-688
13. Farquhar GD, von Caemmerer S, Berry JA (1980) Planta 149: 78-90
14. Sharkey TD (1985) Bot. Rev.51: 53-105
15. Loreto F, Harley PC, Di Marco G, Sharkey TD (1992) Plant Physiol. 98: 1437-1443

MODULATION OF EFFICIENCY OF PRIMARY CONVERSION IN LEAVES, MECHANISMS INVOLVED AT PS2.

B. Genty[1], Y. Goulas[2], B. Dimon[3], G. Peltier[3], J.M Briantais[1] and I. Moya[2] , Lab. Ecologie Vég.[1], LURE[2], Université Paris-Sud, Orsay, Dep[t] Physiol. vég. et Ecosystèmes[3] CEN Cadarache, St Paul lez Durance, France.

1. INTRODUCTION

Non stressed C_3 plants show almost identical quantum yield for O_2 evolution with value around 0.106 mol O_2 mol^{-1} absorbed quanta (1). This result indicates that during steady state light limited photosynthesis, plants are able to coordinate PS 1 and PS 2 close to their maximal potential quantum efficiency.

As under natural conditions, photosynthetic metabolic capacity often limits turn over of the products of the light reactions (as e.g. under light saturation, CO_2 uptake stomatal limitation, during photosynthesis induction) maintenance of this high photochemical efficiency at photosystems will result in an overload in primary conversion products and consequently in possible photoinhibitory damage (2).

Recent experiments in leaves using measurements of chlorophyll fluorescence, absorbance changes at 820 nm and net photosynthetic gas exchange have provided evidence that this overload situation rarely occurs in vivo as at steady state photosynthesis, photochemical efficiencies of both photosystems are modulated down in unisson largely by pigment deexcitation via thermal dissipation (3,4,5). Thus less excitation energy will be available for photochemistry.

In air, under a wide range of conditions, leaf photosynthesis has been found to operate under a rate limited by electron transport between the photosystems (3,5,6,7), thought to be at the level of PQH_2 oxidation by Cyt b6f complex (8). At PS 1, an accumulation of oxidised P700 results from this restriction of electron donation to P700 (3,4,5,9). In its oxidised form P700 traps excitation energy as efficiently as P700 (10) but whereas energy quenching by P700 results in charge separation and electron transport, quenching by oxidised P700 results only in thermal dissipation. Therefore the greater the proportion of oxidised P700 pool the less excitation will be available for PS 1 photochemistry and the less will be the overall photochemical efficiency of PS 1. Thus PS 1 photochemistry will adjust to the demand of metabolism and the reducing side of PS 1 will be maintained oxidised (7,9).

At PS 2, an accumulation of reduced Q_A results from the limited electron transport beyond PS 2. However, a reduction of intrinsic photochemical efficiency also occurs and closure of PS 2 centres remains limited (3,11,12). This phenomenon is associated with large non photochemical quenching of fluorescence and with the acidification of the intrathylakoid lumen (7,9). It has been attributed to thermal dissipation processes at PS 2 (3,7).

The location and mechanistic basis for this light induced modulation of PS 2 efficiency has been subject of much debate. Two main hypothesis have been proposed to explain such processes. Weis and Berry (3,11) have suggested that a fraction of the PS 2 centres are converted to an energised state which is able to dissipate excitation energy and is associated with a low fluorescence yield and less efficient photochemistry. A pH dependent slowdown of electron donation to the PS 2 reaction centre will result in $P680^+$ quenching or

N. Murata (ed.), Research in Photosynthesis, Vol. IV, 603–610.

in a fast recombination between the reducing and the oxidising sides of PS 2 (9,13,14,15). Recently an involvement of a release of bound Ca^{++} has been proposed (16). The second suggestion is that an increased dissipation of excitation energy by non radiative processes occurs within the antennae pigment matrices associated with PS 2 reaction centres (12,17). In vivo, quenching of Fo (11,18,19) and the consistent proportional relationship between the photochemical efficiency of PS 2 measured using chlorophyll fluorescence and photochemistry estimated from net gas exchange support this last hypothesis. As the amount of zeaxanthin resulting from the light dependent deepoxidation of violaxanthin has been found to correlate closely with the existence of these phenomena, zeaxanthin has been postulated to quench excitation in the antenna (20,21). However a plausible quenching mechanism remains to be identified. Recently, it has been suggested that these dissipation phenomena result from a pH dependent aggregation of LHC 2 increasing thermal deactivation in the LHC 2 (22,23). Presence of zeaxanthin may facilitate these structural changes.

In this work, we examine the relationship between quenchings of chlorophyll fluorescence and photochemistry in leaves in air. We used gross photosynthetic O_2 evolution measured using $^{18}O_2$ and mass spectrometry to unambiguously determine the quantum yield of photosynthetic electron transport in vivo. Such experiments confirm that photochemical efficiency of PS 2 is modulated by thermal dissipation processes associated with the antenna and that in leaves these dissipative changes fully account the observed changes in PS 2 efficiency.

We further characterize the nature of these thermal dissipation processes by probing lifetime and amplitude of chlorophyll fluorescence emission in intact leaves in conditions promoting photoinduced qE (energy dependent non photochemical quenching). Firstly we show that fluorescence decay measurements can be performed on intact leaf using single photon counting detection and picosecond pulse excitation. Analytic pulses of variable intensity and length were used to analyse non destructively fluorescence decay times at Fo and Fm. The data presented, particularly a reduction of fluorescence lifetime in the presence of qE at Fo suggest that thermal dissipation processes associated with qE are mediated in the pigment matrix of PS 2 complexes and do not involve primary photochemical events at reaction centre. Experiments with isolated thylakoids which show that light induced non photochemical quenching qE is not sensitive to dithionite addition are also presented.

2. MATERIALS AND METHODS

Barleys (Hordeum vulgare) were grown as previously described (24). Beans (Phaseolus vulgaris, cv Rungally) were grown in a glasshouse in CEN Cadarache (southern France) during spring and summer 1991. Intact chloroplasts were isolated from peas as previously shown (24). Chloroplasts were assayed, after brief osmotic shock, at a concentration of 50 $\mu g\ ml^{-1}$ in a medium containing 330 mM sorbitol, 10 mM KCl, 1 mM EDTA, 25 mM $MgCl_2$, 25 mM ascorbate, 0.1 mM methyl-viologen and 50 mM Hepes buffer ajusted to pH 7.8. Temperature of the chloroplast assay chamber was controlled by a Peltier unit permitting rapid temperature changes (<30 s from 20°C to 2°C).

Measurements of leaf O_2 exchange were made in a closed leaf chamber in $^{18}O_2$ enriched air. The chamber was included in a gas circuit (volume = 63 ml) as previously described (25). Before measurements, the gas circuit was rinsed with air, then closed and 2 ml $^{18}O_2$ were injected. CO_2 concentration in the chamber was kept constant by injection of CO_2 into the system using a peristaltic pump. Mass signals of $^{16}O_2$ (m/e = 32), $^{18}O_2$ (m/e = 36) and Ar (m/e = 40) , (Ar was used as an internal reference) were recorded continuously using a tricollector mass spectrometer (VG Gas Analysis 14-80). O_2 uptake and evolution rates were calculated according to (25). Measurements of fluorescence parameters were made simultaneously with gas exchange measurements according to (12).

Relative chlorophyll fluorescence amplitude in leaves and chloroplasts was recorded either using a commercial fluorometer (Walz PAM101) or using a red filtered photodiode. Room temperature chlorophyll fluorescence lifetime measurements using time correleted single photon counting were essentially carried out and analysed as described by Moya *et al* (26). A temperature controled leaf holder was specially designed. Measurements at Fo and Fm were made using two different light pulse sources and two different protocols.

Fluorescence decays at Fo.

A mode-locked and cavity dumped dye laser system (dye Rhodamine 6 G) synchroneously pumped by a mode locked Ar^+ laser provides 630 nm pulses of 10-15 ps duration at a repetition rate of 0.4 Mhz. Fluorescence was excited and detected on a 3 mm^2 area of the upper surface of the leaf. A lens images the target in the entrance slit of a monochromator (Jobin & Yvon M25). The band width was 3 nm and the analysis wavelength was 685 nm. An interference short pass filter ($\lambda <$ 700 nm, Ditric Optics) was set in front of the entrance slit. In addition, a red filter was introduced after the monochromator, (Schott RG 665, 3 mm), which was removed when measuring the scattered ligth. The detector was a micro-channel plate photomultiplier tube (Hamamatsu R1564U having an S20 spectral response) kept at -30°C by a Peltier cooler in order to reduce the dark counts to < 5 counts/s. As a consequence, no background was recorded in the time window used (20 to 40 ns). A shutter protected the photomultiplier from actinic light and was opened during measurement time.

Under these conditions, the full-width at half maximum of the instrumental response function was approx. 60 ps, when scattered ligth was examined instead of fluorescence. The counting rate was kept below 500 counts/s for both flash and fluorescence in order to avoid any significant variable fluorescence induced by the picosecond laser beam. The decays were accumulated over 1024 channels in a multichannel analyzer (Tracor Northern 1750) with 10^4 to 3.10^4 counts at the peak channel. Deconvolution of the decays into a sum of exponential was carried out on line by means of a least squares programme using the Marquardt search algorithm for the non linear parameters. Quality of the fits were judged by the reduced Ki2 and the distribution of the weighted residuals.

Typical protocol was as follows: A dark adapted leaf was initially exposed to the weak picosecond laser beam and the fluorescence decay accumulated during $\approx$ 20 min. An exposure to a continuous actinic white light (600 μmol m^{-2} s^{-1}) followed to induce large qE. When maximum qE was achieved (after 120 s), leaf temperature was rapidely changed from 25°C to 5°C. Then during dark periods of cycles of 20 s dark - 25 s actinic light, fluorescence decays in the presence of qE were measured. During the first 2 s of the dark period, weak far red light was applied, and no decay was recorded.

As at 5°C dark reversion of qE is largely inhibited ($t_{1/2} \approx$ several minutes) this protocol allowed maintenance of qE during measurements. Fluorescence decays were also recorded after dark reversion of qE at 5°C.

Fluorescence decays at Fm.

The synchrotron radiation of the Super Aco storage ring (Orsay) was used both as an actinic light to induce transitory PS2 traps closure and as an analytic light to measure fluorescence decays. This emission consists in a continuous train of pulses of "white light", repeating at 8 Mhz. Laser source used in Fo experiments was not suitable as a fluorescence quenching, probably generated by singlet-singlet fusion during the 5-10 ps pulse was observed at average intensity needed to close PS 2 traps. The longer pulse duration of Super-Aco (FWHM$\approx$ 400ps) avoids the additional quenching effect evoked above and is still short enough to permit accurate lifetime measurements in the nanosecond time range. Synchrotron light was filtered through a 5 mm 4-96 Corning blue filter and focused on a 1 mm^2 area. Light irradiance (> 15 mmol m^{-2} s^{-1}) was sufficiently high to induce maximal fluorescence after 0.2 s exposure . Total light pulse train duration was 0.7 s. Fluorescence decays were measured during the last 0.5 s of this pulse. A single 0.5 s acquisition was used to determine average life time. 300 counts at the peak channel and 20000 counts in the 20 ns window were obtained during this period of time. When multicomponent deconvolution was needed, the decays were accumulated until 16000 counts at the peak channel either by using repetitive pulses with a 200 s period between pulses to avoid light induced quenching or by using different parts of the leaf. Typical protocol was as following. A dark adapted leaf was initially exposed to the synchrotron light pulse and the fluorescence decays at Fm were measured. Then leaf was given a pretreatment of 120 s irradiation with actinic white light of 600 μmol $m^{-2}s^{-1}$ to induce a large qE. 0.1 s after the end of the preillumination, an other synchrotron light pulse is triggered and the fluorescence decays at F'm were measured. A dark recovery period followed, then a third pulse was applied and the fluorescence decays were recorded.

3. RESULTS AND DISCUSSION

Relationships between fluorescence emission and the quantum yield of gross O_2 evolution.

Assuming that light induced non photochemical quenching of fluorescence results from energy dissipation in the pigment antennae, Fv/Fm should be a good estimate of photochemical efficiency of open PS 2 reaction centres and the parameter ΔF/Fm (=Fv/Fm ·qP) taking account of the loss of photochemical efficiency due to PS 2 traps closure should estimate PS 2 photochemical efficiency at steady state photosynthesis (12,27).

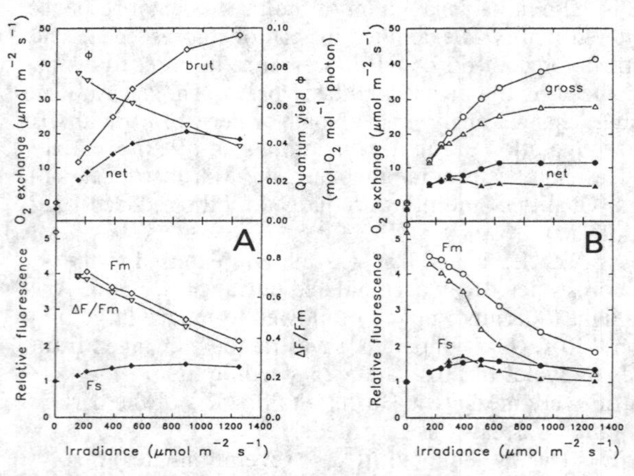

Fig. 1A&B. Irradiance response curve of gross and net O_2 evolution, quantum yield of gross O_2 evolution, Fs, Fm and ΔF/Fm for well hydrated (A) and dehydrated (B) bean leaf discs measured at steady state in air. (o ,•) 9% and (Δ,Δ) 15% water deficit.

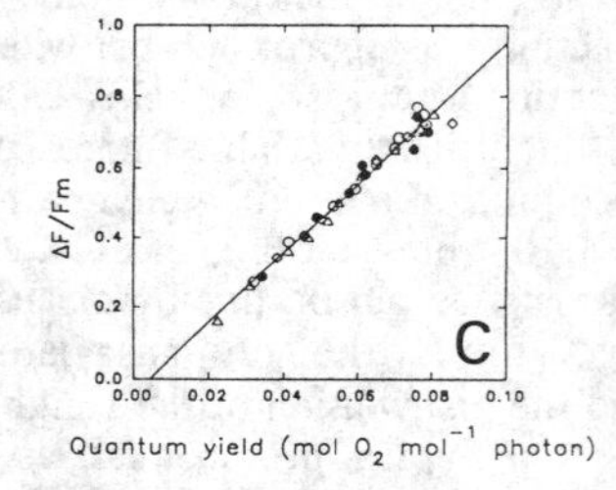

Fig. 1C. The relationship between the quantum yield of gross O2 evolution (calculated on incident photon flux density basis) and ΔF/Fm at steady state photosynthesis under increasing irradiances. (◇) well hydrated leaf discs in air, (o ,Δ) dehydrated leaf discs in air, (•) well hydrated leaf discs in 5% CO2 enriched air.

In order to test this prediction, gross O_2 exchange and fluorescence parameters Fm, Fs and ΔF/Fm were measured simultaneously at steady state in air over a range of irradiance in well hydrated and dehydrated leaves (Fig.1A, B). By using $^{18}O_2$ and mass spectrometry, unidirectional O_2 fluxes were measured and linear electron transport can be directly estimated as gross O_2 evolution. Thus artefacts due to residual photorespiration, respiration or Melher reaction, which affect commonly used estimation of leaf photochemistry from O_2 net exchange, are eliminated.

The relationships between $\Delta F/Fm$ and the quantum yield of gross evolution obtained in these conditions is illustrated by Fig.1C (data obtained in 5% CO_2 enriched air under variable irradiance are also presented). The predicted linear relationship was observed between the decrease of $\Delta F/Fm$ and the decrease of the quantum yield of gross O_2 evolution during saturation of photosynthesis by light. This relationship is maintained in dehydrated leaves where O_2 reduction (presumably via the glycolate pathway) become the major sink for electron and maintained high electron transport activity(Fig.1B).

This correlation and the large increase in non-photochemical quenching of Fm during saturation of photosynthesis (in air Fm at 1280 μmol $m^{-2}s^{-1}$ is 52% of Fm at 153 μmol $m^{-2}s^{-1}$ in well hydrated leaves, 29% in dehydrated leaves (15% water deficit)) suggest that in vivo photochemical efficiency of PS 2 is modulated largely by non photochemical thermal dissipation in the antennae pigments. They also indicate that this exitation quenching fully accounts for the observed changes in open PS 2 centres efficiency.

Fluorescence decays during qE.

As only little information is available about the chlorophyll fluorescence decays of intact leaves, special attention has been devoted to validating measurements done in leaves by comparison with those obtained with isolated choroplasts or algae. Theoretical considerations on the effect of reabsorption on the fluorescence quantum yield and lifetime suggest that the lifetime will not be significantly modified whereas the yield will be strongly decreased by reabsorption (data not shown).

Three exponential decay components were required to fit the chlorophyll fluorescence decay of a dark-adapted barley leaf measured at 685 nm at Fo (table 1). Two slower components with lifetime of 0.18 and 0.43 ns represent 95% of the fluorescence emission at Fo. A fast component with lifetime of 0.04 ns is present and remains small. These results are comparable with data obtained at Fo with algae and chloroplasts (15,28,29).

Table 1: Lifetime (ns) and relative yield (%) of the fluorescence decay components obtained in dark adapted barley leaves.

	Aver. tau (ns)		Deconvolved components C1	C2	C3
Fo	0.323 ± 0.04	tau	0.04 ± 0.03	0.18 ± 0.05	0.432 ± 0.05
		yield	7.2 ± 4.6	36 ± 7	57± 11
Fm DCMU	1.87 ± 0.11	tau	0.5 ± 0.2	1.68 ± 0.11	3.21 ± 0.46
		yield	8 ± 5	71 ± 11	21 ± 13
Fm (light)	1.96 ± 0.05	tau	.27 ± 0.19	1.55 ± 0.18	2.63 ± 0.35
		yield	4 ± 1	51 ± 17	45 ± 17

At Fm, chlorophyll fluorescence decays of dark adapted leaves were measured using synchrotron light pulses to both transiently induce Fm and non destructively analyse fluorescence emission as described in materials and methods. As a comparison, chlorophyll fluorescence decays of dark adapted leaves which have been fed through transpiration stream by a DCMU saturated water solution were also measured using weak average light pulses intensity. Three lifetime components were needed to describe fluorescence decays obtained. Characteristics of fluorescence decays were similar in both protocols. However, a small decrease of the average lifetime was consistently observed in the presense of DCMU. Such result might be explain by fluorescence quenching by oxidised plastoquinones (30). The fluorescence emission is dominated by two long lived components of (1.3 to 1.8 ns) and (2.3 to 3.7ns) (>90%) as it was already noticed in algae and chloroplasts (15,28,29). A rapid component was also found. Our Fm data lacks the 0.04 ns fast component observed in algae and spinach leaves. As this component was present at Fo, it may be infered that the 20 to 40 ns window and the large instrumental response we used at Fm did not allow it resolution.

When leaves were given a light pretreatment to induce a large qE, a quenching of Fo and Fm was observed, with quenching of Fm being considerably greater than that of Fo, as has been reported already. A 38% decrease of the fluorescence average lifetime at Fo corresponds to a 16% decrease in relative fluorescence (Table 2). After dark reversion, Fo quenching was abolished and average lifetime almost reached it initial value. Fig.2 compares the changes of lifetime and amplitude of the components seen at Fo as a function of the average lifetime during qE. The lifetime of the longest lived component, C3, decreases while the one of the middle component C2 was less affected. Lifetime of the rapid component C1 did not significantly change. The yield of the long lived component C3 markedly decreases while that of the two others, C1 and C2, remain stable. This suggests that at Fo, decrease of the average lifetime during qE is mainly related to the decline of C3. These results contradict in vitro studies where no changes at Fo were reported during pH induced qE.

Table 2.

	Fo *	Fm*	Fv/Fm*	qN*	Aver. Tau
Control	24.6 ± 0.33	100	0.77 ± 0.03	0	342 ± 50 ps
Quenched	20.6 ± 3.5	34.2 ± 4	0.45 ± 0.10	0.80 ± 0.04	212 ± 10 ps
Reversed	25.6 ± 2	75 ± 5	0.68 ± 0.04	0.33 ± 0.07	324 ± 40 ps

* Measured with PAM fluorimeter

At Fm, average lifetime declined markedly during qE. Average lifetime decreased proportionally with relative yield during qE, (data not shown) as was reported for photochemical quenching (28). This relationship implies that the average lifetime is a valid estimation of the yield. Two exponential decay components well described stastistically chorophyll fluorescence decays at F'm and during its recovery, as only a reduced amount of counts at the peak could be accumulated. Lifetimes of these two long lived components C2 and C3 declined in the presence of qE, lifetime of C3 being less diminished than that of C2 (Fig.2). During qE, the yield of the longest component, C3, tends to zero while that of the shortest was less decreased. This behaviour is not really different from that reported during trap closure (photochemical quenching) and suggests that during qE, quenching processes affect excitation distribution in a way comparable to photochemical quenching by decreasing the probability that excitation stays in the antenna (28). No appearance of 5 to 20 ns long lived components were seen during qE.

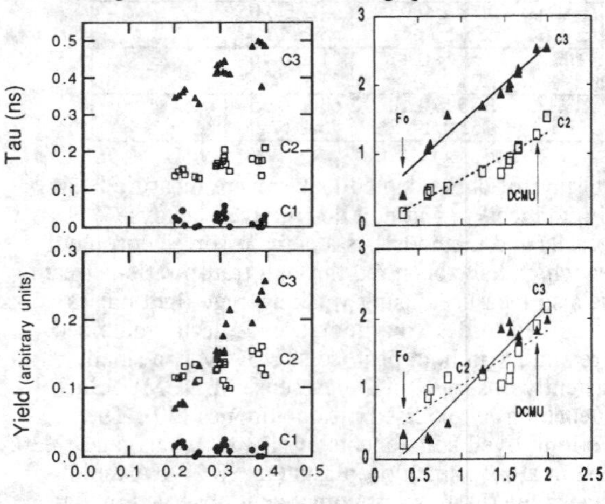

Fig. 3 Relationships between the average lifetime and the specific lifetimes (top) and the yields (bottom) of C1, C2, C3 at Fo (left) and of C2,C3 at Fm measured in barley leaves during qE.

The fact that at Fo the yield of the main component, clearly identified as originating from PS 2, markedly declined shows that qE is associated with quenching processes which compete effectively with photochemical quenching for exciton capture. This last result confirms differences between data obtained in intact systems during light induced qE and those obtained in isolated particles or chloroplasts upon acidification, where no change of Fo was observed.

On the whole, increasing thermal dissipation processes localised in the pigment antennae fully accounts for the observed changes in fluorescence decays. A precise location of these quenchings in the pigment matrices (near the reaction centre, in the LHC 2) remains to be done. Deexcitation by pH dependant conversion of PS 2 to centres with inactive donor side (13),through luminescence by recombination between $P680^+$ $Pheo^-$ or $P680^+$ Q_A^- (14,15,16) or through a competitive cycle for electron (14) appears highly unlikely in vivo.

Reversion of qE by reductants

Fig.3. presents experiments obtained on osmotically shocked chloroplasts comparing the effect of additions of an electron transport inhibitor DBMIB and of a reducing mediator dithionite on light induced qE at steady state fluorescence Fs. Chloroplasts were assayed in presence of 25 mM ascorbate and $MgCl_2$ and presented similar changes of Fo and Fm to those observed in leaves during qE and violaxanthin conversion to zeaxanthin (data not shown) as previously reported (21). Temperature was used to modulate the rate of qE relaxation as a temperature drop markedly slows down its reversion. After chloroplasts suspension have been illuminated at 20°C to induce steady state maximal qE, temperature either was unchanged or decreased to 2°C and 90 s later DBMIB or dithionite was added. Just before dithionite addition, the actinic light was switched off as in reducing conditions minimal light intensity is required to avoid $Pheo^-$ accumulation. During experiments with dithionite, the analytic beam of the fluorometer was set as low as possible (1.6 kHz pulse frequency). On addition of DBMIB, a rapid increase of fluorescence emission was seen, followed by a slow increase of large amplitude.The rapid phase represents reversion of photochemical quenching whereas the slower one reversion of qE. In our conditions qE was largely predominant.

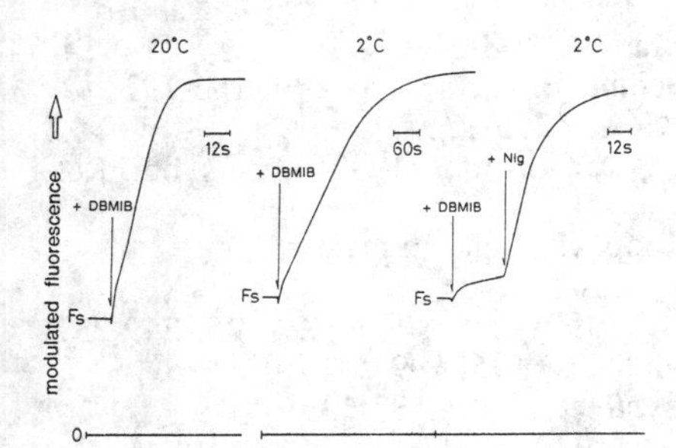

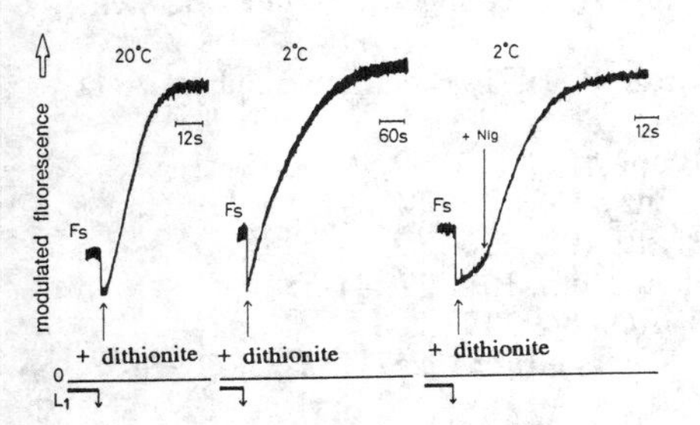

Fig. 4 Comparison of the effect of addition of DBMIB or dithionite on light induced qE at Fs in osmotically shocked pea choroplasts. Additions were done at 20°C or 2°C. Final concentrations were 2.5 μM Nig, 2μM DBMIB, 2.5 mM dithionite.

On addition of dithionite, these two phases could not be determined as in our low light intensity the disappearance of photochemical quenching was slow ($t_{1/2}$ < 11 s when dithionite was added in the absence of qE at both 20°C and 2°C) However as qE was predominant in our condition at 2°C, increases of fluorescence under dithionite should mainly represent qE reversion. The decrease of temperature from 20°C to 2°C induced a marked slowdown of qE reversion in the presence of both DBMIB and of dithionite. In both cases, rate of reversion was markly increased upon addition of an uncoupler nigericin which dissipated the ΔpH. Therefore the reducing effect of dithionite *per se* did not affect qE significantly as its reversion remains sensitive to ΔpH changes.

Moreover, with our chloroplasts preparations, maximal qE was only seen in the presence of 25mM ascorbate a reducing mediator which, like dithionite, reverses low pH induced non photochemical quenching of fluorescence (14). This result strongly suggests that a pH dependant inactivation of PS 2 donor side and an accumulation of quenching species $P680^+$ are not the mechanism underlying thermal dissipation processes associated with qE in vivo.

4. REFERENCES

(1) Demmig B & Bjorkman O (1897) Planta 171, 171-184
(2) Powles SB (1984) Annu. Rev. Plant Physiol. 35, 15-44
(3) Weis E, Ball JT & Berry J (1987) Progress Photosynth. Res. 2, 553-556
(4) Harbinson J, Genty B & Baker NR (1989)Plant Physiol. 90, 1029-1034
(5) Genty B, Harbinson J & Baker NR (1990) Plant Physiol. Biochem. 28, 1-10
(6) Harbinson J & Hadley CL (1989) Plant Cell Environ. 12, 357-369
(7) Foyer C, Furbank R, Harbinson J & Horton P (1990) Photosynth. Res. 25, 83-100
(8) Haehnel W (1984) Annu. Rev. Plant Physiol. 35, 659-693
(9) Weis E & Lechtenberg D (1989) Phil. Trans. R. Soc. Lond. B233, 253-268
(10) Nuijs AM, Shuvalov VA, Von Gorkom HJ, Plijter JJ & Duysens LNM (1986) Biochim. Biophys. Acta 850, 310-318
(11) Weis E & Berry J (1987) Biochim. Biophys. Acta 894, 198-208
(12) Genty B, Briantais JM. & Baker NR (1989) Biochim. Biophys. Acta 849, 183-192
(13) Schreiber & Neubauer C (1987) Z Naturforsch C 42, 1255-1264
(14) Rees D, Noctor G, Ruban AV, Crofts J, Young A & Horton P (1992) Photosynth. Res. 31, 11-19
(15) Kreiger A, Moya I & Weis E (1992) Biochim. Biophys. Acta, in press
(16) Krieger A & Weis E (1992) Photosynthetica, in press
(17) Genty B, Harbinson J, Briantais JM & Baker NR (1990) Photosynth. Res. 25, 249-257
(18) Rees D, Noctor G and Horton P (1990) Photosynth. Res. 25, 199-212
(19) Genty B, Wonders J & Baker NR (1990) Photosynth. Res. 26, 133-139
(20) Demming-Adams B (1990) Biochim Biophys. Acta 1020, 1-24
(21) Gilmore A.M & Yamamoto HY (1991) Plant Physiol. 96, 635-643
(22) Horton P, Ruban AV, Rees D, Noctor G, Pascall AA & Young A (1991) FEBS Lett. 292, 1-4
(23) Ruban AV, Rees D, Noctor G, Young A & Horton P (1991) Biochim. Biophys. Acta 1059, 355-360
(24) Cerovic ZG & Briantais JM (1992) Biochim. Biophys. Acta 1099, 247-252
(25) Dimon B, Gans P & Peltier G (1988) Methods Enzymol 167, 686-691
(26) Moya I, Hodges M & Barbet JC (1986) FEBS Lett. 198, 256-262
(27) Havaux M, Strasser RJ & Greppin H (1991) Photosynth. Res. 27, 41-55
(28) Hodges M & Moya I (1986) Biochim. Biophys. Acta 849, 193-203
(29) Holzwarth A.R (1990) in The Chlorophylls (H Sheers ed) pp1125-1152, CRC Press Boca Raton
(30) Vernotte C, Etienne A & Briantais JM (1979) Biochim. Biophys. Acta 545, 519-527

SCREENING A BIOTOPE BY FLUORESCENCE TECHNIQUES : TWO WAVELENGTHS FLUORESCENCE AMPLITUDE ANALYSIS AND O-J-I-P FLUORESCENCE RISE ANALYSIS

PETER EGGENBERG, BEATRIX SCHWARZ and RETO J. STRASSER
University of Geneva, Bioenergetics Laboratory,
CH-1254 Jussy, Switzerland. Fax: +41 22 759 19 45

Chl *a* fluorescence techniques are powerful tools for analyzing photosynthetic systems as small as isolated reaction center complexes or as big as whole biotopes like a forest, a field or a tree. For *in vitro* experiments the questions focus to problems on a molecular level. When analyzing a field, however, one would like to get informations about the agronomic productivity, or when analyzing a tree or a complex biotope one would like to know about its general state of health, its vitality and its stability in its actual environment. Completely different methods have to be developed in order to describe such complex samples. Two ways appear possible to go:

1. Widening the observation angle to gain an integrated view by **remote sensing**. This is surely the technique of the future for controlling large areas up to the size of continents and oceans. Areas with abnormal behavior will be easily recognized and can subsequently be further investigated by scientists directly in these areas.
2. Using the same methods as for homogeneous samples; but then a **big number of measurements** is needed to get an impression of the heterogeneity of the system. Actually we are developing screening techniques which should allow an overall picture of vitality and stability of photosynthesizing areas. The following requirements for such an approach have already been published [1,2]:

1. More than 100 samples have to be measured in 1 hour.
2. The sampled signals are transformed to normalized expressions exhibiting values between zero and unity.

Theory, Methods and Results.

The following kinetic and spectroscopic parameters are considered, which are typical for all photosynthetic systems:

1. Two wavelengths fluorescence amplitude analysis.

1.1. Quantitative criterion r: The fluorescence emission of chlorophyll containing systems show one emission band between 680 and 700 nm (labelled F") and an other emission band between 710 and 750 nm (labelled F'). The ratio F'/F" has been reported as a power function of the chlorophyll concentration measured by extraction [4] or by reflection [5]. For our purposes we define: $r = F'/(F'+F")$ what is an indirect and nonlinear

N. Murata (ed.), Research in Photosynthesis, Vol. IV, 611–614.

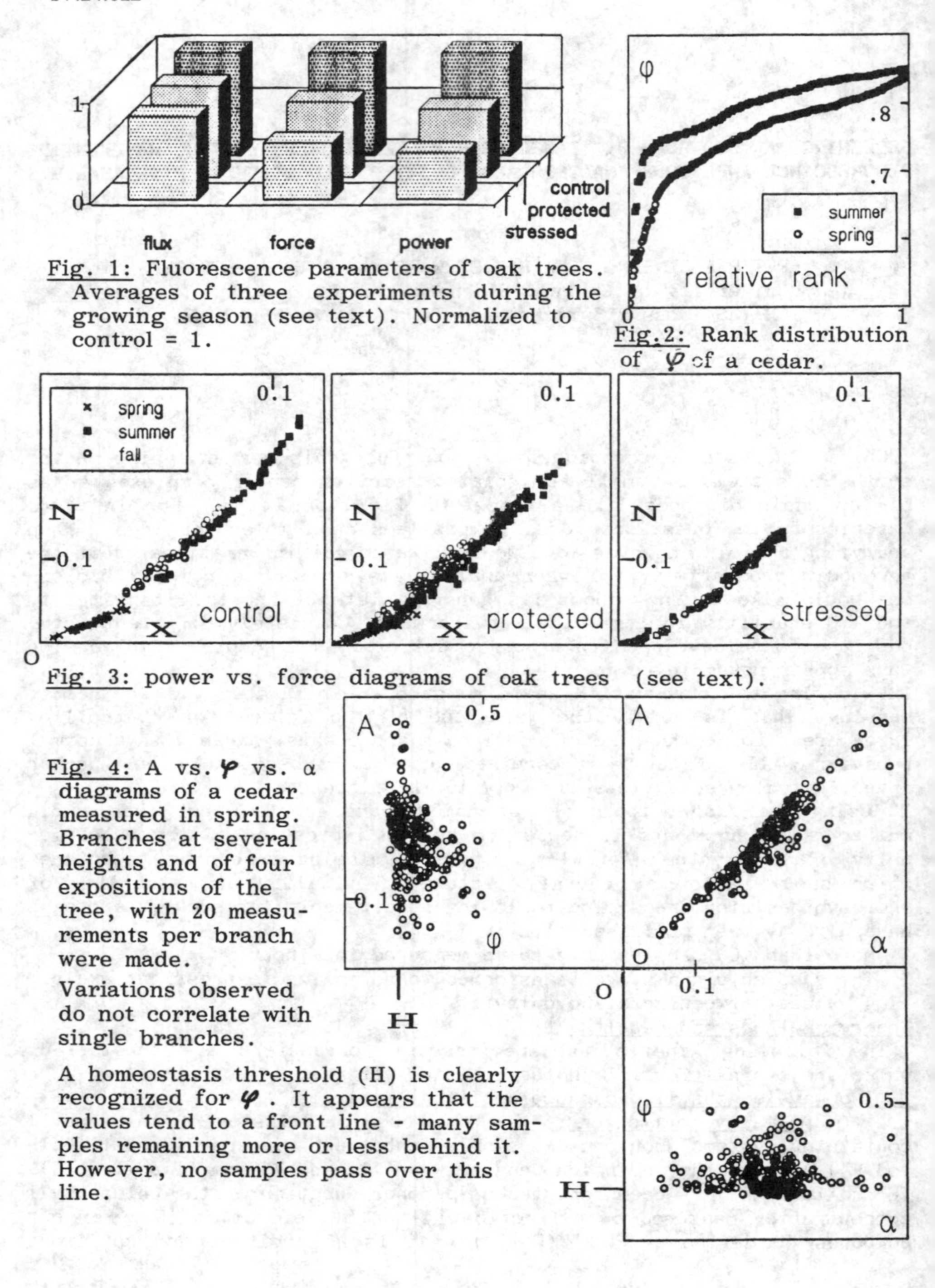

Fig. 1: Fluorescence parameters of oak trees. Averages of three experiments during the growing season (see text). Normalized to control = 1.

Fig. 2: Rank distribution of φ of a cedar.

Fig. 3: power vs. force diagrams of oak trees (see text).

Fig. 4: A vs. φ vs. α diagrams of a cedar measured in spring. Branches at several heights and of four expositions of the tree, with 20 measurements per branch were made. Variations observed do not correlate with single branches.

A homeostasis threshold (H) is clearly recognized for φ. It appears that the values tend to a front line - many samples remaining more or less behind it. However, no samples pass over this line.

index from zero to one indicating the relative amount of chlorophyll per unit area. The index r represents somehow the visual impression of the green color of the sample and, therefore, is also an estimate for the total energy absorbed by the sample.

1.2. Activity criterion φ: We use the maximum quantum yield of PS II as a relative activity criterion of the sample. This expression can be derived from the fluorescence signals of samples with only open (F_o) or only closed (F_{max}) reaction centers as follows: $\varphi = 1 - F''_o / F''_{max}$.

1.3. Complexity criterion α: Excitation energy distribution between antennae of PS I and PS II within the different types of photosynthetic units modify the spectroscopic and kinetic behavior of the sample. Therefore the ratio F_o/F_{max} becomes dependent upon emission wavelength. The complexity of the sample is determined by the organization of the different pigment-protein complexes and the energy distribution therein, and their heterogeneity. We define therefore:

$\alpha = 1 - [F''_o / F''_M (1 - F'_o / F'_M)] / [F'_o / F'_M (1 - F''_o / F''_M)]$.

1.4. Stress adaptation index A: Based on the observation that fluorescence transients from dark adapted state to steady state in the light differs at different emission wavelengths a so called maximum stress adaptation index has been defined [4,5]:

$A = 1 - (F''_o / F''_M) / (F'_o / F'_M)$. This correlates to: $A = \varphi \cdot \alpha$

1.5. Flux index I: A flux index can be defined as follows: $I = r \cdot \varphi$

1.6. Force index X: Multiplying r with A leads to an expression of the type of a force. We define the force index as $X = r \cdot A = r \cdot \varphi \cdot \alpha$

1.7. Power index N: The product of force and flux is a power term. Therefore we define a power index as $N = X \cdot I$

The experimental ratios F'/F'', F'_o/F'_M and F''_o/F''_M can be used to calculate all seven expressions defined above.

Results

A fluorimeter which measures simultaneously the modulated and the direct fluorescence at two different wavelengths before and during a saturating light pulse allows to record the three experimental ratios needed in only a few seconds (Twin Channel Modulated Fluorometer by Hansatech, UK). For every expression a so called **rank distribution** can be plotted. Thereby all data of the same expression are sorted and ranked between zero and one (Fig. 1). Fig. 2 shows the response (average of > 100 measurements) of a free standing (control) oak tree and an alley of oak trees besides recently finished big apartment and deep underground constructions. Special care had been taken during the construction period for some of these trees (protected) in order to disturb as little as possible their root systems and to minimize additional soil draining and erosion. For some other trees (stressed) no protection had been made. Fig. 3 shows the *power* vs. *force* diagram of the individual measurements of the same oak trees as in Fig. 2. Fig. 4 shows the individual measurements of a cedar in the A versus φ versus α diagrams.

2. O-J-I-P fluorescence rise analysis

As reported earlier [6,7] the fluorescence rise from F_o to F_{max} shows two intermediate steps called J and I. The values of Fo-J-I-P are drastically changed if the sample is illuminated a second time (see Fig. 5). Using a shutterless instrument with integrated data acquisition system (Plant Efficiency Analyser PEA by Hansatech, UK) these measurements can be made within 10 seconds. For every selected time (*e.g.* t_1 = 2 ms, t_2 = 30 ms and t_3 = 500 ms) a relative variable fluorescence $V_x = (F_t - F_o)/F_M - F_o)$ where x stand for t_1, t_2 and t_3 can be defined. These ratios are measured during a first illumination and after six seconds dark during a second illumination (Fig. 5). They are very sensitive to environmental changes and react very fast to short term stress conditions. According to the type of stress a different constellation of the parameters appear.

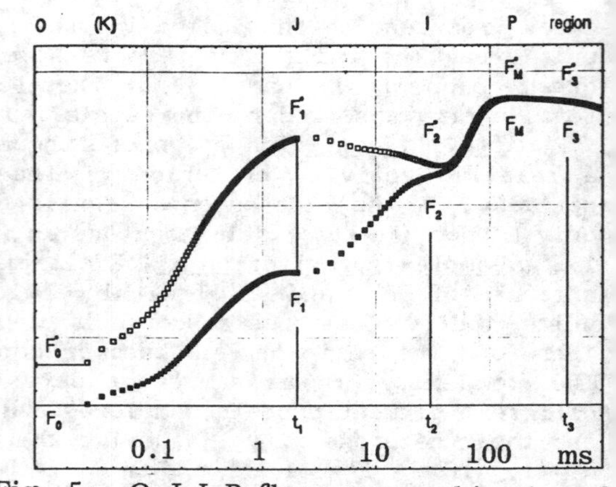

Fig. 5: O-J-I-P fluorescence kinetics of a pea leaf: ■ dark adapted, □ six seconds dark after first flash.

Conclusions

- Many experiments are needed in order to analyze the asymmetric heterogeneity of the energetic constellation of a sample.
- The fluorescence amplitude analysis reveals the overall heterogeneity of behavior of *e.g.* a tree and the trend of slow (seasonal) changes can be followed. Homeostasis thresholds can be estimated.
- The fluorescence rise analysis gives access to the actual dynamic behavior of the sample and its heterogeneity. It is very sensitive to any perturbation of the primary photochemistry of PS II.
- These two techniques can be used to screen biotopes and to establish a checklist containing vitality, complexity and stability criteria.
- It is only a question of time until the fluorescence amplitude and fluorescence rise analyses can be performed with one unique instrument. Intense blue, green or yellow light emitting diodes are needed.
- All measurements can be done in the laboratory, in a mobile laboratory nearby the experimental site or even directly in the field. However, climbing on a tree with sophisticated instruments is an unpractical task for a *Homo sapiens*.

References

1. Strasser,R.J. and Eggenberg,P. (1992) Arch. Sc. Genève, in press.
2. Eggenberg,P., Pasche,A., Truan,R. and Strasser,R.J. (1992) Arch. Sc. Genève, in press.
3. Hak,R., Lichtenthaler,H.K. and Rinderle,U. (1990) Radiat. Environ. Biophys. 29, 229-336.
4. Strasser,R.J.,Schwarz,B. and Eggenberg,P. (1988) in Applications of Chlorophyll Fluorescence (Lichtenthaler, K.H., ed.), pp 181-187, Kluwer Academic Publishers, Dordrecht/Boston/London.
5. Strasser,R.J, Schwarz,B. and Bucher, J.B. (1987) Eur. J. Forest Path. 17, 149-157.
6. Strasser,R.J. and Govindjee (1991) in Regulation of Chloroplast Biogenesis (Argyroudi-Akoyunoglou, J.H.,ed.) pp. 423-426, Plenum Press, New York.
7. Strasser, R.J. and Govindjee (1992), these abstracts.

FORMATION OF INACTIVE PS2 CENTERS IN SPINACH LEAVES DURING LIGHT ADAPTATION.

Jan F.H. Snel, Hans Boumans and Wim J. Vredenberg. Department of Plant Physiological Research, Wageningen Agricultural University, Gen. Foulkesweg 72, 6703 BW Wageningen, The Netherlands.

1. INTRODUCTION

In inactive PS2 ($PS2_I$) centers electron flow from Q_A to the plastoquinone pool is impaired, while watersplitting and the PS2 herbicide binding sites seem to be normal (1,2,3). The lifetime of the closed state of $PS2_I$ centers was reported to be about 1.5-1.7 s (3). The very low rate of electron flow implies that $PS2_I$ centers do not evolve oxygen at a significant rate. As $PS2_I$ centers are among the first PS2 centers to be reduced during photosynthetic induction (4), the O-I phase in the fluorescence induction transient should be characterized by a increase in fluorescence without an associated decrease in the yield of oxygen evolution. We have determined $PS2_I$ centers in spinach leaf-discs by measuring photosynthetic oxygen evolution with high time-resolution by means of the photoacoustic method (5,6). Chylla and Whitmarsh (1989) have reported that 9 to 18% of the total amount of reaction centers is in the inactive form. The data presented in this contribution show that the fraction $PS2_I$ centers in spinach leaves is small after dark adaptation for 18 hrs. During light adaptation up to 45% of the PS2 centers were found to be in the inactive form. The lifetime of the inactive state was found to be 300 ms, which is much shorter than previously reported (3).

2. MATERIAL AND METHODS

Intact chloroplasts were isolated from spinach (*Spinacia oleracea cv.* BERGOLA) grown in the greenhouse and stored on ice (8). Chloroplasts were taken from stock suspensions on ice after dark adaptation of 2 hours and broken in 50 mM sodium phosphate (pH 7.5). After 1 min an equal volume of double strength reaction medium consisting of 660 mM sorbitol, 20 mM NaCl, 10 mM $MgCl_2$, 4 mM EDTA, 10 mM ascorbic acid, 150 mM Hepes/KOH (pH 7.8) was added. The chlorophyll concentration was 20 $\mu g\ ml^{-1}$ Chl $a+b$. Hydroxylamine treated chloroplasts were obtained as described (4). Leaf-discs (∅ 12mm) were cut immediately before the start of the experiment from harvested leaves kept in darkness between moist tissue. Water was removed from the leaf-surface using dry tissue paper and the leaf-disc was then transferred to the PA-cell. Flash-induced P515-signals were measured at 8° C with a modified Aminco Chance spectrophotometer using saturating single-turnover light flashes (7). The amplitude of Reaction 1/RC was determined by subtracting the non-electrochromic absorbance changes (8). Photoacoustic measurements were done at room temperature with leaf-discs using a combined fluorescence and photoacoustic measuring system (6,9). The modulation frequency was 171.6 Hz and the photon flux density 200 $\mu E\ m^{-2}\ s^{-1}$. After the initialization procedure, in which F_0, F_M were measured and the phase of the lock-in amplifier was set to the phase of the thermal signal, the leaf-disc was dark-adapted for 300 s. Fluorescence was measured simultaneously with a PAM chlorophyll fluorometer operating at 100 kHz. Fluorescence induction from isolated chloroplasts was measured in the MKS-101 cuvette (Walz, FRG) thermostatted at 8° C.

N. Murata (ed.), Research in Photosynthesis, Vol. IV, 615–618.

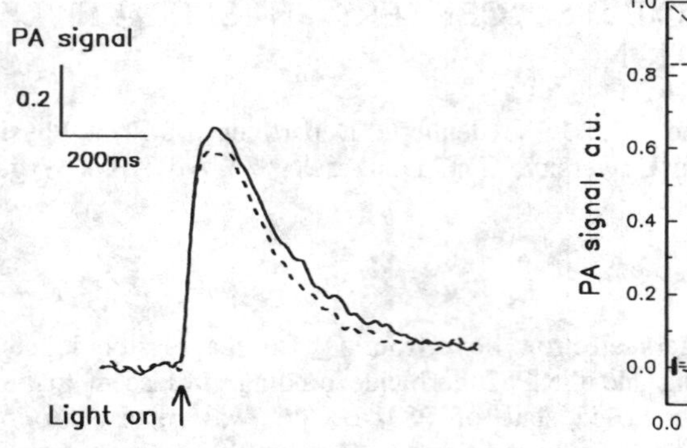

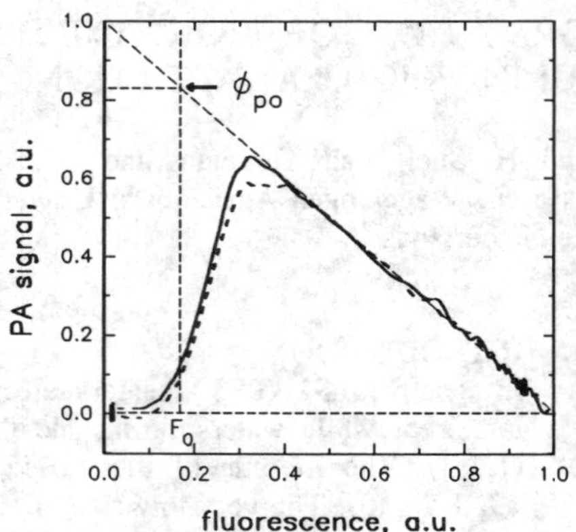

FIGURE 1 (left). Photoacoustic oxygen signal transients from leaf-discs obtained from dark (continuous line) and light (dashed line) adapted spinach plants. The arrow marks the point at which the PA-measuring light was switched on. Time-constants were 30ms for the PA-signal and 24 ms for the fluorescence signal (not shown). Ten independent measurements on different leaf-discs were averaged to improve the signal-to-noise ratio.

FIGURE 2 (right). XY-plot of the oxygen signals shown in Fig.1 and the simultaneously measured fluorescence transient. The fluorescence axis is normalized to $F_M=1$. The F_o level is indicated by the vertical dashed line. Φ_{PO} was obtained by linear regression of the PA and F data between F=0.5 and F=1. The oxygen signal was scaled by extrapolating the dashed line to a (hypothetical) fluorescence yield of 0. In this state, which can only be reached by "increasing" the rate of trapping to infinity, photochemistry proceeds with 100% efficiency.

3. RESULTS AND DISCUSSION

Photoacoustically detected oxygen evolution and chlorophyll fluorescence were simultaneously measured from dark-adapted leaf-discs. Figure 1 shows the kinetics of oxygen signal during the first 1 s of photosynthetic induction of dark-adapted spinach leaf-discs from plants kept in the dark for 18 hr or adapted to daylight for 7 hr. The maximum rate of oxygen evolution is reached in 100 ms with a half time of 30 ms at the light intensity used, which is close to the response time of 30 ms of the lock-in amplifier. As the amplitude of the PA signal can only be expressed in relative units, we have used the chlorophyll fluorescence data to calibrate the PA signal. As the rate of electron flow is proportional to photochemical quenching, a plot of the rate of oxygen evolution versus fluorescence yield should yield a straight line with a direction coefficient of -1. Figure 2 shows the relation between the oxygen signal and chlorophyll fluorescence yield during the first 1 s of photosynthetic induction. At $F=F_O$ the rate of oxygen evolution is proportional to Φ_{PO}, the intrinsic yield of PS2. At $F=F_M$ the rate of oxygen evolution is zero. The well-established complementarity between the rate of electron flow (oxygen evolution) and fluorescence yield is represented by the dashed line from the point denoted as Φ_{PO} at $F=F_O$ to the point characterized by zero oxygen evolution at $F=F_M$. After the time-lag related to the response time of the setup, the oxygen signal shows a linear relation with q_P. There is, however, a distinct difference between the response of dark and light-adapted leaves. Figure 2 shows a lower O_2 evolution rate in the region between F=0.25 and F=0.4 as compared to the dark-

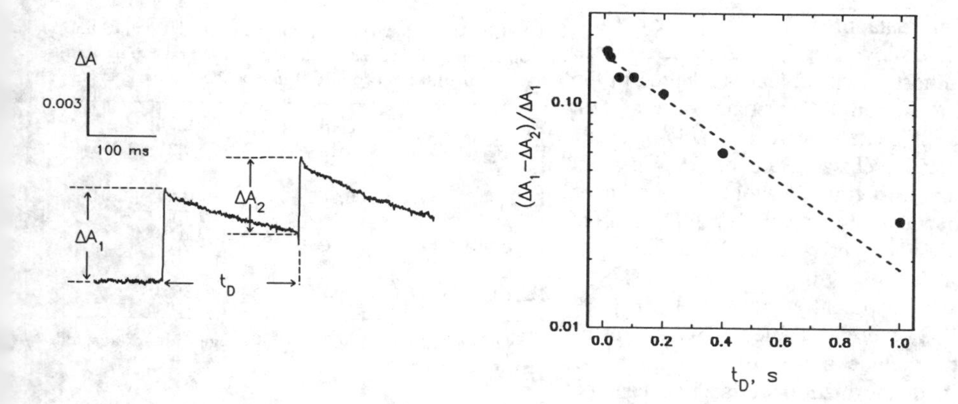

FIGURE 3 (left). Flash-induced P515 signals from spinach thylakoids isolated from spinach leaves adapted to daylight for 7 hrs.

FIGURE 4 (right). Dependence of the number of closed PS2 centers of thylakoids isolated from light-adapted spinach leaves on the dark time t_D between two consecutive single-turnover saturating light flashes. The fraction closed PS2 centers was calculated from the relative decrease of the amplitude of Reaction 1/RC: $(\Delta A_1-\Delta A_2)/\Delta A_1$ and corrected for the contribution of PS1 as measured in a similar experiment using NH_2OH-treated thylakoids in the presence of 1 μM DCMU and 450 μM DQH_2.

adapted leaf. This would indicate the presence of PS2 centers in which the primary processes, including charge separation and Q_A reduction, are normal but in which oxygen evolution is somehow suppressed. From Figs. 1 and 2 one can estimate that about 12% of the PSII centers are inactive in these light-adapted leaves. The number of inactive centers thylakoids isolated from dark and light-adapted leaves was verified using the P515 technique to estimate the number of open reaction centers (2,3). Figure 3 shows the P515 response of dark-adapted thylakoids upon application of two consecutive saturating single-turnover flashes. The amplitude of the initial fast phase, *i.e.* the amplitude of R1/RC (8) is smaller in the second flash. After 18hr dark-adaptation of the plants the amplitude of R1/RC in the two flashes were found to be identical (data not shown). The fraction inactive centers and the lifetime of the inactive state were determined by varying the dark-time (t_D) between the two flashes from 10 ms to 1 s. The fraction $PS2_I$ centers was calculated from the relative decrease of the amplitude of Reaction 1/RC as indicated in Fig.3 and corrected for the contribution of PS1. Figure 4 shows that $PS2_I$ centers amount to about 17% of the total number of reaction centers. The PS2 contribution to the amplitude of Reaction 1/RC was 38%. This suggests that up to 45% of PS2 was inactive. The lifetime of the closed state of the $PS2_I$ centers is about 300 ms (Fig.4). To see whether the occurrence of inactive centers might be correlated with photoinhibition, we have measured F_V/F_M from dark and light-adapted leaf-discs and found no significant differences (Table 1). The fluorescence induction transient of leaves and of isolated thylakoids in the presence of ferricyanide (FeCy) shows a plateau (F_{PL}), which has been correlated with the fraction $PS2_\beta$-centers (4). The relative magnitude of F_{PL} was found to be uncorrelated with the fraction $PS2_I$ centers as determined by means of the P515 or the photoacoustic method (Table 1).

The data presented in this contribution show that i) $PS2_I$ centers were almost absent in leaves adapted to the for 18 hours, ii) primary processes in $PS2_I$ centers were probably normal, iii) the closed state of $PS2_I$ centers had a lifetime of about 300 ms under our conditions and iv) $PS2_I$ centers are not identical to $PS2_\beta$ centers.

TABLE 1. Summary of properties of dark and light adapted spinach leaves. Data are the average plus standard error of the mean of 6-9 independent experiments.

Parameter	Dark	Light
F_{PL}/F_M	0.19±0.01	0.21±0.015
F_V/F_M	0.862±0.01	0.845±0.015
$PS2_I/(PS1+PS2)$[1]	0.03	0.17
Peak PA signal[2]	100%	88%

[1] As estimated from Fig.3. [2] Peak-height in dark-adapted leaves defined as 100%.

The apparently normal F_V/F_M of $PS2_I$ centers (Table 1), which seems to exclude a role of photoinhibition in the formation of inactive centers, and the variable lifetime of the closed state, 300 ms compared to 1.5-1.7 s (3), might suggest that the PS2 environment could play an important role in determining its kinetic properties. Two kinetic phases in fluorescence induction of active PS2 centers have been suggested to reflect the existence of two distinct PQ pools (10,11). Clustering of PS2 units might lead to PS2 centers which are poorly accessible to PQ (12) and therefore to PS2 centers that can only make one turnover. The reduction of the effective antenna size of $PS2_I$ centers by approximately 50% (13) suggests that $PS2_I$ centers belong to the $PS2_\beta$ type centers which are believed to be located in the stroma exposed regions, far away from the $PS2_\alpha$ centers where PQ is reduced. These mechanisms involving PS2-PQ interactions might be sensitive to phase transitions in the membrane. The lifetime of the closed state of $PS2_I$ centers could therefore be temperature dependent, which might explain the longer lifetime of the $PS2_I$ closed state observed in leaves at 22-25°C (3).

4. ACKNOWLEDGEMENT

We thank Wilma Versluis for technical assistance and experimental contributions.

REFERENCES

1 Graan, T. and Ort, D.R. (1986) Biochim. Biophys. Acta 852:320-330
2 Chylla, R.A., Garab, G. and Whitmarsh, J. (1987) Biochim. Biophys. Acta 894:562-571
3 Chylla, R.A. and Whitmarsh, J. (1989) Plant Physiol. 90:765-772
4 Melis, A. (1985) Biochim. Biophys. Acta 808:334-342
5 Poulet, P., Cahen, D. and Malkin, S. (1983) Biochim. Biophys. Acta 724:433-446
6 Vredenberg, W.J., Snel, J.F.H. and Ooms, J.J.J. (1991) in Light in Biology and Medicine, Vol. 2, (R.H. Douglas, J. Moan, and G. Ponto, eds.) Plenum Press, London, 101-110
7 Snel, J.F.H. (1985) PhD Thesis Wageningen Agricultural University
8 Ooms, J.J.J., Vredenberg, W.J. and Buurmeijer, W.F. (1989) Photosynth Res 20:119-128
9 Vredenberg, W.J., Boumans, H., Buurmeijer, W.F. and Snel, J.F.H. (1992) Photosynthetica, submitted
10 Snel, J.F.H., Van Kooten, O. and Vredenberg, W.J. (1987) Progress in Photosynth. Res., Vol. II, (J. Biggins ed.), Martinus Nijhoff Publishers, Dordrecht, 617-620
11 Meunier, P.C. and Bendall, D.S. (1992) Photosynth. Res. 32:109-120
12 Lavergne, J. and Joliot, J. (1991) Trends in Biochem. Sci. 16: 129-134
13 Chylla, R.A. and Whitmarsh, J. (1990) Photosynth. Res. 25:39-48

DIFFERING PATTERNS OF ENHANCEMENT BY O_2 OF PHOTOCHEMICAL EFFICIENCY IN PHOTOSYSTEM 2 AMONG C_3, C_3-C_4, AND C_4 SPECIES OF PANICUM

Richard B. Peterson, Department of Biochemistry & Genetics, The Connecticut Agricultural Experiment Station, Box 1106, New Haven, CT 06504 USA

INTRODUCTION

The process of photorespiration is an important sink for NADPH and ATP and contributes substantially to recycling of orthophosphate, amino groups, CO_2, and reduced carbon in the plant cell. Feedback regulation from carbon metabolism to primary light harvesting processes could be expected, therefore, to respond to variations in photorespiratory activity. This study shows that the photochemical yield of photosystem II (Φ_{II}) based on fluorescence measurements may be enhanced substantially when the [O_2] is elevated. This effect is diminished in species possessing adaptations for reducing photorespiration.

MATERIALS AND METHODS

Panicum bisulcatum (C_3), P. milioides (C_3-C_4), and P. antidotale (C_4) were grown in a greenhouse in a commercial potting mix.

Measurements of CO_2 and H_2O exchange by leaf tissue at 25° C and an external [CO_2] of 200 μbars were conducted in an open system as described previously (1,2). In vivo variable fluorescence yield was assessed using the Chlorophyll Fluorescence System (H. Walz, Effeltrich, Germany). The magnitude of Φ_{II} is given by $(F_m'-F_s)/F_m'$ where F_s is the steady state fluorescence yield and F_m' is that recorded during a 0.7s superimposed saturating light pulse. The photochemical yield of photosystem I (Φ_I) was estimated from the light-dark leaf absorbance change around 830nm (i.e. ΔA830), the absorption band of $P700^+$ (3). Thus, $\Phi_I = 1 - \Delta A830/\Delta A830_{max}$ where $\Delta A830_{max}$ corresponds to full oxidation of P700 and was determined as the x-intercept of plots of Φ_s (=4·CO_2 uptake rate/PFD of incident white light) versus ΔA830 at 14mbars O_2.

RESULTS AND DISCUSSION

Measurements of Φ_{II} and Φ_I (dimensionless) were concentrated at high irradiance since interactive effects of O_2 are greatest when significant quenching of absorbed excitation occurs. Figure 1 shows that Φ_{II} declined with increasing irradiance for each [O_2] and species.

N. Murata (ed.), Research in Photosynthesis, Vol. IV, 619–622.

Nevertheless, the O_2-dependent (and irradiance-independent) increases in Φ_{II} at any irradiance level were greatest in the C_3 tissue, virtually absent in C_4 leaves, and of intermediate magnitude in C_3-C_4 leaves. The O_2-dependent changes in Φ_{II} were associated with changes in both the redox state of the primary quinone electron acceptor in photosystem II (Q_A) and the degree of thermal deactivation of excited singlet states. The changes in Φ_{II} occurred simultaneously with changes in $[O_2]$ on a time scale of seconds implying regulation by the intrathylakoid pH. An increase in $[O_2]$ from 213 to 432mbars did not affect Φ_{II} significantly for any species. Increases in Φ_{II} with $[O_2]$ reached a lower plateau for C_3-C_4 tissue compared to that observed for C_3 tissue (Table 1). A simple upscale shift in the response of Φ_{II} to $[O_2]$ for C_3-C_4 compared to C_3 leaves is not indicated. Note that Φ_{II} was significantly higher in C_4 tissue than in C_3 and C_3-C_4 leaves at 14 mbars O_2.

TABLE 1. Effects of low (14mbars) and high (213 and 432mbars) O_2 levels on Φ_{II}. For each condition data were normalized to the corresponding mean for the four highest irradiance levels in Figure 1 to remove light intensity as a source of variation. Means associated with the same letter did not differ significantly (Tukey's test, p=0.002).

Species	Low $[O_2]$	High $[O_2]$
C_3	0.281 a	0.427 c
C_3-C_4	0.271 a	0.355 d
C_4	0.342 b	0.342 bd

Table 2 shows that the tendency for Φ_{II} to increase with $[O_2]$ (Table 1) correlates with the susceptibility of net photosynthesis to inhibition by O_2. P_{diss} is the proportion of noncyclic electron transport diverted to O_2-dependent processes and is given by $(\Phi_s' - \Phi_s)/\Phi_s'$ where Φ_s' is the predicted quantum yield of linear electron flow obtained by substitution of Φ_{II} measured at high $[O_2]$ into the nearly linear Φ_s versus Φ_{II} relationship observed at 14mbars O_2. The magnitude of P_{diss} is thus free of bias associated with O_2-dependent increases in noncyclic electron transport. The mean P_{diss} was 13% lower in C_3-C_4 compared to C_3 tissue at 213mbars O_2 while the substomatal aqueous phase molar ratio of $[O_2]/[CO_2]$ did not change appreciably.

The magnitude of Φ_I (fraction of P700 in the nonoxidized state) did not vary in a precise linear manner with Φ_{II}' (=measured Φ_{II} divided by the Φ_{II} for the same dark-adapted leaf). The ratio

TABLE 2. Inhibition of net photosynthesis by O_2 for species of Panicum. Means (±standard error) were computed from measurements obtained at the four highest irradiance levels for the experiments of Figure 1.

Species	213 mbars O_2		432 mbars O_2	
	P_{diss}	$[O_2]/[CO_2]$	P_{diss}	$[O_2]/[CO_2]$
C_3	0.560 ± 0.012	56.9 ± 1.3	0.732 ± 0.009	97.4 ± 1.1
C_3-C_4	0.486 ± 0.014	56.3 ± 1.1	0.667 ± 0.008	102.2 ± 2.2
C_4	-0.003 ± 0.014	114.5 ± 7.9	0.051 ± 0.015	347.5 ± 67.1

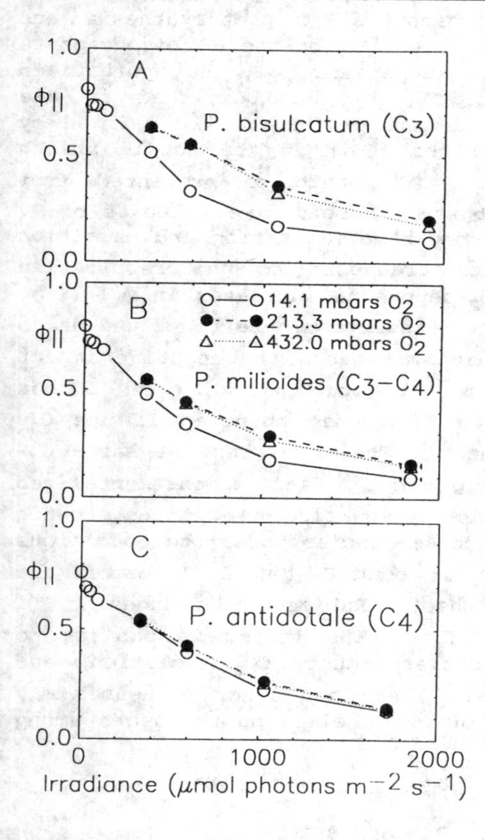

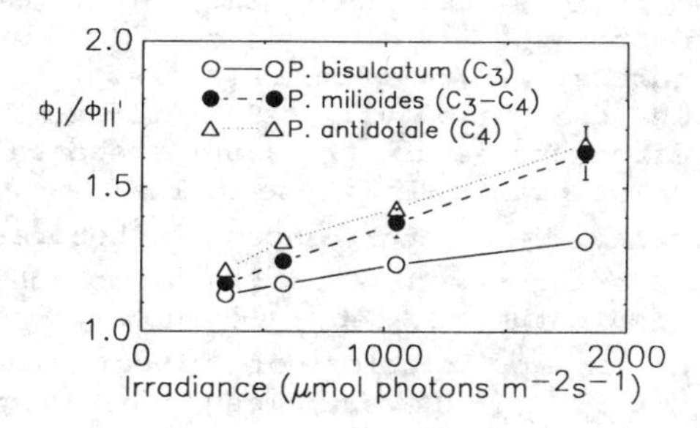

Figure 2. Dependence of the Φ_I/Φ_{II}' (see text) on irradiance for species of Panicum. P. milioides (C_3-C_4) behaved similarly to P. antidotale (C_4) with respect to this ratio. In comparison, the Φ_I/Φ_{II}' was substantially lower at high irradiance for P. bisulcatum (C_3). This is consistent with a relatively greater role for photosystem I in energy metabolism of bundle sheath cells of leaves possessing Kranz or Kranz-like anatomy.

Figure 1. Effects of irradiance and $[O_2]$ on Φ_{II} $[=(F_m'-F_s)/F_m']$ for species of Panicum. The external $[CO_2]$ was 200 μbars. Simultaneously measured values of Φ_s increased nearly linearly with Φ_{II} but the dependencies varied slightly among species (not shown).

Φ_I/Φ_{II}' increased almost linearly with irradiance. The effect of irradiance was greatest in the C_3-C_4 and C_4 leaves and may indicate enhancement of photosystem I-driven cyclic photophosphorylation in these species. Effects of $[O_2]$ on the Φ_I/Φ_{II}' were relatively small.

The differing responses of Φ_I and Φ_{II} to irradiance and $[O_2]$ among species are surely functionally related to cellular differentiation and compartmentalization of pathways in C_3-C_4 and C_4 leaves. Since C_4 leaves fix CO_2 via O_2-insensitive phosphoenolpyruvate carboxylase they photorespire slowly (Table 2) and little effect of changing $[O_2]$ was expected nor observed (Table 1). Leaves of P. bisulcatum and P. milioides use the same biochemical pathways of photosynthesis and photorespiration which begin with ribulose bisphosphate carboxylase/oxygenase (Rubisco). Photorespiratory glycine synthesized in the mesophyll cells of P. milioides is decarboxylated in the mitochondria of the bundle sheath cells and preferentially refixed by chloroplasts in these cells (4). If the $[CO_2]$ in the bundle sheath cells were high enough, photorespired CO_2 would be prevented from entering the dissipative glycolate pathway a second time. Leaves of P. bisulcatum (C_3) show no such obvious compartmentalization and partition a larger fraction of linear electron transport to photorespiration (Table 2). Nevertheless, the large O_2-dependent increases in Φ_{II} (i.e. increases in gross photosynthesis) in C_3 tissue could be construed as an adaptive response to elevated $[O_2]$ which mitigates the negative impact of photorespiration on net CO_2 fixation. In other words, rates of net CO_2 uptake at high $[O_2]$ would be even less than observed if the O_2-dependent enhancement of Φ_{II} were absent. The occurrence of large O_2-dependent increases in Φ_{II} in P. bisulcatum and compartmentalized photorespiration in P. milioides tends to equalize net photosynthetic rates at high $[O_2]$ and irradiance for these species under the conditions employed. The responses of Φ_{II} to O_2 in both C_3 and C_3-C_4 leaves are mediated in large part by the CO_2 response of Rubisco and changes in CO_2 availability in the mesophyll tissue (2). The latter is subject to influence by the external $[CO_2]$, photorespiratory CO_2 evolution, and internal leaf diffusional resistances. These and other processes may interact to produce distinct effects of O_2 on electron transport among species. Supported by NRICGP 9000663.

REFERENCES

1 Peterson, R. B. (1990) Plant Physiol. 94, 892-898
2 Peterson, R. B. (1991) Plant Physiol. 97, 1388-1394
3 Schreiber U., Klughammer C. and Neubauer C. (1988) Z. Naturforsch.43c, 686-698
4 Hylton C. M., Rawsthorne S., Smith A. M., Jones D. A. and Woolhouse H. W. (1988) Planta 175, 452-459

MERCURY-INDUCED LIGHT-DEPENDENT ALTERATIONS OF CHLOROPHYLL FLUORESCENCE KINETICS IN BARLEY LEAF SLICES

Choon-Hwan Lee, Hosik Chang, Suk-Bong Ha, [1]Byoung Yong Moon, [2]Chin Bum Lee, Department of Molecular Biology, Pusan National University, Pusan, [1]Department of Biology, Inje University, Kimhae, [2]Department of Biology, Dongui University, Pusan, Korea.

1. INTRODUCTION

Mercury containing compounds inhibit photosynthetic functions at multiple sites. Mercury inhibits electron transport both in higher plants (1, 2, 3) and in algae and cyanobacteria (4, 5, 6). The inhibitory effects on photosystem II (PSII) activity were reversed by adding electron donor, hydroxylamine (2, 6) and 1,5-diphenylcarbohydrazide (DPC). Chlorophyll a fluorescence provides information on the absorption, distribution, and utilization of light energy in photosynthesis. Recently Moon et al. (7) has shown that mercury ions inhibited the energy-depending quenching significantly compared with copper and zinc ions in barley chloroplasts. Our effort to reveal the primary targets of the mercury inhibition in barley leaf slices lead us to report that the inhibitory effects of mercury are different depending on the presence of light.

2. MATERIALS AND METHODS

Barley (*Hordeum vulgare* L. cv. Albori) plants were grown at 25°C under continuous white light from fluoresent tubes giving PAR of 65-80 $\mu molm^{-2}s^{-1}$. Two centimeter segments, 2 cm below the tip of the first leaves, were taken from 8-9 day-old plants, and scratched by shaking in a flask filled with fine powders of quartz sand. The scratched leaves were left in a petridish filled with H_2O for 30 min and treated with chemicals. Normally shaking by hand about fifty times did not cause any dectectible changes in their fluorescence emission.

Modulated fluorescence emission from the two leaf-segments was measured by using a PAM chlorophyll fluorimeter (Walz Co., Germany). Data were collected by using a data acquisition board (DAS16G, Metrabyte Co, USA) and handled with computer programs written in Basic and Assembly languages. Actinic light was provided by using light emitting diodes (H1000, H2000, or H3000, Stanley Co., Japan). Actinic light intensity was adjusted to 140 $\mu molm^{-2}s^{-1}$. Otherwise it is mentioned in the text. Saturation light was provided by a Schott KL1500 light source (Schott Co., Germany).

3. RESULTS AND DISCUSSION

In our preliminary experiments with isolated barley chloroplasts both whole chain electron transport and PS II-supported O_2 evolution were inhibited about 50 % of the control rate with 50 μM of $HgCl_2$. This inhibitory effect of mercury in isolated chloroplasts was almost

N. Murata (ed.), Research in Photosynthesis, Vol. IV, 623–626.

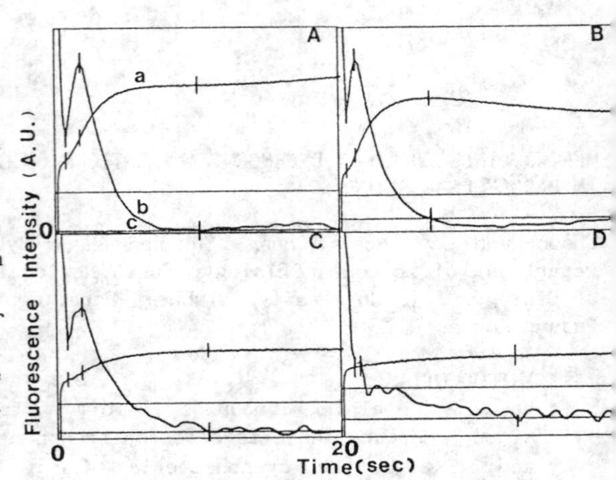

Fig. 1. Time course of the inhibitory effect of 50 μM $HgCl_2$ under light condition on fluorescence induction kinetics of barley leaf slices. (A) 0 min, (B) 15 min, (C) 45 min, (D) 120 min after the treatment, (a) original curve, (b) curve for smoothed first derivatives, and (c) zero line for the first derivatives (vertical axis scale is normalized).

Table 1. Parameters obtained from fluorescence induction kinetics measured from barley leaf slices treated with 50 μM $HgCl_2$ for various time periods*.

Time of Treatment (min)	Fo (V)	Fm (V)	(Fv)m / Fm	Fp (V)	Fp/Fm	T-Fd (ms)	Fd (V)	T-Fr (ms)	Fr mV/s	ΔS(D-Fr (mV/s)
0	0.27 (0.02)	1.31 (0.04)	0.76 (0.05)	1 (0)	0.80 (0.67)	60 (0)	0.5 (0)	153 (12)	12.2 (0.8)	4.5 (0.86)
15	0.25 (0.01)	1.15 (0.14)	0.79 (0.13)	0.95 (0.07)	0.82 (0.20)	40 (0)	0.4 (0)	100 (0)	14.2 (0.8)	5.06 (0.32)
45	0.22 (0.02)	0.68 (0.92)	0.68 (0.22)	0.56 (0.05)	0.84 (0.74)	60 (0)	0.4 (0)	133 (23)	4.5 (0.67)	1.30 (0.29)
120	0.30 (0.38)	0.51 (0.58)	0.41 (0.35)	0.53 (0.05)	0.96 (0.35)	80 (0)	0.4 (0)	127 (50)	1.0 (0.56)	0.11 (0.15)

* Values are means from three equivalent measurements and 1 standard deviatior are given inside parentheses (see text for details).

instaneous. The inhibitory effect of mercury in leaf slices was depending both on the concentration of mercury treated and on the duration of the treatment (Fig. 1). At 45 min (T-45) after the treatment of 50 μM $HgCl_2$ under light condition, the (Fv)m/Fo ratio decreased by 10 % and at T-120, dropped by 50%. Fig. 1 also shows the sequential changes appearing after the treatment of mercury and the changes could be distinguished clearly in the plot of the first derivatives. Several parameters obtained from the fluorescence induction curves are listed in Table 1. At T-15, primary changes observed were negative dF/dt points after P(peak), which diappears after T-45 (Fig. 1) and the decrease in ΔS(D-Fr) (absolute value of the first minimum slope minus the first maximum slope after the first one). This ΔS(D-Fr) value reflects the equilibration time between first electron acceptor of PSII, Qa and Qb. At T-15, both Fp (fluorescence intensity at

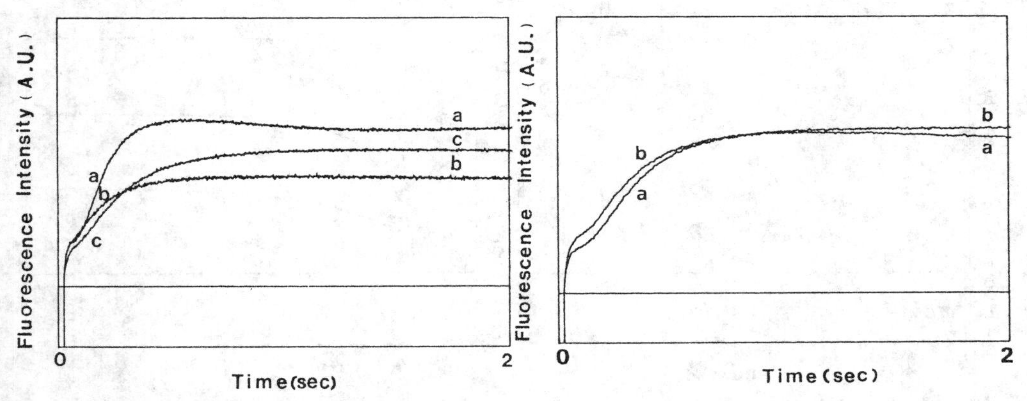

Fig. 2. Hydroxylamine recovery of the effect of 50 μM $HgCl_2$ on barley leaf slices under light condition. (a) control, (b) $HgCl_2$ (60 min), and (c) $HgCl_2$ (60 min) + 5 mM NH_2OH (10 min).

Fig. 3. The inhibitory effect of 50 μM $HgCl_2$ on barley leaf slices under dark condition. (a) control and (b) 50 μM $HgCl_2$ (50 min).

peak) and Fm (maximum fluorescence) values decreased only by about 10%. Fo values did not changed noticebly but increased after T-45. These results suggest that the first inhibitory sites are at near Qa-Qb binding sites and at near or after PSII oxidizing side. After T45, Fp decreased significantly by upto 40%.

As shown in Fig. 2, the decrease in Fp value could be partially recovered by addition of hydroxylamine, but the distinct P-S-M curves were not restored (Fig. 2). This result indicates that inhibitory site of mercury in PS II is located at the oxygen-evolving complex, which agrees with earlier obserbations (2, 6). Samson and Popovic (6) suggested that some PSII centers are inactivated because the rate of Qa photoreduction was unchanged although the complementary area was decreased. However Fd (fluorescence intensity at dip position) values did not show any noticible increase even at T-120 (Table 1).

Under dark condition, the inhibitory effects of mercury was somewhat different from those under light condition. As shown in Fig. 3, the initial fluorescence rise became faster and the P-S-M curves became less distinct. However there was no noticible change in Fp (Fig. 3). Only small drop in the Fm value from mercury treated leaves and there was no change in the initial O-I rise, but the I-P slope decreased slightly as the time proceeds (Fig. 4).

This light-dependent effect of mercury may be due to photoinhibition. However when the light intensity was lowered from 70 $\mu molm^{-2}s^{-1}$ to 3 $\mu molm^{-2}s^{-1}$, noticible decrease in Fp value was still observed from the leaf slices treated under very low light intensities (Fig. 5). Therefore the light-dependent effect of mercury is not essentially due to photoinhibition. One more finding was that the decrease in fluorescence yield under light condition could be recovered under dark condition (Fig. 6).

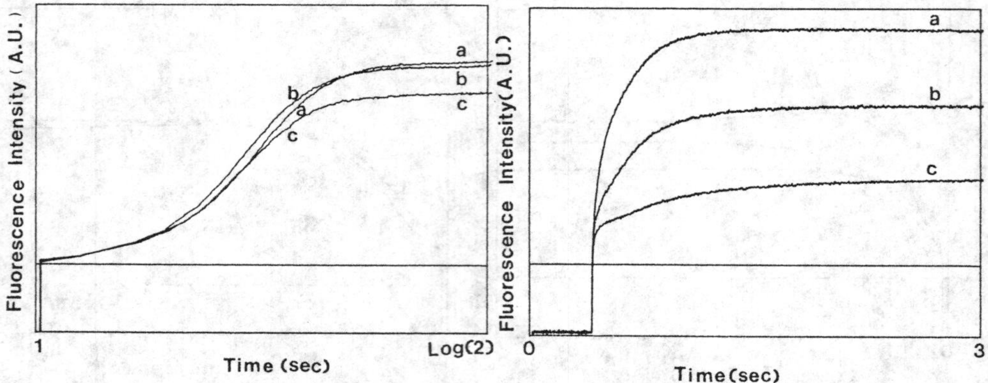

Fig. 4. The inhibitory effect of 50 μM $HgCl_2$ on 50 μM DCMU-poisoned barley leaf slices under dark condition. (a) control and (b) 50 μM $HgCl_2$ (60 min), and (c) 50 μM $HgCl_2$ (90 min) (horizontal axis is in logarithmic scale).

Fig. 5. Light intensity dependency of the inhibitory effect of 50 μM $HgCl_2$ on barley leaf slices. (a) dark, (b) 3 $\mu molm^{-2}s^{-1}$, and (c) 70 $\mu molm^{-2}s^{-1}$.

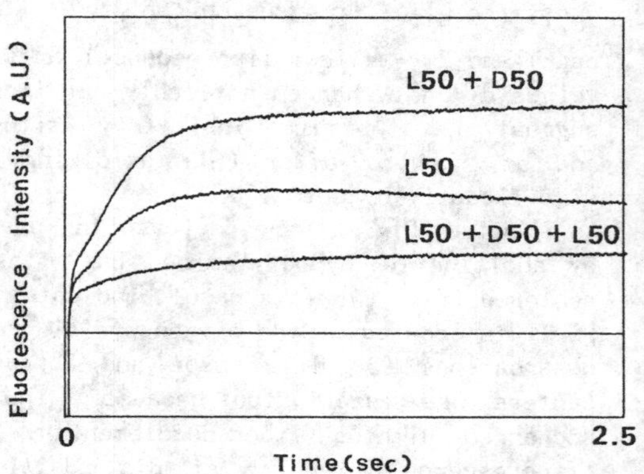

Fig. 6. Light-dependent effect of 50 μM $HgCl_2$ on barley leaf slices. L50, light (50 min), D50, dark (50 min).

Thess results suggest that some of the inhibitory sites of mercury under light condition, e.g. the water splitting system, are not accessible under dark condition, and those are remained to be studied.

4. ACKNOWLEDGEMENT

This work was in part supported by grants from Korea Science and Engineering Foundation..

REFERENCES

1. Kimimura, M. and Katoh, S. (1972) *Biochim. Biophys. Acta* 283, 279-292
2. Honeycutt, R.C. and Krogmann, D.W. (1972) *Plant Physiol.* 49, 376-380
3. Tripathy, B.C. and Mohanty, P. (1980) Plant Physiol. 66, 1174-1178
4. De Filippis, L.F., Hampp, R. and Ziegler, H. (1981) *Arch. Microbiol.* 128, 407-411
5. Murthy, S.D.S., Bukhov, N.G. and Mohanty, P. (1990) *J. Photochem. Photobiol.* B: Biology 6, 373-380.
6. Samson, G. and Popovic, R. (1990) *J. Photochem. Photobiol.* B. Biology 5, 303-310.
7. Moon, B.Y., Jun, H.S., Lee, C.-H. and Lee, C.B. (1992) J. Korean Environ. Sci. Soc. 1 (in press).

EFFECT OF CO_2 CONTENT IN GAS MIXTURE ON THE MILLISECOND DELAYED LIGHT EMISSION IN HWEAT LEAVES

JI-YU YE, SHANGHAI INSTITUTE OF PLANT PHYSIOLOGY, ACADEMIA SINICA,
300 FENGLIN ROAD, SHANGHAI 200032 CHINA

1. INTRODUCTION

Oscillations in photosynthetic carbon assimilation have been widely observed. The phenomena of oscillation had detected by different methods such as chlorophyll fluorescence (!,2), light scattering (3) and photooxidation of P700 (4). When oscillations in photosynthesis are induced, these optical signals mentioned above also oscillate. Explanations of these phenomena heve sought to relate carbon assimilation to chlorophyll fluorescence by the operation of Q_g and Q_e quenching mechanisms (6) or by imbalances between the supply of NADPH and ATP for carbon reduction in leaves (4). If the ATP/ADP ratio was changed during photosynthetic oscillation, the pH oscillation in cells of leaves should be occured. The ms-delayed light emission (ms-DLE) is usually regarded as an indirect indicator of pH gradient across the thylakoids in leaves. In order to obtain information about proton gradient change in leaves during photosynthetic oscillation, we have investigated the effect of CO_2 content in gas mixture on the ms-DLE in illuminated leaves.

2. MATERIALS AND METHODS

WHEAT (TRITICUM AESTIVUM) seedlings were grown for 8-10 d in water culture in the glasshouse under sunlight. 2 cm length of leaf pieces cut in the middle of the first leaf were used in experiment. ms-DLE measurement was made with a Becqerell type phosphoroscope (5). The flash light was provided by a projection incandescent lamp and filtered through a 2 cm thick water in order to remove heat. The ms-DLE between 2.8 ms and 3.8 ms after every flash was measured by photomultiplier with a red glass filter. The intensity of flash light was $5x10^6$ erg $cm^{-2}.sec^{-1}$. The signal passing through a amplifies was recorded by a XWT-204 chart recorder. The CO_2-free air was ensured by a soda lime column. The leaf pieces were placed in the leaf compartment and gas mixture were passed the leaf chember at 360 ml/min with a CD-I type pump. Using the method of vacuum infiltration leaf pieces were treated by Nigericin.

3. RESULTS AND DISCUSSION

Figure 1 (A) shows a recording of CO_2-dependent damping oscillation of ms-DLE. The leaf piece was placed in ambient air under

N. Murata (ed.), Research in Photosynthesis, Vol. IV, 627–630.

unchanged illumination. When the DLE approached a steady state level, the gas mixture was switched from air (0.03% CO_2, 21% O_2) to 5% CO_2 air. The DLE signal showed initial fall, then followed by a large increase and a series of oscillation of declining amplitude until a new steady state level was reached.

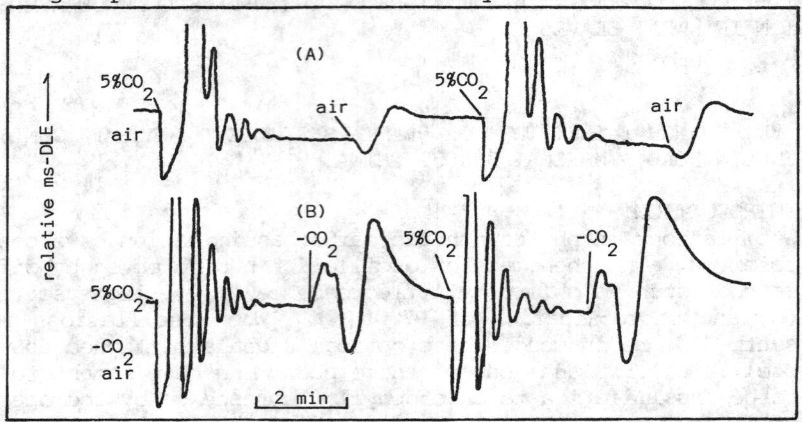

FIGURE 1. ms-DLE oscillation was initiated by increasing the CO_2 concentration from o.o3% to 5% in air (A) or from CO_2-free air to 5% CO_2 air (B). The gas mixture was passed through the leaf chember at 360 ml/min. The leaf was illuminated until the DLE approched a steady state level (about 10 min). The temperature is about 20 C.

On return to air, a small decrease of DLE was appeared and then it was increased to the initial level. This excursion can be repeated when the high CO_2 concentration was switched on again. The experiment in figure 1(B) was carried out at the same intensity of light when the gas mixture was changed from CO_2-free air to 5% CO_2 air. The amplitude and frequency of DLE oscillation were greater than that of figure 1(A). On return to CO_2-

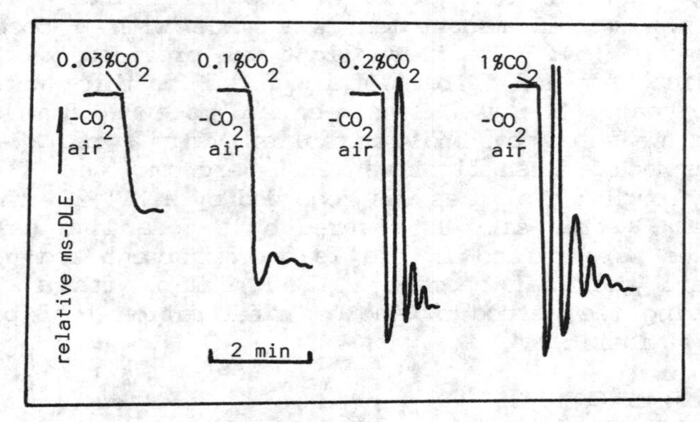

FIGURE 2. Effect of different concentration of CO_2 on the ms-DLE

oscillation of wheat leaf pieces. The value on each curve indicates CO_2 concentration, experimental procedure as in figure 1.

free air a rapid increase in DLE with biphasic rise was induced and then a decrease to the initial level was followed. The figure 2. showing the effect of various CO_2 concentration on the DLE excursion. It indicates that the oscillation appear at the CO_2 concentration of 0.1% and become more significant on increasing of CO_2.

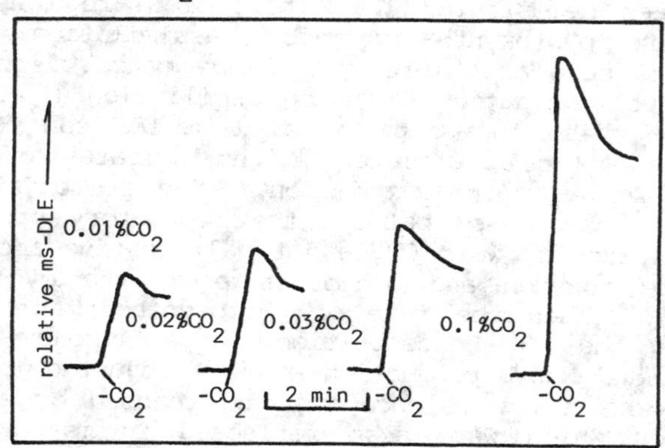

FIGURE 3. ms-DLE excursion was initiated by changing the gas mixture from lower CO_2 concentration to CO_2-free air.

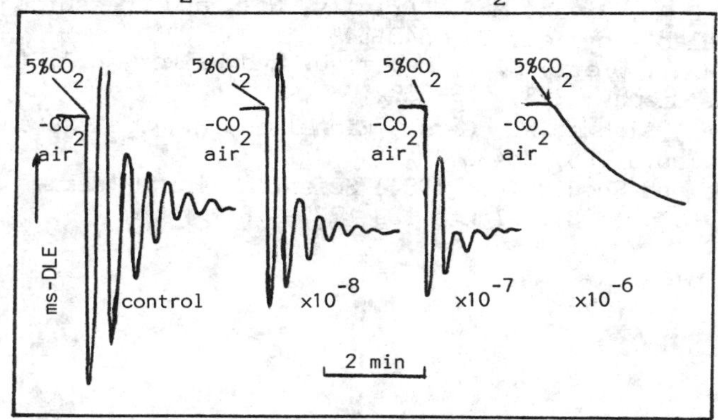

FIGURE 4. Effect of nigericin on the ms-DLE in illuminated leaves. In the presence of $1x10^{-3}$ mol/L KCL the leaf pieces were infiltrated by the nigericin solution with the concentration of $1x10^{-8}$, $1x10^{-7}$ and $1x10^{-6}$ mol/L respectively using the method of vacuum infiltration.

The steady state of DLE was influenced by very low concentration of CO_2. In figure 3 the leaf pieces were placed in 0.01%, 0.02%

and 0.03% CO_2 with constant 21% O_2 respectively. A rapid rise in DLE was induced by switching to CO_2-free air the extent of the excursion was determined by the change of the relative concentration of CO_2. In order to understand the relationship between the pH shifts in cells of leaf and DLE oscillation, we have investigated the effect of nigericin on ms-DLE oscillation. In the presence of K^+, nigericin did diminsh the amplitude of DLE oscillation (figure 4). When the concentration of nigericin was increased to $1x10^{-6}$ mol/L the DLE oscillation was inhibited completely.

It has been demostrated that there is a regular relationship between the photosynthetic carbon assimilation and optical parameter (such as chlorophyll fluorescence, light scattering, and P700 photooxidation) during oscillation (2,3,4,). The results of this study indicate that ms-DLE can be regarded as an another optical parameter which indicates pH changes in cells of leaves upon irradiation. The photosynthesis in any state is a compromise between the regulatory processes determining electron flow to CO_2 and to alternative acceptors (such as nitrite, oxygen and oxaloacetate or the cyclic electron pathway). When the rate of photosynthesis is suddenly by increasing the CO_2 concentration of gas mixture, the ATP synthesis and NADPH production must be adjusted to one another. In this case a new balance will be reached by a series of oscillation which were also reflected in ms-DLE oscillation.

REFERENCES

1 Ogawa, T. (1982) Biochim. Biophy. Acta 681, 103-109
2 Walker, D.A., Sivak, M.N., Prinsly, R.T. and Cheesbrough, J.K. (1983) Plant Physiol. 73, 542-549
3 Sivak, M.N., Dietz, K.J., Heber, U. and Walker, D.A. (1985) Arch. Biochem. Biophy. 273, 513-519
4 Laisk, A., Siebke, K., Gers., Eichelman, H., Oja, V. and Heber, U. (1991) Planta 185, 554-562
5 Xu, C.H. and Shen, Y.K. (1984) Scientia Sinica (series B) 27,37-47
6 Walker, D.A. (1981) Planta 153, 273-278

PLEIOTROPY IN TRIAZINE RESISTANT *Brassica napus*: DIFFERENTIAL STOMATAL AND LEAF RESPONSES TO THE ENVIRONMENT

JACK DEKKER, Weed Biology Laboratory, Agronomy Department, Iowa State University, AMES, IOWA, 50011, USA

INTRODUCTION

S-triazine resistance in higher plants is due to a single base pair mutation to the psbA chloroplast gene (6). The codon 264 change in the psbA gene caused a change in its product, the D-1 protein, a key functional element in PSII electron transport (18). The genetic change in R plants leads to a profound reorganization of functional units in the chloroplast. This pleiotropic cascade includes both structural and functional changes (2, 16, 20). The dynamic nature of the chloroplast to reach a new, markedly different, structural and functional equilibrium in response to the mutation of a key plastidic gene has been observed previously (9, 12). This profound pleiotropic cascade of functional and structural changes conferred by changes in the D-1 protein could imply that the amino acid substitution is close to a primary functional and structural source of photosynthetic regulation. Mattoo (13) has suggested that the rapid anabolism-catabolism rate of the D-1 protein could serve as a signal resulting in the reorganization of membranes around the PSII complex. The dynamic nature of these responses have led several to conclude that the primary effect of R is complex, involves more than one aspect of photosynthesis, and can be mitigated by other processes in the system (10, 14). Dekker and Sharkey (5) have shown that the primary limitation to photosynthesis changes with changes in leaf temperature, and that electron transport limitations in R may be significant only at higher temperatures.

Several studies have shown lower photosynthetic carbon assimilation rates (A) in R relative to S (1, 8, 15, 19). Others have found A in R and S biotypes similar (19) or greater in R (26). These inconsistent responses by R and S biotypes have led several to conclude that the change conferring R is not necessarily directly linked to inferior photosynthetic function (7, 11, 26). An assessment of these and other studies reveals several possible reasons why different responses may have been observed. They include pleiotropic reorganization of the R chloroplast and the dynamic interelationship between components of photosynthesis; the role of environment in altering responses; genetic factors, such as differences between biotypes and genome interactions within a biotype; and the possibility of an unnamed factor controlling photosynthesis (10).

The equivocal nature of our understanding of how photosynthesis differs between R and S, and how it is regulated, has led us to focus experimental efforts on

N. Murata (ed.), Research in Photosynthesis, Vol. IV, 631–634.

chronobiological understandings under more dynamic, but closely controlled, growth conditions. In particular we have observed other pleiotropic effects in R: differential patterns of both carbon assimilation (A) and chlorphyll fluorescence over the course of the light-dark diurnal cycle. Herein we also report that R plants have markedly different leaf and stomatal responses to temperature.

METHODS AND MATERIALS

Experiments reported herein were conducted under two different methods of controlling leaf temperature. Growth environments, plant material and gas exchange measurements reported in controlled leaf temperature conditions (Table 1) are as described in Dekker and Sharkey (1992); those in which only air temperature was controlled (Table 2) are as reported in Dekker and Burmester (1989). Additionally, studies in table 2 were conducted at 15°C, 25°C and 35°C air temperatures. Carbon assimilation (A) and mean leaf temperature and total conductance to water vapor (g) for each period for each biotype were calculated as well as the associated S.E. A, mean leaf temperature, and g for R and S within each period were compared using an F-test, with the associated probability (P) of the null hypothesis (R = S) being true.

RESULTS

Leaf responses in controlled leaf temperature conditions. At 15°C A in R and S was similar, but as leaf temperature increased to 35°C S assimilated increasing more carbon than R (Table 1). Often associated with this was a greater total conductance to water vapor in R relative to S under similar temperature conditions. For both biotypes, the optimal temperature for A was ca. 28-29°C.

TABLE 1. Leaf temperature (Leaf Temp) versus A (μmol $m^{-2}s^{-1}$), total conductance to water vapor (g) (mmol m^{-2} s^{-1}) in 4 leaf R and S *Brassica napus*.

Susceptible			Resistant		
Leaf Temp (°C)	A	g	Leaf Temp (°C)	A	g
15.6	17.1	156	14.7	16.0	243
17.3	21.2	224	16.9	18.7	242
20.5	24.7	222	19.7	22.0	248
23.5	25.4	256	22.8	23.7	262
25.8	29.3	247	25.5	24.5	287
28.2	30.3	262	27.5	23.6	289
30.4	29.7	266	29.5	23.9	296
-	-	-	31.8	22.4	301
33.0	27.7	270	33.4	20.7	307
35.0	25.5	268	35.1	18.7	304

Leaf responses in controlled air temperature conditions. S plants assimilated more carbon over the entire day than R plants at 15°C and 25°C air temperatures, but assimilated less than R at 35°C air temperatures (Table 2). During the early part of the light period, A in R plants was either similar (15°C air temperature), or greater (25

TABLE 2. Changes in carbon assimilation (A) in 4 leaf s-triazine resistant (R) and susceptible (S) *Brassica napus* plants with time grown at 15°C, 25°C and 35°C air temperatures; mean accumulatedA (μmol CO_2 m^{-2} $period^{-1}$), mean leaf temperature (°C), and mean total conductance to water vapor (mmol m^{-2} s^{-1}) (g), within a period of the diurnal (early (0600-0950 (or 1000 for 15°C and 35°C)), midday (0950 or 1000-1800), late (1800-2150) and all day (0600-2150)) compared using F-Test and the associated probability (P; *) of R and S being similar; n=9 plants.

	-----EARLY------		-----MIDDAY-----		---LATE----		-ALL DAY-	
	0600-0950/1000		1000/0950-1800		1800-2150		0600-2150	
Photosynthetic carbon assimilation (A) (μmol $m^{-2}s^{-1}$)								
	R	S	R	S	R	S	R	S
15°C	14.9	14.0	86.5	94.2	12.9	11.0	114.3	119.2
P=*	NS		0.0003		0.0008		0.0256	
25°C	16.2	13.9	109.1	117.3	16.6	14.4	141.9	145.6
P=*	0.0001		0.0001		0.0001		0.0192	
35°C	11.4	9.9	89.8	82.6	12.0	10.4	113.2	102.9
P=*	0.0014		0.0003		0.0025		0.0001	
Leaf Temperature (°C)								
	R	S	R	S	R	S	R	S
15°C	22.1	21.7	23.3	22.5	23.0	22.7	22.8	22.3
P=*	NS		0.0004		NS		NS	
25°C	25.8	26.0	28.0	29.0	26.4	26.2	26.7	27.2
P=*	NS		0.0001		NS		0.0066	
35°C	30.1	31.2	31.0	32.8	30.4	31.1	30.6	31.6
P=*	0.0170		0.0001		0.0037		0.0001	
Total conductance to water vapor (g) (mmol $m^{-2}s^{-1}$)								
	R	S	R	S	R	S	R	S
15°C	60	56	279	240	130	79	174	158
P=*	NS		NS		0.0260		NS	
25°C	163	124	226	175	128	129	174	145
P=*	0.0038		0.0001		NS		0.0003	
35°C	211	157	405	302	209	157	268	196
P=*	0.0280		0.0009		0.0360		0.0001	

and 35°C) compared to that in S. During the midday part of the light period, A in S was greater than that at 15 and 25°C air temperatures, while A in R was greater than that in S at 35°C. A in R was greater than in S at all 3 air temperatures. In most instances, leaf temperatures and g was similar in R and S at 15°C air temperatures. At 25°C, S leaf temperatures were greater than, or equal to, R. At 35°C, R leaf temperatures were less than those of S during all parts of the light period. At 25 and 35°C, g in R plants was almost always greater than that of S.

DISCUSSION

At lower leaf and air temperatures (15°C), R and S leaves function in a similar way. But, as the temperature of their environment increases, their responses diverge considerably. If leaf temperature is controlled externally, R leaves assimilate considerably less carbon than S leaves, especially at hyper-optimal temperatures (e.g. 35°C). If leaf temperature is not directly controlled, and both R and S are immersed in an identical air temperature environment, there responses to the same air temperature is different. R leaves generally are cooler and total conductance to water is greater than in S, probably due to greater stomatal aperature size. The consequence of this is that at higher air temperatures (e.g. 35°C) R leaves photosynthesize at cooler leaf temperatures, leaf temperatures closer to the optimal for both biotypes. In this way R plants compensate for their high temperature sensitivity.

In addition to other pleiotropic effects of the mutation to the psbA gene in R, R plants appear to be stomatal mutants. R and S *Brassica napus* biotypes may constitute a good model system to study regulation of stomatal function and the relationship between environmental cues and stomatal behavior.

REFERENCES

1 Ahrens, W.H., and E.W. Stoller (1983) Weed Sci 31:438-444
2 Arntzen, C., D. Ditto , and P. Brewer (1979) Proc. Natl. Acad. Sci. USA 76: 278-282
3 Dekker, J. and R. G. Burmester. (1990) Z.Naturforsch. 45c:474-477
4 Dekker, J.H. and R.G. Burmester. (1992) Plant Physiol.: In review
5 Dekker, J. and T. D. Sharkey. (1992) Plant Physiol.98:1069-1073
6 Hirschberg, J., L. McIntosh (1983) Science 222:1346-1349
7 Holt, J.S., and D.P. Goffner (1985) Plant Physiol 79:699-705
8 Holt, J.S., A.J. Stemler, and S.R. Radosevich (1981) Plant Physiol. 67:744-748
9 Hugly, S., L. Kunst, J. Browse, C. Somerville (1989) Plant Physiol. 90:1134-1142
10 Ireland, J., P.S. Telfer, P. Covello, N. Baker, J. Barber (1988) Planta 173:459-467
11 Jansen, M., J. Hobe, J. Wesselius, J. van Rensen (1986) Physiol. Veg. 24: 475-484
12 Kunst, L., J. Browse, and C. Somerville (1989) Plant Physiol. 90:846-853
13 Mattoo, A.K., J.B. St. John, and W.P. Wergin (1984) J. Cell Biochem. 24:163-175
14 McClosky, W.B., and J.S. Holt (1990) Plant Physiol. 92:954-962
15 Ort, D.R., W.H. Ahrens, B. Martin, E. Stoller (1983) Plant Physiol. 72:925-930
16 Pillai, P., and J.B. St. John (1981) Plant Physiol. 68: 585-587
17 Schonfeld, M., T. Yaacoby, O. Michael , B. Rubin (1987) Plant Physiol. 83:329-333
18 Trebst, A. (1987) Z. Naturforsch. 42c:742-750
19 van Oorshot, J.L.P., and P.H. van Leeuwen (1984) Z. Naturforsch. 39c:440-442
20 Vaughn, K.C. (1986) Plant Physiol. 82:859-863

RELATION BETWEEN PHOTOSYNTHETIC ACTIVITIES AND CONTENTS OF CHLOROPLAST PIGMENTS IN GREEN AND RED LEAVES OF *PERILLA* GROWN UNDER DIFFERENT GRADES OF SHADING.

Kazuko Ida[1], Hiromichi Koyama[2] and Satomi Takeda[1], [1]Dept. of Natural Science, Osaka Women's Univ., Sakai, 590, and [2]Botanical Garden, Fac. of Sci., Osaka City Univ., Katano, 576 Japan

1. Introduction

Shade leaves are known to be thinner and their chloroplasts to be larger and richer in chlorophyll as compared with sun leaves. The chlorophyll a/b ratio tends to be smaller in shade leaves than in sun leaves. These difference are maintained not only between the leaves of sun and shade plants but also between the leaves of the same species grown under different light intensities (Boardman 1977, Ida 1981). Carotenoids represent another important group of chloroplast pigments responsible for capture of light energy in photosynthesis as well as for the protection against aerobic photooxidation by strong light (Rau 1988, Demmig and Bjorkman 1987, Demmig et al. 1987, 1988, Thayer & Bjorkman 1990).

This study is intended to examine the quantitative influence of incident light intensity on photosynthetic activities and the composition of leaf pigments, especially of carotenoids were studied with green and dark-red (red) leaves of *Perilla* grown under different grades of shade in summer when the growth is most vigorous. The red leaves have contained five kinds of anthocyanin, main pigment is Cyanidin 3-p-coumarylglucoside-5-glucoside (Ishikura 1981).

2. Material and Methods

Plant materials A green variety of *Perilla frutescens viridis* Makino and a red variety of *Perilla frutescens* Britton var. *acuta* Kudo were used.

Light climate Five different levels of shading were produced by using appropriate numbers of plastic mesh sheets (cremona-lawn) covering cubic frames ($2x2x11m^3$). Each sheet was black. Solar radiation was measured by a self-recording Robitzsch pyrheliometer (Tamiya & Co. Tokyo). The average value of relative light light intensity for each level of shading is given in Table 1.

Photosynthesis measurements UV-VIS recording spectrophotometer (Shimazu, UV-2200)was used for spectrophotometric analysis of fresh leaves. Portable system for photosynthesis and transpiration measurement (Shimazu, SPB-H3 & PLC-3B) was used for the measurement of photosynthetic activities.

Anthocyanin Fresh mature leaves were repeatedly extracted with 1% methanolic

N. Murata (ed.), Research in Photosynthesis, Vol. IV, 635–638.

hydrochloric acid. The absorbance of the extracts, clarified by filtration, was measured at 530 nm (Shimazu MPS-2000).

Chlorophyll and carotenoid Leaf pigments were extracted with acetone at 5-10 C in the dark for 20-24 hrs. Chlorophyll content was determined by the method of Arnon (1949). Leaf pigments in acetone were then transferred to ether:n-hexane (1;1, v/v)after water was added.The extracted materials were saponified with 10% KOH in methanol at room temperature in the dark for 1 hr. Unsaponifiable matter was extracted with ether: n-hexane (1:1, v/v). The organic phase was concentrated. Analytical thin-layer chromatography on silica gel 60 (Merk, Art. 5553) was performed with *tert* -amyl alcohol : petroleum ether (1:4, v/v) (Francis and Isaksen, 1988). Contents of respective yellow carotenoids were determined spectrophotometically by using absorption coefficient $E^{1\%}_{1cm}$ at λ max. (Davies, 1976).

Table 1. Relative light intensities under the shade produced by different numbers of plastic mesh sheets.

Numbers of mesh sheets used	Mean relative solar radiationd (%)	solar radiation ($MJ/m^2/day$)
0* *	100	18.1
1	58	10.5
2	33	6.0
3	18	3.3
4	11	2.0

* : daily mean solar radiation during 10 days prior to the measurement of photosynthetic activities.

* * : Full day light

3. Result and discussion

The leaf area per leaf decreased with decreasing relative daylight intensity in the habitats and specific leaf area (leaf area per leaf wt.) increased with decreasing light intensity. Red color of shade red leaves were pale in comparison with sun red leaves.Observations by optical microscope were shown that red pigment of anthocyanin in the red leaves was present only in the cells of leaf epidermis. The mesophyll tissues appeared to be surrounded by a layer of red cells containing anthocyanin.

Photosynthesis The photosynthetic activities of green and red leaves measured on July 7-10, 1990. The rate of photosynthesis was expressed on a leaf area basis and on a chlorophyll basis. The maximum gross photosynthesis tended to be reduced with decreasing daylight intensity in the habitats. Green and red leaves had shown almost the same photosynthetic activities in the same daylight intensity (Fig. 1).

The maximum gross photosynthesis rate / respiration rate ratio in green and red leaves of different shaded plots were almost the same (0.12-0.17).

Fig. 1. Comparison of the light-photosynthesis curves in summer green and red leaves of *Perilla* grown under different grades of shading.

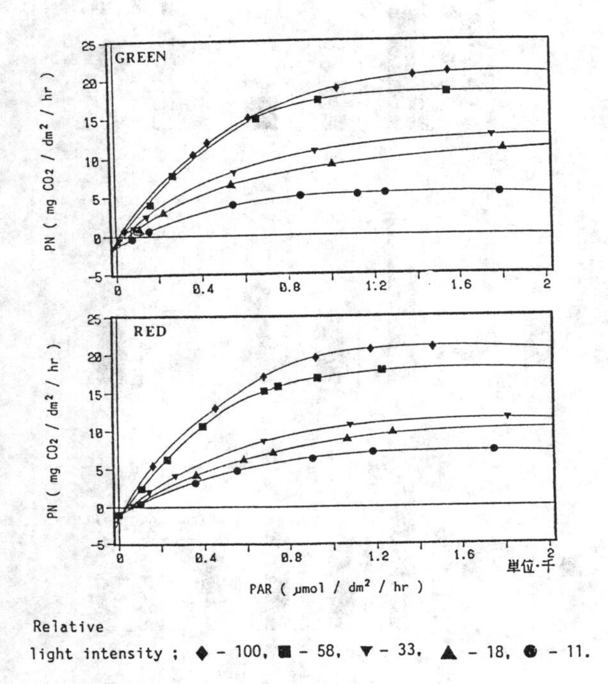

Leaf pigments The contents of anthocyanin decreased with decreasing daylight intensity,

Effect of shading on leaf chlorophyll and carotenoidcontent on a leaf area basis and fresh wt. basis was almost the same in 100-33% relative daylight intensity, Green and red leaves had almost the same amountof chlorophyll and carotenoid. In the habitats of 18-11% light intensity, chlorophyll and carotenoid content in green and red leaves decreased with decreasing light intensities. Chlorophyll a/b ratio was almost the same value in 100-11% of day light intensity.

Each carotenoid composition in total carotenoid was almost the same value in the green and red leaves under different grades of shade in summer.

Fig. Relation between the content of leaf pigment (chlorophyll, carotenoid and anthocyanin) and relative solar radiation.

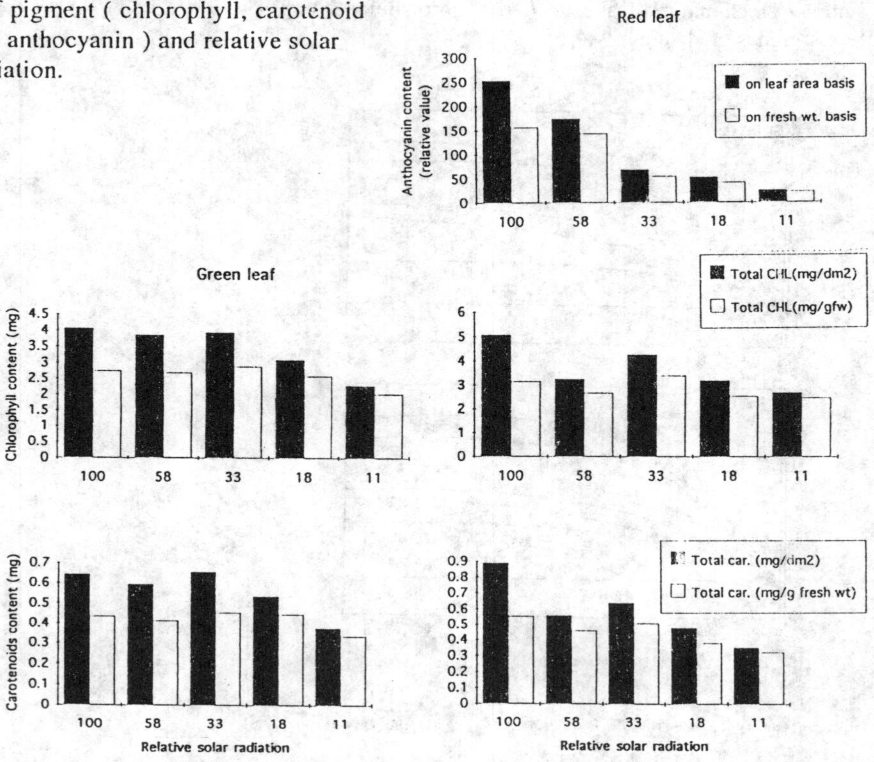

Table Relative amounts of chloroplast pigments found in green and red leaves of <u>Perilla</u>

Color of leaf	Red	Green	Red + Green
Chlorophyll a:b ratio	2.18 ± 0.14	2.44 ± 0.17	2.31 ± 0.20
Percentage of total carotenoids			
β- carotene	27.9 ± 2.6	28.7 ± 3.0	28.3 ± 2.8
Lutein	43.3 ± 2.6	46.8 ± 0.9	45.1 ± 1.3
Violaxanthin	17.3 ± 2.5	13.8 ± 1.4	15.6 ± 1.9
Neoxanthin	11.6 ± 1.7	10.8 ± 1.3	11.2 ± 1.5

CHANGES IN LEAF FLUORESCENCE SPECTRAL SHAPE DURING THE KAUTSKY KINETICS.

Giovanni Agati, Ilaria Ambrosini, Franco Fusi, Piero Mazzinghi
Istituto di Elettronica Quantistica - CNR, Via Panciatichi, 56/30, 50127 Firenze, Italy

1. INTRODUCTION

Chlorophyll (Chl) fluorescence measurement is a useful method to monitor the photosynthetic activity of plants and bacteria. Several authors correlated the changes in Chl fluorescence parameters with the damages to the photosynthetic apparatus induced from environmental stress factors (1-3). The most used and best known method consists in measuring the Chl fluorescence induction kinetics (Kautsky effect) which is produced by irradiation of dark adapted leaves (2,3). The fluorescence increases rapidly from the initial level O to a maximum P as result of the reduction of the primary electron acceptors. A lower fluorescence decline from P to the terminal level T follows. Its interpretation is complex since many mechanisms of fluorescence quenching are involved. Recently, with the development of new instrumentation, the interest has been focused on the information provided by changes in the Chl fluorescence spectrum (2,4). The spectrum consists of two broad bands at about 685-690 and 730-735 nm. The relative intensity of the two fluorescence peaks is used as a stress indicator (2,4,5). The shape of the Chl fluorescence spectrum is dependent on the Chl concentration since a strong fluorescence reabsorption occurs at the shorter-wavelength band (2,6). Moreover, the F685/F735 ratio has been observed to decrease during the Kautsky kinetics (7-10). The physiological interpretation of these experimental data is still poorly developed since several competitive mechanisms contribute to the Chl fluorescence spectral shape (11-13).

This work is focused on the changes in the laser-induced Chl fluorescence (LICF) spectrum during the fluorescence induction kinetics. Since the reabsorption inside the leaf affects greatly the leaf fluorescence spectrum, we checked if variations of leaf absorption occur during the Kautsky kinetics.

2. MATERIALS AND METHODS

2.1 *Plant material*

The study was performed using different plant species: *Lycopersicon esculentum* Mill., *Epipremnum aureum* (Marbel Queen) and *Ocimum basilicum* L..

2.2 *Fluorescence measurements*

Fluorescence spectra induced by laser light (HeNe at 632.8 nm and argon-ion from 457.9 to 514.5 nm) were detected by an Optical Multichannel Analyzer (EG&G PAR OMA III mod. 1460) with a diode array detector (EG&G PAR mod 1421), using the

N. Murata (ed.), Research in Photosynthesis, Vol. IV, 639–642.

apparatus previously described (6). Laser intensities were measured by a laser power meter (Ophir Optics, Jerusalem, Israel). A low photosynthetically active photon fluence density (PPFD) (about 20 μE m^{-2} s^{-1}) was used to record LICF spectra very close to the initial fluorescence F_O. Steady state LICF spectra (F_s) were recorded after the Kautsky kinetics was induced.

The fluorescence induction kinetics was monitored by the above described system or by a Laser Excited Automatic Fluorometer, LEAF®, built in our laboratory (4). Both systems acquire fluorescence values at the two maxima, 685 and 730 nm, within a narrow (5 or 10 nm) band-width centered at the fluorescence peaks. The LEAF® instrument used a diode laser emitting at 635 nm through a 400 μm optical fiber which delivered at the leaf surface a PPFD of about 250 μE m^{-2} s^{-1}.

Measurements were performed at room temperature (20 ± 2 °C) on plants grown in a pot, without detaching the leaves, after dark adapting the plant for at least 20 min.

2.4 *Total transmittance measurements*

Total transmittance (T) spectra of a leaf were measured using an integrating spheroid (PU7908/24, Pye Unicam, Cambridge, England) fitted inside a double beam spectrophotometer (PU8800, Pye Unicam, Cambridge, England). In these experimental conditions (very low PPFD less than 0.01 μE m^{-2} s^{-1}) the fluorescence induced by the measuring beam was negligible (6). The leaf was irradiated at the entrance port of the integrating spheroid by a HeNe laser beam at higher excitation PPFD (about 230 μE m^{-2} s^{-1}). The laser beam was expanded and deflected towards the leaf by a prism. The intensity was chosen to be comparable with that of the LEAF® instrument. The irradiation beam was shut off while the T spectra were recorded.
Measurements were performed at room temperature (20 ± 2 °C) on plants of *Epipremnum aureum* and *Ocimum basilicum* L. grown in a pot, without detaching the leaves.

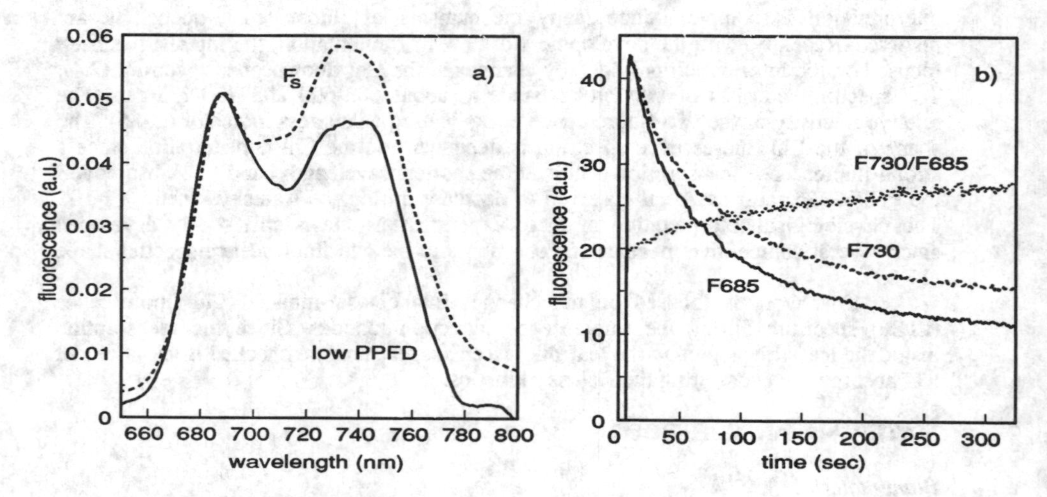

FIGURE 1. Laser-induced Chl fluorescence excited at 632.8 nm of *Lycopersicon esculentum* Mill., normalized at 685 nm. a) spectra at low excitation intensity (solid line) and at the steady-state, F_s (dashed line). b) Fluorescence induction kinetics, PPFD = 2000 μE m^{-2} s^{-1}.

3. RESULTS AND DISCUSSION

LICF spectra at low PPFD and at the steady state of *Lycopersicon esculentum* Mill. for excitation at 632.8 nm are reported in Fig.1a. There is a large increase in the F730/F685 fluorescence ratio going from the initial to the terminal level as better showed in Fig.1b. Similar behaviors are observed in *Epipremnum aureum* (Fig 2a) and in *Ocimum basilicum* L.(data not shown). Values of the F730/F685 ratio at the maximum P and the terminal T level of the Kautsky kinetics are reported in Tab.1 for the different species.

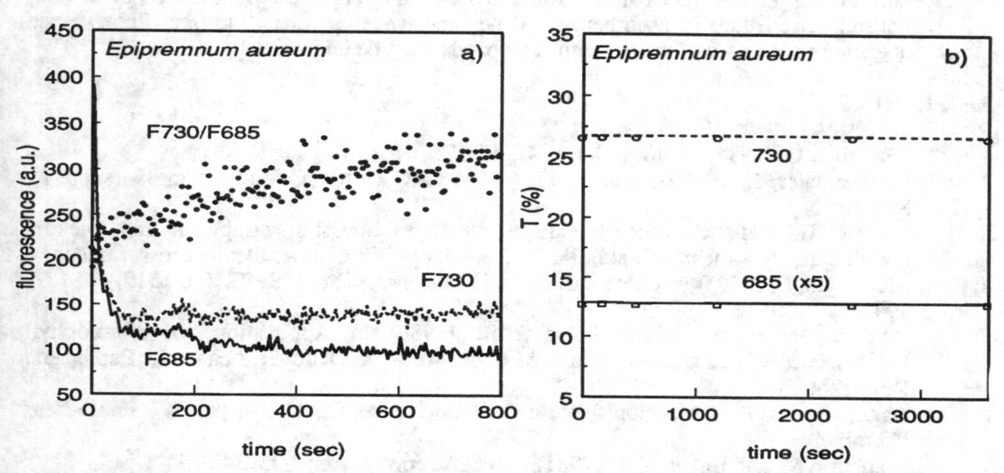

FIGURE 2. a) Fluorescence induction kinetics in Epipremnum aureum; excitation at 635 nm, PPFD = 250 μE m^{-2} s^{-1}. b) Leaf total transmittance kinetics in Epipremnum aureum; excitation at 632.8 nm, PPFD = 230 μE m^{-2} s^{-1}.

TABLE 1. F730/F685 values for maximum (F_m) and steady-state (F_s) fluorescence

Plant species	F730/F685 F_m	F730/F685 F_s
Lycopersicon esculentum Mill. (excitation at 457.9 nm)	0.59	0.83
Lycopersicon esculentum Mill. (excitation at 632.8 nm)	0.98	1.30
Epipremnum aureum	0.70	1.00
Ocimum basilicum L.	0.67	0.87

The effect of irradiation on the leaf transmittance was evaluated on *Epipremnum aureum* and *Ocimum basilicum* L. by measuring the T spectra between 600 and 780 nm at different irradiation times. The measurement was performed on the same leaves on which the Kautsky kinetics was monitored and at similar PPFD values. T values at 685 and 730 nm are plotted in Fig. 2b for *Epipremnum aureum*. Similar results were found in

Ocimum basilicum L. Transmittance does not change within the time interval investigated, which is much longer than that of the Kautsky kinetics (400-800 sec). This result confirms previous observation about the action spectrum for leaf absorbance changes (14). Inoue and Shibata (14) showed that blue light induces a rearrangement of the chloroplasts which changes the leaf absorption, but the effect is lacking when red light is used. Indeed, when we used white light to irradiate the leaf, changes in T with the irradiation time were recorded (data not shown).

In conclusion, we demonstrated that the changes in the F730/F685 fluorescence ratio during the red light induced Kautsky kinetics are not due to variations of the leaf transmittance (that is absorbance). Other mechanisms related to the fluorescence quenching processes of the two emission bands must be important.

REFERENCES

1 Schreiber, U. (1984) Photosynth Res 4, 361-372

2 Lichtenthaler, H.K. and Rinderle, U. (1988) CRC Crit Rev Anal Chem 19 (suppl.1), S29-S85

3 Renger, G. and Schreiber, U. (1986) in Light emission by plants and bacteria (Govindjee, D., Amesz, J. and Fork, D.C. eds.), pp. 587-614, Academic Press, London

4 Mazzinghi, P. (1991) in Chemical and medical sensors, Proc. SPIE Vol. 1510, pp. 187-194

5 Rinderle, U. and Lichtenthaler, H.K. (1988) in Applications of Chlorophyll Fluorescence (Lichtenthaler, H.K., ed.), pp. 189-196, Kluwer Academic Publishers, Dordrecht

6 Agati, G., Fusi, F., Mazzinghi, P., and Lipucci di Paola, M. (in press) J Photochem Photobiol

7 Bradbury, M. and Baker, N.R. (1981) Biochim Biophys Acta 635, 542-551

8 Hák, R., Lichtenthaler, H.K. and Rinderle, U. (1990) Radiat Environ Biophys 29, 329-336

9 D'Ambrosio, N., Szabo, K. and Lichtenthaler, H.K. (1992) Radiat Environ Biophys 31, 51-62

10 Agati, G., Lipucci di Paola, M., Fusi, F. and Mazzinghi, P. (1993) Med Biol Environ in press

11 Butler, W. (1978) Annu Rev Plant Physiol 29, 345-378

12 Briantais, J.M., Vernotte, C., Krause, G.H. and Weis, E. (1986) in Light emission by plants and bacteria (Govindjee, D., Amesz, J. and Fork, D.C. eds.), pp. 539-583, Academic Press, London

13 Krause, G.H. and Weis, E. (1991) Ann Rev Plant Physiol Plant Mol Biol 42, 313-349

14 Inoue, Y. and Shibata, K. (1973) Planta 114, 341-358

THE TURNOVER OF PHOTOSYSTEM II REACTION CENTRE PROTEINS AS A FUNCTION OF LIGHT

B. Geiken, C. Critchley* and G.Renger
Max-Volmer-Institut, Technische Universität Berlin, 1000 Berlin 12, Germany.
* Department of Botany, The University of Queensland, QLD 4072, Australia.

1. INTRODUCTION

The photosystem II reaction centre consists of two polypeptides, D1 and D2 with chlorophyll binding proteins CP43 and CP47 closely associated (1). Plants are exposed to wide fluctuations in the prevailing irradiance conditions. To maintain maximal photosynthetic activity plants continually adjust the composition of pigments and pigment-protein complexes, protein turnover, grana stacking and gene expression in response to light. The D1-protein was found to exhibit an exceptionally fast degradation, not only under photoinhibitory, but also under normal light conditions (2,3). However, not much is known about either D1-protein synthesis or the turnover properties of the other reaction centre proteins in higher plants as a function of light. Our results indicate that also D2, CP43 and CP47 protein synthesis is regulated by light *in vivo*. The D2 protein appears most strongly affected.
We are also interested to understand whether light regulated assembly and disassembly of the PSII reaction centre takes place and the possible involvement of thylakoid membrane stacking. Therefore we studied the *in vivo* synthesis of the reaction centre proteins using simultaneous radiolabeling with ^{14}C-Leucine and ^{14}C-Lysine as a function of growth light intensity (reflecting long term responses and changes in grana stacking) and of short term exposure to limiting, saturating and excess (photoinhibitory) irradiance.

2. MATERIALS AND METHODS

Plants: Pea plants (*Pisum sativum* L. cv 'Mossy Gem') were grown in a glasshouse with maximal light intensity of 1200 $\mu Em^{-2}s^{-1}$ for 2-3 weeks (HL-plants). For the low light condition, the same plants were transferred to a growth cabinet with an irradiance of approx. 90 $\mu Em^{-2}s^{-1}$ for 4-6 days until the newest leaves had unfolded under this low light environment (LL-plants).
After pretreatment with cycloheximide (20 μg/ml) under saturating (SL) or limiting light (LL), respectively, for 60 minutes (to inhibit the synthesis of nuclear coded proteins), the leaf pairs were fed through the petiole with 8 μCi of ^{14}C-Lysine and ^{14}C-Leucine (ratio 7:1), to be taken up in 20-30 min. The leaves were cut into discs and floated on 1 μg/ml cycloheximide. Samples were taken at intervals of 10 min up to 2.5 hours and frozen in liquid nitrogen. This labeling procedure was carried out at irradiances of 90 $\mu Em^{-2}s^{-1}$ (LL), 350 $\mu Em^{-2}s^{-1}$ (SL) and 1500 $\mu Em^{-2}s^{-1}$ (VHL), as indicated in the figures.

N. Murata (ed.), Research in Photosynthesis, Vol. IV, 643–646.

The photosynthetic activity was monitored under all light conditions by measuring the chlorophyll fluorescence parameter Fv/Fm. Thylakoid membranes were isolated according to (3). Chlorophyll concentration was determined as in (4). The thylakoid membrane proteins were separated on lithium-dodecylsulfate PAGE (6% stacking/ 8-16% gradient resolving gel). The radioactive protein bands on the dried gels were analyzed and quantitated with an Ambis beta scanner. From the scan images graphs of time courses of label incorporation into D1, D2 and CP43 were generated, background corrected, normalized to equal label uptake rate and equal lysine/leucine content.

3. RESULTS AND DISCUSSION

In previous experiments (5) we used ^{14}C-lysine to monitor the synthesis of the reaction centre proteins D2, CP43 and CP47. This made use of the fact that the D1-protein in peas does not contain lysine. To be able to study simultaneously the synthesis of the D1-protein and the other reaction centre proteins we employed ^{14}C-leucine together with ^{14}C-lysine. Leucine was almost exclusively taken up by D1 (data not shown) whereas lysine was incorporated into the other proteins of interest.

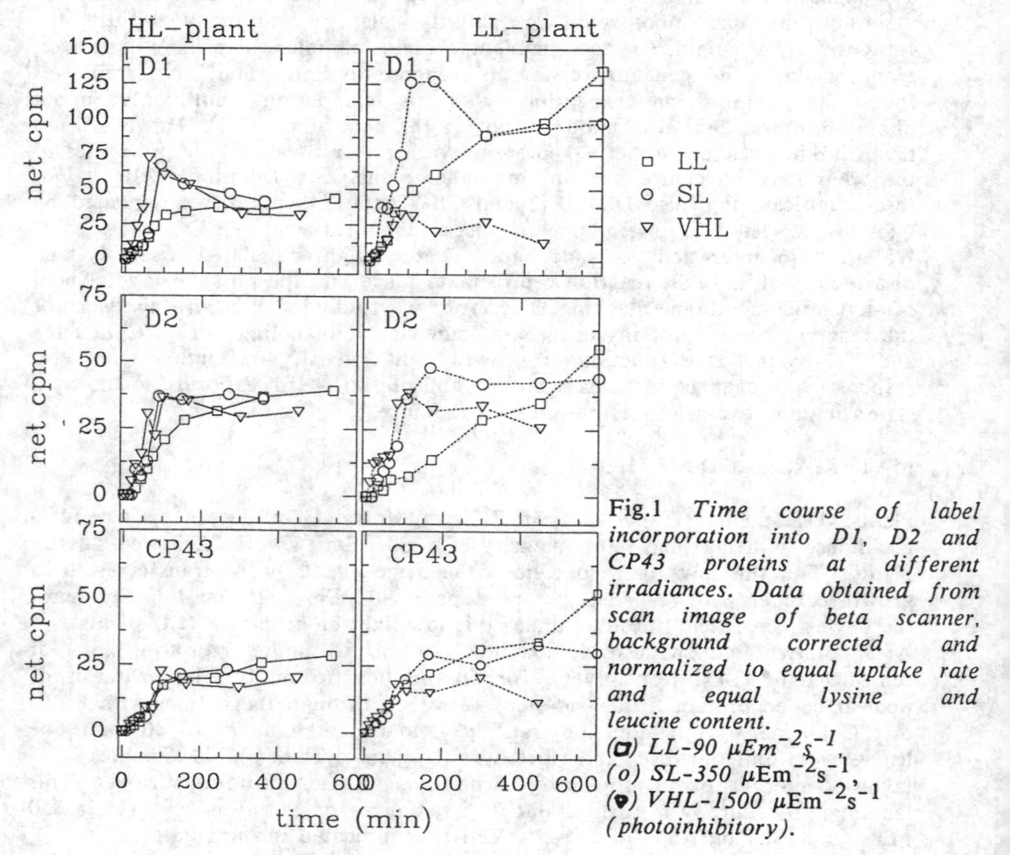

Fig.1 *Time course of label incorporation into D1, D2 and CP43 proteins at different irradiances. Data obtained from scan image of beta scanner, background corrected and normalized to equal uptake rate and equal lysine and leucine content.*
(□) LL-90 μ$Em^{-2}s^{-1}$,
(o) SL-350 μ$Em^{-2}s^{-1}$,
(▽) VHL-1500 μ$Em^{-2}s^{-1}$
(photoinhibitory).

In Figure 1 the time courses of radiolabel incorporation into D1, D2 and CP43 are presented. For up to 10 hours high light plants (HL) with small grana stacks or low light plants (LL) with extensive grana stacks were exposed to limiting (LL, 90 $\mu Em^{-2}s^{-1}$) saturating (SL, 350 $\mu Em^{-2}s^{-1}$) and excess (VHL, 1500 $\mu Em^{-2}s^{-1}$ light.

Comparing HL- and LL-plants it is obvious that protein synthesis in LL-plants is much more susceptible to changes in irradiance. Both the amount of protein synthesised and the rate of synthesis (data not shown for rate of synthesis) vary much more in LL-plants than they do in HL-plants. Depending on the irradiance the overall amount of all proteins tends to be higher in LL-plants than in HL-plants, with the D1-protein synthesis being particularly affected, followed by D2 and CP43 synthesis.

Figure 2A shows the maximum amount of incorporated label as a function of irradiance. These results clearly demonstrate, that in LL-plants an increase in irradiance accompanied by a decrease in photosynthetic activity (Fig.2B) leads to a decrease in incorporation of radiolabeled amino acids into proteins. This effect is very drastic for the D1-protein and less pronounced for D2 and CP43. The strong decrease in label incorporation into D1 under photoinhibitory conditions cannot be explained just by a high degradation rate of D1 occurring concomitently with synthesis. Comparable degradation studies (2) reveal an initial degradation rate of about 10% degradation of labeled D1 per hour, which is in accordance with our data. This can by no means account for a label incorporation that is five times lower than it is under limiting light.

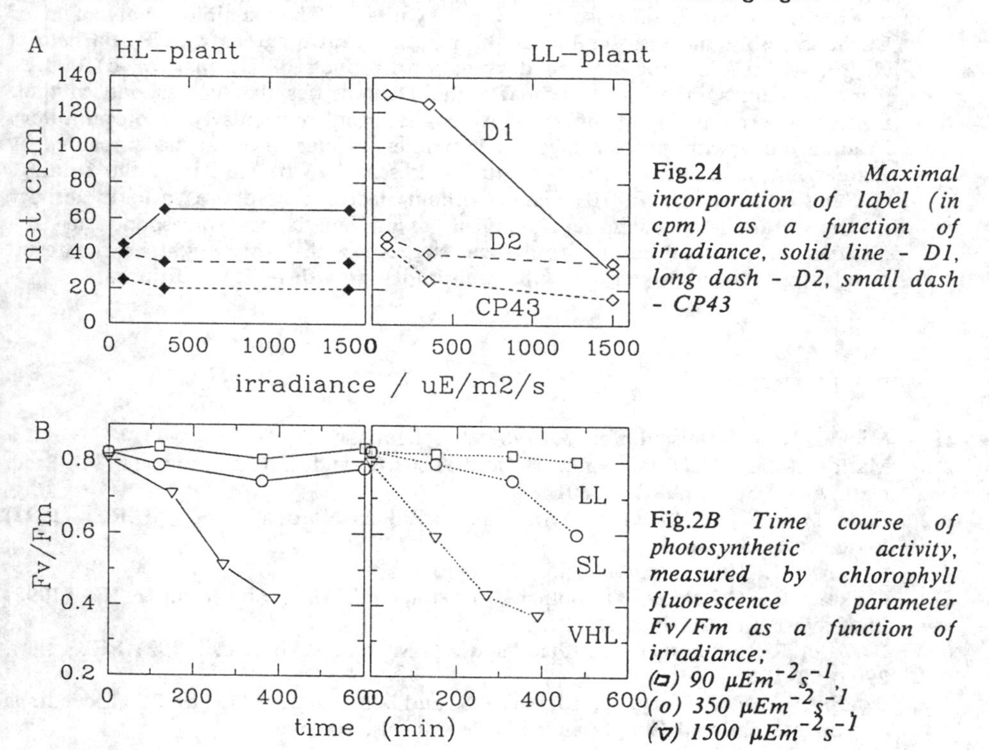

Fig.2*A* *Maximal incorporation of label (in cpm) as a function of irradiance, solid line - D1, long dash - D2, small dash - CP43*

Fig.2*B* *Time course of photosynthetic activity, measured by chlorophyll fluorescence parameter Fv/Fm as a function of irradiance;*
(□) 90 $\mu Em^{-2}s^{-1}$
(o) 350 $\mu Em^{-2}s^{-1}$
(▽) 1500 $\mu Em^{-2}s^{-1}$

Furthermore, in LL-plants D1-degradation does not only occur under photoinhibitory conditions, but also under saturating light and no such decrease in maximal label incorporation can be observed. Of all three light intensities employed we find the highest amount of protein being synthesised at the irradiance that corresponds to the growth light conditions i.e. 90 $\mu Em^{-2}s^{-1}$ and in this case label incorporation does not even reach saturation after 10 hours. This effect can be observed clearly not only for D1, but also for the D2- and CP43-proteins. It suggests that in LL-plants less than the maximal available radiolabel is incorporated at light intensities that lead to a great loss in photosynthetic activity .
Protein synthesis in HL-plants does not show a strong irradiance dependence in any of the studied proteins. The maximum level of synthesised protein, however, corresponds more to that of LL-plants under photoinhibitory conditions. One might therefore speculate that HL-plants, by adapting to high light and at times photoinhibitory conditions (about 1200 $\mu Em^{-2}s^{-1}$), downregulate protein synthesis, mainly D1- and to a lesser extent D2 protein synthesis.

Our results can be summarized as follows: a) LL-plants are much more responsive to changes in the light environment than HL-plants. b) Of all three proteins studied D1-protein synthesis and turnover is most strongly light regulated. c) D2 synthesis is also quite susceptible to different light environments, much more so than CP43 synthesis. The possible involvement of D2 in assembly and disassembly of the reaction centre agrees with R. Barbato et al. (6), who finds light induced degradation products of D2 *in vitro*. d) In LL-plants protein synthesis is maximal at light intensities that correspond to their respective growth light intensity. At higher and particularly photoinhibitory irradiance a downregulation of protein synthesis seems to occur, accompanied by a great loss in photosynthetic activity. This seems to be similar to the findings of Sundby et al. (7). In HL-plants without decrease in photosynthetic activity the maximum level of protein synthesis at all irradiances corresponds to LL-plant under photoinhibitory irradiance, suggesting that this might be the result of adaptation to high and even photoinhibitory growth light conditions.

4. REFERENCES

1 Michel, H. and Deisenhofer, J. (1988) Biochemistry 27, 1-7
2 Mattoo, A.K., Hoffman-Falk, H. Marder, J.B. and Edelman, M. (1984) Proc. Natl. Acad. Sci USA 81, 13801384
3 Critchley, C., Russell, A.W. and Bolhar-Nordenkampf, H.R. (1992) Photosynthetica, in press
4 Arnon, D.I. (1949) Plant Physiol. 24, 1-15
5 Geiken, B., Critchley, C. Bolhar-Nordenkampf, H.R. and Renger, G. (1992) Photosynthetica 27, in press
6 Barbato, R., Shipton, C.A., Giacometti, G.M. and Barber, J. (1992) FEBS Lett. 290, 162-166
7 Sundby, C. McCaffery. S., Chow, W.S. and Anderson, J.M. (1992) Proceedings of 9th International Congress on Photosynthesis, Nagoya

DIFFERENCE IN PHOTOSYNTHETIC RATES AMONG LEAVES AT EQUIVALENT POSITIONS ON THE MAIN STEM AND ITS TILLERS IN RICE PLANTS

Taiichiro OOKAWA, Eiki KURODA and Kuni ISHIHARA, Faculty of Agriculture, Tokyo University of Agriculture and Technology, Fuchu, Tokyo 183, Japan

1. INTRODUCTION

A large variation (6-8 umolCO_2 m^{-2} sec^{-1}) in single leaf photosynthetic rates was found among a group of leaves in a rice canopy, each of which was situated at the equivalent position on a stem (the same numerical leaf from the uppermost fully expanded leaf on each stem), even though the measurements were conducted at the same time of day and under the same light regime (saturation light intensity) in the paddy field[1,2]. Since the stems of a hill in the rice plant were divided into the main stems and tillers, the photosynthetic rates and their related processes and factors were compared between the leaves at the equivalent positions (between the synchronously expanded leaves) on the main stems and their tillers in order to clarify the causes of the variation and the factors responsible for the difference in the photosynthetic rates, using the Japanese standard cultivar, Nipponbare (short culm and ear number type). Furthermore, we examined whether the differences in the photosynthetic rates among leaves at equivalent positions would change due to the cultivars with different number of tillers using Nipponbare and Tainung 67 (long culm and ear weight type).

2. MATERIALS AND METHODS

2.1 Rice seedlings were transplanted on June 10 with a planting density of 15x30cm (three plants per hill) and were grown under submerged conditions in the paddy field of the University farm. The leaves at the equivalent positions on the main stem and tillers were marked with ink of the same color immediately after expansion.

2.2 Photosynthesis measurements: The rates of CO_2 exchange and transpiration of the attached single leaf in the field were determined using the open gas exchange system described by Kuroda et al.[3] Photosynthetic rates were measured at the photon flux density above 1,200umol $m^{-2}sec^{-1}$ during the morning.

2.3 Chlorophyll and RuBPCase contents: After the photosynthetic measurements, leaves were cut off and then frozen at -80 C. Chlorophyll contents were measured specrophotometrically by the method of Wintermans[4], and the amount of RuBPCase were determined by the single radial immuno diffusion method[5].

N. Murata (ed.), Research in Photosynthesis, Vol. IV, 647–650.

3. RESULTS AND DISCUSSION

3.1 The photosynthetic rates of the leaves at the equivalent positions on the main stem and its primary tillers of Nipponbare were compared. Immediately after they fully expanded, little difference was noticed between the photosynthetic rates of the leaves at the equivalent positions. At 16 days after expansion, however, the photosynthetic rates of the leaves on the tillers were smaller than those on the main stem(Table 1.).

Table 1. Comparison of the photosynthetic rates ($\mu molCO_2 \cdot m^{-2} \cdot sec^{-1}$) of the 14th leaf on the main stem and the synchronously expanded leaves on the primary tillers of cv. Nipponbare.

Plant No.	Main stem	Primary tillers 6th	7th	8th *
		Immediately after the leaves fully expanded		
1	17.3	20.3 (117.4) **	15.3 (88.4)	19.9 (115.0)
2	19.8	18.2 (92.3)	19.3 (97.8)	20.3 (103.0)
3	22.5	21.9 (97.5)	22.7 (100.8)	22.3 (99.5)
		16days after the leaves fully expanded		
1	18.3	8.8 (38.0)	10.2 (55.8)	—
2	18.7	17.7 (94.6)	11.7 (62.3)	—
3	21.3	14.3 (43.9)	14.3 (66.9)	12.2 (57.5)

* The node of the main stem from which the tiller emerged.
** Percent values relative to the photosynthetic rate of the leaf on the main stem.

3.2 Percent values of the photosynthetic rates of the leaves on the tillers relative to the photosynthetic rate of the synchronously expanded leaf on the main stem were distributed normally around 100% immediately after expansion, but most of those values were smaller than 100% at 2 or 3 weeks after expansion(Fig.1.).

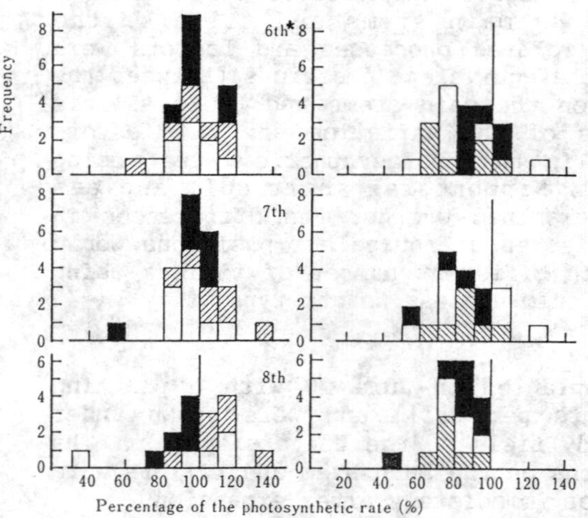

Fig.1. Photosynthetic rates of the expanded leaves on the primary tillers expressed as percentages relative to the photosynthetic rate of the synchronously expanded leaf on the main stem, immediately after they fully expanded (left) and at 2 or 3 weeks after they fully expanded (right). (cv.Nipponbare)
■ : 16th** , ▨ : 15th
□ : 14th , ▧ : 13th
* The node of the main stem from which the tiller emerged.
** The leaf position on the main stem of which expanded synchronously with the leaves on its primary tillers.

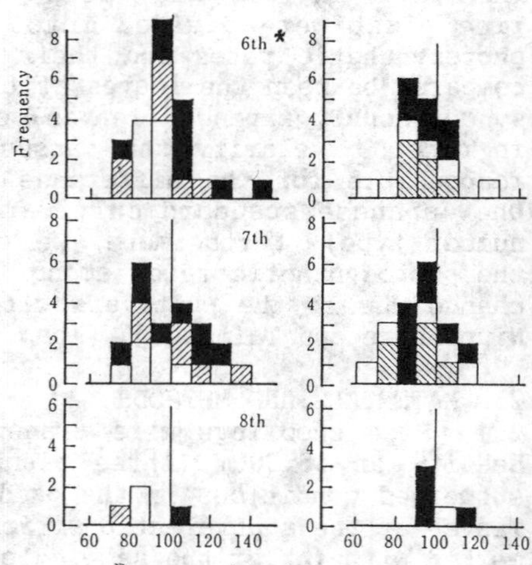

Fig.2. Photosynthetic rates of the expanded leaves on the primary tillers expressed as percentages relative to the photosynthetic rate of the synchronously expanded leaf on the main stem, immediately after they fully expanded (left) and at 2 or 3 weeks after they fully expanded (right). (cv.Tainung 67)
■ : 16th** , ▨ : 15th
□ : 14th , ▧ : 13th
* The node of the main stem from which the tiller emerged.
** The leaf position on the main stem of which expanded synchronously with the leaves on its primary tillers.

3.3 In rice plants, immediately after the 14th leaf on the main stem fully expanded, the photosynthetic rates of the upper (14th and 13th) leaves on the main stem and the synchronously expanded leaves on the tillers were almost the same. However, the photosynthetic rates of the leaves (12th and 11th) at lower positions on the main stem were larger than the synchronously expanded leaves on the tillers. Also the differences in the photosynthetic rates of the lower leaves on the tillers and those of the main stem were more remarkable with tillers that emerged from the higher nodes of the main stem(Table 2.).

Table 2. Comparison of the photosynthetic rates ($\mu molCO_2 \cdot m^{-2} \cdot sec^{-1}$) of the synchronously expanded leaves on the main stem and the primary tillers of cv. Nipponbare immediately after the 14th leaf fully expanded.

Leaf position on the main stem	Main stem	Primary tillers 2nd	3rd	5th	6th	7th	8th
14th	25.1	26.5 (105.4)**	27.8 (110.6)	30.0 (119.6)	27.6 (109.9)	24.7 (98.5)	24.5 (97.6)
13th	24.9	26.1 (104.9)	24.9 (99.9)	22.9 (91.7)	24.9 (100.2)	22.0 (88.5)	24.9 (99.8)
12th	23.5	24.1 (102.4)	21.0 (89.3)	19.8 (84.1)	18.2 (77.3)	19.9 (84.4)	15.3 (64.9)
11th	16.7	17.0 (101.5)	12.9 (77.1)	2.8 (16.9)	12.8 (76.6)	9.8 (58.5)	8.5 (50.8)

* The node of the main stem from which the tiller emerged.
** Percent values relative to the photosynthetic rate of the leaf on the main stem.

3.4 Small differences in the diffusive conductance, chlorophyll content and RuBPCase content were noticed among leaves immediately after expansion on the main stem and its tillers. As the photosynthetic rates of leaves on the tillers decreased more largely with time at 16 days after leaf expansion, the diffusive conductance, chlorophyll content and RuBPCase content of the same leaves decreased(Fig.3.).

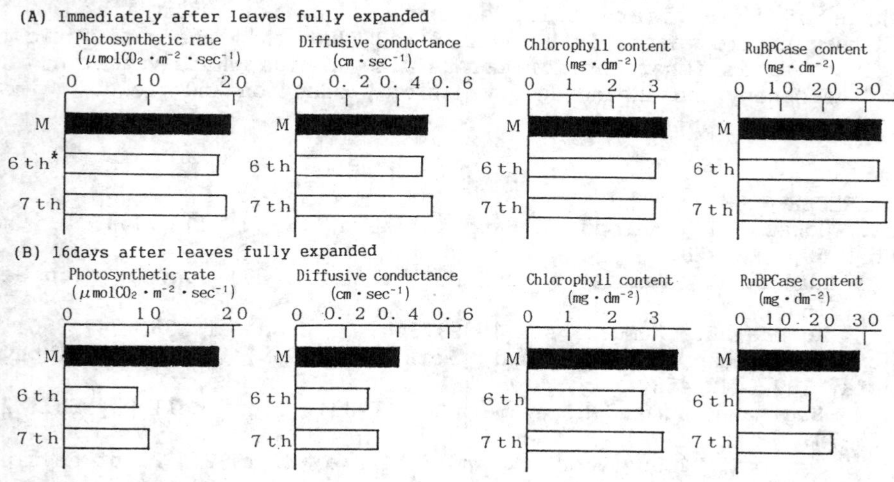

Fig.3. Comparison of the photosynthetic rates, the diffusive conductance, chlorophyll content and RuBPCase content of the 14th leaf on the main stem and the synchronously expanded leaves on the primary tillers of cv. Nipponbare.
* The node of the main stem (M, ▬) from which the tiller emerged.

3.5 These results indicate that one of the factors responsible for the difference in the photosynthetic rates of the leaves at the equivalent positions on the stems in a hill was an earlier leaf senescence of the leaves on the primary tillers, especially those emerging from the higher node on the main stem, than the leaf on the main stem. To examine the causes of the difference in the time of senescence of the main stem leaves and that of tiller leaves, exudation rates from the cut surface of the stems were measured. Since the exudation rates of the tillers which emerged from the higher node on the main stem were much smaller (Table 3.), it was suggested that the amount of cytokinin transported to the leaves was little[6]. Further study is needed to elucidate this mechanism.

Table 3. Comparison of the exudation rates of the main stem and the primary tillers immediately after the 14th leaf on the main stem fully expanded in cv. Nipponbare.

	M *	2nd	3rd	5th	6th	7th	8th
Exudation rate ($mg \cdot hr^{-1}$)	309	380 (123.0)**	341 (110.5)	286 (92.7)	215 (69.6)	252 (81.7)	204 (65.9)

* The node of the main stem (M) from which the tiller emerged.
** Percent values relative to the exudation rate of the main stem.

3.6 In Tainung 67 with a small number of the tillers, the photosynthetic rates among leaves at the equivalent positions on the main stem and the primary tillers were not different even at 2 or 3 weeks after expansion(Fig.2.). Even with aging of leaf, there were no differences in the senescence of the leaves of the main stem and those of the primary tillers, both of which maintained high photosynthetic rates. It is considered that this characteristic of Tainung 67 is important for maintaining a high photosynthetic rate of the canopy and enhancing dry matter production and yield.

4. REFERENCES

1 Ookawa, T., Kuroda, E. and Ishihara, K. (1991) Jpn. J. Crop Sci. 60, 413-420.
2 Kuroda, E., Kumura, A. and Murata, Y. (1987) Jpn. J. Crop Sci. 56, 51-58.
3 Kuroda, E., Kumura, A. (1989) Jpn. J. Crop Sci. 58, 347-356.
4 Wintermans, J.F.G.I. and Mots, A. (1965) Biochim. Biophys. Acta 109, 448-453.
5 Sugiyama, T. and Hirayama, Y. (1983) Plant Cell Physiol. 24, 783-787.
6 Soejima, H, Sugiyama, T. and Ishihara, K.(1992) Plant Physiol. (in press)

COMPARATIVE STUDIES ON THE PHOTOSYNTHETIC TRAITS AND CHLOROPLAST ULTRASTRUCTURE IN DIFFERENT GENOME WHEAT SPECIES

Zhang Rongxian Ma Guoying Wu Yuanying
Dept. of Agronomy, Nanjing Agri. Univ., Nanjing, 210014, P.R.China
(Supported by NSFC)

1. INTRODUCTION

It was reported that the leaf photosynthetic rate of *Triticum boeoticum* and *Aegilops squarrosa* was 40-60% higher than that of *Triticum aestivum* cv. Chinese Spring (Austin 1982, 1984; Zhang et al. 1990). This paper deals with the photosynthetic traits and the ultrastructure of leaf chloroplast in these species in order to elaborate the mechanism of the higher photosynthetic rate in two wild species and the effect of different genomes on wheat photosynthesis.

2. MATERIALS AND METHODS

T.boeoticum (2X, AA), *Ae.squarrosa* (2X, DD) and *T. aestivum* cv. Chinese Spring (6X, AABBDD) were planted in the Experimental Farm of Nanjing Agri. Univ. of China. The photosynthetic traits and the ultrastructure of chloroplasts were measured with the 1st, 5th and flag leaves.

2.1 Isolation of chloroplasts and measurement of photosynthetic rate: The protoplasts were obtained by enzymolysis and the chloroplasts obtained from the broken protoplasts. The photosynthetic rate and the Hill reaction were measured with a clark-type oxygen electrode (Ma et al. 1992).

2.2 PS II activity of chloroplast: Estimated from the measurement of the rate of O_2 evolution by interrupting electron transport between PS II and PS I (Li et al. 1987).

2.3 Chlorophyll content: Determined by Arnon's method (1949).

2.4 Ultrastructure of chloroplasts: Leaf samples were taken from the middle parts of the leaves, fixed immediately after cutting in 4% OsO_4. The fixed material was dehydrated in an ethanol series and was embedded in Epon 812 resin. The sections were viewed with a JEM-100CXII.

3. RESULTS

3.1 Photosynthetic rate of chloroplast and its responses to light intensity and temperature: The photosynthetic rate of chloroplast in *T. boeoticum* was the highest, on average 21.2% and 58.8% higher than that in *Ae. squarrosa* and *T. aestivum* and became much higher under high light intensity and high temperature (above 35°C) (Figs. 1, 2).

N. Murata (ed.), Research in Photosynthesis, Vol. IV, 651–654.

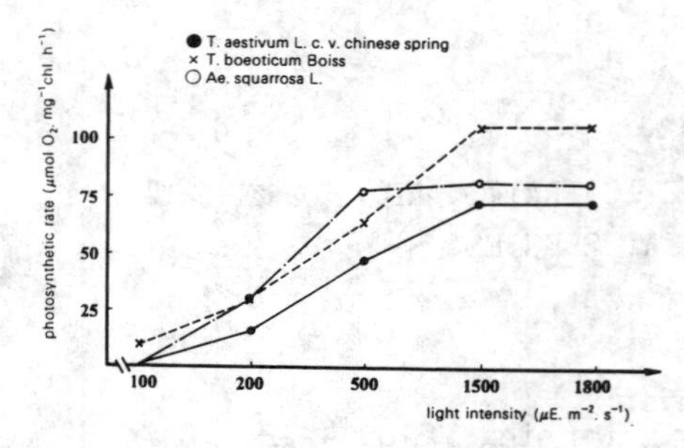

Fig. 1. Effect of light intensity on photosynthetic rate of wheat chloroplast (5th leaf)

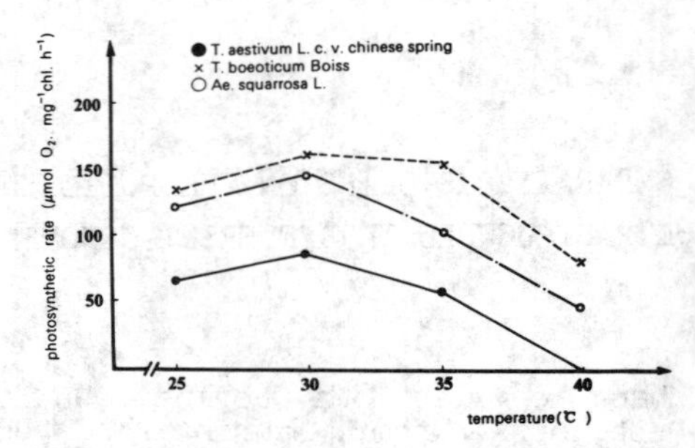

Fig. 2. Effect of temperature on photosynthetic rate of wheat chloroplast

3.2 Hill reaction of chloroplasts and photoinhibition: As the average value of the 1st, 5th and flag leaves, the Hill reaction of chloroplast in T. boeoticum was 16% and 39% higher than that in Ae. squarrosa and T. aestivum respectively (Fig. 3). Under high light intensity (1800uE. m^{-2}.s^{-1}), the uncoupled Hill reaction activity of T. aestivum, Ae. squarrosa and T. boeoticum began to decline after 1, 3 and 5 minutes respectively. So it is supposed that the photoinhibition is lowest in T. boeoticum and highest in T. aestivum(Fig. 4).

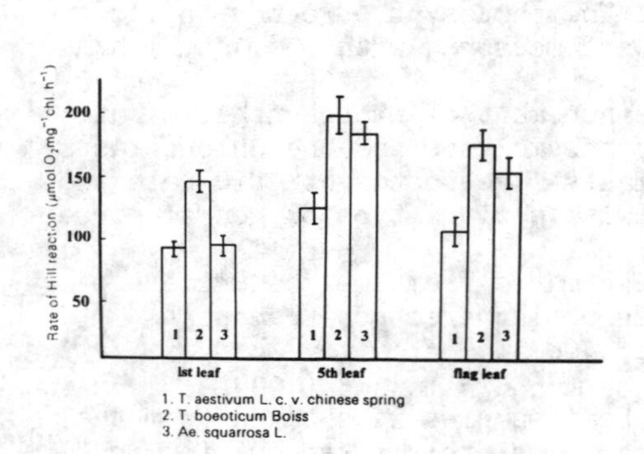

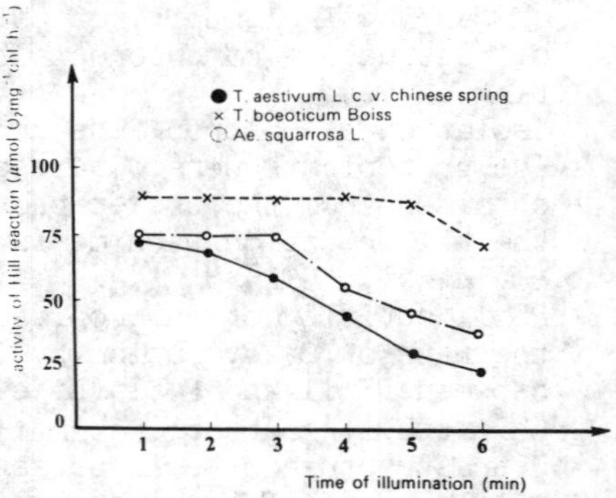

Fig. 3. Hill reaction of wheat chloroplast

● T. aestivum L. c. v. chinese spring
× T. boeoticum Boiss
○ Ae. squarrosa L.
activity of Hill reaction (μmol O₂mg⁻¹chl h⁻¹)
Time of illumination (min)

Fig. 4. Changes of the uncoupled Hill reaction activity of wheat chloroplast under saturation light

3.3 PS II activity of chloroplast: Fig.5 shows that the PS II activities of T. boeoticum and Ae. squarrosa were 49% and 22% higher than that of T. aestivum respectively.

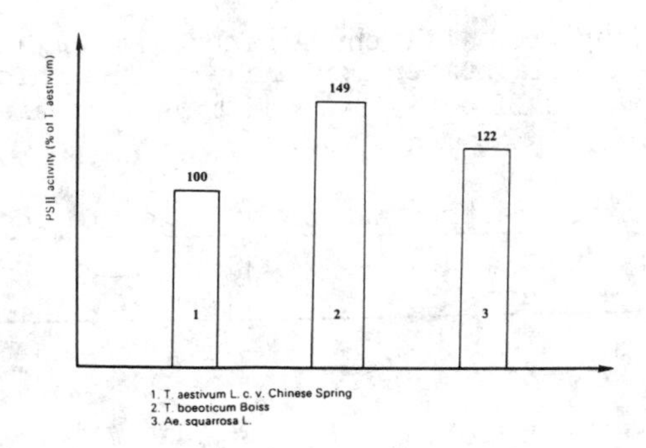

Fig. 5. Comparision of PS II activity of wheat chloroplast

3.4 The ultrastructure of chloroplast: The results in Table 1 show that the number of chloroplast per cm^2 section was higher in the two wild species than that in the cultivated species. The lamella number per grana in T. boeoticum was much higher than that in the other two species.

Table 1. The characteristics of chloroplast ultrastructure of wheat (5th leaf)

Item	T. aestivum L.cv. Chinese Spring	T. boeoticum Boiss	Ae. squarrosa L.
major axis (u)	5.6	5.9	6.1
minor axis (u)	3.1	2.6	2.3
chloroplast no./ cm^2 section	963	1079	1233
grana no./ chloroplast	25.8±7.3	26.0±2.4	24.6±6.0
lamella no./ grana	4.5±1.3	7.9±2.7	4.2±1.3
osmiophilic granule no./ chloroplast	28.8 ± 2.2	20.5 ± 1.9	20.0 ± 1.0

4. DISCUSSION

Table 2 shows that all the measured items for T. boeoticum were about 20% higher than those for Ae. squarrosa. Besides, T. boeoticum was more adapted to the environment with high light intensity and high temperature and had lower photoinhibition. The ultrastructure of chloroplast of T. boeoticum (especially the lamella number per grana) coincided with its high photosynthetic rate. So it is supposed that the A genome is beneficial for increasing the lamella number per grana of the chloroplast, which results in higher PS II activity, and thus increases leaf photosynthesis.

Table 2. Photosynthetic traits of wheat of A genome and D genome

Item	wheat with A genome	wheat with D genome	A higher than D (%)
photosynthetic rate of leaf disc	135.32	112.4	20.1
photosynthetic rate of protoplast	180.1±8.4	141.4±5.7	22.1
photosynthetic rate of chloroplast	169.0±6.8	133.2±2.1	21.0
Hill reaction rate of chloroplast	170.7±12.2	143.0±12	16.2
PS II activity of chloroplast	65.45	50.7	22.5

Unit: u mol O_2 . mg^{-1} chl. h^{-1}

REFERENCES

1. Austin, R.B. et al. (1982) Ann. Bot. 49, 177-189
2. Austin, R.B. et al. (1984) Advances in Photosynthesis Research, Vol. IV, pp.103-110. Printed in Netherlands
3. Zhang, R.X. et al. (1990) Jiangsu Journal of Agricultural Science 6(1), 1-9
4. Ma, G.Y. et al. (1990) Plant Physiology Communications 27(1), 53-55
5. Li, G.F. et al. (1987) Acta Phytophysiologica Sinica 13(3), 295-301

Differences in the Relationships between Rubisco, Carbonic Anhydrase, and Photosynthesis in Wheat and Several Other C_3 Plants in Response to Nitrogen Nutrition

Amane Makino, Hiroshi Sakashita, Jun Hidema, Tadahiko Mae, Kunihiko Ojima and Barry Osmond*; Department of Agricultural Chemistry, Tohoku University, Sendai 981, Japan and Research School of Biological Sciences, The Australian National University*, Canberra ACT 2601, Australia

Introduction

The highly positive correlation between photosynthetic capacity and nitrogen content in leaves is widely found. Evans and Terashima (3), who used spinach, clarified the relation between N nutrition and N partitioning into the various photosynthetic components and activities. They found that although N supply increased the ratio of Rubisco activity to electron transport activity, Chl or total leaf-N, the in vivo balance between the activities of Rubisco and electron transport remained constant. They concluded that this difference was compensated by the presence of a CO_2-transfer resistance between intercellular air spaces and the carboxylation sites. The increase in the ratio of Rubisco to total leaf-N or Chl with N supply is frequently found for other C_3 species, such as cotton, Solanum, and bean (see refs in 3).

However, in spite of the existence of significant CO_2-transfer resistance in wheat (1,8), the ratio of Rubisco to total leaf-N or Chl in fully expanded young leaves seems to be independent of N nutrition (1,4,5). In this study, we used fully expanded, young leaves of several C_3 plants including wheat, rice, spinach, bean and pea, and first clarified differences in the effects of N nutrition on the ratio of Rubisco content to Chl content, electron transport activity or total leaf-N between wheat and the other C_3 plants. We then examined the in vivo balance between Rubisco and electron transport. In addition, we found a distinctly different response of carbonic anhydrase (CA) activity to changing leaf-N content in wheat.

Materials and Methods

Plant Culture --Wheat (Triticum aestivum L. cv Asakaze), pea (Pisum sativum L. cv Sugar snap), spinach (Spinacia oleracea L. cv Nobel), rice (Oryza sativa L cv Sasanishiki) and bean (Phaseolus vulgaris L cv Tendergreen) were grown hydroponically in growth chambers or in a greenhouse under natural sunlight conditions. The hydroponic solution used was described in Makino and Osmond (5), and was continuously aerated. All measurements were made on fully expanded, young leaves of 4- to 10-week-old plants. About 10 to 14 d before the measurements, plants were supplied with a nutrient solution containing different N concentrations (0.2 to 12 mM) as described previously (5).

Determination of Chl, Total leaf-N and Rubisco --These were deter-

N. Murata (ed.), Research in Photosynthesis, Vol. IV, 655–658.

mined as described elsewhere (5). The Chl and total leaf-N contents were measured from part of leaf homogenate. After adding 25% (w/v) Li-DS solution to the homogenate (final conc. 1% [w/v]), this preparation was immediately heated at 100 C for 45 s and centrifuged. The supernatant was used for SDS-PAGE to determine Rubisco. The Rubisco content was determined spectrophotometrically by formamide extraction of Coomassie Brilliant Blue R on the gel, using calibration curves made with Rubisco purified from wheat or rice leaves (5).

Assay of Rubisco, Electron Transport and CA --The Rubisco and whole chain electron transport activities were measured as described previously (5). The CA activity was measured by the method of Wilbur and Anderson with some modifications. Leaves were homogenized in 50 mM Hepes-NaOH (pH 7.5) containing 10 mM DTT, 0.5 mM EDTA and 10% (v/v) glycerol. Triton X-100 was added to a portion of the homogenate to a final concentration of 0.1% (v/v), followed by centrifugation. The supernatant was used for enzyme assay. Addition of 0.1% Triton X-100 enhanced CA activity by 10 to 20%. The CA activity was determined by measuring the pH decrease at 0 to 2 C with a pH electrode. The centrifuged crude extract and 2 mL of 20 mM Na-barbital (pH 8.3 with H_2SO_4) were stirred at a constant rate in a small cuvette, and the reaction was by addition of 1.0 mL CO_2-saturated H_2O. Enzyme activity was defined as 1 unit (U) = 10(To-T)/T, in which T and To represent the time(s) needed for a pH decrease from 8.3 to 7.5, with and without enzyme, respectively.

Gas Exchange --The rate of CO_2 and H_2O-vapor exchange were measured with an open gas-exchange system using a temperature-controlled chamber equipped with two fans. The system was detailed in Makino et al. (4). Measurements were made at an irradiance of 1800 umol quanta m^{-2} s^{-1} and a leaf temperature of 25 C.

Results and Discussion

The ratio of Rubisco to total leaf-N and its relationship to leaf-N content are shown in Fig. 1. There was a difference in N partitioning in response to changing leaf-N content among the C_3 species examined here. The ratio of Rubisco to leaf-N in wheat was independent of leaf-N content, but this ratio from the other plants increased with increasing leaf-N content. In addition, differences in the absolute ratio were found among species. For example, in wheat and rice, about 28% and 28 to 37% of the leaf-N content were present in Rubisco, respectively, while its proportion from spinach was only 13 to 25%. The greater ratio of N in Rubisco for wheat and rice were also pointed out by Evans (2). However, the values of Rubisco ratio to leaf-N given in Fig. 1 are appreciably higher than those previously seen in literature. This may be ,in part, because we obtained complete extraction of membrane-bound Rubisco by addition of detergent (6).

The ratio of Rubisco to Chl in wheat was relatively constant, but that from other plants increased with increasing leaf-N content. These relationships between Rubisco and Chl are quite similar to those in Fig. 1. This is because the proportion to leaf-N as Chl remained almost constant in all plants including wheat, irrespective of N treatment.

We next determined the ratio of Rubisco to electron transport activity. In wheat leaves, this ratio was unaffected by N treatment, but in spinach and rice it increased with increasing leaf-N content Thus, except for wheat, the greater increase in Rubisco with leaf-N was quite similar to that reported by Evans and Terashima (3) with spinach.

The response of the photosynthetic rate to intercellular partial CO_2 pressure was examined using intact leaves of wheat, rice and spinach. According to the photosynthetic model for C_3 species developed by Farquhar and co-workers, the photosynthetic rate at low CO_2 partial pressure is limited by Rubisco capacity, while the rate at high CO_2 is limited by electron transport capacity. In addition, photosynthesis under saturating CO_2 conditions can be also limited by the capacity of Pi-regeneration during starch and sucrose synthesis (7). Thus, if the in vivo ratio of Rubisco to electron transport capacities is affected by N supply, we would expect to observe a difference in the ratio of the photosynthetic rate at low CO_2 pressure to the rate at high CO_2 among the various N treatments. For all plants examined, however, when the CO_2-response curve for each N treatment was normalized to the rate at 200 ubar, the respective curves for the three species collapsed to nearly identical curves, showing that there is no difference among species in the relationship between photosynthesis at low and high CO_2 pressures in response to N nutrition. This means that the in vivo balance between the capacities of Rubisco and electron transport in wheat, spinach and rice remained almost constant, irrespective of N treatment. This finding suggests that wheat has a special mechanism(s) for this in vivo balance. According to the view of Evans and Terashima (3), we considered that the difference in mechanisms for the in vivo balance between Rubisco and electron transport between wheat and other plants possibly lies in a difference in the response of the CO_2-transfer resistance to changing N content. Therefore, we examined CA activity as one of the components of the CO_2-tranfer resistance.

Fig. 2 shows the relationship between the ratio of CA activity to Rubisco content and leaf-N content. Although CA activity on a Rubisco basis in rice, spinach and pea remained essentially constant irrespective of N treatment, this enzyme activity from wheat was markedly enhanced with increasing leaf-N content. In addition, the absolute in vitro activity of CA per unit leaf area in wheat was much lower than that from the other C_3 plants examined over a wide range of leaf-N content, being only 3 to 10% of that from the other plants at any given leaf-N content (Fig. 3). If CA is closely related to the CO_2-transfer resistance, these results suggest that the CO_2-transfer resistance in wheat may be significantly affected by N treatment, decreasing with increasing leaf-N content. Thus, the change in this resistance may be responsible for the balance between Rubisco and electron transport activities in vivo.

Von Caemmerer and Evans (8), using a combination of conventional gas-exchange measurements with concurrent measurements of carbon isotope discrimination during CO_2 uptake, found a inverse correlation between the CO_2-transfer resistance and leaf-N content in wheat. Our results suggest that this interspecific comparison using on-line carbon-isotope discrimination analysis might be useful in evaluating the role of CA in the CO_2-transfer resistance of leaves. They also found that the CO_2-transfer resistance in rice is smaller than in wheat at any given leaf-N content, which might be caused to a greater or lesser extent by the much greater CA activity ,in rice noted here.

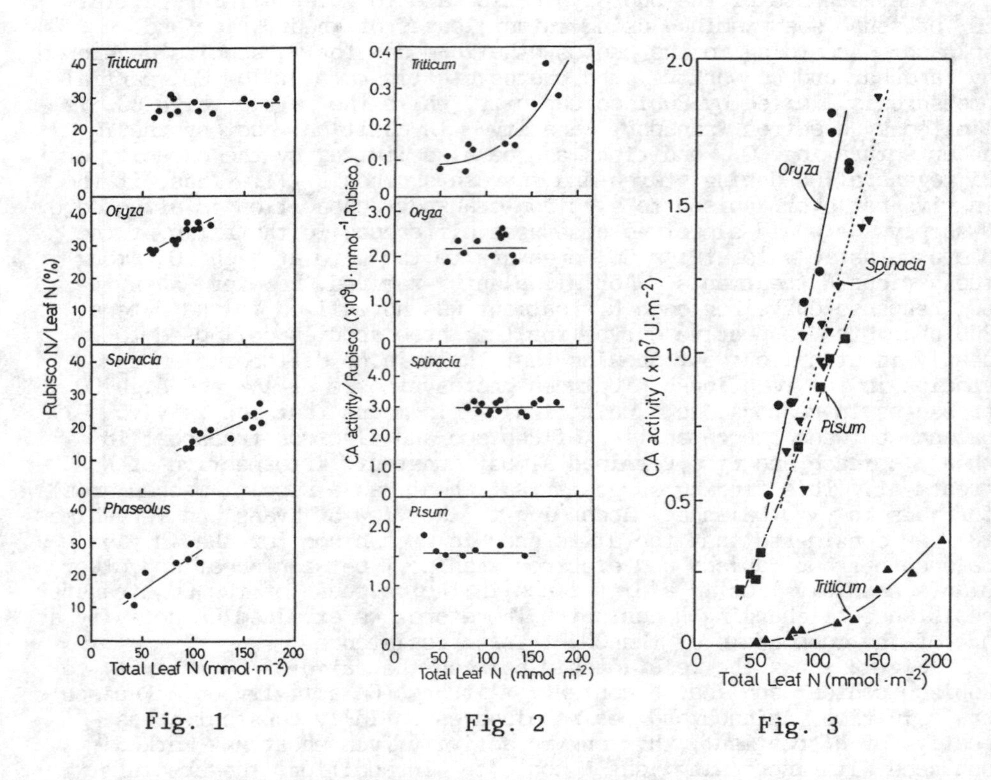

Fig. 1 Fig. 2 Fig. 3

Fig. 1 Ratio of Rubisco to total leaf-N *versus* total leaf-N content in fully expanded, young leaves of wheat, rice, spinach and bean.

Fig. 2 Ratio of CA activity to Rubisco content *versus* total leaf-N content in leaves of wheat, rice, spinach and pea.

Fig. 3 CA activity per unit leaf area *versus* total leaf-N content in leaves of wheat, rice, spinach and pea

References

1. Evans, J.R. (1983) Plant Physiol. 72, 297-302
2. Evans, J.R. (1989) Oecologia 78, 9-19
3. Evans, J.R. and Terashima, I. (1988) Plant Cell Physiol. 29, 157-165
4. Makino, A., Mae, T. and Ohira, K. (1988) Planta 174, 30-38
5. Makino, A. and Osmond, B. (1991) Plant Physiol. 96, 355-362
6. Makino, A. and Osmond, B. (1991) Photosynth. Res. 29, 79-85
7. Sharkey, T.D. (1985) Plant Physiol. 78, 71-75
8. von Caemmerer, S. and Evans, J.R. (1991) Aust. J. Plant Physiol. 18, 287-305

THE EFFECT OF LOW TEMPERATURES ON THE OPERATION OF PHOTOSYNTHESIS IN SAINTPAULIA IONANTHA (African Violet) LEAVES

JEREMY HARBINSON and PIETER VAN VLIET, ATO-DLO, P.O. Box 17, 6700 AA WAGENINGEN, THE NETHERLANDS

Saintpaulia ionantha is a tropical lowland herb found on the coastal plain around Tanga, Tanzania. It grows in shaded habitats in an area where the mean screen minimum temperature of the coldest month is only 20°C (1). The cultivars derived from this species are therefore, not susprisingly, very chilling sensitive. This is a brief report of the effects of a comparatively mild chilling treatment on the photosynthesis of these plants.

MATERIALS AND METHODS

All plants used were of Saintpaulia ionantha Fischer's Ballet 'Vivien'. Each measurement cycle lasted two days. During the first day the irradiance response of CO_2 fixation and the quantum efficiencies of photosystems I and II were measured in a leaf in a gaseous phase of either 2% O_2, 360ppm CO_2, remainder N_2, or 20% O_2, 360 ppm CO_2, remainder N_2, and at a temperature at 23°C. Overnight the whole plant was chilled at 8°-9°C in darkness for 14 h, and the next day the photosynthesis of the chilled leaf was measured again. The equipment and techniques used to make these measurements are described in Foyer et al (2) and Harbinson and Foyer (3) (and references therein).

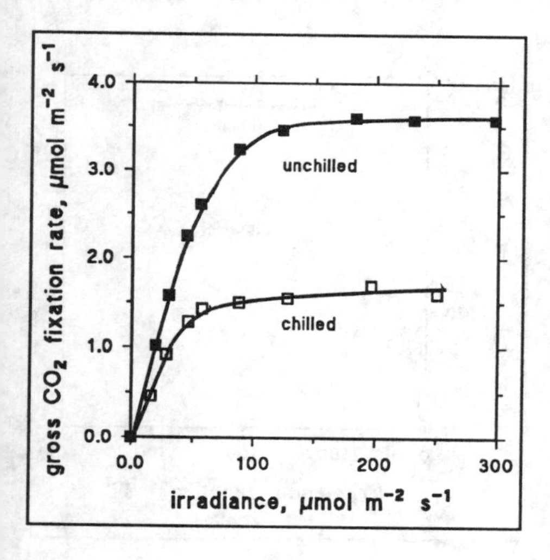

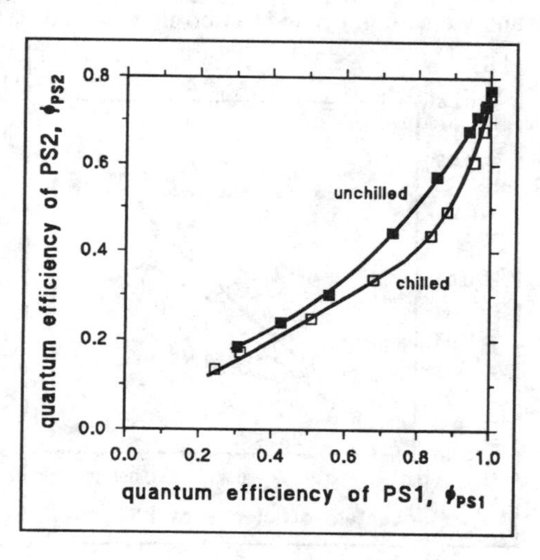

Fig. 1 (left)
The response of gross CO_2 fixation to irradiance in a leaf of Saintpaulia ionantha before and after chilling. Photosynthesis was measured at 23 °C in a gaseous phase of 360 ppm CO_2, 2% O_2, remainder N_2, and the leaf was chilled at 8 °C for 10 h in darkness in air.

Fig. 2 (right)

N. Murata (ed.), Research in Photosynthesis, Vol. IV, 659–662.

The relationship between ϕ_{PSI} and ϕ_{PSII} for the same leaf of Saintpaulia ionantha as in fig. 1. Measurements of ϕ_{PSI} and ϕ_{PSII} were made at progressively higher irradiances both before and after chilling.

RESULTS AND DISCUSSION

The consequences of chilling on CO_2 fixation, measured in a 2% O_2 atmosphere to suppress photorespiration, are shown in fig. 1. Two things are apparent; firstly, chilling can produce a large decrease in the light saturated rate of CO_2 fixation, in this case by over 50%; secondly, the limiting quantum efficiency of CO_2 fixation also declines following chilling. Measurements of c_i showed no fall after chilling, nor did leaf chlorophyll concentration decline. This implies that whatever produces the effect on the maximum rate of CO_2 fixation it is not due to stomatal resistance, nor is a fall in light absorption by the leaf responsible for the fall of photosynthetic quantum yield.

The relationship between ϕ_{PSI} and ϕ_{PSII} (fig. 2) shows three important points. The ϕ_{PSII}/ϕ_{PSI} is clearly significantly curvilinear for these leaves. In most previous studies (4, 5) the relationships between ϕ_{PSI} and ϕ_{PSII} were linear, implying a predominant role for linear electron transport. Other studies (2, and unpublished observations) suggest that curvilinear relationships between ϕ_{PSI} and ϕ_{PSII} of the kind shown here are due to the existence of significant cyclic electron flow about PSI; this is the first time that such a curvilinear relationship has been observed in a leaf with open stomata in air. Secondly, chilling in the dark does not significantly reduce the maximum dark adapted ϕ_{PSII}, so the fall in the limiting CO_2 quantum yield (fig. 1) is not due to a fall in the maximum value of ϕ_{PSII}. Lastly, following chilling the ϕ_{PSII}/ϕ_{PSI} relationship is more curvilinear than before; this may imply and increase in cyclic electron flow around PSI.

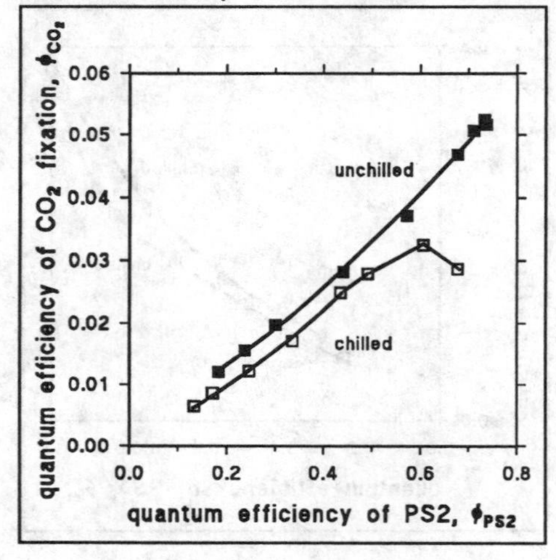

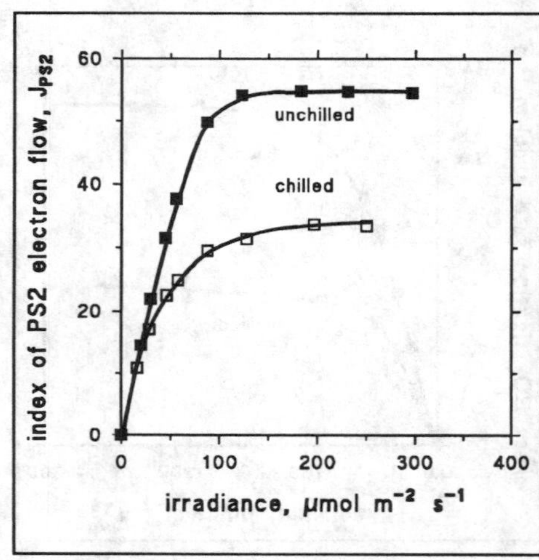

Fig. 3 (left)
The relationship between the index of electron flow through PSII (ϕ_{PSII} x irradiance) and irradiance for the Saintpaulia ionantha leaf used in figs. 1 and 2.

Fig. 4 (right)
As for the previous figures but showing the relationship between the quantum efficiency of CO_2 fixation at each irradiance and the quantum efficiency of PSII. Measurements were made before and after chilling.

The product of ϕ_{PSII} and irradiance provides an index for electron flow through PSII, J_{PSII}. This is not a calibrated measure of PSII electron flow but it is, based on certain reasonable assumptions, linearly related to PSII electron flow. The relationships between J_{PSII} and irradiance before and after chilling (fig. 3) are superficially similar to those between CO_2 fixation and irradiance (fig 1). Following chilling the maximum J_{PSII} declines, but the decline is not so great as the fall in the maximum rate of CO_2 fixation. The reason for this can be seen in fig. 4 which shows the relationship between ϕ_{PSII} and ϕ_{CO2}. After chilling it is clear that the ϕ_{PSII}/ϕ_{CO2} relationship has shifted to lower values of ϕ_{CO2}; this effect is particularly conspicuous at high efficiences (low irradiances) where ϕ_{CO2} seems to be largely decoupled from ϕ_{PSII}. The shift in the relationship between ϕ_{CO2} and ϕ_{PSII} following chilling, taken together with the decline in the maximum values of J_{PSII} and CO_2 fixation, implies that after chilling CO_2 fixation is, in absolute terms, a less effective sink for reducing equivalents.
This decrease of the maximum J_{PSII} appears to be a controlled one, and may be connected with the greater curvature to ϕ_{PSII}/ϕ_{PSI} (fig. 2) relationship after chilling, which could be due to more cyclic electron transport about PSI. However the decline of J_{PSII} is less than that of the rate of CO_2 fixation, as is clear from fig. 4. This implies that proportionally CO_2 fixation is a less effective sink after chilling than before.

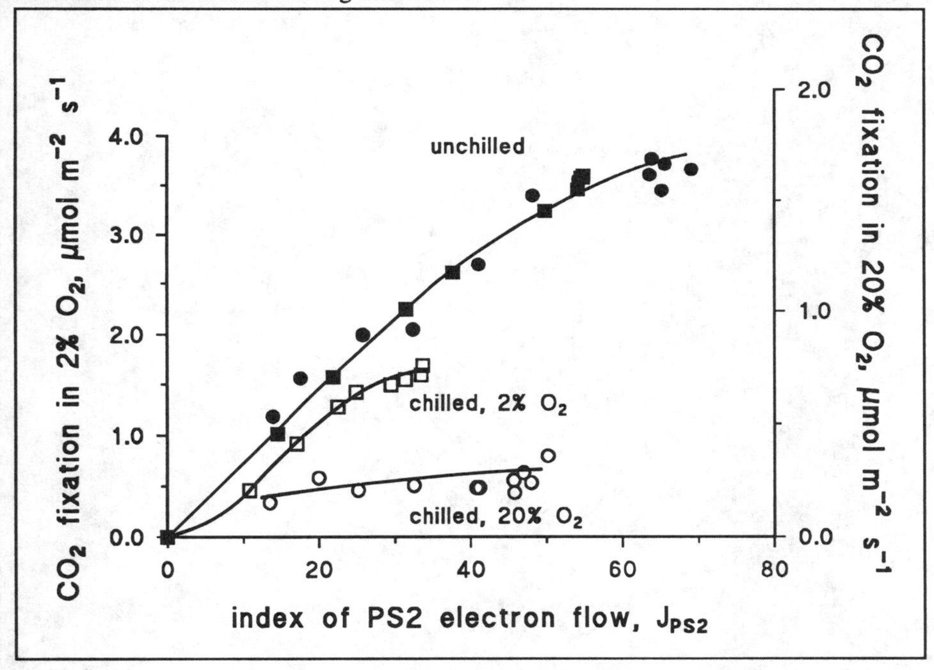

Fig. 5
The relationship between J_{PSII} and the rate of CO_2 fixation for two leaves of Saintpaulia ionantha; one as used in figs. 1-4 and measured in a 2% O_2 gaseous phase (open and solid square symbols) before and after chilling, and the other a leaf measured in a 20% O_2 gaseous phase (open and solid circles) but chilled identically. The scales of the ordinates have been adjusted to superimpose the data obtained from both leaves before chilling.

For a leaf in air photorespiration acts as a significant sink for reducing equivalents, and the effectiveness of this sink activity can change with irradiance. Figure 5 shows the relationships between J_{PSII} and the rate of CO_2 fixation for leaves measured in either 2% O_2,

360 ppm CO_2 and remainder N_2, or 20% O_2, 360 ppm CO_2 and remainder N_2, and before and after chilling. Note that the CO_2 fixation rate scales on the ordinates of this figure have been adjusted to superimpose the paths of the J_{PSII} - CO_2 fixation relationships before chilling. It is evident that following chilling the decline of the rate of CO_2 fixation, in terms of J_{PSII}, is greater under photorespiratory conditions than under nonphotorespiratory conditions. It appears that photorespiration can act as a 'dump' for reducing equivalents (as has been alluded to previously) (5). However as c_i was relatively unaffected by chilling it is not yet clear how this shift to relatively greater photorespiration occurs.

REFERENCES

1 Johansson, D.R. (1978) Biol. Conserv. 14, 45-62
2 Foyer, C., Lelandais, M. and Harbinson, J. (1992) Plant Physiol. 99, 979-986
3 Harbinson, J. and Foyer, C. (1991) Plant Physiol. 97, 41-49
4 Harbinson, J., Genty, B. and Baker, N.R. (1989) Plant Physiol. 90, 1029-1034
5 Harbinson, J., Genty, B. and Baker, N.R. (1990) Photosynth. Res. 25, 213-224

PHOTOSYNTHETIC RESPONSE TO CO_2 CONCENTRATION AND LIGHT INTENSITY IN MUNGBEAN (*VIGNA RADIATA* (L.) WILCZEK) LEAVES WITH AND WITHOUT EPIDERMIS.

MUHAMMAD TAJUL ISLAM[1], FUMITAKE KUBOTA[1], WAICHI AGATA[1] AND ABDUL HAMID[2], PRACTICAL BOTANY LAB., FACULTY OF AGRICULTURE, KYUSHU UNIVERSITY[1], HAKOZAKI, HIGASHI-KU, FUKUOKA 812, JAPAN AND INSTITUTE OF POSTGRADUATE STUDIES IN AGRICULTURE[2], SALNA, GAZIPUR 1703, BANGLADESH.

INTRODUCTION

Carbon dioxide exchange rate (CER) is regulated by two main factors, stomatal opening and enzymatic activity related to CO_2 fixation. Of environmental factors which play significant roles in the regulation of stomatal opening, light and CO_2 concentration are taken up as highly influential factors. Boyer (1) stated that plants grown in natural conditions were often prevented from expressing their full genetic potential of photosynthesis. CER determined in the absence of stomatal limitations is regarded as a way to know photosynthetic potential of the plant. Stomata can be removed by peeling off the epidermis of leaf. Few reports (2,3,4) are available on the epidermis peeling effect on photosynthetic characteristics, but none of them is on mungbean. This study was carried out with mungbean leaves to evaluate the influence of abaxial epidermis peeling on the photosynthetic characteristics and elucidate the photosynthetic potential without CO_2 gas exchange limitations at variable light intensities and CO_2 concentrations.

MATERIALS AND METHODS

Mungbean seeds (cultivar Chinese) were sown in 8 L pots in early April, 1992. Each pot contained sandy loam soil mixed with 5 g of compound chemical fertilizer (N:P:K=16:16:16). The plants were grown in a glass house with 30/22 C of day/night temperature. Terminal leaflets of the 3rd trifoliate leaves (fully expanded) were used for measurements. Data collection started 40 days after emergence of seed. N (Normal leaf), Fl (the adaxial surface of leaf was covered with transparent plastic film) and Pl (the adaxial surface was covered with film and the abaxial

N. Murata (ed.), Research in Photosynthesis, Vol. IV, 663–666.

epidermis was peeled) were subjected to different light intensities (PAR) of 0 to 3,000 $\mu Em^{-2}s^{-1}$ and CO_2 concentrations of 350 to 2,700 ppm to determine photosynthesis (Pn), transpiration rate (Tr) and related parameters. The transparent film was used to prevent gas exchange through adaxial surface allowing gas exchange through abaxial surface only. Abaxial epidermis was peeled by a technique described by Kubota et al.(4). The peeled area was a little more than the measurement area (6.25 cm^2) of a assimilation chamber used. A slide projector (Master Hilux-Zoom 300) with halogen lamp (1,000W) was used to create differential light intensities. Measurements of CER and Tr were made by a portable photosynthesis apparatus (SPB-H3, ADC).

RESULTS AND DISCUSSION

The leaves selected with low stomatal conductance had a Gs of 0.06 $molm^{-2}s^{-1}$ in N (Table 1); whereas Gs of leaves with normal conductance rate was over two-fold of the above value. Mesophyll conductance (Gm) had a similar trend observed in Gs. Gs and Gm in Fl were reduced by the restriction of gas exchange through the adaxial surface. The removal of abaxial epidermis increased both Gs and Gm of leaves with low and normal conductances. At 850 $\mu Em^{-2}s^{-1}$ PAR and 360 ppm CO_2, epidermis peeling resulted in 52% increase of Pn in leaves with low Gs; while for leaves with normal stomatal opening, the increase in Pn by epidermis peeling was only 2% (Table 1). This suggests that Pn was greatly reduced by stomatal restriction but photosynthetic potential of mesophyll kept a relatively high level even if the stomata were closed. Increase in Pn by epidermis peeling has also been reported on leaves of *Ipomoea batatas* Lam. in previous papers(4,5).

TABLE 1. Photosynthetic rates of leaves with low and normal stomatal conductances under peeled and unpeeled conditions.

	Low Gs			Normal Gs		
	N	Fl	Pl	N	Fl	Pl
Pn	4.9	0.2	10.3	11.5	7.9	11.7
Gs	60	5	330	150	120	370
Gm	22	7	38	42	30	449
Ci	221.6	280.5	272.3	225.1	230.1	261.4

Measurements were made at 850$\mu Em^{-2}s^{-1}$ light intensity and 360 ppm CO_2 concentration. Pn, photosynthetic rate ($\mu mol\ m^{-2}s^{-1}$);Gs, stomatal conductance ($mmolm^{-2}s^{-1}$).

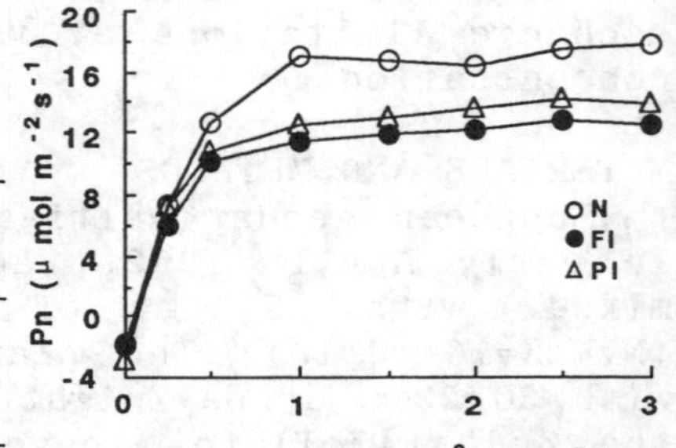

FIGURE 1. Light response of photosynthetic rates (Pn) of peeled and unpeeled leaves.

Effects of light intensity on Pn in N, Fl and Pl were investigated using a leaf with fully open stomata (Fig.1). Light saturation points were detected around 1,000 $\mu Em^{-2}s^{-1}$ in common. Pn of N was higher than those of Fl and Pl. Pn in N, Fl and Pl increased curvilinearly with increasing PAR above 250 $\mu Em^{-2}s^{-1}$ but below 250 $\mu Em^{-2}s^{-1}$ measurable effects of peeling on Pn were not found. This is because the initial slope in the light photosynthetic response curve is not dependent on stomatal aperture but mainly dependent on the photochemical reaction. Photochemical reaction is assumed to be unchangeable by peeling (4,5). Dark respiration was the highest (-2.89 $\mu mol\ m^{-2}\ s^{-1}$) in Pl.

Fig. 2 shows the influence of PAR on Tr. In N and Fl Tr increased with increase in PAR, while the variation in Pl was little.

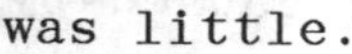

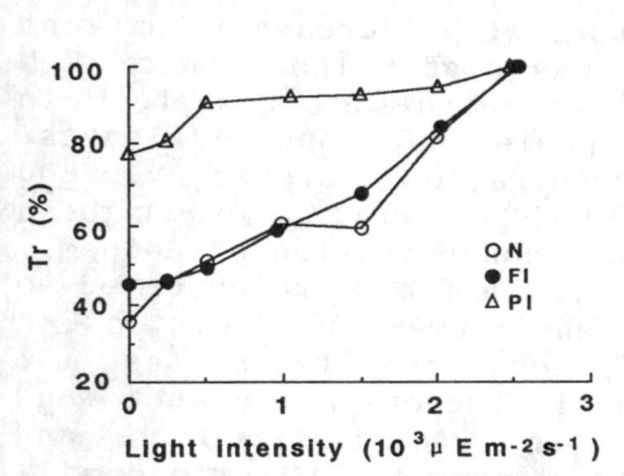

FIGURE 2. Transpiration rates (Tr) of peeled and unpeeled leaves at variable light intensities.

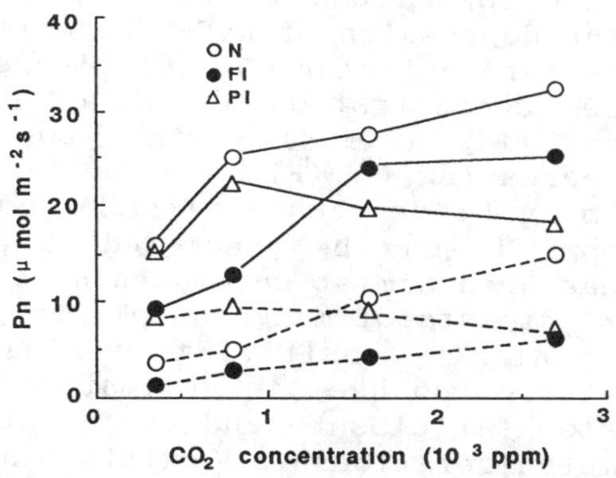

FIGURE 3. Photosynthetic rates (Pn) of peeled and unpeeled leaves at different CO_2 concentrations in day (——) and night (----).

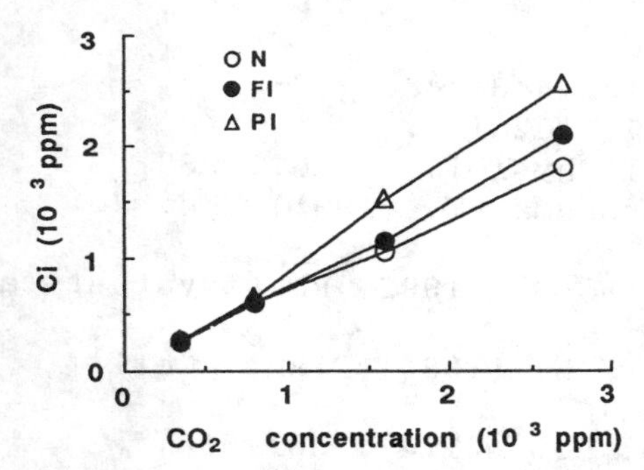

FIGURE 4. Intercellular CO_2 concentration (Ci) of peeled and unpeeled leaves at differrent ambient CO_2 concentrations.

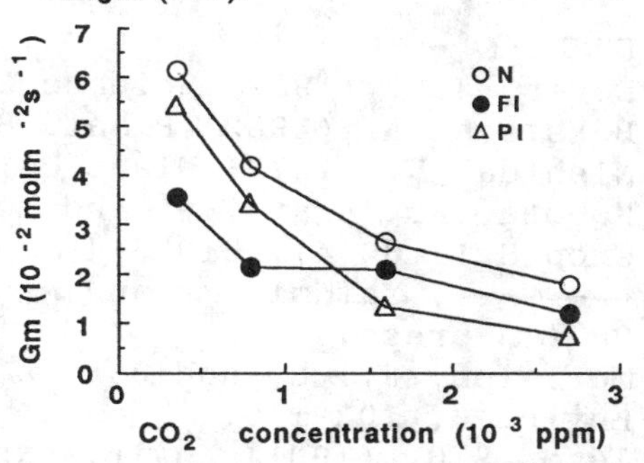

FIGURE 5. Effect of CO_2 concentrations on the mesophyll conductance (Gm) of peeled and unpeeled leaves.

Fig. 3 represents effects of CO_2 concentrations on Pn during day and night. It was observed that increase in CO_2 concentrations resulted in curvilinear increase of Pn in both N and Fl. Increase in Pn and concomitant decrease in stomatal conductance with CO_2 concentration increase were reported by Morision and Jarvis (6) and Idso (7). Pn increased with CO_2 concentration increase in N and Fl, but in Pl the highest Pn was found at 800 ppm in both day and night measurements. This might be due to some adverse effects of excessively high concentration of CO_2 on the enzymatic activity. Pn at night was remarkably low in N and Fl compared to the day measurements because of stomata closure. High CO_2 concentration and epidermis peeling were effective on Pn at night as well, but the levels of Pn were much lower than those of day time. This might be caused by the depression of RuBPCase activity at night.

Intercellular CO_2 (Ci) increased with increase in ambient CO_2 concentration and Ci of Pl was higher than those of N and Fl (Fig.4). High CO_2 concentration resulted in decreasing Gm (Fig. 5) in both peeled and unpeeled leaves. Gm in Pl decreased with CO_2 concentration increase over 800 ppm. It may be predicted that RuBPCase action in mungbean has been almost saturated at a CO_2 concentration of 800ppm.

Stomata of mungbean plants grown in field are observed to be highly sensitive to various environmental conditions. A little change in climatic factors readily causes the stomatal closure and photosynthetic reduction. To know what mutualrelationship exists between stomatal action and photosynthetic potential without stomatal limitations will be taken up as a physiological subject in the project of the improvement of mungbean productivity and photosynthesis.

REFERENCES

1. Boyer, J.S. (1982) Science 218, 443-448.
2. Berstsch, A. (1969) Planta 87, 102-109.
3. Nishida, K. (1977) Plant Cell Physiol. 18, 627-930.
4. Kubota, F., Agata, W. and Morokuma, M. (1991) Jpn. J. Crop Sci. 60(4), 510-514.
5. ————, Yatomi, M. and Agata, W. (1992) Photosynthetica 26 (in press).
6. Morision, J.I.L. and Jarvis, P.G. (1983) Plant, Cell Envir. 6, 103-109.
7. Idso, S.B. (1991) Envir. exp. Bot. 31(4), 381-383.

EFFECTS OF INTERMITTENT ILLUMINATIONS ON PHOTOSYNTHESIS IN SWEET POTATO (*IPOMOEA BATATAS* LAM.) LEAF.

KAZUYOSHI NADA, FUMITAKE KUBOTA AND WAICHI AGATA, FACULTY OF AGRICULTURE, KYUSHU UNIVERSITY, HAKOZAKI, HIGASHI-KU, FUKUOKA, 812, JAPAN.

INTRODUCTION

Light environment for the photosynthesis of plants grown under the natural conditions always fluctuates in various ways. For the purpose of elucidating the photosynthetic state in light fluctuations, CO_2 exchange rates and biochemical responses to intermittent illuminations with short light and dark intervals have been studied so far. It has been described that the light utilization efficiency of photosynthesis is often enhanced by intermittent illuminations (4,5,6). The efficiency is also varied with light/dark intervals, light intensities and light preconditionings on leaf (1,2). In this study the balance between energy supply from photosystem and energy consumption in CO_2 fixation have been varied by changing light/dark intervals, light intensity and CO_2 concentration,and its effects on stomatal aperture, CO_2 exchange rate and light utilization efficiency have been analyzed using a leaf of *Ipomoea batatas* Lam.

MATERIAL AND METHOD

Ipomoea batatas Lam. plants, cv. Koganesengan grown in pots under full sunlight and heavy shade (20% in relative light intensity) was used as an experiment materials. CO_2 exchange rates (CER) were measured on young expanded leaf ($6.2 cm^2$) by a portable CO_2 assimilation and transpiration measurement system (ADC;model SPB-H3). As a light source a slide projector (1,000w, halogen lamp) was used. Intermittent illuminations with short light/ dark repeating intervals were created by intercepting the beam from projector to leaf by a motor-driven rotating disk (Fig.1). The disk was 28cm in diameter and partially opened to allow light to pass through. Light/dark ratios of disks ranged from 20:3 to 3:20. Rotating speed was controlled by changing voltage with a variable resistor and measured with a rotating meter. Light time and dark time were changed by rotating speed and light dark ratio of disk. Higher CO_2

FIGURE 1. Intermittent illumination system.

N. Murata (ed.), Research in Photosynthesis, Vol. IV, 667–670.

concentration was obtained by mixing N_2 gas including 1.5% CO_2 with the atmospheric air and CO_2 concentration was reduced by CO_2 absorbent (sodalime).

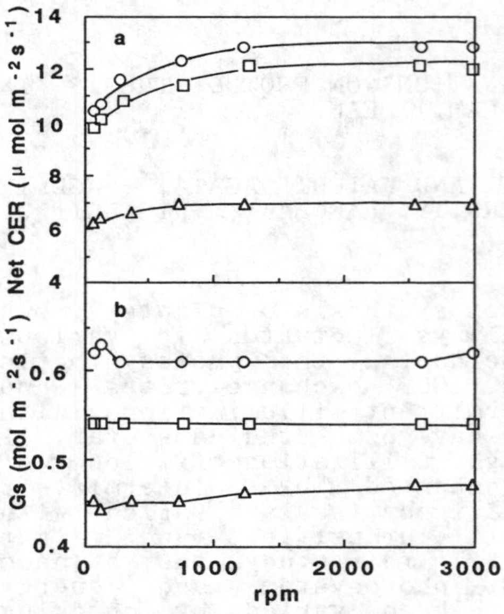

FIGURE 2. Change in CER (a) and Gs (b) with rotating speed (Light / dark ratio =1:1) at different light intensities, 3,860 (○), 2,940 (□) and 1,930 (△) μ mol m^{-2} s^{-1}.

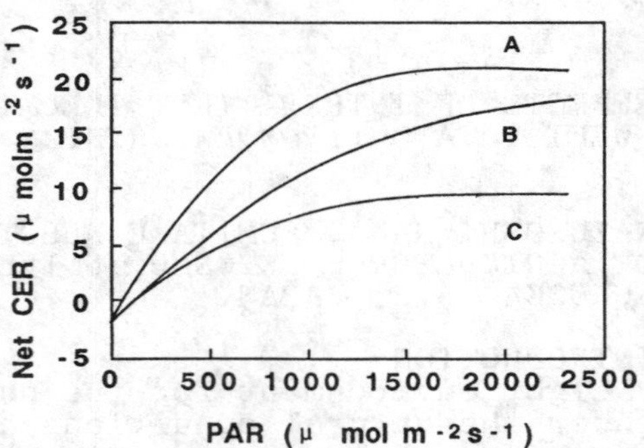

FIGURE 3. Response of CER under continuous illuminations (A), intermittent illuminations (light/dark ratio = 1:1) (B). C is a calculated value (C = A/2).

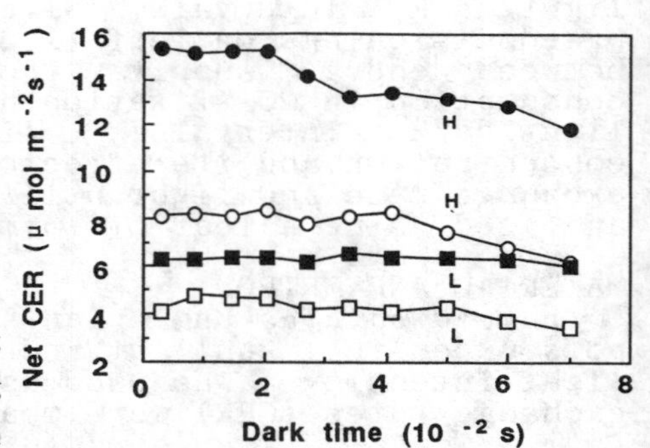

FIGURE 4. Changes in CER of sun-leaf (●, ■) and shade-leaf (○, □) with dark time at different light intensities,660 (H) and 240 μ mol m^{-2} s^{-1} (L).

RESULT AND DISCUSSION

CER at a constant light intensity increased with increase in rotating speed of disk and reached a stable level at 700 to 1200 rpm (Fig. 2, a). During this treatment no change were found in the stomatal conductance (Fig. 2, b). This indicated that the increase of CER was not caused by stomatal openings but depended solely on the shortening of light/dark alternating intervals with rotation speed increase. CERs were measured at intermittent illuminations with light/dark = 1/1 at rotating speeds over 700 rpm and compared with those measured at continuous illumination (Fig.3). CER at this intermittentillumination exceeded the value of 50 % of CER at continuous illumination. The intermittent illumination was effective in increasing the light utilization efficiency (LUE) in photosynthesis. It is

TABLE 1. Arrangement of leaf-received light intensity by chaging the combination of disk type and light intensity.

Disk type	LT	DT	SR
1/0.148	20	2.96	0.328
1/0.414	20	8.28	0.404
1/0.733	20	14.65	0.495
1/1.027	20	20.53	0.579
1/1.349	20	26.97	0.671
1/1.692	20	33.83	0.769
1/2.052	20	41.04	0.872
1/2.500	20	50.00	1.000
1/3.000	20	60.00	1.140
1/3.500	20	70.00	1.280

Disk type, Light/dark ratio of disk; LT, Light time (10^{-3}s); DT, Dark time (10^{-3}s); SR, Shading ratio (1.00= no shade). LT was constant (0.02 s) and DT was variable from 0.00296s to 0.07s in this experiment.
Leaf-received light intensity (LL) was caluculated by the equation (2).

$$SR \cdot LT/ (LT+DT) = 0.2857 \quad (1)$$

$$LL = 0.2857 \cdot SL \quad (2)$$

SL, Supplied light intensity .

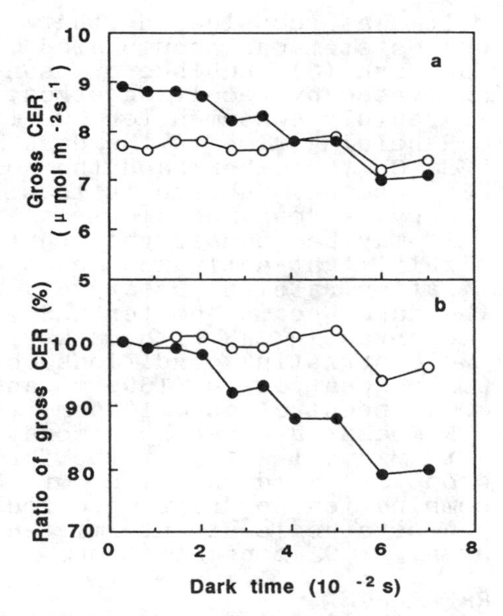

FIGURE 5. Changes in gross CER (a) and the ratio (b) of sun-leaf with dark time at low CO_2 concentrations (160 ppm) and high light intensity (780 μ mol m^{-2} s^{-1}) (●) and at high CO_2 concentrations (2100 ppm) and low light intensity (170 μ mol m^{-2} s^{-1}) (○).

suggested that the enhanced LUE in photosynthesis at intermittent illuminations is caused by the post-illumination carboxylation which is supported by using a stored light energy in photosystem (3,5).

Responses of CER to intermittent illuminations were compared between sun- and shade-leaves (Fig.4). Light energy per unit time (LES) under intermittent illuminations was adjusted to constant by changing the combination of light intensity (PAR) and light/ dark ratio of rotating disk (Table 1). CER changed with dark time. In short dark time CER did not drop but began to gradually decrease when the dark time was over a certain length. At high LES (660μmol m^{-2}s^{-1}) CER of sun-leaf held at a maximal level within a dark time below 0.02s. While at low LES (240μmol m^{-2}s^{-1}) CER was low but held a constant level up to 0.07s in the dark, several times longer than that of high light intensity. In shade-leaves CER holding time in the dark was 0.04s at high LES and 0.05s at low LES.

It was considered that a part of light energy in photosystem was accumulated , and used for CO_2 fixation in the dark (3). Rubisco of sun-leaf may be highly light-activated by receiving strong light and the pooled energy is rapidly consumed for CO_2 fixation in the dark. Therefore CER holding time in the dark may become shorter at high LES. On the other hand the holding time was longer at low LES, because Rubisco is less light-activated and the pooled energy is consumed slowly.

It may be considered that in shade-leaf Rubisco was highly light-activazed even at low LES, by which CO_2 fixation rate was relatively high and CER holding time in the dark became shorter LES.

Changes in CER with dark time were investigated under the two contrasting conditions, high LES (780μmolm^{-2}s^{-1})+ low CO_2 concentration (160ppm) and low LES (167μmolm^{-2}s^{-1}) high CO_2 concentration (2100ppm) (Fig.5 a,b). Maximum values of CER measured under both conditions were almost same levels, 8 to 9 μmolm^{-2}s^{-1}. At the former combination CER began to drop at a dark time of 0.02s. While at the latter combination no drops were found in CER up to 0.05s. LUE in photosynthesis at intermittent illuminations was enhanced by high CO_2 concentration.

REFERENCE

1 Chazdon,R.L. and Pearcy,R.W. (1986) Oecologia 69,517-523
2 Chazdon,R.L. and Pearcy,R.W. (1986) Oecologia 69,524-531
3 Kirschbaum,M.U.F. and Pearcy,R.W. (1988) Planta 174,527-533
4 Kriedemann,P.E.,Törökfalvy,E. and Smart,R.E. (1973) Photosynthetica 7,18-27.
5 Pearcy,R.W.,Osteryoung,K. and Calkin,H.W. (1985) Plant Physiol. 79,896-902
6 Pollard,D.F.W. (1970) Can.J.Bot.48,823-829

STUDY ON THE PHOTOSYNTHETIC CHARACTERISTICS OF CROP IN SHELTERBELT NETWORK

Northeast Forestry University, Harbin , China

Chen Jie , Wang Wenzhang , Zhang Baoyou, Wang Yitao , Feng Yulong

1. INTRODUCTION

Shelterbelt has become one of the effective measures to increase crop output and improve its quality by improving farmland ecological environment and protecting crops from natural disaster. Although there are quite a few reports on this, the extent and mechanism of the influence of various shelterbelt systems in different regions are still in need for a further study.

From 1986 to 1990, the physiological and ecological indices, such as photosynthesis, of corn growing inside the shelterbelt network were measured in semi–arid windy and dusty grassland region. The relationship between photosynthetic characteristics and corn output, crop grain quality, and the mechanism of increasement had been expounded. The theoritical basis for the reasonable construction of sheterbelt and the scientific evaluation of agricultural and ecological effects of shelterbelt network system had been founded.

2. MATERIALS AND METHODS

The main research crop was corn–one of the staple crops in northeastern China . The research areas of Zhaozhou County , Daqing City, and Zhaodong County were located in the western part of Heilongjiang province, all of those areas belong to the temperate region with the semi–moist continental monsoon climate. The tree species of shelterbelt is Popular (Populus pseudosimonii) with an average height of 10–14m. Inside the shelterbelt network, plots were set up at 1, 5, 10, 15, 20, and 25 times the tree height (H), and the control plot was located in an open area. A series of observations and measurements were made with Beckman Model–865 CO_2 infrared analyzer and many other physiological and ecological instruments.

3. RESULTS AND DISCUSSION

3.1 Photosynthetic charateristics of corn under the influence of shelterbelt network.

The shelterbelt has a benefitial influence on corn photosynthesis and leads to a great change in photosynthetic rate and in daily and seasonal process of photosynthesis. The photosynthetic rate of corn was higher measured at 10H、15H and 5H, and lower at 20H and 1H in the shelterbelt network in Daqing area in June of 1988. Also the photosynthetic rate of corn was highest measured at 10H in the shelterbelt network in Zhao zhou area in July , 1987. The "noon nap" phenomenon was alleviated or dispelled. This made corn accumulate suf–

N. Murata (ed.), Research in Photosynthesis, Vol. IV, 671–674.

ficient photosynthetic products for grain maturing. The daily photosynthetic process of corn was bipeak curve form in the control plot outside the shelterbelt network, with an apparent"noon nap"and a low photosynthetic rate.

During the whole growing season, the seasonal photosynthetic process of corn shows a monopeak curve form and the peak point occurs at the end of July.The photosynthetic assimilation of corn at different plots within the shelterbelt network has a similar seasonal process, but the photosynthetic rate of corn community was the highest at 10H and decreased from this point to the two other sides.The size of the shelterbelt network has also an influence on the corn photosynthetic rate.The size of $500 \times 500 m^2$ is better than $460 \times 160 m^2$.

Shelterbelt has a benefit influnce on corn photosynthesis.It can raise the potential capacity of photosynthesis and utilization of sun energy.This can be seen by the increasement of production, especially in the situation of drought, strong wind and frost

3.2 The physiological and ecological influence on corn photosynthesis

The length and width of corn leaf are longer and broader measured at 5H and 10H plots than those at the control plot. The maximum leaf index of corn inside the shelterbelt network during the growing season appeared earlier with a long stable period .This can slow down the scenessence and increase the utilization of solar energy.

Before the end of corn jointing stage the leaves grow quite fast, and at this time the increasement of leaf–area is the main factor to determine the productivity in shelterbelt network.After the cron jointing stage the growth rate of corn leaves are gradually slow down. At this time the leaf– area in different places in the shelterbelt network has an evident influnce on the corn productivity.After the wax–mature period, the corn leaves become aged , but the photosynthetic rate of the green corn leaves after frost is still a little bit incrcase.

Other physiological function of corn at different plots inside the shelterbelt network changed correspondingly (Table 1) . There are a more reasonable chlorophyll content, a more optimum water state, a lower transpiration, and a higher respiration at 10H plot than those outside the shelterbelt network. All of those are benefitial to the corn photosynthesis.

Table1 physiological characteristics of corn in shelterbelt networks

physiological characteristics	1H	5H	10H	15H	20H
chlorophyll content (mg / g)	1.91	2.08	2.31	1.81	1.93
relative turgor (%)	84.1	85.2	91.2	89.1	86.9
water saturation deficit (%)	15.9	14.8	8.8	10.9	13.1
max.nct photosynthetic rate ($mg \cdot co_2 / m^2 / s$)	0.6972	0.8139	0.8589	0.7806	0.7361

A close possitive correlation existed between corn photosynthesis and air temperature, light intensity, and air humidity. The results of measurement and analysis show that the short time and daily photosynthesis of corn are positively related to air temperature and relative humidity. The regression curve shows that the daily photosynthetic production rises along with the increasement of air temperature and relative humidity, although the rate of increasement is gradually slow. So that the sunlight , air temperature and relative humidity in different shelterbelt network area have different influnce on corn photosynthetic rate and production. During the whole growth period, the corn individals growing at 1H area have a low grain production and quality limited by the low daily air temperature and relative humidity at that area. At the 5H and 10H area, the photosynthetic rate of corn is high and there is no "noon nap"because of the higher sunlight, air temperature and relative humidity. At the 15H and 20H area there are a higher air temperature, but a lower relative humidity; and at the 25H area there are a lower air temperature and a higher relative humidity. So at those area of 15H, 20H and 25H, the daily photosynthetic rate and production of corn are higher than those at 1H area, but lower than those at 5H and 10H area. The photosynthic characteristics of corn can be forecast by the microclimate in the shelterbelt network. Based on this we can take some means to regulate and control environment factors to increase corn production. Water status can become a limiting factor for corn photosynthesis under some given situation, but the main influencing factors changed with the different growth stage of corn. Shelterbelt was benefiteial to the efficient utilization of soil water. Meanwhile, the vertical change of CO_2 concentration inside shelterbelt network was benefit to the photosynthesis of corn, especially in July and August.

3.3 The influence of shelterbelt network on the output and quality of corn

The photosynthetic rate, output, and grain quality of corn increased with the better change of climate and soil improved by the shelterbelt network. The output of corn was highest at 5H, 10H, and 15H plots, where are the optimum protective areas of shelterbelt network. The mean biomass of corn inside $500 \times 500 m^2$ shelterbelt network increased by 3.3%, and output increased by 16.1%.

The decreasement of corn production at 1H area is influnced by the shelterbelt. The shade and the water absoption of tree roots created by shelterbelt are both unbenefit to the corn growth at this area . In addition, a severe frost and a relatively short growth period of leaves also influnce the corn growth and production at 1H area . The unbenefit influnce of shelterbelt to corn growth is limited within 1H.

The similar results were obtained about the content of starch, protein, fat (Fig.3), amino acids (lysine and tryptophan), and vitamins (V_{B1}, V_{B2}, V_{PP}) . The total content of the three chief types of organic substance increased by about 5.5%.

In one word, the influence of shelterbelt on the physiological and ecological characteristics of corn is benefitial and effective.

REFERENCES

1 We L., Jiang Ai.L., Song Zh.M. (1981), The relationship between output and microclimate factors in forest net. For Sci.2, 155−161

2 Han F.Sh., Zhao M., Zhao S.Sh, (1987), The study of the causes of "noon nap"of wheat. Ⅱ. The relationship between physiological factors

and "noon nap". Acta crop sinica 13 (4), 330–334

3 Boardman, N.K., (1977) .Comparative photosynthesis of sun and shade plants. Ann. Rev. Plant Physiol 28.355–377

4 Cao X.S., (1983) .Shelterbelt, Chinese forest press, Peking, China.

STUDY ON THE PHOTOSYNTHETIC CHARACTERISTICS AND THE PRIMARY PRODUCTIVITY OF LARIX OLGENSIS

Northeast Forestry University, Harbin, China

Wang Wenzhang Chen Jie Zhang Baoyou Feng Yulong Wang Yitao

1. INTRODUCTION

The photosynthetic characteristics of Larix olgensis growing in different sites are studied in this paper. The net photosynthetic rate (Pn) is selected as the main index. The relationship between Pn, biomass and economic production has been found out, because Pn can be looked upon as the best expression of multiple environment.

There are many reports on the study of Larix biomass in the past, but there are few reports on the photosynthetic characteristics of Larix, The resrarh results can provide a theoretic base to the reasonable management of manmade forest resource and to the fundation of the management plan of man– made Larix forest ecosystem with high biomass, high productivity, resonable structure, perfect function, and high stability.

The experiments were conducted on three forest farms with different soil conditions, those forest farms are Erlongshan Forest Farm (with Baijiangized–black soil), Bin county; Maoershan Forest Farm (with Baijiang soil), Shangzhi County, and Harbin Forest Farm (with Black soil) in Heilongjiang province. The photosynthetic rates and the respiratory rates of Larix olgensis were measured with Beckman–865 Infrared Analyzer in different soil conditions. Meanwhile, the co_2 gradient distribution and the primary productivity of the Larix olgensis stands in different soil sites were also measured. The results show that the net photosynthetic rates and the respiratory rates of Larix olgensis are quite different in different sites.

2. MATERIALS AND METHODS

The experiment is conducted with the individals of Larix olgensis and Larix gmelini distributed in above three areas.

2.1 Photosynthesis and respiration are measured with Beckman–865 infrared CO_2 Analyzer.

2.2 Leaf area is measured with Li–3000 Easy to Carry leaf area Instrument

3 RESULTS AND DISCUSSION

The measerment results show that the net photosynthesis and respiration of Larix olgensis growing in different sites are quite different.

3.1 Erlongshan Forest Farm, Bin county

The average daily net photosynthetic rates of 14–Year–old Larix olgensis in east, south, west, and north crown direction are 0.1907, 0.2110, 0.2418, and 0.200 $mgco_2 \cdot m^{-2} \cdot s^{-1}$ respectively. The daily processes of net photosynthetic rates at different crown layers (upper, middle, and lower) in south direction all show a monopeak curve form. The respiratory rates in different crown layers (upper, middle, and lower) in south direction all show a monopeak curve form. The respiratory rates in different crown parts are lower than the net photosynthetic rates respectively, but the daily processes also show a monopeak curve form.

This is related to the sunlight density at that time. The net photosynthesis at the middle position is a little bit higher than those at the upper and lower position in south corwn side.

N. Murata (ed.), Research in Photosynthesis, Vol. IV, 675–678.

But the peak time ocurred differently in each crown side.
The daily net photosynthetic rates of 7—year—old Larix olgensis in four crown directions all show a bipeak curve form. The peaks appear at 9: 00 am and 3: 00 pm, and the depression appears at 1: 00 pm. The average daily net photosynthetic rates in east, south, west, and north crown direction are 0. 148, 0. 147, 0. 152, and 0. 1237 mg • m^{-2} • s^{-1} respectively. The net photosynthetic rate in west crown side is a bit higher than those in other three crown sides. The respiration rate in four crown directions show a bipeak curve form, but lower than the net photosynthetic rate.
The average net photosynthetic rates of Larix olgensis growing in the mixed coniferous stand were measured in June, August, and September; and the results are 0. 1886, 0.1989, and 0.1832 mg • m^{-2} • s^{-1} respectively. The measurment results can be seen in Table 1. The net photosynthetic rates are different in different growing season during the whole year. Three measurement results show that the net photosynthetic rate is highest in August, lower in June and September, especially for the different crown directions

Table 1 The net photosynthetic rate of Larix olgensis in different crown directions

time \ Net photosynthetic Rate mg • m^{-2} • s^{-1}	Eest	South	West	North	Average
June, 27	0.1141	0.1877	0.1553	0.2076	0.1886
Aug, 11	0.1300	0.2393	0.1391	0.2874	0.1989
Sept.20	0.1793	0.2065	0.1757	0.1714	0.1832

The net photosynthetic rate seasonal process of Larix olgensis
The net photosynthetic rate of 14—year—old Larix olgensis is measared monthly: the net photosynthetic rate of Larix olgensis is low measured on May 18, incrcases in july, reachs its highest is August with the meascrement result of 0.3604 mg • m^{-2} • s^{-1} and begins to decrease in September with the similar situation in May. This shows that the net photosynthetic rate seasonal change of Larix olgansis shows a monopeak curve form

3.2 Laoshan Ecological Experiment station, Maoershan Forest Farm

The seasonal process of the net photosynthetic rate of Larix olgensis shows a monopeak curve form. The peak point of 0.3604 mg • m^{-2} • s^{-1} appears in August, and the depression point appears on September 18.
Experiment results at Laoshan Ecological Experiment Station of Maoershan Forest Farm
The daily net photosynthetic rates of Larix olgensis in its mixed stand with Fraxinus mandshurica show a bipeak curve form. The average values in the east, south, west, and north crown directions are 0.2246, 0.214, 0.233 and 0.224 mg • m^{-2} • s^{-1} respectively. The values measured in its pure stand in the above four crown directions are 0.1578, 0.1719, 0. 1301, and 0. 1691 mg • m^{-2} • s^{-1} respectively. The results show that the daily net photosynthetic rate of Larix olgensis in its mixed stand (0.224mg • m^{-2} • s^{-1}) is 42.5% higher than that in its pure stand (0.1575 mg • m^{-2} • s^{-1}).
The daily net photosynthetic rates of Larix gmelini show a bipeak curve form both in different crown directions and in different crown layers. Its seasonal changes mensured in July, August, and September are 0.446, 0.1823, 0.1561 mg • m^{-2} • s^{-1} respectively.

3.3 Experment reaults on Harbin Forest Farm

The daily net photosynthetic rate of young Larix olgensis shows a bipeak curve form.The two peak points appear at 10.00 am.and 3.00 pm.The depression point appears at 1.00 pm. The daily net photosynthetic rates in the four crown directions (E, S, W, N) are 0.1945, 0.2322, 0.1852, and 0.1973 mg · m^{-2} · s^{-1} respectively.

The seasonal change of the net photosynthetic rate of Larix olgensis shows a monopeak curve form with the peak point on August 10.

4. Energy fixed in the stands with different structures and sites.

Based on the quantity of fixed energy and accumulated glucose the primary productivities were calculated for Larix olgensis in its pure stand, mixed coniferous stand, broad leaved coniferous stand and Larix gmelini in its pure stands distributed in different soil sites.The biomass and economic production at the early stage can be estimated by the primary productivities.This can provide a theoretical base for the reforestation with rapid growth and high yield, and for the scienfific management of artificial resources.

The results show that the highest fixed energy of Larix olgensis is 8.597 MJ · m^{-2} · h^{-1} in its mixed Fraxinus mandshurica stand (Maoershan Forost Farm) and in its pure stand (Harbin Forest farm); The middle value is 7.632 MJ · m^{-2} · h^{-1} in its mixed coniferous stand (Erlongshan Forest Farm); and the lowest is 6.023 MJ · m^{-2} · h^{-1} in its pure stand (Maoershan Forest Farm) .The reason is that the mixed broad–leaved coniferous stand has a abundant soil nutrient, a rich soil water, a high air humidity, and a low evaporation.For instance, the individals of Larix olgenois grow more rapidly in Black soil (Harbin forest Farm) with the abundent soil water and nutrient supply.The quantity of fixed energy of Larix olgensis (8.410 MJ · m^{-2} · h^{-1} is higher than that of Larix gmelini (6.177mj · m^{-2} · h^{-1}.This shows that, not only in theory, but also in practice, Larix olgensis grows much better than Larix gmelini (Fable 2)

Table2 **The Fixed Energy and Dextrose**

Foresttype Energy andDextrose	purestand Bigtree L.olgensis	L.gmelini	yougetree L.olgensis	Mixedstand youngtree L.olgensis	L.gmelini	Harbin Forest farm L.olgensis
Pn mg · m^2S^{-1}	0.2196	0.160	0.1572	0.210	0.244	0.2439
FixedEnergy mj · $m^{-2}s^{-1}$	8.410	6.117	6.023	7.632	8.597	8.597
FixedDextrose g · $m^{-2}s^{-1}$	6.6485	4.7423	4.630	6.1857	6.598	6.595
FixedDextrose t · ha–1yr^{-2}	19.513	14.306	18.063	24.135	25.74	25.73

Calculated either by fixed energy or by accumulated glucose, the energy quantity fixed by Larix olgensis is 42.5% higher in its broadleaved–coniferous stand and 33.61% higher in its mixed coniferous stand than that in its pure stand.The energy fixed by Larix olgensis is 36.39% higher than that by Larix gmelini.The primary productivity measured has a similar result with The biomass and economic production.

The results also show that different Larix olgensis stands have a different co_2 distribution. co_2 concentration is higher in the early morning, in the later afternoon, and at noon; and lower during the rest time of the day.The co_2 distribution in a tree crown shows that the concentration at upper and lower parts is higher than that at middle part, all of those are resulted from photosynthesis.

Conclusion

1. The net photosynthetic rate and the respiratory rate of Larix olgensis vary with different soil conditions, different crown directions, and different crown parts. The daily net photosynthetic rate represents a bipeak curve form.
2. The primary productivities of Larix olgensis vary with different sites .The highest primary productivity is 8.597 MJ · m^{-2} · h^{-1} in its pure stand (Harbin Forest Farm) and in its mixed stand (Maoershan Forest Farm); The middle is 7.632 MJ · m^{-2} · h^{-1} in its mixed coniferous stand (Erlongshan Forest Farm), and the lowest is 6.023 MJ · m^{-2} · h^{-1} in its pure stand (Maoershan Forest Farm) .
3. Different Larix species has differeat energy fixed ability.Larix olgensis can fix energy with 8.41 mj · m^{-2} · h^{-1} and Larx gmelini fix energy with 6.033 mj · m^{-2} · h^{-1}
4. The fixed energy of Larix in mixed forest is 8.597 mj · m^{-2} · h^{-1}, higher than that in pure stand of 6.023 mj · m^{-2} · h^{-1}
5. Different stands have different co_2 gradient distribution.The co_2 concentration in upper or lower parts is higher than that in middle part of the crown.

REFERENCES

1 Cannell, M.G.R and Last, F.T. (1976) Tree physiology and yield improvement, Academic press.
2 Deng Ruiwen et.al. (1986) The influence of photosynthesis on co$\pm$2 in stand, the paper anthology of the fourth national meeting of the society of chinese plant physiology, 96
3 Larcher w, 1957, physiological plant ecology, 54–79.
4 Lin JiHui et. al. (1983) The application and improvement of the method of the meaasurement of photosynthesis of tree with IR co_2 analyzer, research of stand ecological system, 3,303–306
5 Yao Yuan (1983) The research of the ecophysiological characteristic of Larix olgensis Henry.Research of stand ecological system 3.265–269.

HOW TO IMPROVE CO_2 BALANCE IN OBLIGATE CAM, PINEAPPLE, *Ananas comosus* (L.) Merr.

AKIHIRO NOSE, COLLEGE OF AGRICULTURE, UNIVERSITY OF THE RYUKYUS,
1 SENBARU, NISHIHARA-CHO, OKINAWA, 903-01, JAPAN

1. INTRODUCTION

CAM photosynthesis possessed high water use efficiency to CO_2 absorption as an ecological superiority. The exchange rate and the balance of CO_2, however, were lower than those of C_3 and C_4 photosynthesis. In other words, the high water use efficiency was a useful trait in agriculture, but the low CO_2 balance had prevented the utilization of CAM plants as economic plants.

Traits of the carbon gain in CAM photosynthesis were summarized as follows(1): CO_2 absorbed by CAM photosynthesis in the dark was stored in vacuole as malate. Consequently, the total CO_2 absorption in the dark was determined by vacuole's capacity to store the malate. In the light, especially in CO_2 absorption of phase IV, however, there was no limitation to carbon gain as in the malate storage in the vacuole, because the CO_2 was converted to carbohydrates through the Calvine cycle, while parts of CO_2 were recycled by phosphoenopyruvate carboxylase(2). In a word, increasing the CO_2 absorption in the light is the key point to improving the carbon gain in CAM photosynthesis. To examine the CAM photosynthesis in the aspects mentioned above, the ratio of CO_2 absorption in phase I, dark period, to the daily CO_2 balance was defined as CAM ability(3). In other words, the decrease of the CAM ability implied the relative increase of the CO_2 absorption in light period.

To make clear indexes for improving the CO_2 balance in obligate CAM of pineapple, relationships of the CAM ability and the daily CO_2 balance were examined on the bases of average light intensity in light period(4), day length(3), leaf temperature(5), soil moisture(6), and nitrogen nutrient(7).

2. MATERIALS and METHODS

Five experiments were conducted to examine the relationships of the CAM ability and the daily CO_2 balance. Pineapple, *Ananas comosus* (L.) Merr. cv. smooth cayenne was used as experimental plants in every experiment. In temperature experiment, the results of the gas exchange were obtained on single leaf, D leaf. In other experiments, shoots were used for the measurements. In nitrogen experiment, plants were grown with hydroponic culture using Siders's solution. In the experiments of temperature and the others respectively, plants were grown in Wagner pots (0.05 m^2) filled with volcano sand and red soil. The CO_2 exchanges were measured in the open system with infra red CO_2 analyzer, using acrylic assimilation chambers. Ambient air was provided in every measurement of the CO_2 exchange, and humidity in the assimilation chambers was not controlled exactly, except in soil moisture experiments.

2.1 Experiment for light intensity(4)

Experiments were done with plants of 516 to 587 days after planting. Conditions of the gas exchange were as follows: Average light intensities on the top of the plant were 0, 220, 440, 880, 1760 μmol m^{-2} s^{-1}. Leaf temperatures were 30.0±1.0 °C and 26.5±1.0 °C at light and dark periods respectively.

N. Murata (ed.), Research in Photosynthesis, Vol. IV, 679–682.

Day length was 11.5 hours.

2.2 Experiment for day length(3)

Long day treatments, 16 hours of the natural day length and additional irradiance of 220 μmol m-2 s-1 at the top of the plants supplied with incandescent lamps after sunset, were started at 85 days after planting. The gas exchanges were measured at 64 to 72 days after treatment. Short day treatments, 10 hours from 7:00 to 17:00, were started at 98 days after planting with a setting device placed outdoors. The measurements of the gas exchange were done at 64 to 73 days after the short day treatments. Control plants were grown under natural day length in a grass house, and the gas exchange was measured from 25th September to 12nd October, at 163 and 180 days after planting respectively. Day length in the measurement was 12 hours. Leaf temperatures were 30.0±1.0 °C and 25.0±1.0 °C at light and dark periods respectively.

2.3. Experiment for leaf temperature(5)

Combinations of leaf temperatures at light and dark periods were as follows: Light / dark, 19 °C/10, 13, 16, 19, 22, and 25 °C, 25 °C/16, 19, 22, 25, 28, 31, and 34 °C, and 31 °C/16, 19, 22, 25, 28, 31, 34, and 37 °C. Day length was 10.5 hours. Light intensity on leaf surface was 316±33 μmol m-2 s-1. The gas exchanges were measured with plants of 94 to 156 days after planting.

2.4 Experiment for soil moisture(6)

Experimental blocks of soil moisture were 1.3, 2.5, 3.8, and 4.5 pF. Moisture treatments were started at 72 to 109 days after planting and continued for one month until the gas exchange measurements. Leaf temperatures in light and dark periods were 29.4±0.7 °C and 23.4±1.1 °C, day length was 11 hours, and relative humidities in assimilation chambers were 50.2±8.8% and 62.8±4.3% at light and dark periods respectively.

2.5 Experiment for nitrogen nutrition(7)

Experimental plants were cultured with Sideris's solution for 44 day after planting. After that, nitrogen treatments of 14, 28, 69, 138, 277, 554 ppm were provided, and the gas exchanges were measured at 14 to 28 days and 25 to 49 days after treatments. Experimental conditions for the gas exchange were as follows: Day length was 11 hours, leaf temperatures were 24.8±0.7 °C and 18.9±1.1 °C at light and dark periods, and average light intensities were 1235±75, 560±22, 210±33 μmol m-2 s-1 at the top of the plant.

3. RESULTS and DISCUSSION

Figure 1 showed effects of the light intensity on the CAM ability and the daily CO_2 balance. A significant relation, such as r=-0.855, P<0.001, was obtained. In other words, the light intensity in light period improved the CO_2 balance by decreasing the CAM ability, that is, increasing the CO_2 absorption in light period.

Effects of the day length on relationships of the CAM ability and the daily CO_2 balance were shown in Fig. 2. There were no significant correlations. When the relationships were examined in each day length treatment, however, the CAM ability showed significant relations to the daily CO_2 balance. Since the results in each day length treatment included effects of light intensity in light period, these results were the same as in Fig. 1. Nevertheless, the distributions of the daily CO_2 balance and the CAM ability were different in each day length treatment.

When the relations of the CAM ability and the CO_2 balance were grouped by the condition of light quantity in light period, the CAM ability showed positive relations to the daily CO_2 balance, except in light quantity block of 2 mmol m-2 s-1, while those relation were not statistically significant. In brief, there were some possibilities that the day length improved the daily CO_2 balance by increasing the CO_2 absorption in dark period. These results suggested that short day conditions were suitable for CAM photosynthesis.

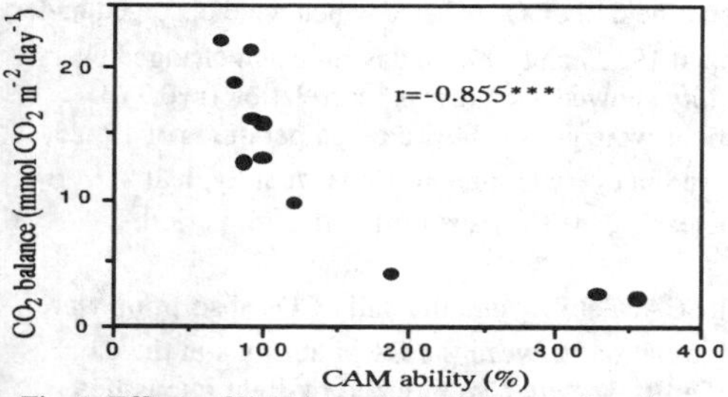

Fig. 1. Effects of light intensity in light period on the relationships of CAM ability and CO_2 balance. *** indicates statistical significance at 0.1%.

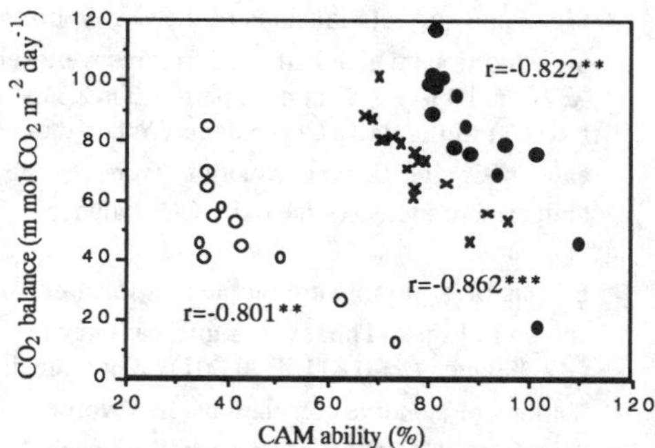

Fig. 2. Effects of day length on the relationships of CAM ability and CO_2 balance.
●, o, and x means short day length, long day length, and control respectively. ** and *** indicates statistical significance at 1.0 and 0.1% respectively.

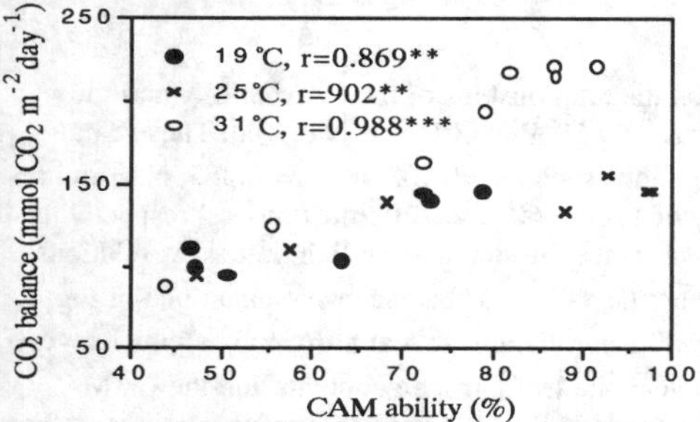

Fig. 3. Effects of leaf temperatures on the relationships of CAM ability and CO_2 balance.
** and *** indicates statistical significance at 1.0 and 0.1% respectively. Figures in the graph mean leaf temperatures in light period.

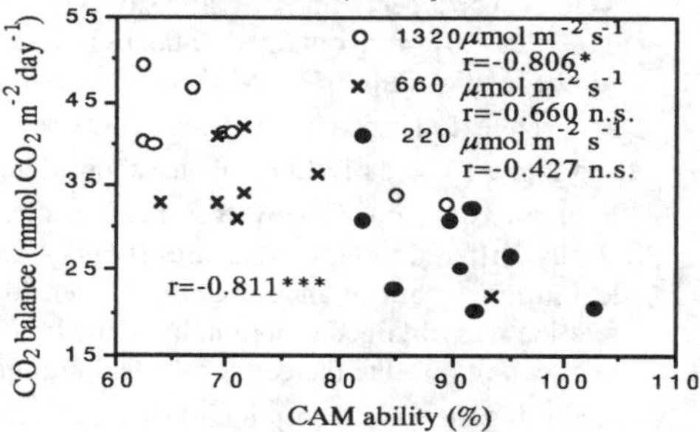

Fig. 4. Effects of soil moisture on the relationships of CAM ability and CO_2 balance.
Figures in the graph mean light intensities in light period. ***, * and n.s. indicates statistical significance at 0.1 and 5%, and non of siginificance respectively.

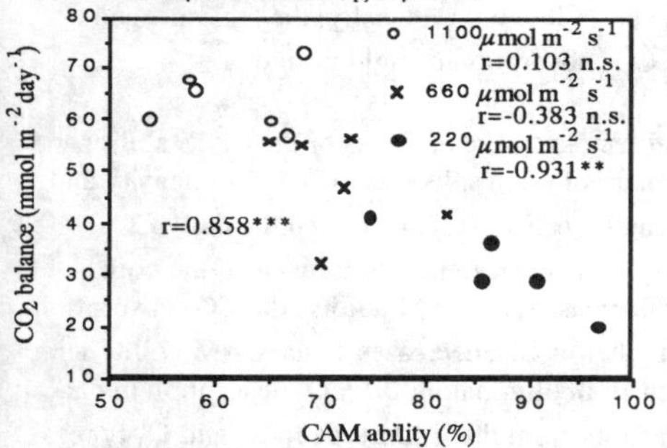

Fig. 5. Effects of nitrogen nutrient on the relatioships of CAM ability and CO_2 balance.
Figures in the graph meand light intensitys in light period. ***, **, and n.s. indicates statistical significance at 0.1 and 1%, and non respectively.

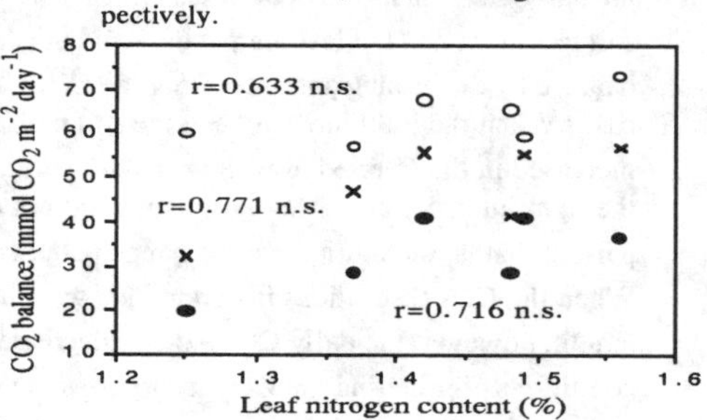

Fig. 6. Relationships of leaf nitrogen content and CO2 balance. o, x, and ● meaned light intensitis in light period of 1100, 660, 220 μmol m^{-2} s^{-1}. n.s. meanes non of statistical significance.

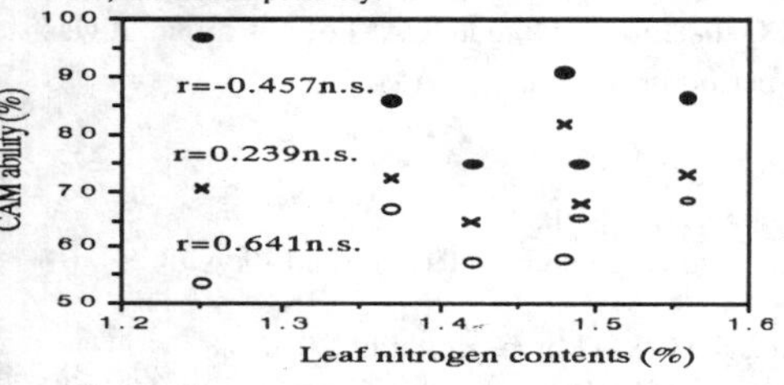

Fig. 7. Relationships of leaf nitrogen contents and CAM abilities.
o, x, and ● in the figure means light intensities in light period of 110, 660, and 220 μmol m^{-2}s^{-1} respectively. n.s. means non of significance.

Fig. 3 showed relationships of the CAM ability and the daily CO_2 balance which were observed under the conditions which leaf temperatures were set up at 19, 25 and 31°C in day time and changed every 3 °C from 10 to 37 °C in dark period. The CAM ability showed a significant correlation ($r=0.773$, $P<0.01$) to the daily CO_2 balance. When the relations were grouped by day temperatures of 19, 25, and 31 °C, significant correlations were also observed in every treatment. Consequently, leaf temperature increases the daily CO_2 balance by increasing the CO_2 absorption in dark period.

Effects of soil moisture on the relationships of the CAM ability and the daily CO_2 absorption were shown in Fig. 4. There was significant negative correlation between the CAM ability and the daily CO_2 balance ($r=-0.811$, $P<0.001$). When the data in Fig. 4 were also grouped by light intensities, there were negative correlations. In a word, soil moisture improved the daily CO_2 balance with increasing the CO_2 absorption in light period.

Figure 5 showed effects of the nitrogen nutrients on the relationships of the CAM ability and the daily CO_2 balance. Significant negative correlation ($r=-0.858$, $P<0.001$) was observed. These data were also grouped with light intensity. Then correlations such as $r=0.103$, n.s., $r=-0.383$, n.s., and $r=-0.931$, $P<0.01$ were obtained in the light intensity of 1100, 660, and 220 μmol m^{-2} s^{-1} respectively. As the relationships of CAM ability and daily CO_2 balance differed in each light intensity, relations between leaf nitrogen contents, the CAM ability, and the daily CO_2 balance were examined in Fig. 6 and Fig. 7 . The daily CO_2 balance showed the positive correlations to leaf nitrogen contents in every light intensity (Fig. 6). However, relationships between the leaf nitrogen contents and the CAM ability differed in light intensities (Fig. 7). That is, CAM ability showed significant relations to the leaf nitrogen content under high light intensities of 660 and 1320 μmol m^{-2} s^{-1}, but a negative relation was obtained in low light intensity of 220 μmol m^{-2} s^{-1}. These results implied that in high light conditions, the increase of the leaf nitrogen content improved the daily CO_2 balance by increasing the CO_2 absorption of dark period. However, in low light intensity, the leaf nitrogen content increased the CO_2 balance by increasing the CO_2 absorption of light period.

As described above, the effects of five environmental factors on the relations of the CAM ability and the daily CO_2 balance had been examined. The summary of the results was: The light intensity and soil moisture, and the leaf temperature and the day length, respectively, increased the daily CO_2 balance by decreasing and increasing the CAM ability. The nitrogen nutrition revealed the both cases.When the light intensity and the soil moisture decreased the CAM ability, the CO_2 absorption increased in light period as well as in dark period. In other words, decreases of the CAM ability with the light intensity and the soil moisture did not result from eliminating the CO_2 absorption in dark period, that is, the diurnal gas exchange patterns changing from the CAM type to C_3 and C_4 type. When the CO_2 absorptions in dark period were depressed in the treatments by temperature and day length, however, the daily CO_2 balance decreased. Consequently, in pineapple plants, under the conditions eliminating the CO_2 absorptions in the dark period, the daily CO_2 balance did not improve positively. In other words, to improve the daily CO_2 balance in obligate CAM of pineapple, it was necessary to increase the CO_2 absorption of light period in continuing CAM.

REFERENCES

1 Nose, A. (1986) Sci. Bull. Coll. Agric. Univ. Ryukyus 33, 1-70.
2 Cote, F.X., Andre, M., Folliot, M., Massimino, D. and Daguent, A. (1989) Plant Physiol. 89, 61-68.
3 Nose, A., Heima, K., Miyazato, K. and Murayama, S. (1986) Photosynthetica 20,20-28.
4 Nose, A., Siroma, M., Miyazato, K. and Murayama, S. (1977) Japan. Jour. Crop Sci. 46, 580-587.
5 Nose, A., Abe, S., Kawamitsu, Y. and Murayama, S. (1991) Jpn. J. Crop Sci. 60(E. I. 1), 154-155.
6 Nose, A., Miyazato, K. and Murayama, S. (1981) Japan. Jour. Crop Sci. 50, 525-535.
7 Nose, A., Matake, S., Miyazato, K. and Murayama, S. (1985) Japan. Jour. Crop Sci. 54, 195-204.

CHANGES OF CO_2 TRANSFER AND CARBOXYLATION RESISTANCES IN THE SENESCING PROCESS OF RICE LEAVES (ORYZA SATIVA L.)

H.Sasaki, M.Samejima* and R.Ishii
(Faculty of Agriculture, The University of Tokyo, Bunkyo-ku, Tokyo 113, Japan; *National Institute of Agrobiological Resources, Tsukuba, Ibaraki 305, Japan)

INTRODUCTION

Our previous paper (1) showed that cultivar difference of flag leaf photosynthesis (LPS) in rice (*Oryza sativa* L.) was determined mainly by the factors relating to mesophyll CO_2 resistance (r_m). However, r_m involves different sorts of physical and chemical resistances in CO_2 diffusion and fixation processes. Isolation of physical CO_2 resistance from r_m has been so far attempted by several researchers, some of whom acknowleded physical CO_2 resistance to be important (2)(3)(4)(5). We have also attempted to divide r_m to CO_2 transfer resistance (r_r), and carboxylation resistance (r_c) in rice leaves by $\delta^{13}C$ and gas exchange measurement to approach the mechanism of cultivar difference of LPS in rice (6). But, it is still obscure whether and how the relative values of these resistances vary with leaf senescence. In this paper, we have examined the change of r_r and r_c with progress of leaf senescence in 31 rice plants cultivars.

MATERIALS AND METHODS

Plant materials: Thirty one cultivars of rice plants (*Oryza sativa* L.), which were bred in Japan in the last 100 years, were used for the experiment. The plants were grown in the paddy field by the normal cultivating methods.

Measurement of LPS: The LPS and transpiration rate per unit leaf area, and leaf temperature were simultaneously measured on three flag leaves of each cultivar, in the field under the irradiance above 1450 $\mu mol\ m^{-2} s^{-1}$ PPFD. The measurements were conducted in 0, 2, and 4 weeks after heading, which corresponded to the heading, grain filling, and grain maturing time, respectively.

Extraction of soluble sugars: To measure $\delta^{13}C$ in the current photosynthetic products, soluble sugars were extracted from the flag leaves, and served for the measurement. Fifteen flag leaves were covered with aluminium foil at 1200h on the precedent day to LPS measurement, to make the leaves starved for the photosynthetic products. In the next morning (on the day of LPS measurement), the flag leaves were exposed to the sunlight in fine weather from 0900h to 1200h, and then, they were cut off from the plant. The soluble sugars

N. Murata (ed.), Research in Photosynthesis, Vol. IV, 683–686.

were extracted following to the method of Sasaki et al. (6).

Assay of carbon isotope discrimination and calculation of transfer resistance: The measurement of $\delta^{13}C$ of soluble sugars was made according to the method of Sasaki et al. (6), with mass spectrometer (Finnigan MAT, San Jose, USA).

TABLE 1. The mean values of flag leaf photosynthesis (LPS), carbon isotope discrimination (Δ), and CO_2 stomatal (r_s), transfer (r_r), and carboxylation (r_c) resistance, and CO_2 concentration in the stomatal cavity ($[CO_2]_{stc}$) and at the reaction site of RubisCO ($[CO_2]_{cht}$) in different time of flag leaf senescence.

	Time		
	Heading	Grain filling	Grain maturing
LPS ($\mu mol\ m^{-2} s^{-1}$)	20.3±1.6	16.0±1.5	11.6±1.6
Δ (10^{-3})	18.25±0.44	18.45±0.63	18.61±0.66
Resistance ($m^2 s\ mol^{-1}$)			
r_s	4.24±0.61	4.49±0.63	6.08±1.23
	(28±3)	(23±4)	(22±4)
r_r	1.45±0.46	2.61±0.89	3.57±1.12
	(10±3)	(13±4)	(13±3)
r_c	9.42±0.90	12.53±1.40	17.57±3.45
	(62±2)	(64±3)	(65±3)
CO_2 concentration ($\mu l\ l^{-1}$)			
$[CO_2]_{stc}$	245±10	261±13	263±12
$[CO_2]_{cht}$	212± 6	216± 8	219±10

Values are expressed as Mean ± SE.
Figures in the parentheses are percentage ratio of each resistance to total resistance.

RESULTS AND DISSCUSSIN

The mean values of leaf photosynthesis (LPS) and its related parametwers of 31 cultivars are shown in TABLE 1 to know the changing tendency of each parameters with the progress of leaf senescence. In heading time, the r_r was so low as 1.45±0.46 $m^2 s\ mol^{-1}$, and r_c was as high as 9.42±0.90 $m^2 s\ mol^{-1}$. The values of r_r were in almost the same level as those previously reported in other papers (3)(4)(5). The mean percentage ratios of stomatal CO_2 resistance (r_s), r_r, and r_c to the total CO_2 resistance (r_t), was 28, 10, and 62%, respectively. This indicates that the contribution of r_c to the determination of LPS is particularly large, compared with r_s or r_r. The frequency distributinon of the extent of change from heading to grain maturing time in relative values of r_s, r_r and r_c is shown in FIGURE 1. The relative values of r_s, r_r and r_c in most cultivars varied in the range within $\pm$ 10%. This indicates that the relative r_s, r_r and r_c are maintained comparatively constant in most cultivars through the leaf senescence, although the absolute value of each resistance increased with the progress of leaf senescence. Furthermore, CO_2 concentration at the reaction site of RubisCO ($[CO_2]_{cht}$) was maintained almost

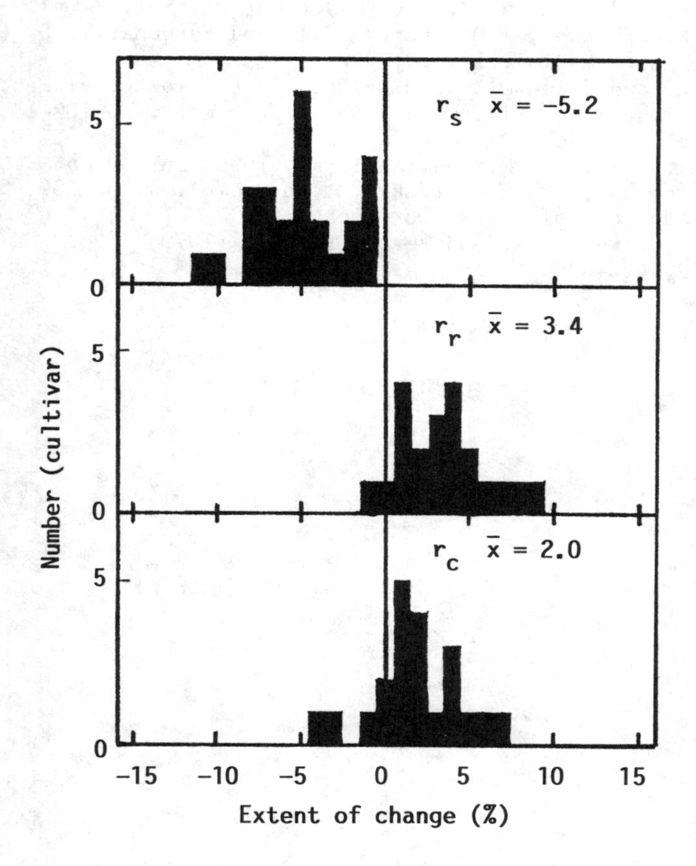

FIGURE 1. Frequency distribution of the extent of change from heading to grain maturing time in r_s, r_r and r_c.
The extent of change was expressed as difference of relative resistance in the period from heading to grain maturing time.

constant through leaf senescence at about 215 $\mu l\ l^{-1}$, while CO_2 concentration in the stomatal cavity ($[CO_2]_{stc}$) increased from 245 to 263 $\mu l\ l^{-1}$. Wong et al. (7) suggested that $[CO_2]_{stc}$ was maintained constant. Our paper is not necessarily coinciding to this result. It would be considered as the reason for constant $[CO_2]_{cht}$ through the leaf senescence that the resistance from atmospheric air to the reaction site of RubisCO ($r_s + r_r$) is balanced with that of carboxylation reaction (r_c). This implies that CO_2 transfer step is feed-back controlled by CO_2 fixation step.

REFERENCES

1 Sasaki, H. and Ishii, R. (1992) Photosynthesis Res. 32, 139-146
2 Čatský, J. and Tichá, I. (1982) Photosynthetica 16, 253-284
3 Evans, J.R. and Seemann, J.R. (1984) Plant Physiol. 74, 759-765
4 Evans, J.R., Sharkey, T.D., Berry, J.A. and Farquhar, G.D. (1986) Aust. J. Plant Physiol. 13, 281-292
5 Raven, J.A. and Glidewell, S.M. (1981) in Physiological Processes Limiting Plant Productivity (Johnson, C.B., ed.), pp 109-136, Butterworths, London
6 Sasaki, H., Samejima, M. and Ishii, R. (1990) in Current Research in Photosynthesis (Baltscheffsky, M., ed), Vol. 4, pp. 895-898, Kluwer Academic Publishers, Dordrecht
7 Wong, S.C., Cowan, I.R. and Farquhar, G.D. (1979) Nature 282, 424-426

THE EFFECTS OF FIRE AND TREE-FELL ON PHOTOSYNTHESIS IN *Quercus ilex* RESPROUTS

FLECK,I., SANJOSE,M., GRAU,D., VIDAL,D.
Departament de Biologia Vegetal. Facultat de Biologia.
Universitat de Barcelona. Spain.

1. INTRODUCTION

Several photosynthesis-related parameters were measured during the course of one year in **Quercus ilex** leaves from a mediterranean-type forest. The annual trends were compared with those of the resprouting vegetation which appeared after an experimental fire and after tree-felling. The aim of this study was to evaluate the effects of these disturbances on the physiological characteristics of the resprouting vegetation and to compare them with those of the original vegetation.

2. MATERIALS AND METHODS

2.1 Experimental Design: Three holm oak (**Quercus ilex**) forest plots of 800 m^2 were studied in the Prades mountains (Tarragona, N.E. Spain). In two plots, all the trees were cut down and trunks and big branches were removed. Remaining branches were uniformly distributed over the soil surface and one of these plots was burned. The front fire power was 9350 $cal.cm^{-2}$ s^{-1}, which can be considered a medium value.

2.2 Plant Material: The material studied was mature leaves of **Quercus ilex** from the undisturbed (control), burned and tree-felled stands, respectively.

2.3 Measurements: Measurements were carried out five times during the course of the second year after the disturbances: winter, spring, early summer, late summer and autumn. Net photosynthesis (NP), transpiration (E) and leaf conductance (G) were determined using a portable photosynthesis system (ADC Irga-porometer). At least twelve replicates were measured per stand and day. Measurements were always taken between 12am and 2pm (Table 1). Thereafter, leaves were frozen in liquid nitrogen and kept in a freezer at 80ºC until assay. Ribulose

N. Murata (ed.), Research in Photosynthesis, Vol. IV, 687–690.

bisphosphate carboxylase (RuBPCase) activity was determined by spectrophotometric end point titration of formed D-PGA in a 60 s. assay at 25ºC (1) with several modifications because of the high concentration of protein-precipitating tannins in sclerophylls. Three replicates of eight leaves each were assayed per stand and day. Total Nitrogen content was determined by using gas chromatography (HPLC) after freeze-drying and grinding. Three replicates of twenty leaves were assayed per stand and day. Statistical analysis of the data was accomplished at the 0.05 level of significance using one-way unbalanced ANOVA.

3. RESULTS AND DISCUSSION

3.1 The results did not show significant differences in the parameters measured between the two kind of resprouts (originated after burning or after tree-felling). Their rates or concentration and their annual course were the same, indicating that the physiological characteristics studied were independent of the kind of disturbance.

Differences in photosynthesis, transpiration and leaf conductance were observed between the resprouting vegetation and control. Differences in the successional state of the stands are not thought to be responsible for the results obtained, as was shown in a previous work (4).

The seasonal trends in photosynthesis (Fig.1) were the same for the three stands, with maximum in the spring and minimum in the summer. The marked NP decline may indicate the presence of midday depression in net CO_2 uptake, characteristic of mediterranean schlerophylls in dry seasons (5). It is remarkable that significant differences between control and resprouts were only obtained in early and late summer, indicating the advantage of the resprouting vegetation in high temperature months. This has already been observed in a previous paper on **Arbutus unedo** and **Coriaria myrtifolia** resprouts after wildfire (4).

Transpiration (Fig. 2) and leaf conductance (G) (Fig. 3) were significantly higher in the resprouts except in the winter. During the annual course, the resprouts showed increases in transpiration in spring and summer whereas foliar conductance was maintained.

FIGURE 1. Photosynthesis, FIGURE 2. Transpiration and FIGURE 3. Leaf Conductance rates of **Quercus ilex** leaves during the course of one year in control, burned and tree-felled stands.

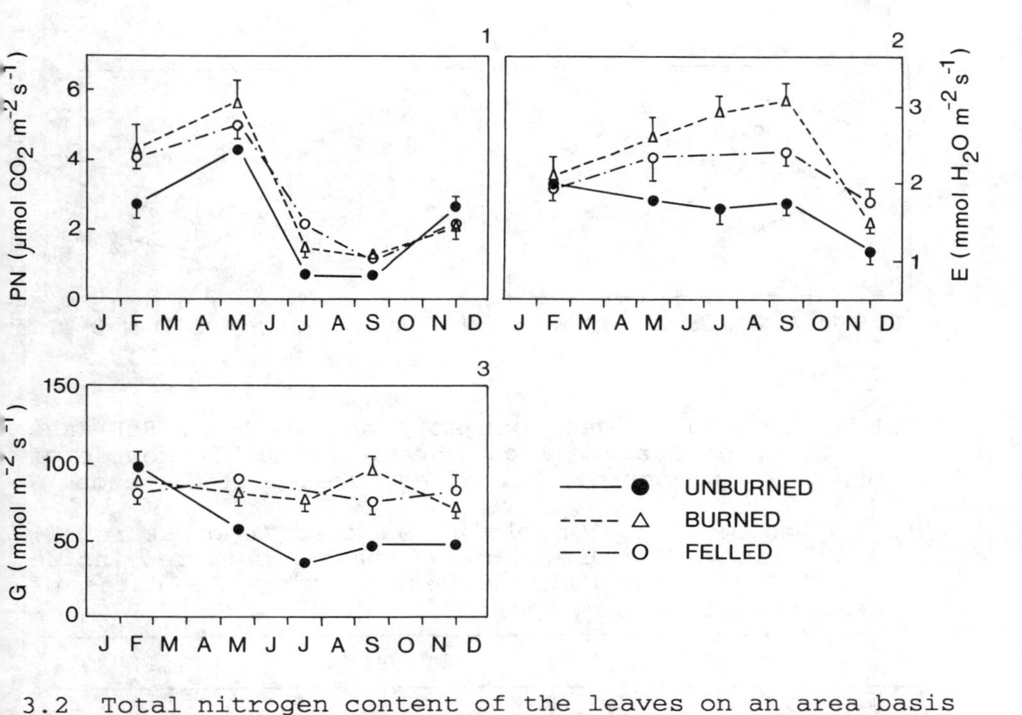

3.2 Total nitrogen content of the leaves on an area basis (Fig. 4) was constant during the year in the three stands but was twice as high in the resprouts with respect to the controls. The results show high nitrogen content per unit area and low photosynthetic rates in all the stands, as already observed in other sclerophylls (3), probably due to proportionally lower allocation of nitrogen to photosynthesis in this species.
Higher leaf nitrogen content in the resprouts may account for their higher RuBPCase activity (Fig.5), since it reflects the amount of this protein (2). The results indicate that enzyme activity did not change significantly in control leaves during the year, whereas it showed seasonal variations in the resprouts, especially in those originating after fire. Moreover, the differences in RuBPCase activity between stands were not significant in early or late summer, suggesting that the photosynthesis advantage of the resprouts in these periods may not be due to increased carboxylating activity but to improved water relations.

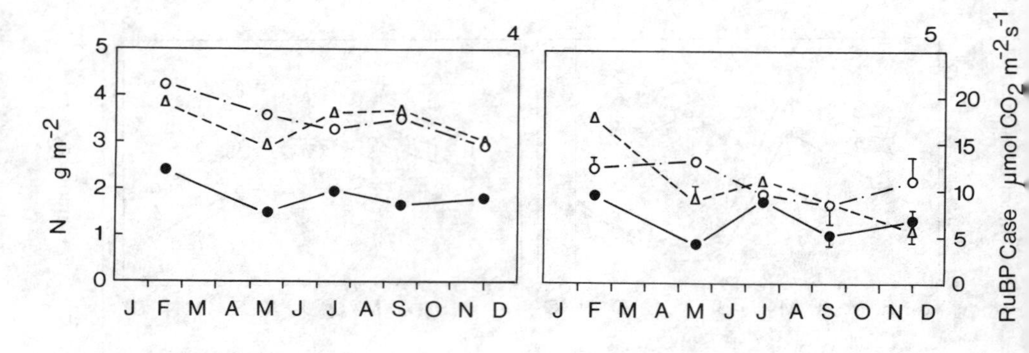

FIGURE 4. Total nitrogen content and FIGURE 5. RuBPCase activity of **Quercus ilex** leaves during the course of one year in control, burned and tree-felled stands.

TABLE 1. Incident PAR ($\mu mol \cdot m^{-2} \cdot s^{-1}$), Leaf temperature (T) and Relative Humidity (RH) of the air measured inside the ADC-Irga porometer cuvette during the dates of measurement (12am-2pm).

	PAR	T(°C)	RH(%)
WINTER	1563 ± 98	21.6 ± 1.2	26.0 ± 1 6
SPRING	898 ± 60	26.4 ± 0.1	23.0 ± 2.5
EARLY-SUMMER	1613 ± 68	30.9 ± 0.1	14.8 ± 1.2
LATE-SUMMER	846 ± 63	28.6 ± 0.2	22.4 ± 2.0
AUTUMN	1635 ± 24	18.6 ± 0.1	15.7 ± 1.1

REFERENCES

1 Di Marco, G. and Tricoli, D. (1983) Photosynth. Res.4, 145-149

2 Evans, J.R. (1989) Oecologia 78, 9-19

3 Field, C. and Mooney, H.A. (1986) in On the Economy of Plant Form and Function (Ginvish, T.J. ed.), pp. 25-55, Cambridge

4 Fleck, I., Iñiguez, F.J., Diaz, C. and Pascual, M.(1990) in Currrent Research in Photosynthesis (Baltscheffsky, M., ed.), Vol. 4, pp 695-698, Kluwer Academic Publishers, Dordrecht

5 Tenhunen, J.D., Beyschlag, W., Lange, O.L. and Harley, P.C. (1987) in Plant Response to Stress. Functional Analysis in Mediterranean Ecosystems (Tenhunen J.D., Catarino, F.M., Lange O.L. and Oechel W.C. eds.), NATO ASI Series, Vol.3, pp 305-327, Springer Verlag, Berlin

This research was supported by CICYT (NAT 90/350).

WATER STRESS EFFECTS ON PHOTOSYNTHESIS IN SUBTERRANEAN CLOVER LEAVES

Socias, X., Aguiló, F., Pol, A., Vadell, J. and Medrano, H.
Lab. Fisiologia Vegetal; Dept. Biologia Ambiental. Institut d'Estudis Avançats; Universitat de les Illes Balears. 07071 Palma de Mallorca; Spain.

1. INTRODUCTION

Different models or "strategies" for plant response to water stress have been described often in relation with the ways in which water stress is developed (1,2). When water stress is gradualy imposed, as is most common under natural conditions, plants develop an acclimation response in which changes in growth and physiology of the whole plant contribute to improve water economy (3). Accordingly, the particular way in which water stress is imposed could be of special significance to observe the acclimation response as well as to evaluate the plants capacity to acclimate (4).

Many different methods have been developed for inducing water stress on pot growing plants (5). In the present work the leaf response to rapidily and slowly induced water stress are compared in three different environments in order to achieve a more complete understanding of this response in subterranean clover plants. A clear effect of the method to impose water stress is demonstrated as well as an interaction between plant response and environmental growth conditions.

2. MATERIAL AND METHODS

Subterranean clover (*Trifolium subterraneum* ssp. *brachycalycinum* cv. Clare) seeds were sown both, in pots (vermiculite:perlite, 3:1; growth chamber and greenhouse experiments), or in clay-calcareous soil (field). Three environments were tested: growth chamber (23±2 °C, 50±5% RH, 12/12 h light/dark period, 350 µmol photons m^{-2} s^{-1}), greenhouse (April-May, 12-28 °C) and field conditions (Mediterranean climate, March-May, 10-28 °C).

When plants completely cover the pot, three treatments were established: Irrigation (I), replenishing the evaporated water in each pot every day. Withholding

N. Murata (ed.), Research in Photosynthesis, Vol. IV, 691–694.

watering (WW), and Slowly induced drought (SID), replenishing with a fraction of evaporated water. For growth chamber experiment, such fraction was 1/2 of average water loss by I plants, Ei. For greenhouse experiment the watering dose (WD) was calculated according with Ei and the water loss by SID plants Ed, applying a drought factor F of 1/3. Watering dose was obtained as follows: WD=(2FxEi)-Ed. Under field conditions water stress was developed by withholding irrigation, preventing any rainfall on the experimental plot.

Pre-dawn leaf water potential (Ψ) was determined with Scholander's chamber, and gas exchange measurements in attached leaves with a portable IRGA (Li-Cor 6250 system).

3. RESULTS AND DISCUSSION

3.1. Leaf water potential: After a short period of treatment, WW plants showed a steep decline in Ψ. This decline was not so apparent in SID ones, which remained lower than irrigated but following similar pattern. As the present data shows, the way in which water-stress is imposed clearly affected leaf Ψ evolution. Lowering water availability in a gradual way, leaf Ψ declines much more slowly, maintaining moderate low values after a long treatment period (Figure 1).

3.2. Leaf characteristics: Fully-expanded leaf area reduction in response to water stress was early showed both in WW and SID plants. The new "acclimated" SID leaves showed much lower leaf area (50 % of I ones). Specific leaf weight did not show a coincident pattern (Table 1).

Table 1: Leaf Area (LA) and Specific Leaf Weight (SLW) at the end of each experiment.

	Growht chamber	Greenhouse	Field
LA (cm^2):			
I	19.4±1.6	15.6±4.8	12.4±1.3
WW	7.3±0.5	9.0±2.3	
SID	8.3±0.5	8.9±1.2	5.4±1.8
SLW ($g\ m^{-2}$):			
I	34.8±0.8	58.5±4.8	41.6±2.8
WW	38.9±2.1	50.2±4.5	
SID	35.4±0.4	55.1±4.1	35.4±6.5

3.3. Leaf photosynthesis and related parameters: Stomatal conductance (g) was early reduced both in WW and SID to values around 50% of I plants. Later, WW leaves showed a

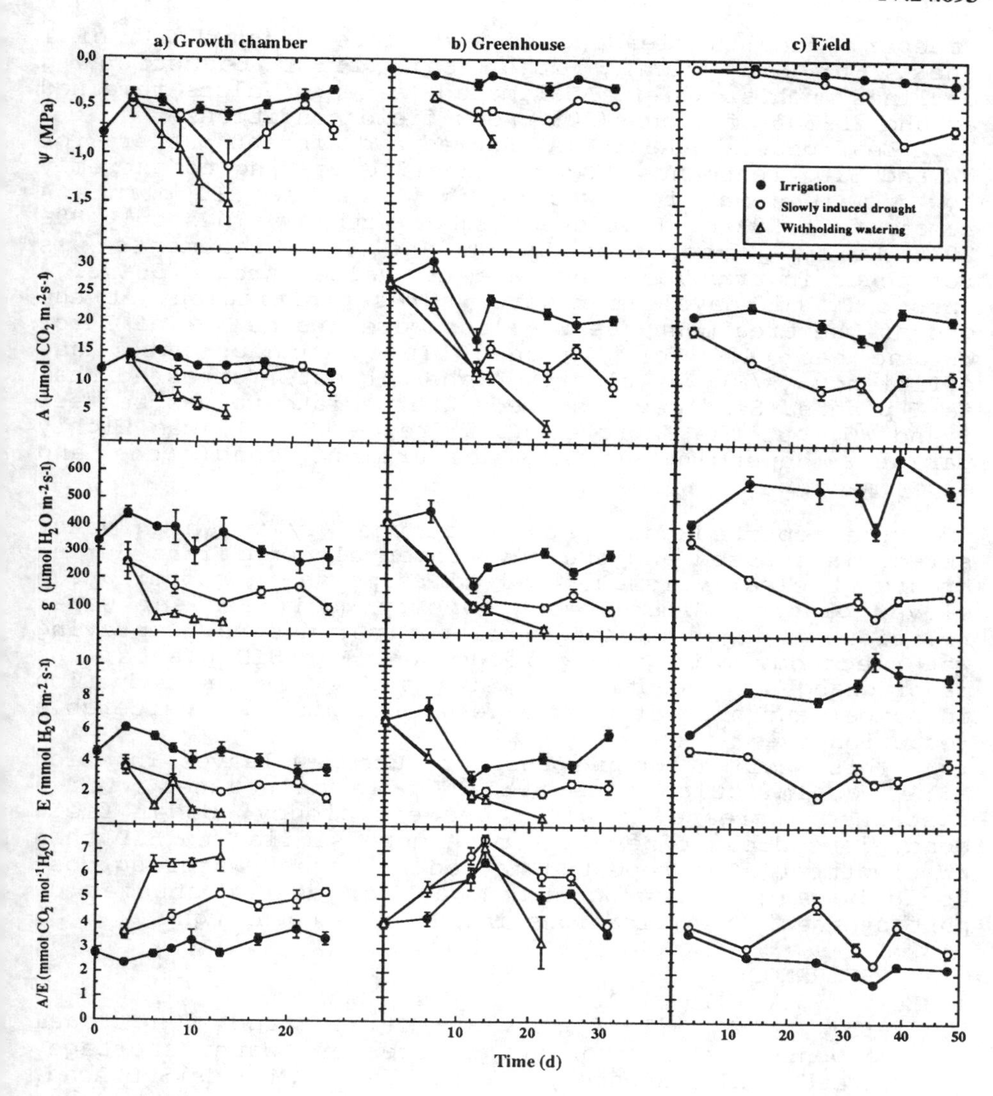

Figure 1: Water Potential (Ψ) CO_2 Assimilation Rate (A), Stomatal Conductance (g), Transpiration Rate (E) and Instantaneous Water Use Efficiency (A/E) of subterranean clover leaves growing in three different environments and submited to different water stress treatments: Irrigation (I), Withholding Watering (WW) and Slowly Induced Drought (SID).

steeper g decline leading to end values around 10% of I ones. For SID plants, after this first reduction, g declines much slowlier. Acclimated leaves g values remained around 25-30% of I ones(20% under field conditions).

Leaf photosynthesis (A) showed a different pattern for WW and SID treatments. A steep decline leading to extremly low A values was followed by WW while the SID plants A remained at 50% of I or even higher with g values only 30-20%. Early g reduction in WW and SID treatments was reflected in transpiration rate (E) values around 50% of I ones only few days after water stress initiation. At the end of the treatment the E values were around 15% of I for WW and near 40% for SID ones. Instantaneous water use efficiency (A/E) was clearly higher in water stressed than in I plants. SID leaves showed intermediate values between I and WW, but the improvement in respect to I, was highly variable depending on the measurement conditions and experiment.

The reported data shows that the way in which water stress is imposed and the environmental conditions during treatment clearly influence leaf response in subterranean clover plants. WW treatment quickly modifies leaf water relations and gas exchange related parameters, improving water economy mainly by g reduction. For SID plants, the major changes in relation to water saving are the reduction in number and size of the leaves joint with a considerable reduction in g.

This acclimation response produce new leaves in which a net assimilation rate 50% of I is maintained with a sustained increase in water use efficiency. Under field conditions drought develops much more similar to SID than WW treatment. The reported method to adjust watering dose could be a good reproductive way for deeper studies of photosynthesis modifications in response to drought.

REFERENCES

1. Levit, J.V. (1972) Academic Press, New York.
2. Ludlow, M.M. (1989) in Structural and functional responses to environmental stresses: Water shortage. (Kreeb, K.H., Richter, H. Hinckley, T.M. eds) SPB Acad. Pub. The Hague.
3. Schulze, E.D. (1991) in Response of plants to multiple stresses (Mooney, H.A., Winner, W.E., Pell, E.J., Chu, E. eds.) Academic Press, Inc.
4. Chaves, M.M. (1991) J. Exp. Bot. 234, 1-6
5. Pennypacker, B.W., Leath, K.T., Stout, W.L., Hill, R.R. Jr. (1990) Agron. J. 82, 951-57.

EVIDENCE FOR ^{18}O LABELING OF PHOTORESPIRATORY CO_2 IN PHOTOAUTOTROPHIC CELL CULTURES OF HIGHER PLANTS ILLUMINATED IN THE PRESENCE OF $^{18}O_2$.

Laurent COURNAC, Bernard DIMON and Gilles PELTIER.

Département de Physiologie Végétale et Ecosystèmes; Commissariat à l'Energie Atomique - Sciences du Vivant; Centre d'Etudes de Cadarache ; 13108 Saint-Paul-lez-Durance; France.

1. INTRODUCTION

Photorespiration is initiated by the oxygenase activity of Rubisco (1,2). The fixation of one molecule of O_2 on RuBP leads to the formation of one molecule of phosphoglycerate and one molecule of phosphoglycolate (2). By using $^{18}O_2$ and mass spectrometry it was established that one atom of oxygen was incorporated into the carboxylic group of glycolate (3) and was conserved into glycine and serine (4,5). However, although it is generally admitted that CO_2 produced in the light should be ^{18}O enriched when C_3 plants are photorespiring in the presence of $^{18}O_2$, no conclusive evidence for an ^{18}O enrichment has been reported.

We hypothesized that the carbonic anhydrase activity, which is contained in plant cells in large amounts, could provoke, by catalyzing the exchange of oxygen atoms between CO_2 and H_2O (6), the lost of label of the CO_2 produced during photorespiration (5). In the present paper, using a photoautotrophic cell suspension of *Euphorbia characias* characterized by a low carbonic anhydrase activity (7), we show that the CO_2 released in the light in photorespiratory conditions in the presence of $^{18}O_2$ is enriched in ^{18}O. We also observe that the burst of CO_2 (PIB) produced in the dark immediately after this light period is labeled by ^{18}O.

2. MATERIAL and METHODS

The photoautotrophic strain of *Euphorbia characias* L. was cultivated as described in reference (8) and was aerated (5 $l.h^{-1}$) with 2% CO_2-enriched. For mass spectrometer experiments, the cell suspension was introduced into a thermostated (25°C) illuminated reaction vessel. Dissolved gases were introduced into the ion-source of a mass spectrometer (MM14-80, V.G. Instruments) through a membrane inlet system. $^{18}O_2$ (1 ml at 99.4 ^{18}O atom %) was introduced in the vessel and mass-peaks m/e = 44 ($C^{16}O^{16}O$), m/e = 46 ($C^{18}O^{16}O$) were recorded.

When in solution in water, the ^{18}O isotopic content of ^{18}O labeled CO_2 progressively decreases due to an exchange between oxygen atoms of CO_2 and water occurring through the chemical equilibrium between dissolved CO_2 and hydrated CO_2 species (6). The time constant of the exchange ke is determined as the exponential time constant of the decay of ^{18}O isotopic content of $^{13}C^{18}O_2$ (6). The exchange activity of the culture medium had a time constant ke of 0.57 min^{-1} and the exchange activity of the photoautotrophic cell suspension was not significantly different thus indicating a low carbonic anhydrase activity.

N. Murata (ed.), Research in Photosynthesis, Vol. IV, 695–698.

In the experiment shown on Fig. 4, the actual $C^{18}O^{16}O$ concentration in the vessel was calculated by substracting to the recorded mass signal the estimated background of the mass spectrometer and the $C^{18}O^{16}O$ concentration due to the natural abundance of CO_2.

3. RESULTS

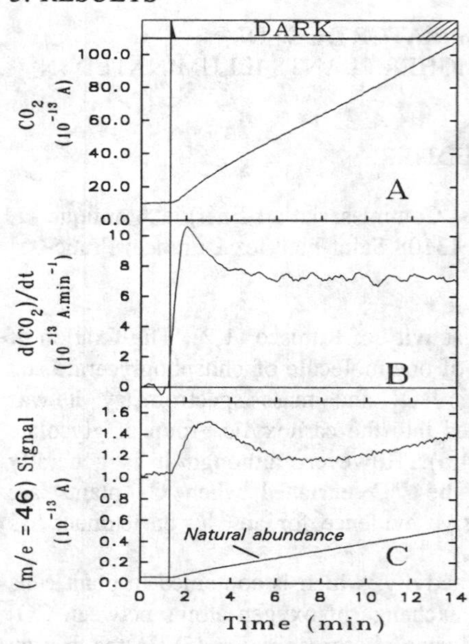

Fig. 1 : Mass spectrometric measurements of CO_2 exchange in photoautotrophic cells of *Euphorbia characias* during a light to dark transition.

Because of their low carbonic anhydrase level, photoautotrophic cells of *Euphorbia characias* appear as a suitable plant material to investigate a possible $^{18}O_2$ labeling of photorespiratory CO_2.

When the cell culture was illuminated in the presence of $^{18}O_2$ without exogenous CO_2 supply, dissolved CO_2 concentration was stable in the light and increased when the light was turned off (Fig. 1A). During the first minutes of darkness the rate of CO_2 production was higher than in the stationary dark period (Fig. 1B). This phenomenon well-known as the PIB (9) has been already reported and extensively studied in C_3 plants. The recorded m/e = 46 signal (Fig. 1C) was much higher than the rate of $C^{18}O^{16}O$ production that could have been expected from the ^{18}O natural abundance of CO_2 (lower curve on Fig. 1C). The m/e = 48 signal could not be detected either in the light or in the dark indicating that $C^{18}O^{18}O$ production did not occur at a significant extent.

When carbonic anhydrase was added in the light at the CO_2 compensation point, the stationary level of the m/e = 46 signal rapidly decreased. Moreover, the m/e = 46 post-illumination burst completely disappeared (Fig. 2b).

These data show that a significant $C^{18}O^{16}O$ production occurs in the light as well as during a light to dark transition. Carbonic anhydrase, by accelerating the isotope exchange with water decreases the $C^{18}O^{16}O$ level.

Aminooxyacetate (AOA), an inhibitor of serine-glyoxylate aminotransferase activity has been reported to stop both glycine

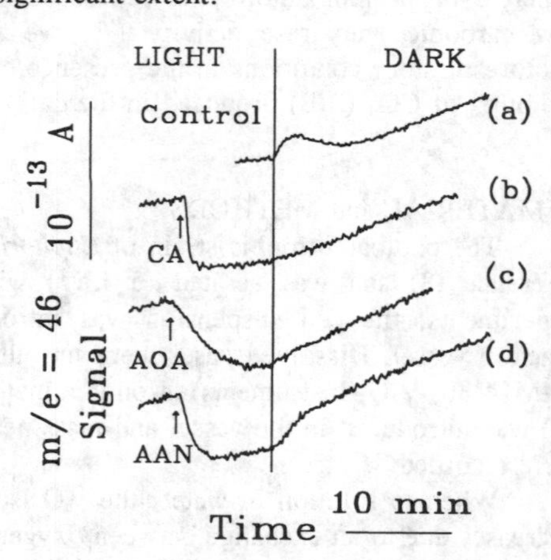

Fig.2 : Effect of anhydrase carbonic and of inhibitors of the photorespiratory pathway on $C^{18}O^{16}O$ production in the light and during the PIB.

production and decarboxylation (10). Aminoacetonitrile (AAN) is a known inhibitor of the glycine decarboxylase complex (10). When added at the CO_2 compensation point both of these inhibitors decreased the m/e = 46 steady state signal as well as the transient burst observed after a light to dark transition (Fig. 2c,d).

When the CO_2 level was increased from 150 (compensation point value) to 600 $\mu l.l^{-1}$, both the PIB (Fig. 3A) and the m/e = 46 signal burst (Fig. 3B) were strongly diminished. At very high concentrations of CO_2 (corresponding to atmospheric concentrations of about 1%), both the PIB and m/e = 46 signal burst were not detectable (data not shown).

The sensitivity of the m/e = 46 signal burst to the CO_2 level and the action of photorespiration inhibitors clearly indicates that the $C^{18}O^{16}O$ produced has mainly a photorespiratory origin.

The decrease in $C^{18}O^{16}O$ concentration was found to be exponential (time constant of 0.6 min^{-1}). The time constant of the decrease was similar to the value (0.57 min^{-1}) deduced from the unlabeling of exogenous ^{18}O labeled $^{13}CO_2$ (see Material and Methods). This indicates that isotope exchange is the main process responsible for the disappearance of $C^{18}O^{16}O$ after extinction of the PIB.

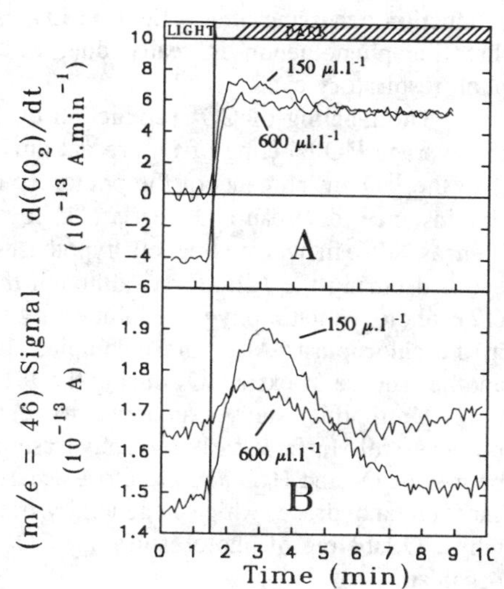

Fig. 3 : Effect of CO_2 concentration (150 or 600 $\mu l.l^{-1}$) on the PIB (A) and on the $C^{18}O^{16}O$ production (B) during a light to dark transition.

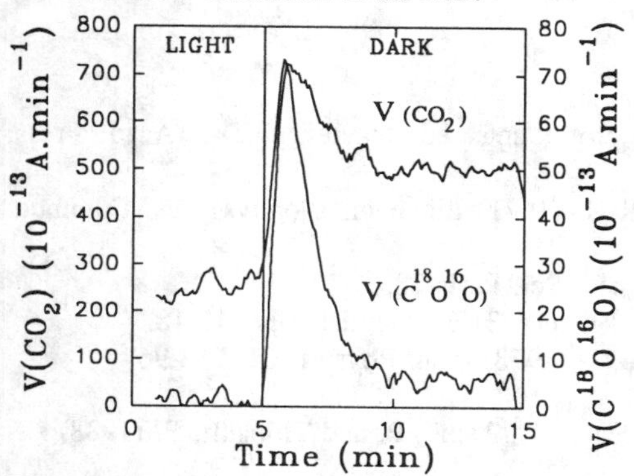

Fig. 4 : Production rates of CO_2 and of $C^{18}O^{16}O$ after isotopic exchange correction during a light to dark transition at the CO_2 compensation point.

By assuming that isotope exchange was occurring with the same time constant during the dark period it was possible to calculate the actual production rate of $C^{18}O^{16}O$ (Fig. 4). Production rates were used to estimate ^{18}O labeling of CO_2 produced during the PIB. The ratio between the labeling of CO_2 evolved during the PIB and the labeling of O_2 present during the preceding light period averaged at a value of 0.46 ± 0.15 (10 experiments).

4. DISCUSSION

By using a photoautotrophic cell suspension culture containing a low carbonic anhydrase activity, we show that the CO_2 produced by illuminated cells in the presence of $^{18}O_2$ in photorespiratory conditions is labeled with ^{18}O. The production of ^{18}O enriched CO_2 is affected by the CO_2 level and by inhibitors of the photorespiratory pathway such as

AOA or AAN. These experiments supply direct and clear evidence that the $C^{18}O^{16}O$ produced in the light directly originates from the photorespiratory pathway initiated by the oxygenasic activity of Rubisco.

In addition, we show that the PIB, which is defined as the stimulation of CO_2 production occurring after a light period, is also labeled with ^{18}O. This observation confirms that this phenomenon is really due, at least partially, to the continuing activity of the photorespiratory cycle.

The labeling of CO_2 production during the PIB was found to be about 46 ± 15 % of the average ^{18}O labeling of O_2 present during the photorespiratory period. This value is lower than the ^{18}O enrichments of the photorespiratory intermediates previously observed in leaves. For instance, de Veau and Burris (11) found that the relative labeling of glycine could be as high as 80% in wheat. Several hypotheses may explain the incomplete labeling of the CO_2 evolved during the PIB. First, although this process was reported to be negligible in leaves (12), photosynthetic oxygen evolution by photosystem II could reduce actual oxygen labeling in the chloroplast. Also, the incomplete labeling of the PIB could indicate the existence of another source of extra CO_2 during the PIB.

Until this study, attempts to detect ^{18}O labeling of CO_2 remained essentially unsuccessful. In fact, carbonic anhydrase catalyzes the reactions of hydratation-dehydratation between CO_2 and H_2O and therefore accelerates unlabeling of ^{18}O-labeled CO_2. This effect of carbonic anhydrase, which is generally present at high levels in plant cells, probably explains why ^{18}O labeling of photorespiratory CO_2 has not been observed until now in photosynthetic organisms.

This work establishs for the first time a direct link between O_2 uptake in the light, CO_2 production and the PIB. Isotopic ^{18}O labeling of CO_2 will probably supply a powerful tool to elucidate the components implicated in the CO_2 production flux occurring in the light or during light to dark transitions. It will be however necessary to adapt experimental procedures in order to generalize these results to other plant materials such as protoplasts or leaves.

5. REFERENCES

(1) Tolbert, N.E. (1980) in The Biochemistry of Plants, ed. Davies, D.D., (Acad. Press, New York), Vol. 2, pp. 487-523.

(2) Bowes, G., Ogren, W.L. and Hageman, R.H. (1971) Biochem. Biophys. Res. Commun. 45, 716-722.

(3) Dimon, B. and Gerster, R. (1976) C. R. Acad. Sci. Paris 283, 507-510

(4) Andrews T.J., Lorimer G.H. and Tolbert N.E. (1973) Biochemistry 12, 11-18.

(5) Berry, J.A, Osmond, C.B. and Lorimer, G.H. (1978) Plant Physiol. 62, 954-967

(6) Gerster, R. (1971) Planta 97, 155-177

(7) Rebeille, F., Gans, P., Chagvardieff, P., Pean, M., Tapie, P. and Thibault, P. (1988) J. Biol. Chem. 263, 12373-12377

(8) Chagvardieff, P., Péan, M., Carrier, P., and Dimon, B. (1990) *Plant Physiol. Biochem.* 28, 231-238

(9) Decker, J.P (1959) Plant Physiol. 34, 100-102

(10) Husic, D.W., Husic, H.D. and Tolbert, N.E. (1987) Critic. Rev. in Plant Sci. 5, 45-100

(11) de Veau, E.J. and Burris, J.E. (1989) Plant Physiol. 90, 500-511

(12) Samish, Y.B. (1971) Photosynthetica 9, 372-375

PHOSPHATE-DEFICIENCY REDUCES THE PHOTOSYSTEM II EFFICIENCY OF CHINESE CABBAGE LEAVES

Park, Youn-Il and Young-Nam Hong, Biol. Dept. Seoul Nat'l Univ. Seoul 151-742, Korea

1. INTRODUCTION

The inorganic phosphate content in higher plant leaves has been known as the internal regulator of photosynthesis [1]. Hence, there have been many reports on the primary action of the phosphate deficiency on leaf photosynthesis [2-4]. However, there is a rare attention on the modulation of photochemical activity of PSII to the internal metabolic perturbations in leaves by phosphate deficiency [5,6]. Recently, it was reported that phosphate deficiency in Chinese cabbage leaves by mannose feeding increased the nonphotochemical quenchings during the induction of photosynthesis, accompanying the decline of photosynthetic CO_2 exchange rate [7]. In present paper we describe the further work conducted to investigate the changes of intrinsic quantum yield of PSII ($\varphi_{PSII} = \varphi_{CO2}/qQ$) in relation to the development of nonphotochemical quenchings.

2. MATERIAL AND METHODS

Primary leaves of Chinese cabbage (*Brassica campestris* L. cv Seoul) were detached from 15-day-old plants and treated with DW or 25 $mmolm^{-3}$ mannose for various periods under the growth light condition (PFD; 80 $\mu molm^{-2}s^{-1}$) [7]. Rates of CO_2 exchange from the detached leaves were measured by using an open-gas exchange systems with infra red gas analyzer (LCA2, ADC CO., U.K.) [7]. Modulated chlorophyll fluorescence emission from the upper surface of the detached leaves were measured by using a PAM fluorimeter (Walz Co., F.R.G.). Data for fast fluorescence changes and fluorescence relaxation kinetics following single turnover saturation flashes (XST 103, Walz Co., F.R.G.) were collected with an IBM compatible computer mounted with a data acquisition board. Quenching coefficients of photochemical (qQ) and nonphotochemical (qNP) during steady state photosynthesis were determined as described in Ref. [8], and "energy"-dependent quenching (qE) as described in [9]. The proportion of oxidized P700 (a820) during steady state assimilation was determined according to [10] by using a modified emitter-detector unit [11]. All fluorescence parameters and a820 values in control leaves did not change for 12 hrs after the treatment of mannose.

3. RESULTS AND DISCUSSION

The kinetics of two step fluorescence rise upon dark-light transition in Chinese cabbage leaves are shown in Fig. 1. Both the fluorescence rises from the constant fluorescence (F_O) to the intermediate fluorescence (F_I) and F_I to peak fluorescence (F_P) were decreased gradually upto 9 h of mannose-feeding time and then remained unchanged. Increase in F_O level were observed in 9 h - and 12 h - treated leaves. The fluorescence

N. Murata (ed.), Research in Photosynthesis, Vol. IV, 699–702.

rise from Fo is dependent on the redox state of primary PSII electron acceptor, Q_A [12]. Thus, the decrease in variable fluorescence might be caused by the changes in the electron transfer rate from Q_A^- to the secondary acceptor, Q_B (and PQ). The reoxidation kinetics of Q_A^- of mannose-fed leaves for various time periods were measured (Fig. 2). Their decay constants calculated as described in [13] did not show any significant differences (data not shown), but the maximal intermediate fluroscence yields (F_{MI}) declined gradually upto 9 hrs of feeding time. This result suggests that the decrease in variable fluorescence shwon in Fig. 1 is not due to the changes in the electron transfer rate from Q_A^- to the secondary acceptor, Q_B, (and to PQ pool) but due to the restriction of Q_A because the F_{MI} level is consistent with the approximate fraction of reduced Q_A^- [14].

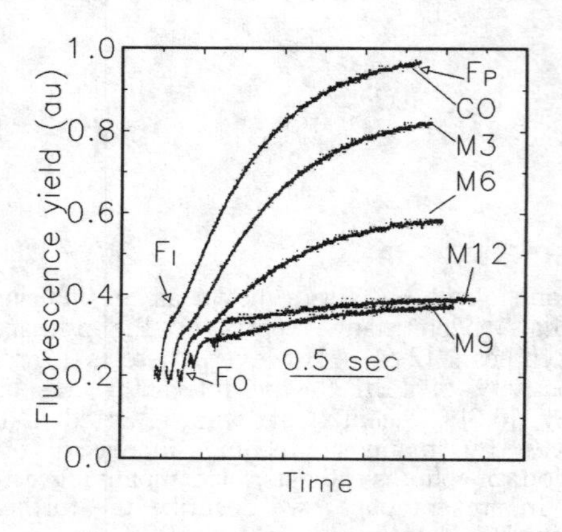

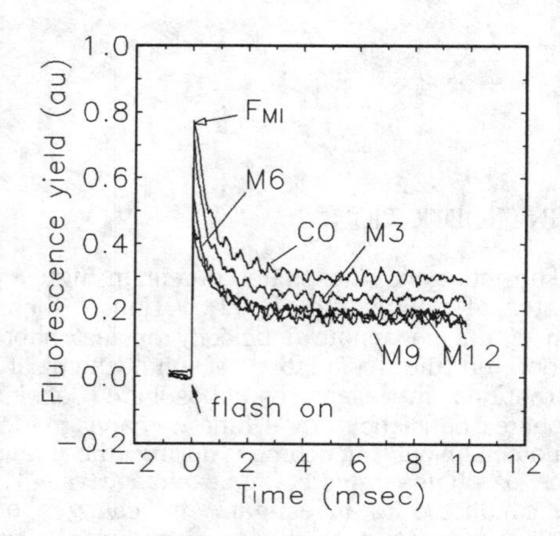

Fig. 1 (left). Changes of fluorescence induction kinetics as a function of mannose feeding time. CO: DW treated, M: mannose treated. Each numbers represents the mannose feeding time. Actinic light intensity: 80 μmolm^{-2}s^{-1}.

Fig. 2 (right). Changes of fluorescence relaxation kinetics following a saturating single turnover flash (XST 103, Walz Co.).

This view was confirmed by the decreases in the variable fluorescence yields (Fv) resulted from the full reduction of PQ pools (Fig. 3). Decline of Fv yields lead to the decrease of excitation energy capture efficiency by PSII, which revealed as the ratio of variable to maximal fluorescence (Fv/Fm) [12]. Consequently it is assumed that nonphotochemical quenching at PSII increased in mannose-fed leaves.

By mannose feeding, the inorganic phosphate (Pi) level inside in chloroplasts is decreased [15] through the restriction of the Pi recycling between cytosol and chloroplast [16], which may restrict the formation of ATP. ATP level in mannose-fed leaves declined by 66 % as compared to controls (Table 1). This decreasing availability of Pi in turn might lead to the development of pH gradient across the thylakoid membrane or the acidification of inner-lumen of thylakoid.

Table 1. Changes in the ATP contents (nmol/leaf) in the 15-day old primary leaves of Chinese cabbage

Treatment	Co- 0h	C0- 6h	Ma- 6h	Co-12h	Ma-12h
ATP	0.44±0.06	0.45±0.07	0.15±0.03	0.32±0.06	0.14±0.02

In order to check the development of pH gradient across the thylakoid membrane in the mannose-fed leaves, quenching analysis of chlorophyll fluorescence were conducted (Fig. 4). As the time of mannose feeding increased, the fraction of reduced PSII (1-qQ) and oxidized P700 (a820) were gradually increased in parallel to the treatment time. Furthermore, nonphotochemical quenchings (qNP) increased. Especially, "energy"-dependent quenching (qE) was promptly reached plateau after 6 h and then remained high, which means the development of pH gradient across the thylakoid membrane [12]. The formed pH gradient across the thylakoid membranes would restrict the electron transport through the limitation of the reoxidation of plastoquinol by cytochrome b_6 f complex [17]. Therefore, the formed pH gradient in Pi deficient leaves would lead to the increases both the fractions of reduced Q_A (high 1-qQ) and oxidized PSI reaction centres (high a820) during steady - state photosynthesis. These two opposing effects of pH on the reduction of Q_A (Fig. 2) and reoxidation of PQH_2 (Fig. 4) were also reported on the spinach thylakoids [18].

The photochemical efficiencies of PSII ($\varphi_{PSII} = \varphi_{CO_2}/qQ$, [10]) during steady - state photosynthesis rapidly declined upto 6 h after mannose treatment and remained then unchanged (Fig. 5). These decreases in φ_{PSII} might be attributable to the development of pH gradient across thylakoid membrane.

Because the increase in Fo and the decrease in the ratio of (Fv)/Fm from Fig. 3 are regarded as the symptons of impaired photosynthetic appparatus [12], we analyzed the photosynthetic performance of thylakoid membranes. Whole chain electron transport rates of thylakoid membranes from mannose - treated leaves for 12 hrs was declined by 30 % as compared to controls (Table 2). Consequently it is assumed that prolonged Pi-deficiency impaired photosynthetic appparatus by prolonged Pi-deficiency.

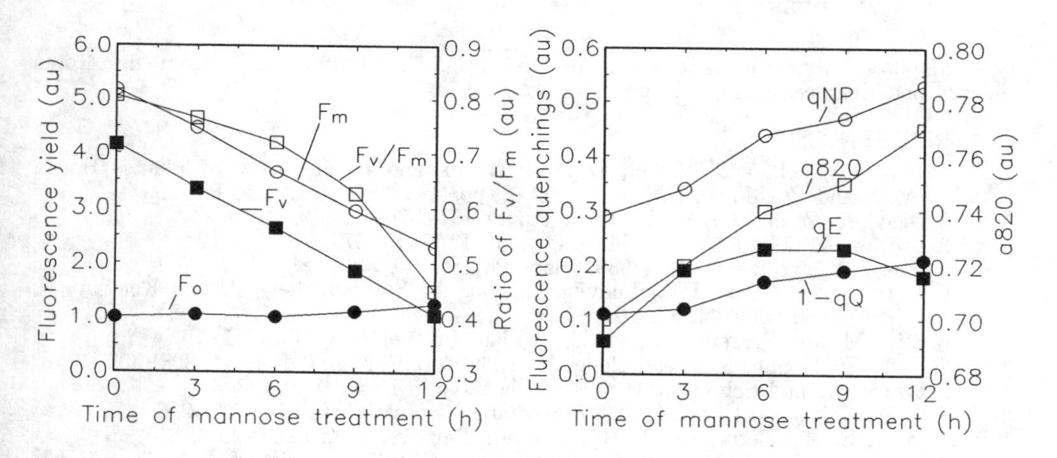

Fig. 3 (left). Changes of fluorescence parameters upon dark-light transitions as a function of mannose feeding time. Saturation light intensity; 3700 μ molm^{-2}s^{-1}, Light pulse; 800 msec.

Fig. 4 (right). Changes in the coefficients of chlorophyll fluorescence quenchings and fraction of oxidized P700 (a820) at steady-state photosynthesis.

In conclusion the decreases of PSII efficiency in phosphate-deficient Chinese cabbage leaves are resulted from the inhibition of the redox change of Q_A probably due to the build-up of proton gradient across the thylakoid membrane. Furthermore the photosynthetic apparatus were impaired by the prolonged phosphate deficiency.

Table 2. Changes in the whole chain electron transport rates (O_2molmgChlh^{-1}) in the 15-day old primary leaves of Chinese cabbage

Treatment	Co- 0h	C0- 6h	Ma- 6h	Co-12h	Ma-12h
O_2 uptake rate	230.3±3.1	224.9±19.6	215.9±20.7	228.6±20.6	159.4±18.5

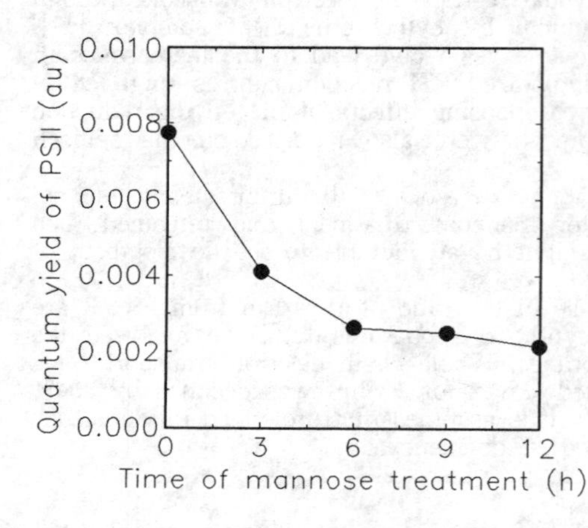

Fig. 5. Changes of the photochemical efficiency of PSII (φ_{PSII}) at steady - state photosynthesis as a function of mannose feeding time. φ_{PSII} in control leaves did not change during 12 h.

This work was supported by a research grant 911-0408-022-2 from the Korea Science and Engineering Foundation

4. REFERENCES

1 Robinson, S.P. and Walker, D.A. (1981) in The Biochemistry of Plants (Hatch, M.D. and Boardman, N.K. eds), Vol. 8, pp. 193-236, Academic Press.
2 Dietz, K.-Z. and Foyer, C. (1986) Planta 167, 376-381
3 Brooks, A. (1986) Aust. J. Plant Physiol. 13, 221-237
4 Rao, I.M., and Terry, N. (1989) Plant Physiol. 90, 820-825
5 Harris, G.C., Gibbs, P.B., Ludwig, G., Un, A., Sprengnether, M. and Kolodny, N. (1986) Plant Physiol. 82, 1081-1089
6 Stitt, M. and Schreiber, U. (1988) J. Plant Physiol. 133, 263-271
7 Park, Y.-I., Suh, K.H. and Hong, Y.-N. (1991) Korean J. Bot. 34, 303-309
8 Bilger, W. and Schreiber, U. (1986) Photosynth. Res. 10, 303-308
9 Quick, P.W. and Stitt, M. (1989) Biochim. Biophys. Acta 977, 287-296
10 Weis, E. and Berry, J.A. (1987) Biochim. Biophys. Acta 894, 198-208
11 Schreiber, U., Klughammer, C. and Neubauer,C. (1988) Z. Naturforsch. 43, 686-698
12 Krause, G.H. and Weis, E. (1991) Ann. Rev. Plant Physiol. Plant Mol. Biol. 42, 313-349
13 Cao, J. and Govindjee. (1990) Biochim. Biophys. Acta 1015, 180-188
14 Schreiber, U. and Neubauer, C. (1987) Z. Naturforsch. 42, 1255-1264
15 Sharkey, T.D. and Vanderveer, P.J. (1989) Plant Physiol. 91, 679-684
16 Herold, A., Lewis, D.H. and Walker, D.A. (1976) New Phytol. 76, 397-407
17 West, K.R. and Wiskich, J.T. (1968) Biochem. J. 109, 533-594
18 Rees, D. and Horton, P. (1990) Biochim. Biophys. Acta 1016, 219-227

SENESCENCE AND THE PHOTOSYNTHETIC PERFORMANCE OF INDIVIDUAL LEAVES OF DECIDUOUS BROADLEAVED TREES AS RELATED TO FOREST DYNAMICS

KOIKE,T., SANADA,M. LEI,T.T.[1] KITAO,M. AND LECHOWICZ,M.J.[1]
Forestry and Forest Products Research Institute, Sapporo 062, JAPAN
[1]Department of Biology, McGill University, Montreal, PQ, Canada H3A 1B1

1. INTRODUCTION

Leaf development and senescence are regulated by the specific response of tree species to the environment(1,2). In fact, autumn coloration of late successional species begins from the top part of a crown while early successional species start from the inner part of a crown(3). Based on an analysis of Chl.fluorescence, senescence of leaves starts in mid summer(4). Does the timing of leaf shedding depend upon the specific patterns of trees with different successional characteristics(5)? What about the functional performance of individual leaves during leaf senescence?

To answer these questions, we monitored the time course of the photosynthesis of individual leaves in order to ascertain the timing of inactivation of leaves. We measured the photosynthesis, Chl.fluorescence and nitrogen content in different aged leaves before leaf shedding. We discussed the physiological changes in individual leaves of seral tree species as related to the successional strategy in a forest stand.

2. Materials and Methods

2.1 Plant materials: Leaves of the sunny and shady crown of early successional species, birch (*Betula maximowicziana*; Heterophyllous type) and alder (*Alnus hirsuta*; indeterminant type); late successional species, maple (*Acer japonicum*; determinant type) were used. In mid August, the edge of the sun leaves of the maple turned slightly reddish. Trees were planted in the experimental forest of the Forestry and Forest Products Research Institute (Sapporo; 42°58'N, 141°23'E, 140m a.s.l.).

2.2 Measurements: Photosynthesis of the odd numbered leaves as counted from the base was measured with an infra red gas analyzer(Shimadzu URA2S) under conditions of saturated PPFD(800 $\mu mol \cdot m^{-2} s^{-1}$), an optimum leaf temperature(20°C), ambient CO_2(340ppm), regulated by a climatized chamber(Koito KG) and flow rate of 83 $cm^3 \cdot s^{-1}$. Relative humidity in an assimilation chamber(20x18x2cm) monitored with a Vaisala humidity sensor(HMP 31UT) was kept at ca.80%. Chl.fluorescence was detected with a fluorometer(Hansatech PEA) in mid August. Chl. content in a leaf was analyzed using 80% acetone extracts. Leaf nitrogen concentration was determined using a C/N corder(Yanagimoto MT 500W). Chl. and nitrogen analysis was carried out in early October.

N. Murata (ed.), Research in Photosynthesis, Vol. IV, 703–706.

3. Results

3.1 Photosynthesis and leaf nitrogen concentration of individual leaves

Except for the first leaves of birch(early leaves), the maximum photosynthetic rate at light saturation(Pns) of alder and birch increased with increasing leaf age then decreased rapidly as the individual leaves aged(Fig.1). The max. Pns of early leaves of birch and maple was maintained over most of the growing season. In maple, there was little difference in Pns between individual leaves. Pns of all leaves unfolded at spring began to decrease in early September irrespective of the green color of the leaves. The younger leaves of birch and alder expanded in July which kept a high Pns of 8 $\mu mol \cdot m^{-2}s^{-1}$ even in early October.

With increasing leaf order, Pns and leaf nitrogen concentration of birch and alder increased(Fig.2). On the contrary, those of maple decreased with increasing leaf order. A positive correlation between Pns and leaf nitrogen concentration was found.

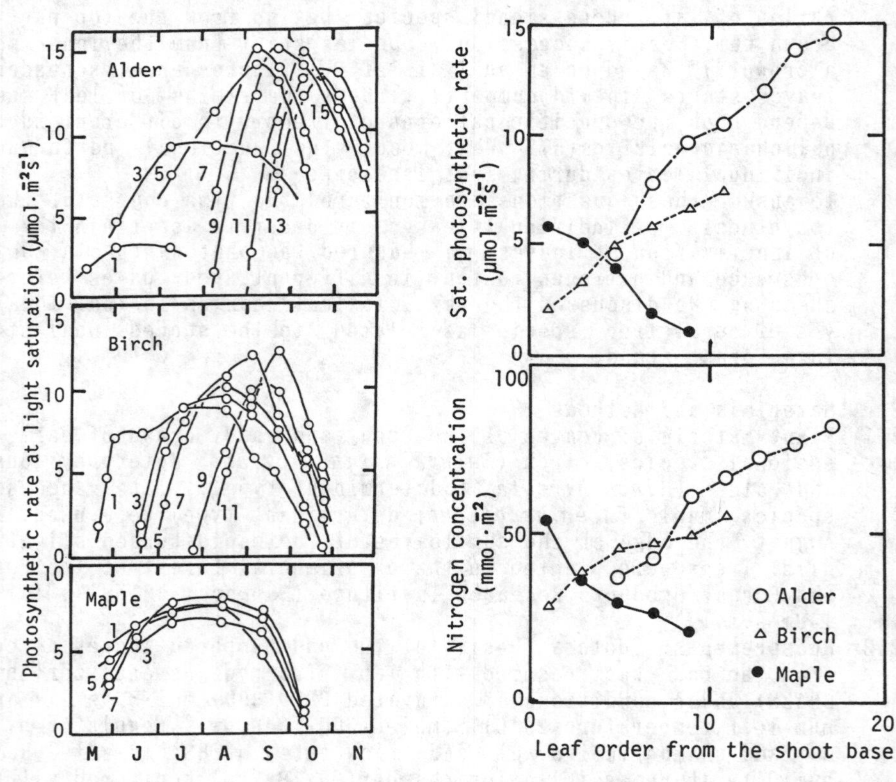

FIGURE 1. Seasonal change in the photosynthesis of individual leaves. Numbers indicate leaf order counted from the shoot base.

FIGURE 2. Photosynthesis at light saturation and nitrogen concentration of each leaf order. Measurement in early October.

3.2 Chlorophyll content and Chl.fluorescence of sun and shade leaves

Chl. content of alder and birch leaves increased from the bottom part of a shoot to the top(Fig.3). In contrast, Chl. content of maple leaves decreased with increasing leaf order. Except for the older leaves of alder, Chl.b content was more stable than Chl.a. The older leaves of the alder decreased both Chl.a+b. Chl.b of maple leaves was almost constant at 0.1 $mmol \cdot m^{-2}$.

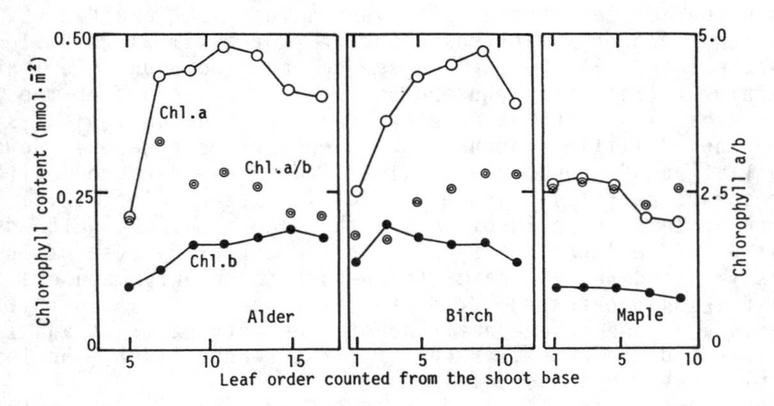

FIGURE 3. Chlorophyll content and chlorophyll a/b ratio determined in early October. Measurement replicated was three times in each.

The Chl.fluorescence curve of sun leaves of alder and birch decreased more rapidly after reaching the peak (P) than with shade leaves (Fig.4). In maple, the curve of sun leaves initially showed higher

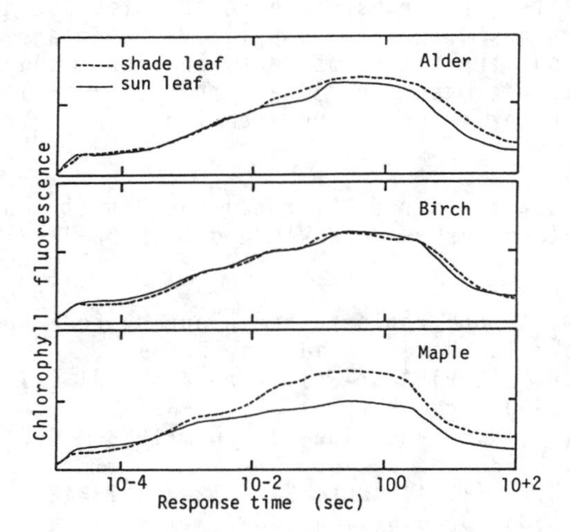

FIGURE 4. Chlorophyll-fluorescence induction kinetics in sun and shade leaves. In maple, autumn coloration started from the top part of a crown in mid August with lower temperature.

values then lower than shade leaves. The difference between sun and shade leaves of birch was the smallest. Despite the green color of the alder leaves, the Chl.fluorescence of shade leaves was higher after the 10^{-2} sec. passed.

4. Discussion

Photosynthetic rate, Chl.content and leaf nitrogen concentration of each species decreased with increasing leaf age(Figs.2,3). Leaf nitrogen concentration may allocate for maximizing the leaf photosynthesis(6,7,8). During senescence, many compounds in leaves, containing nitrogen and phosphorous, are recycled from the leaf into the stem(1). Alder leaves stay green in color until leaf shedding(3) and showed little response to a supply of nitrogen(9). However, the initiation of senescence in alder leaves was detected with Chl.fluorescence curve(4) irrespective of its green color(Fig.4). The pattern of leaf aging in birch was the same as alder, which may be related to the light environment in the canopy because of the continuously expanding new leaves throughout the growing season. In maple, leaf aging progressed from the outer part of a crown (Fig.2,3,4) because of the severe environment, eg. strong light and large temperature differences. Except for the second flush, the leaf age of maple leaves was the same(3).

Trees indeterminant leaf development produce a high photosynthetic capacity with a short lifespan, which may be advantageous for achieving as long a growth space as possible. Before leaf shedding, little nitrogen in alder was recycled, which may be attributed to the nitrogen fixative microorganism in its root system. In contrast, trees with determinant leaf growth, such as maple, quickly complete shoot elongation and have long leaf lifespans. Most of the nitrogen in maple leaves may translocate to the stem for next growing season. This pattern may confer a competitive advantage to an old forest. In conclusion, the timing of leaf senescence and the photosynthetic capacity and nitrogen recycling are closely related to the successional characteristics of tree species.

ACKNOWLEDGEMENTS

Financial support in part by the Japan Ministry of Agriculture, Forestry and Fisheries is acknowledged (BCP 92-II-2).

REFERENCES

1 Šesták, Z.D. (1985) Photosynthesis during Leaf Development. pp.396 Dr.Junk Pub., The Hague; Academia, Praha
2 Dickson, R.E. (1989) Ann. Sci. For. 46S, 631-647
3 Koike, T. (1990) Tree Physiol. 7, 21-32
4 Lichtenthaler, H.K. and Rinderle, U. (1988) CRC Crit. Rev. Analy. Chem. 19S1, 29-85
5 Lechowicz, M.J. (1984) Amer. Nat. 124, 821-842
6 Field, C. (1983) Oecologia 56, 341-347
7 Harper, J.L. (1989) Oecologia 80, 53-58
8 Hirose, T. and Werger, M.J.A. (1987) Oecologia 72, 520-526
9 Koike, T. and Sanada, M. (1989) Ann. Sci. For. 46S, 476-478

FLAG LEAF PHOTOSYNTHESIS AND SENESCENCE OF THE UPPER THREE LEAVES DURING SPIKELET FILLING IN RICE (Oryza sativa L.)

PARK, T.S., A.A. ALEJAR and B.S. VERGARA, UNIVERSITY OF THE PHILIPPINES AT LOS BAÑOS and INTERNATIONAL RICE RESEARCH INSTITUTE, LAGUNA, PHILIPPINES

INTRODUCTION

The timing of decline in photosynthetic capacity of leaves during reproductive development differed among species (1,2). It also showed poor or no correlation with senescence of source leaves (3). This relationship has not been fully investigated in rice.

MATERIALS AND METHODS

Thirteen rice cultivars, two advanced lines, and three isogenic lines were grown in waterlogged potted soil inside the greenhouse. Chlorophyll was determined on intact flag, penultimate, and third leaves at 0, 5, 10, 15, 20, 25 and 30 d after heading (DAH) using a handy chlorophyll meter. Carbon dioxide exchange rate in flag leaves during the same period was measured by an infrared gas analyzer (4).

RESULTS AND DISCUSSION

The pattern of chlorophyll loss in the individual upper three leaves (Fig. 1) exhibited reduction typical of an acropetal progression of foliar senescence in rice (5). The figure shows that 75% of chlorophyll at heading time or initial level was reached at 14 DAH in the third leaves, 20 DAH in the penultimate leaves, and 26 DAH in the flag leaves. The data suggest that it is better to use the penultimate leaves at 20 DAH to compare leaf chlorophyll of rice varieties for senescence studies, since chlorophyll loss comes late in the flag leaves and very early in the third leaves. However, the other two leaves could also be used because there was a high correlation of the rate of chlorophyll loss among the leaves.

Senescence of the flag leaves was accompanied by decline in photosynthetic activity showing a quadratic linear regression curve (Fig. 2). The maximum level was observed at 5 DAH (flowering) followed by a rapid decline, reaching the minimum at 26 DAH. This characteristic pattern in rice also demonstrates the positive relationship ($r = 0.76^{**}$) between chlorophyll degradation and photosynthetic activity of flag leaves.

REFERENCES

1. Ong, C.K. and Marshall C. (1975) Ann. Bot. 39,413-421.
2. Woodward, R.G. and Rawson H.M. (1976) Aust. J. Plant Physiol. 3,257-267.
3. Thomas, H. and Stoddart J.L. (1980) Annu. Rev. Plant Physiol. 31,83-111.
4. Cruz, R.T, O'toole J.C. Dingkuhn M., Yambao E.B., Thangaraj M. and de Datta S.K. (1986). Aust. J. Plant Physiol. 13,657-675.
5. Mondal, W.A. and Choudhuri, M.A. (1986) Physiol. Plant. 61,287-292.

N. Murata (ed.), Research in Photosynthesis, Vol. IV, 707–708.

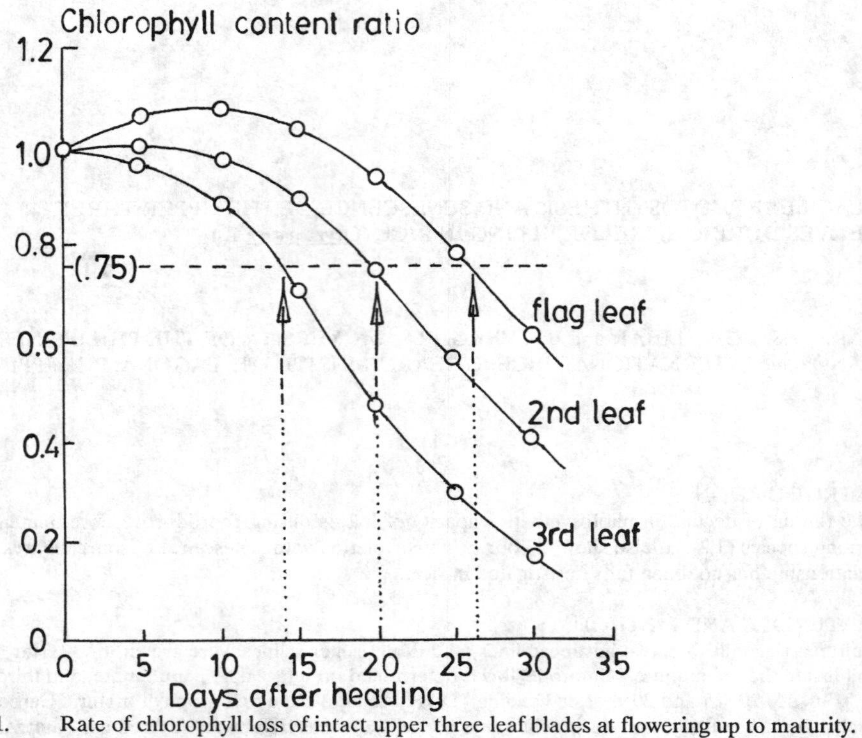

FIGURE 1. Rate of chlorophyll loss of intact upper three leaf blades at flowering up to maturity.

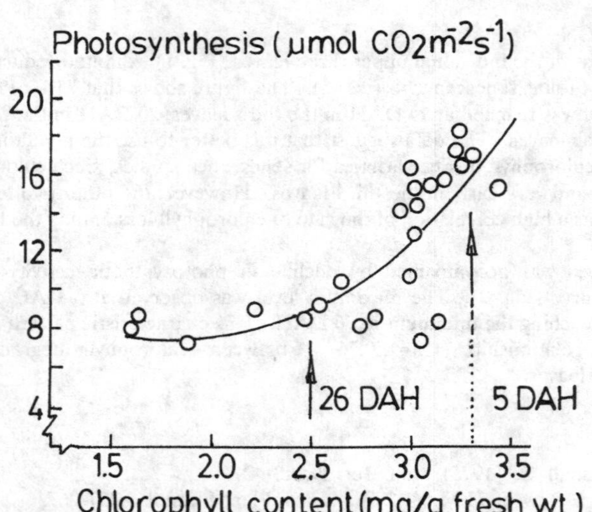

FIGURE 2. Relationship between photsynthetic rate and chlorophyll content of intact flag leaves at flowering up to maturity of two isogenic lines.

[^{14}C] SUCROSE UPTAKE OF INDIVIDUAL SPIKELETS IN RICE

KIM, J.D., A.A. ALEJAR and B.S. VERGARA, UNIVERSITY of the PHILIPPINES at LOS BAÑOS and INTERNATIONAL RICE RESEARCH INSTITUTE, LAGUNA, PHILIPPINES

INTRODUCTION

The production of more high-density (HD) grains or spikelets to increase the yield potential of rice have shown other various beneficial effects (1,2). These HD spikelets are usually located on the number five position of the primary branch of a panicle in contrast to the lowest density spikelet number two (3). Studies have shown that the final spikelet weight is highly correlated to rate and duration of spikelet filling (4) but could be limited by sink activity (5). Since dry matter accumulation in the spikelet of most indica rice is highest shortly after flowering (3,5), this study investigates sink activity of individual spikelets 5 days after heading (DAH).

MATERIALS AND METHODS

Rice cultivar IR30 was grown in potted waterlogged soil inside the greenhouse. At five DAH, the panicles, including 5 cm internode were cut and placed in a test tube containing 5 ml of [^{14}C] sucrose with 0.5 uci/ml activity, 30 mg sucrose/ml and 0.1% glutamine. Sucrose-UL-^{14}C with specific gravity of 553.2 uci/mmol was purchased from Sigma Chemical Co., USA. The test tubes with panicles were kept in a dark room at 25 ^{o}C. After 24 h, the panicles were taken out of the solution and the spikelets separated and dried at 70 ^{o}C for 3 d and pulverized. The total ^{14}C content of 20 mg spikelets were oxidized and determined by Packard liquid scintillation counter.

RESULTS AND DISCUSSION

Figure 1a shows that the individual spikelets had different sink activity regardless of their attachment to the different branches. The top branch had a stronger sink force than the middle and lowest branch at early heading time. Generally, the second and third spikelets of a branch showed weaker ^{14}C activity or sink force than the other spikelets. Although the fifth spikelet in the middle branch did not exhibit anthesis earlier than did spikelets of the top branch (Fig 1c), it had stronger sink force at 5 DAH (Fig 1a). Similarly, the same spikelets on the lowest branch was the heaviest (Fig 1b), although it flowered later and showed very low ^{14}C activity at 5 DAH. The sink activity of the fifth spikelet must have increased later and was also highest within the lower primary branch. These observation resulted in high density of the first and fifth spikelets. The results confirm the earlier findings that spikelet filling occurs first at the top branch and that high density spikelets are located on the first and fifth spikelets of any branch.

N. Murata (ed.), Research in Photosynthesis, Vol. IV, 709–710.

of the fifth spikelet must have increased later and was also highest within the lower primary branch. These observation resulted in high density of the first and fifth spikelets. The results confirm the earlier findings that spikelet filling occurs first at the top branch and that high density spikelets are located on the first and fifth spikelets of any branch.

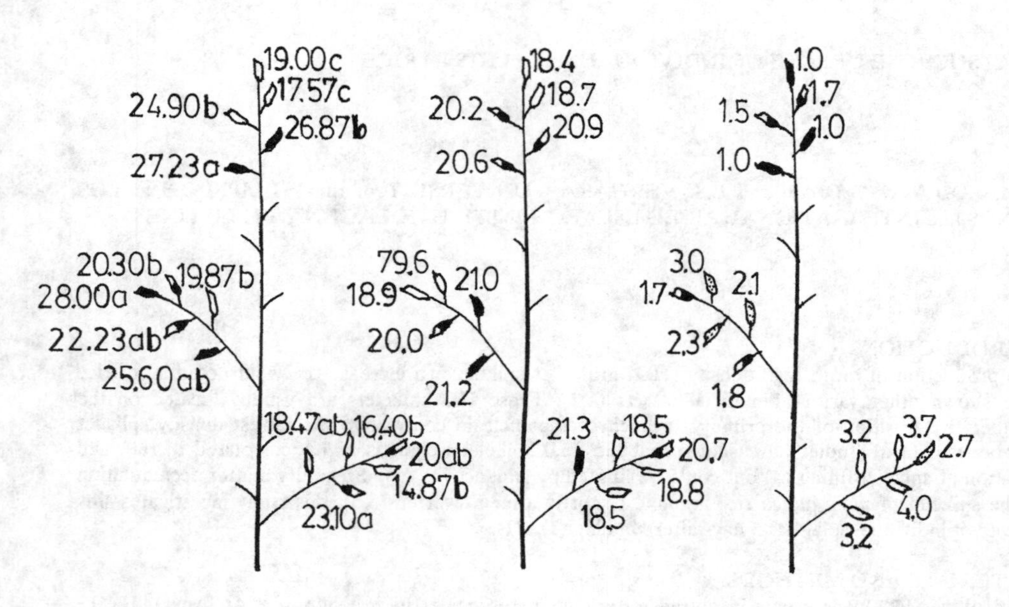

FIGURE 1. ^{14}C activity (a), spikelet weight (b) and days to anthesis (c) of individual spikelet of rice IR30. ^{14}C activity was measured five days after heading while spikelet weight was taken at maturity.

REFERENCES

1. Vergara, B.S., Ventakeswarlu, B., Janoria, M., Ahn, J.K., Kim, J.K., and Visperas R.M. (1990). Philipp. J. Crop Sci. 15(1);33-40.
2. Arain, A., Vergara,B.S., and Visperas R.M. (1990). Philipp. J.Crop Sci. 5(3);137-145.
3. Ahn, J.K. (1986). Ph.D. Thesis, University of the Philippines at Los Baños 127p.
4. Mallik, S., Aguilar A.M. and Vergara B.S. (1989) Phillip. J. Crop Sci. 14 (Suppl);S40.(Abst.).
5. Kim, J.D. 1990. Ph.D Thesis University of thePhilippines at Los Baños, Laguna, Philippines

TRANSLOCATION OF PHOTOASSIMILATES FROM LEAVES TO FRUITS IN GRAPE SHOOTS.
Nagoya Congress Center, Nagoya, Japan, August 30 - September 4, 1992

YOSHIE MOTOMURA, FAC. AGR., HIROSAKI UNIV., HIROSAKI, 036, JAPAN

1. INTRODUCTION

The patterns of 14C-asimilate transported from individual source leaves to sink organs are influenced by the vertical position with respect to the phyllotaxic arrangement. In the grape shoot, translocation of assimilates from the leaves to the cluster are also coupled with the orthostichy(1). In this experiment, to survey the factors affecting to the partitioning of assimilates in the grape shoots, the effects of relative position of two clusters on the shoot(4), shoot pinching, leaf-halving and girdling of the shoot(5) on the incorporation of 14C-assimilates from individual leaves into the cluster were investigated. On the other hand, it is understood that the translocation substance in grape is sucrose in Concord(2), and monosaccharides and sucrose in Delaware(3). In this experiment, chemical changes of translocation substances in the tissues from source leaf to berries were investigated.

2. MATERIALS AND METHODS

Actively growing Delaware grape shoots of uniform size were used, and the leaves on the shoots were numbered from the base.

Experiment I: One week before full bloom, their clusters were thinned to three configurations (Fig.1).

Treatment A: One cluster on the third node from the base of the shoot.
Treatment B: Two clusters on the second and third nodes, on the opposite side of the shoot.
Treatment C: Two clusters on the third and fifth nodes on the same side of the shoot.

Every week from one week before through to three weeks after full bloom, a leaf of a shoot was fed with 14CO2, in each treatment, and ten basal leaves were used for this experiment. For 14CO2 labaling, each individual leaf was enclosed in a polyethylene bag. 14CO2 was released inside the bag for two hours. Twenty four hours after feeding, the shoots were sampled and divided into four or five parts: the fed leaf, cluster(s), and apical and basal parts above and below the node of the fed leaf, repectively. The shoot parts were oven dried, weighed, grounded, and oxidized by combustion using a oxidizer. The 14C activity was counted with a liquid scintillation spectrometer. The results

N. Murata (ed.), Research in Photosynthesis, Vol. IV, 711–714.

were expressed as percentage distribution into cluster and percentage contribution of the leaves on each side of the stem (odd-numbered and even numbered leaves), calculated as follows:
Percentage distribution of 14C to the cluster = (14C recovered in the cluster/total 14C recovered in the whole shoot including fed leaf) x 100
Percentage contribution of odd or even numbered leaves = (Percentage distribution into cluster from odd- or even-numbered leaves/percentage distribution into cluster from all fed leaves on the shoot) x 100

Experiment II: Clusters were thinned leaving one at the third node. Every week from full bloom to three weeks after full bloom, shoots were trimed to five configurations (FIg.1), as follows:
Treatment D: Untreated
Treatment E: Shoots were pinched off above the 10th leaf.
Treatment F. Shoots were pinched off above the 5th leaf.
Treatment G. Shoots were pinched off above the 10th leaf and half of each remaining individual leaf was cut off along the midvein.
Treatment H. Shoots were pinched off above the 5th leaf and half of each remaining individual leaf was cut off along the mid vein.
14CO2 feedings were carried out as above, every week from two weeks before through to three weeks after full bloom.

Experiment III: Clusters were thinned leaving one at the third node, from seven weeks through to ten weeks after full bloom, and the shoots were trimmed to two configurations (Fig.1), as follows:
Treatment I. Shoots were pinched off above the 5th leaf.
Treatment J. Shoots were pinched off above the 5th leaf and the basal node of the shoot was girdled.
Feedings of 14CO2 were carried out as Experiment II.

Experiment IV: Shoots of Delaware three weeks after full bloom were used. 14CO2 was fed to the fouth leaf, with the same method as the above experiments. Two, 4, 8 and 24 hours after the begining of feeding, the 14C-fed leaf blade, the petiole of the fed leaf, the bark of the stem between the fed leaf and cluster(the fourth node), the peduncle and berries were sampled and extracted with 80% ethanol. Each extract was fractionated to fructose, glucose, sucrose and other fraction by paper chromatography. The chromatogram was divided into each sugar fraction and was oxidized by combustion, and 14C-activity was counted with a Liquid Scintillation Spectrometer.

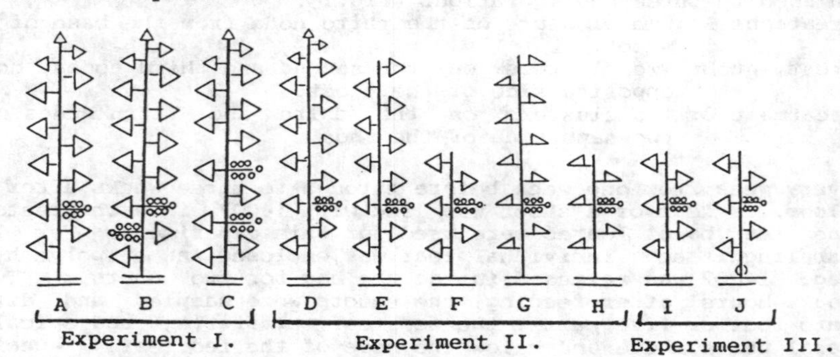

Fig. 1. Illustration of the position of cluster(s) and leaves on the shoot.

3. RESULTS AND DICUSSION

Experiment I. Effect of relative position of two clusters.
Before full bloom, percent distributions of 14C of the cluster on the third node in Treatment A were higher from the second and fourth leaves on the same side as the cluster, just below and above the cluster. After full bloom, however, the 14C-assimilates distributed a high percentage into the cluster not only from the second and fourth leaves but also from the leaves above them, including those on the opposite side to the leaves, but distribution from the even-numbered leaves were higher than those from the odd-numberd ones. The percentage contribution of the even-numbered leaves to the cluster were 69% to 90% for the cluster on the third node in Treatment A.
In the shoots with two clusters, the supply of 14C to each cluster was similar to that for the shoot with one cluster. In Treatment B, the cluster on the second node took up 14C-assimilates mostly from the odd-numbered leaves. On the contrary, the percentage distribution into the cluster on the third node was higher from the even-numbered leaves. Thus, in Treatment B, almost all of the leaves supplied a high percentage of 14C-assimilates to the clusters on their own sides. In Treatment C, both of the clusters received the assimilates mostly from the even-numbered leaves. Therefore, the leaves on the same side as the cluster on the shoot contributed 69% to 98% of the assimilate supply to the cluster growth in these stages through the treatments.

Experiment II. Effects of shoot pinching and leaf-halving.
Regardless of shoot pinching and leaf-halving, the mean values of percentage distribution of 14C-assimilates into the cluster from even-numbered leaves were higher than those from odd-numbered leaves, at all feeding times. The percentage contributions of 14C-assimilate to clusters from even-numbered leaves was 80-90% in all treatments. Regardless of pinching and leaf halving, the leaves supplying the greatest amount of labeled assimilates to the developing cluster were in the orthostichies adjacent to the position of the cluster on the stem.

Experiment III. Effect of girdling of shoot.
In Treatment I, the mean values of percentage distribution of 14C-assimilates into the cluster from even-numbered leaves were higher than those from odd-numbered leaves, at all feeding times, while, in the girdled shoot(Treatment J), percentage contributions were approximately 50%, which means similar contributions were made to the leaves on either sides. These facts show that by the increase of 14C-assimilates translocated to the cluster from the leaves on the side opposite to the shoot, traversing the vascular bundles in the stem, they were of similar quantities to assimilates translocated from the leaves on the same side as the cluster of the stem.

Experiment IV. Sugar composition of translocated substances.
Translocated substances, which assimilated in the leaf blade and translocated to petiole and stem, were mainly monosaccharides and sucrose, while sucroe was not detected in peduncle and berries. Sucrose in the translocation substances was inverted to monosaccharides between the stem and peduncle. These results may suggest that the sucrose translocated during longitudial movement in the stem, it was inverted during the transverse movement in the stem.

Table 1. Percentage contributions of the even-numbered leaves.

Treat- ment	Node of cluster	Weeks after full bloom				
		-1	0	1	2	3
A	3	83.4	90.0	85.0	86.2	69.8
B	2	3.1	8.4	8.9	5.3	14.0
	3	95.0	74.1	94.8	86.1	80.0
C	3	94.8	96.1	81.9	90.7	85.0
	5	78.0	88.9	86.8	86.5	81.7
		Weeks after full bloom				
		0	1	2	3	
D	3	90.7	84.4	87.4	85.0	
E	3	87.7	91.0	75.8	71.7	
F	3	87.0	91.3	79.9	73.0	
G	3	85.5	90.8	77.3	68.3	
H	3	83.6	84.7	68.4	75.0	
		Weeks after full bloom				
		7	8	9	10	
I	3	73.8	79.5	58.3	64.4	
J	3	51.4	53.8	52.0	51.9	

Table 2. Percentage distribution of 14-C into sugar fractions in each tissue.

Sugar fraction	Leaf blade				Petiole					
	Hours after feeding				Hours after feeding					
	2	4	8	24	2	4	8	24		
Fructose	43.8	33.0	30.5	46.3	39.1	39.5	46.6	41.3		
Glucose	45.5	56.9	62.3	46.7	33.4	41.0	38.7	44.1		
Sucrose	1.1	2.6	2.4	3.4	7.9	11.4	6.2	9.7		
Others	9.6	7.6	4.8	3.6	19.7	8.0	8.6	4.8		
	Stem(bark)				Peduncle			Berries		
	Hours after feeding				Hours after feeding			Hous after feeding		
	2	4	8	24	4	8	24	4	8	24
Fructose	30.5	33.2	39.2	40.0	49.9	53.3	43.6	41.3	35.4	31.3
Gluose	40.2	35.1	38.0	37.2	47.2	43.7	49.9	43.2	40.0	40.5
Sucrose	17.2	26.5	19.7	17.3	0.5	1.2	2.4	1.3	2.5	5.7
Others	12.1	5.3	3.1	5.5	2.4	1.7	4.1	14.2	22.2	22.5

4. CONCLUSION

Translocation of photoassimilates in grape shoots were greatly affected by phyllotaxi, and photoassimilates accumulated into clusters were mainly from the leaves on the same side as the cluster on the shoot.

Such a tendency was less affected by the position of the cluster on the shoot, shoot pinching, leaf-halving, then affected by ringing of the shoot. Translocation substances in Delaware were monosaccharides and sucrose, but sucrose was inverted to monosaccharides during translocation between stem and peduncle.

REFERENCES

1. Hale C.R. and Weaver,R.J. (1962) Hilgardia 33, 89-131
2. Swanson C.A. and EL-Shishiny,E.D.H.,(1958) Plant Physiol. 33, 33-37
3. Matsui,H., Yuda,E. and Nakagawa,S., (1985) J. Japan. Soc. Hort. Sci., 54(2), 184-191.
4. Motomura,Y.,(1990) Amer. J. Enol. Vitic., 41(4), 306-312
5. Motomura,Y.,(1992) Amer. J. Enol. Vitic., 44(1), in press

SIGNAL TRANSDUCTION IN BLUE LIGHT RESPONSE OF STOMATAL GUARD CELLS

Ken-ichiro Shimazaki, Biological Laboratory, Kyushu University, Fukuoka, Japan

1. INTRODUCTION

Gas exchange between plant and atmosphere is regulated by the aperture of stomatal pore which is surrounded by a pair of guard cells. Stomatal opening is efficiently induced by blue light (1). Blue light activates the proton pump in plasma membrane of guard cells, and creates an electrochemical gradient across the membrane, which induces the K^+ uptake through a K^+-selective channel (2,3,4). An accumulation of K-salt in guard cells decreases the water potential and causes water uptake, resulting in the stomatal opening. Several evidence indicate that blue light acts as a signal rather than an energy source, however, the mechanism by which the light perception is transduced into activation of the pump is still unknown. This paper presents recent results on the properties of blue light response of stomata using *Vicia* guard cell protoplasts and *Commelina* epidermis, suggesting that Ca^{2+}/calmodulin is involved in the blue light response of stomatal guard cells.

2. MATERIALS AND METHODS

Vicia faba plants were cultivated hydroponically in a green house. Plants of *Commelina benghalensis* ssp. were cultivated in soil with leaf mold in a green house. Guard cell protoplasts were isolated from *Vicia* epidermis according to the previous method (3). Epidermal layers of *Commelina* were obtained by the method of Weyers and Travis (5). Proton extrusion induced by blue light was measured according to the previous method using a glass pH electrode in *Vicia* guard cell protoplasts (3). Leaf tissue was fixed in 2% paraformaldehyde in 0.1 M sodium phosphate buffer (pH 7.2) and the dehydrated tissue was embedded in paraplast, sectioned by a microtome. Antiserum raised against spinach calmodulin was kindly provided by Dr. Muto in Tokyo University (6).

3. RESULTS AND DISCUSSION

3.1 Effect of various protein kinase inhibitors were investigated on blue light-dependent proton extrusion in *Vicia* guard cell protoplasts. Among these inhibitors, calmodulin-dependent myosin light chain kinase (MLCK) inhibitors, ML-7 and ML-9 were most effective to inhibit the proton extrusion. Preferential inhibitors of protein kinase C, H-7 and calphostin C had a slight effect. Other protein kinase inhibitors, H-8 (inhibitor of protein kinase A and G) and KN-62 (inhibitor of calmodulin kinase II) had no inhibitory effect (Table 1).

N. Murata (ed.), Research in Photosynthesis, Vol. IV, 715–718.

TABLE 1. Effect of protein kinase inhibitors on blue light-dependent proton extrusion in *Vicia* guard cell protoplasts.

Inhibitors	Concentrations	Magnitude of H^+ extrusion
	μM	nmol H^+ μg^{-1} protein pulse^{-1} (%)
H-7	0	0.301 (100)
	200	0.266 (88)
Calphostin C	0	0.585 (100)
	1	0.470 (80)
H-8	0	0.331 (100)
	200	0.321 (97)
KN-62	0	0.368 (100)
	50	0.360 (98)
ML-7	0	0.300 (100)
	50	0.073 (24)
ML-9	0	0.619 (100)
	50	0.129 (45)

3.2 Since activity of MLCK is regulated by calmodulin, the inhibitory action of calmodulin antagonist on blue light-dependent proton extrusion was expected. Table 2 shows the inhibition of the proton extrusion by calmodulin antagonists. All antagonists tested here strongly suppressed the proton extrusion in guard cell protoplasts. The result that W-5, a structural analogue of W-7 with less activity, had only a slight inhibition of the proton pump in compared with the severe inhibition of it by W-7, suggested that the action of the antagonists was specific to calmodulin.

TABLE 2. Inhibition of blue light-dependent H^+ extrusion by calmodulin antagonists in *Vicia* guard cell protoplasts.

Antagonists	Concentrations	Magnitude of H^+ extrusion
		nmol H^+ μg^{-1} protein pulse^{-1} (%)
Trifluoperazine	0	0.388 (100)
	50 (μM)	0.141 (36)
Compound 48/80	0	0.393 (100)
	10 (μg/ml)	0.014 (4)
Prenylamine	0	0.323 (100)
	50 (μM)	0.200 (62)
HT-74	0	0.315 (100)
	25 (μM)	0.053 (17)
W-7	0	0.455 (100)
	100 (μM)	0.261 (57)
W-5	0	0.448 (100)
	100 (μM)	0.411 (92)

3.3 Possible involvement of calmodulin in light-dependent stomatal opening was investigated using epidermal peels of Commelina benghalensis. When peels were illuminated with light (blue + red), stomata opened up to 14 um in 2hrs. If blue light was omitted, the stomatal aperture was reduced to less than 30% of in widely-opened stomata. This light-dependent opening was strongly inhibited by W-7, but only slightly inhibited by W-5 (Table 3).

TABLE 3. Inhibition of light-dependent stomatal opening by calmodulin antagonists in epidermal peels of Commelina benghalensis ssp.

Antagonists	Stomatal aperture
	μm
Control	13.80 ± 2.38
W-7 (200 μM)	2.52 ± 3.24
W-5 (200 μM)	11.61 ± 3.20

3.4 Calmodulin seems to be involved in blue light-dependent proton extrusion by Vicia guard cells and in stomatal opening in Commelina. We investigated the presence of calmodulin in guard cells by immunocytochemical method. Immunochemical staining of cross sections (6 μm thick) of Commelina green leaves using an antiserum against spinach calmodulin indicated that the immuno-reaction product was localized inside guard cells, in the vicinity of plasma membrane, in particular (Fig.1). When non-immune serum was used instead of the antiserum, the staining was drastically reduced, suggesting that the staining was specific to calmodulin or calmodulin-like proteins. Similar results were obtained in Vicia leaves (not shown).

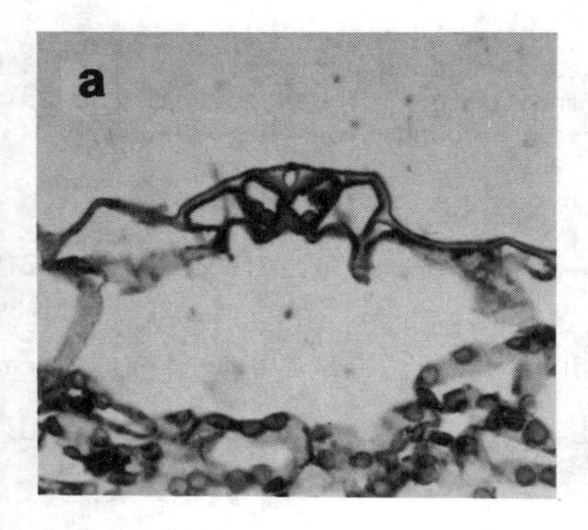

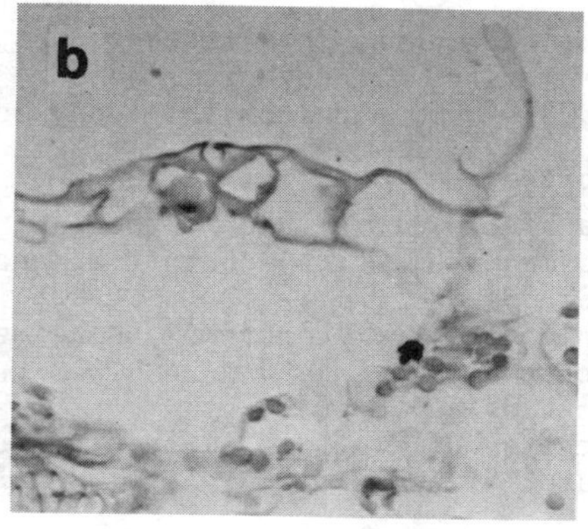

FIGURE 1. Immunochemical staining of cross sections of Commelina leaves.

Antiserum raised against spinach calmodulin was used as a first antibody. a) antiserum b) non-immune serum. Alkaline-phosphatase conjugated antiserum was applied as a secondary antibody to stain. Arrows indicate a pair of guard cells.

3.5 If calmodulin is involved in blue light-response of stomata, intracellular Ca^{2+} concentration in guard cells must be increased by the light signal. Ca^{2+} may come from external medium or internal Ca^{2+} stores such as endoplasmic reticulum and/or vacuole in guard cells. We tested the effect of several Ca^{2+} channel blockers on blue light-dependent proton extrusion. Among them, verapamil at 0.5mM inhibited the proton extrusion, suggesting the involvement of Ca^{2+} in the blue light response of stomata (Table 4). Verapamil at 1mM completely inhibited the light-dependent stomatal opening in *Commelina* epidermis, and the inhibition was restored by further addition of fusicoccin (not shown). The result indicates that verapamil does not inhibit the proton pump itself.

TABLE 4. Inhibition of the proton extrusion in *Vicia* guard cell protoplasts by verapamil.

	Magnitude of H^+ extrusion
	nmol H^+ μg^{-1} protein pulse^{-1} (%)
Control	0.317
Verapamil (0.5 mM)	0.104

From these results, it is concluded that Ca^{2+}/calmodulin plays an important role in the signal transduction processes in the blue light response of stomata in green leaves. However, more direct evidence will be needed to demonstrate the role of Ca^{2+}/calmodulin in the response, because most of the data were provided from the use of pharmacological tools.

Acknowledgements: This research was supported in part by grants from the Ministry of Education, Science and Culture of Japan (Nos. 03640570, 03304006) and from the Toray Science Foundation (No. 89-3005).

REFERENCES

1. Mansfield, T. A. and Meidner, H. (1966) J. Exp. Bot. 17, 510-521.
2. Assmann, S. M., Simoncini, L. and Schroeder, J. I. (1985) Nature 318, 285-287.
3. Shimazaki, K., Iino, M. and Zeiger, E. (1986) Nature 319, 324-326.
4. Schroeder, J. I., Raschke, K. and Neher, E. (1987) Proc. Natl. Acad. Sci. 84, 4108-4112.
5. Weyers, J. D. B. and Travis, A. J. (1981) J. Exp. Bot. 32, 837-850.
6. Muto, S. and Miyachi, S. (1984) Z. Pflanzenphysiol. 114, 421-431.

DEPHOSPHORYLATION OF THE LHCII PROTEIN BY LIGHT IN GUARD CELL PROTOPLASTS FROM VICIA FABA L.

Toshinori Kinoshita[1], Ken-ichiro Shimazaki[2] and Mitsuo Nishimura[1]
Dept. Biol., Kyushu Univ.[1], Fukuoka 812, Japan and Biol. Lab., Kyushu Univ.[2], Fukuoka 810, Japan

1. INTRODUCTION

Protein phosphorylation is an ubiquitous mechanism for the control of intracellular events and cellular function in animal and plant cells (1). Phosphorylation status of many proteins in plant cells have been known to be altered in response to light (2). The light-harvesting chlorophyll *a*/*b* protein complex associated with photosystem II (the LHCII protein) in mesophyll cell chloroplasts is a phosphoprotein which responds to light (3, 4). The LHCII protein is phosphorylated by LHCII kinase under illumination and is dephosphorylated in the dark by protein phosphatase. Reversible phosphorylation of the LHCII protein seems to be closely correlated to the control of light-energy distribution between photosystem I (PSI) and photosystem II (PSII) (4), and it strongly affects the yield of fluorescence from PSII at room temperature. Chl *a* fluorescence transients from guard cells have different properties from those from mesophyll cells. Rate of fluorescence quenching was slow when guard cells were excited by blue light, but it was faster under the green actinic light. In contrast, the fluorescence induction in mesophyll cells showed similar time courses with both blue and green actinic lights (5). This observation indicates that the light-energy distribution in thylakoid membranes of guard cells may have a particular property in the response to light quality. In the present study, we investigated protein phosphorylation in guard cell protoplasts from *Vicia faba* L. by incubating the protoplasts with [^{32}P]orthophosphate. We found that a protein with molecular mass of 26 kD was phosphorylated in the dark and was dephosphorylated by red light. Several evidence indicated that the 26 kD protein was the LHCII protein in guard cells.

2. MATERIALS AND METHODS

2.1 Plant material: Plants of *Vicia faba* L. were grown as described previously (8). Guard cell and mesophyll cell protoplasts were isolated enzymatically as described previously (6, 7).

2.2 Protein phosphorylation: The assay mixture (350 μl) for guard cell protoplasts contained 0.39 M mannitol, 1 mM $CaCl_2$, 10 mM KCl, 10 mM Mes-NaOH (pH 6.1) and guard cell protoplasts (250 μg protein). The assay mixture (350 μl) for mesophyll cell

N. Murata (ed.), Research in Photosynthesis, Vol. IV, 719–722.

protoplasts contained 0.6 M mannitol, 1 mM $CaCl_2$, 4 mM $NaHCO_3$, 50 mM HEPES-KOH (pH 7.5) and mesophyll protoplasts (250 μg protein). Phosphorylation was started by the addition of 1,850 kBq [^{32}P]-orthophosphate to the assay mixture and the mixture was incubated for 80 min in the dark at 24°C. In illumination experiments, the mixture was illuminated after the 80-min dark incubation. The reaction was terminated by the addition of SDS-solubilization medium to the protoplasts suspension. Solubilized samples were subjected to SDS-PAGE according to the method of Laemmli (8). The separation gel contained 12.5% polyacrylamide. After electrophoresis, the gel was stained with CBB, destained and dried. Phosphorylated proteins were determined by exposing Fuji RX film to the dried gel for 12-48 hours at room temperature.

2.3 Fractionation of guard cell protoplasts: Guard cell protoplasts were fractionated into chloroplasts, mitochondria and cytosol according to the methods described previously (9, 10) with modifications.

3 RESULTS AND DISCUSSION

3.1 Figure 1 shows phosphorylation status of proteins in guard cell protoplasts from *Vicia faba* L. There were several proteins phosphorylated in the dark, with apparent molecular masses of 42, 34, 32, 26 and 19 kD (Fig. 1, D). Illumination of dark-adapted protoplasts with red light for 20 min induced a dephosphorylation of the 26 kDa protein (Fig. 1, L), without affecting the polypeptide patterns in SDS-PAGE (data not shown). We investigated the wavelength dependency in the dephosphorylation of the 26 kD protein by light (Table 1). Illumination by monochromatic lights in the wavelength range of 700-730 nm was most effective for dephosphorylation. Monochromatic lights with the wavelengths at 400-660 nm were less effective. Okadaic acid is a specific inhibitor of serine/threonine protein phosphatases. In animal cells, the serine/threonine protein phosphatases are classified into PP-1, PP-2A, PP-2B and PP-2C; PP-1, PP-2A and PP-2B are inhibited by okadaic acid with I_{50} values of 20 nM, 0.2 nM and 5 μM, respectively, while PP-2C is insensitive to okadaic acid (11). The light-induced dephosphorylation of the 26 kD protein was inhibited by okadaic acid at 1 nM, suggesting that PP-2A was involved in dephosphorylation of the 26 kD protein. Subcellular distribution of the 26 kD protein in guard cell was investigated (Fig. 2). Guard cell protoplasts were fractionated into chloroplasts, mitochondria and cytosol. The phosphorylated 26 kD protein was located in the chloroplast fraction.

3.2 Phosphorylation status of mesophyll-cell proteins was investigated using isolated mesophyll protoplasts in the same manner. The LHCII protein in mesophyll cells was dephosphorylated in the dark and was phosphorylated by red light illumination. These results were consistent with the generally accepted observations of light-induced phosphorylation of the LHCII protein in leaf and intact chloroplasts (3, 4). Molecular mass of the LHCII protein in *Vicia* mesophyll cell was 26 kD. The 26 kD protein in guard

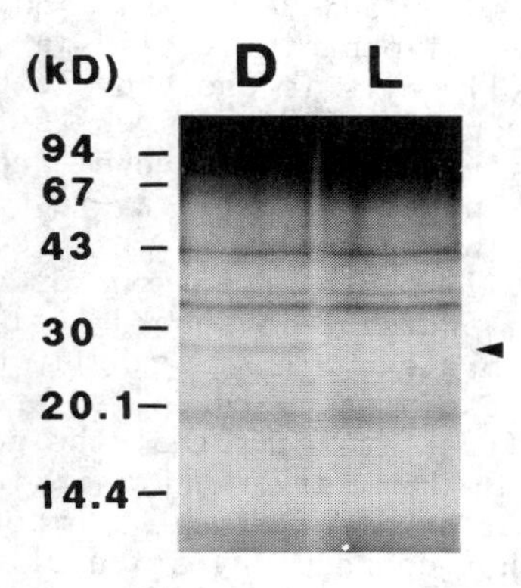

Figure 1. Protein phosphorylation of Vicia guard cell protoplasts. Guard cell protoplasts were incubated with [^{32}P]orthophosphate in the dark for 80 min (D), then illuminated with red light at 600 μmol m^{-2} s^{-1} for 20 min (L). Guard cell proteins were separated by SDS-PAGE. Phosphorylated proteins were visualized by autoradiography. Solid arrow indicates the 26 kD protein.

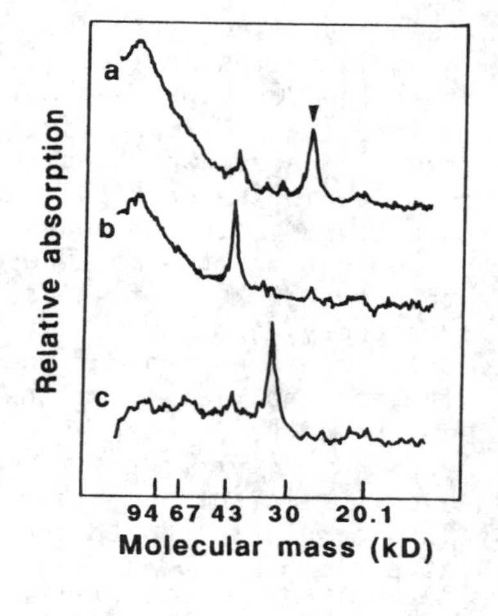

Figure 2. Subcellular distribution of phosphorylated proteins in guard cells. Guard cell protoplasts were incubated with [^{32}P]orthophosphate in the dark. Proteins in each fraction were separated by SDS-PAGE. Densitometric scans in autoradiograms of (a) chloroplast fraction, (b) mitochondrial fraction and (c) cytosolic fraction. Solid arrow indicates the phosphorylated 26 kD protein.

Table 1. Wavelength dependency in dephosphorylation of the 26 kD protein by light. Guard cell protoplasts were illuminated at 15 μmol m^{-2} s^{-1} for 10 min. Monochromatic light was obtained by passing the white light through an appropriate interference filter. Phosphorylation levels were densitometrically determined and were presented as the percentages of the phosphorylation level in the dark.

Wavelength (nm)	Phosphorylation level (%)
400	74
510	93
601	89
660	75
700	32
730	26

cells had exactly the same molecular mass with that of the LHCII protein in mesophyll cells determined by SDS-PAGE. This indicates that the 26 kD protein may be the LHCII protein itself in guard cells. The LHCII protein in mesophyll cells is phosphorylated by reducing agent which reduces plastoquinone (PQ) pool and Cyt b/f complex in the dark (4). When dithionite, a strong reducing agent, was added to guard cell protoplasts under far-red light illumination, the 26 kD protein was phosphorylated. This suggests that the 26 kD protein is the LHCII protein in guard cells. Phosphorylation status of the LHCII protein in guard cells is different from that of the LHCII protein in mesophyll cells: the phosphorylation of the LHCII protein in guard cells proceeds in the dark. In guard cells, therefore, it seems that the pool PQ and Cyt b/f complex are reduced in the dark, and that far-red light preferentially absorbed by PSI oxidizes these components. This agrees well with the result that dephosphorylation of the 26 kD protein by 660 nm light was stimulated by DCMU (data not shown). It is concluded that in guard cells of *Vicia*, the LHCII protein is phosphorylated in the dark and is dephosphorylated by the type-2A protein phosphatase under far-red light absorbed by PS I. Clarification of the physiological significance of the reversible phosphorylation of the LHCII protein in guard cells, in relation to stomatal function, awaits further investigation.

ACKNOWLEDGMENT

This work was supported in part by grants from the Ministry of Education, Science and Culture of Japan (Nos. 03640570, 03304006) and from the Toray Science Fundation (No. 89-3005).

REFERENCES

1. Ranjeva, R. and Boudet, A. M. (1987) Annu. Rev. Plant Physiol. 38, 73-93
2. Budde, R. J. A. and Randall, D. D. (1990) Plant Physiol. 94, 1501-1504
3. Bennett, J. (1977) Nature 269, 344-346
4. Bennett, J. (1991) Annu. Rev. Plant Physiol. Plant Mol. Biol. 42, 281-311
5. Mawson, B. T. and Zeiger, E. (1991) Plant Physiol. 96, 753-760
6. Shimazaki, K., Kinoshita, T. and Nishimura, M. (1992) Plant Physiol. 99, in press.
7. Shimazaki, K., Gotow, K. and Kondo, N. (1982) Plant Cell Physiol. 23, 871-879
8. Laemmli U. K. (1970) Nature 227, 680-685
9. Gotow, K., Tanaka, K., Kondo, N., Kobayashi, K. and Syono, K. (1985) Plant Physiol. 79, 829-832
10. Shimazaki, K., Terada, J., Tanaka, K. and Kondo, N. (1989) Plant Physiol. 90, 1057-1064
11. Cohen, P. (1989) Annu. Rev. Biochem. 58, 453-508

LIGHT-INDUCED CHANGES IN MEMBRANE POTENTIAL AND CYTOPLASMIC PH IN AQUATIC PLANTS, *EGERIA* AND *CHARA*

MASASHI TAZAWA[1], NAOHIKO IWASAKI[2], YOSHIJI OKAZAKI[2]
[1]FUKUI INSTITUTE OF TECHNOLOGY, GAKUEN 3-6-1, FUKUI 910, JAPAN; [2]OSAKA MEDICAL COLLEGE, SAWARAGICHO 2-41, TAKATSUKI, OSAKA 569, JAPAN

1. INTRODUCTION

In green plants light induces changes in membrane potential (E_m). The E_m in plant cells is composed of the diffusion potential and the potential generated by the electrogenic H^+-pump or the H^+-ATPase (1). In tonoplast-free cells of *Chara* light-induced potential change (LPC) is caused by an increase in the ATP level via photophosphorylation (2). The plasma membrane H^+ pump activity is dependent on the cytoplasmic pH (pH_c). In tonoplast-free cells of *Chara* and *Nitellopsis*, the intracellular pH optimum for ATP-dependent electrogenesis is about 6.5 (3,4). The pH_c in plant cells is kept between 7.1-7.6 (5). Cytoplasmic acidification caused by acid-loading or fusiccocin results in membrane hyperpolarization, verifying the importance of pH_c in electrogenesis (6,7,8). Light also causes pH_c shift; alkalization in characean cells (9,10,11) and transient alkalization followed by acidification in *Riccia* (12). However, in tonoplast-free cells of *Chara*, LPC is induced even under strongly buffered internal pHs ranging between 6.2-7.9 (3). This implies that pH_c is not a sole regulating factor of LPC.

Under such a situation, we wanted to know in **intact** characean cells whether a causal relationship exists between the light-inducd pH_c change and activation of the H^+ pump. For this we developed a triple-barreled pH microelectrode which was tough and allowed continuous simultaneous measurements of pH_c and E_m. As a material, we also used *Egeria densa*. Since both *Chara* and *Egeria* are known to utilize both CO_2 and HCO_3^- (13,14), we examined whether or not inorganic carbon species could influence light-induced potential change and pH_c.

2. MATERIALS AND METHODS

2.1 Materials

Before use isolated internodal cells of *Chara corallina* were incubated in an artificial pond water of pH 7.5 (APW-pH 7.5) under dim light for several hours. APW-pH

N. Murata (ed.), Research in Photosynthesis, Vol. IV, 723–726.

7.5 contained 0.1 mM each of KCl, NaCl and $CaCl_2$ and 5 mM Hepes/Tris. Isolated leaves of *Egeria densa* were incubated in APW-pH 7.5 under dark at least 4 days.

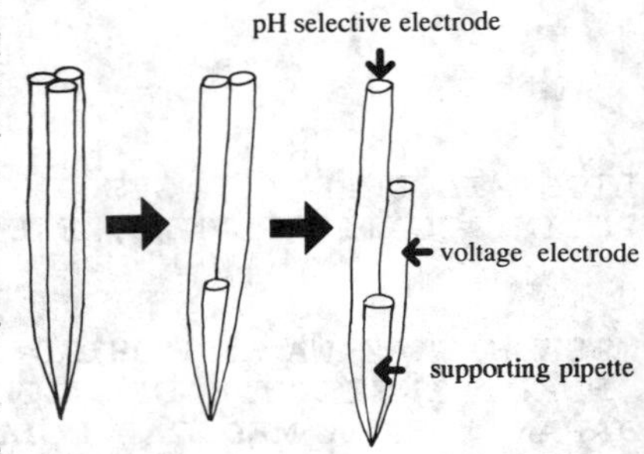

Fig. 1 Triple-barrelled microelectrode

2.2 pH-selective microelectrodes
Microelectrodes were fabricated in an ordinary manner (15,16). But it was new that triple-barreled microelectrodes were made from three pipettes. Two pipettes were trimmed for their length as shown in Fig. 1. The longest pipette containing a hydrogen cocktail at the tip was filled with the reference solution of pH 6 (100 mM Mes/Tris, 0.5 M KCl). The middle long pipette filled with 3 M KCl solution was used for measurements of E_m. The shortest pipette served as a supporter.

2.3 Measurement of intracellular pH and E_m
The E_m and the potential difference between the pH-sensitive electrode and the voltage electrode were measured with a dual electrometer of high impedance and recorded with a pen-writing recorder. The pH-microelectrodes were calibrated for the standard solutions of pHs 4,5,6,7 and 8 containing 100 mM KCl.

2.4 Experimental solutions and light source
When otherwise stated, experimental solution was APW-pH 7.5. To supply carbon either in the form of CO_2 or HCO_3^-, 2 mM $NaHCO_3$ was added to APW with the pH adjusted to 4.8 with Mes or to 8.1 with Hepes. The light source was a microscope incandescent lamp. The light intensity was about 25 µmol photon m^{-2} s^{-1}.

3. RESULTS AND DISCUSSION

3.1 Effect of light

When *Chara* cells were transferred from dark to light, pH_c increased by ca. 0.3 pH units, while E_m first hyperpolarized slightly and soon depolarized significantly (Fig. 2A). The alkalized pH_c was maintained during illumination at least for 10 min and recovered to the original value on turning off the light. Both reactions were completely inhibited by 10 µM DCMU. The alkalization of the cytoplasm can be interpreted as the result of either activation of the H^+ pump or uptake of H^+ into stroma. The light-induced membrane depolarization can be interpreted as follows. Light increases membrane conductance (g_d) of the passive ion channels through which the inward current flows that is equivalent to outward pump current (i_p) (17). Since the pump-

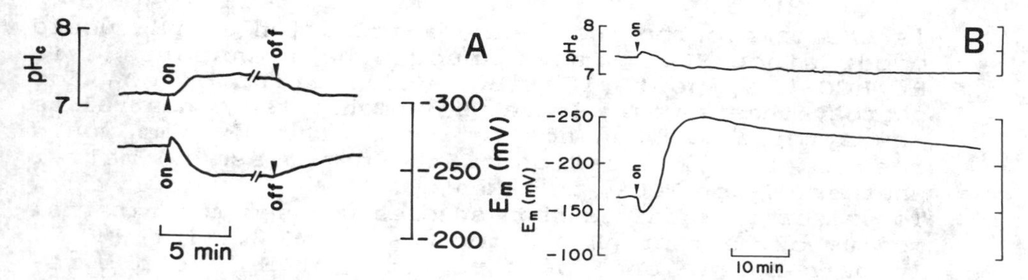

Fig. 2 Light–induced changes in pH_c and E_m in *Chara* (A) and *Egeria* (B)

dependent electrogenesis can be calculated as $-i_p/g_d$, a large increase in g_d may depolarize E_m even when i_p is increased.

When *Egeria* cells were illuminated, a large hyperpolarization was observed after a first small depolarization, while pH_c transiently increased and then recovered the original value or turned slightly acidic within 5 min (Fig. 2B). Both reactions were also completely inhibited by 10 µM DCMU. The membrane hyperpolarization is thought to reflect the activation of the plasma membrane H^+ pump, which was supported by the increase in H^+ efflux in *Elodea* cells (18). The pump activation can be interpreted as the result of acidification of the cytoplasm. This effect of acidification was verified by observation that the membrane hyperpolarization induced by fusicoccin, an activator of the plasma membrane H^+-ATPase, is preceded by a decrease in pH_c in root hairs of *Sinapis alba* (8) and in rhizoids of *Riccia fluitans* (12). We also observed similar results in *Egeria*. Cytoplasmic acidification may be caused by production of malate in the cytosol by PEP-carboxylase. In photoautotrophic suspension culture of a C_3-type plant, *Chenopodium ruburum*, Hüsemann et al. (19) found that light caused a rapid (in 10 s) production of malate amounting to 20-40% of total photosynthetic intermediates depending on external pH. They suggested that malate produced by stimulation of pH-sensitive PEP-carboxylase may counteract the pH rise induced by the H^+ pump activation. Recently, in internodal cells of *Chara corallina* Ding et al. (20) found a significant incorporation of ^{14}C-bicarbonate into malate in the cytoplasm, about 14 mM in the chloroplast layer and about 3 mM in the cytosol after 10 min.

3.3 Light-induced changes in pH_c and E_m in relation to inorganic carbon species

If plant cells utilize external CO_2 for photosynthesis, no change in pH_c would occur with CO_2 uptake. If HCO_3^-

is the main carbon source, acidification of pH_c would occur since HCO_3^- is assumed to be transported via H^+/HCO_3^- symport (13). But utilization of CO_2 for photosynthesis would leave OH^- which acts to neutralize the cytoplasm. Thus activation of the H^+ pump would results in alkalization of the cytoplasm no matter whether CO_2 or HCO_3^- is taken up.
To select inorganic carbon species we used the external medium of either pH 4.8 for CO_2 or pH 8.1 for HCO_3^-. In both *Egeria* and *Chara* patterns of E_m and pH_c responses obtained at both pHs were similar to those obtained at pH 7.5 (Fig. 2). These results are in harmony with the hypothesis of H^+/HCO_3^- symport.

REFERENCES

1 Tazawa, M., Shimmen, T. and Mimura, T. (1987) Ann. Rev. Plant Physiol. 38, 95-117
2 Mimura, T. and Tazawa, M. (1986) Plant Cell Physiol. 27, 319-330
3 Fujii, S., Shimmen, T. and Tazawa, M. (1979) Plant Cell Physiol. 20, 1315-1328.
4 Tazawa, M. and Shimmen, T. (1982) Bot. Mag. Tokyo 95, 147-154
5 Felle, H. (1988) Physiol. Plant. 74,583-591
6 Brummer, B., Felle, H. and Parish, R.W. (1984) FEBS Lett. 174, 223-227
7 Brummer, B., Bertle, A., Potrykus, I., Felle, H. and Parish, R.W. (1985) FEBS Lett. 189, 109-114
8 Bertle, A. and Felle, H. (1985) J. Exp. Bot. 36, 1142-1149
9 Mimura, T. and Kirino, Y. (1984) Plant Cell Physiol. 25, 813-820
10 Smith, F.A. (1984) J. Exp. Bot. 35, 43-50
11 Walker, N.A. and Smith, F.A. (1975) Plant Sci. Lett. 4, 125-132
12 Felle, H. (1991) J. Exp. Bot. 42, 645-652
13 Lucas, W.J. (1983) Ann. Rev. Plant Physiol. 34, 71-104
14 Eighmy, T.T., Jahnke, L.S. and Fagerberg, W.R. (1991) Plant Cell Environ. 14, 157-165
15 Felle, H. and Bertl, A. (1986) Biophys. Biophys. Acta 848, 176-172
16 Reid, R.J. and Smith, F.A. (1988) J. Exp. Bot. 207, 1421-1432
17 Kawamura, G., Shimmen, T. and Tazawa, M. (1980) Planta 149, 213-218
18 Marre, M.T., Albergoni, F.R., Moroni, A. and Marre, E. (1989) J. Exp. Bot. 212, 343-352
19 Hüsemann, W., Callies, W. and Leibfritz, D. (1992) Bot. Acta 105, 116-120
20 Ding, Q.D., Amino, S., Mimura, T., Sakano, K., Nagata, T. and Tazawa, M. (1992) J. Exp. Bot. 43,1045-1051

25. Photosynthesis Control by Sink

THE POSSIBLE EFFECTS OF SINK DEMAND FOR ASSIMILATE ON PHOTOSYNTHESIS

L.C. HO, PLANT PHYSIOLOGY DEPARTMENT, HORTICULTURE RESEARCH INTERNATIONAL, LITTLEHAMPTON, WEST SUSSEX BN17 6LP, UK

The production and utilisation of leaf assimilates are in dynamic balance within a plant. In nature, this is achieved by adjusting either the source strength (i.e. capacity of production) or sink strength (i.e. capacity of utilisation) for leaf assimilates, when one of them becomes limiting. In fact, there is always either a source-limiting (i.e. insufficient production) or sink-limiting (i.e. insufficient utilisation) situation. It is now clear that the rate of photosynthesis is not just affected by environmental factors, such as light, CO_2, water and temperature on the biochemical and biophysical processes of photosynthesis (i.e. carbon assimilation), but is also regulated by the utilisation of the products of photosynthesis (i.e. photoassimilates) within the plant. It is easy to appreciate that when the supply of assimilates is limited there should be a reduction in the growth of sink organs, as the latter is relying on the supply of assimilates. How a change of sink demand (i.e. the fulfilment of the potential sink strength of sink organs by the supply of assimilates) should retard or enhance the photosynthetic rate of leaves is not readily explained.

There are two obvious links between source and sink within a plant: the transport of assimilates and water and the transmission of electrical or chemical signals. Therefore, a change of sink demand may result in changes of (a) the export rate of assimilates, (b) the water relations in the leaves, and (c) the balance of endogenous hormones in the whole plant. For this reason, a change of photosynthesis, in response to sink demand, may be caused by more than just the dispersal of assimilates from the source leaf. For instance, girdling of the petiole may cause a transient enhanced accumulation of ABA, as well as the temporary closure of the stomata, resulting in a corresponding change of photosynthesis within 3 hours (1). However, most of the responses of photosynthesis to a change of sink demand would only take place over a longer period, up to several days. Therefore, we have to identify whether they are short-term, transient responses or long-term adaptive responses. Despite the attractive nature of hormonal regulation of photosynthesis, very little evidence is available to assess the hormonal feedback mechanism on photosynthesis (2). I will limit this

N. Murata (ed.), Research in Photosynthesis, Vol. IV, 729–736.

review to assessing the popular concept that the possible effect of sink demand on photosynthesis is operated by biochemical feedback mechanisms.

A substantial volume of research has been carried out to determine to what extent the rate of photosynthesis can be regulated by sink demand upon the dispersal or accumulation of the photosynthetic products in leaves, since the first end-product inhibition hypothesis was proposed by Boussingault, 124 years ago (see 3). A number of reviews (3-7) have shown that the rate of photosynthesis, under certain situations, is increased or decreased by the sink demand of assimilate, as a result of positive or negative feedback, respectively. Negative feedback (i.e. decreased photosynthesis due to low sink demand) has been observed more frequently, when export of assimilate from the leaf was insufficient to disperse the newly formed assimilate (e.g. low sink/source ratio, 'midday depression'), or reduced (e.g. phloem chilling, reduced sink size or activity), or stopped (e.g. leaf detachment, phloem girdling). Positive feedback (i.e. increased photosynthesis due to high sink demand) has occasionally been observed when there is an increase of sink/source ratio (e.g. reduction of leaf area, initiation or addition of new sink), or of sink activity (e.g. warming of the sink). However, it appears that (a) a change or alteration of sink demand does not always affect the rate of photosynthesis, and (b) a change of the rate of photosynthesis does not always relate to the accumulation of a certain product of photosynthesis such as sugars or starch. The aim of this review is to answer the following questions: (a) In what kind of source/sink relationship does the rate of photosynthesis change in response to sink demand? (b) What are the biochemical factors determining the extent of change in the rate of photosynthesis in response to sink demand?

1. SINK DEMAND ON ASSIMILATE PARTITIONING IN THE PLANT

Assimilate partitioning among sink organs is regulated by both the availability of assimilates in the source and the competition between the sink organs (8). In most plants, the source leaves would supply more than one sink, while a sink would be supplied by more than one source. Therefore, a change of demand by an individual sink may only alter the priority of sink competition or source/sink relationships, rather than the export rate of the corresponding source leaves. For instance, in tomato the import of assimilates by an inflorescence targeted for abortion can be increased by hormone treatment at the expense of the apex (9). As a result, the total export rate of those source leaves may not be altered. It may be the reason for the lack of response occasionally observed in the source, even when the import of assimilates to an individual sink was altered or the source size was reduced (4).

2. SINK DEMAND ON AVAILABILITY OF TRANSPORTABLE ASSIMILATES IN THE SOURCE LEAF

The availability of transportable assimilates in the leaves to meet the sink demand is determined by (a) the rate of photosynthesis (b) the effective photosynthetic area, (c) the duration of photosynthesis and (d) the storage and remobilization of reserves. In general, the long-term, adaptive response of the source to an increase of sink demand is to increase the capacity of canopy photosynthesis. Thus, during the evolution or agricultural selection of crop plants, the higher fruit yield is often accompanied by a higher canopy photosynthesis, rather than a higher photosynthetic rate (8).

However, there are concomitant responses, in either the storage/remobilization of reserves or the rate of photosynthesis in the source, to sink demand. The rate of export is determined by both the concurrent photosynthesis and remobilization of reserves. For a great number of plant species, sucrose is the principal end product of photosynthesis and the major transportable sugar. Among these species, some of them would store the surplus newly produced assimilates mainly as starch, sucrose or hexoses. When the rate of export is altered, the rate of accumulation of these assimilates and the rate of carbon flow from newly fixed carbon into intermediates often changes in response. For instance, with enhanced sink demand in a tomato leaf, after partial defoliation, the initial incorporation of carbon into amino acids was enhanced, more starch was mobilized and more protein was made (10). In cucumber, cotton and bean, a decrease in carbon flow to 3-phosphoglycerate (PGA), phosphoenolpyruvate (PEP) and sugars and an increase in sugar-P and amino acids were also observed, in response to low sink demand (1,11). On the contrary, when the sink demand was reduced in tomato by truss removal, the initial incorporation of carbon into starch was enhanced and the subsequent mobilization of starch was less (10). However, not all these changes in the compartmentation of assimilates in response to sink demand resulted in a change of the rate of photosynthesis (11).

3. SINK DEMAND ON PHOTOSYNTHETIC RATE OF THE SOURCE LEAF

When the total sink demand is substantially higher or lower than the potential rate of export of assimilate from all the leaves, the rate of photosynthesis may change.

3.1 Source/sink relationships in the plant: The response time of photosynthesis of a certain leaf to sink demand is determined by the extent of the change of its export rate. In a two-truss tomato plant, for instance, the photosynthetic rate was only reduced two weeks after truss removal (10). However, a reduction was observed in 3 days in a simplified one-truss/one-leaf tomato system (12), or even within 24 hours when the photosynthetic rate of the leaf was increased, under continuous illumination at high light intensity (13). The extent of negative feedback inhibition in photosynthesis may be in proportion to the degree of sink removal and the resulting accumulation of starch in the source leaf, as observed in cotton (11). Furthermore, the duration of the negative feedback inhibition in photosynthesis is also determined by the stability of the source/sink relationships. As in the cucumber, once the new sink was allowed to develop, the starch was remobilized and the rate of photosynthesis in the source leaf was restored (1).

3.2 Compartmentation and accumulation of assimilates in the source leaf: The extent of negative feedback inhibition of photosynthesis may depend on either the amount of assimilates being accumulated or inhibitory factors being generated as a result of assimilate accumulation. The assimilate being accumulated in response to low sink demand is not always the principal end product of photosynthesis. For instance, *Amaranthus*, a C_4 plant, normally accumulates about 94% of the newly-fixed surplus carbon as starch in the light period. In response to petiole chilling, the sucrose pool increased 5-6 fold, whereas the starch content was unchanged (14). On the other hand, the principal assimilate accumulated in wheat is sucrose. When the sink demand was lower, the surplus assimilate was mainly accumulated as sucrose and starch. However, photosynthesis was inhibited only when the accumulation of total carbohydrate was above 100 mmol C m^{-2}, while the surplus carbon began to be accumulated as hexoses (15). Furthermore, the degree of photosynthetic inhibition, may be related to the potential capacity of sugar accumulation. For instance, the severe inhibition of photosynthesis observed in chilling-susceptible rice cultivars was related to a smaller potential sugar pool size and a higher accumulation of sugars at low sink demand (16).

The response of a source leaf to a change of sink demand is not just determined by the absolute strength of the sink (i.e. import rate of assimilates), but by the source strength (i.e. rate of photosynthesis). The inhibition of photosynthesis, caused by low sink demand at high CO_2, did not occur in leaves with a low photosynthetic rate in low CO_2, as in peanut (18). Similarly, the inhibition of photosynthesis in cucumber due to petiole girdling was observed one day after treatment in high CO_2, but after 3 days in low CO_2 (1).

3.3 Potential photosynthetic rate in the source leaf at source- or sink-limiting situations: Intrinsically, the potential photosynthetic rate of a plant is inversely related to the leaf size and the accumulation of carbohydrates in it, e.g. among rice cultivars (19). In this case, it appears that the low photosynthetic rate of the large leaf cultivars may be caused by the accumulation of assimilates in a sink-limiting situation. However, in response to changes of sink demand, the change of photosynthetic rate is more related to source/sink ratios (i.e. the ratio of assimilate production capacity to assimilate utilisation capacity) than the potential photosynthetic rate alone. For instance, among maize cultivars, the extent of photosynthesis inhibition by ear removal was greater in cultivars with a low source/sink ratio. On the other hand, when sink demand was enhanced by partial defoliation, the photosynthetic rate was increased only in cultivars with a high source/sink ratio (20). Therefore, a negative feedback on photosynthesis would be more profound in a source-limiting situation, while the potential photosynthetic rate is already high. On the contrary, in a sink-limiting situation, a further reduction in sink demand may not have the negative feedback to photosynthesis in the source leaf if the photosynthetic rate is below its potential. The new balance may be achieved by establishing new sinks. Furthermore, the rate of photosynthesis of the remaining leaves, after the source size was reduced, may only be increased in a sink-limiting situation if the photosynthetic rate prior to the treatment was below potential. In a source-limiting situation, a further reduction of source size may not have a positive feedback on photosynthesis if the rate of photosynthesis was already high. The new balance may be achieved by establishing new source leaves.

4. BIOCHEMICAL FEEDBACK MECHANISMS ON PHOTOSYNTHESIS

Accumulation or remobilization of assimilate is frequently associated with negative or positive feedback, respectively, of sink demand on photosynthesis. There are a number of possible mechanisms for consideration.

4.1 Starch accumulation and breakdown: Storage and remobilization of starch is a normal process within the chloroplast after carbon fixation. While an excess of starch accumulation has been frequently suggested as the cause of negative feedback (1,11), remobilization of starch is only associated with the restoration of photosynthetic rate when the previous sink demand was restored (1), but is not always proposed as the cause of positive feedback. However, even in the starch accumulating plant, e.g. *Amaranthus*, negative feedback is more likely due to the accumulation of sugars rather than starch (14). Furthermore, even when more starch was accumulated than sugars, in response to higher light, as in red clover, the reduction of photosynthesis appeared to be more related to a sharp increase of sugars (17). Nevertheless, excessive accumulation of starch in the chloroplast may increase the physical resistance to CO_2 diffusion toward the carboxylation enzymes or cause interference of light transmission within the chloroplast (3). In response to low sink demand, starch grains occupied most of the chloroplast space, resulting in reduction of free volume of stroma, grana distortion and thus lower density of the thylakoid membrane (21,22). Apart from the possible physical obstruction for CO_2 fixation, it has been tentatively suggested that the inhibition of photosynthesis may also be caused by certain biochemical effects of starch accumulation (17,23).

4.2 Sugar accumulation and dispersal: Accumulation of sucrose, hexoses or sugar phosphates in the cytosol has been considered as the cause of negative feedback of low sink demand on photosynthesis. It is unlikely that inhibition of photosynthesis is due to a direct mass inhibition as a result of the accumulation of these end products. Recent progress on intermediary metabolism studies suggests that photosynthesis may be inhibited by low inorganic pyrophosphate (Pi) or high triose phosphate (TP) concentration in the chloroplast, as a result of end product accumulation.

For sucrose-transporting species, the immediate result of reduced sink demand is the accumulation of sucrose. Due to mass inhibition effects of sucrose on the activity of either sucrose synthase (SS) or sucrose phosphate synthase (SPS), further sucrose synthesis will be inhibited (24). As a result of less Pi being released from the reduced conversion of sucrose-P to sucrose, the cytosol Pi concentration will be lower, and consequently, so will the stroma Pi (5). A lower cytosol Pi can also be induced by an inhibition of conversion from Fru-1,6-P_2 to Fru-6-P by excessive Fru-2,6-P_2 which inhibits the activity of Fru-1,6-bisphosphatase (25,26). Therefore, accumulation of hexoses, the hydrolysis product of accumulated sucrose, may also induce low cytosol Pi by preventing the regeneration of Pi through stimulation of the synthesis of Fru-2,6-P_2 (6). Limitation of Pi in the stroma is the consequence of low cytosol Pi. As the production of ATP or the regeneration of carboxylation substrates such as ribulose 1,5-bisphosphate (RuBP) in the chloroplast will be limited by low stroma Pi (15,27), the rate of photosynthesis will be reduced.

This working hypothesis has been supported by observations in transgenic tobacco plants with yeast invertase expressed in the apoplast to reduce the export of assimilate, presumably due to the impairment of phloem loading (28). As a result of excessive accumulation of carbohydrate, the level of some Calvin-cycle enzymes, i.e. RuBPC, Fru-1,6-phosphatase and NADP-glyceraldehyde-3-phosphate dehydrogenase, decreased. Consequently, there was a decrease in photosynthesis accompanied by a decrease of RuBP and PGA, but an increase of TP and Fru-1,6-P_2. In this negative feedback inhibition of photosynthesis, SPS activity was not inhibited in the transgenic plants. Indeed, by expressing the inorganic pyrophosphatase from *E.coli* in transgenic plants of tobacco and potato, to reduce the cytosolic Pi level, a substantial accumulation of sugars was accompanied by a reduction in chlorophyll content of up to 85%, which is the possible cause of photosynthesis inhibition (29). Therefore, low cytosol Pi is one of the main factors in negative feedback. Another consequence of low cytosol Pi is a high TP in the chloroplast, caused by a reduced 'shuttle exchange' of Pi and TP between the chloroplast and cytosol (5). It has been tentatively suggested that as the activity of RuBPC can be reduced by excess PGA or ribulose-5-phosphate (Ru5P), the rate of photosynthesis will be reduced (30). Observations in phosphorus deficient spinach plants demonstrated that low activity of RuBPC and a low regeneration rate of RuBP are the main causes of reduced photosynthesis (31).

Furthermore, accumulation of sucrose in the source leaf can also be caused by a direct repression of nuclear gene expression by sucrose and glucose on the small subunits of RuBPC and of the chlorophyll a/b binding protein (32). Therefore, negative feedback inhibition of photosynthesis may involve both biochemical and genetic regulation.

4.3 Accumulation of other intermediates: Although accumulation of sugars and starch is frequently associated with negative feedback inhibition of photosynthesis, accumulation of other intermediates may also play a role in regulating the photosynthetic rate. For instance, negative feedback inhibition of photosynthesis in CAM plants may be due to the accumulation of glucans in chloroplasts (22). In comparison with negative feedback, the mechanism of positive feedback is less certain. However, a higher compartmentation of newly-fixed carbon in amino acids (10) and a higher protein content (33) in the source leaf has been observed in response to increased sink demand. It is possible that a higher photosynthetic rate may be achieved by a higher level of RuBPC, as a result of changes of carbon metabolism.

5. CONCLUDING REMARKS

Analysis of the existing evidence suggests that there are certain rules in the possible mechanisms:

(A) If the change of sink demand of individual sinks only affects the priority of sink competition, but not the total sink demand, no change of photosynthetic rate is expected.

(B) If the change of total sink demand causes a change of export rate and the compartmentation of assimilate, but within the potential capacity of storage and remobilization, no immediate change of photosynthetic rate is expected.

(C) The extent of changes of photosynthetic rate in response to feedback may be determined by (a) the source/sink ratio; (b) the potential photosynthetic rate, and (c) the compartmentation of intermediates. As there is a dynamic source/sink situation in plants, an increased or decreased photosynthesis due to feedback may not be permanent. However, photosynthesis is more likely regulated by negative rather than positive feedback from sink demand.

(D) Due to the diversity of patterns in carbon metabolism among plants, the principal assimilates involved in feedback control would be variable. However, the most common biochemical step may be the change of RuBPC activity regulated by the Pi level in the stroma or the rate of protein synthesis from the newly-fixed carbon.

REFERENCES

1 Mayoral, M.L., Plaut, Z. and Reinhold, L. (1985) Plant Physiol. 77, 712-717
2 Wareing, P.F., Khalifa, M.M. and Treharne, C.J. (1968) Nature 220, 453-457
3 Neales, T.F. and Incoll, L.D. (1968) Bot. Rev. 34, 107-125
4 Geiger, D.R. (1976) Can. J. Bot. 54, 2337-2345
5 Herold, A. (1980) New Phytol. 86, 131-144
6 Foyer, C.B. (1987) Plant Physiol. Biochem. 25, 649-657
7 Wardlaw, I.F. (1990) New Phytol. 116, 341-381
8 Ho, L.C. (1988) Ann. Rev. Plant Physiol. Plant Mol. Biol. 39, 355-378
9 Kinet, J.M., Hundebise, D., Parmentier, A. and Stainier, K. (1978) J. Amer. Soc. Hort. Sci. 103, 724-729
10 Ho, L.C. (1979a) in Photosynthesis and Plant development (Marcelle, R. et al, ed.), pp. 243-250, Dr. Junk Publishers, The Hague
11 Plaut, Z., Mayoral, M.L. and Reinhold, L. (1987) Plant Physiol. 85, 786-791
12 Ho, L.C., Shaw, A.F., Hammond, J.B.W. and Burton, K.S. (1983) Ann. Bot. 52, 365-372
13 Ho, L.C. (1979b) Ann. Bot. 43, 437-448
14 Blechschmidt-schneider, S., Ferrar, P. and Osmond, C.B. (1989) 177, 515-525
15 Azcon-Bieto, J. (1983) Plant Physiol. 73, 681-686
16 Huang, L.K., Wong, S.C., Terashima, I., Zhang, X., Lin, D.X. and Osmond, C.B. (1989) Aust. J. Plant Physiol. 16, 321-337
17 Grub, A. & Machler, F. (1990) J. Exp. Bot. 41, 1293-1301
18 Bagnall, D.J., King, R.W. and Farquhar, G.D. (1988) Planta 175, 348-354
19 Lafitte, H.R. and Travis, R.L. (1984) Crop Sci. 24, 447-452
20 Barnett, K.H. and Pearce, R.B. (1983) Crop Sci. 23, 294-299
21 Natziger, E.D. and Koller, H.R. (1976) Plant Physiol. 57, 560-563
22 Mayoral, M.L., Medina, E. and Garcia, V. (1991) J. Exp. Bot. 42, 1123-1129
23 Piazza, G.J. and Gibbs, M. (1982) in Crassulacean acid metabolism (Ting, I.P. and Gibbs, M. Waverly, eds), pp. 128-152
24 Huber, S.C. (1981) Z. Pflan. 102, 443-450
25 Huber, S.C. (1986) Ann. Rev. Plant Physiol. 37, 233-246
26 Stitt, M. (1990) Ann. Rev. Plant Physiol. Plant Mol. Biol. 41, 153-185
27 Furbank, R.T, Foyer, C. and Walker, D. (1987) Biochem. Biophys. 894, 165-173
28 Stitt, M., von Schaewen, A. and Willmitzer, L. (1990) Planta 183, 40-50
29 Sonnewald, U. (1992) Plant J. 2, 571-581
30 Sharkey, T.D. (1985) Bot. Rev. 51, 54-105
31 Brooks, A. (1986) Aust. J. Plant Physiol. 13, 221-237
32 Sheen, J. (1990) Plant Cell 2, 1027-1038
33 Lauer, M.J. and Shibles, R. (1987) Crop Sci. 27, 1197-1201

THE ROLE OF SUCROSE PHOSPHATE SYNTHASE IN DETERMINING ASSIMILATE PARTITIONING AND PHOTOSYNTHETIC CAPACITY IN TOMATO LEAVES

Christine H. FOYER[1], Nathalie GALTIER[1], Steven C. HUBER[2] and Paul QUICK[3]

[1] Laboratoire du Métabolisme, INRA, Route de St Cyr, 78026 Versailles Cedex, France; [2] USDA Agriculture Research Service, North Carolina State University, Box 7631, Raleigh, North Carolina, USA; [3]Robert Hill Institute, Department of Animal and Plant Sciences, University of Sheffield, PO Box 601, Sheffield S10 2UQ, UK.

1. INTRODUCTION

The maximum rates of photosynthesis in conditions of saturating irradiance and CO_2 are determined by the capacity of the photosynthetic machinery (1). Metabolic limitations might arise at the level of (a) the electron transport processes (b) the carbon reduction cycle or (c) the synthesis of end products, mainly sucrose and starch (1-5).
Two enzymes of the sucrose biosynthetic pathway, sucrose phosphate synthase (SPS) and fructose-1,6-bisphosphatase (Fig.1) are instrumental in regulating the rate of carbon flow to sucrose. It is, therefore, possible that by increasing the activities of either of these enzymes the maximal rates of photosynthesis might be increased. SPS is also considered to be important in the regulation of the partitioning of assimilate between starch and sucrose in the leaf (6,7). Interspecific variation in SPS activity has been reported (8). Furthermore, it has been found that SPS activity is inversely related to the starch content of leaves (8). SPS activity is also highly correlated with the rate of assimilate export (9,10) and also with plant growth rate (11,12). Changes in the activity of SPS in leaves would thus be predicted to have effects on assimilate partitioning, export and growth characteristics.
In the present study transgenic plants of the cultivated tomato, *Lycopersicon esculentum* Var. UC82B, expressing both the native SPS and also the SPS gene from maize, under the control of the promotor of the small subunit of ribulose-1,5-bisphosphate carboxylase (13), were used to investigate the role of SPS in the regulation of photosynthetic capacity and assimilate partitioning in the leaves.

N. Murata (ed.), Research in Photosynthesis, Vol. IV, 737–744.

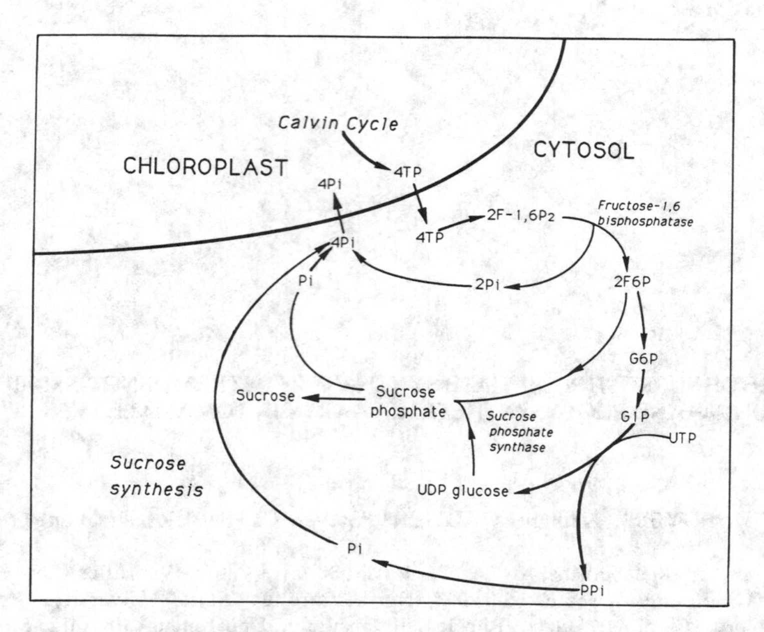

Figure 1. Scheme for the sucrose synthesis pathway in leaves. F6P: fructose-6 phosphate; F-1,6P_2: fructose-1,6-bisphosphate; GIP: glucose-1-phosphate; G6P: glucose-6-phosphate; Pi: orthophosphate; PPi: inorganic pyrophosphate; TP: triose phosphate

2. MATERIALS AND METHODS

2.1 Plant material. Seed of transgenic and non-transgenic tomato (*Lycopersicon esculentum* var UC82B) was obtained from the Roussel Agri-Vet Company (France) and Calgene Inc (Davis, USA). Plants were grown in glasshouses in Versailles (France) with supplemented lighting and in growth chambers in Sheffield, UK and Raleigh, USA. Plants in chambers were exposed to either a 12h or 16h photoperiod at either 160 μmol m^{-2} s^{-1} or 400-700 μmol m^{-2} s^{-1} irradiance. Mature adult leaves were used in all the experiments reported here.

2.2 Measurements of sucrose phosphate synthase (SPS) activity, starch and sucrose contents. Leaves were harvested at mid-day or following 12h darkness and were frozen immediately in liquid N_2. Leaf samples were ground in an extraction medium consisting of 0.2 M Tris-HCl (pH 8.2), 20 mM $MgCl_2$, 5 mM EDTA, 10 mM dithiothreitol, 20% glycerol and 1 mg ml^{-1} bovine serum albumin. The extracts were filtered and centrifuged at maximum speed in an Ependorf centrifuge for 5 mins. The soluble fraction was assayed for SPS activity by either the method of Salerno *et al* (14) except that the reaction medium was modified as in (15), or by the method described in (16).

For the analysis of sucrose and starch contents extracts of leaf material were made either (1) in $HClO_4$ (1 M), centrifuged and neutralised with K_2CO_2, or (2) in 80% ethanol and incubated at 85°C for 1 h. Glucose, fructose and sucrose were measured enzymatically as described previously (15). Starch was extracted from the insoluble leaf material via digestion with amylase (0.66 U ml^{-1}) and amyloglucosidase (15 U ml^{-1}) and the glucose liberated was assayed as described above (15).

2.3 Photosynthesis measurements. CO_2 dependent O_2 evolution in leaf segments was measured in saturating CO_2 in the leaf disc oxygen electrode (Hansatech, UK). Irradiance was either 160 μmol m^{-2} s^{-1} or 1600 μmol m^{-2} s^{-1} as stated in the legends to the figures and tables.

3. RESULTS AND DISCUSSION

3.1 Modulation of assimilate partitioning.

When the maize leaf SPS is expressed in tomato, the leaf cells are unable to regulate the activity of the introduced enzyme such that the SPS activity is substantially higher in both the light and darkness (13, 15). The tomato plants appear to tolerate the elevated levels of SPS with no detrimental effects. The plants have a changed shoot: root ratio that favours proliferation of the shoot (15) such that the transformed plants are rather more bushy than the untransformed controls. Tomato is considered to be a high leaf starch former (17). The presence of the maize SPS dramatically changed the balance of partitioning in favour of sucrose (Table 1). The total amount of carbohydrate (starch plus sucrose, glucose and fructose) remained relatively constant despite the re-orientation of carbon allocation towards sucrose synthesis (Table 1).

Table 1: Total leaf carbohydrate contents in the light, mid-way through the photoperiod of control, a high SPS expressing (TR 2) and the highest SPS expressing (TR 9) transgenic tomato plants. Values are means ± standard errors, with (n) the number of samples.

Plant type	Total leaf carbohydrate content (mmol m^{-2})	% starch	% sucrose
Control	70.0 ± 21.1 (7)	83	14
TR 2	71.3 ± 30.6 (8)	72	20
TR 9	60.3 ± 25.7 (10)	56	29

Worrell *et al* (13) found that the starch contents of leaves from transformed plants were about 25% decreased at mid-day and were 50% decreased at 4 pm in comparison with untransformed controls, while the sucrose levels were about doubled. Our studies with plants grown in the glasshouse or a growth chamber (15) led us to conclude that the partitioning of photosynthate in the leaf is directly determined by the SPS activity in the leaf and this is illustrated by Fig. 2 where leaf starch and sucrose contents were measured at 160 $\mu E\ m^{-2}\ s^{-1}$. It is important to note that this change in partitioning was always observed and was evident at all irradiances used. The amount of starch in the leaves decreased (Fig. 2B) while that of sucrose increased (Fig. 2A) as a function of the extractable SPS activity. The levels of starch and sucrose within the leaves was consistently found to vary according to the SPS activity whatever the conditions such that when the ratio of sucrose of starch present in the leaves is plotted as a function of SPS activity a strong correlation is observed (Fig. 2C).

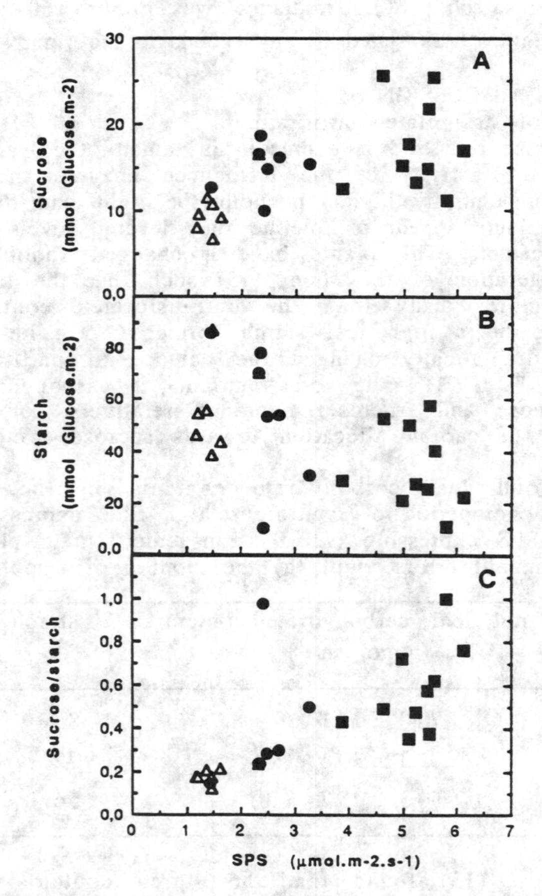

Figure 2. The relationship between the SPS activity of control ( ) and transformed (,) tomato leaves and their sucrose and starch contents. Plants were grown in a growth chamber at 160 $\mu mol\ m^{-2}\ s^{-1}$ irradiance and leaves were harvested at approximately mid-day.

The carbon budget of the leaf is thus modified as a result of the increases in SPS activity, the rate of sucrose synthesis and export is increased while that of starch synthesis and storage is decreased (data not shown). We conclude that the level of SPS is a major determinant of carbon partitioning and, as we demonstrate below, this has important repercussions for photosynthesis. The maximum rate of photosynthesis in saturating CO_2 and high light was increased by up to 20% in the transformed plants relative to controls (Fig. 3). The control plants in Table 2 had an SPS activity of 15.4 ± 4.2 in the light while the TR2 transformants had more than double this activity and the TR9 transformants had about four times the activity. The over-expression of SPS in the TR2 transformants increased the maximal capacity for photosynthesis, while the greater SPS activity in the TR9 transformants increased the maximal rate of photosynthesis even more (Table 2). We conclude that increases in SPS increased the capacity for sucrose synthesis and, thereby, increased the maximal photosynthetic rate, in all of our studies. When photosynthesis was measured in air and high irradiance an increase in photosynthetic rate was evident but the variation between leaf samples was large and the differences were not statistically relevant (15).
In order to further examine the possibility of limitation of the rate of photosynthesis by the capacity for sucrose synthesis we used a treatment of rapid light transitions as described by Stitt (5). When leaf discs that have been illuminated in high light are subjected to a brief exposure in low light the subsequent return to high light produces a temporary (15-30 s) enhancement of the photosynthetic rate which is illustrated in Fig. 3.

Table 2: CO_2-saturated rates of photosynthesis measured at 400 µmol m^{-2} s^{-1} and 1600 µmol m^{-2} s^{-1} irradiance in control, a high SPS expressing (TR 2) and the highest SPS expressing (TR 9) transgenic tomato plants. Values are means ± standard errors, with (n) the number of samples. At 400 µmol m^{-2} s^{-1} plants were obtained from in a growth chamber; at 1600 µmol m^{-2} s^{-1} plants were obtained from in a greenhouse.

Plant type	Photosynthesis (µmol m^{-2} s^{-1})			
	light intensity 400 µmol m^{-2} s^{-1}		light intensity 1600 µmol $m^{-2} \cdot s^{1}$	
Control	16.44 ± 0.76	(6)	23.43 ± 4.41	(7)
TR 2	17.09 ± 0.73	(7)	- -	
TR 9	18.29 ± 0.65	(10)	26.95 ± 2.55	(7)

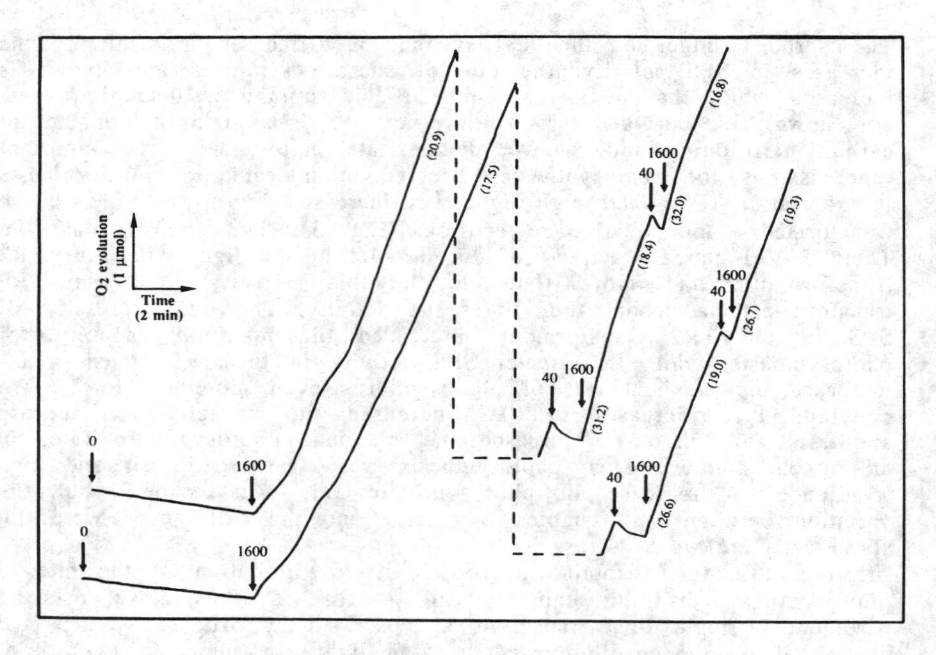

Figure 3. O_2 evolution during transitions in irradiance measured in the leaf disc oxygen electrode. Changes in irradiances (µmol m^{-2} s^{-1}) are indicated above the arrows. Rates of CO_2-dependent O_2 evolution, in µmol m^{-2} s^{-1}, are given in brackets beside the appropriate section of the trace. The upper trace was taken from a transformed tomato leaf disc, the lower trace from a control.

CO_2-dependent O_2 evolution was measured in the leaf disc oxygen electrode at saturating CO_2 and high irradiance (1600 µmol m^{-2} s^{-1}) (Fig. 3). The upper trace was made from the leaf disc of a high SPS expressor while the lower trace was made from a control leaf disc. The relative rates of photosynthesis are given in the brackets on the figure. It is clear that the high SPS expressor had a higher maximum photosynthetic rate than the control. At the points indicated the light intensity was rapidly decreased to 40 µE m^{-2} s^{-1} for a brief period. Following this brief exposure to low irradiance the rate of photosynthesis was transiently, but substantially, increased when the leaf disc was returned to high light. Photosynthetic rates are given in the figures in brackets adjacent to the curves. In the example shown the temporary enhanced rate of photosynthesis was about 50% above that of the steady-state rate of O_2 evolution. In the transgenic tomatoes expressing high SPS activities the elevated rate could be much higher (up to 300%) than the steady-state rate (14). The transformed tomato plants may, thus, have a slight advantage in a fluctuating light environment since carbon gain in this situation will be higher than in the untransformed controls. Since a steady-state situation with regard to irradiance rarely exists in natural environments increased SPS activities may be beneficial. The transgenic tomato plants have a higher photosynthetic rate in the steady-state in optimal conditions of irradiance and CO_2, plus an additional advantage in terms of photosynthesis when subjected to transitions in irradiance. This is possibly related to the increased capacity for cycling Pi afforded by the presence of higher SPS activities.

In conclusion, our results confirm that SPS activity plays a pivotal role in the regulation of assimilate partitioning in leaves and that an increase in the capacity for photosynthetic sucrose formation has the effect of elevating the maximal rate of photosynthesis when the supply of light and CO_2 are adequate. Our data also shows that the regulated capacity of sucrose synthesis is a major natural determinant of the amount of starch in the leaves as well as sucrose. Furthermore, at high irradiance the activation state of SPS, similar to the activation states of the Calvin cycle enzymes, may be a limitation on electron transport capacity (2).

ACKNOWLEGEMENTS

These experiments were carried out under contract to Roussel-Uclaf (France).

REFERENCES

1 Leegood, R.C., Walker, D.A. and Foyer, C.H. (1985) in Topics in photosynthesis, Vol. 6, Photosynthetic mechanisms and the environment (Barber J. and Baker N.R. eds), 189-258, Elsevier, Amsterdam
2 Heber, U., Neimanis and Dietz, K.J. (1986) Biochim. Biophys. Acta 852, 144-155
3 Heber, U., Neimanis and Dietz, K.J. (1988) Planta 173, 267-274
4 Foyer, C.H., Furbank, R., Harbinson, J. and Horton, P. (1990) Photosynth. Res. 25, 83-100
5 Stitt, M. (1986) Plant Physiol. 81, 1115-1122
6 Stitt, M., Huber, S. and Kerr, P. (1987) in The biochemistry of plants (Hatch M.D. and Boardman N.K., eds), Vol. 10, Photosynthesis, Academic Press, New York, 327-409
7 Stitt, M. and Quick, P. (1989) Physiol. Plant. 77, 633-641
8 Huber, S.C. (1981) Z. Pflanzenphysiol. 102, 443-450
9 Huber, S.C., Rufty, T.W. and Kerr, P.S. (1984) Plant Physiol. 75, 1080-1084
10 Rocher, J.P. (1988) Aust. J. Plant Physiol. 15, 677-685
11 Rocher, J.P., Prioul, J.L., Lecharny, A., Reyss, A. and Joussaume, M. (1989) Plant Physiol. 89, 416-420
12 Kerr, P.S., Huber, S.C. and Israel, D.W. (1984) Plant Physiol. 75, 483-488
13 Worrell, A.C., Bruneau, J.M., Summerflelt, K., Boersig, M. and Volker, T.A. (1991) Plant Cell 3, 1121-1130
14 Salerno, G.L., Gramundi, S.S. and Pontis (1979) Ann. Biochem. 93, 196-199
15 Galtier, N., Foyer, C.H., Huber, J., Voelker, T.A. and Huber, S.C. (1992) Plant Physiol., in press

16 Huber, J.L., Hite, D.R.C., Outlaw, W.H. Jr and Huber, S.C. (1991) Plant Physiol. 95, 291-297
17 Hammond, J.B.W., Burton, K.S., Shaw, A.F. and Ho, L.C. (1984) Ann. Bot. 3, 307-317

MOLECULAR BIOLOGY AND BIOCHEMISTRY OF THE 62 kD SUCROSE BINDING PROTEIN AND ITS POSSIBLE ROLE IN SUCROSE TRANSPORT

Nagoya Congress Center, Nagoya, Japan, August 30 - September 4, 1992

HOWARD D. GRIMES, Department of Botany, Washington State University, Pullman, WA 99164-4238, UNITED STATES OF AMERICA

1. INTRODUCTION

The entire life cycle of higher plants is intimately linked with carbon fixation and partitioning this carbon between various tissues. During the process of photosynthesis carbon is fixed into carbohydrate energy sources. Carbon partitioning describes the distribution of this carbohydrate, usually in the form of sucrose, between various organs throughout the plant. Two of the most critical steps in carbon partitioning are 1) phloem loading or transport of sucrose against a concentration gradient into phloem for long-distance transport and 2) phloem unloading at the sink tissue and transport of sucrose into the sink tissue cells. The relationship between carbon fixation in photosynthesis and carbon partitioning in the soybean plant is shown in figure 1. We have used the soybean cotyledon to investigate the mechanism of sucrose transport because this organ is actively engaged in sucrose uptake into its parenchyma cells after sucrose unloading and is an excellent model system to investigate the biochemistry and molecular biology of sucrose transport across the plasma membrane.

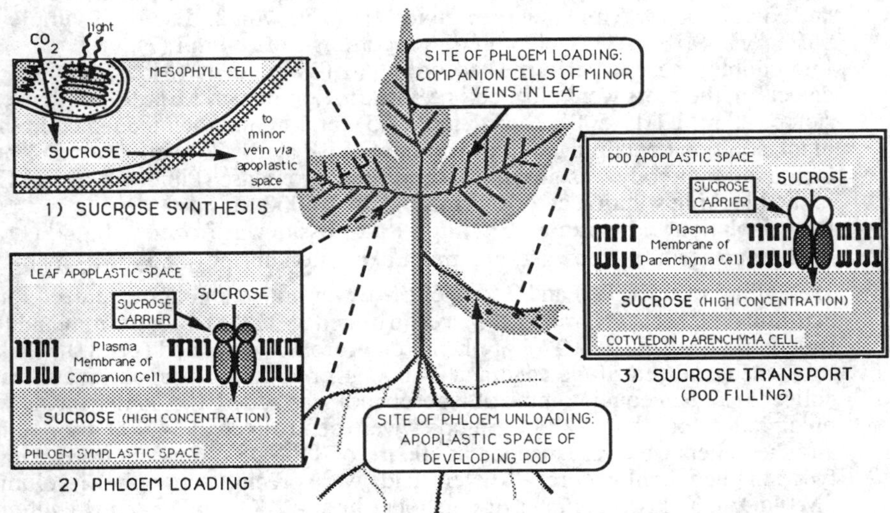

Figure 1. Critical Steps in Sucrose Transport in the Soybean Plant

N. Murata (ed.), Research in Photosynthesis, Vol. IV, 745–751.

Two proteinaceous candidates have been implicated in sucrose transport in higher plants. The first is a 62 kD membrane protein that was initially identified using the sucrose-analog photoaffinity probe, 6'-deoxy-6'-(4-azido-2-hydroxy)-benzamidosucrose, to label isolated microsomal membranes from the soybean cotyledon (1). Immunocytochemical experiments indicate that this protein is a plasma membrane protein that is strongly associated with cells that are actively transporting sucrose (1, 2, 3). Because of its' proven ability to bind sucrose, this protein is termed the 62 kD sucrose binding protein or 62SBP. The second candidate is a 42 kD group of proteins identified by differential labeling with N-ethylmaleimide (4). Antiserum raised against this protein group is somewhat inhibitory to sucrose transport in isolated membrane vesicles (5) and these polypeptides have been reconstituted in liposomes with a partial restoration of sucrose transport (6).

2. MATERIALS AND METHODS

2.1 Plant Material: Soybean (*Glycine max* cv Wye) seeds were planted in potting compost in gallon pots and grown in a controlled environment chamber with a photon flux density of 360 to 400 µE / m • sec PAR at canopy height, with a 16-hr photoperiod and 24°C / 18°C day / night temperatures. Plants were grown to flowering (about 3 months) for cotyledon harvest. The cotyledons used were collected from plants at 10 - 20 days after flowering unless otherwise specified.

2.2 Protein Extraction, Electrophoresis, and Immunoblotting: Cotyledons were removed from the pod and seed coat and ground in a Warring blender using a buffer consisting of 250 mM sucrose, 2.5 mM DTT, 10 mM EGTA, 10 mM $MgSO_4$, 0.5% gelatin (w/v) in 25 mM Mes-KOH at pH 7.0. 2 ml of buffer per g FW cotyledons was used and grinding was for 1 minute. The ground mixture was poured through 4 layers of cheesecloth and centrifuged twice at 13,000 g for 10 min each time. The supernatant was then centrifuged at 100,000 g for 45 min. The resulting microsomal pellet was resuspended in 25 mM Tris-HCl (pH 6.8) and 0.5% SDS. For electrophoresis, the resuspended microsomes were heated at 80°C for 5 min and then mixed 1:1 (v/v) with 2x Laemmli sample buffer (7). SDS-PAGE gels were run according to Laemmli (7). Immunoblotting was performed according to Towbin et al. (8). For antigen detection, the blots were blocked in 5% Carnation Instant Milk in Tris-buffered saline (20 mM Tris, 500 mM NaCl, pH 7.5) for 1 hr and then incubated in the block solution containing antibody to the 62SBP at a 1:5000 dilution for 1 hr. Secondary antibody was goat anti-rabbit IgG peroxidase (Pierce Chemical Co.) in the blocking solution at a concentration of 1:5000 for 1 hr.

2.3 RNA Isolation and Northern Blotting: 1 g of tissue was frozen in liquid N_2 and ground to a fine powder. 9.5 ml of extraction buffer (0.85 mM Tris pH 9.0, 1% SDS, 5 mM EDTA) and 0.5 ml of βME was added and homogenized for an additional 30 sec. The mixture was centrifuged at 31,000 g for 15 min and the supernatant collected. 10 ml of phenol:chloroform was added (pH 8.0), shaken for 10 sec, and centrifuged again at 31,000 g for 20 min. Aqueous phase was collected and an equal volume of isopropanol was added and nucleic acids were precipitated for 1 hr at -20°C. Samples were centrifuged at 14,000 g for 10 min and the pellets were resuspended in 600 µL of TE/SDS. Samples were extracted twice in phenol:chloroform. Nucleic acids were precipitated with 0.1 volume of 3M NaOAc and two volumes of ethanol (1 hr at -20°C). After centrifugation in a microfuge, samples were dried in a speed-vac. The pellets were resuspended in 1 ml of TE/SDS to which was added 250 μL of LiCl and the RNA was precipitated overnight at 4°C. RNA was pelleted in a microfuge, dried, and resuspended in 100 μL of TE/SDS. Total RNA was separated on agarose gels containing formaldehyde and transferred to GeneScreen (DuPont) membranes according to Sambrook et al. (9). Hybridizations were done according to standard methods.

2.4 DNA Sequencing: Selected clones from the screening were purified. The plasmid pBluescript SK+ was excised from the vector, and the plasmid containing E. coli strain was increased. Plasmid from the clone chosen for sequencing was purified through PEG precipitation and sequenced by dideoxy sequencing from the 5' end beginning with a primer to the T3 promoter and continuing using oligonucleotides based on the previous sequence as primers. The sequence was checked by sequencing from 3' to 5'.

3. RESULTS AND DISCUSSION

3.1 The 62 SBP was cloned and sequenced. Analysis of the nucleotide sequence has yielded sever al important pieces of information concerning the 62SBP that the cDNA encodes. First, there is a 29 amino acid hydrophobic region that is cleaved off of the mature protein (figure 2A). This conclusion was reached after the sequences of the cDNA and the isolated mature protein were compared. The hydrophobic leader peptide may be involved in directing this protein to the plasma membrane. Second, the 62SBP is not an invertase. We have examined the nucleotide and deduced amino acid sequences of this cDNA and compared it to the published sequence of the carrot extracellular β-fructosidase (10). There is no conservation of sequence even in the regions that are most highly conserved in the invertase gene family. Hence, the role of the 62SBP in sucrose transport is not to simply cleave sucrose into its hexose sugars. Third, both Kyte-Doolittle and Goldman et al. hydropathy plots indicate that the 62SBP is not a hydrophobic protein and has no recognizable membrane-spanning domains (figure 2B). Extensive computer-assisted secondary structure predictions indicate that no significant hydrophobic patches exist on the 62SBP nor are any helical wheel structures found that are large enough to span the bilayer. These results suggest that the 62SBP is not an integral membrane protein. Fourth, there is no significant homology of the 62SBP to other known protein or gene sequences.

3.2 Because the sequence analysis indicates that the 62SBP is not an integral membrane protein, the extent to which the 62SBP is associated with the membrane was determined by performing hypotonic washes on the microsomes. These washes cause the vesicles to burst and then to spontaneously revesiculate. Thus, if soluble proteins are "trapped" inside of the vesicles, these washes should release them. Figure 3 shows that even with 4 hypotonic washes the 62SBP is found associated with the membrane vesicles. Hence, the 62SBP is a membrane protein and is not merely a soluble protein that is trapped inside of membrane vesicles during homogenization.

A.

MGMRTKLSLAIFFFFLLALFSNLAFGKCKETEVEEEDPELVTCKHQCQQ
ETEVEEEDPELVTCKHQCQQ

B.

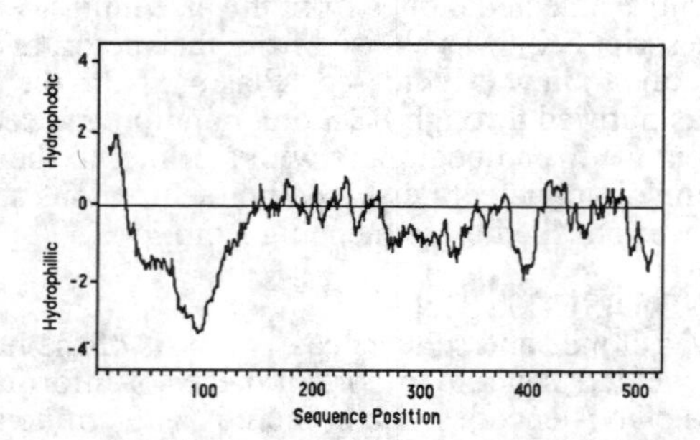

Figure 2. A) Upper line shows the deduced amino acid sequence at the N-terminus of the 62SBP. The bottom line (in italics) is the amino acid sequence obtained from the isolated, mature 62SBP. The underlined region in the upper line indicates a 29 amino acid sequence that is cleaved off of the mature protein. B) Kyte-Doolittle hydropathy plot of the 62SBP.

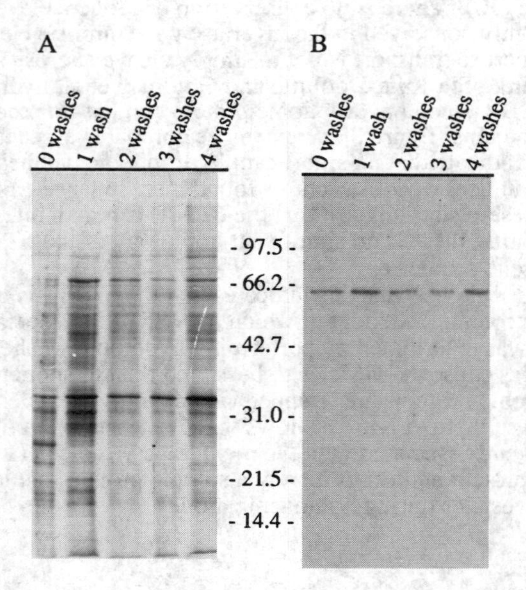

Figure 3. A) SDS-PAGE gel stained with coomassie after a series of hypotonic washes to open the membrane vesicles and release any trapped soluble components. B) An immunoblot to the same hypotonic washes shown in panel A probed with the 62SBP antibody.

Further experiments using salts (KI, KCl) and sulfhydryl reagents (β-mercaptoethanol, DTT) demonstrate that the 62SBP is not removed by these reagents (data not shown). Since even 2M salt treatments will not remove the 62SBP from the membrane, we conclude that the 62SBP is not interacting with the membrane solely through ionic interactions. The only treatments which remove a significant amount of the 62SBP from the membrane are strong chaotropic reagents (such as 0.6 M urea) or detergents (2% CHAPS or 1% Triton X-100) (data not shown). Collectively, these experiments indicate that the 62SBP is tightly associated with the membrane even though it is not an integral membrane protein.

3.3 So far, we have discussed the sucrose transport properties and the 62SBP associated with the soybean cotyledon. The soybean cotyledon is used because sucrose is transported to this tissue, unloaded into the apoplastic space, and then virtually all of the cells in the cotyledon are actively transporting sucrose across the plasma membrane into the symplast. Another important aspect of sucrose transport, however, is loading of sucrose into the phloem against a concentration gradient (i.e. phloem loading) and sucrose transport into young tissues, such as leaves, while they are still sinks. In this latter case, a soybean leaf is a net carbon, or sucrose, importer until it makes the transition to a source leaf. If the 62SBP is involved in sucrose transport in sink leaves, then we might expect to observe its mRNA transcript expressed at significant levels at a very young age while the leaf is a sink. This is because many of the cells of the leaf need to import sucrose from the apoplast since they are not yet highly photosynthetic. We have examined the expression of the mRNA for the 62SBP in leaves of three distinct stages: 1/8 expanded where the leaf is a strong carbon sink, 1/4 expanded where the leaf has just made the transition to a source leaf, and fully expanded where the leaf is a strong source of carbon. When immunolocalization is performed on these different stages, the 62SBP is associated with the plasma membrane of most cells in the 1/8 expanded leaf. As the leaf matures, however, the 62SBP signal is observed only associated with the companion cells of the phloem (data not shown). When the 62SBP transcript level is assayed by northern blotting, we observe that the 1/8 expanded leaf has a significant amount of hybridization while 1/4 expanded and fully expanded leaves have no detectable 62SBP mRNA (figure 4).

The northern data are consistent with the immunolocalization data because in the 1/8 expanded leaves, most of the cells are actively transporting sucrose and, hence, most of the cells are actively transcribing this message. As the leaf develops further, we observe a restriction of the 62SBP to the phloem and we no longer have detectable levels of 62SBP transcript (figure 3). The reason that no transcript is found is because the population of phloem cells in the leaf is fairly small and consequently the amount of transcript is too low to be detected in fully expanded leaves. Because of our observations at the immunocytochemical level demonstrating that the 62SBP is associated with leaf cells and phloem cells that are actively engaged in sucrose transport, we postulate that the 62SBP is involved in sucrose transport associated with phloem loading as well as in the soybean cotyledon.

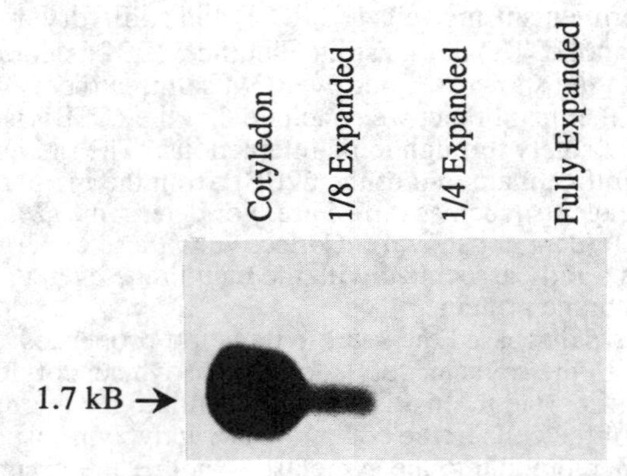

Figure 4. Northern blot of 62SBP mRNA levels in 1/8, 1/4, and fully expanded soybean leaves.

3.4 Most of the evidence that we have presented and that is in the literature suggesting that the 62SBP is involved in sucrose transport is derived from a) its method of identification (i.e. its ability to bind sucrose and its association with the membrane fraction) and b) extensive immunolocalization studies demonstrating that the 62SBP is associated only with tissues and cells that are actively involved in sucrose transport. Recently, however, antibodies against the 62SBP were shown to inhibit sucrose transport in *Vicia faba* protoplasts (11) lending strong support to the argument that the 62SBP is involved in sucrose transport. Thus, we now have several observations concerning the 62SBP and its potential role in sucrose transport. First, the 62SBP binds sucrose tightly and appears to be involved in sucrose transport. Second, the 62SBP is not an integral membrane protein and yet is tightly associated with the membrane. Third, available data indicate that it is located on the external leaflet of the plasma membrane. Fourth, the 62SBP is not an invertase. Considering all of these observations, we propose the following model for sucrose transport in higher plants (figure 5).

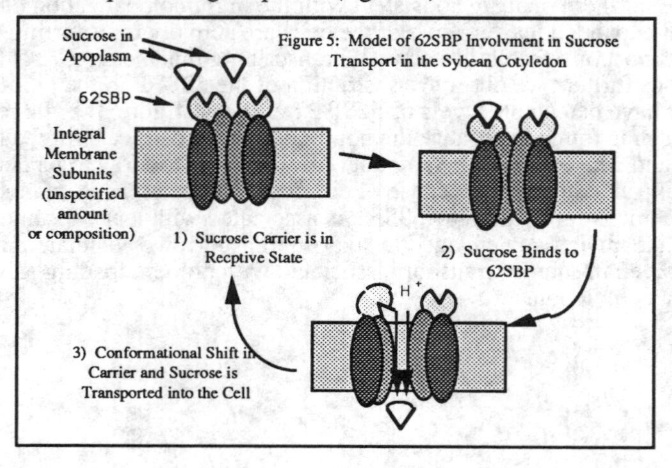

Figure 5: Model of 62SBP Involvment in Sucrose Transport in the Sybean Cotyledon

Although this model is speculative, it is consistent with all currently available observations of the 62SBP and sucrose transport in higher plants. We propose that the 62SBP initially binds sucrose prior to translocation across the membrane through a multiprotein complex. As such, the 62SBP may be a regulator of sucrose transport.

REFERENCES

1 Ripp, K.G., Viitanen, P.V., Hitz, W.D., and Franceschi, V.R. (1988) Plant Physiol186: 1435-1445
2 Warmbrodt, R.D., Buckhout, T.J., and Hitz, W.D. (1989) Planta 180: 105-115
3 Warmbrodt, R.D., Vanderwoude, W.J., and Hitz, W.D. (1991) New Phytol 118: 501-512
4 M'Batchi, B. and Delrot, S. (1984) Plant Physiol 75: 154-160
5 Lemoine, R.E., Delrot, S., Gallet, O., and Larsson, C. (1988) Biochem. Biophys. Acta 778: 65-71
6 Li, Z.S., Gallet, O., Gailard, C., Lemoine, R., and Delrot, S. (1991) FEBS Letters 286: 117-120
7 Laemmli, U.K. (1970) Nature 227: 680-685
8 Towbin, H., Staehlin, T., and Gordon, J. (1979) Proc. Natl. Acad. Sci. USA 76: 4350-4354
9 Sambrook, J., Fritsch, E.F., and Maniatis, T. (1989) Molecular Cloning: A Laboratory Manual, 2nd Ed (Cold Spring Harbor, NY: Cold Spring Harbor Laboratory)
10 Sturm, A. and Chrispeels, M.J. (1990) Plant Cell 2: 1107-1119
11 Fieuw, F., Franceschi, V.R., Hitz, W.D., and Patrick, J.W. (1992) Plant Physiol. 99:40 (#240)

SUGARS, FATTY ACIDS, AND PHOTOSYNTHETIC GENE EXPRESSION

Jen Sheen, Hai Huang, Anton R. Schäffner, Patricia Leon, and Jyan-Chyun Jang

DEPARTMENT OF MOLECULAR BIOLOGY, WELLMAN 11, MASSACHUSETTS GENERAL HOSPITAL, BOSTON, MA 02114, USA

INTRODUCTION

Bacteria and unicellular eukaryotes are able to respond swiftly to change in environmental nutrient supplies and internal metabolite levels by switching on and off the genes involved in catabolic and anabolic pathways. This behavior is thought to allow them to adapt to capricious fluctuations in nutrient supplies from the environment and to maintain an economical balance of essential biomolecules (1). In contrast, multicellular organisms maintain energy homeostasis in a changing environment through the regulation of metabolic pathways in cells of defined and differentiated tissues. For instance, in vertebrate, glucose homeostasis is maintained by liver cells which are principle sites for gluconeogenesis and glycogen storage and mobilization. In higher plants, an energy balance is achieved between the photosynthetic (source) and non-photosynthetic (sink) cells. When the rate of photosynthesis in source tissue exceeds the demand of sink tissue, a feedback or sink regulation of photosynthesis is observed. Therefore, sink-source relationships are not only central to crop yield, but also tightly linked to plant development (2, 3, 4). Although abundant information has accumulated on the metabolic regulation of gene expression in *E. coli* and yeast (1, 5) much less is known about the molecular mechanisms mediating metabolic regulation of gene expression in proliferating and differentiated cells of multicellular eukaryotes, especially in photosynthetic higher plants (6). The development of a physiological and simplified cellular system should facilitate the understanding of the molecular mechanisms mediating metabolic regulation of photosynthesis.

Although abundant and homogeneous population of mesophyll protoplasts can be easily obtained from fresh leaves of most plants, the study of photosynthetic gene regulation in freshly isolated mesophyll protoplasts has not been vigorously pursued. It has been widely believed that photosynthetic genes are suppressed in mesophyll protoplasts by osmotic stress after isolation (7). We discovered that the inhibition of photosynthetic gene expression in mesophyll protoplasts is likely the result of photosynthetic endproduct repression by

N. Murata (ed.), Research in Photosynthesis, Vol. IV, 753–760.

sucrose and glucose. Sucrose and glucose are two commonly used osmotica in tobacco protoplast culture (8) in which repression of photosynthetic genes was shown previously (7). We have presented evidence that the transcriptional activity of seven maize photosynthetic gene promoters is specifically and coordinately repressed by the photosynthetic endproducts sucrose and glucose, and by the short chain fatty acid acetate (6). The metabolic repression of photosynthetic genes overrides regulation by light, tissue type, and developmental stage. Repression by sugars and repression by acetate are mediated by distinct mechanisms and can act synergistically (1, J.-C. Jang and J. Sheen, unpublished). The discovery represents the first molecular evidence suggesting an intimate connection between the level of photosynthetic endproducts and the transcriptional potential of genes required for photosynthesis. The identification of conditions that avoid sugar repression overcomes a major obstacle to the study of photosynthetic gene regulation and reveals a new aspect of metabolic regulation. Lately, metabolic repression of photosynthetic gene expression has also been found in other plants, such as <u>rbcS</u> gene in <u>Arabidopsis</u> (9), and <u>cab</u> and <u>rbcS</u> genes in tobacco (10). In addition, sugars as positive or negative gene regulators have also been detected in various plant tissues, e.g., an amylase gene in rice callus and embryo (11, 12), proteinase inhibitor gene promoter in transgenic tobacco leaves (13), chalcon synthase gene promoter in transgenic <u>Arabidopsis</u> (14), and sucrose synthase genes in maize callus and root (15, 16). Therefore, metabolic regulation of gene expression appears to be a universal and fundamental problem common to all higher plants.

MATERIALS AND METHODS

To study monocot-specific, tissue-specific, developmental, light, and metabolic regulation of maize photosynthetic genes, a convenient and physiological transient expression method has been developed based on protoplasts isolated from fresh tissues of maize seedlings. Two constructs containing the promoter of the cauliflower mosaic virus 35S RNA, and the chloramphenicol acetyltransferase gene (CAT) or β-glucuronidase gene (GUS) were used as indicators to optimize the expression in protoplasts freshly isolated from root, stem, and leaf of various chloroplast developmental stages (6, 17, 18, 19). The 35SCAT and 35SGUS constructs both contain the 3′ region of the nopaline synthase gene (<u>nos</u>) as a transcription termination signal. A promoterless construct was used as a control to estimate background levels. DNA samples were routinely introduced into 10^5 protoplasts by electroporation. Transient expression is extremely reproducible usually with less than 5% variation among different protoplast samples (6). Results are consistent between different batches of protoplasts isolated in the past five years in our laboratory. The protoplast isolation procedure and electroporation condition have been extensively optimized (J. Sheen,, unpublished). The construction of various maize photosynthetic fusion genes for transient expression assays has been described (6, 17, 18, 19).

RESULTS AND DISCUSSION

Using maize mesophyll protoplasts and fusion genes, we show that seven maize photosynthetic gene promoters are specifically and coordinately repressed by the photosynthetic endproducts sucrose and glucose (Table 1) and by the short chain fatty acid acetate (Table 2)(6). The repression is concentration-dependent and overrides regulation by light, tissue-type, and developmental stages. Acetate repression is generally 10-fold stronger than glucose repression for most promoters except the C4ppdkZm1 promoter. The non-photosynthetic cyppdkZm1 promoter is repressed by sugars but not acetate. Repression by sugars and repression by acetate are likely mediated by different mechanisms (6). Further analysis indicates that the two mechanisms can act synergistically (J.-C. Jang and J. Sheen, unpublished). The repression is triggered at low and physiological concentration of glucose (5 mM) and acetate (1 mM), suggesting that the sensory mechanism of metabolite signals is highly sensitive. Obviously, osmotic stress can not account for the repression effect (J.-C. Jang and J. Sheen, unpublished).

Promoter and CAT Fusions (Cotransfection GUS Fusion)	Relative CAT (GUS) Activity	
	No Acetate	3 mM Acetate
C_4ppdkZm1CAT (cyppdk-Zm1GUS)	25.3 (23.0)	1.5 (11.7)
C_4pepcZm1CAT (cyppdk-Zm1GUS)	8.5 (25.5)	0.1 (8.8)
C_4meZm1CAT (cyppdk-Zm1GUS)	7.5 (24.8)	0.2 (6.2)
cabZm1CAT (cyppdkZm1GUS)	24.8 (24.6)	0.3 (8.6)
cabZm5CAT (cyppdkZm1GUS)	30.1 (19.9)	0.2 (6.6)
rbcSZm1CAT (cyppdk-Zm1GUS)	13.3 (15.1)	0.5 (7.1)
rbcSZm3CAT (cyppdk-Zm1GUS)	8.9 (17.1)	0.04 (6.7)
35SCAT (cyppdkZm1GUS)	54.9 (33.3)	6.3 (19.4)
nosCAT (cyppdkZm1GUS)	28.6 (38.5)	4.8 (10.9)
Adh1CAT (cyppdkZm1GUS)	8.3 (28.1)	1.0 (8.3)
cyppdkZm1CAT	13.2	8.8

CAT assay was the same as described in Table 3. Cell extract from 10^4 protoplasts was used for GUS assay. Relative GUS activity of cotransfection is shown in parentheses. Similar results were obtained when the experiment was repeated three times without cotransfection and once with cotransfection.

Table 1. Effect of Sugars

Promoter and CAT Fusions (Cotransfection GUS Fusion)	Relative CAT (GUS) Activity		
	Mannitol	Sucrose	Glucose
C_4ppdkZm1CAT (35SGUS)	9.6 (37.1)	0.7 (21.1)	0.4 (18.9)
C_4pepcZm1CAT (35SGUS)	7.2 (35.7)	2.3 (18.3)	0.9 (17.6)
C_4meZm1CAT (35SGUS)	5.4 (26.7)	1.3 (13.2)	0.6 (12.4)
cabZm1CAT (35SGUS)	18.2 (30.4)	4.9 (15.5)	1.8 (16.2)
cabZm5CAT (35SGUS)	21.8 (27.6)	2.0 (15.2)	1.8 (17.4)
rbcSZm1CAT (35SGUS)	22.0 (30.9)	1.7 (18.6)	0.6 (19.1)
rbcSZm3CAT (35SGUS)	7.5 (33.2)	1.6 (15.8)	0.3 (15.1)
35SCAT	34.2	20.1	19.7
nosCAT	20.7	12.7	11.9
Adh1CAT	5.6	4.7	4.3
cyppdkZm1CAT (35SGUS)	19.3 (27.6)	3.4 (17.7)	0.6 (19.6)

Cell extract from 5×10^4 protoplasts was used for CAT assay except the 35SCAT sample (2×10^3 protoplasts). Cell extract from 2×10^3 protoplasts was used for GUS assay. Relative GUS activity of cotransfection is shown in parentheses. Similar results were obtained when the experiment was repeated three times without cotransfection and once with cotransfection. The construction of photosynthetic gene promoter and CAT fusions will be described elsewhere (J. Sheen, A. Schäffner, and H. Huang, unpublished data).

Table 2. Effect of Acetate

All the photosynthetic fusion genes studied in this laboratory contain complete 5′ untranslated regions. It is possible that repression occurs at the level of posttranscriptional regulation mediated through 5′ untranslated regions. However, promoter deletion analysis suggests that upstream sequences between -348 and -69 of the C4ppdkZm1 promoter and sequences between -138 and -54 of the cabZm5 promoter are important for glucose and acetate repression (Fig. 1)(6). The truncated promoters containing only TATA box and transcription initiation site show low level of activity, and are insensitive to sugars and acetate. In addition, study of a hybrid promoter shows that the addition of an ocs enhancer element confers the cabZm5 promoter (-92 to +71) glucose insensitive (Fig. 2). The hybrid promoter is also 10-times less sensitive to acetate (Fig. 3). Therefore, the sequences between -138 and -92 of the cabZm5 promoter are important for metabolic repression (6). Using site-directed mutagenesis, we have also replaced two different positive regulatory elements of the C4ppdkZm1 promoter with the ocs enhancer. In both cases, the mutated C4ppdkZm1 promoters are no longer sensitive to glucose and acetate (Figs. 2 and 3) (6). These results indicate that metabolic repression is mediated through upstream regulatory elements at transcriptional level. Although repressor binding is important for glucose repression in yeast (20), our data suggest that negative regulatory elements are perhaps not essential for metabolic repression of the C4ppdkZm1 promoter. Unless the ocs enhancer but not the C4ppdkZm1 enhancers can overcomes the effect of repressor. It is likely that metabolic repression is mediated through multiple upstream positive regulatory elements of maize photosynthetic gene promoters by the modification of either DNA-protein binding activity or protein-protein interactions.

The results described here also demonstrate that transient expression in protoplasts is a viable and attractive alternative to transgenic plant analysis for the study of photosynthetic gene regulation. The previously observed inhibition of photosynthetic gene expression in mesophyll protoplasts is likely the result of "endproduct repression" by the sugars chosen to stabilize protoplasts. Substitution of sucrose or glucose with mannitol, sorbitol, or other carbohydrates releases the repression. The most striking advantages of protoplast transient expression are rapidity, convenience, and versatility. Starting from the isolation of protoplasts to the collection of quantitative data, the whole process takes less than two days, while it takes months to obtain equivalent results with transgenic plants. In addition, the electroporation and CAT assay used here yields highly reproducible results when samples from different batchs of protoplasts are tested. It is especially convenient for the analysis of a large number of constructs. Large variations among similar samples associated with transgenic plant analysis has never been encountered using the transient expression assay. Compared with tissue transient expression, the homogeneous mesophyll protoplast system is more rapid, quantitative, and economical. Moreover, protoplasts can be easily and uniformly treated with metabolites and chemical inhibitors and activators which offers another advantage over intact tissues for the study of signal transduction pathways mediating metabolic regulation. Like the tissue transient expression assay, the protoplast transient assay requires little tissue culture and plant care, and can be applied to both dicot and monocot plants.

It has been shown by Foyer (2) that the removal of sinks causes an increase in the sucrose concentration of leaves and a severe inhibition of photosynthesis. Huber (21) has also shown that the feeding of the leaves with sucrose or glucose causes a substantial increase in leaf sugar content and a significant decrease in photosynthetic capacity. Recently, Dickinson et al. (22) and von Schaewen et al. (3) have independently shown that overexpression of a yeast invertase gene in source leaves of transgenic tomato or tobacco can increase sugar content and inhibit photosynthesis and growth. Based on these observations, it has been proposed that sugars play a crucial role in the biochemical feedback regulation of carbon assimilation and can act as the modulators of source and sink interaction when the production of photosynthate significantly exceeds the capacity of photosynthate utilization or transportation. In this work, we present evidence that sugars can play another role in the feedback regulation of photosynthesis, namely switching off the expression of photosynthetic genes. It is also possible that sugar repression is used, in part, as a regulatory mechanism for the developmental (germination and senescence), stress-repressible (wounding and pathogen attack), and tissue-specific expression of photosynthetic genes in higher plants.

Sugar repression allows a basal level of expression and is reversible when the concentration of sugars decreases. The concentration dependence and leaky features of sugar repression in higher plants resemble that found in end-product repression of the tryptophan operon in *E. coli* (5). Because sugars are the major endproducts of photosynthesis, it is more appropriate to classify the "glucose repression" of photosynthetic genes as a type of end-product repression in higher plants. Moreover, because sugars inhibit the expression of genes involved in an anabolic pathway--photosynthesis. Glucose repression in higher plants is a type of anabolite repression in contrast to catabolite repression in bacteria and yeast.

Besides sugar repression, transcriptional repression of photosynthetic genes was found with acetate and other short chain fatty acids, propionate and butyrate (J.-C. Jang and J. Sheen, unpublished). Repression mediated by acetate and repression mediated by sugars are quite different. Usually, acetate repression is 10 times stronger than sugar repression for photosynthetic gene promoters, with the exception of the cytosolic *ppdkZm1* promoter that is inhibited by sugars but not acetate (Tables 1 and 2). Thus, there must be at least two pathways for metabolic repression at the transcriptional level in maize.

The reasons for acetate repression can probably be best explained by the unique ability of plant cells to use acetate for gluconeogenesis and by the central role played by acetyl CoA (the direct cellular derivative of acetate) in the global cellular metabolism of plant cells (Fig. 4) (23, 24, 25, 26). It has been shown that acetate can be used as the sole exogenous carbon source by several green algae. In algal cells fed with acetate, the glyoxysome, a single membrane-bound organelle, is involved in using acetyl CoA for gluconeogenesis through the glyoxylate cycle (23, 27, 28, 29). The presence of acetate inhibits the expression of photosynthetic genes under light but activates the expression of glyoxysome enzymes for the metabolism of acetate (27, 28, 29, 30). These observations suggest that, in algae, acetate is a more favorable exogenous carbon source than CO_2, probably because the utilization of CO_2 involves the expression of more complex photosynthetic pathways. The repression of genes involved in other metabolic pathways by preferred exogenous carbon sources in green algae is a type of metabolic repression similar to that found in E. coli and yeast. However, an anabolic pathway, photosynthesis, is inhibited in green algae instead of the catabolic pathways inhibited in bacteria and yeast.

In higher plants, glyoxysomes are particularly abundant in germinating seedlings that are metabolizing fat. In these cells, acetate (or acetyl CoA) plays an important role for the generation of energy through the TCA cycle and the generation of carbohydrates through the glyoxylate cycle (Fig. 4) (23, 24, 25, 26). The presence of acetate repression in the mesophyll cells of maize seedlings might suggest the adaptation of an economical strategy by higher plants to ensure the use of stored fat first before switching over to the operation of more complex photosynthetic pathways. This model is consistent with the recent discovery by Graham et al. (31) that acetate can activate malate synthase gene of the glyoxylate cycle pathway during postgerminative growth of cucumber. The glyoxylate cycle enzyme synthesis stops when the developing seedlings become photosynthetic competent presumably after the stored fat in seed is consumed. Alternatively, plants can also absorb nutrients from organic acid-enriched soil, and the presence of excess acetate can act as a signal to convert plants to the utilization of easily available fuel from the environment. Because glyoxysomes and acetate repression are found in plant kingdom from green algae to higher plants, the evolutionary conservation strongly suggests that they play a role of fundamental importance in cellular metabolism.

Promoter and CAT fusions	Positions	Relative CAT activity: mannitol	glucose	acetate
C4ppdkZm1CAT	-507 +72	23.3	0.7	0.8
C4ppdkdel1CAT	-348 +72	22.0	1.8	1.3
C4ppdkdel2CAT	-158 +72	9.7	0.8	1.4
C4ppdkdel3CAT	-69 +72	0.4	0.3	0.2
cabZm5CAT	-838 +71	27.1	1.6	0.3
cabdel1CAT	-384 +71	30.1	3.2	0.3
cabdel2CAT	-138 +71	16.1	0.8	0.2
cabdel3CAT	-54 +71	0.2	0.2	0.2
35SCAT	-430 +1	185.7	115.1	50.0
35SC4ppdkhyb1CAT	-430 -40/-51 +72	178.7	135.1	66.7
35SC4ppdkhyb2CAT	-430 -25/-29 +72	188.6	147.9	59.2
C4ppdk35Shyb1CAT	-507 -44/-45 +1	19.0	0.6	2.0

Figure 1. Deletion Analysis

Promoter and CAT fusions	Positions	Relative CAT activity (Relative GUS activity): mannitol	sucrose	glucose
cabZm5CAT	-838 +71	21.8 (27.6)	2.0 (15.2)	1.8 (17.4)
ocscab5CAT	-155	57.8 (21.8)	27.2 (39.0)	43.3 (40.9)
C4ppdkZm1CAT	-507 +72	9.2 (19.8)	0.8 (10.9)	0.6 (17.0)
C4ppdkmut1CAT	-282/-273	50.4 (22.8)	22.4 (45.8)	47.1 (48.6)
C4ppdkmut2CAT	-97/-88	28.1 (23.1)	12.3 (40.7)	23.0 (46.5)

Figure 2. Effect of Sugars on the Activity of Mutated Promoters.

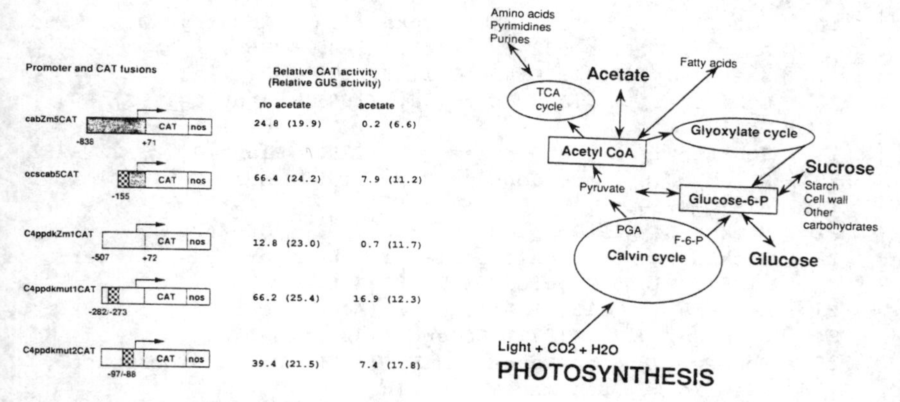

Figure 3. Effect of Acetate on the Activity of Mutated Promoters.

Figure 4. Acetyle-CoA as a Central Metabolite

REFERENCES

1 Saier, M.H.Jr. (1991) New Biol. 3, 1137-1147.
2 Foyer, C.H. (1988) Plant Physiol. Biochem. 26, 483-492.

3 Von Schaewen, A., Stitt, M., Schmidt, R., Sonnewald, U., and Willmitzer, L. (1990) EMBO J. 9, 3033-3044.
4 Stitt, M., von Schaewen, A., and Willmitzer, L. (1990) Planta 183, 40-50.
5 Miller, J., and Reznikoff, W. (1978) The Operon (Cold Spring Harbor, New York: Cold Spring Harbor Laboratory).
6 Sheen, J. (1990) Plant Cell 2, 1027-1038.
7 Fleck, J., Durr, A., Fritsch, C., Vernet, T., and Hirth, L. (1982) Plant Science Lett. 26, 159-165.
8 Nagy, J.T., and Maliga, P. (1976) Z. Pflanzenphysiol. 78, 453-455.
9 Cheng, C.-L., Acedo, G.N., Cristinsin, M., and Conkling, M.A. (1992) Proc. Natl. Acad. Sci. USA 89, 1861-1864.
10 Criqui, M.C., Durr,A., Parmentier, Y., Marrach, J., Fleck, J., and Jamet, E. (1992) Plant Physiol. Biochem. in press.
11 Yu, S.-M., Kuo, Y.-H., Sheu, G., Sheu, Y.-J., and Liu, L.-F. (1991) J. Biol. Chem. 266, 21131-21137.
12 Karrer, K. and Rodriguez, R. (1992) Plant J. 2, 517-524.
13 Kim, S.-R., Costa, M.A., and An, G. (1991) Plant Mol. Biol. 17, 973-983.
14 Tsukaya, H., Ohshima, T., Naito, S., Chino, M., and Komeda, Y. (1991) Plant Physiol. 97, 1414-1421.
15 Maas, C., Schaal, S., and Werr, W. (1990) EMBO J. 9, 3447-3452.
16 Koch, K.E., Nolte, K.D., Duke, E.R., McCarty, D.R., and Avigne, W.T. (1992). Plant Cell 4, 59-69.
17 Sheen, J. (1991) Plant Cell 3, 225-245.
18 Schäffner, A., and Sheen, J. (1991) Plant Cell 3, 997-1012.
19 Schäffner, A., and Sheen, J. (1991) Plant J. 2, 221-232.
20 Flick, J.S., and Johnston, M. (1990) Mol. Cell. Biol. 10, 4757-4769.
21 Huber, S. (1989) plant Physiol. 91, 656-662.
22 Dickinson, C.D., Altabella, T., and Chrispeels, M.J. (1991) Plant Physiol. 95, 420-425.
23 Beevers, H. (1969) Ann. N. Y. Acad. Sci. 168, 313-324.
24 Bassham, J.A. (1971) Science 172, 526-534.
25 Bonner, J., and Vanner, J.E. (1976) Plant Biochemistry. (New York: Academic Press, Inc.).
26 Kuhn, D.N., Knauf, M., and Stumpf, P.K. (1981) Arch. Bioch. Bioph. 209, 441-450.
27 Gibbs, M., Gfeller, R.P., and Chen, C. (1986) Plant Physio. 82, 160-166.
28 Steinbiβ, H.J., and Zetsche, K. (1986) Planta 167, 575-581.
29 Monroy, A.F., and Schwartzbach, S.D. (1984) Proc. Natl. Acad. Sci. 81, 2786-2790.
30 Kindle, K.L. (1987) Plant Mol. Biol. 9, 547-563.
31 Graham, I.A.,Leaver, C.J., and Smith, S.M. (1992) Plant Cell 4, 349-357.

CHANGES IN ACTIVITY OF ADPGLUCOSE-PYROPHOSPHORYLASE FROM MAIZE LEAF DURING DAY / NIGHT CYCLE

Emmanuelle JEANNETTE and Jean-Louis PRIOUL,
Structure et Métabolisme des Plantes, Bât. 430, Université de Paris-Sud,
associé au CNRS, URA 1128, 91405 Orsay Cedex, France.

1. INTRODUCTION

ADPglucose pyrophosphorylase (E.C.2.7.7.27) catalyzes the interconversion between ADPglucose and glucose 1P (ADPglucose + PPi <=> G1P + ATP). In vivo, this enzyme is considered to function in the direction of ADPglucose synthesis, providing the glycosyl for starch synthesis. PGA/Pi ratio controls activity *in vitro* and probably *in vivo* (1, 2). However simultaneous synthesis and degradation of starch have been reported in the light (3) which could introduce more complex regulation of starch accumulation. Under constant irradiance, starch content increases linearly during the most of the light period but decline in starch storage may occur a few hours before the beginning of the dark period (4).
In the present work, changes in extractable ADPglucose pyrophosphorylase activity were observed during light/dark cycle. These variations were shown to be dependent upon leaf carbohydrate status in conjunction to light.

2. MATERIAL and METHODS

2.1 Maize plants (*Zea mays* L. cv F7F2) were grown in a greenhouse. Natural light was supplemented 16 h a day (from 6 a.m. to 10 p.m.) with fluorescent "Phytoclaude" lamps (400 µmol quanta m^{-2} s^{-1}). Minimum temperatures were 25°C and 15°C during light and dark period, respectively. Leaf discs (0.5 cm^2) were punched out from mature fourth leaf, i.e. one or two days after its ligule was visible and immediately stored in liquid nitrogen.

2.2 Leaf extracts :
Leaf discs were individually ground in Eppendorf tubes at liquid nitrogen temperature with a glass pestle and then suspended at 4°C in 200 µl extraction buffer (50 mM Hepes-NaOH pH 7.5, 5 mM Mg Cl_2, 1 mM EDTA, 2.6 mM DTT, O.6% BSA, 0.02 % (v/v) Triton X100). Homogenate was centrifuged 4 min, 12000 g, 4°C. The same supernatant was used for determination of carbohydrate content and for enzyme assays. Desalted extracts were obtained by centrifugation (4 min, 3000g, 4°C) of the crude extracts on Sephadex G25 (Pharmacia Fine Chemicals) columns pre-equilibrated with extraction buffer.

2.3 Measurement of carbohydrate content :
Sucrose and glucose contents were measured by enzyme coupling method as in (5). Starch was determined on pellets from glucose obtained after amyloglucosidase digestion.

2.4 Assay of ADPglucose pyrophosphorylase/synthase :
The pyrophosphorylase activity was determined at 30°C from pyrophosphate-dependent degradation of ADPglucose. Glucose-1P formation was

N. Murata (ed.), Research in Photosynthesis, Vol. IV, 761–764.

spectrophotometrically monitored at 340 nm using coupling enzymes as in (6). Reaction mixture contained 77 mM Hepes-NaOH pH 7.5, 7.7 mM.$MgCl_2$, 1 mM NAD, 1 unit phosphoglucomutase (Sigma), 1 unit glucose 6P dehydrogenase from *Leuconostoc* (Boehringer) and 20 µl extract. Sodium pyrophosphate (1mM) was added to start the reaction when absorbance at 340 nm reached a plateau (<5 min). Assay in the ADPglucose synthesis direction was performed as in (7). Reaction mixture (200µl) contained 100 mM Hepes-NaOH pH 7.5, 5 mM $MgCl_2$, 2.5 mM ATP, 1 mM ^{14}C glucose 1 P (specific activity 10^6 dpm μmol^{-1}) and 20 µl extract The concentration of 3-PGA, when added, was 1 mM. The reaction was performed at 30°C for 10 min and terminated by heating in a boiling bath for 30 s. The unreacted glucose-1 P was hydrolyzed by adding 0.1 mg alkaline phosphatase from *E. Coli* and incubating for 40 min at 30°C. The mixture was absorbed on DEAE cellulose discs (Whatman DE 81) which were washed individually by vacuum evacuation using a multiwell apparatus. The discs were dried and counted by liquid scintilation.

2.5 Immunoprecipitation :

A volume of extract necessary to get 400 nkat (7 to 20 µl) was mixed with 0 to 10 µl antibodies previously diluted to 1/10 in extraction buffer. Final volume was adjusted to 40µl. After 2h incubation at 4°C the mixture was centrifuged 10 min at 12000g and the activity remaining in the supernatant was measured. The antibodies raised against one of the enzyme subunit from maize (Bt2) were kindly provided by L.C. Hannah and M. Giroux (University of Florida, Gainesville) who are gratefully acknowledged.

3 RESULTS

3.1 Diurnal changes in activity :

In a preliminary experiment we observed for 5 successive days that activity of ADPglucose pyrophosphorylase (ADPG-PPase) was consistently higher at the beginning of the light period than at the end. Precise measurements during a 24 h cycle (Fig.1) showed that activity was maximum at the end of the night and during the first 8 h in the light, then it declined to half the initial value in the second part of the light period. In this second part, starch (St.) accumulation levelled off but sucrose (Su.) content increased markedly.

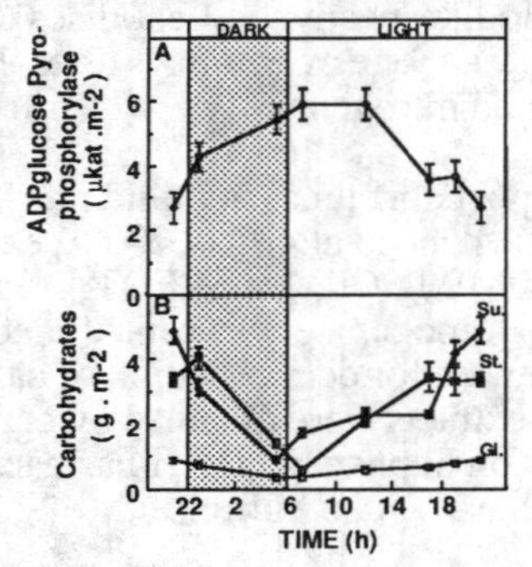

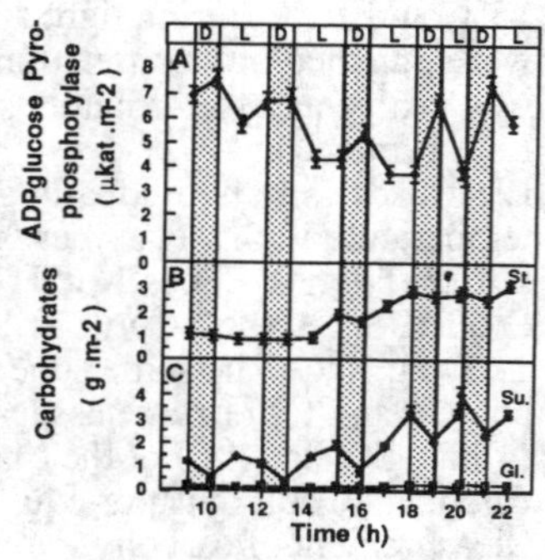

FIGURE 1. Time course of (A) ADPG-PPase activity and (B) starch (St.), sucrose (Su.) and glucose (Gl) contents during light and dark period. Mean ± SE from 3 plants.

FIGURE 2. Effect of one hour light interruption on (A) ADPG-PPase activity, (B) starch, (C) sucrose and (D) glucose content. Mean ± SE from 3 plants.

The effect on ADPG-PPase pattern of one hour light interruption at different times during the photoperiod was examined (Fig. 2). The dark period caused the recovery of a high activity whatever the time in the light period at which the light was interrupted.
However, it was a transient effect since activity returned back to its low value after one hour in the light. The light /dark transitions produced large fluctuations in sucrose content (Su.) and slightly affected starch (St.) accumulation, effect on glucose was negligible.The duration of the dark period for optimum recovery of a high activity was approximately one hour (not shown). The lowering of activity in the light, after one hour dark treatment, was irradiance dependent. Above a threshold value of 50µmol quanta m^{-2} s^{-1} the higher was irradiance the faster was the decline (data not shown).

3.2 In order to further test the interactions between soluble carbohydrate level and ADPG-PPase activity, leaves were excised and placed at 19:00, either on sucrose or sorbitol solutions at the same osmolarity (137 mM). ADPG-PPase activity in sorbitol treatment followed the same pattern as in control attached leaves (Fig. 1) whereas sucrose treatment limited the night increase and induced a rapid decline at the onset of light (Fig. 3). This decline corresponded to a massive increase in leaf sucrose content (data not shown).

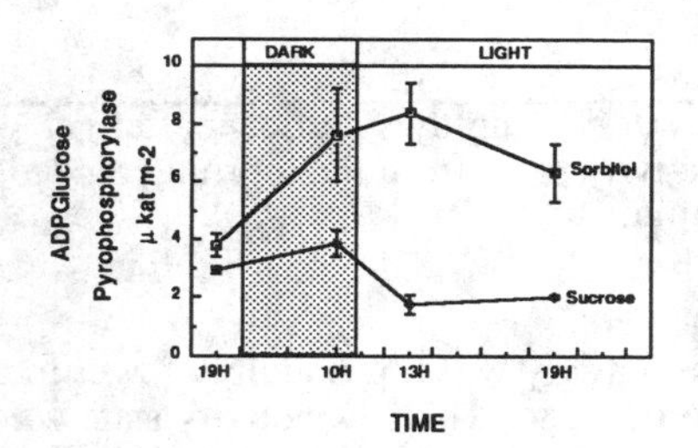

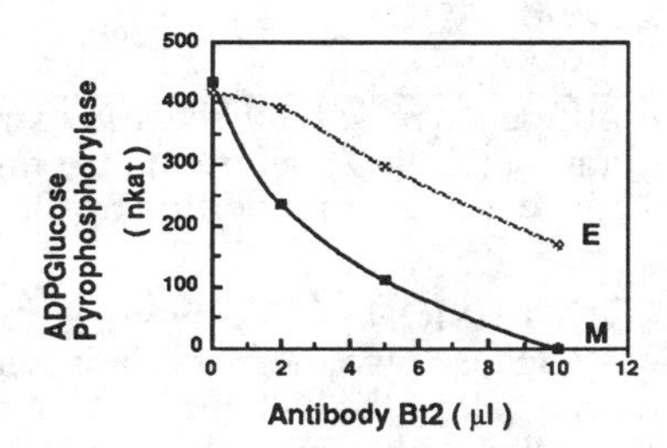

FIGURE 3. ADPG-PPase activity of excised leaves placed on 137 mM sucrose or sorbitol. Mean ± SE from 3 plants.

FIGURE 4. ADPG-PPase activity remaining in the supernatant after immuno-precipitation with Bt2 antibodies. Crude extracts from the morning (M) or evening (E).

3.3 Comparison of morning and evening extracts :
Immunoprecipitation curves from morning (M) and evening (E) extracts were compared by adjusting volume of extracts to get the same initial enzyme activity per tube (400 µkat) and by mixing with antibodies. We observed that for any given amount of antibody, a much higher proportion (Fig. 4) of the activity was immuno-precipitated from morning extracts than for evening ones. The experiment tends to indicate a higher specific activity for the enzyme in the morning than in the evening.

TABLE 1. Measurement of activity in the ADPglucose synthesis (mean ± SE from 30 determinations).

Morning Extracts (μ kat m^{-2})		Evening Extracts (μ kat m^{-2})	
no PGA	1 mM PGA	no PGA	1 mM PGA
0.78 ± 0.07	3.68 ± 0.17	0.41 ± 0.03	1.55 ± 0.08

Enzyme activity measured in the ADPglucose synthesis direction in the presence or absence of PGA (1mM) was also higher in the morning that in the evening (Table 1). Activation by PGA was slightly higher (x 4.7) in the morning than in the evening (x 3.8).

TABLE 2. Gel filtration on Sephadex G25 spun-columns (columns were pre-equilibrated with 0.6% BSA and loaded with leaf extracts).

MORNING EXTRACTS				EVENING EXTRACTS			
Crude		Desalted		Crude		Desalted	
µkat m^{-2}	%	µkat m^{-2}	%	µkat m^{-2}	%	µkat m^{-2}	%
4,5 ± 0,2	100 %	2,9 ± 0,3	64 %	1,9 ± 0,3	100 %	1,6 ± 0,2	87 %

A difference in activity between extracts was still highly significant after gel filtration (Table 2). However, the high activity form from the morning tended to be retained in higher proportion by the column.

CONCLUSION

ADPglucose pyrophosphorylase/synthase activity was reproducibly lower in the second half of the light period than in the first part. This low activity state was associated with high sucrose and starch contents. It can be transitorily reversed by a short dark period. Immunoprecipitation and gel filtration indicated that the enzyme seems to be in different states at the beginning and at the end of the light period. This difference should be confirmed by further purification allowing detailed kinetic analysis of the enzyme. At present, the relationships between the observed changes in activity and the regulation of leaf starch synthesis are still unclear since maximum *in vitro* activity was associated either with no starch synthesis (dark interval) or with very active synthesis (first half of the light period). Consideration of *in vivo* PGA/Pi ratio could probably explain this discrepancy.

REFERENCES

1 Preiss, J. (1982). Annu. Rev. Plant Physiol., 33, 431-454.
2 Beck, E. and Ziegler, P. (1989). Annu. Rev. Plant Physiol., Plant Mol. Biol., 40, 95-117.
3 Stitt, M. and Hedlt, H.W. (1981). Biochem. Biophys. Acta, 638, 1-11.
4 Fondy, B.R. and Geiger, D.R. (1982). Plant Physiol., 70, 671-676.
5 Bergmeyer, H.U. (1974). Methods of enzymatic analysis. Vol. 3, Academic Press, New-York.
6 Plaxton, W.C. and Preiss, J. (1987). Plant Physiol., 83, 105-112.
7 Spilatro, S.R. and Preiss, J. (1987). Plant Physiol., 83, 621-627.

EXPRESSION OF YEAST DERIVED INVERTASE IN THE APOPLAST OF POTATO PLANTS: EFFECT ON METABOLISM

D. HEINEKE,[1] U. SONNEWALD,[2] G. GÜNTER,[1] K. LEIDREITER,[1] D. BÜSSIS,[1] I. WILKE,[1] K. RASCHKE,[3] L. WILLMITZER,[2] H. W. HELDT[1], INSTITUT FÜR BIOCHEMIE DER PFLANZE, GÖTTINGEN, GERMANY[1], INSTITUT FÜR GENBIOLOGISCHE FORSCHUNG, BERLIN, GERMANY[2], INSTITUT FÜR PFLANZENPHYSIOLOGIE, GÖTTINGEN, GERMANY[3]

1. INTRODUCTION

In most plants sucrose is the main photosynthesis product exported from the source cells in the leaves to the sink tissues. The expression of a chimeric yeast invertase gene in the apoplast of plant cells as achieved with tobacco (1,2), Arabidopsis (1), tomato (3) and potato (shown here), in order to decrease the phloem loading of sucrose, provides a means to change source-sink interactions and to study the response of the leaf mesophyll cells on such a change. Because of their high sink capacity potato plants are expected to respond differently to such a transformation as the other species described. In the present report we studied the adaptation of fully expanded green source leaves to the transformation.

2. MATERIALS AND METHODS

Potato plants (Solanum tuberosum v. Desirée, were transformed using the Agrobacterium system (4), propagated from tissue cultures and grown in a climatized chamber on 12 h light/12 h dark cycle of 23/18°C and a light intensity of 300 µmol photons m^{-2} s^{-1}. Measurements of photosynthesis, enzyme activities and metabolite contents were carried out by modified standard methods (5). Phloem sap was collected by aphid technique (6) or from detached leaves placed with their petiole into 20 mM EDTA solution. Apoplast sap was sampled from potato leaves as described in (5).

3. RESULTS AND DISCUSSION

3.1. In this study we analyzed three different transformants to ascertain that the alterations observed are due to the expression of the yeast invertase and are not the result of an independent mutation. Multiple plants were propagated from these transformants, along with wild type plants as controls. As the studies with the 3 different transformants yielded very similar results, for the sake of brevity only the results from one transformant are shown.

3.2. The activity of the invertase in the transformant (15 µmol mg chl^{-1} min^{-1}) was two orders of magnitude higher than in the wild type plants (< 0.1 µmol mg chl^{-1} min^{-1}). The sucrose level in the apoplast of the transformant was reduced to about one twentieth, and those of glucose and fructose were increased 20 fold, indicating that the invertase was indeed functionally active in the apoplast (Table 1).

N. Murata (ed.), Research in Photosynthesis, Vol. IV, 765–768.

Table 1. Carbohydrate content of the leaf apoplast space and in the total leaves of illuminated potato plants

	Wild type total leaf	Wild type apoplast	Transformant total leaf	Transformant apoplast
	(nmol/mg chl)			
Sucrose	4100	36	4050	2
Fructose	2060	20	3820	342
Glucose	1410	17	2050	314

3.3. Although in the transformant plants the ratio of hexoses to sucrose increased in the apoplast by two orders of magnitude, as compared to the wild type, the carbohydrate pattern in the phloem sap remains unaltered; 96% of the carbohydrate in the phloem sap consisted of sucrose (table 2). This demonstrates the strong specifity of phloem loading.

Table 2. Distribution of carbohydrates in the phloem sap of potato leaves

	Sucrose	Glucose	Fructose
		%	
Wild type	95	2	3
Transformant	96	1	3

3.4. The transformant showed a modified phenotype characterized by a reduced number and size of leaflets and an earlier senescence, resulting in a loss of leaves in the lower region of the plant. Necroses and pale areas were not observed in the fully expanded young leaves of the transformants, but they showed a tendency to curl. Their photosynthesis was strongly inhibited, accompanied by a closure of the stomata (Table 3). The content of chlorophyll and the activity of Rubisco was not largely changed showing that the photosynthesis machinery is not markedly altered (Table 3). The increase of RuBP indicates an inhibition of the carboxylation step (Table 3). This inhibition does not seem to be caused by a feed back control by metabolites of

Table 3. Photosynthesis, evaporation, respiration, chlorophyll content, Rubisco activity and metabolite content of illuminated potato leaves

	Wild type	Transformant	
Photosynthesis	58	15	µmol CO_2 (mg chl h)$^{-1}$
Evaporation	5.6	1.1	mmol H_2O (mg chl h)$^{-1}$
Respiration	1.1	5.1	µmol CO_2 (mg chl h)$^{-1}$
Chlorophyll content	0.048	0.055	mg chl cm^{-2}
Rubisco activity	128	146	µmol (mg chl h)$^{-1}$
RuBP	208	375	nmol (mg chl)$^{-1}$
Glc6P	173	176	"
UDPGlc/UTP	9.4	7.6	

sucrose synthesis, as the intermediate Glc6P did not accumulate and UDPGlc/UTP ratio remained nearly constant (Table 3).

3.5. Glucose and fructose derived from invertase catalyzed sucrose hydrolysis in the apoplast accumulated in the leaves of the transformant to large extent (Table 1,4). Also amino acids, which are translocated in the mass flow of sucrose (6), accumulated in the leaves, probably as a result of the reduced sucrose transfer into the sieve tubes (Table 4). This led to an increase in the sum of the solutes causing a large increase of the osmolality of the leaf sap (Table 4).

Table 4. Metabolite contents and osmolality of illuminated potato leaves

	wild type	transformant	
Sucrose	7.6	8.2	μmol/mg chl
Glucose	0.6	5.5	"
Fructose	1.5	12.8	"
Σ Sugars	9.8	26.5	"
Malate	13.1	15.5	"
Σ Aminoacids	4.0	10.4	"
Proline	0.002	4.3	"
ΣΣ	26.9	52.5	"
Osmolality	243	357	mosmol kg^{-1}

The large accumulation of proline, earlier observed when plants subjected to water or salt stress, indicates that in the transformant the accumulation of hexoses and amino acids results in a stress. As water- and salt-stress are known to inhibit photosynthesis, it is postulated that the inhibition of photosynthesis in the transformant was caused by an increase of the osmotic pressure in the leaf mesophyll cells.

3.6. The increase in the amino acids to sucrose ratio in the leaves of the transformant was accompanied by an increase of this ratio in the sieve tubes leading to a higher amino acid content in the tubers (Table 5). Probably as a result of this, the protein to starch ratio in the tubers of the transformant was increased by a factor of 2 (Table 5).

Table 5. Relative content of metabolites in the leaves, the phloem exudate and the tubers of wild type and transformed potato plants

	Amino acids / sucrose		Protein / Starch
	Leaves	Phloemsap	tuber
wild type	0.53	0.035	0.041
transformant	1.26	0.104	0.095

4. CONCLUSIONS

The results clearly demonstrate that in potato leaves phloem loading involves the apoplastic compartment. A decrease of sucrose export from the plant source cells to the sink tissues, as caused by the introduction of the yeast invertase gene into the apoplast, affects the partitioning of the products of photosynthesis between carbohydrates and amino acids, which ultimatly leads to an increase in the protein to starch ratio in the potato tubers.

REFERENCES

1. von Schaewen, A., Stitt, M., Schmidt, R., Sonnewald, U. and Willmitzer, L. (1990) EMBO J. 9, 3033-3044
2. Stitt, M., von Schaewen, A. and Willmitzer, L. (1990) Planta 183, 40-50
3. Dickinson, C.D., Altabella, T. and Crispeels, M.J. (1991) Plant Physiol. 95, 420-425
4. Rocha-Sosa, H., Sonnewald, U., Frommer, W., Stratmann, M. Schell, J. and Willmitzer , L. (1989) EMBO J. 8, 23-29
5. Heineke, D., Sonnewald, U., Büssis D., Günter, G., Leidreiter, K., Wilke, I., Raschke, K., Willmitzer, L. and Heldt, H.W. (1992) Plant Physiol. in print
6. Winter, H., Lohaus, G., Heldt, H.W. (1992) Plant Physiol. in print

THE ROLE OF INORGANIC PHOSPHATE IN ACTIVATION OF RUBPCASE ACTIVITY IN RESPONSE TO CHANGES IN SOURCE/SINK BALANCE

Shinichi Sawada[1] and Hideaki Usuda[2]
[1]*Dept.Biol., Fac.Sci., Hirosaki Univ., Hirosaki 036 and* [2]*Lab.Chem., Fac. Medi., Teikyo Univ., Hachioji 192-03, Japan*

We demonstrated the end-product inhibition of photosynthesis with the model plants, composed of single-rooted soybean leaves without petioles, kept under sink-limited conditions (1). The purpose of the present study was to investigate the role of free Pi in chloroplast in the regulation of RuBP-case activity which has been shown to play an important part in reduction in rate of photosynthetic CO_2 fixation in the sink-limited model plant (2, 3, 4).

Single-rooted leaves of soybean(*Glycine max* L.) were prepared and cultured as described previously (1). Sink-limited leaves were obtained by prolonging the duration of photosynthesis for 5d under continuous illumination(1). This prolonged photosynthesis increased available photosynthates in the source while the sink capacity remained constant. As a result, each plant was in what we refer to as a "sink-limited" condition(1). The levels of acid-extractable free Pi and of total phosphate, the contents of chlorophyll and of soluble protein, preparations of leaf extracts for assays of RuBPcase and of deactivated crude RuBPcase and the assay of these enzymes were carried out according to the methods(4).

RESULTS AND DISCUSSION

With the sink-limited leaves, the rate of photosynthesis was inhibited by 59%, levels of all most of the phosphorylated intermediates of photosynthetic metabolism increased by 142-458% and the "initial" activity of RuBPcase decreased by 35%(2,3). Therefore, we suggested that the reduced activity of RuBPcase caused a reduction in the rate of photosynthesis and the decrease in RuBPcase activity is the result of decrease in the level of Pi in the sink-limited leaves. A decrease in the level of free Pi and an increase in level of esterified phosphates were found in the sink-limited leaves(Table 1). If we assumed that 30% of free Pi is evenly distributed between cytosol and chloroplast stroma without vacuoles(5) and that the combined volume of these two compartments is $50 \mu l \cdot (mg\ Chl)^{-1}$ (6), then the concentrations of free Pi in cytosol and chloroplasts can be calculated to be 6.2 and 4.1mM in the control and sink-limited leaves (Table 1), respectively. These estimations are roughly consistent with the previous reported values(7). The previous studies(8, 9) reported that Pi at 1-2.5mM in chloroplast may be metabolically inactive. Taken all together, the concentration of metabolically active Pi in the stroma of sink-limited chloroplast may be even lower than the estimated level of Pi and no higher than 3 mM.

N. Murata (ed.), Research in Photosynthesis, Vol. IV, 769–772.

TABLE 1. Amounts of phosphate in sink-limited leaves.

Condition	Phosphate content [μmole·(mg Chl)$^{-1}$ ± SE]		
	Fee Pi	Esterified P[a]	Total P
Control	1.03±0.08(87%)	0.15±0.02(13%)	1.18±0.04(100%)
Sink-limited	0.69±0.02(69%)	0.31±0.02(31%)	1.00±0.02(100%)

[a]Amount of esterified phosphate was calculated from the difference between total phosphate and free Pi contents. Each value is expressed as the mean ± SE of results of four or more determinations.

TABLE 2. Effect of CO_2 and Pi on RuBPcase activity in sink-limited leaves.

Sample	Extraction medium	Activation medium			RuBPcase activity [μmole CO_2·(mg Chl)$^{-1}$·min^{-1}]± SE	
	Pi	Pi	CO_2	Mg^{2+}	"Initial"	After activation
Control	−	−	+	+	4.3±0.6(80%)	5.3±0.5(100%)
leaves	+	+	−	+	5.0±0.4(95%)	6.4±0.7(121%)
Sink-limited	−	−	+	+	1.6±0.7(35%)	4.6±0.3(100%)
leaves	+	+	−	+	4.1±0.3(89%)	6.0±0.4(131%)

Activation was allowed to take place for 20 min at 0°C. The concentrations of Na_2HPO_4, $NaHCO_3$ and $MgCl_2$ in activation and extraction media were 5, 20 and 5 mM, respectively. The values in parentheses are the percentage of the activities after activation by CO_2 and Mg^{2+}. Each value is expressed as the mean ± SE of results of four determinations.

The "initial" activity of RuBPcase in the sink-limited leaves was lower than that in the control leaves(Table 2). This deactivated enzyme was activated by Pi and Mg^{2+} in the absence of CO_2(Table 2). This type of activation by Pi was also observed with the deactivated crude enzyme obtained by removal of Mg^{2+} and CO_2 by gel filtration(Figs. 1a,b; Table 3). The activation was maximal at approximately 5mM Pi in each case(Fig. 1a). Maximum activation was achieved within 5 min and was maintained for up to 20 min of preincubation(Fig.1b). Therefore, it is reasonable to suggest that the level of Pi in chloroplast plays an important role in the regulation of RuBPcase activity.
Recently, Sharkey(10) proposed another mechanism for feedback inhibition of photosynthesis: the extent of carbamylation of RuBPcase declines as a result of deactivation of RuBPcase activase caused by reductions in levels of ATP. Our previous results(2) showed, however, that the estimated decrease in the stromal concentration of free Pi could not influence the rate of photophosphorylation because the level of ATP and the ratio of ATP to ADP in sink-limited leaves were more than sufficient to permit

photosynthesis at the same high level of activity as in the control leaves. Thus, the carbamylation of RuBPcase in sink-limited soybean leaves seemed not to decrease even under the lowered level of stomatal Pi.

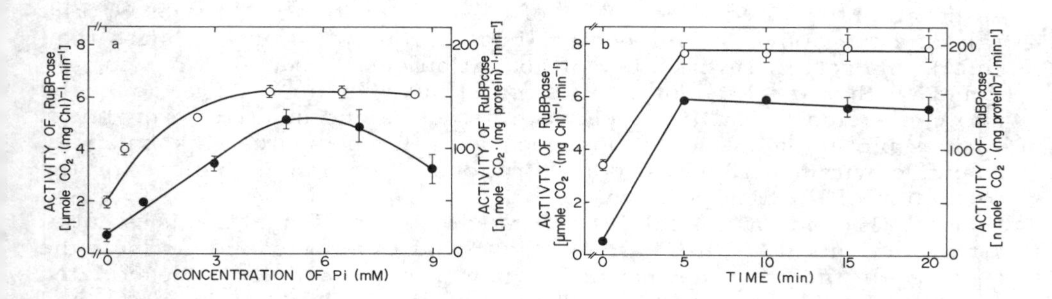

FIGURE 1a. Effects of the concentration of Pi on activation of RuBPcase (O) in extract from sink-limited leaves and of crude RuBPcase(●) fully deactivated by removal of CO_2 and Mg^{2+} by passage through Sephadex G-25. The activation of both enzymes was carried out by preincubation in medium contained 5mM $MgCl_2$ and various concentrations of Na_2HPO_4 at pH 8.0 for 5 min at 0°C. Each value is expressed as the mean ± SE of results of four or more determinations.

FIGURE 1b. Time courses of activation of RuBPcase(O) in extract from sink-limited leaves and of crude RuBPcase(●) fully deactivated by removal CO_2 and Mg^{2+} by passage through Sephadex G-25. The activation of both enzymes was carried out by preincubation in the medium contained 5mM $MgCl_2$ and 5mM Na_2HPO_4 at pH 8.0 at 0°C. Each value is expressed as the mean ± SE of results of four or more determinations.

TABLE 3. Reversibility of activation of crude RuBPcase by CO_2 and Mg^{2+} and/or Pi and Mg^{2+}.

Treatment[a]		Activity of RuBPcase [nmole CO_2·(mg protein)$^{-1}$.min^{-1}]	
		+ CO_2, Mg^{2+}	+ Pi. Mg^{2+}
(i)	GF	5.2 (4%)	5.2 (4%)
(ii)	GF--I	138.6 (100%)	151.1 (100%)
(iii)	GF--I--GF	9.3 (7%)	9.3 (7%)
(iv)	GF--I--GF--I	145.2 (104%)	147.0 (97%)

[a]Treatment, in the order indicated, consisted of gel filtration(GF) to remove CO_2 plus Mg^{2+} and/or Pi plus Mg^{2+} and incubation(I) with 20mM $NaHCO_3$ plus 5mM $MgCl_2$ and/or 5mM Na_2HPO_4 plus 5mM $MgCl_2$ at pH 8.0 at 0°C for 5 min. The activaty was determined after each treatment.

The cycle of activation and inactivation of crude RuBPcase was perfectly reversible by the addition of Pi and Mg^{2+} to the enzyme and by their removal from the enzyme(Table 3). The extent of activation and inactivation of the enzyme by these two effecters was almost equal to that obtained by the addition of CO_2 and Mg^{2+} and their removal. In addition to the observation that the concentration of Pi for full activation was 5mM (Fig. 1a) and the above mentioned estimated concentration of Pi(less than 3mM), this perfect reversibility of activation clearly supports our suggestion(2, 4) that the level of Pi in stroma plays an important role in the interconversion of RuBPcase between its active and inactive forms under various physiological conditions, such as different source/sink balances, changing within a range of concentrations of Pi that is critical for the regulation of RuBPcase activity.
Bhagwat(11) and Parry et al.(12) suggested that some bound CO_2 is essential for the activation of RuBPcase by Pi and that Pi alone cannot activate the enzyme. In the present experiments, however, the activity of deactivated crude RuBPcase was activated 29 times by Pi and Mg^{2+} without CO_2 and reached to the almost equal level obtained by activation with CO_2 and Mg^{2+} (Table 3). This observation and the perfect reversibility of the enzyme activation by incubation with Pi and Mg^{2+} and removal of these effecters suggest the possibility that the bound CO_2 is not necessary for the activation by Pi of the enzyme and that the enzyme may be activated directly by addition of Pi and Mg^{2+} alone.
It is, however, difficult to completely eliminate CO_2 from the medium(13). Therefore, the complete deactivation of the enzyme by total elimination of endogenous CO_2 from the medium has been impossible up to the present. Thus, the significance of bound of CO_2 to the enzyme in the activation by Pi is open to question.

REFERENCE

1. Sawada,S., Hayakawa,T., Fukushi,K. and Kasai,M. (1986) Plant Cell Physiol. 27, 591-
2. Sawada,S., Hasegawa,Y., Kasai,M. and Sasaki,M. (1989) Plant Cell Physiol. 30, 691-
3. Sawada,S., Usuda,H., Hasegawa,Y. and Tsukui,T. (1990) Plant Cell Physiol. 31, 697-
4. Sawada,S., Usuda,H. and Tsukui,T. (1992) Plant Cell Physiol. 33, (in press)
5. Foyer,C. and Spencer,C. (1986) Planta, 167, 369-
6. Gerhardt,R., Stitt,M. and Heldt,H.W. (1987) Plant Physiol. 83, 399-
7. Sharkey,T.D. and Vanderveer,D.J. (1989) Plant physiol. 91, 679-
8. Furbank,R.T., Foyer,C.H. and Walker,D.A. (1987) Biochim.Biophys. Acta, 894, 552-
9. Robinson,S.P. and Giersch,C. (1987) Aust.J.Plant Physiol.14, 451-
10. Sharkey,T.D. (1990) Bot.Mag.Tokyo, Special Issue, 2, 87-
11. Bhagwat,A.S. (1981) Plant Sci.Lett. 23, 197-
12. Parry,M.A., Schmidt,C.N.G., Cornelius,M.J., Keys,A.J., Millard,B. and Gutteridge,S. (1985) J.Exp.Bot. 36, 1396-
13. Lorimer,G.H., Badger,M.R. and Andrews,T.J. (1976) Biochemistry, 15, 529-

CONCENTRATIONS OF AMINO ACIDS AND SUCROSE IN VARIOUS SUBCELLULAR COMPARTMENTS AND IN THE PHLOEM SAP OF BARLEY LEAVES

G. LOHAUS[1], H. WINTER[1], D.G. ROBINSON[2], H.W. HELDT[1]

[1]Inst. für Biochemie der Pflanze, [2]Pflanzenphysiologisches Institut, Universität Göttingen, Untere Karspüle 2, D-3400 Göttingen, FRG

1. INTRODUCTION

The products of photosynthesis generated in the leaf are exported to other parts of the plant by phloem transport. In the present communication the properties of phloem loading are studied by comparing metabolite concentrations in the cytosol and the apoplastic space of source leaves and in sieve tubes.

2. MATERIALS AND METHODS

Primary leaves of 21 day-old barley (*Hordeum vulgare L.*, var Apex), grown hydroponically in 14 mM nitrate (1) were used.

3. RESULTS AND DISCUSSION

3.1. In order to evaluate subcellular metabolite concentrations, the sizes of the respective compartments of barley leaves have been determined by morphometry of electron microscopic data(Table 1).

TABLE 1. Aqueous spaces in mature barley leaves after 9 h of illumination (Winter, H.,Robinson, D.G., Heldt, H.W., in prep.)

Epidermis cells	246	µL/mg chl
vacuole	243	"
cytosol	1.2	"
nucleus	0.2	"
Mesophyll cells	355	"
vacuole	270	"
cytosol	21	"
chloroplast	60	"
stroma	29	"
thylakoid	25	"
mitochondria	3.5	"
nucleus	1.1	"
Apoplast		
aqueous	41	"
gas space	213	"
Sieve tubes		
companion cells	<1.7	"

3.2. Barley leaves, which had been frozen in liquid nitrogen and then lyophilized were fracionated by nonaqueous means (2). The contents of various metabolites in the vacuolar, stromal and cytosolic fraction of the leaf material were analyzed. Based on the subcellular volumes shown in Table 1, subcellular concentrations were then calculated. Since a permeability barrier for small molecules between the cytosolic compartment

N. Murata (ed.), Research in Photosynthesis, Vol. IV, 773–776.

TABLE 2. Subcellular metabolite concentrations in barley leaves after 9 h of illumination

	Total leaf content	Vacuole	Stroma	Cytosol
	µmol/mg chl	mM	mM	mM
3-PGA	0.39	0	7.4	5.7
Nitrate	97	212	<30	<30
Sucrose	17	21	<6	241
Glutamate	5.3	≤0.4	89	93
Glutamine	1.4	≤0.1	21	27
Aspartate	1.8	≤0.1	28	33
Serine	2.2	≤0.1	25	52
Glycine	1.4	0.8	10	26
Alanine	0.9	≤0,1	8	22
Σ Amino acids	14.4	≤1,8	204	285

and the nucleus does not exist, the cytosolic concentrations were related to the sum of these two spaces. Since subcellular fractionation does not differentiate between epidermis and mesophyll cells, the volumes of the epidermal and mesophyll cells were added together for the evaluation of metabolite concentrations in the subcellular compartments. The results in Table 2 show that 3-PGA is confined to the cytosolic and stromal compartment, whereas nitrate is almost exclusively found in the vacuoles. Amino acids mainly occur in the stromal and cytosolic compartment; their concentration in the vacuolar compartment is very low.

3.3. The metabolite content in the apoplast of illuminated barley leaves was determined (5) and related to the apoplastic volume shown in Table 1 (Table 3). Phloem sap was collected from these leaves using aphid stylets, which had been severed by a ruby laser beam (3), for about 4 h under conditions preventing any marked evaporation of the samples (1). The absolute values for the phloem sap concentrations of amino acids and sucrose shown in Table 3 can be therefore regarded as highly reliable.

3.4. Similar to spinach (2), a comparison of metabolite concentrations in the cytosol and in the phloem sap (Table 3) reveals that sucrose is concentrated by a factor of 5 during transfer from the cytosol into the sieve tubes, whereas the amino acids remain in the sieve tubes at a similar concentration as in the cytosol. Previous results (see ref 4) indicated that phloem loading proceeds via passage through the apoplast. Table 3 indicates that the passage of amino acid through the apoplast is accompanied by a concentration decrease of a factor of 100 which is compensated again upon entering the sieve tubes by a concentration increase of a similar extent. It should be noted that the amino acid pattern in the apoplast is very similar to that in the cytosol and the phloem sap. In the case of sucrose, the apoplastic concentration is even 1000 and 5000 times lower than the respective concentrations in the cytosol and in the sieve tubes. Proton symport translocators for sucrose and various amino acids in plant plasma membranes have been characterized and their participation in the phloem loading has been discussed (6-9). On the reasonable assumption that, not only the uptake of amino acids and sucrose from the apoplast, but also their efflux from the cytosol to the apoplast proceeds by proton symport, the low metabolite concentrations in the apoplast can be explained as a mere consequence of its high

TABLE 3. Metabolite concentrations in phloem sap, cytosol and apoplast from barley leaves (Percentage of total amino acids).

Metabolite	Cytosol mM	Apoplast mM	Phloem sap mM
Sucrose	214	0.2	1030
Glutamate	93 (33)	0.5 (27)	97 (44)
Glutamine	27 (10)	0.06 (3)	10 (5)
Aspartate	33 (12)	0.3 (14)	29 (13)
Serine	52 (18)	0.4 (20)	32 (15)
Glycine	26 (9)	0.2 (11)	7 (3)
Alanine	22 (8)	0.16 (8)	14 (6)
Σ Amino acids	285	1.9	219
Sucrose/Amino acids	0.9	0.1	4.7

proton concentration (pH 5.6) as compared to the cytosol (pH≈7.8) and phloem sap (pH 7.5-8.5) (10).

3.5. As the amino acid pattern in the cytosol is not very different from the amino acid pattern in whole leaves, it seems sufficient to determine the whole leaf content as a reasonable measure of cytosolic amino acid levels. We therefore compared amino acid patterns in barley leaves and in the phloem sap obtained from these leaves in a diurnal cycle (Fig 1). For many amino acids the diurnal changes of the concentrations in the phloem sap closely reflected changes in the leaf content.

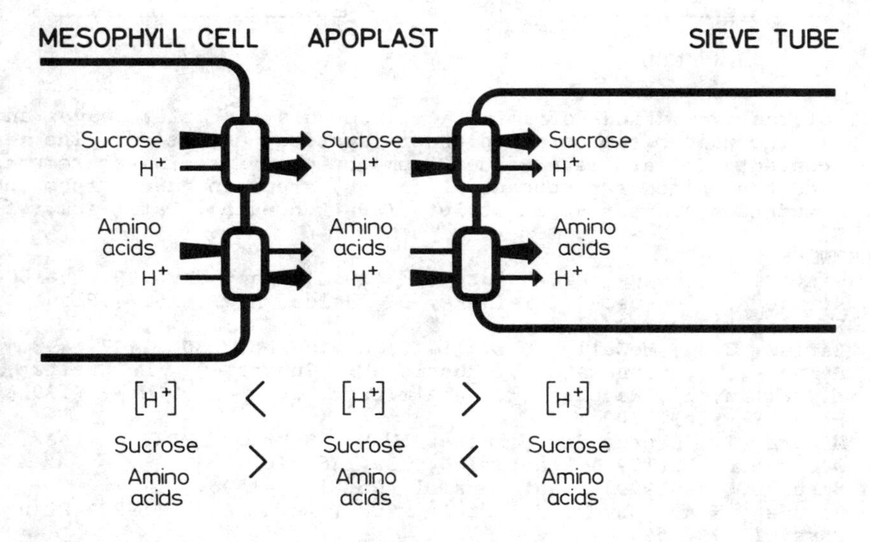

3.6. Whereas carbohydrates are translocated via the sieve tubes in the form of sucrose, there is no special transport form for nitrogen compounds. All amino acids are translocated, and the amino acid pattern in the phloem sap is dependent on the metabolism in the cytosol of the source cells. In connection with the suggestion that the phloem loading of both amino acids and sucrose occurs by proton symport, it remains to be elucidated why it is only sucrose which is concentrated during transfer from the mesophyll cells to the sieve tubes.

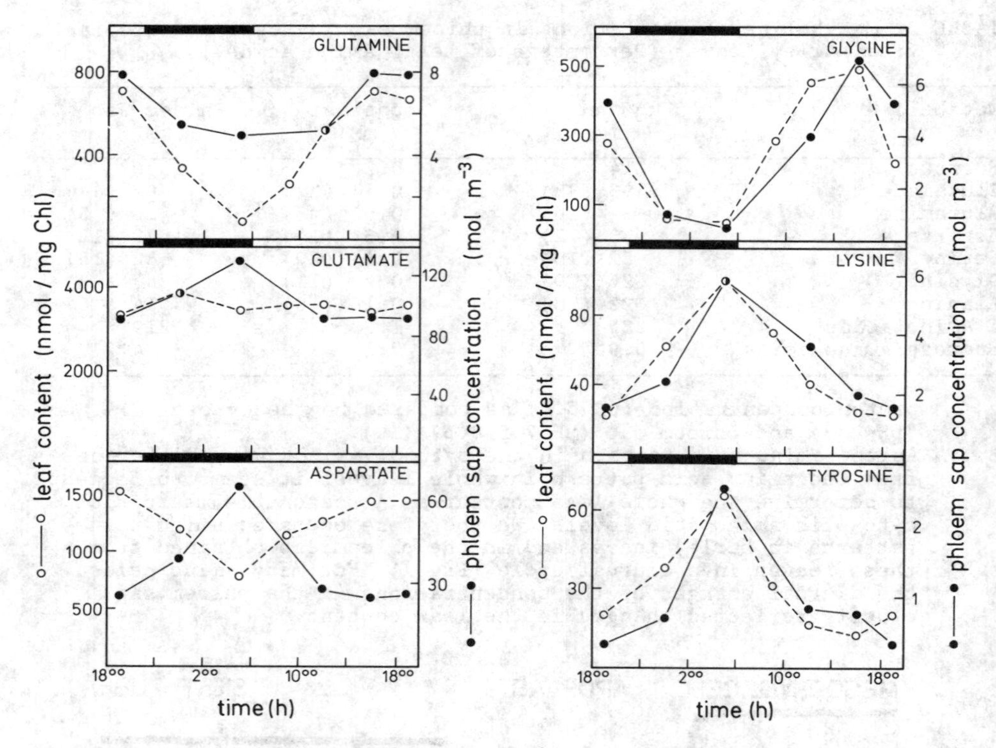

Fig.1 Diurnal variations of amino acid contents in barley leaves and in the phloem sap obtained under identical conditions. The leaf contents (o) are mean values from three series of measurements and the phloem sap concentrations (●) are mean values from the exudation of four aphid stylets (20-60 h each). Data from ref.1.

REFERENCES
1. Winter, H.,Lohaus, G., Heldt, H.W.(1992) Plant Phys.**99**,996-1004.
2. Riens, B., Lohaus, G., Heineke, D., Heldt, H.W. (1992) Plant Physiol. **97**,227-233.
3. Barlow, C.A., McCully, M.E.,(1972) Can.J.Zool. **50**, 1497-1498.
4. Heineke, D., Sonnewald, U.,Büssis, D., Günter, G., Leitreiter, K., Wilke, I., Raschke, K., Willmitzer, L., Heldt, H.W. (1992) Plant Physiol. **100**
5. Mimura, T., Dietz, K.J., Kaiser, W.M., Schramm, M.J., Kaiser, G., Heber, U.(1990) Planta **180**, 139-146.
6. Bush, D.R., (1990) Plant Physiol. **96**, 1590-1596.
7. Snedden, W.A., Chung, J., Pauls, R.H., Bown, A.W. (1992) Plant Physiol. **99**, 665-671.
8. Despeghel, J.P., Delrot, S. (1983) Plant Physiol. **71**, 1-6.
9. Li, Z.-C., Bush, D.R., (1990) Plant Physiol. **94**, 268-277.
10. Giaquinta, R.T., (1983) Ann, Rev. Plant Physiol. **34**, 347-387.

ACKNOWLEGDEMENT
This research has been supported by the Deutsche Forschungsgemeinschaft. We thank B. Raufeisen for the artwork.

POLAR TRANSPORT OF PHOTOASSIMILATES IN CHARA CORALLINA

DA-QIAO DING[4], SHIN-ICHI AMINO[2], TETSURO MIMURA[1], MASASHI TAZAWA[3] and TOSHIYUKI NAGATA[2], DEPT. LIFE SCIENCE, HIMEJI INSTITUTE OF TECHNOLOGY[1], HYOGO 678-12; DEPT. BOT., FACULTY OF SCIENCE, UNIVERSITY OF TOKYO[2], HONGO, TOKYO 113; DEPT. APPLIED PHYSICS AND CHEMISTRY, FUKUI INSTITUTE OF TECHNOLOGY[3], GAKUEN, FUKUI 910; COMMUNICATIONS RESEARCH LABORATORY[4], IWAOKA, KOBE 651-24, JAPAN.

1. INTRODUCTION

Intercellular transport of photoassimilates is crucial in understanding the source-sink relationship in plants. The chemical and physical compartmentation of transported substances in source and sink cells may be regulatory points for intercellular transport. In higher plants, little is known about the distribution of photoassimilates in subcellular compartments because of the difficulty in separating each compartment from mesophyll cells immediately after photosynthesis. In contrast to higher plants, the large cell size and simple construction of characean plants facilitate these kinds of studies at the cellular level. No vascular systems exist in characean plants, so the main form of transport is symplastic transport, which is enhanced by rapid cytoplasmic streaming. The long-distance transport of nutrients, such as nitrate, phosphate and carbon assimilates, from rhizoids or branchlets to the apical part in *Chara hispida* has been studied (1,2). Apices (primary and secondary) were the most important sinks for carbon and phosphate. In order to elucidate the source-sink relationship of photoassimilates in whole plants, we developed an isolated system composed of two cells which facilitates the quantitative analysis of intercellular transport.

2. MATERIALS and METHODS

2.1 Photosynthetic fixation of ^{14}C and intercellular transport

A detached internode-branchlet complex of *Chara corallina*, which is composed of one internode and one branchlet, was used to measure the intercellular transport of photoassimilates (Fig. 1). Internodes or branchlets were loaded with ^{14}C-labeled bicarbonate for 10 min, and then incubated in unlabeled medium for 50 min to 3 hours. The cells loaded with ^{14}C-medium behaved as "the source" of photoassimilates, and accordingly, the other cells which were incubated in unlabeled medium and received the transported ^{14}C-substances are designated as "the sink". Radioactivity of ^{14}C was measured in a liquid scintillation counter as the result of photosynthesis and intercellular

N. Murata (ed.), Research in Photosynthesis, Vol. IV, 777–780.

transport of photoassimilates (3).

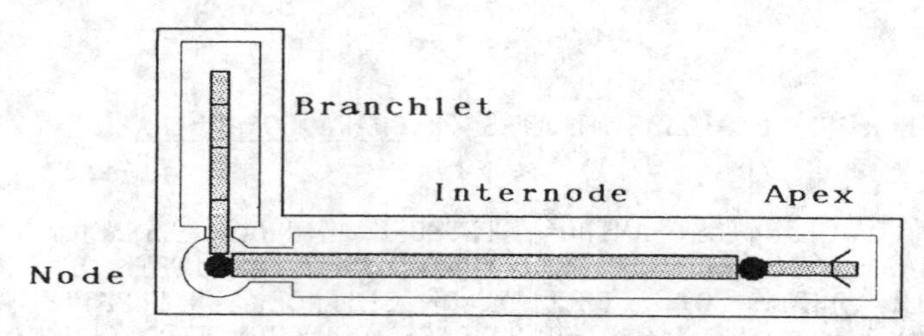

FIGURE 1. Experimental system for measuring transport of photoassimilates between the internode and the branchlet through the node. The apex remained in some experiments.

2.2 Photosynthetic evolution of oxygen in isolated chloroplasts and RuBPCase activity.

The photosynthetic activity and the electron transport activity of isolated chloroplasts were measured in terms of evolution of oxygen. Evolution of oxygen was measured with a Clark-type oxygen electrode. The activity of ribulose-1,5-bisphosphate carboxylase of both internodes and branchlets was measured by an enzyme assay (3).

2.3 Measurement of concentrations of intercellularly transported photoassimilates

In internode and branchlet cells of _Chara corallina_, there are three main compartments, i.e. the cortical chloroplast layer, the streaming sol endoplasm and the vacuole, occupying 0.5 %, 4.5 % and 95 %, respectively, of the total cell volume. The intracellular perfusion technique was used to isolate each subcellular compartment (4). The radioactivities in each subcellular compartment was determined (5), and the ^{14}C-photoassimilates were identified using two dimensional thin layer chromatography (TLC)(6).

The soluble photoassimilates in each subcellular compartment were extracted with 80 % (v/v) methanol after perfusion (6). The amount of sucrose was measured by an enzyme assay. Amino acids were analyzed with an automatic amino acid analyzer (Hitachi 8500). Malate was analyzed with an ion chromatographic analyzer (Yokogawa IC7000M).

3. RESULTS AND DISCUSSION

3.1 Polar transport of photoassimilates

Table 1 shows the photosynthetic activities of the source cells, and the apparent rate of transport (J) of ^{14}C from these cells. The photosynthetic activity of the branchlet was always higher (1.4 to 1.5 times higher) than that of the internode in these complexes. However, when the apices was removed, the photosynthetic activities of both branchlets and internodes decreased by about 30%. When the apex remained to the internodal cell, the intercellular flux (J) from the branchlet to the internode was about 5 times higher than that from the internode to the branchlet. When the apex was removed from the internode, the apparent rate of transport (J) from the branchlet to the internode decreased, while the transport from the internode to the branchlet increased. These results show that there is a polarity in the transport of photoassimilates from the branchlet to the internode, and that the polarity is influenced by the presence of the apex. As the photosynthetic activity in the branchlet is always higher than that in the internode (Table 1), the polar transport may be caused by the difference in photosynthetic activities in the branchlets and the internodes.

TABLE 1. The photosynthetic activities of the source cell (Aso) and the apparent rate of intercellular flux of ^{14}C (J) into the sink cell (From Reference 3).

Source cell	Sink cell	Apical complex	Aso(nmol $cm^{-2}min^{-1}$) (mean$\pm$s.e.)	J (Bq h^{-1}) (mean$\pm$s.e.)	No.
Branchlet	Internode	+	1.68 $\pm$ 0.28	7.14 $\pm$ 1.55	11
Internode	Branchlet	+	1.13 $\pm$ 0.06	1.44 $\pm$ 0.33	12
Branchlet	Internode	-	1.14 $\pm$ 0.06	2.66 $\pm$ 0.30	15
Internode	Branchlet	-	0.84 $\pm$ 0.11	1.78 $\pm$ 0.22	7

3.2 Differences in photosynthetic activity between internode and branchlet

Branchlets always show a higher photosynthetic activity than internodes (Table 1). The chlorophyll content, measured in terms of the surface area in internodes and branchlets, was almost identical. However, the activity of ribulose-1,5-bisphosphate carboxylase (RuBPCase) in the branchlets was 1.6 times higher than that of the internodes, and the rate of ferricyanide-dependent evolution of oxygen in the branchlets was 1.4 times higher than that in the internodes. Therefore, the higher photosynthetic activities of branchlets result from their higher RuBPCase activities and higher rates of photosynthetic electron transport.

3.3 Subcellular distribution of photoassimilates and intercellular transport

In order to elucidate the relationship between the polarity of transport and the photosynthetic activity, the subcellular distribution of photoassimilates was investigated. After the internode or branchlet of an internode-branchlet complex was exposed to ^{14}C-bicarbonate for 10 min, 70 to 80 % of the total fixed carbon was found in the sol endoplasm. Following a chase in an unlabeled solution, the content of ^{14}C-photoassimilates in the sol endoplasm of the source decreased. By contrast, there were no significant changes in the ^{14}C-content in the cortical

chloroplast layer and the vacuole. Therefore, we conclude that the photoassimilates distributed in the sol endoplasm mainly participated in the intercellular transport.
When the apex remained, the higher photosynthetic activity of the branchlet resulted in a ^{14}C-concentration difference of 13.5 mM in the sol endoplasm of branchlets compared to that of the internodes after 10 min of photosynthesis. In the subsequent 3 h-chase period, this difference decreased to about 1 mM. In cases where we measured transport from the branchlet to the internode without the apex and transport from the internode to the branchlet with or without the apex, the intercellular difference of ^{14}C in the sol endoplasm after 10 min photosynthesis was only about 7 mM. Therefore, when the apex remains, the greater gradient of photoassimilate levels between the sol endoplasm of branchlets and the internodes is the major cause of the polar intercellular transport from branchlet to internode.

3.4 Identification of intercellularly transported photoassimilates

The ^{14}C-photoassimilates transported intercellularly were identified using thin layer chromatography. After feeding $NaH^{14}CO_3$ to the branchlet for 10 min, the ^{14}C-photoassimilates in the sol endoplasm included sucrose, amino acids, malate and sugar phosphates. Within 10 min, ^{14}C-photoassimilates of the source branchlet were transported to some of the sink internode. Qualitatively the composition of ^{14}C-photoassimilates was almost the same in the sol endoplasm of both cells.
Quantitatively, the absolute amounts of sucrose, amino acids and malate in both branchlet and internodal cells with or without the apex revealed that there were concentration gradients of sucrose and glutamic acid between the sol endoplasm of the two cells; higher in the branchlet and lower in the internode. The gradients decreased when the apex was detached. It was concluded that sucrose and glutamic acid were the major photoassimilates transported polarly in *Chara*.

References

1 Andrews, M., Box, R., Fyson, A., and Raven, J. A. (1984) Plant, Cell and Environment, 7, 683-687
2 Box, R. J. (1986) Plant, Cell and Environment, 9, 501-506
3 Ding, D. Q., Mimura, T., Amino, S. and Tazawa,M. (1991a) J. Exp. Bot. 42, 33-8
4 Tazawa, M., Kikuyama, M. and Shimmen, T. (1976) Cell Structure and Function, 1, 165-176
5 Ding, D. Q., Amino, S., Mimura, T., Nagata, T. and Tazawa, M. (1991b) J. Exp. Bot. 42, 1393-8
6 Ding, D. Q., Amino, S., Mimura, T., Sakano, K., Nagata, T. and Tazawa, M. (1992) J. Exp. Bot. 43,1045-1051

EFFECT OF EAR REMOVAL ON DRY MATTER PRODUCTION, ITS PARTITIONING AND PHOTOSYNTHESIS IN RICE.

Hideo NAKATANI, Kano KOIDE and Kuni ISHIHARA, Fac. of Agric., Tokyo Univ. of Agric. and Tech., Fuchu, Tokyo 183, Japan.

1. INTODUCTION

It has been suggested that sink size and its activity are affected by leaf photosynthesis through the amount and rate of supply of photosynthates, and that source activity of leaf photosynthesis is affected by sink activity and its size through the amount and rate of sink accumulation of photosynthates.

We found that the high yielding ability in any recently bred high yielding rice variety could be attributed to an increase in the number of spikelets per panicle as well as per unit area. These results have often been considered to be one of the examples in which more dry matter was produced due to a higher source activity accelerated by an increase in the sink capacity.

In the present study, we examined the effects of ear removal on dry matter production, its partitioning into various organs and on photosynthesis in order to investigate the sink-source relationship.

2. MATERIALS and METHODS

2.1 Rice plants (Oryza sativa L., cv. Nipponbare) were grown under submerged condition at three plants per 1/2000a Wagner pot. Five days after heading date ears of all culms in one half of the pots were cut at their respective neck nodes. The newly developed tillers after ear removal were not removed.

2.2 Six control and six no-ear plants were respectively sampled and the dry weights measured on the 0, 7th, 14th, 28th, and 42nd day after ear removal. The rate of photosynthesis and transpiration were measured on the attached first (flag), second and third leaves on the main culm using an open gas analysis system under a controlled environment. After every photosynthetic measurement, the contents of chlorophyll and ribulose-1,5-bisphosphate carboxylase/oxygenase (RuBPCase) in every leaf were determined spectrophotometrically and by the single radial immuno diffusion method, respectively.

3. RESULTS and DISCUSSION

3.1 There was no significant difference in the total dry weights of the control and no-ear plants till the 28th day after ear removal. However, the weight of no-ear plants was significantly larger on the 42nd day (Table 1). The dry weight of each organ was different for the two plants (Fig. 1). The weight of the flag

N. Murata (ed.), Research in Photosynthesis, Vol. IV, 781–784.

leaf blade was larger in the no-ear plants than in the control and the difference increased with time (Fig. 2).

3.2 The effects of ear removal on photosynthesis and related processes were different depending on leaf position and the period after ear removal (Fig. 3A). The photosynthetic rates and diffusive conductance in the flag leaves of the no-ear plants were significantly lower than those in the control plants during the first 7 days. The rates were correlated with the conductance on the same regression line in both plants during the test period. Thus, the lower photosynthetic rates of the flag leaf in the no-ear plants during the first 7 days were considered to be due to smaller stomatal aperture.

Table 1. Effects of ear removal on changes in total dry weight.

Days after ear removal	0	7	14	28	42
Control	60.9±1.7	67.9±3.6	69.6±2.4	77.8±5.3	81.8±2.4
No-ear	—	69.4±4.0	72.2±3.1	78.1±2.0	96.3±5.4

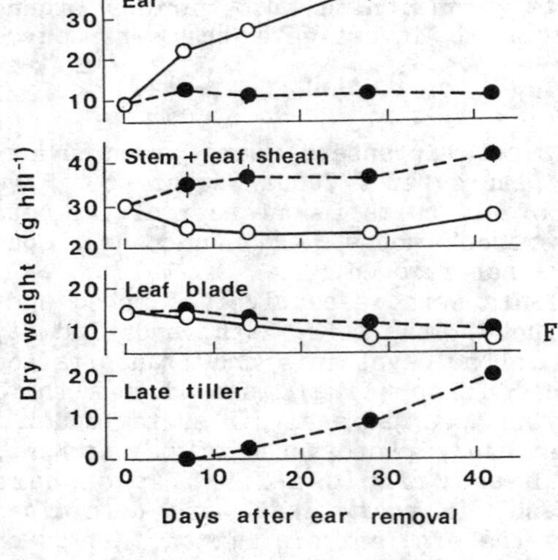

Fig. 2. Effects of ear removal on weight per area of leaf blade at different leaf positions. Roman numerals indicate the leaf positions (e.g. I: the flag leaf), which are similar to those of Fig. 3 and 5.

Fig. 1. Effects of ear removal on dry matter partitioning into various organs.
○—○ control, ●- -● no-ear plant. (These symbols are similar for Fig. 2-5). Ear weights in no-ear plants are values at the time of ear removal. The ranges of standard error were the length of vertical bars or narrower than size of symbols, which are similar to those of Fig. 2 and 3.

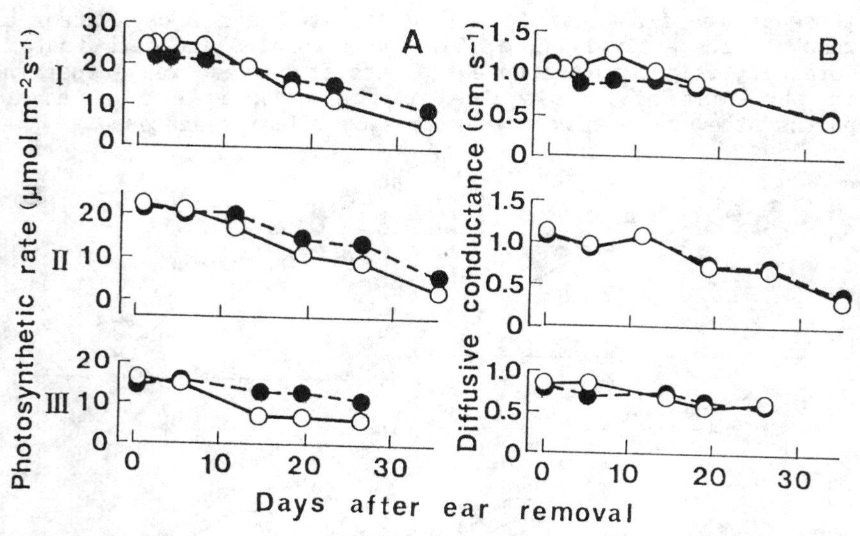

Fig. 3. Effects of ear removal on photosynthetic rate (A) and diffusive conductance (B) in the flag, second and third leaves.

3.3 The photosynthetic rates in the flag leaf after the 12th day as well as in the second and third leaves of the no-ear plants were maintained always higher than those of the control. However, there was no significant difference in the diffusive conductance of these leaves for both plants (Fig. 3B). The photosynthetic rates of these leaves in the no-ear plants were always higher at the same diffusive conductance than in the control (Fig. 4).

3.4 Chlorophyll and RuBPCase contents of the flag, second and third leaves in both plants decreased with time and were always higher in all leaves in the no-ear plants except

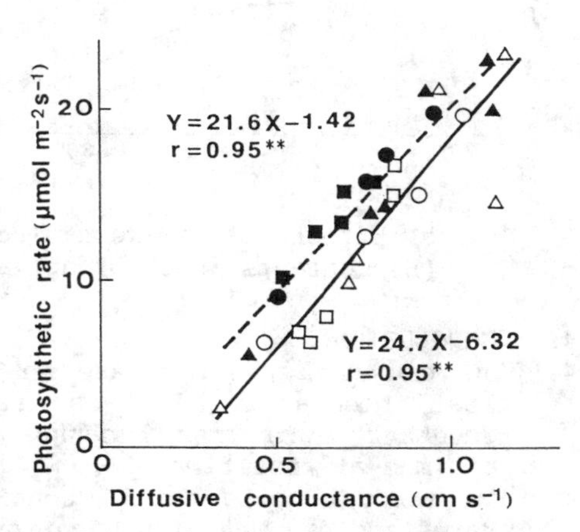

Fig. 4. Effects of ear removal on the relationship between diffusive conductance and photosynthetic rates in the flag leaf from the 12th day, the second and third leaves. Circles, flag leaf; triangles, second leaf; squares, third leaf. **Significant at $P<0.01$.

those in the flag leaf during the first 7 and 3 days after ear removal, respectively (Fig. 5). These results indicate that the total dry weight in the no-ear plants at harvest was larger than in the control mainly due to the maintenance of higher photosynthetic rates coupled with slower leaf senescence.

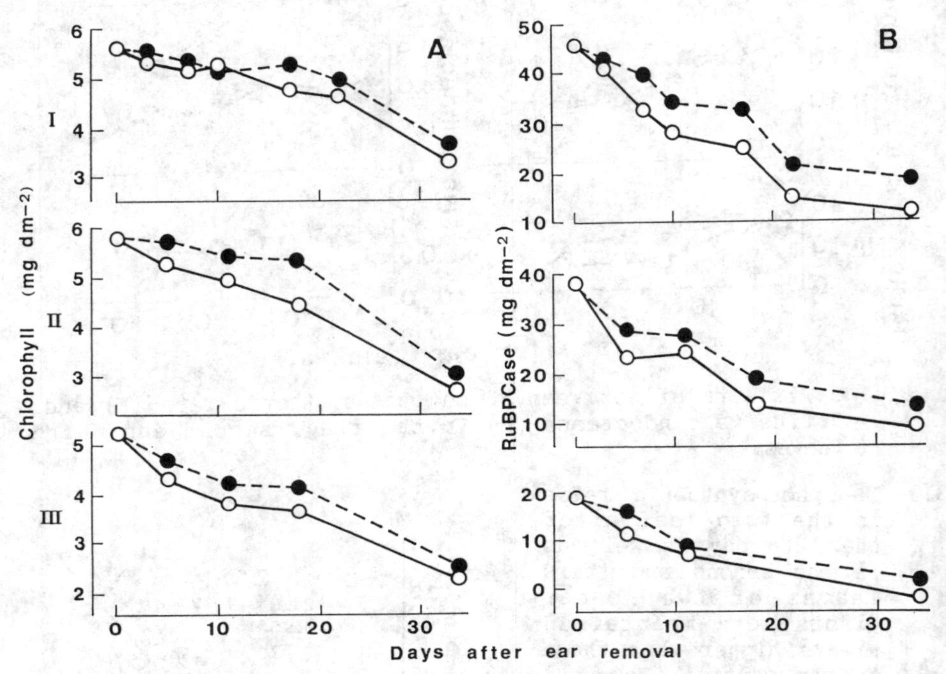

Fig. 5. Effects of ear removal on chlorophyll (A) and RuBPCase (B) contents in the flag, second and third leaves.

4. CONCLUSION

4.1 The cause of the decrease in photosynthetic rates in the flag leaf immediately after ear removal was hormonal rather than a feedback inhibition because the leaf weight increased to the minimum at that time.

4.2 Ear removal could not be considered to limit the photosynthetic rates and dry matter production through carbohydrate accumulation in leaves.

4.3 It could be concluded that the high yielding ability of rice varieties should not be explained simply on the basis of an increase in spikelet number per panicle as well as per unit area i. e. the increase in sink capacity by which a higher source activity of leaf photosynthesis was accelerated and maintained.

EAR REMOVAL EFFECT ON DIURNAL CHANGE OF THE FLAG LEAF PHOTOSYNTHESIS IN WHEAT.

Kano KOIDE and Kuni ISHIHARA, Fac. of Agric., Tokyo Univ. of Agric. and Tech., Fuchu, Tokyo 183, Japan.

1. INTRODUCTION

Many investigators have studied the effects of the sink restriction on the source activity to clarify the sink-source relationship. However, the mechanism of how the sink restriction affects the source activity has not been elucidated yet.
In our previous paper[1,2] on sink-source relationship using ear removal as the sink restriction, we reported the following results; 1 The dry matter production was not affected but its partitioning was changed. 2 Photosynthetic rates of the flag leaf during grain filling were not reduced though the sucrose was accumulated. The rates were maintained by slower leaf senescence due to the ear removal.

In the present study, we examined the effect of ear removal on diurnal change of the flag leaf photosynthesis in wheat to clarify its short-term response to sink restriction. To clarify the mechanism of the effects of sink restriction on source activity, we examined the ear removal effects on the activity of CO_2 fixation system and on diurnal change of the photosynthesis with midday dark treatment, which interrupted the photosynthesis, and midday low CO_2 treatment, which reopened stomata.

2. MATERIALS and METHODS

2.1 Plant materials and ear removal: Winter wheat (cv. Aoba), grown at three plants per 1/2000 a Wagner pot, was used as the test crop. Ears of the main culm and tillers were cut at their basal nodes about one week after anthesis. Ears of the late tillers, which developed after ear removal, were not removed.

2.2 Gas exchange measurement: Gas exchange rate of the attached flag leaf of the main culm was measured using an open gas analysis system with assimilation chamber. Light intensity, CO_2 concentration, air temperature, leaf temperature and leaf to air water vapor pressure difference were maintained at 1200μE $m^{-2}s^{-1}$, 350±4 μL L^{-1}, 24±1°C, 24±1°C and 8.0±1mmHg, respectively, expect during the dark or low CO_2 treatment. Diffusive conductance was calculated from the transpiration rate and leaf to air water vapor pressure difference. Intercellular CO_2 concentration (Ci) was calculated using the following equation;

$$Ci = Ca - 1.56\ Pr\ Dc^{-1}$$

where Ca is CO_2 concentration inside the chamber; Dc, diffusive conductance; Pr, Photosynthetic rate and 1.56, the ratio of gas

N. Murata (ed.), Research in Photosynthesis, Vol. IV, 785–788.

diffusion coefficient of CO_2 to H_2O.
Maximum photosynthetic capacity (Amax) was determined by the Hansatech leaf disc oxygen electrode in 5% CO_2.

3. RESULTS and DISCUSSION

3.1 Under constant environmental conditions, the photosynthetic rate (Pr) of the flag leaf in the control and no-ear plant gradually declined with a decrease in diffusive conductance (Dc) as time proceeded . The decline of Pr and Dc was greater in the no-ear plants. Intercellular CO_2 concentration (Ci) in the control plants remained practically constant but Ci in the no-ear plants declined (Fig. 1).

3.2 Apparent carboxylation efficiency (ACE) in the evening was lower than that in the morning. There was no significant difference in the degrees of the decrease between the control and no-ear plants both on the day of ear removal and 8 days after (Table 1). From these results, we presumed that the drop in Pr with time was due to a decline in mesophyll activity but the greater decline of Pr in the no-ear plants was due to the decline in their Ci i.e. decrease in stomatal aperture.

3.3 Midday dark treatment reduced the decline in Pr with time but did not reduce the differences in both the Pr and Dc between the control and no-ear plants. Pr and Dc in the no-ear plants were

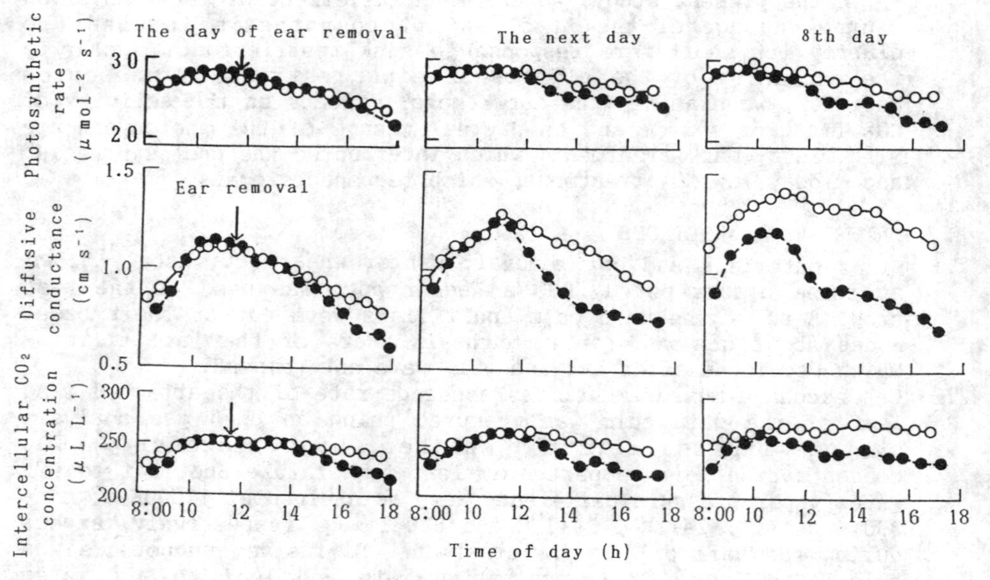

Fig. 1. Effects of ear removal on diurnal changes of photosynthetic rates, diffusive conductance and intercellular CO_2 concentration of the flag leaf in wheat under constant environmental conditions.
○—○ control, ●- -● no-ear plants.

Table 1. Apparent carboxylation efficiency of the flag leaf in wheat in the morning and evening.

	Apparent carboxylation efficiency[1] (10^{-3} μmol m^{-2} s^{-1}/μmol m^{-3})					
	Day of ear removal			8 days after ear removal		
	Morn[2]	Evg[2]	Evg/Morn(%)	Morn	Evg	Evg/Morn(%)
Control	3.43	3.23	94.6	3.98	3.41	85.0
No-ear	3.41[3]	3.39	96.7	3.92	3.22	84.0

1) Apparent carboxylation efficiency was caluculated from the slope of the regression line of the photosynthetic rates to intercellular CO_2 concentration.
2) Measurement was done between 7:00 and 10:00 in the morning and between 17:00 and 20:00 in the evening.
3) Measurement was done before ear removal treatment

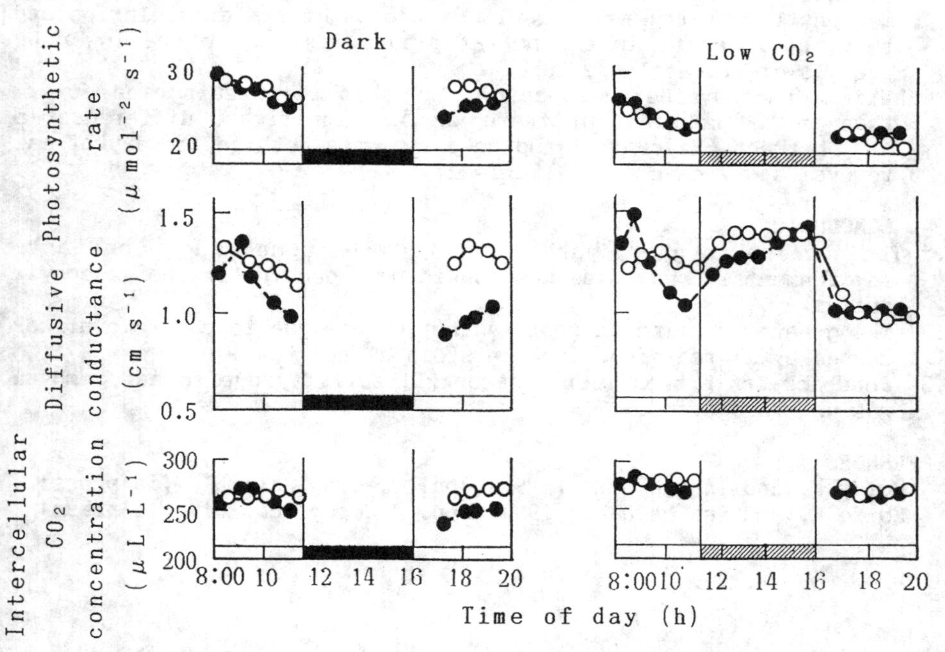

Fig. 2. Effects of ear removal on diurnal changes of photosynthetic rates, diffusive conductance and intercellular CO_2 concentration of the flag leaf in wheat with midday dark treatment (left) and midday low CO_2 treatment (right) at 10 days after ear removal. ○—○ control, ●- -● no-ear plants.

Table 2. Maximum photosynthetic capacity of the flag leaf in wheat in the morning and evening.

	Maximum photosynthetic capacity (μmol m^{-2} s^{-1})					
	Day of ear removal			7 days after ear removal		
	Morn[1]	Evg[1]	Evg/Morn(%)	Morn	Evg	Evg/Morn(%)
Control	64.2	52.5	81.8	58.9	54.2	92.0
No-ear	64.9[2]	56.1	86.6	62.8	54.9	87.5

1) Measurement was done between 9:00 and 10:00 in the morning and between 17:00 and 18:00 in the evening.
2) Measurement was done before ear removal treatment

lower than in the control plants in the evening (Fig. 2). Midday low CO_2 treatment reduced the difference in Pr and Dc between the control and no-ear plants in the evening (Fig. 2). These results suggest that the decline in Pr with time was due to a decrease in mesophyll activity as a result of photosynthate accumulation and that the lower Pr in the no-ear plants was due to the lower Dc i.e. lower stomatal aperture.

3.4 Maximum photosynthetic capacity (A_{max}) in the evening was lower than in the morning but there was no significant difference in A_{max} between the control and no-ear plants both on the day of ear removal and 7 days after (Table 2).

4. CONCLUSION

4.1 The decline in photosynthetic rate with time under constant environmental conditions was caused by a decline in the mesophyll activity .

4.2 The greater decline in photosynthetic rate due to ear removal was caused by a greater decline in stomatal aperture.

4.3 Feedback inhibition in the mesophyll activity due to ear removal was not recognized.

REFERENCES

1 Koide K. and Ishihara K. (1992) Jpn. J. Crop Sci. 61, (in press)
2 Koide K. and Ishihara K. (1992) Jpn. J. crop Sci. 61, (in press)

NITROGEN EFFECTS ON RELATIONSHIPS BETWEEN LEAF GROWTH AND LEAF PHOTOSYNTHESIS

C. J. NELSON[1], S. Y. CHOI[2], F. GASTAL[3] AND J. H. COUTTS[1], UNIVERSITY OF MISSOURI[1], USA, CHONBUK NATIONAL UNIVERSITY[2], CHONJU, KOREA, AND INRA[3], LUSIGNAN, FRANCE

1. INTRODUCTION

Leaf elongation rate (LER) of tall fescue (Festuca arundinacea Schreb.) in the field was 3-fold higher when nitrogen (N) was increased from 0 to 75 kg ha^{-1} (1). N concentration in developed leaf tissue increased by 1.6 fold, but concentration of soluble N in the leaf growth zone was less affected. This suggested N flux through the growth zone is more critical in regulating leaf growth than is N concentration of the leaf blade. Studies in growth chambers showed similar responses (2), with the N effect on growth being due almost exclusively to increased cell production, as cell elongation rate and final cell size were largely unaffected (3).

This raised the question-does leaf growth compete for N with the development of photosynthetic machinery, i.e. chloroplasts and associated enzymes? Earlier, Evans (4) found increased N had little effect on CO_2 exchange rate (CER) of wheat flag leaves, but canopy development was enhanced markedly. However, he did not report data on leaf growth rates. We have developed a detailed understanding of cellular dynamics (3), carbohydrate metabolism (5), and N responses (6) in leaf growth zones of tall fescue. Therefore, we determined N effects on both LER and CER. We compared low rates of N, expecting competition among processes would be stronger than at high rates.

2. MATERIALS AND METHODS

2.1 Experiment 1: Vegetative tillers of a tall fescue genotype selected for rapid leaf growth rate (HYT) were transplanted into soil in plastic pots that were 10-cm diameter by 15-cm deep. Conditions were 500 µmol m^{-2} s^{-1} PFD, constant 20°C, and a 14-h photoperiod. After plants were established, top growth was removed to leave a 5-cm stubble, and pots received the equivalent of 5, 20, 40, or 60 kg ha^{-1} of N as NH_4NO_3. Elongation rates of four leaves per pot were determined by regressing daily leaf length vs. time. The CER of the developing leaf was measured weekly at 500 µmol PFD and 350 µL L^{-1} CO_2 using an open system, beginning when the tip appeared above the whorl of sheaths. After 12 weeks of growth plants were washed from the soil, leaf tissue was removed from the stubble, tillers were counted, and tissue dried. Total N was measured in the harvested leaf material.

N. Murata (ed.), Research in Photosynthesis, Vol. IV, 789–792.

2.2 Experiment 2: The basic experiment was repeated as above, but N rates were 5, 25, and 45 kg ha^{-1}. Dark respiration of the youngest leaf blade was measured with the CO_2 analyzer. Photorespiration was estimated by the enhanced CER in 2% O_2 (350 µL L^{-1} CO_2) compared with 21% (350 µL L^{-1} CO_2).

3. RESULTS AND DISCUSSION

Just prior to initiating N treatments in Experiment 1 the LER was 4.8 mm d^{-1}, which is much lower than the 25 to 35 mm d^{-1} we normally expect for well-fertilized plants (3,5). LER responded to N rate by 2.5-fold in a near linear manner (Table 1). Similarly, in Experiment 2 LER increased by more than 2-fold over a smaller change in N. Response was 0.19 mm in Experiment 1 and 0.22 mm d^{-1} kg^{-1} N in experiment 2. In all cases, however, N concentration in harvested leaf tissue remained low and near 1.0%.

In contrast, CERs on dates the ligule appeared above the sheath, i.e. the blade was maximum size, were similar at 20, 40, and 60 kg ha^{-1}, and only about 20% higher than at 5 kg ha^{-1} (Figure 1). Thus, LER responded to N (Table 1) to a much greater degree than CER. The CER of leaves gradually decreased over the next 7 weeks, slowly for the first 2 to 3 weeks, then more rapidly, with little difference due to N rate. This suggests that leaf senesence, for this species at least (7), was independent from N rate. Total CO_2 fixed over the 9-week period was 9.7, 9.8, 11.5, and 11.7 g dm^{-2}, respectively, for increasing N treatments.

Maximum CER in Experiment 2 increased with increasing N rates, from 13.2 at 5 kg N ha^{-1} to 20.0 and 25.2 mg CO_2 dm^{-2} h^{-1} at 25 and 45 kg N ha^{-1}, respectively. Rates of dark respiration were not affected by N (2.1 mg CO_2 dm^{-2} h^{-1}), and the increase in CER in 2% O_2 was also similar over N rates (30%). Thus, the major response to N involves relationships between leaf growth and CER.

TABLE 1. Growth responses of tall fescue to N nutrition.

N-rate	LER	N	Root	Leaf	Stub	Total	Tillers
kg ha^{-1}	mm d^{-1}	%DM	--------g pot^{-1} --------				no. pot^{-1}
Experiment 1							
5	6.1	0.7	3.3	2.2	2.9	8.5	-2
20	10.5	1.1	5.8	4.1	4.5	14.6	3
40	13.6	1.0	9.2	7.4	8.5	25.9	16
60	16.3	1.0	13.2	10.1	11.7	36.4	29
LSD 0.05	1.7	0.2	1.1	1.0	1.0	3.1	5
Experiment 2							
5	7.1	1.1	7.4	2.4	4.1	14.0	2
25	12.8	1.0	11.5	5.6	7.9	25.2	8
45	15.8	1.0	15.9	8.6	11.2	35.6	12
LSD 0.05	1.3	ns	2.2	1.0	1.0	3.5	2

Leaf growth is not carbohydrate limited (5,8,9), thus additional carbon provided by increased photosynthesis is used to support root growth and tillering (Table 1), the latter directly increasing the number of leaf sinks. Tillering increased in both experiments (Table 1), leading directly to increased stubble weight, i.e. tissue consisting of leaf sheaths within 5 cm of soil level.

Leaf width responded curvilinearly to N, increasing from about 5.2 mm at 5 kg N ha^{-1} to 7.4 mm at 40 or 45 kg N ha^{-1}. Leaf length was closely associated with LER as the time interval between leaves was affected very little. These results suggest that diameter of the apical meristem enlarges as N increases allowing more cell columns to be initiated as the primordium circumscribes the terminal. Then, as N rates are further increased, rate of cell production for each cell column is enhanced, subsequently contributing directly to faster leaf growth rate. LER and leaf width are weakly associated, with genetic changes in LER contributing 1.6 to 1.8 times more than leaf width to leaf area expansion rate (10).

Most N used in leaf growth is imported at the base of the elongating leaf (Figure 2) where cell division predominates (3) and stomatal frequency is determined. Thereafter, concentration of soluble protein decreases rapidly as cells expand (2). Little or no new N is imported to the leaf during rapid biosynthesis of Rubisco and other aspects of chloroplast development (6), suggesting protein is recycled as the cells divide, expand, differentiate and develop photosynthetic competency.

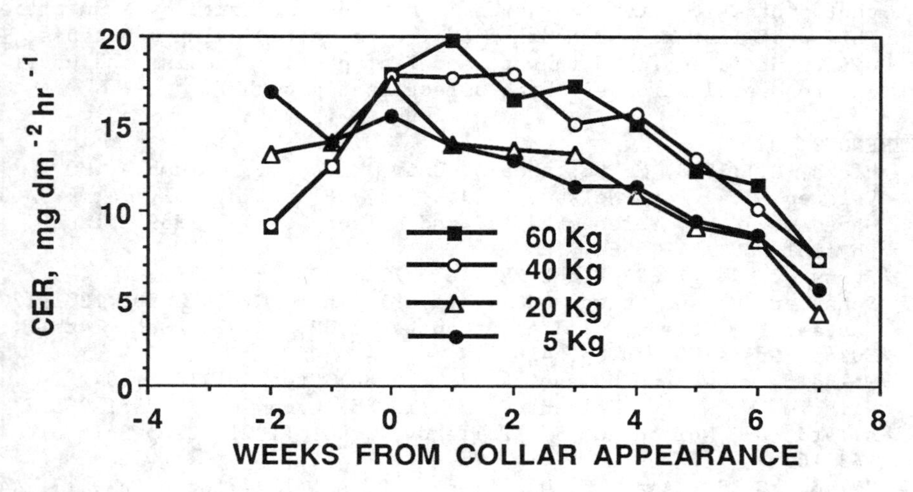

FIGURE 1. Photosynthesis at time of collar emergence (time 0) was slightly higher with high rates of N. Subsequent rates of decline were largely independent from N nutrition. Experiment 1.

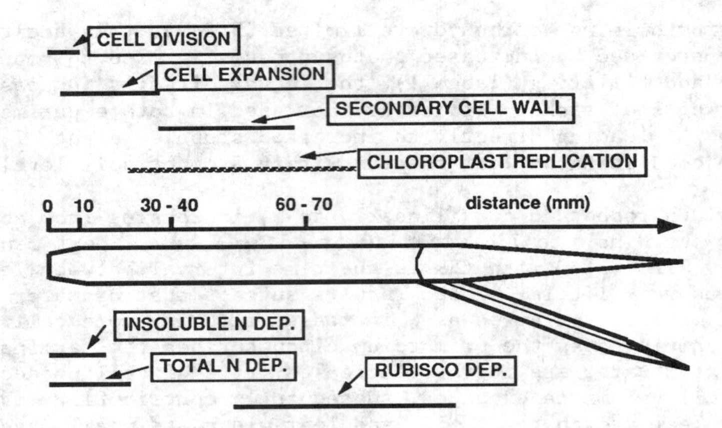

FIGURE 2. Growth zones and deposition positions for N along the base of an elongating leaf. Exact positions depend on genotype and growth conditions. Data for chloroplast replication of wheat (11) are adjusted to tall fescue. Adapted from (6).

4. CONCLUSION

Responses to N should be considered in terms of sequential use rather than competition between leaf growth and photosynthetic machinery. Leaf growth (i.e. cell division) is the primary responder. Subsequent cell expansion causes N-containing compounds to be diluted to a more common level. This N is likely recycled and reallocated to the mesophyll for synthesis of photosynthetic proteins, the end result being leaf elongation rate, but not leaf photosynthetic rate of grasses is markedly affected by N nutrition. This protein-turnover model needs to be tested using genotypes differing in leaf growth rate and leaf photosynthesis, and under environmental stresses which affect leaf growth.

REFERENCES

1 Hicks, N. (1988) M. Sc. thesis, Univ. Missouri, Columbia, MO
2 Volenec, J. J. and Nelson, C. J. (1984) Plant Physiol. 74, 595-600
3 MacAdam, J. W., Volenec, J. J. and Nelson, C. J. (1989) Plant Physiol. 89, 549-556
4 Evans, J. R. (1983) Plant Physiol. 72, 297-302
5 Schnyder, H. and Nelson, C. J. (1989) Plant Physiol. 90, 1201-1206
6 Gastal, F., Nelson, C. J. and Coutts, J. H. (1992) Proc. 14th Europ. Grassld. Fed. p. 418-419
7 Wilhelm, W. W. and Nelson, C. J. (1978a) Crop Sci 18, 769-772
8 Wilhelm, W. W. and Nelson, C. J. (1978b) Crop Sci 18, 951-965
9 Allard, G., Nelson, C. J., Pallardy, S. G. (1991) Crop Sci. 31, 163-167
10 Nelson, C. J., Asay, K. H., Sleper, D. A. (1977) Crop Sci. 17, 449-452
11 Dean, C., and Leech, R. M. (1982) Plant Physiol. 69, 904-910

26. Photosynthesis and Global Climate Change

MODELLING PHOTOSYNTHESIS AND TRANSPIRATION IN PLANTS GROWING IN AN ATMOSPHERE ENRICHED IN CO_2

Ian Woodrow, Department of Botany, James Cook University of North Queensland, Townsville 4811, Australia.

1. Introduction

There are many uncertainties regarding the way in which humankind will impact upon the earth and its atmosphere in the decades to come. One certainty, however, is that the concentration of CO_2 in the atmosphere will continue to rise at a significant rate; the only uncertainty is how fast the rise will occur and at what point it will cease. The increase in atmospheric CO_2 concentration has important consequences for plant growth which seem to relate to two primary effects—the effect of CO_2 on the aperture of stomata and the kinetics of ribulose 1,5-bisphosphate carboxylase/oxygenase (Rubisco) [1]. As the concentration of CO_2 rises, carboxylase activity is stimulated, oxygenase activity is inhibited and stomatal conductance decreases which, taken together, may result in a rise in water use efficiency (WUE, defined as the rate of CO_2 assimilation/the rate of transpiration) in both C_3 and C_4 plants under certain environmental conditions [2]. We are, however, still left with the challenge of determining whether WUE is as large as it could be under relatively high CO_2 conditions and if not, how it can be improved upon. This paper addresses the issue of the optimisation of water use efficiency in C_3 plants grown in a high CO_2 atmosphere. The acclimation of the photosynthetic system to high CO_2 is examined first, then the broader question of the optimisation of stomatal conductance and WUE is examined.

2. Materials and Methods

Plants of sunflower (*Helianthus annuus*) and *Eucalyptus grandis* were grown in pots in a glasshouse at either 350ppm or 800ppm CO_2. Otherwise, all environmental conditions were largely identical: plants were watered daily with 1/4 strength Hoagland's solution; the maximum photon flux density (PFD) was approximately 2000 μmole m^{-2} s^{-1}; the ambient relative humidity was 35%; and the daytime maximum and night-time temperatures were 30^0C and 25^0C, respectively. Transpiration and CO_2 assimilation rates, intercellular CO_2 concentration and stomatal conduc-

N. Murata (ed.), Research in Photosynthesis, Vol. IV, 795–802.

tance were measured on fully expanded leaves using a gas exchange system similar to the one described by Mott [3]. Rubisco flux control coefficients were calculated from measurements of the effect of small changes in O_2 and CO_2 concentration on the assimilation rate (for details see [4]). In some experiments the transpiration rate of small canopies (4×4 plants, 20 cm apart) was calculated using a hydroponic system in which the amount of water needed to maintain a constant soil water content was measured at 40 minute intervals (the system is based upon [5]). Leaf temperature was measured using thermocouples attached to the under surface of leaves. Average boundary layer conductance was calculated from the wind speed above the canopy and the canopy dimensions

3. Results and Discussion

3.1. *Biochemical Acclimation of the C_3 Photosynthetic System*

Studies of a range of C_3 species have shown that acclimation to a relatively high CO_2 concentration often involves a reduction in the amount of ribulose bisphosphate carboxylase/oxygenase (Rubisco) (see [6]). On the surface such a reduction in enzyme activity is logical because an enhanced CO_2 concentration in the stroma allows Rubisco to catalyse the same total flux with a lower concentration of active sites, all other factors being equal. Nevertheless, there is no reason to assume that acclimation to enhanced CO_2 concentrations should involve simply an adjustment to the Rubisco concentration such that the rate of CO_2 assimilation is the same as in plants grown at 350ppm CO_2. An understanding of the acclimation response to high CO_2 will most probably require a quantitative model showing how resources should be distributed within a plant in order to achieve the maximum rate of carbon gain. Such a model of C_3 carbon flux requires a description of the elements (enzymes etc.) which determine the flux together with estimates of their 'value' or 'maintenance and construction costs' (in common terms), the efficiency with which each element sustains the flux, and the proportion of the total flux that is 'carried' by each element. Many limits would need to be included in such a model. For example, there may be a limit to the total number of rapidly growing and dividing cells which consume much of the sucrose produced by the photosynthetic system (i.e. carbon sinks). Clearly such an optimisation model would be very difficult to construct.

A simpler approach to assessing the acclimation of the C_3 photosynthetic system is taken here. Control analysis was used to describe the degree to which certain enzymes determine the rate of CO_2 assimilation in 3-week-old sunflowers and 2-month-old *E. grandis* plants. It was assumed that the control coefficients (see [4] and Section 3.3. for a mathematical definition) reflect an allocation of resources that is approximately optimal for the rate of CO_2 assimilation and that the values of the coefficients are independent of the total amount of resources within the system.

Since raising the atmospheric CO_2 concentration stimulates Rubisco activity, and is therefore equivalent to adding extra ('flux-generating') resources to the C_3 photosynthetic system, optimal acclimation should involve a modification of the concentration of enzymes such that the sensitivity coefficients resume the values measured for plants grown at 350ppm CO_2. This hypothesis was tested for Rubisco in leaves that were exposed to a PFD that was largely saturating for the rate of CO_2 assimilation. Sensitivity or flux control coefficients were calculated as described in Section 2 using equations presented elsewhere [4]. In the plants grown at 350ppm CO_2 the Rubisco control coefficients were about 0.6 and 0.7 for sunflower and *E. grandis*, respectively (Fig. 1). These coefficients indicate that for both species, the rate of CO_2 assimilation is quite sensitive to Rubisco activity. A control coefficient of unity indicates that the flux is directly proportional to enzyme activity. However, when identical measurements were made using leaves from sunflowers grown at 800ppm CO_2, the Rubisco control coefficient was relatively low at about 0.15 whereas the coefficient for *E. grandis* was unchanged at about 0.7 (Fig. 1). These data, according to the hypothesis discussed above, indicate that sunflower does not acclimate optimally with respect to the rate of CO_2 assimilation but *E. grandis* does. This conclusion is supported by growth rate data which shows that *E. grandis* is more stimulated under high CO_2 than sunflower (data not shown).

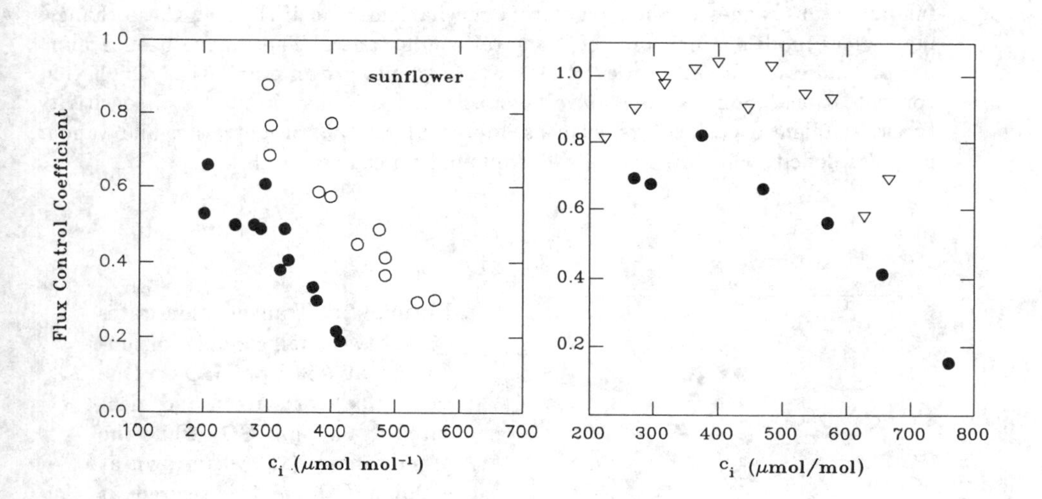

Figure 1: Flux Control or Sensitivity Coefficients for Ribulose bisphosphate carboxylase (Rubisco) as a function of intercellular CO_2 mole fraction in sunflowers (left) and *Eucalyptus grandis* (right) grown at 350ppm (•) and 800ppm (○,▽) CO_2. Measurements were made on fully expanded leaves under a PFD that was largely saturating for the rate of CO_2 assimilation. Arrows indicate the average intercellular CO_2 concentration for each treatment. The magnitude of the coefficient indicates the degree to which the activity of Rubisco limits the flux.

The reason why *E. grandis* can apparently acclimate optimally with respect to assimilation rate may relate to its ability to become 'bushy'—i.e. to grow rapidly at a number of apices. In other words there are relatively few limits placed upon the ability of the sink tissues to utilize sucrose, and when sucrose production is stimulated, a decrease in the amount of Rubisco and an increase in the amount of 'sink' activity occurs. In sunflower, however, there is a genetic limit placed upon the capacity of the 'sink' tissues to consume sucrose. Thus, given this limit, optimal reallocation of resources under high CO_2 may not be reflected by the Rubisco control coefficient of the plant grown at 350ppm CO_2, and greater rates of CO_2 assimilation could only be attained if extra regions of rapidly growing and dividing cells were made available. These data also indicate that as the rate of CO_2 assimilation under high CO_2 and high PFD may not always be determined by Rubisco activity, our models of C_3 photosynthesis will need to be altered to incorporate feedback inhibition deriving from sink tissue capacity [7].

3.2. *Acclimation of Stomata*

Having examined the acclimation of the photosynthetic systems of two C_3 species to 800ppm CO_2, it is pertinent to examine briefly whether stomata undergo any fundamental changes to their regulatory mechanisms and if so, how these changes may affect models which predict stomatal conductance. There have been a number of studies of the properties of stomata in plants grown at relatively high CO_2 concentrations. Some studies have demonstrated a change in stomatal sensitivity to environmental parameters, such as intercellular CO_2 concentration and vapour pressure deficit, while other studies have found no change at all [2].

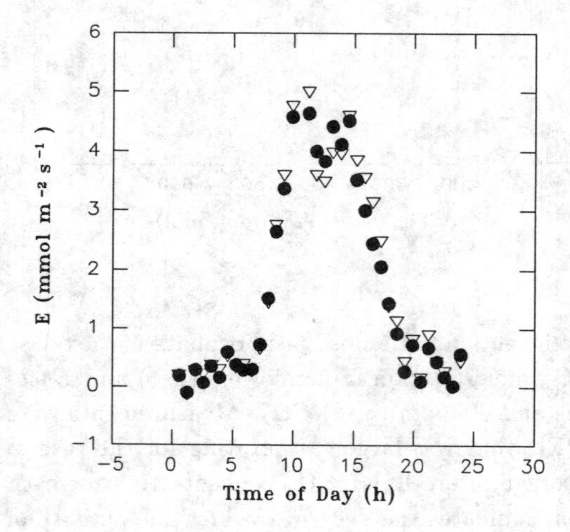

Figure 2: Transpiration rates (E) for two small canopies of sunflowers at 350 ppm CO_2. One canopy (•) was grown and measured at 350ppm CO_2 while the other canopy (▽) was grown at 800ppm CO_2 and measured at 350ppm CO_2. Measurements began at 10.00am. Transpiration rates are given on a leaf area basis and were measured as outlined in the *Materials and Methods.*

Acclimation of a large population of sunflower stomata was tested by growing plants at 350ppm and 800ppm CO_2. Then the transpiration rates of small canopies (16 plants) of sunflowers were compared with those of transferred canopies (i.e. canopies grown at one CO_2 level and transferred to the other). Figure 2 shows the transpiration rate on a leaf area basis of a control and transferred canopy at 350ppm CO_2. Both the transpiration rate at any time and the total amount of transpired water were not significantly different when measurements were made at 350ppm and 800ppm CO_2. As both canopies were at a similar stage of maturity (i.e. the number of expanded leaves per plant was the same) and environmental conditions were identical, it is probable that no significant change in the regulation of stomatal conductance—at least over the range of conditions to which the canopies were exposed—had occurred in the plants acclimated to 800ppm CO_2. The density of stomata on fully expanded leaves of plants grown at both CO_2 levels was also measured and shown not to be significantly different (ANOVA, $p \leq 0.01$) on both surfaces of the leaf [8].

Gas exchange measurements of stomatal conductance and CO_2 assimilation rate were also made on a variety of leaves from both sunflower and *E. grandis* over a range of conditions. The data were plotted according to the empirical model of Ball

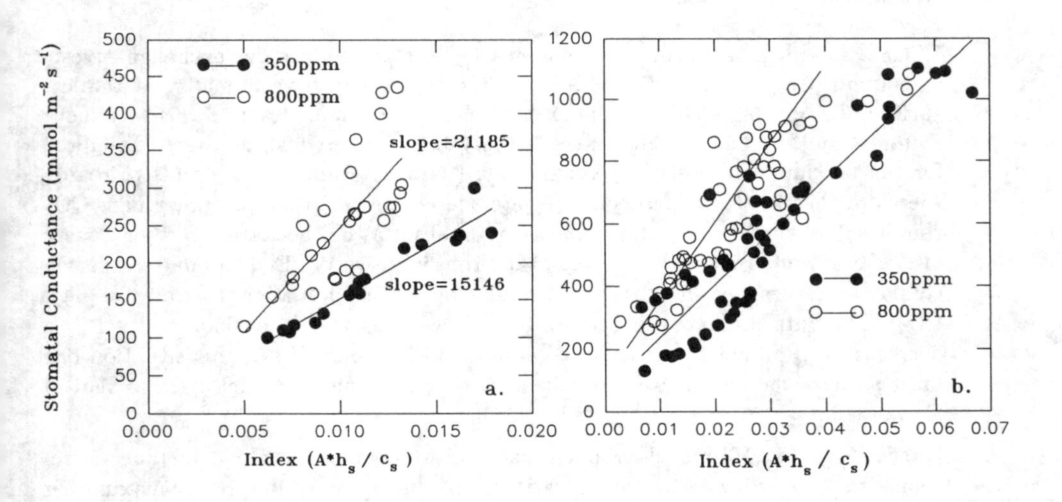

Figure 3: Empirical model of stomatal conductance for sunflowers (a) and *Eucalyptus grandis* (b) grown at 350ppm and 800ppm CO_2. Assimilation rates (A), relative humidity (h_s) and CO_2 mole fraction (c_s) at the leaf surface, and stomatal conductance (g_s) were measured on individual leaves using a gas exchange system. Several leaves of both species were used and conditions ranged as follows: c_s, 300-800μmol mol^{-1}; h_s, 30-60%; PFD, 200-1200μmol m^{-2} s^{-1}; leaf temperature, 25^{0}C and 27^{0}C.

et al. [9] which relates stomatal conductance (g_s) to an index as follows:

$$g_s = m\frac{Ah_s}{c_s} + b$$

where A is the rate of CO_2 assimilation, h_s and c_s are the relative humidity and CO_2 mole fraction at the leaf surface, respectively, m is the slope of the line, and b is the ordinate intercept. The data show that both slope and intercept change for plants acclimated to 800ppm CO_2 (Fig.3). Moreover, these and other data (not shown) indicate that the scatter of the points increases for high CO_2 plants and that some of the scatter derives from the division by c_s—i.e. the fit of the line can be improved under some conditions by making measurements at an approximately constant c_s.

For both species the slope of the line—the 'composite stomatal sensitivity' [9]—increases for the plants grown at 800ppm CO_2. Much of this variation may simply be due to biochemical acclimation of the photosynthetic system which reduces the CO_2 assimilation rate per unit leaf area in both species. Thus, at any g_s the index will be less and m greater for plants grown at 800ppm CO_2. Further research is needed to confirm the utility of this relatively simple model for plants grown at a range of CO_2 concentrations and under a range of other conditions.

3.3. *Optimisation of Stomatal Conductance*

When a sunflower leaf grown at 350ppm CO_2 was placed in a gas exchange cuvette at 800ppm CO_2, a PFD of 1000μmol m^{-2} s^{-1} and a relative humidity at the leaf surface of about 50%, the calculated intercellular CO_2 mole fraction (c_i) was about 650μmol mol^{-1}. This c_i value exceeds the value of about 500μmol mol^{-1} required for the maximum rate of CO_2 assimilation (data not shown). It stands to reason therefore that in this experiment, despite the closure of stomata, under high CO_2 conditions stomatal conductance is not optimal for WUE because a further closure of stomata would reduce both c_i and E and thus increase WUE. The same conclusion cannot necessarily be drawn from a similar appraisal of sunflowers grown at high CO_2. The data presented in Section 3.1. shows that at a c_i of 650μmol mol^{-1}, a decrease in g_s would result in a decrease in both A and E. In this situation one must address the question of the optimisation of g_s using a model, such as that of Cowan [10].

Briefly, Cowan's [10] model assumes that variations in stomatal conductance in response to changes in environmental variables can be explained in terms of maximising carbon assimilation and minimising transpiration. Over a single day, for example, if soil water content does not change significantly then total assimilation ($\overline{A}$) and total transpiration ($\overline{E}$) should vary as follows:

$$\overline{A} - \frac{\overline{E}}{\lambda} = maximum.$$

where λ is the benefit (in terms of plant 'fitness') of carbon gain relative to the cost (also in terms of plant 'fitness') of water loss. In other words stomatal conductance should vary such that no other variation could have produced a smaller $\overline{E}$ at $\overline{A}$ or a larger $\overline{A}$ at $\overline{E}$. It follows from the above equation that at any time

$$A - \frac{E}{\lambda} = maximum$$

must also hold. In this equation A and E are the instantaneous rates of carbon assimilation and transpiration, respectively. The constant λ should only change when the 'value' of water changes—i.e when the soil water content changes.

In order to assess whether stomatal conductance is optimal (as defined by Cowan [10]) in sunflowers grown at 800ppm CO_2, λ values for plants grown at both high and low CO_2 concentrations were compared. One could argue that if the soil water content is the same for plants under both CO_2 regimes, then λ should also be the same—in other words, plants of a single variety should adopt the same long term water use and carbon gain strategy.

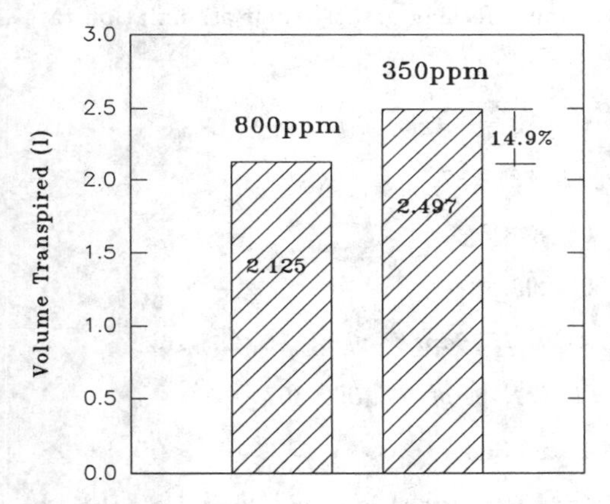

Figure 4: Total amount of transpired water from small canopies of sunflowers grown at 350ppm and 800ppm CO_2 between 10.00am and 3.00pm. The canopies (16 plants) were grown in a glasshouse and transpiration was measured as described in the *Materials and Methods*. The average boundary layer conductance over the canopies was approximately 0.7 mol m^{-2} s^{-1}.

Values of λ were calculated from the results of flux control studies of sunflowers acclimated to 350ppm and 800ppm CO_2. As outlined in Section 3.1. a flux control or sensitivity coefficient expresses the effect on a flux of a small change in enzyme concentration or diffusional conductance, for example. From the above equation

$$\lambda = \frac{\partial E}{\partial A} = \frac{\frac{\partial E}{\partial g_s} \cdot \frac{g_s}{E}}{\frac{\partial A}{\partial g_s} \cdot \frac{g_s}{A}} = \frac{C^E_{g_s}.E}{C^A_{g_s}.A}$$

where $C^E_{g_s}$ and $C^A_{g_s}$ are the flux control coefficients for stomatal conductance with respect to transpiration and carbon assimilation, respectively.

Small canopies (16 plants) of sunflowers grown at 800ppm CO_2 showed a reduction both in stomatal conductance and in the total amount of water used during the day relative to canopies grown at 350ppm CO_2 (Fig.4). Under the conditions occurring at 10.00am (PFD=1100μmol m^{-2} s^{-1}; see *see Materials and Methods*), the λ values were approximately 1100 and 8000 for sunflowers at low and high CO_2, respectively. These values are obviously far from identical, and they indicate that the canopy acclimated to 800ppm CO_2 transpires much more water than the water use strategy of the 350ppm-grown plants (reflected by λ) would dictate.

What then should stomatal conductance be in order for the high CO_2 plants to maintain a λ value of about 1100? An estimate was made using a model of the leaf energy budget, stomatal conductance and assimilation (based upon the outline presented elsewhere [11]). A λ value of 1100 for the plants acclimated to 800ppm CO_2 requires a stomatal conductance which is some 25% of that conductance which was estimated for these plants. This proportion is by no means applicable to all plants acclimated to high CO_2 concentrations. Nevertheless, it is relatively clear that most plants acclimated to high CO_2 could reduce their stomatal conductance and reduce their transpiration rate without affecting greatly their assimilation rates.

References

[1] Mott, K.A. (1990) *Plant Cell Environ.* **13**, 731-737.

[2] Eamus, D. (1991) *Plant Cell Environ.* **14**, 843-852.

[3] Mott, K.A. (1988) *Plant Physiol.* **86**, 200-203.

[4] Woodrow, I.E. and Mott, K.A. (1988) *Aust. J. Plant Physiol.* **15**, 253-262.

[5] Snow, M.D. and Tingley, D.T. (1985) *Plant Physiol.* **77**, 602-607.

[6] Bowes, G. (1991) *Plant Cell Environ.***14**, 795-806.

[7] Woodrow, I.E. and Berry, J.A. (1988) *Ann. Rev. Plant Physiol. Plant Mol. Biol.* **39**, 533-594.

[8] Gardener, M.R. (1992) Honours Thesis, James Cook University of North Queensland.

[9] Ball, J.T., Woodrow, I.E., and Berry, J.A. (1987) **In:** *Progress in Photosynthesis Research*, ed. J. Biggins, 4, 221-224.

[10] Cowan, I.R. (1986) **In:** *On the Economy of Plant Form and Function*, ed. T. Givnish, Cambridge: Cambridge University Press.

[11] Woodrow, I.E., Ball, T.J. and Berry, J.A. (1987) See ref. 9, pp. 225-228.

PHYTOPLANKTON PHOTOSYNTHESIS IN THE OCEAN IN RELATION TO THE GLOBAL CARBON CYCLE

Paul G. Falkowski, Oceanographic and Atmospheric Sciences Division, Brookhaven National Laboratory, Upton, New York 11973, USA

1. INTRODUCTION

Phytoplankton in the oceans accounts for <1% of the plant biomass, but is responsible for approximately 50% of the photosynthesis on Earth. Over the past 2 billion years, the efflux of O_2 from the oceans due to the photosynthetic activity of these single-celled organisms has produced almost all of the oxygen in the Earth's present-day atmosphere, while simultaneously, depleting it of CO_2. Most of the carbon fixed by phytoplankton in the upper 150 m of the ocean, is oxidized below the main thermocline as the organisms sink. The photosynthetic fixation of carbon in the upper ocean and subsequent sinking and oxidation of the organic carbon below the thermocline has effectively sequestered atmospheric CO_2 in the deep ocean (Fig. 1). Thus, while the upper ocean is very close to equilibrium with the atmospheric CO_2 concentrations, below the thermocline, the concentration of total inorganic carbon is much higher than the air-sea equilibrium value. This inverse gradient, due to the action of the so-called "biological pump", was crucial in maintaining atmospheric levels of CO_2 at a steady-state concentration of about 275 ppm prior to the industrial revolution.

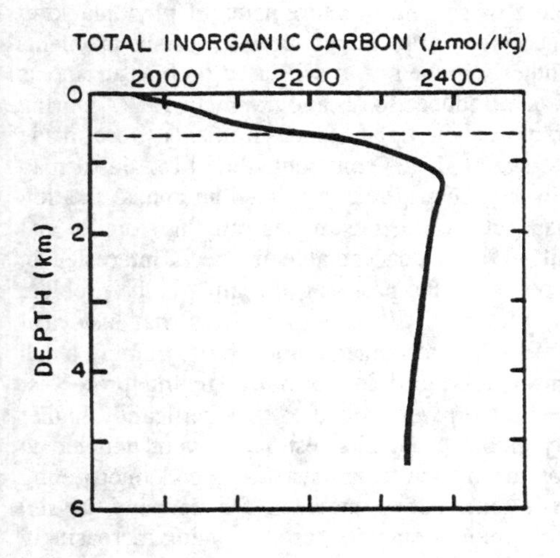

Fig. 1. A representative vertical profile of the total inorganic carbon in the upper 5000m of the central oceans.

A small fraction (<1%) of the CO_2 fixed by phytoplankton arrives at the sea floor. On the shallow continental shelves, or relict inland seas, the sedimenting organic material can accumulate over millions of years, becoming buried in sediments. As it is buried, the organic matter is subjected to high pressures and temperatures and undergoes chemical transformations, forming oil and natural gas. The anthropogenic oxidation of these fossil fuels presently adds about 7.4 ($\pm$ 1.2) x 10^9 metric tons (GT) of carbon, as CO_2, to the atmosphere, and this rate is increasing by about 0.35% each year.

Of this, about 3.5 GT C per year are removed from the atmosphere by one or more sinks (1, 2). Thus, at the present time, the gas composition of the atmosphere is no longer in steady-state. CO_2 absorbs infrared radiation, and its accumulation in the atmosphere helps to reradiate outgoing long-wave radiation back to the surface of the Earth, thereby forcing an

N. Murata (ed.), Research in Photosynthesis, Vol. IV, 803–810.

increase in surface temperature. As we come to the end of the 20th century, a major challenge facing scientists in general is to (a) identify and quantify the sinks for the anthropogenic CO_2, and (b) understand how the changes in the gas composition of the atmosphere will affect the biological processes which, prior to the industrial revolution, maintained a relative balance between photosynthetic carbon fixation and heterotrophic carbon oxidation. Here I will focus on the present understanding of the role of phytoplankton photosynthesis in the oceans in the steady-state and non-steady state global carbon cycle.

2. STRATEGIES FOR ESTIMATING PHYTOPLANKTON PHOTOSYNTHESIS

Two fundamental questions concerning the role of photosynthesis in the global carbon cycle are: (a) If the atmospheric CO_2 levels are not in steady-state, has the annual mean photosynthetic carbon fixation changed since the beginning of the industrial revolution, and if so why? and (b) What are the feedbacks between changes in radiative forcing and global patterns of photosynthesis? To address these questions, it is necessary to derive accurate estimates of photosynthesis, to determine the factors limiting the rates of photosynthesis, and to assess how the limitations have been and will be affected by changes in radiative forcing.

In oceanography, two general strategies for deriving global estimates of phytoplankton photosynthesis have emerged. The first is based on direct fixed point, *in situ* measurements of photosynthetic rates which are then scaled to basin or global areas. The second is based on synoptic global satellite-based maps of ocean chlorophyll. Photosynthetic rates are derived from these maps using radiative transfer and photosynthetic response models. Model parameters are derived from *in situ* measurements. Both approaches are imperfect, and major efforts are under way to improve and integrate them.

2.1 As phytoplankton are not fixed in space and the oceans can be extremely dynamic environments, measurements of phytoplankton biomass and photosynthetic rates from ships are spatially and temporally biased. While the problem of scaling measurements of phytoplankton photosynthesis is much more tractable than scaling terrestrial plant production, serious problems persist. Most estimates of phytoplankton photosynthesis in the ocean are based on measurements of the uptake of radiocarbon; the basic technique was introduced to oceanography in 1952. During the following decades, tens of thousands of radiocarbon uptake measurements were made throughout the world oceans. In 1970, Koblenz-Miske et al. (3) constructed the first global map of the average spatial patterns of carbon fixation in the oceans, and calculated an annual fixation of 23 Gt C. Subsequent maps, based on larger data sets, yielded estimates ranging from 20 and 35 Gt C/y (4). This range of uncertainty (about 40%) is unacceptable if one is interested in constraining the sink of anthropogenic CO_2. Compounding the problem of scaling is the problem of the accuracy of the radiocarbon method itself. In the 1980s it was realized that historical radiocarbon measurements in the open ocean were subject to contamination by extremely small amounts of trace metals which were inadvertently introduced in normal sampling protocols. Carbon fixation rates obtained using ultra-clean techniques were found to be significantly higher than those previously measured, and consequently global production estimates were doubled to about 50 gigatons C per annum (5). Because of the difficulty in measuring and interpreting radiocarbon-based measurements of photosynthesis, alternative methods for deriving *in situ* photosynthetic rates, based, for example, on variable fluorescence (6), are becoming increasingly accepted. The advantages of fluorescence-based methods are that no incubation is required and the instruments are capable of being moored in the ocean for extended periods (months), thereby producing long time series.

2.2 One of the major oceanographic tools to emerge in the past decade has been satellite measurements of ocean color. For eight years, beginning in 1978, the Coastal Zone Color Scanner (CZCS) orbited the earth aboard the satellite Nimbus 7. CZCS high resolution measurements of ocean color were used to construct global maps of the seasonal and spatial distribution of phytoplankton chlorophyll in the upper ocean. The quantitative relationship between ocean color and chlorophyll is based on an understanding of the optical properties of pure seawater and phytoplankton. Pure seawater absorbs red and infrared light but scatters light isotropically (7). Scattering increases as a reciprocal of the fourth power of wavelength. Thus, to an observer looking down from above, the ocean appears blue due to absorption of red light and the intense backscattering of blue light. Superimposed on the optical properties of the seawater itself are the optical properties of phytoplankton. Because phytoplankton contain chlorophylls and carotenoids, they absorb blue and red light, but backscatter only about 2% of the light at angles $> 90^{\circ}$. Algorithms based on the reflectance ratios of blue to green light leaving the ocean surface (water leaving radiances) can be used to quantitatively derive the chlorophyll concentration in the upper ocean. These algorithms include a correction for scattering and absorption in the atmosphere. The relationships used for calculating chlorophyll from the inherent optical properties of the ocean are empirical, but relatively accurate; as long as chlorophyll concentrations are lower than 1 μg/l, the coefficient of determination is > 0.95 and the relative error $< 20\%$. As chlorophyll concentrations increase, the accuracy of the algorithms deteriorates; in coastal waters, where chlorophyll concentrations can exceed 10 μg/l and there is further absorption of light by yellow humic substances, it is not possible to derive chlorophyll based on water leaving radiance measurements. Such areas account for about 10% of the ocean surface.

Satellite measurements of ocean color made global scale maps of phytoplankton chlorophyll biomass readily accessible, and more or less eliminated the problems of sampling bias and scaling. However, deriving credible and accurate photosynthetic rates from satellite-based estimates of phytoplankton chlorophyll requires additional information and modeling.

3. BIO-OPTICAL MODELS OF PHYTOPLANKTON PHOTOSYNTHESIS

Chlorophyll is a pool, photosynthesis is a flux. The calculation of a flux from a pool requires a time-dependent variable. The models which use satellite-derived estimates of phytoplankton chlorophyll to estimate the global phytoplankton photosynthesis incorporate irradiance as the time-dependent parameter; the transfer functions are a cross section and a quantum yield. Various so-called bio-optical models have been developed to derive photosynthesis (see review in ref. 8); the conceptual basis underlying most of the models is straightforward.

At any point on the Earth the average incident photosynthetically active (400 to 700 nm) scalar irradiance at the top of the atmosphere can be readily computed from knowledge of the spatial and temporal coordinates. The propagation of light through a clear sky is relatively well modeled and clouds can be treated statistically. The propagation and modification of scalar irradiance through the water column can also be computed for open ocean systems, so, that at any depth, z, the spectral irradiance $E_{(z,\lambda)}$ can be computed from knowledge of $E_{(\lambda)}$ at the surface and the chlorophyll concentration [Chl]. The basis for the calculation is a reasonable understanding and parameterization of the absorption and scattering coefficients of seawater and phytoplankton. Because the optical properties of the ocean are comparatively simple compared with terrestrial systems, model calculations of scalar spectral irradiance are reasonably accurate (within 5% error).

Instantaneous or time-integrated photosynthetic rates can be calculated from the spectral irradiance at any depth, the light-intensity behavior of the quantum yield (assumed to be a spectrally independent property) and the chlorophyll specific absorption cross section, a* (a spectrally dependent property), thus:

$$P = \int E_\lambda \, a^*_\lambda \, \phi \, [Chl] \, d_\lambda \quad (1)$$

where P is chlorophyll-specific carbon fixation.

Accurate numerical solution to Eq. (1) requires an understanding of the variability in a* and ϕ. Chlorophyll-specific rates of photosynthetic carbon fixation vary significantly in the ocean. The variability is found in both the light saturated rates as well as in the light limited rates. Variability in chlorophyll-specific rates of light-limited photosynthesis implies variability in either the effective absorption cross section normalized to chlorophyll, and/or in the maximum quantum yield. Variations in the light saturated rates of photosynthesis imply variability in either the number of photosynthetic units (n, the reciprocal of the Emerson-Arnold number) and/or the maximum rate of whole chain photosynthetic electron transport from water to CO_2. We have used *in situ* pump-and-probe fluorescence methods to investigate the contribution of these parameters to the variability and causes thereof in natural phytoplankton communities in the ocean (9).

3.1 The chlorophyll-specific absorption cross section of phytoplankton varies by about a factor of five. The variations are due to two basic phenomena: (a) changes in the ratio of accessory pigments/chlorophyll and (b) the "package" effect. Phytoplankton can rapidly acclimate to varying irradiance levels by markedly changing the cellular composition and concentration of pigments. Changes in the ratio of carotenoids to chlorophyll account for about 50% of the variance in a*. Moreover, as chlorophyll concentrations increase (due, for example to acclimation to low irradiance levels), there is an increase in the stacking of thylakoid membranes. This self-shading of pigment molecules results in a decrease in the optical absorption cross section normalized to chlorophyll (Fig. 2). Thus, a doubling or trebling in intracellular chlorophyll may confer as little as a 20% increase in light harvesting efficiency. Similarly, nitrogen or iron limitation, while leading to a decrease in cellular chlorophyll, simultaneously lead to an increase in the chlorophyll specific absorption cross section because of a reduction in thylakoid membrane stacking.

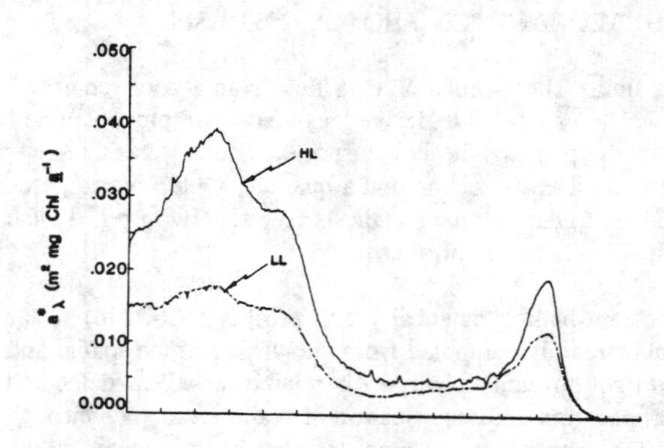

Fig. 2. The chlorophyll specific absorption cross section for high light and low light adapted *Dunaliella tertiolecta*. Note the lower absorption cross sections at low light adapted cells due to the "package" effect.

It is extremely difficult to measure a* accurately in natural phytoplankton. The concentration of chlorophyll is so low in the ocean that direct absorption measurements are almost impossible. To

To overcome this problem, phytoplankton are concentrated on filters and the absorption of the filter is determined. Multiple light scattering on filters increases the probability of light absorption, and consequently yields and overestimate of the true absorption cross section. Additionally, light absorption by non-photosynthetic particles, such as bacteria, produce a non-linear distortion of the baseline. These technical problems have seriously impeded parameterization of bio-optical models.

It is relatively straightforward to derive the absorption cross section of PSII without a direct absorption measurement by following the saturation curve of variable fluorescence using a pump-and-probe technique. The flash intensity saturation curve follows a cumulative one-hit Poisson function (10). The PSII cross-section is related to the total absorption cross section, a*, by the function:

$$\sigma_{PSII} = (a^* \phi)/(4\ n) \qquad (2)$$

where n is the concentration of PSII reaction centers per chlorophyll and ϕ is the maximum quantum yield. Variations in σ_{PSII} in the ocean reveal strong effects of nutrient regimes in modifying photoacclimation (Fig. 3).

3.2 In laboratory continuous cultures of phytoplankton, the maximum variable fluorescence yield (F_v/F_m), measured with a pump-and-probe fluorometer (11), is remarkably independent of species composition and growth irradiance, averaging about 0.65. This efficiency is comparable to that obtained in higher plants under ideal conditions. We attribute the constancy of this efficiency to the conservation of both PSII reaction center core proteins (D1, D2, cyt b_{559}) and the two proximal antenna chlorophyll protein complexes CP43 and CP47. The changes in the maximum quantum yield of fluorescence decrease as a hyperbolic function of nitrogen or iron deficiency and are quantitatively linked to the maximum quantum yield of photosynthesis. Western blots reveal that nitrogen deficiency leads to selective losses of CP43 and D1 relative to other thylakoid proteins, while iron deficiency leads to a loss of cyt b_6/f and D1. Based on these results, we have investigated the quantum yields of phytoplankton photosynthesis in major ocean basins using pump-and-probe fluorescence techniques.

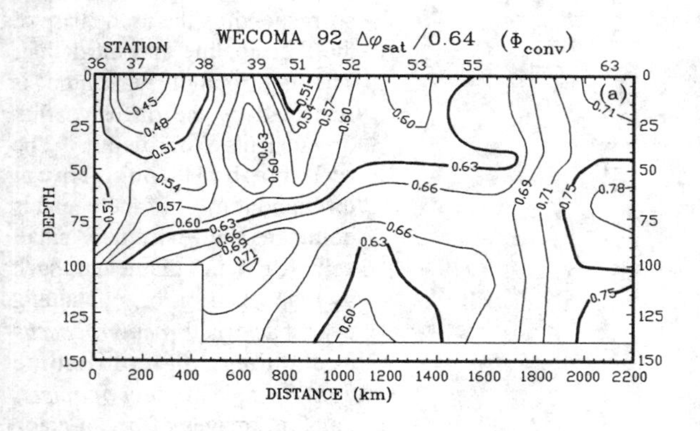

Fig. 3. A section of the maximum quantum efficiency of Photosystem II measured by FRR fluorometry in the equatorial Pacific from 0°, 140°W to 15°N, 149°W.

We hypothesized that if the phytoplankton photosynthesis were limited only by light in the ocean, then the quantum yield would be relatively constant. Instead we found that the quantum yield of photosynthetic energy conversion varies by a factor of about 3, from a maximum of 0.65 to a minimum of 0.25. Maximum values are obtained in nutrient rich areas, such as off the coast of northwest Africa, where strong westerly winds cause intense upwelling and nitrate values at the sea surface are as high as 10 uM. Minimum values are found in the upper 20 m in the central of the subtropical gyres, where nitrate concentrations are undetectable (below 5 nM). Transects across the equatorial Pacific (which is thought to be iron limited) to the *central Pacific gyre (which is thought to be nitrogen limited), from the oligotrophic Sargasso Sea to the nutrient rich continental margin of the eastern United States, show that the variations in the quantum yield are strongly influenced by the availability of nutrients. For example, the addition of 5 μM nitrate to surface seawater from the central subtropical Atlantic results in a marked increase in quantum yields over a 72 h period (Fig. 4), and enrichment of surface waters from the equatorial Pacific with nanomolar concentrations of $FeCl_3$ also promotes large increases in quantum efficiency. These types of enrichments strongly indicate that throughout most of the open ocean, phytoplankton photosynthetic energy conversion efficiency, not simply biomass, is limited by the availability of nutrients. Due to the difficulty in obtaining sufficient material from the ocean, we have not yet been able to confirm using western blot techniques whether the variations in quantum yields are due to a reduction in CP43 and/or D1.

4. WHAT LIMITS PHYTOPLANKTON PHOTOSYNTHESIS IN THE OCEAN?

Global maps of ocean chlorophyll and sea-surface temperature distributions reveal the importance of nutrients such as nitrate and phosphate in determining the abundance of phytoplankton. With three important exceptions, nutrient-rich areas of the ocean are associated with cold water. In the surface ocean, phytoplankton biomass is generally limited by availability of nutrients. For example, in the center of the warm ocean gyres, chlorophyll concentrations are extremely low (on the order of 0.1 μg chl/l) and total inorganic nitrogen is less than 0.1 μM. Vertical profiles of chlorophyll in such regions reveal a strong gradient, with a chlorophyll maximum of 0.3 to 1 μg/l at 100 to 120 m, corresponding the to the base of the thermocline and nitrocline. The chlorophyll maximum is sustained by the diffusive flux of nutrients from depth. The chlorophyll maximum throughout most of the ocean is dominated by extremely small cells (ca. 1 um diameter), such as the Chl a/b containing cyanobacteria, *Prochlorococcus* and the phycobilisome containing *Synechococcus*. Satellite images of ocean color do not record the chlorophyll maximum in such areas, as it is much too deep to influence the water leaving radiances;

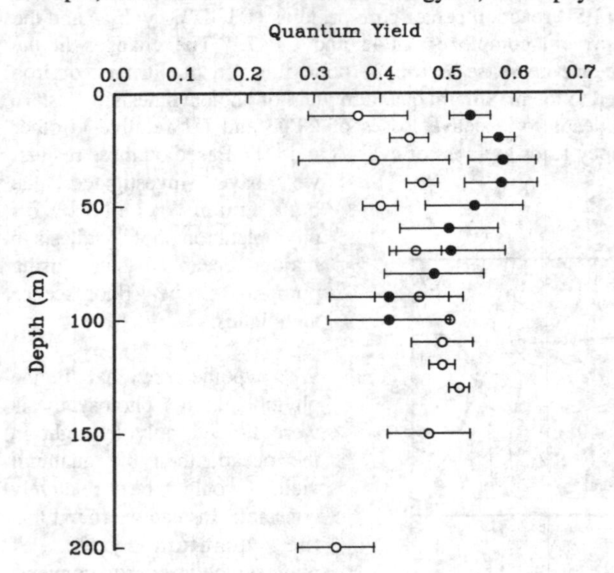

Fig. 4. Comparison of vertical profiles of the maximum quantum efficiency of Photosystem II (F_v/F_m) in a nutrient-rich upwelling region (●) off northwest Africa and in a nutrient-depleted area in the central subtropical Atlantic gyre (○).

consequently, it can only be inferred from statistical analysis of ship-based *in situ* profiles. Chlorophyll concentrations in the upper ocean are highest in coastal upwelling regions, such as off the coast of Peru, northwest Africa and in the tidally stirred areas of Georges Bank (off the northeast coast of the United States) and the Bering Sea. In such areas the vertical distribution of chlorophyll is relatively homogeneous in the upper mixed layer of the ocean. Seasonal changes in phytoplankton chlorophyll are especially strong in the temperate regions, such as the North Atlantic, where the progressive increase in incident solar radiation in the spring results in thermal stratification of the upper ocean. By setting a thermal floor to mixing nutrients are trapped in the upper ocean and the incident radiation is sufficient to simultaneously allow the integrated water column photosynthetic rate to exceed the integrated respiration. The result is a net increase in phytoplankton biomass; i.e., a "spring bloom." In late fall, as stratification dissipates and the mixing depth exceeds the compensation depth, phytoplankton chlorophyll diminishes to very low levels.

4.1 In most areas of the world ocean the essential inorganic nitrogenous nutrients either are or become depleted at some time during the year as a result of phytoplankton photosynthesis. There are three major ocean regions where inorganic nutrient concentrations are perennially high and phytoplankton chlorophyll is perennially low, namely the Southern Ocean, the equatorial Pacific and the subarctic Pacific. In all three areas the availability of reactive (ferrous) iron has been suggested to be limiting. Iron is supplied to the ocean primarily from the atmospheric transport of iron-rich particles from the continents. Major sources of such particles are the Gobi and Sahara deserts. Nanomolar additions of iron to surface seawater samples often result in the assimilation of the available inorganic nitrogen with a concomitant increase in phytoplankton chlorophyll. Simple geochemical box-diffusion models suggest that if iron was limiting, and iron supplementation could would act to drawdown all the available nutrients in the three areas, a significant decrease in atmospheric CO_2 would occur (12).

4.2 Phytoplankton photosynthesis can significantly reduce the concentration of free CO_2 in the upper ocean. As the rate constant for the dehydration of HCO_3^- is relatively long, the photosynthetic processes can facilitate the diffusion of CO_2 across the air-sea interface. In the absence of phytoplankton photosynthesis and sinking, the concentration of pCO_2 in the surface waters would come into equilibrium with the higher concentration of TCO_2 in the deep ocean, and a net out-gassing of CO_2 to the atmosphere would ensue. However, in order for phytoplankton photosynthesis (or any other biological process) to have a significant influence on the anthropogenic CO_2 it must be changing.

5. CONCLUSIONS: PHYTOPLANKTON PHOTOSYNTHESIS AND THE GLOBAL CARBON CYCLE

Direct observational data on phytoplankton biomass and photosynthetic rates in the ocean only extend back in time to the mid 1950s - which, given the sampling biases and natural variability, is not long enough to deduce a significant time-dependency. However, using optical data of ocean transparency based on Secchi disc measurements, which extend back to the beginning of the 20th century, it is possible to construct a century long time series of phytoplankton biomass and production for the North Pacific and North Atlantic Oceans. The results of that analysis reveal that subtle changes in ocean circulation, presumably climatically forced, have occurred in the North Pacific Ocean; phytoplankton chlorophyll has increased slightly at the ocean margins and decreased in the central ocean basins. These changes are consistent with increased atmospheric iron loading to the surface ocean, presumably due to increased desertification. Overall, however, the changes in carbon fixation in the open ocean are small compared with the annual anthropogenic flux of CO_2, and for practical purposes phytoplankton photosynthesis in central ocean basins should be considered to be in steady-state. In contrast, however, on continental margins, where additional nutrient loadings have accelerated phytoplankton growth, the additional photosynthetic uptake of CO_2 may be significant. The fate of this additional carbon in the sediments or the or ocean interior remains unclear (13).

Acknowledgments: This research was supported by the U.S. Department of Energy under Contract DE-AC02-76CH00016, the Centre National pour Recherche Scientifique, and the John Simon Guggenheim Memorial Foundation.

REFERENCES

1 Sarmiento, J. (1992) Nature 356, 589-593

2 Tans, P., Fung, I., Takahashi, T. (1990) Science 247, 1431-1438

3 Koblentz-Mishke, O.J., Volkovinsky, V.V. and Kabanova, J.G. (1970) in Scientific Exploration of the South Pacific (Wooster, W.S., ed.), U.S. National Academy of Science

4 Malone, T.C. (1980) in Primary Productivity in the Sea (Falkowski, P.G., ed.), pp. 301-319, Plenum Press, New York

5 Barber, R.T. and Chavez, F.P. (1991) Limnol. Oceanogr. 36(8), 1803-1815

6 Falkowski, P., Ziemann, Kolber, Z. and Bienfang, P. (1992) Nature 352, 55-58

7 Kirk, J.T.O. (1983) Light and Photosynthesis in Aquatic Ecosystems, Cambridge University Press, 401 pp

8 Bidigare, R., Prézelin, B.B. and Smith, R.C. (1992) in Primary Productivity and Biogeochemical Cycles in the Sea (Falkowski, P.G. and Woodhead, A.D., eds.), pp. 175-212, Plenum Press, New York

9 Kolber, Z., Wyman, K. and Falkowski, P.G. (1990) Limnol. Oceanogr. 35, 72-79

10 Falkowski, P.G., Wyman, K., Ley, A. and Mauzerall D. (1986) Biochim. Biophys. Acta 849, 183-192

11 Kolber, Z., Zehr, J. and Falkowski, P.G. (1988) Plant Physiol. 88, 923-929

12 Sarmiento, J. and Orr, J. (1991) Limnol. Oceanogr. 36(8) 1928-1950

13 Falkowski, P.G. and Wilson, C. (1992) Nature (in press)

THE IMPLICATIONS OF CONCURRENT INCREASES IN TEMPERATURE AND CO_2 CONCENTRATION FOR TERRESTRIAL C_3 PHOTOSYNTHESIS.

S.P. LONG[1,2], G.Y. NIE[2], B.G. DRAKE[3], G. HENDREY[2] AND K. LEWIN[2]. DEPT. OF BIOLOGY[1], UNIVERSITY OF ESSEX, COLCHESTER, CO4 3SQ, UK. DEPT. OF APPLIED SCI.[2], BROOKHAVEN NATL. LAB., UPTON, NY 11973, USA. SMITHSONIAN ENV. RES. CNTR.[3], POB28, EDGEWATER, MD 21037, USA.

1. INTRODUCTION

Atmospheric CO_2 concentration (C_a) is expected to rise from the current mean of ca.360 μmol mol^{-1} to ca. 530 μmol mol^{-1} by 2050 and to ca.700 μmol mol^{-1} by the end of the next century (1). Rising concentrations of infra-red absorbing gases, including CO_2, are predicted to increase mean air temperatures by ca. 2-3°C by 2050 and ca. 3-4°C by 2100 (1). Whilst much is known about the responses of photosynthesis and photosynthetic capacity to variation in temperature little is known of how long-term elevation of C_a will modify these responses to temperature. Understanding of this interaction will be critical to predicting photosynthetic carbon uptake by crops and natural vegetation with climate change (2).

Photosynthesis is not only the major physiological process by which plants sense change in C_a, but is also the process a priori by which plant production is most likely to be affected by change in C_a and the process which sets the upper limit on potential C-uptake into vegetation (2). Increase in C_a will lead to increased efficiency of net leaf photosynthetic CO_2 uptake (A) by increasing the velocity of carboxylation of ribulose-1:5-bisphosphate (RubP) and by competitive inhibition of oxygenation of RubP and hence photorespiration (2,3). Since photorespiration decreases the efficiency of photosynthesis, increase in C_a will result in increased photosynthetic CO_2 uptake, regardless of whether light is limiting or saturating and regardless of whether efficiency of carboxylation or maximum electron transport rate are limiting. However, if end-product utilisation results in inorganic phosphate (P_i) limitation within the chloroplast, then increase in C_a will not stimulate CO_2 uptake (3,4). Several studies have shown that Rubisco activity is depressed in leaves developed in elevated C_a (3,4,5). Under conditions where Rubisco activity is limiting to photosynthesis, this will partially or wholly offset the gain from decreased photorespiration. The effect of decreased Rubisco activity should be of particular significance at low temperatures, where the gain from decreased photosynthesis will be smallest (2,4). Conversely thought, it has also been argued that the decrease in photorespiratory losses resulting from rising C_a may be offset by an increase in photorespiration resulting from the projected concurrent rise in mean temperature (6). Evidence of decreased Rubisco quantities and activities has come largely from controlled environment studies where decrease could be an artefact of pot-size restricting the development of below-ground sinks for photosynthate (4). Growth of plants in elevated CO_2 has frequently been reported to result in increased leaf carbohydrate concentrations, increasing the likelihood of end-product inhibition (3,4). Any factor suppressing photosynthetic capacity may be expected to increase the probability of photoinhibition, and thus elevated C_a, particularly when coupled with supra-optimal temperatures may be expected to promote photoinhibition.

This study utilises a mechanistic model of leaf photosynthesis to examine the potential quantitative significance of the interaction of rising C_a and temperature on leaf

N. Murata (ed.), Research in Photosynthesis, Vol. IV, 811–817.

photosynthesis. Predictions are compared to experimental measurements in which plants have been grown either in elevated C_a in the field for extended periods or from seed in controlled environments, to examine the interaction of low temperature with elevated C_a. Three questions are addressed. 1) To what extent will increase in C_a modify the response of leaf photosynthetic CO_2 uptake (A) to temperature. 2) Is the decrease in photosynthesis at sub-optimal temperatures predicted for plants grown at elevated C_a, realised in practice? 3) Is photoinhibition accentuated in plants grown in the field at elevated C_a for long-periods.

2. METHODS

2.1 Model: Understanding of the effects of rising C_a and temperature on the rate of leaf photosynthesis has been effectively incorporated into the mathematical model of Farquhar et al. (7), and subsequent models developed from its principles (3,8,9). These models of steady-state leaf photosynthesis are centred upon the kinetics of the reactions catalysed by Rubisco, and encapsulate the primary mechanism by which the photosynthetic process responds to changes in intercellular CO_2 concentration, i.e. RubP carboxylation/oxygenation. Details of the mathematical model used here have been published elsewhere (4).

Parameters, except where stated otherwise, were as given previously (2). These parameters are assumed to represent an average for healthy C_3 mesophytes. To examine the effects of variation in temperature, rate constants and solubilities were recalculated here, relative to their values at 25°C, as were the solubilities of CO_2 and O_2 (2). In comparisons of predictions with measurements, in vivo maximum velocity of carboxylation and electron transport rate were calculated from light and c_i responses determined for the same populations of leaves (9). Stomatal conductance is affected independently by C_a. For a range of C_3 species stomatal conductance appears to interact with CO_2 uptake to maintain an intercellular CO_2 concentration (C_i) which is a constant proportion of the ambient concentration at a given leaf-air water vapour concentration deficit, assumed here to be 0.7 (2,4). It was assumed that the intercellular O_2 concentration did not differ significantly from that of the atmosphere (210 mol mol^{-1}). Jordan & Ogren (10) provide data on the response of the kinetic constants of Rubisco (K_c, K_o, V_{cmax}) to temperature. Activation energies determined from these plots (2) were used in preference to those of Farquhar et al. (7). The quantum yield of CO_2 uptake (ø) was estimated as the predicted initial slope of the response of A to absorbed photon flux (2).

2.2 Plant material, photosynthetic gas exchange and chlorophyll fluorescence: Plants of Scirpus olneyi growing on a Maryland tidal marsh were exposed, over three consecutive years to a CO_2 concentration elevated to ca. 680 mmol mol^{-1} via 10 open-top chambers, ten further chambers were maintained at current atmospheric concentrations (11). Crops of Gossypium hirsutum cv. Delta Pine 77 grown with sub-soil irrigation at Maricopa in Arizona and were exposed to a CO_2 concentration elevated to 550 μmol mol^{-1} from germination to harvest. CO_2 concentration was controlled via four free-air CO_2 enrichment (FACE) rings within the crop, four further rings provided controls (12). Details of the experimental design and exposure systems are described elsewhere (11,12). Plants of *Triticum aestivum* cv. Yecora Rojo, were grown in controlled CO_2 environments (E15HL, Conviron, Winnipeg) at 360 and 700 μmol mol^{-1} of CO_2 in air, for control and elevated treatments, respectively. Temperatures were 24°C during the 12 h day and 20°C at night. Photon flux was varied in a pseudo-diurnal pattern, giving 2000 μmol m^{-2} s^{-1} at mid-day. In a second experiment temperatures were 14/10°C day/night.

The responses of leaf photosynthesis to intercellular CO_2 concentration (c_i) and leaf temperature were determined in a semi-closed gas exchange system (MPH-1000, Campbell

Scientific). The maximum quantum yields of CO_2 concentration and ratio of variable to maximal fluorescence of "dark-adapted" tissues were measured as described previously, using portable chlorophyll fluorimeters (PSM, BioMonitor AS, Umeå, Sweden; PEA, Hansatech, King's Lynn, UK) (13).

3. RESULTS AND DISCUSSION

Fig. 1 illustrates generalised responses of light-saturated rates of leaf CO_2 uptake (A_{sat}) to temperature at CO_2 concentrations of 350 and 700 μmol mol^{-1}, predicted by the model of leaf photosynthesis. Rates show little difference at 0°C, but at 30°C, A at 700 μmol mol^{-1} is ca. double the value at a C_a of 350 μmol mol^{-1}. Maximum velocities of carboxylation (V_{max}) and electron transport rate (J_{max}) were calculated from the responses of A to intercellular CO_2 concentration (c_i) and to photon flux (Q) for the fourth leaf of wheat. These values were then used in the model to calculate temperature response curves of A which were compared to the actual measurements for the same population of wheat leaves (Fig. 2). The close fit of the predictions to the measured rates, at least between 10 and 30 °C, suggests that the assumptions of the model, and the values used to describe the thermal behaviour of the kinetic constants, are adequate for the range of conditions simulated.

When the quantity of active Rubisco is rate-limiting, any loss of activity must depress the rate of CO_2 uptake. A survey of studies of the effects of elevated C_a on photosynthesis, suggest that, on average, a doubling of C_a leads to a decrease in Rubisco activity of 15 - 20% (4). However loss of activity varied greatly between experiments and species, with reports ranging from no change to a 40% loss in activity (4). Fig. 1 illustrates the effect of decreases in V_{max}, on photosynthesis at different temperatures. V_{max}, which represents the maximum velocity of Rubisco *in vivo* is decreased by 20 and 40%, to simulate the average and the extreme of decreases that have been observed. When leaves grown and measured at 350 μmol mol^{-1} are compared to hypothetical leaves in which growth at 700 μmol mol^{-1} is assumed to have resulted in a 20% decrease in Rubisco activity, the simulation suggests that leaves in the doubled CO_2 atmosphere would show a lower photosynthetic rate at leaf temperatures below 14°C (Fig. 1). If acclimation is assumed to result in a 40% loss of activity, then rates would be lower than in leaves grown in the current atmosphere at leaf temperatures, below 23°C (Fig. 1). However, at 30°C and above these leaves will show a substantially higher A_{sat}, despite lower activities of Rubisco (Fig. 1). Lower rates at low temperatures despite a doubling of C_a result because photorespiration accounts for only a small fraction of carbon flow at low temperatures. Thus the gain resulting from a partial suppression of photorespiration at low temperatures is small and insufficient to offset the loss resulting from the decrease in carboxylation efficiency. Is this prediction realised when plants are actually grown at low temperatures?

Fig. 3 illustrates measurements of A_{sat} for wheat leaves grown at 10/14°C and in 360 or 700 μmol mol^{-1} of CO_2 in air. When measured at 700 μmol mol^{-1} the leaves grown in 360 μmol mol^{-1} show substantially increased rates at all temperatures, by comparison to measurements of the same leaves at 360 μmol mol^{-1}. However, A_{sat} for leaves grown and measured at 700 μmol mol^{-1} were not significantly higher at leaf temperatures of 10 - 20°C than in leaves grown and measured at 360 μmol mol^{-1} (Fig. 3). Whilst this fails to demonstrate the lower rates predicted from the model, it does illustrate the potential of decreased Rubisco activities to eliminate any increase in photosynthesis due to elevated C_a in cool climates or during the colder periods of growing seasons.

Fig. 4 illustrates the predicted response of the maximum quantum yield of CO_2 uptake (ø) to leaf temperature at three CO_2 concentrations. Because the solubility of, and the specificity of Rubisco for, CO_2 relative to O_2 decreases with temperature (10), the proportion of ATP and NADPH diverted into photorespiratory metabolism will increase with temperature (2,4).

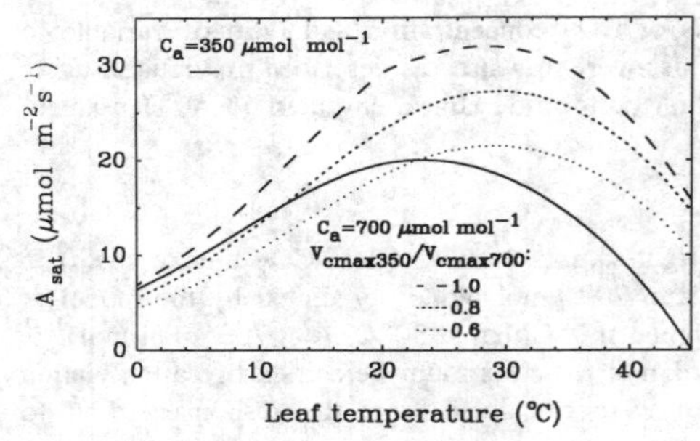

FIGURE 1. The si mulated response of CO_2 uptake of leaves (A) to leaf temperature at CO_2 concentrations in air (C_a) of 350 and 700 μmol mol^{-1}. To simulate the effect of a decrease in Rubisco activity, for a C_a of 700 μmol mol^{-1}, the maximum velocity of carboxylation has been reduced by 20% and by 40%, $V_{cmax700}/V_{cmax350}$ =0.8 and =0.6, respectively.

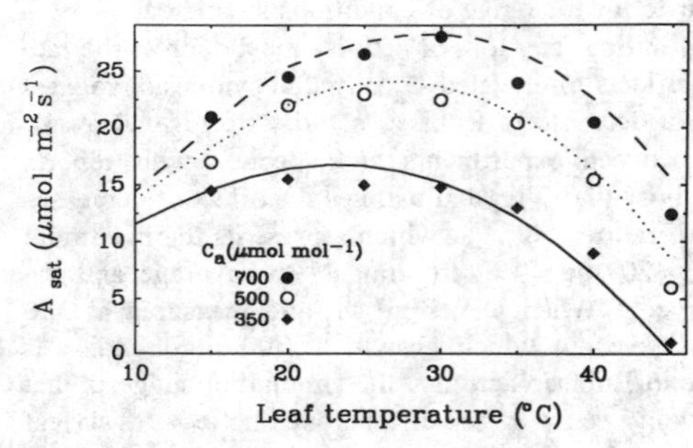

FIGURE 2. Lines indicate the model simulated responses of light saturated photosynthetic CO_2 uptake (A_{sat}) and points the measured responses to variation in leaf temperature, for the 3rd leaf of wheat grown at 20/24°C, a maximum photon flux of 2000 μmol m^{-2} s^{-1}. Each point is the mean of 3 measurements.

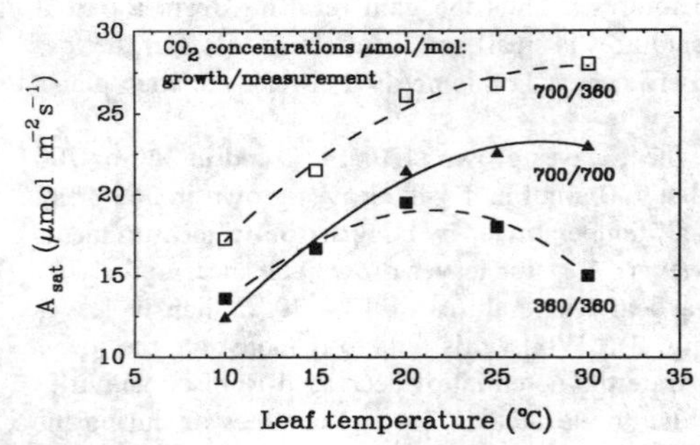

FIGURE 3. The measured response of light saturated CO_2 uptake (A_{sat}) of leaves to leaf temperature. Squares illustrate the mean response of leaves grown at 360 μmol mol^{-1} to temperature when measured at CO_2 concentrations in air of 360 (closed squares) and 700 μmol mol^{-1} (open squares). Triangles indicate the response for leaves grown and measured in a C_a of 700 μmol mol^{-1}. All data are for the 3rd leaf of wheat plants grown at 10/14°C. Each point is the mean of 3 measurements.

Since, by definition, CO_2 uptake on the initial linear phase of the light response curve of photosynthesis is light-limited, any diversion of ATP or NADPH away from photosynthesis will depress the quantum yield. This has often been observed in C_3 species (14). Increase in CO_2 concentration to 700 μmol mol^{-1} is insufficient to completely inhibit photorespiration, but is sufficient to decrease the sensitivity of ø to temperature. This simulation predicts that at 28°C, ø would rise from 0.060 at 350 μmol mol^{-1} to 0.078 at 700 μmol mol^{-1}. These values agree closely with the experimental points obtained for shoots of Scirpus olneyi grown and measured at 700 and at 350 μmol mol^{-1}(13). When strictly light limited, the rate of CO_2 fixation will be limited by the rate of regeneration of RubP and will be independent of Rubisco activity. Changes described as "acclimation" or "down-regulation" (reviewed 4) in the photosynthetic apparatus leaves developed in elevated CO_2 concentrations would only decrease photosynthetic potential at or near to light saturation, as yet there is no evidence of any mechanism of acclimation that could offset the increase in quantum yield predicted for elevated C_a (4). This has important implications for shade environments, particularly in the tropics, and for the lower layers of dense canopies. If the maximum quantum yield is increased by elevated C_a, but leaf respiration unaffected, then it follows that the light compensation point of photosynthesis will decline, increasing the range of shade habitats that C_3 plants could colonise.

Many studies have shown that exposure of leaves of crops and other plants to high light levels in the field induces a decrease in the photochemical efficiency of photosystem II. These leaves show a decrease in the maximum quantum yield of photosynthesis, and some decrease in photosynthetic rate at all light levels (15). Since these decreases in photochemical efficiency are reversible, within 2-3 hours, it seems likely that this form of photoinhibition results from the formation of additional quenchers of excitation energy within the photosynthetic apparatus, protecting against the formation of oxidising radicals which would otherwise produce damage and a more permanent decrease in photosynthetic efficiency. This readily reversible form of photoinhibition is amplified under conditions where photosynthetic C-metabolism is inhibited (15). Plants grown in elevated CO_2 commonly show marked increases in leaf soluble and insoluble carbohydrate concentrations (4). In the longer term this leads to the possibility of end-product inhibition of photosynthesis, through the sequestering of stromal and cytosolic inorganic phosphate (P_i) into intermediates of carbohydrate metabolism outside of the Calvin cycle (9). This in turn will lead to P_i-limitation of photosynthesis. Under these conditions it may be expected that photoinhibition would be increased. Figs. 5 and 6 show that in two field studies in which CO_2 concentration has been elevated for prolonged periods, the maximum photochemical efficiency of PSII, as indicated by the fluorescence parameter F_v/F_m showed no greater decrease in plants grown at elevated C_a than in plants grown at the current C_a. In the case of Scirpus olneyi a slight increase is indicated, suggesting increased protection against photoinhibition (Fig. 5). Since plant water status is known to affect the incidence of photoinhibition (15), it is possible that decreased water loss at elevated C_a (4) may afford some protection against photoinhibition. In both cases air temperatures were supra-optimal for photosynthesis, conditions expected to promote photoinhibition (15).

The simulations and measurements made here add support to the hypothesis that there is a strong positive interaction between rising CO_2 and temperature, and that the large increases in leaf photosynthesis in an elevated CO_2 atmosphere will occur under conditions of high temperature. Both model predictions and a limited set of measurements suggest that elevated C_a will increase the temperature optimum of A_{sat} and decrease the rate of decline in maximum quantum yield of CO_2 uptake with increasing temperature. In environments where current temperatures are below the present temperature optimum of leaf photosynthesis, rising temperatures will amplify the stimulatory effect of increased C_a rather than act in the

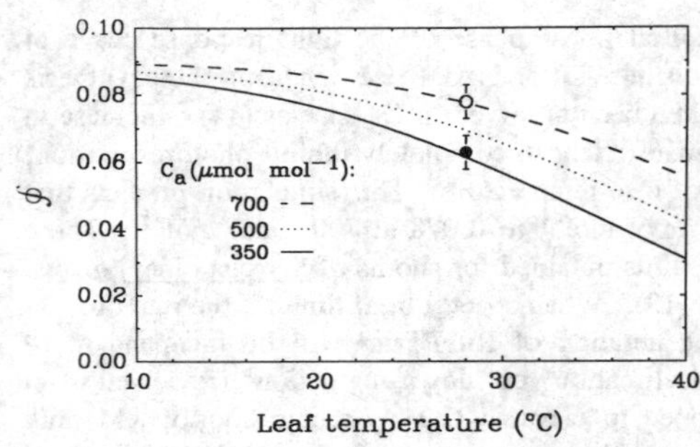

FIGURE 4. The simulated maximum quantum yield of CO_2 uptake (ø) as a function of temperature for three atmospheric CO_2 concentrations (C_a). The two points indicate the mean ø (± 1se) of Scirpus olneyi leaves grown and measured in 350 (closed symbol) and 680 μmol mol^{-1} (open symbol)(13).

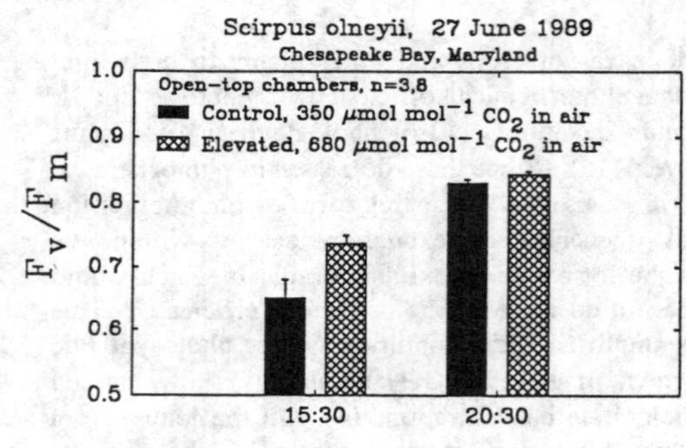

FIGURE 5. The maximum efficiency of photosystem II, as indicated for the ratio of variable to maximal photosystem II fluorescence (F_v/F_m), for shoots of Scirpus olneyi growing in open top chambers on the Chesapeake Bay, Maryland. Measurements were made on a day with clear skies, a mid-day photon flux of 1900 μmol m^{-2} s^{-1} and air temperature of 38°C. Values are given for a point in the early afternoon when decrease in F_v/F_m was greatest and in the evening when F_v/F_m had fully recovered. Each bar is the mean of 24 shoots.

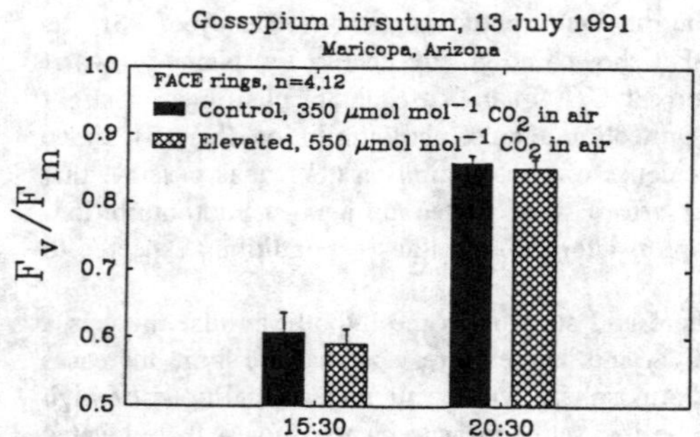

FIGURE 6. As for Figure 5, but for leaves of Gossypium hirsutum grown in field free-air CO_2 enrichment rings from germination, at Maricopa, Arizona. Measurements were made at the beginning of boll formation on a day with clear skies, a maximum photon flux of 2200 μmol m^{-2} s^{-1} and an air temperature of 40°C. Each bar is the mean of 48 measurements.

converse manner, as had been suggested by Eamus (6). Acclimatory response, in the form of decreased Rubisco activity, will offset part of this increase, and could lead to lower rates of photosynthesis in cold environments, despite decreased photorespiration. This however, does not take account of the possibility that photosynthesis in an elevated CO_2 atmosphere could be further inhibited by an increase in the occurrence of P_i-limited photosynthesis. Light limited photosynthesis is increased by elevated C_a, and as yet no mechanism which could counteract this has been identified. Finally, whilst elevated CO_2 could be expected to promote photoinhibition, particularly at supra-optimal temperatures, no evidence to support this was obtained in measurements made within two long-term field studies of the effects of growth at elevated C_a.

ACKNOWLEDGEMENTS

This research was performed in part under the auspices of the U.S. Department of Energy under contract No. DE-AC02-76CH00016.

REFERENCES

1 Watson, R.T., Rodhe, H., Oescheger, H. and Siegenthaler, U. (1990) in Climate Change. The IPCC Scientific Assessment (J.T. Houghton, G.J. Jenkins & J.J. Ephraums, eds.),pp. 1-40, Cambridge University Press, Cambridge
2 Long, S.P. (1991) Plant Cell Env. 14, 729-739.
3 Stitt, M. (1991) Plant Cell Env. 14, 741-762.
4 Long, S.P. and Drake, B.G. (1992) in Topics in Photosynthesis, vol. 12, N.R. Baker and H. Thomas, eds., pp. 69-103, Elsevier, Amsterdam.
5 Bowes, G. (1991) Plant Cell Env. 14, 795-806.
6 Eamus, D. (1991) Plant Cell Env. 14, 843-852.
7 Farquhar, G.D., von Caemmerer, S. and Berry, J.A. (1980) Planta 149, 78-90.
8 Evans, J.H. and Farquhar, G.D. (1992) in Modeling Crop Photosynthesis - from Biochemistry to Canopy, K.J. Boote and R.S. Loomis, eds., pp. 1-15, Crop Science Society of America, Madison
9 Harley, P.C. and Tenhunen, J.D. (1992) in Modeling Crop Photosynthesis - from Biochemistry to Canopy, K.J. Boote and R.S. Loomis, eds., pp. 17-39, Crop Science Society of America, Madison
10 Jordan, D.B. and Ogren, W.L. (1984) Planta 161, 308-313.
11 Curtis, P.S., Drake, B.G., Leadley, P.W., Arp, W.J. and Wigham, D.F. (1989) Oecologia 78, 20-29.
12 Hendrey, G.R., ed. (1992) FACE: Free-Air CO_2 Enrichment for Plant Research in the Field, in press, CRC Press, Boca Raton.
13 Long, S.P. and Drake, B.G. (1991) Plant Physiol. 96, 221-226.
14 Berry, J. and Björkman, O. (1980) Annu. Rev. Plant Physiol. 31, 491-543.
15 Ögren, E. and Öquist, G. (1988) in Applications of Chlorophyll Fluorescence, Lichtenthaler, H.K., ed., pp. 165-172, Kluwer, Dordrecht.

EFFECTS OF CLIMATIC CHANGE ON THE PHOTOSYNTHESIS, BIOMASS PRODUCTION AND YIELD OF FIELD-SOWN WHEAT (Triticum aestivum L.) AND MEADOW FESCUE (Festuca pratensis Hudson) DURING FINNISH GROWING SEASON.

Kaija Hakala, Eeva-Maria Tuhkanen and Timo Mela,
Agric. Res. Centre of Finland, Inst. of Crop and Soil Sci., SF-31600 Jokioinen, Finland.

1. INTRODUCTION

According to current predictions, the climate will be warmer and CO_2 levels higher in the future, due to compositional changes in the earth's atmosphere. The present investigation was undertaken in order to evaluate the impact of these changes on wheat and meadow fescue. The experimental design allowed for the evaluation of the impact of elevated temperatures and CO_2 both together and separately. The experimental crops were sown directly in the field, in normal sward density. An especially interesting aspect of the present investigation was the exploration of the effect of the Finnish growing season, which is characterized by an extremely long photoperiod, on the growth of the crops at higher temperatures and elevated CO_2 levels.

2. MATERIALS and METHODS

The Swedish spring wheat variety "Polkka" and the Finnish meadow fescue variety "Kalevi" were sown in rows in an east-west direction on an outdoor field (sowing date 14th of May) as well as in a greenhouse built for the experiments on the same field (sowing date 29th of April). After sprouting, the sprouts were enclosed by open-top chambers, measuring 3 m in diameter and 2 m high, so that half of the chamber area was covered with wheat and the other half with meadow fescue. The chambers were constructed of corrugated colourless acrylate (PAR light transmission 90 %) and were ventilated by overhead fans. There were two replicates for each treatment.

N. Murata (ed.), Research in Photosynthesis, Vol. IV, 819–822.

The temperatures inside the greenhouse were constantly kept 3 degrees above outside temperatures. Of the 4 chambers situated inside the greenhouse, two were constantly fed with CO_2 to maintain the CO_2 level at 700 ppm. The fans mixed the CO_2 gas with the chamber air. The other two chambers not fed with CO_2 had average CO_2 levels ranging from 350 to 400 ppm. The same CO_2 experiments were performed in outdoor conditions in the field. The field was partly covered with the same plastic as that used in the construction of the greenhouse (EVA sheet, 60 % PAR light transmission no UV-B transmission) to correspond with the radiation and rainfall conditions of the greenhouse.

The photosynthesis of wheat was measured directly in the field and in the greenhouse with a portable IRGA (LCA-3, ADC Company, England). The measurements were performed, when the light intensity exceeded 800 $\mu E\ m^{-2}s^{-1}$, which is the saturating light level for wheat. Biomass samples were taken 3-4 times from each treatment throughout the growing season. The grain yield harvested at the end of the growing season is reported at 15 % moisture level. In order to evaluate the chamber effect, measurements were made also from plots of equal size, but without chambers.

3. RESULTS and DISCUSSION

3.1. Meadow fescue

The elevated CO_2 levels increased the yield of meadow fescue in the first cut (approximately 2 months after sowing) by 19 % at +3°C temperatures and 6 % at ambient temperatures (Table 1). The yield at +3°C temperatures with elevated CO_2 was 16 % more than that at ambient temperatures with elevated CO_2. After the second cut, carried out one month after the first one, the yield of meadow fescue was markedly higher in the field at ambient temperatures than at +3°C temperatures (Table 1). The restricted growth at +3°C temperatures may have been due to the excessive temperatures (30-35°C) before the second cut of the greenhouse material. Elevated CO_2 levels also failed to increase the yield at +3°C temperatures before the second cut, even though elevated CO_2 levels at ambient temperatures increased the yield considerably (20 %). The number of tillers (main shoots)$^{-1}$ increased from cut to cut, but there was no correlation between above ground biomass yield and tiller number. However, at both +3°C temperatures and at ambient temperatures, the number of tillers was greater in the chambers with elevated CO_2 than in those with ambient CO_2 (Table 1).

TABLE 1. Meadow fescue biomass yield in kg ha^{-1} at elevated (+3°C) and ambient temperatures and at elevated (+CO_2, 700 ppm) and ambient (A) CO_2 levels. C=plot without chamber. Number of tillers (main shoot)$^{-1}$ in parenthesis.

	elevated temperatures			ambient temperatures		
	A	+CO_2	C	A	+CO_2	C
1. cut	3101	3834	3085	3013	3218	2342
	(2.4)	(3.1)	(3.1)	(3.1)	(4.1)	(3.8)
2. cut	3612	3426	2900	3975	4968	3783
	(2.8)	(3.4)	(3.9)	(4.9)	(5.2)	(3.9)

3.2. Wheat

3.2.1. Wheat photosynthesis

Wheat photosynthesis appeared to be equally efficient both at the 5-6 leaf stage and at the end of flowering (Table 2). The lower general photosynthesis at +3°C temperatures after flowering was probably due to lower ambient temperatures (23°C) at the time of measurement, the ambient temperature having been 31-35°C during measurement at the 5-6 leaf stage. Both at 5-6 leaf stage and at the end of flowering, the photosynthesis was higher in chambers with elevated CO_2 levels than in those with ambient CO_2 levels. The increases in net photosynthesis in elevated CO_2 levels were 24 % at the 5-6 leaf stage and 18.4 % at the end of flowering at +3°C temperatures, and 11.9 % and 28 % at corresponding stages at ambient temperatures (Table 2).

TABLE 2. Net photosynthesis (Pn, μmol CO^2 $m^{-2}s^{-1}$) of wheat at elevated (+3°C) and ambient temperatures and at elevated (+CO_2, 700 ppm) and ambient (A) CO_2 levels at 5-6 leaf stage (5-6ls) and at the end of flowering (eofl) C=plot without chamber. 5 leaves were measured from each treatment.

	elevated temperatures			ambient temperatures		
	A	$+CO_2$	C	A	$+CO_2$	C
5-6ls	15.6	20.5	16.9	19.3	21.9	17.4
eofl	13.1	16.0	12.3	17.8	24.6	20.3

3.2.2. Shoot biomass measurements

The shoot biomass at the 5-6 leaf stage was at the the same level both at ambient and +3°C temperatures. However, at the end of flowering the shoot biomass was markedly higher at +3°C temperatures (Table 3).Elevated CO_2 levels had no clear effect on the biomass accumulation at ambient temperatures, although at +3°C temperatures elevated CO_2 levels resulted in slightly higher shoot weights, especially with reference to the shoot biomass inside the chambers (Table 3). The plots without chambers occasionally showed better photosynthesis and a better biomass accumulation, compared with the chambers with ambient CO_2 levels. Increased CO_2 levels not only compensated for the negative effects of the chamber, but also induced higher photosynthetic rates than in plots without chambers. The higher biomass yield of wheat at elevated temperatures, despite the fact that photosynthesis was higher at ambient temperatures (Tables 2 and 3) highlights the importance of the mutual effect of increased photosynthesis and temperature on growth.

TABLE 3. Biomass production of wheat shoots at elevated (+3°C) and ambient temperatures and at elevated ($+CO_2$, 700 ppm) and ambient (A) CO_2 levels in g dry weight (g DW) $shoot^{-1}$ at 5-6 leaf stage (5-6ls) and at the end of flowering (eofl) C=plot without chamber.

	elevated temperatures			ambient temperatures		
	A	$+CO_2$	C	A	$+CO_2$	C
5-6ls	0.52	0.60	0.57	0.72	0.66	0.62
eofl	2.19	2.51	2.53	1.62	1.66	1.69

3.2.3. Grain yield

The grain yield of wheat was about 15 % higher with elevated CO_2 levels at +3°C temperatures when compared with wheat in chambers with ambient CO_2 levels (6077 kg ha^{-1} at elevated CO_2 and 5356 kg ha^{-1} at ambient CO_2). The higher yield of wheat grown on plots without chambers (6980 kg ha^{-1}), again demonstrates the adverse effects of a chamber.

FIELD PHOTOSYNTHESIS STUDY IN ARCTIC PLANTS: IMPLICATIONS FOR CLIMATE CHANGES

Tatyana V.Gerasimenko,Erik L. Kaipianen, 197376, Komarov Botanical Institute Acad. of Sci., prof. Popov str.2, St.Petersburg, Russia

1. INTRODUCTION

Although the exact effects of doubling CO2- concentration on the global climate are unknown, consensus is growing among climatic modelers that change will be particulary dramatic in the Arctic (Maxwell, 1992, in Chapin et al.,1992)These will include increased air and soil temperature, higher precipitations and also secondary effects prolonged season lenght, later snowmelt, increased minerali zation and nutrient availability as well as released soils carbon and methane pools back to the atmosphere (Chapin et al., 1992). The extent to which climate changes will affect Northern ecosystems depends on physiological response of plants as main green producers. Comprehensive information about photosynthesis and other vital processes as basis- blocks for global predictions must be taken into account. In this respect photosynthesis data of whole ecosystems may be used as integration result of CO2 flux at normal& artificial conditions (Grulke et al.,1990). Results of this study are important for predicting the response of "todays" ecosystems, but new environment will be occupied by new plant communities in the case of species migration& competition.On the other hand species behavior depend on inherent physiological pathways. Also the challenge is to create a bank of photosynthesis data on, as large as possible number of wild species in different zones of the Earth.

2. MATERIALS and METHODS

2.1 The aim of our investigations was to study photosynthesis(P)and respiration (R) in a large number of species at different tundra sites of Russia: Wrangel Island (71 N), Taymir Peninsula (73 N), Khibin (68 N) and Polar Ural (69 N) mountains tundra. Based on results of diurnal and seasonal patterns of P as well as light and temperature responses of P (Gerasimenko & Shvetzova, in Semikhatova ed, 1989); R data and its relationship to growth (Kaipiainen, 1987; Semikhatova et al.,in Chapin et al., 1992), a bank of data on 59 tundra species has been created.

2.2 We used the concept of species- specific passport (ESP) (Gera-

N. Murata (ed.), Research in Photosynthesis, Vol. IV, 823–826.

simenko & Kaipiainen, 1992), that comprises 23 parameters including light and temperature responses of P, maximal values of P; R and pigments content (chlorophyll a+b (Chl) and carotenoids sum (car)) as well as growth R and maintenance R. This approach provides an appreciation of environmental capacity of species and degree of its realization under concrete environmental circumstances.

2.3 Net P was measured in the field by IRGA "Infralit-4" or by LI-COOR 6200 in closed or in a differential system. The compounds of CO_2 gas exchange were estimated by a mathematical model of O. Bykov (Semikhatova ed, 1989). P was elucidated also at elevated (0.6-1.0%) CO_2 in short-term expositions using a radiometric method with $C^{14}O_2$.

3. RESULTS

3.1 All studied species are C3 plants and the range of P rates among them is narrower than in other biomes. Life form of the plant and leaf longevity are the major factors in both cases (normal and elevated CO_2 level) correlated with P rate. Dominants as rule are species with lower Pn, Pp max but they realize their photosynthetical capacity (realization of daily and seasonal maximum) more effectively than other species.

3.2 24 h. diurnal photosynthesis rhythm is substantial adaptation of photosynthesis. The extent of "night" Pn varied among species (10-25%) and reflected both weather conditions and light response of P. Predicting later snowmelt in Arctic may be negative for the "night" carbon gain in June. Dominants of phytocenosisis as rule have low net photosynthesis during a day but maintain substantial rates during the arctic "night" whereas more light-requiring species photosynthesize only during a day were more effective at sunny days. Interspecific differences in plant responses to temperature and light are significant in this respect.

3.3 Plants of arctic tundra combine as features shade (low light compensation point, low photosaturation, very effective CO_2 uptake at low light) and also sun tolerant plants: There may be seen high requirements for light saturation of Pn, Pp in some species. All studied in the Arctic plants have high Pn in spite of the low Chl content and chloroplasts with poorly developed grana. In spite of the simple vertical structure of phytocenosesis arctic species vary considerably in their light requirements so that the expected increase in Arctic cloudiness may cause differential photosynthetic responses among species.

3.4 Maximal values of Chl content varied in the narrow range for example on the Wrangel Island (0.5- 2.9 mg g^{-1} fm) being close to indexes in desert and high mountains plants. Peculiarity of pigment apparatus is manifested itself in the high content of car (0.3-0.6 mg g^{-1} fm) which may be seen as additional light harvesters. The peculiarity of pigment apparatus organization in arctic species is prononced in low values of the ratio light harvesting Chl/ Chl protein complexes1+ Chl pc2 which are mainly close to 1 or lower, as well as in the small size of photosynthetic units, which are 100- 200 molecules (Gerasimenko et al., 1992).

3.5 Also, acclimation to changes to light condition is obviously more complicated as it requires changes of the whole light- absorbing system. Low Chl content in tundra may be explained by the fact that Chl synthesis is costly, because it needs a complicated enzyme system and formation of special proteins that make up the Chl-protein complex.

3.6 Another way of increasing absorption at low light is to make thicker leaves, which many arctic plants do. But this is also costly, again requiring both carbon and nitrogen. In this regard, the comparatively high car synthesis is cheaper than that of Chl.

3.7 Arctic plants are extremely tolerant of low temperature, they must adapt their main metabolic processes (CO2 uptake, metabolism, transport) to low temperature. The mechanisms are apparently the same for P and R: increased number of structural units: mitochondria and sometimes chloroplasts that entailing a substantial nitrogen cost (Chapin et al.,1992) but compensate for the low temperature effect and an increase in protein flexibility, which enables the enzymes to operate rapidly even at low temperature. Tundra plants have a low temperature optimum (10°-15°C) for Pn. Our data from different tundra regions demonstrate that these physiological traits vary considerably among species and relate to both their phytogeographic origin and present habitat requirements (Semikhatova et al., in Chpin et al., 1992). In spite of this during half a season, air temperatures are significantly lower than the optimum for Pn and Pp. Also even low temperature- adapted arctic plants are still temperature- limited most the time of vegetation. Moreover, max temperature at which arctic plants can uptake CO2 is typically 7-10°C higher than the highest ambient temperature in the field where they grow . This reserve is very important in the case of warming. We can assume, that the acclimation to changes in temperature would be comparatively "easier" for arctic plants than the new light conditions.

3.8 The possible increase in ambient temperatures will not greatly increase P rates because CO2 output in the light will also be greater, and arctic plants have no such special features to increase CO2 reassimilation as do C3 desert plants. If ambient temperature stabilizes at higher levels, the cost of maintenance respiration will decrease, and the growth of plants will be prolonged. While the climate is changing, this maintenance cost could increase, for the process of acclimation itself requires energy.

3.9 The high respiratory potential of arctic plants enables them to maintain at low temperature relative growth rates comparable to those of temperate plants growing under much warmer conditions. The high respiratory potential result in a high maintenance respiration (Ivanova & Vaskovsky, 1976; Kaipiainen, 1987; Semikhatova et al.,in Chapin et al., 1992), reduced in some species growth (Tieszen,1978) under warmer conditions, perhaps explaining the restriction of some arctic elements of flora to relatively cold environments.

3.10 There is a plotted connection in plants between R and growth. If the global warming increases of R, it will directly influence the carbon balance. Coefficient of growth respiration does not depend on temperature variation and the amount of assimilates which is necessary for the growth, it is closed to the theoretical maximal values (Penning de Vries et al., 1979; McCree, 1982). At the same time the temperature has a great effect on maintenance respiration. Thus the warming of climate in the North may stimulate the increase of the cost of maintenance respiration during the process of adaptation to higher temperature, and it would cause a disturbance in the carbon balance in plant leading to a negative one.

REFERENCES

1 Chapin F.S. III, Jefferies,R.L., Reynolds,J.F., Shaver,G.R., Svoboda,J. (Editors), (1992). Arctic ecosystems in a changing climate. Amer. Academic Press Inc.: 469.

2 Gerasimenko T.V., Koroleyva,O.V., Filatova,N.I., Popova,J.A. & Kaipiainen,E.L. (1992). Field investigation in pigment apparatus and photosynthesis in plants of the Arctic. Photosynthetica, 26, N1

3 Grulke, N.E., Riechers,G.H., Oechel, W.C., Hjelm, U, and Jaeger, C. (1990). Carbon balance in tussock tundra under ambient and elevated atmospheric CO2. Oecologia 83, pp. 485- 494

4 Ivanova, T.I. and Vaskovsky, M.D. (1976). Respiration of plants of Wrangel Island. Bot. Zh. 68, pp. 1637- 1643 (In Russian)

5 Kaipiainen, E.L. (1987). Influence of ecological conditions on the interdependency between photosynthesis and respiration in production processes in plants. Dissertation, Leningrad: 22

6 McCree K. J. (1982). Maintenance requirements of white clover at high and low growth rates. Crop. Sci. 22, pp.345-351

7 Penning de Vries F.W.T., J.M. Witlage, D. Kremer, (1979). Rates of respiration and of increase in structural dry matter in young wheat, ryegrass and maize plants. Ann. Bot. 44, pp.595- 609.

8 Semikhatova, O.A. (eds) (1989). Ecophysiological investgation of plant photosynthesis and respiration, Nauka, Leningrad, (in Russian).

9 Tieszen,L.L.(eds) (1978). Vegetation and Production Ecology of an Alaskan Arctic Tundra. New York. Ecological studies, 29

THE EFFECT OF ELEVATED CO2 ON PHOTOSYNTHESIS BIOMASS PRODUCTION AND CHLOROPLAST THYLAKOID STRUCTURE OF CROP PLANTS

A. PENNANEN*, V. KEMPPI**, D. LAWLOR*** AND E. PEHU**
* Dept of Plant Biology and ** Dept of Plant Production, University of Helsinki, Viikki SF-00710 Helsinki, Finland, *** AFRC, Rothamsted Exp. Station, Dept of Biochemistry and Physiology, Harpenden UK

1. INTRODUCTION

Enhanced CO2 stimulates the carboxylation reactions catalyzed by Rubisco enzyme. Reviews show that doubling of CO2 concentrations from 330ppm to 650ppm, increases productivity of crop plants clearly (1,2). Enhanced CO2 has been shown to promote net photosynthesis in high temperatures (3,4). In concordance with activated carboxylation, light reactions in the chloroplast thlakoids are also likely to be activated. It has been found though that reactions associated with the thylakoid membranes are sensitive to envrionmental stresses (5). PSII, in particular, appears to be sensitive to stress factors such as high and low temperatures (6,7). Photoinhibition may occur even at moderate light levels if plants suffer simultaneously from other environmental stresses. Very little is known, however, about the effects of enhanced CO2 on light reactions and thylakoid proteins, especially not when coupled with environmental stresses. The aim of the present study was to monitor the adaptive regulation of photosynthesis regarding the functions of Rubisco and some thylakoid proteins under enhanced CO2 and high temperatures.

2. MATERIALS AND METHODS

2.1. Plant material: The elevated CO2 experiment with wheat (Triticum astivum) and barley (Hordeum vulgare) was conducted in Saxil-growth chambers (Rothamsted Exp. Station), one having a CO2 concentration of 350ppm and the other 700ppm. Day and night temperatures were maintained at 20 and 15°C, resp. Plant material for the studies on light reactions with barley and turnip rape (Brassica rapa) was grown in purpose built greenhouse compartments (Dept. of Plant Production, Helsinki) having the same CO2 concentrations as the Saxil-growth chambers. The daily ambient temperatures ranged from 15 to 23°C. In the temperature stress treatment the temperatures ranged from 25 to 30C.
2.2. Photosynthesis measurements: Rate of photosynthesis was measured from the 7th leaf. Net photosynthesis rates were measured using a 6-chamber open-circuit gas-exchange system with automatic data handling (8). Pn was calculated according to Farquhar and Sarhkey (9).
2.3. Rubisco activity: Leaf samples were stored in liquid nitrogen. Internal activity and total activity were measured as described by Gutteridge et al. (10). Soluble protein was determined by SDS-PAGE and Rubisco protein by Laemmli-method (8).
2.4. Ultrastructure and immunogold labelling:For the ultrastructural studies leaf samples were fixed in 2.9% (v/v) glutaraldehyde in 0.1M Na-phosphate buffer, pH 7.2 for 4 hours at room temperature. For immunogold labelling leaf samples were fixed in 1.25% glutaraldehyde. The samples were washed with PB. After dehydration in an ascending

N. Murata (ed.), Research in Photosynthesis, Vol. IV, 827–830.

ethanol concentration series, the samples were embedded in L.R.White resin (Bio-Rad) which was later polymerized at 60°C. Thin sections were picked up onto nickel grids. All incubations described below were done at room temperature. Incubations and washes were done in 25 mM Tris-HCl, pH 8.0, containing 500 mM NaCl and 0.3% (v/v) Tween-20 (TBS-T). Grids were incubated for 10 minutes in TBS-T containing 1% (w/v) BSA (TBS-T-B). Antibodies were against chloroplast thylakoid proteins LHCII, light harvesting protein, and cyt b559. Grids were blotted and incubated for 2 hours in primary antibody diluted 1:50 in TBS-T-B followed by blotting and incubating for 10 minutes in TBS-T-B and four washes in TBS-T-B. After washing, the grids were blotted and immersed for 1.5 hours in Protein A-gold (10nm particle size; Zymed) solution diluted in TBS-T-B. The grids were then blotted and washed four times in TBS-T-B and two times in TBS-T and rinsed in distilled water. The ratios of particle densities were calculated for each migrograph (enlarged 30000x) and averaged to determine the distribution of antigen within the chloroplasts.

2.5. Fluorescence: Fluorescence measurements were done with Bio Monitor PSM MarkII meter. After 30 min incubation in the dark fluorescence emission of the leaf tissue was measured at a light level of 400 umol m-2 s-1 for 10s.

3. RESULTS AND DISCUSSION

3.1. Net photosynthesis: The observed positive effect of elevated CO2 on net photosynthesis is in agreement with previous studies (see Fig.1; 1,2). An acclimation of net photosynthesis to high CO2 conditions was evident from the fact that when measured in high CO2 conditions the net photosynthesis of plants grown in high CO2 was relatively lower than of those grown in low CO2. This is in agreement with the findings of Cure and Acock (2) and Cure et al. (11). The observed reduction in the rate of photosynthesis has been contributed to end product inhibition resulting from enhanced supply of carbohydrates which exceeds the capacity of the sink (12). This was also evident from the electronmicrographs of chloroplasts of barley, which showed a pronounced accumulation of starch indicating deficiencies in translocation.

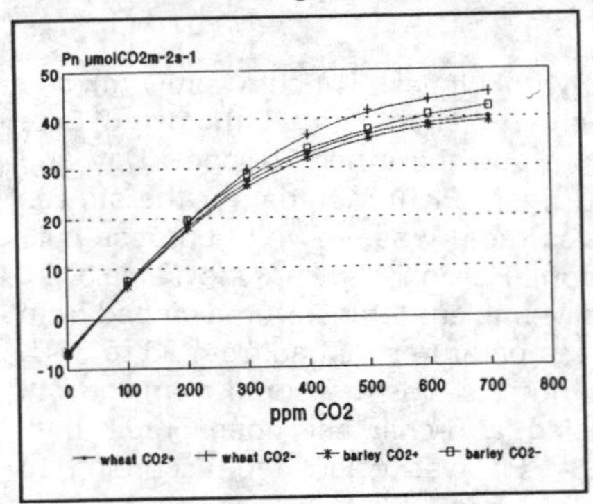

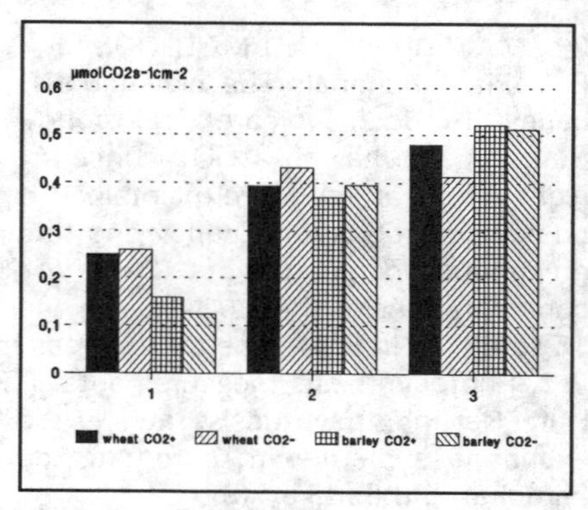

FIGURE 1.a) The effect of CO2 concentration on net photosynthesis in wheat and barley. b) Rubisco activities of wheat and barley, the measurements followed every 7th day.

3.2. Rubisco activity: Internal Rubisco activity increased in both CO2 treatments as the plant matured (Fig.2.). In view of the component characteristics there was no clear association between Rubisco activity with net photosynthesis in either barley or wheat. There are previous reports where the N/C ratio (11,13), enzyme protein concentration and activity of already synthesized proteins has reduced in plants grown in high CO2 conditions (14). However, even a loss of 40% of Rubisco activity has been shown to have no negative effect on net photosynthesis (13).

3.3. Ultrastructure: Ultrastructural changes under enhanced CO2 referred to similar structure as in chloroplasts of older leaves (Fig 2.b.) , where also LCHII is diminished (15). The proportion of appressed thylakoids was initially low in wheat and barley under high CO2 conditions, however, the proportion increased gradually (Figs 2a,2b). The increase in cell number in plants grown in high CO2 reported by Allen (16) was also observed in this study. The increase in cell number could contribute to increased net photosynthesis.

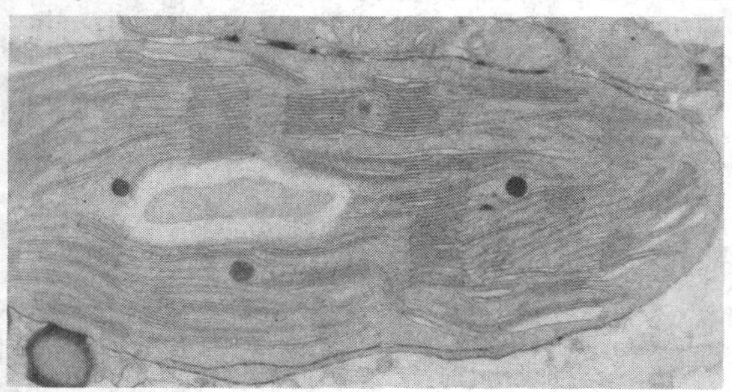

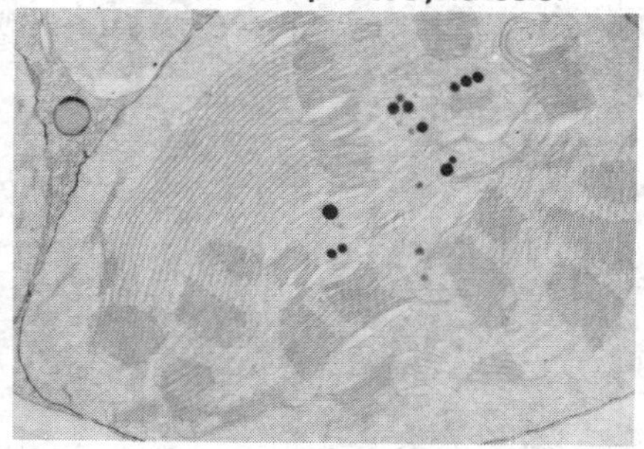

FIGURE 2.a) Chloroplast of barley grown under low CO2 concentration. x 25000 b) Chloroplast of wheat grown under enhanced CO2. x 15000

3.4. Fluorescence: There was a significant decrease in the ratio of variable fluorescence to minimum fluorescence (Fv/Fm Table 1.) in Brassica rapa following high temperature treatment in normal (350ppm) CO2 concentration. This was not observed in the plants grown in high CO2. This indicated in the low CO2 conditions photoinhibition of PSII (6,7), whereas high CO2 concentration seemed to protect PSII (Table 1.). On the contrary in barley only a slight increase was observed in the Fv/Fm ratio in plants grown under enhanced CO2.

TABLE 1. Effect of enhanced CO2 and high temperature (ca. 30°C) on fluorescence emission in barley and turnip rape leaves.

	Fluorescence parameters			
	Fv/Fm	Fm	Fv	Fo
Hordeum control				
normal T -CO2	0.77	1.34	1.1	0.31
High T -CO2	0.73	0.98	0.76	0.27
High T +CO2	0.72	1.06	0.76	0.31
Brassica control				
normal T -CO2	0.78	2.29	1.77	0.51
High T -CO2	0.65	0.91	1.34	0.48
High T +CO2	0.75	1.71	1.28	0.43

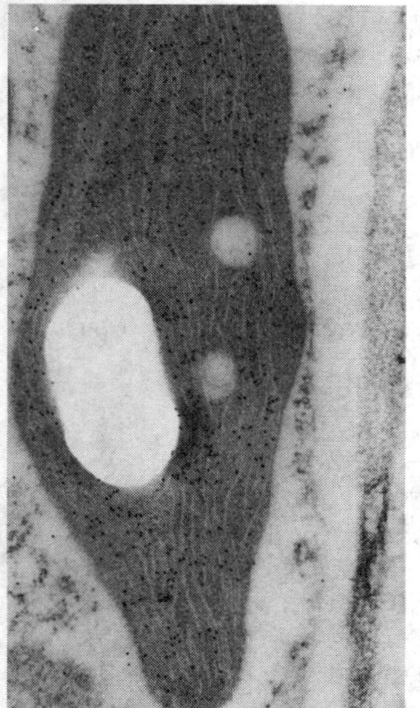

FIGURE 3. Electron micrograph of Brassica (- CO2) labeled with antibody to LHCII.

3.5. Immunogoldlabelling: The labelling of thylakoid proteins indicated significant differences in the organization of these proteins under changing CO2 concentrations. The amount of light harvesting protein LHCII was doubled in Hordeum and Brassica under low CO2 (Fig.3. Table 2). The ratio of cyt b559 (part of the PSII reaction centre) to LHCII was significantly lower in Brassica grown under low CO2 conditions. This further indicated photoinhibition of PSII in Brassica under high temperatures. Contrary to the low CO2 concentration the enhanced CO2 did not result in significantly low ratio of gold labelled cyt b559 to LHCII. The observed changes under high CO2 conditions did not result in reduction in the PSII reactions. These results support the postulations that photoinhibition depends directly on the rate of light absorbtion by the PSII light-harvesting antenna (Fig 4.; 17).

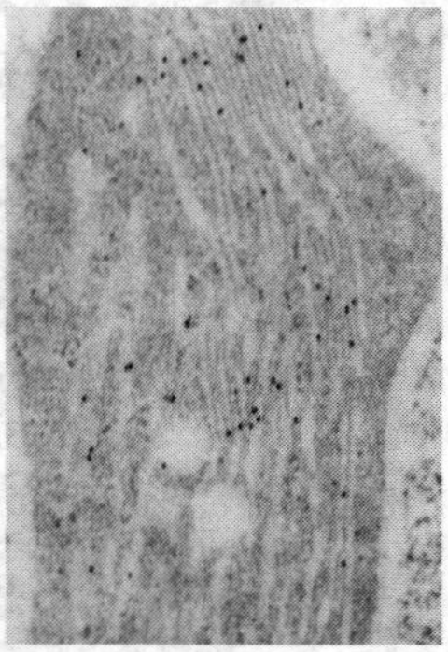

TABLE 2. Density of gold particles in chloroplasts in high and low CO2 concentrations.

plant	antiserum	density (mean) - CO2	density (mean) + CO2
Hordeum	LHCII	203	120
	cyt b559	83	40
Brassica	LHCII	313	147
	cyt b559	49	110

FIGURE 4. Electron micrograph of Brassica (+ CO2) labeled with antibody to LHCII.

Immunogoldlabelling method is not qantitatively as reliable as the chlorophyll protein determination by SDS-PAGE. However, the chloroplast ultrastructure in Hordeum and Brassica plants grown under enhanced CO2 were similar to that of chloroplasts in older leaves where also a reduction of LHCII protein was observed (15).
In conclusion high CO2 concentration appears to provide protection to the thylakoid reactions in high temperature stress.

REFERENCES

1 Kimball BA (1983) Agronomy J 75: 779-788
2 Cure JD, Acock B (1986) Agric and Forest Meterology 38: 127-145
3 Drake BG, Leadley PW (1991) Plant, Cell and Environment 14:853-860
4 Stitt M (1991) Plant, Cell and Environment 14: 741-762
5 Öquist G (1987) In Progress in Photosynthesis Reseach, J Biggins ed, Vol 4, Martinus Nijhoff Publisher, Dordrecht, pp 1-10
6 Berry JA, Björkman O (1980) Rev Plant Physiol 31: 491-543
7 Aro E-V, Tyystjärvi E, Nurmi A (1990) Physiol Plant 79: 585-592
8 Lawlor DM, Kontturi M, Young AT (1989) J of Experim Bot 40:43-52
9 Farquhar GD, Sharkey TD (1982) Ann Rev Plant Physiol 33: 317-345
10 Gutteridge S, Schmidt CNG (1982) European J of Biochemistry 126: 597-602
11 Cure JD, Rufty TW Jr, Israel DW (1987) Bot Gaz 148: 67-72
12 Arp WJ (1991) Plant, Cell and Environmental 14: 869-875
13 Long SP (1991) Plant, Cell and Environmental 14: 729-739
14 Besford RT, Ludwig LJ, Withers AC (1990) J of Experim Bot 41: 229, 925-931
15 Nurmi A (1985) J of Ultrastructure Res 92:190-200
16 Allen LH Jr (1989) Proceedings of the Plant Growth regulator Society of America. 16th Ann meeting: August 6-10, 1-13
17 Cleland RE, Melis A (1987) Plant, Cell and Environment 10:747-752

PREDICTING CANOPY ASSIMILATION OF RICE IN RESPONSE TO CARBON DIOXIDE CONCENTRATION AND TEMPERATURE.

K. J. BOOTE, N. PICKERING, J. T. BAKER, AND L. H. ALLEN,
UNIV. OF FLORIDA AND USDA-ARS, GAINESVILLE, FL 32611, USA.

This paper illustrates the development of a model to predict canopy assimilation of a rice (*Oryza sativa* L.) crop in response to $[CO_2]$ concentration, temperature, photon flux density (PFD), and leaf area index (LAI). Predictions were compared to canopy assimilation measurements on rice grown in sunlit, controlled-environment chambers under various season-long treatments of $[CO_2]$ and temperature (1, 2). The chambers measured 1 m by 2 m and 1.5 m high. Apparent assimilation was based on the amount of CO_2 injected to maintain $[CO_2]$ at the desired setpoint. Measurements were corrected for leakage. Apparent assimilation, $[CO_2]$, air temperature, and PFD were recorded and averaged at 5-min intervals throughout the day.

Leaf level sensitivity to CO_2 and temperature was added to a canopy assimilation model originally developed for row-crop geometry (3). The model accounts for diffuse and direct beam interception of PFD according to Spitters (4), computes irradiance on sunlit and shaded leaf classes, and computes photosynthesis (P) of sunlit and shaded leaf classes with an asymptotic exponential equation (3):

$$P = Pmax \cdot CO_2max \cdot (1 - e^{(-QE \cdot PFD/(Pmax \cdot CO_2max))})$$

Temperature and CO_2 effects on quantum efficiency (QE) and light-saturated photosynthesis (Pmax) are computed using eq. 16.60 a,b of Farquhar and von Caemmerer (5), assuming limiting RuBP, and temperature effects on the specificity factor of rubisco for CO_2 versus O_2 (6).

$$CO2QE = 6.225 \cdot (C_i - G^*) / (4 \cdot C_i + 8 \cdot G^*)$$

$$CO2max = 7.179 \cdot (C_i - G^*) / (4 \cdot C_i + 8 \cdot G^*)$$

The equations are scaled to a relative effect of 1.0 at 30 C and 350 vpm CO_2. Actual QE at any given temperature and $[CO_2]$ is equal to CO2QE times 0.0541 mol/mol. Since QE is defined near the light compensation point, C_i was assumed equal to C_a for computing CO2QE. For computing CO2max, a slope of 0.7 was assumed for C_i versus C_a,

N. Murata (ed.), Research in Photosynthesis, Vol. IV, 831–834.

above the CO_2 compensation point (G*). These equations give QE responses to [CO_2] and temperature very comparable to data of Ehleringer and Bjorkman (7).

Because there were no measurements of single leaf Pmax, the canopy assimilation model was used in solution mode, whereby nonlinear regression was used to solve for Pmax and other coefficients. Using this approach, we evaluated the trends in solved values of Pmax and trends in responses to [CO_2] and temperature. For model comparisons, we entered observed LAI, and 5-min averages of [CO_2], air temperature, and PFD measured throughout the day for each chamber. A spherical leaf angle distribution and a scattering coefficient of 0.20 were assumed.

This approach was used to solve for single leaf Pmax and canopy respiration (RESP) for individual rice canopies growing at 160, 250, 330, 500, 660, and 900 vpm CO_2 (Table 1). Values for Pmax increased with increasing [CO_2] at 29 and 60 days after planting (DAP). At both dates, canopy respiration varied threefold, almost proportional to the amount of aerial biomass, for a given date. The respiration term was needed because measured canopy carbon exchange rates included effects of two concurrent CO_2 fluxes: gross photosynthetic uptake by foliage, and CO_2 efflux from respiring plant parts. Subsequently, gross assimilation rates were computed by subtracting respiration from apparent assimilation values.

Table 1. Single leaf Pmax (per unit leaf area), LAI, crop respiration (RESP, per unit land area), and initial slope of CO_2 activation (z) for rice canopies grown at different [CO_2] and measured at 29 and 60 DAP. PVEM is percentage of variation accounted for by the model.

Growth	At 29 DAP				At 60 DAP			
[CO_2]	LAI	Pmax	RESP	PVEM	LAI	Pmax	RESP	PVEM
vpm		umol m^{-2} s^{-1}		%		umol m^{-2} s^{-1}		%
160	2.37	28.3	-6.1	93.6	6.19	17.1	-6.0	88.9
250	3.13	48.7	-10.3	96.4	9.04	16.3	-9.8	92.9
330	3.67	46.1	-11.0	97.0	9.30	21.9	-12.7	92.7
500	4.10	55.4	-12.8	97.7	11.64	29.3	-14.0	96.1
660	4.40	57.6	-18.0	95.7	11.92	28.9	-18.0	95.3
900	4.12	49.4	-18.3	97.6	10.53	27.1	-19.1	96.6
all		49.6		97.7		24.0		95.5
all		54.9	z=0.00808	98.1		29.8	z=0.00507	96.3

Then, we solved for one Pmax value to represent all [CO_2] treatments, with the assumption that CO_2 effects should be accounted for by the CO2QE and CO2max terms. Pmax thus reflects light-saturated rate at 350 vpm CO_2 and 30 C. One solved Pmax was adequate to predict canopy response for all [CO_2] treatments, except at 160 vpm, where the model consistently overestimated assimilation response in high light. Analysis of individual treatments had also shown an increasing trend in the Pmax with increasing [CO_2]. These two features indicated a problem with the assumption that the complete response to [CO_2] can be modeled on the basis of energy limitation only. Electron-transport rate in high light is reportedly inhibited as C_i falls below 300 vpm (8,9). Thus, an asymptotic equation was added to drive Pmax as a function of C_i. This function alternately describes substrate limitation for RuBP regeneration or CO_2 activation of rubisco. The initial slope (z, umol CO_2 m^{-2} s^{-1} $umol^{-1}$ CO_2 $umol^{-1}$ air) is proportional to rubisco activity. This addition improved the model fit for both dates. As defined, 50% "activation" was achieved at a C_i of 86 or 137 vpm CO_2 for 29- or 60-DAP canopies, respectively. Figure 1 illustrates how well predicted canopy assimilation matched the observed values for 160, 330, and 660 vpm CO_2 treatments at 60 DAP.

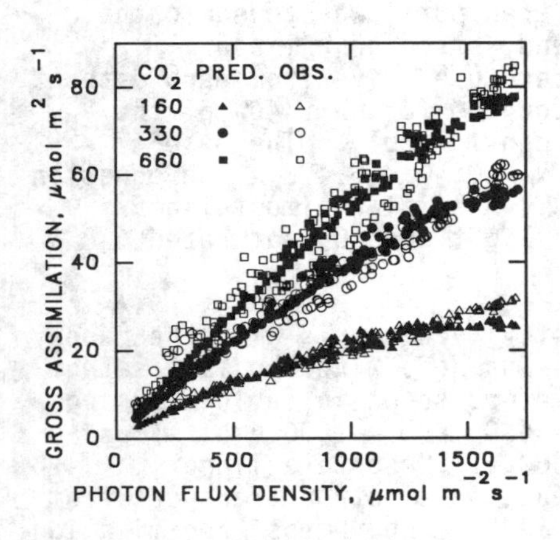

Fig. 1. Gross assimilation vs PFD at 160, 330 and 660 vpm CO_2.

In a second experiment, rice was grown in the controlled-environment chambers at 25, 28, 31, 34, or 37 C day temperature at 660 vpm CO_2, with one chamber at 28 C and 330 vpm CO_2. Single-leaf Pmax and canopy respiration were solved using the same approach. Temperature and CO_2 effects on QE and CO_2max are already built into the equations, but without a temperature effect on electron transport capacity <u>per se</u>. Rice canopies at 17 and 60 DAP showed a trend for Pmax to increase from low to high temperature (Table 2). Solving for a single Pmax to

Table 2. Single leaf Pmax, LAI, canopy respiration (RESP), and initial slope of CO_2 activation (z) for rice canopies grown at various air temperatures and measured at 17 and 60 DAP. PVEM defined in Table 1.

Growth Temp|CO_2	At 17 DAP LAI	Pmax	RESP	PVEM	At 60 DAP LAI	Pmax	RESP	PVEM
C vpm		umol m^{-2} s^{-1}		%		umol m^{-2} s^{-1}		%
25	0.51	21.8	-6.0	80.0	5.57	18.9	-17.0	93.0
28(330)	0.76	14.7	-4.1	72.9	6.84	23.3	-12.4	89.5
28(660)	1.23	16.5	-9.5	94.1	7.46	24.1	-15.2	95.3
31	1.28	20.8	-8.5	90.8	8.77	23.0	-19.6	95.0
34	1.49	34.1	-10.6	93.3	7.53	24.7	-17.7	94.4
37	1.01	22.0	-9.0	92.9	6.63	39.6	-15.7	97.0
all		21.7		88.0		24.4		92.7
all (z*)		22.3		88.7		24.6		92.7
all (z*,temp#)		21.0		91.0		24.0		94.4

* The z values were fixed at 0.00840 and 0.01194 for 17 and 60 DAP.
# Includes temperature effect on Pmax: $R = -0.2724 + 0.0424 \cdot TEMP$

represent all treatments for a given date overestimated assimilation at 25 C and underestimated at higher temperatures. Accounting for the initial slopes of activation (z) only improved the fit slightly. Temperature influence on Pmax (electron transport) was added to the model to account for the temperature trend, based on a linear regression of 10 Pmax values versus temperature (five from each date at 660 vpm CO_2). Although the equation accounted for only 40% of the variation in Pmax, the fit was improved considerably. The base temperature of the equation at which Pmax = 0. was 6.4 C. The equation was normalized to a value of 1.0 at 30 C. A similar almost-linear response to temperature was reported for light-and CO_2-saturated photosynthesis of soybean leaves (6).

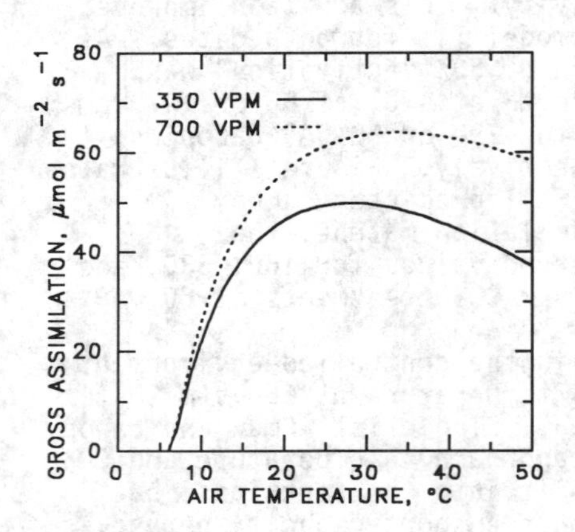

Fig. 2. Gross assimilation vs temperature at 350 or 700 vpm.

Sensitivity analysis with the canopy model was done with the last set of parameters shown in Table 2, using LAI = 5.0, PFD = 1500 umol m^{-2} s^{-1} at midday. Despite a linear increase in electron transport from 6 to 37 C, canopy gross assimilation was within 98% of maximum from 24 to 32 C at 350 vpm CO_2, and from 28 to 40 C at 700 vpm CO_2 (Fig. 2). This shift in temperature optimum with increasing [CO_2] has been suggested previously. The broad temperature optimum for canopy assimilation is consistent with our measurements (e.g., there were no major differences in canopy assimilation from 25 to 37 C).

REFERENCES

1 Baker, J. T., Allen, L. H., Boote, K. J., and Jones, J. W. (1990) Agron. J. 82, 834-840.
2 Baker, J. T., Allen, L. H., and Boote, K. J. (1992) J. Exp. Bot., 43, 959-964.
3 Boote, K. J., and Loomis, R. S. (1991) in Modeling Crop Photosynthesis--From Biochemistry to Canopy (Boote, K. J., and Loomis, R. S., eds.), CSSA Special Publication no. 19, pp. 109-140, American Society of Agronomy, Madison, WI. USA.
4 Spitters, C. J. T. (1986) Agric. For. Meteorol. 38,231-242.
5 Farquhar, G. D., and von Caemmerer, S. (1982) in Physiological Plant Ecology II (Lang, O. L., ed), pp. 549-587, Springer-Verlag, Berlin.
6 Harley, P. C., Weber, J. A., and Gates, D. M. (1985) Planta 165, 249-263.
7 Ehleringer, J., and Bjorkman, O. (1977) Plant Physiol 59, 86-90.
8 Sharkey, T. D., Berry, J. A., and Sage, R. F. (1988) Planta 176, 415-424.
9 Gerbaud, A., and Andre, M. (1980) Plant Physiol. 66, 1032-1036.

CLIMATE CHANGE AND WHEAT PHOTOSYNTHESIS: INTERACTIVE EFFECTS OF CO_2, TEMPERATURE AND NITROGEN NUTRITION

Esteban Delgado, Simon P. Driscoll, Rowan A.C. Mitchell, Valerie J. Mitchell, Martin A. Parry and David W. Lawlor. AFRC IACR, Rothamsted Experimental Station, Biochemistry and Physiology Department, Harpenden, Herts. AL5 2JQ, UK.

1. INTRODUCTION

Atmospheric carbon dioxide is currently increasing at 0.15 Pa (1.5 μmol mol^{-1}) annum^{-1}, and could exceed 70 Pa by 2100. A possible consequence of this increase, and that of other "greenhouse gases", is warmer global temperature of upto 4 °C by 2100.

Because of the kinetic characteristics of the enzyme ribulose 1,5-bisphosphate carboxylase-oxygenase (Rubisco), C_3 plants have poor affinity for CO_2 and photorespire, due to the oxygenase reaction; increased CO_2 will stimulate their photosynthesis and decrease photorespiration. However, the potential for increased rates of carbon assimilation may not be realised by all species because of acclimation which decreases the capacity of photosynthesis to respond to elevated CO_2 (reduction in photosynthetic components) or feedback regulation which decreases the actual rate without decreasing the capacity (1, 2). Response to elevated CO_2 depends on species and upon other environmental factors (1); temperature determines rates of metabolic, physiological and developmental processes, thereby affecting photosynthesis and crop production. Nitrogen profoundly affects the composition and performance of the photosynthetic system.

Winter wheat is a crop of great importance but little is known of its response to elevated CO_2 or of the long-term effects on leaf photosynthetic characteristics of interaction between CO_2, temperature and nitrogen supply. We have analysed the effects of these interacting environmental factors on photosynthetic rate (A) in relation to internal CO_2 concentrations (Ci) and photosynthetic photon fluxes (PPF) throughout growth. The aims: to establish the effects of CO_2, temperature and N on photosynthesis and leaf composition and to determine if acclimation occurs under simulated field conditions.

2. MATERIAL AND METHODS

2.1 Growing conditions: Plants of *Triticum aestivum* L. (var. Mercia) were grown in pots in controlled environment compartments simulating field conditions (natural day length and total integral of radiation) with continuous exposure

N. Murata (ed.), Research in Photosynthesis, Vol. IV, 835–838.

to ambient or elevated CO_2 pressure (35 and 70 Pa) combined factorially with ambient temperature (following outside temperature) or ambient + 4 °C and two nitrogen treatments (total 1.5 g and 0.15 g N per pot over the growing season) in standard nutrient given once or twice weekly.

2.2 Photosynthesis measurements: Three light and CO_2 response curves were determined in a 6-chamber open-circuit gas exchange system for each treatment combination and occasion on fully expanded, attached leaves at 20 °C, water vapour pressure deficit between leaf and chamber atmosphere ca. 1.2 KPa. Intercellular CO_2 (Ci) was calculated from stomatal conductance and assimilation rate (3). An asymptotic curve was fitted to each response curve to give the CO_2 saturated assimilation rate ($Amax_{(Ci)}$), carboxylation efficiency (ϵ), and apparent quantum yield (ϕ) (4). Total soluble protein, RuBisco, chlorophyll and N contents were measured on leaves.

3. RESULTS AND DISCUSSION

This experiment is the first examining the effects on photosynthesis of the interaction of CO_2, N and temperature throughout growth of a winter wheat crop. Photosynthetic capacity (*Amax*), averaged over the experiment, increased by 12% at elevated CO_2 (Fig. 1a and 1b), close to the increase in total plant dry matter (15 %). Apparent quantum yield (Fig. 3a and 3b) also increased but carboxylation efficiency was unchanged (Fig. 2a and 2b) with elevated CO_2. Similar effects of CO_2 have been seen in shorter-term field experiments (5, 6) but contrast with others showing loss of photosynthetic capacity and efficiency (see 2). The increase we observed in *Amax* at elevated CO_2 may be related to improved light capture (larger chlorophyll/protein ratio) and regeneration of RuBP as no change in carboxylation efficiency and Rubisco content was observed (data not shown). The 13 % increase in apparent quantum yield at elevated CO_2 indicates improved light harvesting rather than higher efficiency of electron transport, as there was no difference in photochemical efficiency of photosystem II measured from chlorophyll a fluorescence (data not shown). The crop is normally light limited, therefore investment in light harvesting components would improved light capture, RuBP regeneration and hence photosynthesis.

Nitrogen deficiency decreased *Amax* and ϵ, on average by 21 and 35 % respectively, as expected from the small N content, reflecting the smaller chlorophyll, total soluble protein and Rubisco amounts (decreased by 20-30 %, data not shown) when compared to high N supply. The effect on *Amax* (loss of capacity) and ϵ both early and also late in the crops life when N deficiency accelerated senescence. Apparent quantum yield was not affected.

Ambient +4 °C decreased *Amax* and ϵ but not ϕ. Elevated CO_2 generally has only a small effect on photosynthesis at cool temperatures and larger in the warm (7). In our experiments the effects on photosynthesis of growing plants at +4 °C compared to ambient temperatures changed with time and

N supply. With abundant N, +4 °C decreased carboxylation efficiency over the growing period and the photosynthetic capacity in the early season (Fig. 1b and 2b), with no effect from day 110 onwards. However, at low N, the effect was a decrease in the photosynthetic capacity in the early season and a decrease in both *Amax* and ϕ later, associated with senescence.

Small response of winter wheat to a doubling of current atmospheric CO_2 under conditions very comparable to the field, contrasts to the larger effects of nitrogen supply and +4°C increase in temperature throughout growth. Acclimation is not observed in this plant under these conditions. Effects of N and warmer temperature are related to decreased photosynthetic components resulting from inadequate substrate for protein synthesis and more rapid development of the plant linked to faster senescence, respectively.

CONCLUSIONS

1. Growing winter wheat plants at elevated CO_2 (70 Pa) increased photosynthetic capacity (Amax) of leaves slightly when compared to 35 Pa CO_2, related to greater apparent quantum yield and possibly improved RuBP regeneration.
2. Acclimation, i.e. loss of photosynthetic capacity, under elevated CO_2 did not occur.
3. Temperature 4°C above ambient decreased *Amax* and ϵ compared to ambient, as a consequence of accelerated development and senescence.
4. Deficient N supply decreased *Amax* and ϵ by reducing the amounts of chlorophyll and soluble and Rubisco protein, it decreased the reponse to CO_2 substantially.
5. Elevated CO_2 did not interact with temperature or N supply in affecting photosynthesis.
6. Under conditions comparable to U.K. field, winter wheat may benefit by 15% in photosynthesis and dry matter accumulation from a doubling of CO_2; this will be offset completely by temperatures 4°C above ambient.

REFERENCES

1 Lawlor, D.W. and Mitchell, R.A.C. (1991) Plant, Cell and Environment, **14**, 807-18.

2 Stitt, M. (1991) Plant, Cell and Environment, **14**, 741-762.

3 Farquhar, G.D. and Sharkey, T.D. (1982) Ann. Rev. Plant Physiol. **33**, 317-45.

4 Jacob, J., and Lawlor, D.W. (1991) J. Experimental Botany, **42** (241), 1003-1011.

5 Cambell, W.J., Allen, L.H. and Bowes, G. (1988) Plant Physiology, **88**,1310-16.

6 Havelka, U.D., Wittenbach and Boyle M.G. (1984) Crop Science, **24**, 1163-1168.

7 Sage, R.F. and Sharkey, T.D. (1987) Plant Physiology, **84**, 658-664.

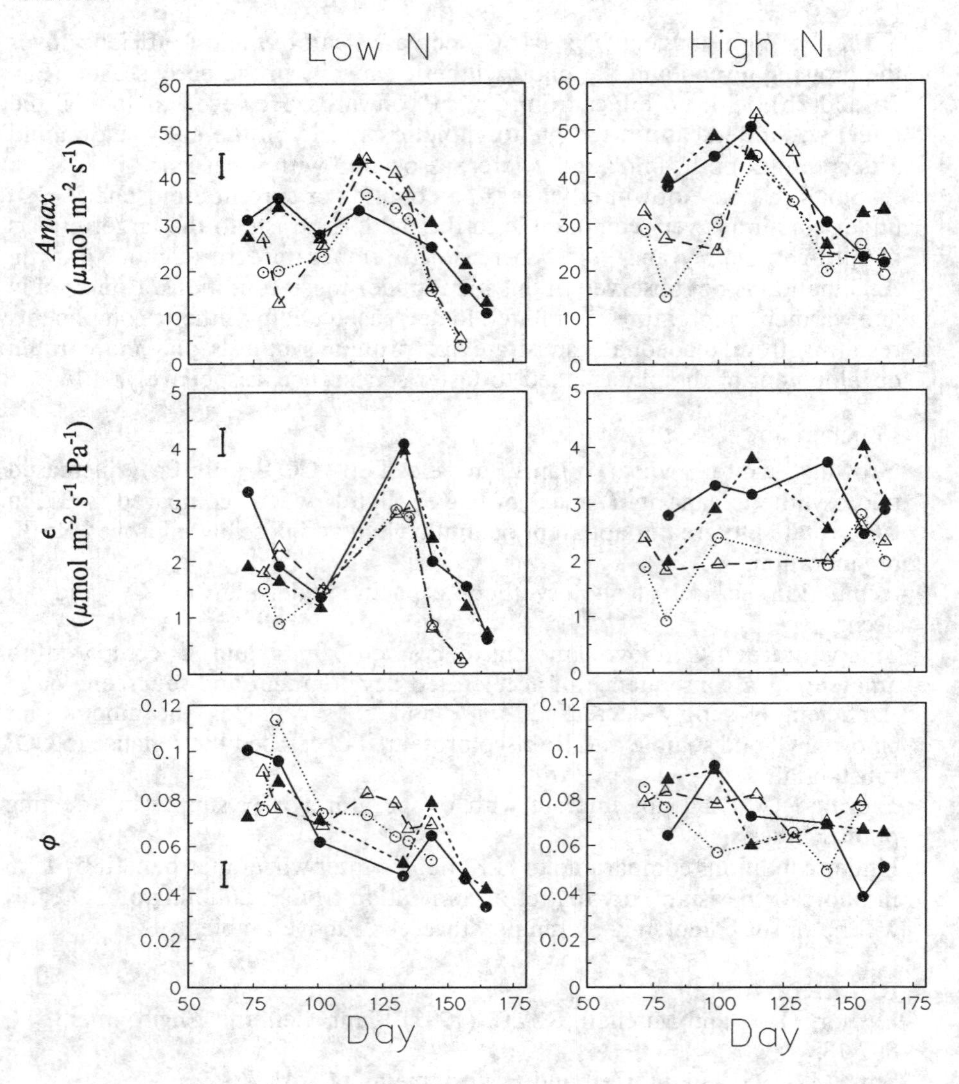

Figure 1. Maximum photosynthetic rates (*Amax*) at saturating light and CO_2 concentrations, carboxylation efficiency (ϵ), and apparent quantum yield (ϕ) of young fully expanded leaves grown at low and high N supply: ●, Amb T and 35 Pa CO_2; ▲, Amb T and 70 Pa CO_2; ○, +4 °C and 35 Pa CO_2; △, +4 °C and 70 Pa CO_2. Mean of 3 replicates. Bars = mean ± SE.

CHANGES OF THE ENZYME ACTIVITIES AND GLUTATHIONE LEVEL IN THE LEAVES OF C_3 AND C_4 PLANTS GROWN UNDER HIGH O_2 ATMOSPHERE

Hiroshi Ohno, Takako Tsuru and Ryuzi Kanai,
Department of Biochemistry, Saitama Univeristy, Urawa 338, Japan

INTRODUCTION

Oxygen concentration in the present atmosphere is too high, while CO_2 concentration is very low for optimum photosynthesis of C_3 plants. Geographically O_2 concentration of the Paleozoic atmosphere had been increasing due to plant photosynthesis and reached almost the same level already in the Carboniferous period. Adaptation to high O_2 atmosphere is an requisite for the survival of the plant; namely, the development of a defense mechanism against increasing photooxidative damage. In addition, the development of C_4 plants itself may be regarded as an evolutionary invention of the plants to reduce photorespiratory loss of the assimilated CO_2. Thus, the plants have acquired the capacity to acclimatize themselves to the environment of higher O_2 and lower CO_2 concentration.

To study the acclimatizing capacity to high O_2, C_3 and C_4 plants were grown for 2-3 weeks in the atmosphere of 60-65% O_2. Activity of various enzymes, namely those in photosynthetic carbon reduction(PCR), oxidation(PCO) and C_4 pathways as well as those for protecting against photooxidation, were compared with the control plants grown in the air. In addition, glutathione and ascorbate levels in the leaf were also compared between barley plants grown under high O_2 and the air.

MATERIALS AND METHODS

Growth of plants: C_3(barley cv. Kashimamugi and wheat cv. Norin 61) and C_4(sorghum cv. M90389 and maize cv. Nagano 2) plant seeds were germinated in small soil-pots for 4-5 days in the air. Pots of each plant species were separated into two groups, transferred to two growth chambers which were maintained in the same conditions except O_2 concentration in the atmosphere: one containing 60-65% O_2 and the other 21% O_2($\pm$1%), both containing 0.05$\pm$0.001% CO_2. Illumination by xenon lamp from 8:00 to 20:00 was added to natural sunlight. Day/night temperature was 25/20^oC. Watering and sampling of plant-pot were done through side-arms without disturbing the gas content. For comparison, leaves of the same position(first to fourth leaves, depending on growth period) were cut, weighed, and ground with sand by a chilled mortar and pestle in a grinding medium(1). Chlorophyll determination and protein assay of the extract were done as in former publication(1).

Assay of enzyme activities: Enzymes of PCR, PCO and C_4 pathways were assayed by the established methods(1). RuBP oxygenase was measured by an O_2 electrode(2). For the assay of superoxide dismutase(3), ascor-

N. Murata (ed.), Research in Photosynthesis, Vol. IV, 839–842.

bate peroxidase(4) and glutathione reductase(5), leaf extract was prepared by a grinding medium containing 100 mM K-phosphate buffer(pH 7.0) and 0.1 mM ascorbate. Each enzyme activity was determined by changing amount of the leaf extract.

Assay of ascorbate, dehydroascorbate and glutathione: Leaf extract was obtained by grinding with 5% metaphosphate. Ascrobate content was calculated from difference of the assays of dehydroascrobate before and after conversion of ascorbate to dehydroascorbate(6). The amount of total and oxidized glutathione was determined before and after removing the reduced form with 2-vinylpyridine(7).

RESULTS AND DISCUSSION

Under this high O_2 condition, all plant species tested were able to grow, and leaf soluble protein on a fresh weight basis was not much different from the control, although their chlorophyll content declined remarkably within 10 days to reach a constant level which was about half of that in control plants(data not shown, see Tables 1 and 2). Thus, enzyme activities are compared on a protein basis.

Two C_3 species grown in high O_2 decreased NADP-glyceraldehyde 3-P dehydrogenase, FuBP 1-phosphatase and Ru5P kinase activities(Table 1), while activities of RuBP carboxylase and oxygenase did not change at least for 2 weeks(data not shown). Among PCO pathway enzymes of barley, glycolate oxidase and hydroxypyruvate reductase increased remarkably by a longer high O_2 treatment(Figure 1).

Two C_4 species grown in high O_2 increased PEP carboxylase activity 1.5-2.0 times of the control within 2 weeks(Figure 1), while enzymes of PCR and PCO pathways generally retained their activities similar to

TABLE 1. Comparison of enzyme activities of PCR and PCO cycles in the leaf extracts of C_3 plants(barley and wheat) grown under high O_2(60%) and normal air for 15 days after germination

Plant	Barley			Wheat		
Atmosphere	High O_2	Air	Ratio[a]	High O_2	Air	Ratio
Enzyme activity[b]						
RuBP carboxylase	469	443	1.06	487	475	1.03
NADP-GA3P dehydrogenase	-	-	-	900	996	0.90
FuBP 1-phosphatase	-	-	-	86	106	0.81
Ru5P kinase	612	1002	0.61	536	856	0.63
Glycolate oxidase	78	57	1.37	-	-	-
Catalase($x10^{-3}$)	107	101	1,06	-	-	-
Hydroxypyruvate reductase	702	502	1.40	-	-	-
Chlorophyll[c]	0.84	1.32	0.64	0.67	1.13	0.59
Leaf soluble protein[d]	22.5	23.5	0.96	32.7	32.1	1.02

[a]Ratio:High O_2/Air; [b] $\mu mol\cdot(mg\ protein)^{-1}\cdot min^{-1}$;
[c]$mg\cdot(g\ fresh\ weight)^{-1}$; [d]$mg\cdot(g\ fresh\ weight)^{-1}$

those of control plants(Table 2). Exceptions are a remarkable increase in the activities of sorghum catalase and maize FuBP 1-phosphatase. Decrease in Ru5P kinase activity in C_4 plants may be common to C_3 plants under high O_2(Tables 1 and 2).

Among the protecting enzymes of photooxidation, glutathione reductase activity increased dramatically in both C_3 and C_4 plants tested (Figure 1). Ascorbate peroxidase showed some increase in the activity,

Figure 1. Enzyme activities and levels of reductants in leaf extract of C_3 and C_4 plants. Comparison between the plant grown under 65% O_2 and the air. Ordinates: ratio of high O_2/normal air(=100). Abscissa: days after sowing. The arrow indicates the time of transfer to high O_2.

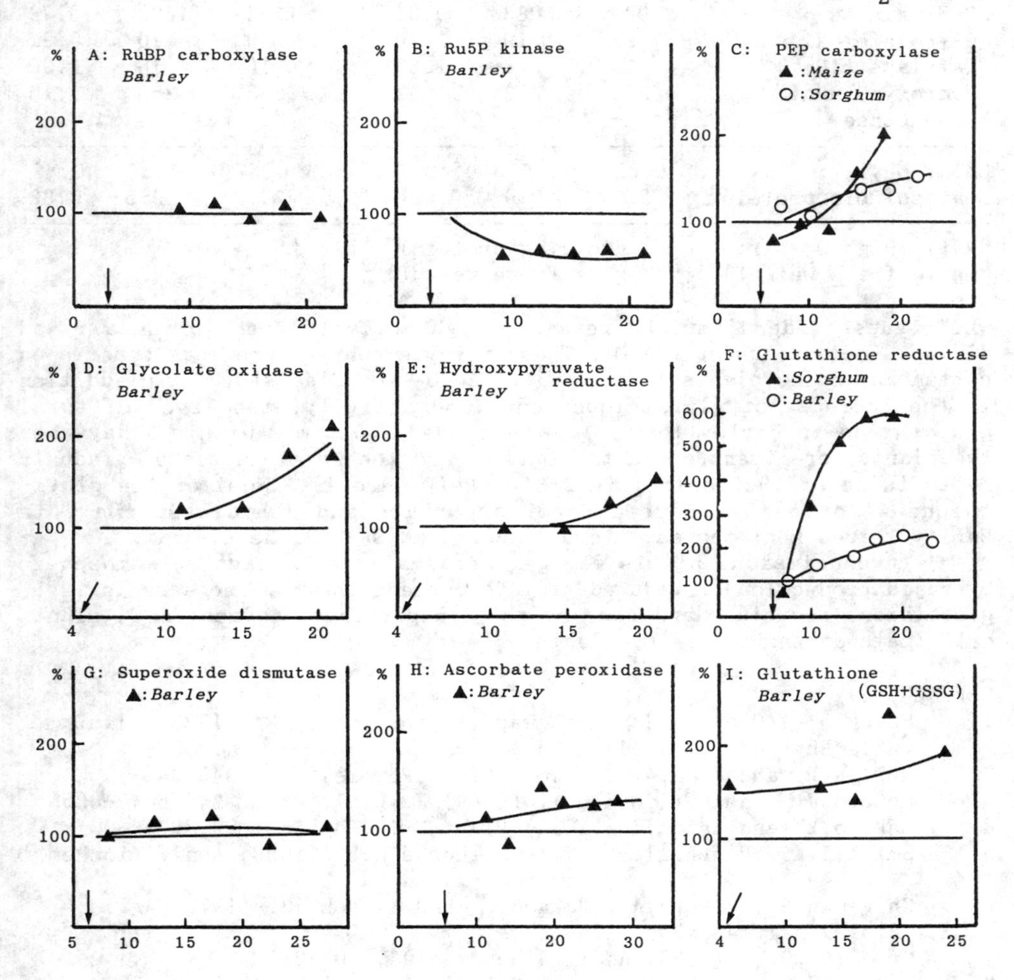

TABLE 2. Comparison of enzyme activities of PCR and PCO cycles in the leaf extracts of C_4 plants(sorghum and maize) grown under high O_2(60%) and normal air for 9 days after germination

Plant	Sorghum			Maize		
Atmosphere	High O_2	Air	Ratio[a]	High O_2	Air	Ratio
Enzyme activity[b]						
RuBP carboxylase	-	-	-	128	147	0.87
NADP-GA3P dehydrogenase	-	-	-	2540	2521	1.01
FuBP 1-phosphatase	182	186	0.98	238	166	1.43
Ru5P kinase	926	1083	0.86	1154	1603	0.72
Glycolate oxidase	21	19	1.10	9	10	0.91
Catalase($x10^{-3}$)	13	8	1.62	16	16	1.00
Hydroxypyruvate reductase	236	232	1.02	298	259	1.15
Chlorophyll[c]	0.65	1.55	0.42	0.57	1.36	0.42
Leaf soluble protein[d]	26.7	29.0	0.92	24.2	29.5	0.82

[a]Ratio:High O_2/Air; [b] $\mu mol\cdot(mg\ protein)^{-1}\cdot min^{-1}$;
[c]$mg\cdot(g\ fresh\ weight)^{-1}$; [d]$mg\cdot(g\ fresh\ weight)^{-1}$

while superoxide dismutase retained high activity even in the air and did not increase under 65% O_2. These results confirm previous reports on cotton and maize plants treated with 75% O_2 for 2 days(8,9). In addition to the increase of glutathione reductase activity, the level of total glutathione in barley leaves was increased 1.5 times within a day when the plants were transferred to high O_2, and the level increased gradually to twice of the control in 2-3 weeks(Figure 1). Most of the glutathione were in the reduced form. Ascorbate and dehydroascorbate in barley leaves kept the same level under high O_2 and the air.

In conclusion, plants may get acclimatized to high O_2 atmosphere by rapid production of reduced glutathione and then by increase in glutathione reductase and some of photorespiratory enzymes in C_3 plants or C_4 pathway enzymes in C_4 plants.

REFERENCES

1 Suzuki,E., Ohnishi,J., Kashiwagi,M. and Kanai, R. (1986) Plant Cell Physiol. 27, 1117-1125
2 Hall,N.P. and Keys,A.J. (1983) Plant Physiol. 72, 945-948
3 McCord,J.M. and Fridovich,I. (1969) J. Biol. Chem. 244,6049-6055
4 Nakano,Y. and Asada,K. (1981) Plant Cell Physiol. 22,867-880
5 Smith,I.K., Vierheller,T.J. and Thorne,C.L. (1988) Anal. Biochem. 175, 408-413
6 Shigeoka,S., Yokota,A., Nakano,Y. and Kitaoka,S. (1979) Agric. Biol. Chem. 43, 2053-2058
7 Griffith,O.W. (1980) Anal. Biochem. 106, 207-212
8 Foster,J.G. and Hess,J.L. (1980) Plant Physiol. 66, 482-487
9 Foster,J.G. and Hess,J.L. (1982) Phytochem. 21, 1527-1532

On the relationship between isoprene emission and photosynthetic metabolites under different environmental conditions

Francesco Loretc and Thomas D. Sharkey, Department of Botany, University of Wisconsin, Madison, WI 53706-1381 USA

Introduction

Isoprene synthesis in plants occurs in the chloroplasts (1) and is closely correlated with photosynthesis under many environmental conditions (2-6). Like photosynthesis, isoprene emission is a light-dependent process. Isoprene emission is also inhibited by low CO_2 partial pressure, although the low-CO_2 inhibition of isoprene emission is sometimes absent during light-limited photosynthesis (6). While some isoprene is still produced when leaves are held in CO_2-free air, the rate is considerably reduced when CO_2 and O_2 are simultaneously removed from air (5, 6). Unlike photosynthesis, isoprene emission from leaves is usually inhibited by exposure of leaves to high CO_2 partial pressure during the assay (1, 5, 6). A full understanding of the relationship between isoprene emission and photosynthesis will require an explanation of why both low and high CO_2 partial pressure inhibits isoprene emission (7).

Gas-exchange and chlorophyll fluorescence measurements and results from inhibitor studies have been interpreted to indicate that the rate of isoprene emission may be regulated by ATP concentration in leaves, which can vary under different environmental conditions. In addition, Loreto and Sharkey (6) hypothesized that PGA may also be involved in regulating the rate of isoprene emission; PGA from the photosynthetic carbon reduction cycle may be the carbon source for the mevalonic acid pathway from which isoprene is formed (8). Monson et al. (7) speculated that other metabolites (e.g. triose phosphates) could also regulate isoprene synthesis.

In order to determine which metabolites are best correlated with the rate of isoprene emission, we measured the concentration of the photosynthetic metabolites which could be directly or indirectly involved with isoprene synthesis (ATP, ADP, PGA, triose phosphates, and RuBP) in leaves after measuring the rate of isoprene emission. Measurements were made at high CO_2, low CO_2, and following a light-to-dark transition. The levels were compared to control values obtained from leaves in high light, 35 Pa CO_2, 20 kPa O_2 (normal air).

Methods

Isoprene detection. Leaf isoprene emission was detected by gas-chromatography. Isoprene was separated from other gases on a 30 m, 5 μm coating fused-silica Megabore DB-1 column (J & W Scientific, Folsom, Cal. USA) of the gas-chromatograph (model GC-14A, Shimadzu, Columbia, Md., USA) maintained at 55°C. Isoprene was detected with a photoionization detector (supplied by Shimadzu) and measured with a computing peak integrator (model SP4400, Spectra Physics, San Jose, Cal., USA).

Metabolite determination. When leaf photosynthesis and isoprene emission was steady, metabolite turnover was rapidly stopped by clamping an 8.4 cm^2 leaf disc between two copper blocks which had

N. Murata (ed.), Research in Photosynthesis, Vol. IV, 843–846.

been cooled in liquid nitrogen. The leaf disc was then ground to a powder and 3.5% $HClO_4$ was added during grinding. After thawing and centrifugation, the supernatant was neutralized using 2 N KOH, 0.15 M Hepes, 10 mM KCl buffer and the precipitate was discarded after further centrifugation. Metabolites were measured spectrophotometrically using enzyme-linked assays.

Results

Darkness rapidly inhibited isoprene emission (Fig. 1). Triose phosphate and RuBP concentrations

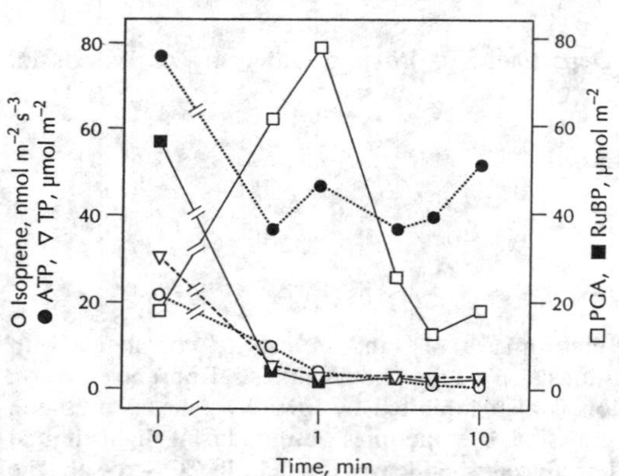

Figure 1. Isoprene emission rate and metabolite concentrations in velvet bean leaves following imposition of darkness at 0 time. The time scale is logarithmic to make it easier to see the rapid changes which occur during the first minute following darkness.

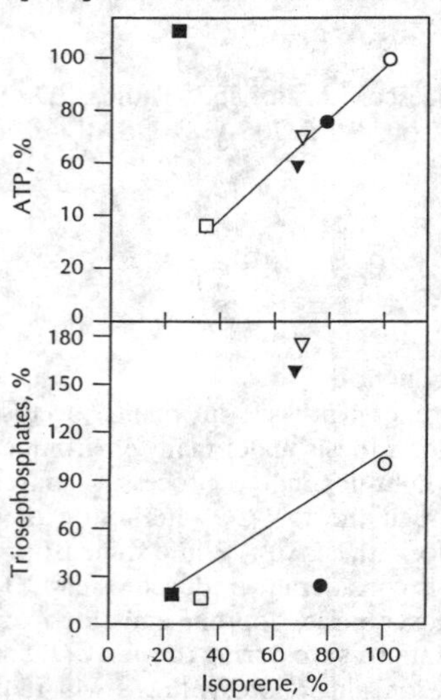

Figure 2. Relationship between isoprene emission and ATP concentration under different environmental conditions. Open circle = 20% O_2, 35 Pa CO_2 (ambient) air composition; Closed circle = 2% O_2, 35 Pa CO_2; Open triangle = 20% O_2, 250 Pa CO_2; Closed triangle = 20% O_2, 100 Pa CO_2; Open square = 20% O_2, 35 Pa CO_2, 30 s after darkness imposition; Closed square = 2% O_2, 0 Pa CO_2. All values represent the average of 4 measurements and are expressed as a percentage of the value measured under ambient air conditions, open circle (= 100).

were reduced more rapidly but to the same extent (to zero) as isoprene. The concentration of ATP also dropped very rapidly. After half a minute, ATP was 48% of the concentration measurable under light, but no further reduction occurred. PGA increased four-fold during the first minute of darkness but then declined to the pre-darkness concentrations.

Changes in the air composition also reduced the rate of isoprene emission (Table 1). Under CO_2-free, low O_2 conditions, isoprene emission was strongly inhibited. RuBP concentration was much higher while PGA and triose phosphate concentrations were significantly lower than in controls. No significant change in ATP occurred. When the CO_2 concentration of the atmosphere was increased to 250 Pa (about 2500 ppm), isoprene emission was again reduced relative to the control. The control rate of isoprene emission varied between this experiment and the last one and so subsequent data manipulations are based on changes in metabolite level relative to controls determined on the same day with the same plants. The inhibition of isoprene emission at high CO_2 was associated with reductions in RuBP and ATP concentrations; PGA and triose phosphates concentrations increased after the treatment with high CO_2. Other metabolites also changed but no metabolite was always well correlated with the rate of isoprene emission (Table 1).

Table 1. Isoprene emission rate and concentration of photosynthetic metabolites in leaves of velvet bean in different atmospheres. Isoprene is given as nmol m^{-2} s^{-1} while the metabolites are given as μmol m^{-2}. Values are means ± SE for 4 or 5 measurements.

Isoprene Metabolites	Control	2 kPa O_2 0 Pa CO_2	Control	20 kPa O_2 250 Pa CO_2
Isoprene	6.1 ± 2.5	1.4 ± 1.1	39 ± 2	27 ± 4
PGA	46 ± 10	2.5 ± 1.0	46 ± 5	139 ± 18
RuBP	22 ± 7	47 ± 12	102 ± 19	44 ± 10
ATP	20 ± 6	22 ± 7	20 ± 4	14 ± 2
ADP	20 ± 6	15 ± 3	16 ± 5	20 ± 5
Triose phosphates	15 ± 4	3 ± 1	8 ± 4	14 ± 1
Glc 6-P	21 ± 5	8 ± 5	14 ± 4	27 ± 6
Fru 6-P	15 ± 3	3 ± 2	10 ± 4	24 ± 5

We made additional measurements on leaves exposed to a variety of conditions and compared the rate of isoprene emission with the metabolite levels. We also included the data after 30 s of darkness. Subsequent data from the light to dark transition were not included since we felt that changes in the activation of isoprene synthase could occur after one min of darkness. When the metabolite concentration was plotted against the rate of isoprene emission, we found an apparent linear relationship between ATP concentration and isoprene emission, except for the data obtained in the CO_2-free, low O_2 atmosphere (Fig. 2). Other metabolites did not appear to be related to isoprene emission, we show only the data for triose phosphates in Fig. 2.

We determined the coefficients of determination (r^2) for ATP, PGA, RuBP, and triose phosphate with isoprene emission rate. In each case we dropped the one data point which reduced the correlation coefficient the most. The coefficients of determination for the relationship between isoprene emission rate and ATP was 0.96 for the velvet bean data and 0.81 for the oak data. The correlation coefficients for the other metabolites were all 0.5 or less.

Discussion

The rate of isoprene emission was best correlated with the concentration of ATP in leaves of velvet bean and red oak. The high CO_2 inhibition of isoprene emission was shown to result from a reduction in the concentration of ATP. On the other hand, the low CO_2 inhibition of isoprene emission was correlated with a reduction in the concentration of PGA. Thus in low O_2, CO_2-free air two potential sources of carbon for isoprene synthesis (8), glycolysis beginning with PGA and pyruvate formation by rubisco (9) substantially reduced.

The important role of ATP in controlling the rate of isoprene emission was foreshadowed by gas exchange studies where it was shown that when photosynthesis in leaves was no longer stimulated by low O_2, isoprene emission was inhibited by low O_2 (5, 6). Other studies have shown that low O_2 reduces the concentration of ATP under these conditions (10). Feeding methyl viologen, which increases the ATP concentration in intact leaves (11) also stimulated the rate of isoprene emission (6). Thus there is gas exchange evidence, inhibitor feeding evidence, and now metabolite measurements to support the important role of ATP concentration in regulating the rate of isoprene emission.

In addition to the importance of ATP concentration, the availability of carbon can influence the rate of isoprene emission as seen in low O_2, CO_2-free air. The drop in the rate of isoprene emission immediately after imposing darkness can be explained by the reduction in ATP concentration. However, the concentration of ATP stabilized at around 50% of the value found in the light within one min, and the concentration of PGA was much higher than before darkness was imposed. To account for the continuing decline in the rate of isoprene emission we speculate either that carboxylation of RuBP to provide pyruvate is required for isoprene synthesis or that the isoprene synthase (12) is light regulated by a mechanism such as phosphorylation or by a strong dependence upon pH, which drops when darkness is imposed. Silver and Fall (12) did not find so strong a pH dependence for isoprene synthase purified from aspen. If PGA can supply the carbon for isoprene emission, the increase in PGA following darkness could explain the post-illumination burst of isoprene reported by Monson et al. (7) and which we have also seen (data not shown).

In summary, we think that when a source of carbon is available, the main limitation to isoprene formation is the availability of ATP. PGA or carboxylation of RuBP is the link between carbon metabolism and isoprene emission (6), but very low levels of PGA or carboxylation are required to make carbon supply a significant factor for isoprene production.

References

1. Sanadze, G.A. (1990) The principle scheme of photosynthetic carbon conversion in cells of isoprene releasing plants. Cur. Res. Photosyn. IV, 231-237
2. Sanadze, G.A., Kursanov, A.L. (1966) On certain conditions of the evolution of the diene C5H8 from poplar leaves. Sov. Plant Physiol. **13**, 184-189
3. Jones, C.A., Rasmussen, R.A. (1975) Production of isoprene by leaf tissue. Plant Physiol. **55**, 982-987
4. Tingey, D.T., Evans, R., Gumpertz, M. (1981) Effects of environmental conditions on isoprene emission from live oak. Planta **152**, 565-570
5. Monson, R.K., Fall, R. (1989) Isoprene emission from Aspen leaves. The influence of environment and relation to photosynthesis and photorespiration. Plant Physiol. **90**, 267-274
6. Loreto, F., Sharkey, T.D. (1990) A gas-exchange study of photosynthesis and isoprene emission in *Quercus rubra* L. Planta **182**, 523-531
7. Monson, R.K., Hills, A.J., Zimmerman, P.R., Fall, R.R. (1991) Studies of the relationship between isoprene emission rate and CO_2 or photon-flux density using a real-time isoprene analyser. Plant Cell Environ. **14**, 517-523
8. Sharkey, T.D., Loreto, F., Delwiche, C.F. (1991) The biochemistry of isoprene emission from leaves during photosynthesis. In: Trace gas emissions from plants, pp. 153-184, Sharkey, T.D., Holland, E.A., Mooney, H.A., eds. Academic Press, San Diego
9. Andrews, T.J., Kane, H.J. (1991) Pyruvate is a by-product of catalysis by ribulosebisphosphate carboxylase/oxygenase. J. Biol. Chem. **266**, 9447-9452
10. Sharkey, T.D., Stitt, M., Heineke, D., Gerhardt, R., Raschke, K., Heldt, H.W. (1986) Limitation of photosynthesis by carbon metabolism. II O_2 insensitive CO_2 uptake results from limitation of triose phosphate utilization. Plant Physiol. **81**, 1123-1129
11. Brooks, A., Portis, A.R.,Jr., Sharkey, T.D. (1988) Effects of irradiance and methyl viologen treatment on ATP, ADP and activation of ribulose bisphosphate carboxylase in spinach leaves. Plant Physiol. **88**, 850-853
12. Silver, G.M., Fall, R. (1991) Enzymatic synthesis of isoprene from dimethylallyl diphosphate in aspen leaf extracts. Plant Physiol. **97**, 1588-1591

ALGAL PHOTOSYNTHESIS: INHIBITION BY UV-B RADIATION, RECOVERY AND UV-ABSORBING PIGMENTS.

Adele Post, Sarah Gentle and A.W.D. Larkum,
School of Biological Sciences, A12,
University of Sydney, 2006, Australia.

INTRODUCTION

As UV-B radiation has been measured at depths up to 70m (1), stratospheric ozone depletion will result in increasing exposure of marine plants to ultraviolet (UV-B) light. Although algae contain UV-absorbing pigments (2), UV-B light inhibits their photosynthesis and extensive exposure leads to severe damage. In higher plants the molecular site of the initial damage to the photosynthetic system appears to be within the reaction centre of photosystem II (PS II) (3) and this damage is not identical to that occurring in photoinhibition (4). Our measurements suggest the initial site of UV-B inhibition of photosynthesis of marine algae also occurs within PS II.

MATERIALS AND METHODS

Samples of *Prasiola crispa* ssp. antarctici (Kutzing) Knebel were collected near Casey, East Antarctica (66°17'S, 110°32'E), and *Ulva* sp. was collected near Sydney, Australia (33°55'S, 151°10'S). *Griffithsia monilis* (Harvey) was cultured in Provosoli enriched seawater and thylakoids were prepared (5).

UV-B radiation was measured with an International Light meter (IL-1350) with a 313nm filter on the sensor. *Prasiola* was maintained in an environment cabinet with low PAR (90μmol quanta m^{-2} s^{-1}) enhanced with UV-B radiation provided by Westinghouse FS20 tubes (0.017mWcm^{-2}). *Ulva* thalli and *Griffithsia* thylakoids were exposed to 0.1mWcm^{-2} of UV-B radiation using a 1kW xenon light source filtered with cellulose acetate and Schott UG-11 filters (324nm centre wavelength transmission, 80nm half-width).

Chlorophyll was extracted from samples using 80% acetone and the concentration calculated (6) from the absorbance. UV-absorbing pigments were extracted into methanol (HPLC grade).

Photosynthetic rates were measured with a Rank oxygen electrode. Continuous white light was used except for the quantum yield measurements when a xenon flash unit was used (7).

Fluorescence kinetics measurements were made at room temperature with a custom built instrument, with excitation light (400-500nm) of 100μE$m^{-2}s^{-1}$. Fluorescence was measured at 685nm and the signal digitised at speeds up to 200μs per data point. Samples were dark adapted for a minimum of 15 minutes.

N. Murata (ed.), Research in Photosynthesis, Vol. IV, 847–850.

RESULTS

Prasiola, a green Antarctic alga, contains very high concentrations of UV-absorbing pigments relative to chlorophyll (Fig. 1, solid line). However even with these high concentrations of pigments, UV-B exposure results in decreased oxygen evolution rates under both light limiting and light saturating irradiance (Fig. 2). The UV-B dose was low but the ratio of UV-B to visible light was double the amount at midday on the day of collection.

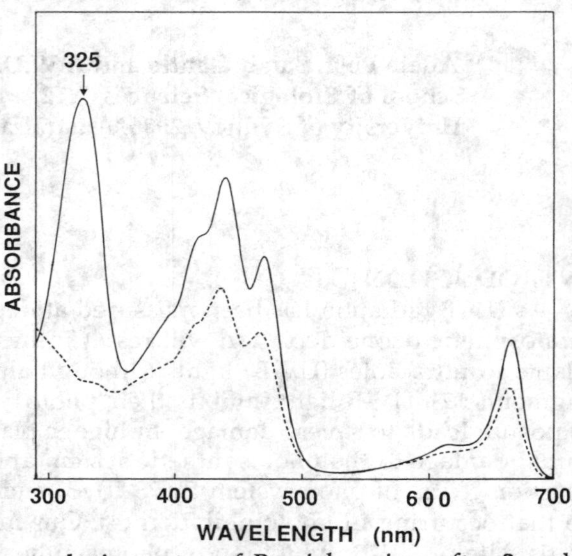

Fig. 1: Absorbance spectra of the methanol extract of *Prasiola crispa*. (solid line) and of *Ulva* (dashed line).

Fig. 2: Photosynthetic oxygen evolution rates of *Prasiola crispa* after 3 and 4 weeks of culturing with PAR and with PAR and UV-B. Means are shown for 6 samples with standard errors.

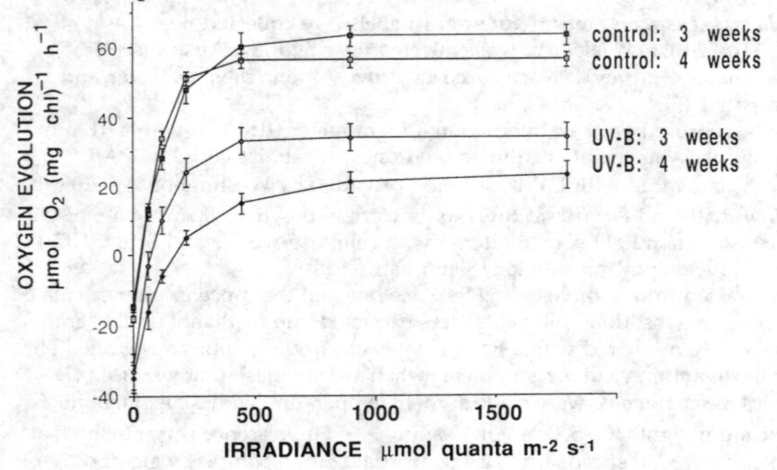

Although many temperate algae are exposed to a much higher yearly dose of UV-B light than Antarctic algae they contain lower levels of UV-absorbing pigments. An example is the intertidal green foliose alga *Ulva* which despite its exposed situation contains little UV-absorbing pigments relative to chlorophyll (Fig. 1, dashed line). UV-B radiation caused inhibition of oxygen evolution, with recovery from this initial inhibition occurring within a few hours although it is slower in the dark than in dim light, 15μmol quanta m^{-2} s^{-1}, (Fig. 3).

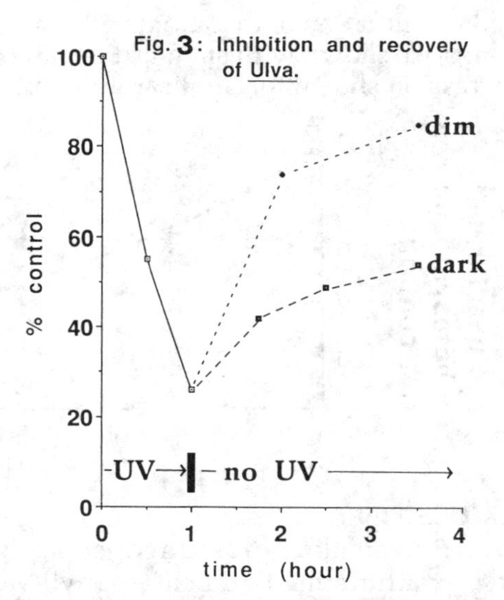

Fig. 3: Inhibition and recovery of Ulva.

To avoid any protection provided by UV-absorbing pigments thylakoids were isolated. A temperate rhodophyte alga *Griffithsia* was chosen as the light harvesting phycobilisomes can be removed conveniently. Photosynthetically active thylakoids with phycobilisomes attached were exposed to UV-B radiation and the effect was monitored by measuring the decrease in variable fluorescence, quantum yield and light saturated oxygen evolution (Fig. 4). A comparison with thylakoids lacking phycobilisomes showed no difference in the extent of UV-B inhibition (Fig. 5).

Fig. 4 : Inhibition of thylakoids with phycobilisomes.
Means are shown with standard deviation. Regression shown for light saturated photosynthetic rates (LSPS).

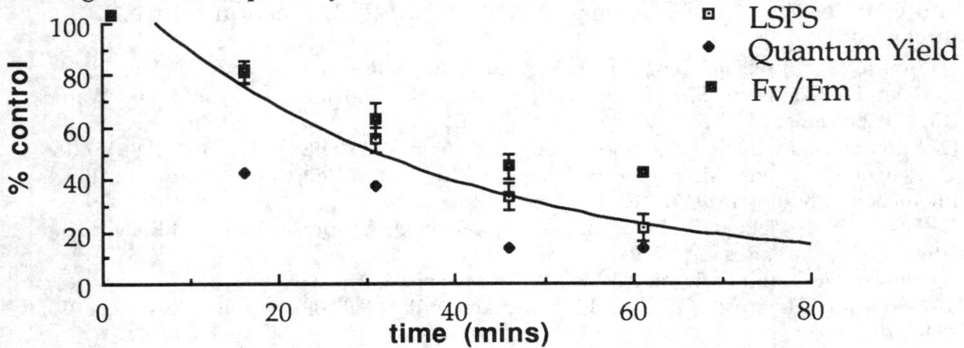

Fig. 5 : Inhibition of thylakoids without phycobilisomes.
Means are shown with standard deviation.
Regression shown for light saturated photosynthetic rates.

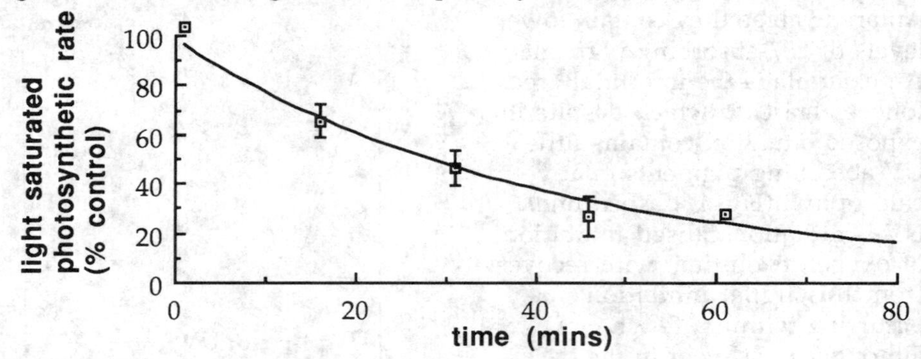

DISCUSSION

UV-B irradiation caused reductions in light saturated oxygen evolution rates, quantum yield and chlorophyll variable fluorescence. The effect of UV-B irradiation on the oxygen evolution of *Prasiola* and *Ulva* thalli are consistent with the UV-B damage occurring in PS II. Even when the alga contains high amounts of UV-absorbing pigments, as in the case of *Prasiola*, a low dose of UV-B results in inhibition over a period of weeks. The decrease in variable fluorescence and quantum yield observed for *Griffithsia* thylakoids with phycobilisomes attached indicates the inhibition occurs in PS II. The similar extent of inhibition of *Griffithsia* thylakoids lacking phycobilisomes suggest the site of UV-B damage is not in the light harvesting components of this alga and that the phycobilisome does not protect for UV-B damage. Microsecond Δ830nm absorbance measurements of PS II can provide data on the state of P680 reduction (3,4). Measurements of ΔA830 made on thylakoids from this rhodophyte alga are in progress to show the effect of UV-B iradiation within the PS II reaction centre.

REFERENCES

(1) Smith, R.C., Prezelin, B.B., Baker, K.S., Bidigare, R.R., Boucher, N.P., Coley, T., Karentz, D., MacIntyre, S., Matlick, H.A., Menzies, D., Ondrusek,M., Wan,Z. and Waters, K.J. (1992) Science 255, 952-959

(2) Karentz, D., McEuen, F.S., Land, M.C. and Dunlap, W.C. (1991) Mar. Biol. 108, 157-166

(3) Renger, G., Volker, M., Eckert, H.-J., Fromme, R., Hohm-Veit, S. and Graber, P. (1989) Photochem. Photobiol. 49, 97-105

(4) Eckert, H.-J., Geiken, B., Bernarding, J., Napiwotzki, A., Eichler H.-J. and Renger, G. (1991) Photosynth. Res. 27, 97-108

(5) Stewart, A.C. and Larkum, A.W.D. (1983) Biochem. J. 210, 583-589

(6) Porra, R.J., Thompson, W.A. and Kriedemann, P.E. (1989) Biochim. Biophys. Acta 975, 384-394

(7) Chow, W.S., Hope, A.B. and Anderson, J.M. (1989) Biochim. Biophys. Acta 973, 105-108

AN ANALYSIS OF OZONE INHIBITION OF PHOTOSYNTHESIS FOLLOWING SHORT- AND LONG-TERM EXPOSURE IN THREE CONTRASTING SPECIES

P.K. FARAGE and S.P. LONG, Department of Biology, University of Essex, Wivenhoe Park, Colchester, Essex, CO4 3SQ, UK.

1. INTRODUCTION

A programme of experiments was undertaken in order to establish the effects of O_3 exposure on whole leaf photosynthesis. Reports of the inhibitory effects of O_3 on photosynthesis are frequent but the sites of limitation to leaf gas exchange have remained unclear (1). The current investigation used *in vivo* techniques to examine the effects of both short- and long-term O_3 exposure on three taxonomically contrasting species representing a cereal, a legume and a broad-leaved tree.

2. MATERIALS and METHODS

Short-term O_3 exposures:
Individual, fully expanded leaves of *Triticum aestivum* (cv. Avalon), *Pisum sativum* (cv. Meteor) and *Quercus robur* were fumigated with O_3 (200 & 400 nmol mol^{-1}) for 4 to 16 hours in a water-jacketed, stirred, glass leaf chamber at 20°C and with a photon flux density of 300 µmol m^{-2} s^{-1}. Ozone was produced by an ultra violet source incorporated in a generator/analyser unit (1008-PC, Dasibi Inc., USA.).

Long-term O_3 exposures:
Whole plants of *T. aestivum* and *P. sativum* were grown from seed in cuboid chambers similar to those described by Lockyer *et al* (2) but with the addition of an internal fan to ensure thorough air mixing and a high boundary layer conductance. The sides of the chambers were covered with polypropylene film which has good transmittance of long-wave radiation and thereby helps prevent the air temperature from rising. The chambers were located inside a temperature controlled glasshouse and fumigated with O_3 at 80 nmol mol^{-1} for 7 hours each day. Ozone was produced from O_2 using electric discharge (BA-023, ozone generator, Wallace & Tiernan Ltd., UK.). Gas exchange measurements were made on leaves which had just reached full expansion and had consequently developed in the elevated O_3 environment. Saplings of *Q. robur* were grown in "solar domes" at the former Central Electricity Research Laboratories, Leatherhead, UK. for one summer season (5 months), at 80 nmol mol^{-1} O_3.

N. Murata (ed.), Research in Photosynthesis, Vol. IV, 851–854.

Leaf gas exchange measurements:
Fluxes of CO_2 and H_2O were measured in a leaf section chamber (LSC, ADC Ltd., UK.) as described previously (3). Control leaves/plants were subjected to identical conditions without O_3 (<5 nmol mol^{-1}) except for *Q. robur* in the long-term experiment where the concentration was 20 nmol mol^{-1} O_3.

3. RESULTS AND DISCUSSION

The short-term fumigations involved each species being exposed to O_3 under identical conditions. However, the effective O_3 dose depends upon the rate of O_3 uptake, which will occur primarily through the stomata. During these experiments the quantity of O_3 absorbed by the leaves did not differ significantly between each species (F, $p>0.05$; Fig. 1) and consequently the effective dose received was very similar.

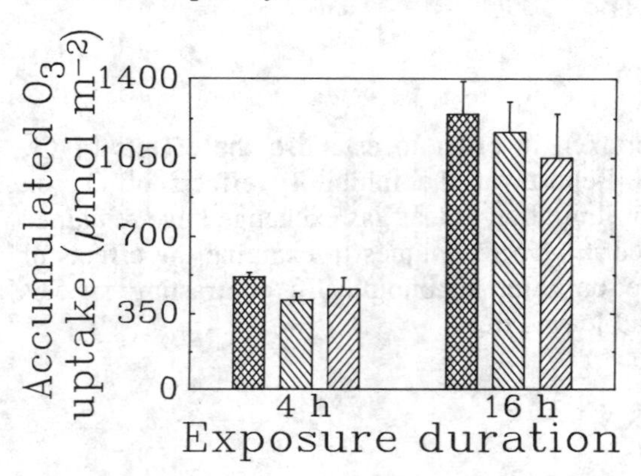

FIGURE 1. The accumulated quantity of O_3 absorbed by *Triticum aestivum* ; *Pisum sativum* ; and *Quercus robur* leaves in air with an O_3 concentration of 200 nmol mol^{-1}. Measurements were made at 20°C, with a photon flux density of 300 μmol m^{-2} s^{-1}. Vertical bars represent standard errors of the mean.

The resulting effect on photosynthesis, as assessed by the light-saturated rate of CO_2 uptake (A_{sat}) was also similar for each species (Fig. 2a). The degree of inhibition increasing with duration of exposure and increasing O_3 concentration. *Quercus robur* was particularly sensitive to the most severe treatment by which time net CO_2 uptake had almost ceased. Species differences were more apparent following the longer-term O_3 exposures (Fig. 2b). Only *T. aestivum* showed a significant decline in A_{sat} (F, $p<0.05$).

Gas exchange analysis using the methods of Farquhar and co-workers (4,5) showed that the decreases in CO_2 fixation were primarily the result of significant reductions in carboxylation capacity which is dependent upon the amount and activity of the enzyme ribulose- 1,5-bisphosphate carboxylase/oxygenase (RubisCO). There was a very close correlation between carboxylation capacity and A_{sat} following short-term O_3 exposure for all three species (t $p<0.01$; Fig. 3). Following long-term exposure the significant decline in A_{sat} of *T. aestivum* was correlated with a corresponding decline in carboxylation capacity (F, $p<0.05$; Fig. 4). The only discrepancy was a significant reduction in carboxylation capacity of *Q. robur* (F, $p<0.05$) without any significant alteration of A_{sat}. This was partly because the results from *Q. robur*, particularly from fumigated leaves, became more variable, but also because the operating point of photosynthesis proved to be just on the plateau of the CO_2 response curve and so was virtually unaffected by the change in carboxylation capacity.

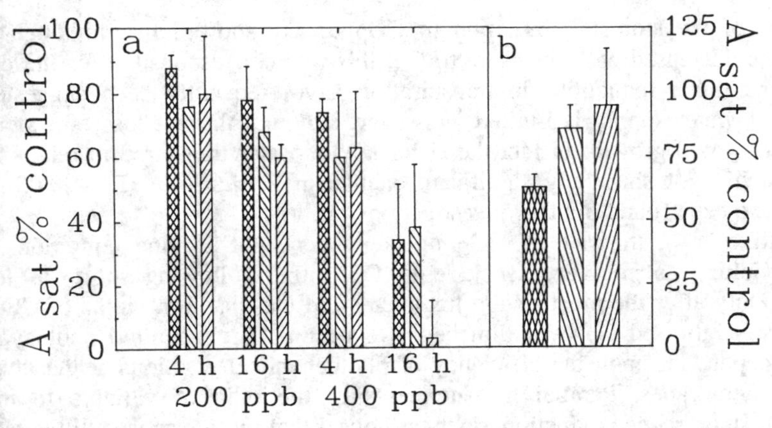

FIGURE 2. Percentage changes in the light-saturated rate of CO_2 uptake (A_{sat}) of *Triticum aestivum* ▩ ; *Pisum sativum* ▧ and *Quercus robur* ▨ leaves following: a) 4 & 16 hours exposure to 200 & 400 nmol mol^{-1} (ppb) O_3; and b) long-term exposure to 80 nmol mol^{-1} O_3, 7 h d^{-1}. Vertical bars represent standard errors of the mean.

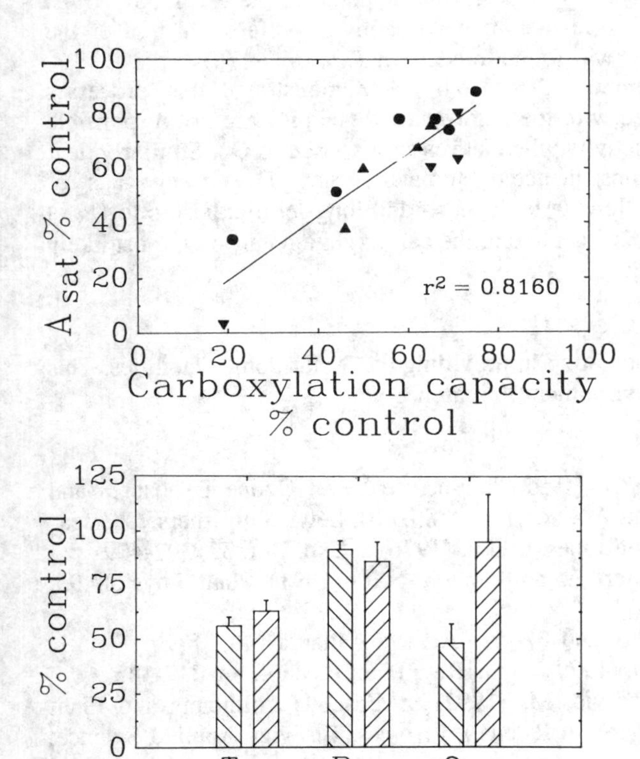

FIGURE 3. Relationship between the carboxylation capacity and the rate of light-saturated CO_2 uptake (A_{sat}) of *Triticum aestivum* ● ; *Pisum sativum* ▲ and *Quercus robur* ▼ leaves exposed to O_3 concentrations of 200 and 400 nmol mol^{-1} for up to 16 hours.

FIGURE 4. Comparison of the effects of exposure to 80 nmol mol^{-1} O_3 during leaf development on the carboxylation capacity ▧ and the rate of light-saturated CO_2 uptake ▨ on *Triticum aestivum* (T.a.), *Pisum sativum* (P.s.) and *Quercus robur* (Q.r.). Vertical bars represent standard errors of the mean.

Calculation of the stomatal limitation to CO_2 uptake showed that although stomatal conductance decreased with exposure to O_3, this was not responsible for the decline in CO_2 uptake. Such reductions in transpiration have frequently been suggested to be beneficial if water supply is limited. However, although the net loss of water will be reduced, so to will growth. In fact the efficiency of water transpired in relation to CO_2 assimilated did not show any significant change in *T. aestivum* (F, $p>0.05$). Similar findings have been found in other investigations (1).

Unlike A_{sat}, the rate of CO_2 uptake under light-limiting conditions, i.e. the quantum yield, was not very sensitive to O_3, either following short- or long-term exposure. Only after the most severe treatments did the quantum yields of CO_2 uptake for absorbed light and O_2 evolution begin to decline. Light-limited photosynthesis is primarily dependent upon the efficiency of photochemical reactions at the level of the thylakoid membranes. Parallel measurements of the ratio of variable to maximum chlorophyll fluorescence induction kinetics showed that there was very little decrease in photosystem II efficiency. That electron transport capacity was mainly unperturbed is further supported by the fact that the CO_2 saturated rate of CO_2 uptake, which depends on the rate of ribulose 1,5-bisphosphate regeneration and hence ATP and NADPH production, showed relatively small decreases compared to A_{sat} and carboxylation capacity. Related biochemical analyses provide further support to these results. Whilst there was no selective loss of thylakoid membrane proteins, a preferential loss of the small and large subunits of RubisCO was found to occur in *T. aestivum* (6).

In conclusion, this programme of research has demonstrated that processes dependent upon reactions associated with the chloroplast thylakoids are not responsible for major losses in photosynthetic activity when leaves are exposed to O_3. Similarly, leaf gas exchange is not inhibited as a consequence of stomatal closure. The primary cause of photosynthetic inhibition *in vivo* following both short- and long-term exposure to O_3 in all of the three species investigated is a decline in the carboxylation capacity, most likely through a decrease in active RubisCO.

4. ACKNOWLEDGEMENTS

We thank Dr. K. Brown for his cooperation in providing the "solar dome" facilities. This work was funded by the Natural Environment Research Council.

REFERENCES

1 Runeckles, V.C. and Chevone, B.I. (1992) in Surface Level Ozone Exposures and Their Effects on Vegetation (Lefohn, A.S., ed.), pp. 189-270, Lewis Publishers, Chelsea
2 Lockyer, D.R., Cowling, D.W. and Jones, L.H.P. (1976) J. Exp. Bot. 37, 397-409
3 Farage, P.K., Long, S.P., Lechner, E. and Baker, N.R. (1991) Plant Physiol. 95, 529-535
4 Farquhar, G.D., von Caemmerer, S. and Berry, J.A. (1980) Planta 149, 78-90
5 Farquhar, G.D. and Sharkey, T.D. (1982) Annu. Rev. Plant Physiol. 33, 317-345
6 Baker, N.R., Nie, G. and Tomasevic, M. (1992) in Gaseous Pollutants and Plant Metabolism (Alscher, R. and Welburn, A.R. eds.), in press, Elsevier Applied Science, Amsterdam

THE EFFECT OF PROLONGED GROWTH IN ELEVATED CO_2 CONCENTRATIONS IN THE FIELD ON THE AMOUNTS OF DIFFERENT LEAF PROTEINS.

G.Y. NIE[1] AND S.P. LONG[1,2], DEPT. OF APPLIED SCI.[1], BROOKHAVEN NATL. LAB., UPTON, NY 11973, USA. DEPT. OF BIOLOGY[2], UNIVERSITY OF ESSEX, COLCHESTER, CO4 3SQ, UK.

1. INTRODUCTION

Atmospheric CO_2 concentration (C_a) is expected to rise to double pre-industrial concentrations within the next century (1). Increased C_a may stimulate photosynthetic CO_2 uptake (A) in C_3 species because of the low affinity of Rubisco for CO_2 and by inhibition of RubP oxygentation. Several controlled environment studies have suggested that this potential stimulation may be offset by decreased Rubisco contents and activities in leaves developed at elevated C_a, which can be related to decreased photosynthetic capacity in these leaves (2). Arp (3) has suggested that this decreased capacity may be an artifact of restriction of below-ground organ development, and hence sink-capacity, imposed by pot size. Four species grown over two or more years in elevated C_a in the field are used to address two questions. 1) Are changes in Rubisco content also observed when plants are grown with elevated C_a in the field without restriction on rooting volume? 2) Is Rubisco the only major leaf protein to show change in quantity in plants grown in elevated C_a over prolonged periods?

2. MATERIALS AND METHODS

The CO_2 concentration of the air around the plants of the C4 grass _Spartina patens_ and the C3 sedge _Scirpus olneyi_ growing on a tidal marsh of the Chesapeake Bay, Maryland, has been elevated to ca. 680 $\mu mol\ mol^{-1}$ for the past 6 years via open-top chambers (OTCs), with control chambers and unenclosed plots at ambient concentrations of 340 - 360 $\mu mol\ mol^{-1}$ (1). Similarly, plants of the understory shrub _Lindera venzion_ growing in the adjacent forest have been exposed to elevated (ca. 680 $\mu mol\ mol^{-1}$ CO_2 in air) and ambient (ca. 360 $\mu mol\ mol^{-1}$) via OTCs over 2 years. Sour orange trees (_Citrus aurantium_ L.) have been grown from the seedling stage in large OTCs in the field in Arizona for 6 years at ca. 650 $\mu mol\ mol^{-1}$ CO_2 with controls at current ambient concentrations (4). In May 1992 samples of fully expanded current year leaves were selected in each chamber, cut and immediately frozen in liquid N_2. To extract total proteins, leaves were ground to a powder in liquid N_2 and then resuspended in 10% TCA (5). Soluble proteins were obtained by removing membranes from the extract by centrifugation (37,000g, 30 min). Thylakoids were isolated as described previously (6). Proteins were separated by SDS-PAGE and Coomassie Blue stained gels scanned with a computing 2-dimensional densitometer (300S, Molecular Dynamics). Protein content was determined using Pierce BCA protein reagent.

N. Murata (ed.), Research in Photosynthesis, Vol. IV, 855–858.

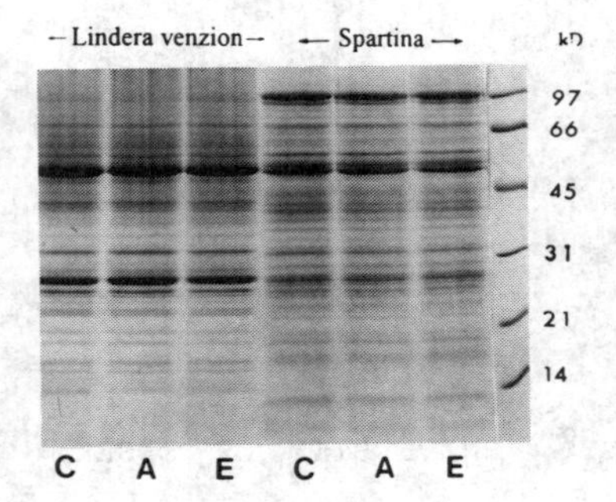

FIGURE 1. 12-18% gradient SDS-PAGE polypeptide profiles for total protein extracts of leaves of Lindera venzion and Spartina patens grown in open-top chambers at an elevated CO_2 concentration of ca. 680 µmol mol^{-1} (E), in chambers at ambient CO_2 concentrations (A) and outside of the chambers (C). Tracks were loaded on an equal leaf area basis. Molecular weights are indicated in kD.

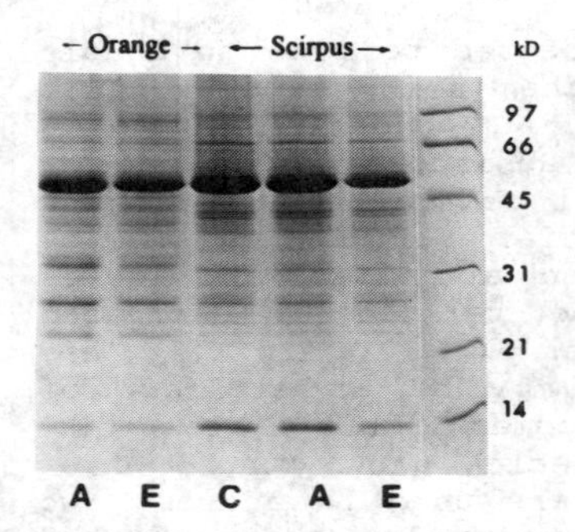

FIGURE 2. As for Fig. 1, but for total protein extracts of shoots of Scirpus olneyi and leaves of orange. For the orange trees the elevated chambers were maintained at ca. 650 µmol mol^{-1} of CO_2 in air.

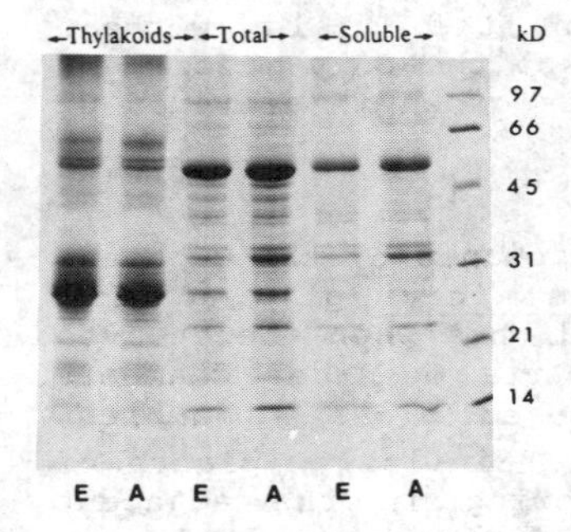

FIGURE 3. 12-18% gradient SDS-PAGE polypeptide profiles for total protein extracts, thylakoids and soluble proteins from leaves of orange grown at elevated CO_2 concentration of ca. 650 µmol mol^{-1} (E) and at current ambient CO_2 concentration (A). Each pair of tracks are loaded for the same area of leaf.

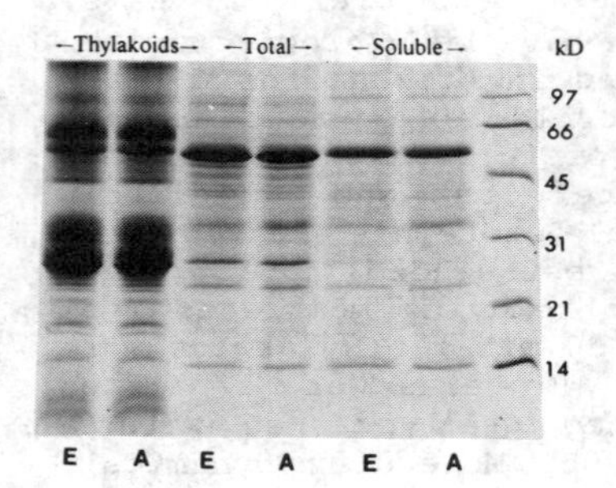

FIGURE 4. As for Fig 3, but with tracks loaded on an equal protein basis.

3 RESULTS AND DISCUSSION

Previous studies have suggested that photosynthesis in C_4 species is largely unaffected by growth in elevated CO_2 concentrations. These results suggest that despite 6 years growth at 680 µmol mol^{-1}, Spartina patens shows no discernible changes in quantities of any of the major leaf proteins on a unit leaf area basis, including the large and small sub-units of Rubisco and the primary carboxylase, PEPcase (Fig. 1). Similarly the understory C_3 shrub Lindera venzion also shows no discernible changes in protein concentrations, suggesting that ecological type may play a part in the capacity of leaf protein concentrations to respond to development in elevated CO_2 concentrations (Fig. 1). Unlike plants of open habitats, plants of the relatively still forest understories may frequently encounter CO_2 concentrations well above the mean for the free atmosphere. Rubisco activity is less likely to be limiting in a shade environment, hence an adaptive response of Rubisco contents is less likely.

In contrast, leaves of Scirpus olneyi and orange, showed reduction in leaf protein concentrations with prolonged growth in elevated CO_2 concentrations (Fig. 2). In both species, the 55 kDa large sub-unit of Rubisco shows a clear reduction in quantity. This may reflect the reduced requirement for Rubisco in an elevated CO_2 atmosphere (2). In S. olneyi this reduction appears to correspond to a decrease in the concentration of all soluble proteins. In orange, the degree of change varies for specific proteins. High MW proteins (>66 kDa) show little change in contrast to Rubisco. No significant differences in the quantities of the major thylakoid proteins could be detected (Fig. 3). On a leaf area basis, both the large and small sub-units of Rubisco show obvious decreases together with other proteins. When loaded on an equal protein basis it can be seen that the profile is still modified by growth in elevated CO_2 concentrations. Of particular note is a decrease in the soluble protein at 33-35 kD(Fig. 4). Densitometric analysis of the total protein profile shown in Fig. 3 suggested, that of the 14 most abundant proteins, 5 were unaffected by growth in elevated C_a, the remaining 9 showed varying degrees of reduction, down to 50% of concentrations in control leaves (Fig. 5). The largest decrease was in a 33-35 kDa soluble protein, which may correspond to carbonic anhydrase. The results suggest: 1) that even when rooting volume is unrestricted and plants are grown with a good supply of N, decrease in the quantity of Rubisco occurs, and 2) that Rubisco is only one of several soluble leaf proteins showing significant change in concentration in plants grown in elevated CO_2 concentrations.

ACKNOWLEDGMENTS

We thank Drs. B.G. Drake and G. Thompson of the Smithsonian Environmental Research Center and Drs. S.B. Idso and B.A. Kimball of the USDA/ARS Water Lab., for providing the plant material, and Keith Lewin and Dr. G.R. Hendrey of Brookhaven National Lab. for making this research possible. This research was performed under the auspices of the U.S. Department of Energy under contract No. DE-AC02-76CH00016.

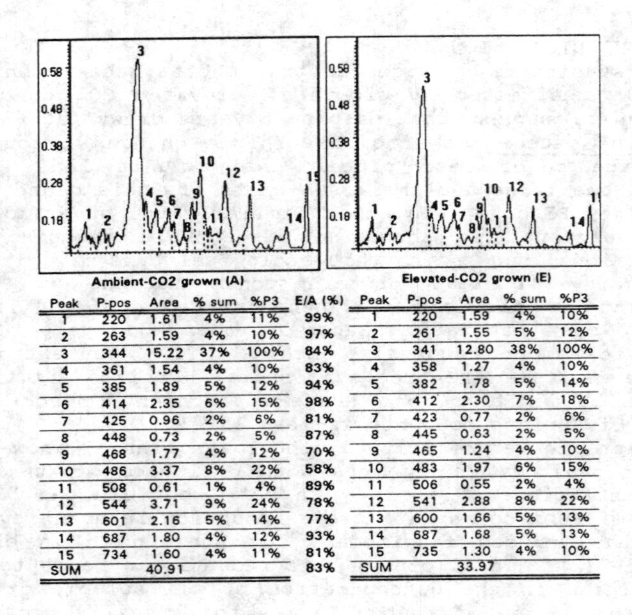

Peak	P-pos	Area	% sum	%P3	E/A (%)	Peak	P-pos	Area	% sum	%P3
1	220	1.61	4%	11%	99%	1	220	1.59	4%	10%
2	263	1.59	4%	10%	97%	2	261	1.55	5%	12%
3	344	15.22	37%	100%	84%	3	341	12.80	38%	100%
4	361	1.54	4%	10%	83%	4	358	1.27	4%	10%
5	385	1.89	5%	12%	94%	5	382	1.78	5%	14%
6	414	2.35	6%	15%	98%	6	412	2.30	7%	18%
7	425	0.96	2%	6%	81%	7	423	0.77	2%	6%
8	448	0.73	2%	5%	87%	8	445	0.63	2%	5%
9	468	1.77	4%	12%	70%	9	465	1.24	4%	10%
10	486	3.37	8%	22%	58%	10	483	1.97	6%	15%
11	508	0.61	1%	4%	89%	11	506	0.55	2%	4%
12	544	3.71	9%	24%	78%	12	541	2.88	8%	22%
13	601	2.16	5%	14%	77%	13	600	1.66	5%	13%
14	687	1.80	4%	12%	93%	14	687	1.68	5%	13%
15	734	1.60	4%	11%	81%	15	735	1.30	4%	10%
SUM		40.91			83%	SUM		33.97		

Figure 5. Densitometric analysis of the total protein extract separated by 12-18% gradient SDS-PAGE orange leaves, as illustrated in Fig. 3. The final columns for the profiles of each treatment (%P3) indicate the area of each peak relative to that for the large sub-unit of Rubisco (peak 3). The column labelled E/A compares each peak from the elevated CO_2 leaves with that from the ambient CO_2 leaves for the 15 major bands.

REFERENCES

1 Curtis PS, Drake BG. Leadley PW, Arp WJ, Wigham DF (1989) Oecologia 78:20-29
2 Bowes G (1991) Plant Cell Env. 14,795-806
3 Arp, W.J. (1992) Plant Cell Env. 14, 869-876.
4 Idso SB and Kimball BA (1992) Plant Physiol. 99, 341-343
5 Damerval C, de Vienne D, Zivy M and Thiellement H (1986) Electrophoresis 7: 52-54
6 Hayden DB, Baker NR, Percival MP and Becwith PB (1986). Biochim. Biophys. Acta 851, 86-92

Index of Names

Aartsma, T.J., **I**.1.105, **I**.1.161, **II**.5.81
Abarca, M.D., **I**.4.557
Abo-Seda, S.A., **II**.8.737
Adamec, F., **I**.2.335
Adamska, I., **III**.12.335, **IV**.23.403
Adamson, H., **III**.10.79
Adir, N., **II**.5.195
Aebersold, R., **I**.2.195
Agalidis, I., **I**.1.33
Agata, W., **IV**.21.235, **IV**.24.663, **IV**.24.667
Agati, G., **IV**.24.639
Ågren, H., **II**.6.421
Aguiló, F., **IV**.24.691
Aida, T., **III**.13.397
Aizawa, K., **IV**.22.301, **IV**.22.329
Ajlani, G., **III**.15.575
Akabori, K., **II**.5.123, **II**.5.127
Akamatsu, T., **II**.5.101
Akasaka, T., **II**.5.215
Åkerlund, H.-E., **I**.2.231, **I**.2.235
Albertsson, P.-Å., **I**.2.283, **II**.7.507, **III**.14.527
Albrecht, A.C., **I**.2.179
Albrieux, C., **III**.13.453
Alden, R.G., **I**.3.377
Alejar, A.A., **IV**.19.107, **IV**.24.707, **IV**.24.709
Alexander, N., **IV**.22.325
Allen, J.F., **I**.2.243, **IV**.22.345, **IV**.23.549
Allen, J.P., **I**.3.377, **I**.3.381
Allen, L.H., **IV**.26.831
Alsaadi, R., **II**.7.567
Amako, K., **IV**.23.529
Ambrosini, I., **IV**.24.639
Ambroz, M., **I**.2.335
America, A., **III**.11.173
Amesz, J., **I**.1.105, **I**.1.161, **I**.3.393, **I**.3.453, **III**.10.3
Amino, S.-I., **IV**.25.777
Amory, A., **III**.13.449
Ananyev, G.M., **II**.6.441
Anastassiou, R., **III**.12.327
Anbudurai, P.R., **III**.13.409
Andersen, B., **I**.4.497, **I**.4.609
Andersen, R.V., **III**.10.27, **III**.10.31
Anderson, J.M., **IV**.22.361, **IV**.23.443
Andersson, B., **I**.2.307, **II**.8.773, **IV**.23.395, **IV**.23.435, **IV**.23.455, **IV**.23.479, **IV**.23.521
Andoh, T., **IV**.21.251
Andréasson, L.-E., **I**.2.235, **II**.6.301, **II**.6.353
Andreo, C.S., **III**.18.855
Andrews, T.J., **III**.16.653, **IV**.24.595
Andrianov, V., **III**.12.299
Angerhofer, A., **I**.1.129
Antohe, S., **II**.9.845
Antonenko, Y.N., **II**.8.689
Aoki, N., **III**.17.737
Apostolova, E., **IV**.20.165
Araga, C., **II**.5.127
Arakawa, K., **IV**.21.247
Arata, H., **II**.7.575, **III**.10.91, **III**.18.835, **III**.18.899
Ardelean, I.I., **II**.7.623
Arellano, J.B., **II**.5.105
Argyroudi-Akoyunoglou, J.H., **III**.12.327
Arieli, B., **II**.7.483
Aro, E.-M., **II**.5.171, **IV**.22.309, **IV**.23.419, **IV**.23.431, **IV**.23.479, **IV**.23.483
Arrabaça, M.C., **III**.18.847, **IV**.21.295
Aruga, S., **III**.18.783
Arvidsson, P.-O., **I**.2.235, **IV**.24.595
Arvidsson, Y.B.C., **IV**.24.595
Asada, K., **II**.5.115, **II**.7.487, **II**.7.559, **II**.7.563, **II**.7.603, **II**.7.607, **II**.7.627, **IV**.23.529, **IV**.23.533
Asada, Y., **I**.3.445, **I**.3.449, **I**.3.477
Asahi, T., **II**.9.787, **II**.9.805
Asakura, M., **IV**.21.235
Asayama, M., **III**.13.397
Ashida, H., **III**.12.307

Aso, A., **II**.7.539
Aso, S., **IV**.21.259
Astier, C., **III**.15.575
Aust, V., **I**.1.129
Avital, S., **II**.8.653
Aviv, D, **IV**.23.557
Axelsen, K.B., **III**.10.31
Baba, K., **IV**.23.553
Baba, T., **III**.18.923
Babcock, G.T., **II**.6.381
Babu, T.S., **II**.7.591
Badenhorst, P., **III**.13.449
Bader, K.P., **II**.6.433
Baker, J.T., **IV**.26.831
Baker, N.R., **IV**.20.153
Bakou, A., **II**.6.337
Balachandran, S., **II**.5.37
Bald, D., **I**.4.629
Ball, K., **III**.17.697
Baltscheffsky, M., **III**.13.385
Bandilla, M., **I**.1.109
Barbato, R., **IV**.23.505
Barber, J., **II**.5.243, **II**.5.247, **III**.13.469, **IV**.23.395, **IV**.23.427, **IV**.23.463
Barkla, B.J., **IV**.21.219
Baron, A.C., **IV**.19.47
Barón, M., **I**.5.105
Barquera, B., **II**.7.463
Barrett, S.J., **I**.1.77
Barzda, V., **II**.7.631
Bassi, R., **I**.2.287, **I**.2.291, **II**.5.13
Battistelli, A., **IV**.21.275
Bauer, C.E., **III**.10.19
Beator, J., **III**.12.331
Beck, J., **IV**.19.95
Becker, T., **IV**.19.11
Bédu, S., **III**.18.771, **III**.18.819
Bei-Paraskevopoulou, T., **III**.12.327
Belyaeva, O.B., **III**.10.75
Ben, G., **IV**.20.173
Benson, A.A., **III**.18.911
Bergantino, E., **II**.5.13
Bernier, M., **II**.5.97
Berry, J.A., **III**.18.915
Berry, J.O., **III**.12.225
Berry-Lowe, S., **III**.10.31
Berthomieu, C., **II**.5.49, **II**.5.53
Bertrand, M., **III**.10.71
Beuf, L., **III**.18.771, **III**.18.819
Bezsmertnaya, I.N., **I**.4.549
Bhagwat, A.S., **II**.7.499, **III**.18.863
Bialek-Bylka, G., **II**.9.849
Biggins, J., **I**.4.537
Bingham, S.E., **I**.4.561
Bishop, N.I., **III**.13.433, **IV**.22.389
Bittl, R., **I**.3.461
Blackwell, R.D., **III**.18.891, **IV**.19.27
Blanchard-Desce, M., **II**.6.273
Blankenship, R.E., **I**.1.53, **I**.1.121, **I**.3.417, **II**.7.595
Blikman, R., **IV**.21.287
Blokesch, A., **II**.7.499
Blubaugh, D.J., **II**.6.361, **IV**.23.451
Blumwald, E., **IV**.21.219
Bocek, J., **I**.2.335
Boekema, E.J., **I**.4.629, **II**.8.645
Böger, P., **III**.10.11
Bögershausen, O., **II**.6.333
Bogorad, L., **I**.4.557
Bohnert, H.J., **IV**.21.195
Boinski, J.J., **III**.12.225
Bolhár-Nordenkampf, H.R., **IV**.22.337, **IV**.22.369
Bolle, C., **III**.12.219, **III**.13.377
Bönigk, B., **I**.3.433
Boote, K.J., **IV**.26.831
Borisov, A., **I**.1.117
Borovkov, V.V., **II**.9.841
Borrias, M., **III**.11.165
Bosch, M.K., **I**.3.457
Boschetti, A., **III**.11.197
Bose, S., **III**.15.551
Böthin, B., **IV**.23.471
Böttcher, B., **II**.8.645
Boumans, H., **IV**.24.615
Boussac, A., **II**.5.21, **II**.5.53, **II**.5.235
Boussiba, S., **III**.13.429
Bowlby, N., **II**.6.381

Bowsher, C.G., **IV**.19.35
Bowyer, J., **II**.5.203, **II**.5.207, **II**.5.211
Boyd, K., **III**.13.421
Boynton, J.E., **III**.13.417, **III**.15.567
Brand, M., **I**.1.153
Bratt, C.E., **I**.2.231, **I**.2.235
Bredenkamp, G.J., **IV**.20.153
Breton, J., **I**.3.437, **I**.4.633, **II**.5.53
Briantais, J.M., **IV**.24.603
Britt, R.D., **II**.6.317
Britton, G., **IV**.23.581
Brock, I.W., **III**.11.141
Brody, S.S., **I**.2.331
Brudvig, G.W., **II**.5.85
Brune, D.C., **II**.7.595
Bryant, D.A., **I**.1.25, **I**.1.69, **I**.4.565
Buchanan, S., **I**.3.341
Büchem-Osmond, C., **III**.16.653
Buetow, D., **III**.12.295
Burghaus, O., **II**.5.109
Burnap, R., **II**.5.179
Buser, C.A., **II**.5.85
Busheva, M., **IV**.20.165
Büssis, D., **IV**.25.765
Bustos, S.A., **III**.13.381
Büttner, M., **I**.4.513, **II**.7.471
Bylina, E.J., **I**.3.369
Caboche, M., **IV**.19.11
Cadiz, N.M., **IV**.19.107
Cai, D., **III**.13.349, **III**.13.377
Camadro, J.-M., **III**.15.543
Campbell, W.H., **III**.17.675, **IV**.19.63
Canja, D., **II**.7.623
Cao, W.-H., **II**.7.559
Cardon, Z.G., **III**.18.915
Carlberg, I., **II**.8.773
Carpentier, R., **II**.5.97, **II**.5.139, **IV**.20.157
Carraro, L., **III**.14.523
Carrasco, J.L., **III**.18.927
Carrillo, N., **III**.12.319
Cases, R., **II**.5.73
Casimiro, D.R., **II**.9.829
Castrillo, M., **IV**.21.279
Cavaco, A.M., **III**.18.847
Chamovitz, D., **III**.10.11
Chan, R.L., **III**.16.641
Chang, H., **IV**.24.623
Chang, J.-Y., **IV**.19.95
Chang, N.K., **I**.4.557
Charland, M., **IV**.23.459
Charng, Y.-Y., **III**.17.697
Chastain, C., **III**.18.757
Chatellard, Ph., **III**.12.255
Chavan, A.J., **III**.16.601
Chen, G.-X., **II**.5.115, **IV**.23.451
Chen, H.-B., **III**.16.645
Chen, J., **IV**.24.671, **IV**.24.675
Chen, Z., **III**.16.593, **III**.18.757
Chen, Z.-L., **III**.16.649
Chen, Z.-Q., **II**.8.769
Cheng, P., **I**.1.121
Cheniae, G.M., **II**.6.361, **IV**.23.451
Cherepanov, D.A., **II**.7.447
Chiang, G.G., **I**.1.157
Chiou, H.-C., **I**.3.417
Chitnis, P., **I**.4.513
Chitty, J., **III**.18.757
Choi, H.-K., **I**.2.303
Choi, S.Y., **I**.4.557, **IV**.25.789
Chollet, R., **III**.18.851
Choquet, Y., **III**.13.359
Chow, W.S., **IV**.22.361, **IV**.23.443
Christensen, H.E.M., **II**.7.523
Christensen, R.L., **I**.1.125
Chu, Z.X., **I**.2.275
Chueca, A., **II**.5.105, **III**.18.927
Chung, S., **I**.1.69
Ciurana, N.R., **III**.11.165
Clarke, A., **III**.18.815
Clausmeyer, S, **III**.13.349
Cline, K., **III**.11.149
Cogdell, R.J., **I**.1.3, **I**.1.77, **I**.1.149
Cohen, Y., **I**.4.505
Collier, J.L., **IV**.19.3
Conrad, L.S., **II**.7.523
Cook, K.M., **III**.13.469
Cooper, M.A., **IV**.19.35

Copertino, D.W., **III**.12.271
Cornic, G., **IV**.21.211
Corten, E.P.M., **I**.1.101
Coryell, V.H., **I**.3.377
Cotton, N.P.J., **II**.8.685
Cournac, L., **IV**.24.695
Coutts, J.H., **IV**.25.789
Crafts-Brandner, S.J., **III**.16.629
Cramer, W.A., **II**.7.447, **II**.7.495
Cresswell, C., **III**.13.449
Crétin, C., **III**.17.701
Crielaard, W., **II**.7.639
Critchley, C., **IV**.22.337, **IV**.23.423, **IV**.24.643
Crofts, A.R., **II**.5.131, **II**.7.463, **II**.7.491, **II**.7.635
Csèplö, A., **III**.12.219
Cunningham, I.J., **II**.8.685
Cunningham, Jr., F.X., **I**.2.315
Cushman, J.C., **IV**.21.195
da Silva, A.B., **III**.18.847, **IV**.21.295
da Silva, J.M. **IV**.21.295
Dai, Y.-L., **II**.7.615
Daie, J., **III**.17.691
Dainese, P., **I**.2.287, **I**.2.291, **II**.5.13
Daldal, F., **II**.8.757, **II**.8.761
Daley, P., **II**.5.37
Daniels, M., **III**.10.47
Darszon, A., **II**.8.741
Dassen, H.J., **II**.8.681
Datta, R., **III**.17.721
Dau, H., **II**.5.239
Davidson, E., **II**.8.757
Davidsson, L., **II**.5.251
de Boer, A.D., **II**.7.519
de Jager, D., **III**.10.119
de Las Rivas, J., **IV**.23.395, **IV**.23.427, **IV**.23.463
de Keyzer, M., **I**.3.457
de Kouchkovsky, Y., **II**.8.709
de Kruijff, B., **III**.11.133, **III**.11.185
de Lamotte, F., **III**.17.659
Decoster, B., **I**.1.125
Decottignies, P., **III**.17.659, **III**.17.701, **III**.17.705
Deinum, G., **I**.1.161
Dekker, J., **III**.11.165, **IV**.24.631
Dekker, J.P., **I**.2.263, **I**.2.271, **II**.6.325
Delgado, E., **IV**.26.835
Deligiannakis, Y., **II**.5.119
DeRocher, E.J., **IV**.21.195
DeRose, V.J., **II**.5.109, **II**.6.281
Dever, L.V., **III**.18.891
Devi, M.T., **III**.18.887
Dian, J., **I**.2.335
Dickerson, N.S., **III**.13.381
Dietz, K.-J., **III**.18.775
Dimon, B., **IV**.24.603, **IV**.24.695
Diner, B.A., **II**.5.119, **II**.5.175
Ding, D.-Q., **IV**.25.777
Dionisi, H.M., **III**.16.637
Dismukes, G.C., **II**.6.257, **II**.6.305
Dobek, A., **I**.4.633
Doi, M., **I**.1.45, **III**.10.99
Dorcus, D., **II**.8.765
dos Santos, C.P., **II**.5., **II**.7.515
Douce, R., **III**.13.453
Draber, W., **III**.15.537
Dracheva, S., **I**.1.53
Drake, B.G., **IV**.26.811
Drepper, F., **II**.8.773
Drews, G., **I**.1.153
Driesenaar, A.R.J., **IV**.23.557
Drincovich, M.F., **III**.18.855
Driscoll, S.P., **IV**.26.835
Ducruet, J.-M., **IV**.20.185
Duff, S.M.G., **III**.18.851
Durnford, D.G., **I**.2.195, **I**.2.211
Durrant, J.R., **II**.5.243, **II**.5.247
Duval, J.C., **IV**.23.581
Eaton-Rye, J.J., **I**.2.239
Ebina, M., **II**.6.389, **II**.6.397
Edwards, G.E., **III**.18.907
Eggenberg, P., **IV**.24.611
Egorov, S.Yu., **III**.10.111
Ehlert, J., **I**.1.109
Ehrenheim, A.M., **I**.2.279
EL-Saad, M.M.A., **II**.8.737

Emes, M.J., **IV**.19.35
Emetarom, C.M., **II**.5.93
Enami, I., **I**.4.581, **II**.6.377
Endo, T., **II**.7.603, **II**.7.607, **III**.11.181
Engels, P.W., **II**.7.639
Erdös, G., **III**.12.295
Erickson, J.M., **II**.5.151, **III**.13.421
Eriksson, J., **III**.13.401
Ermler, U., **I**.3.341
Erokhin, Yu., **I**.3.441
Eskins, K., **IV**.22.325
Espe, M., **II**.6.381
Etchebest, C., **II**.5.147
Evans, J.R., **IV**.24.595
Evans, M.C.W., **I**.4.617, **II**.6.377
Evans, L.T., **IV**.24, **IV**.24.587
Everly, R.-M., **II**.7.447
Ezoe, T., **II**.7.531
Falk, J., **III**.12.267
Falk, S., **III**.18.815
Falkowski, P.G., **IV**.26.803
Farage, P.K., **IV**.26.851
Farhoosh, R., **I**.1.125
Farr, T.J., **IV**.19.51
Feher, G., **I**.3.349, **II**.5.195
Feick, R.G., **I**.1.41
Feiler, U., **I**.3.409
Feng, Y., **IV**.24.671, **IV**.24.675
Ferreyra, R.G., **III**.16.637
Ficner, R., **I**.1.57
Filatova, N.I., **IV**.20.181
Finazzi, G., **I**.2.279
Finkele, U., **I**.3.429
Fischer, K., **III**.17.667
Fleck, I., **IV**.24.687
Flieger, K., **III**.12.219
Foidl, M., **I**.1.89
Flonta, M.L., **II**.7.623
Flügge, U.-I., **III**.17.667
Fonollá, J., **III**.18.927
Forti, G., **I**.2.279
Foyer, C.H., **IV**.25.737
Frackowiak, D., **I**.1.145
Franceschi, V.R., **III**.16.625
Franck, F., **III**.10.71
Frank, H.A., **I**.1.125
Franzén, L.-G., **IV**.23.491
Fraser, P.D., **III**.10.51
Frasch, W.D., **II**.8.745
Fredriksson, P-.O., **IV**.23.491
Freer, A.A., **I**.1.3
Freiberg, A., **II**.5.65
Friso, G., **IV**.23.505
Fritzsch, G., **I**.3.341, **I**.3.397
Frizzo, A., **IV**.23.505
Fromme, R., **I**.4.521, **II**.5.183
Fu, W., **IV**.21.291
Füchsle, G., **I**.3.461
Fujihira, M., **I**.3.449
Fujii, T., **III**.18.903
Fujii, Ch., **IV**.22.333
Fujita, K., **IV**.19.79
Fujita, Y., **II**.7.503, **III**.10.67, **III**.14.491, **IV**.19.103, **IV**.22.301, **IV**.22.329
Fujiwara, S., **III**.12.239
Fukumori, Y., **II**.7.555
Fukuyama, K., **III**.14.491
Fukuyama, T., **IV**.21.271
Fukuzawa, H., **III**.18.799
Furbacher, P.N., **II**.7.447
Furbank, R.T., **III**.18.757
Furuki, M., **I**.4.621
Furuta, Y., **IV**.22.333
Fuse, H., **III**.10.87
Fuse, T., **III**.12.323, **IV**.20.169
Gabay, C., **III**.13.437
Gadal, P., **III**.17.701
Gaines, III, G.L., **II**.9.795
Gal, A., **IV**.23.403
Galun, E., **IV**.23.557
Galtier, N., **IV**.25.737
Gantt, E., **I**.2.315
Gao, Z.-P., **I**.2.251
Gapinski, J., **I**.4.633
Garab, G., **I**.2.171, **II**.7.631
Gardeström, P., **III**.17.709
Gardet-Salvi, L., **II**.7.539
Gardiner, A.T., **I**.1.77, **I**.1.149

Garlaschi, F.M., **I**.2.291
Garnir, H.P., **III**.10.71
Gast, P., **I**.3.413, **I**.3.457, **I**.4.553, **II**.6.325
Gastal, F., **IV**.25.789
Gatzen, G., **II**.5.69
Gause, K., **II**.7.455
Gawronski, S.W., **III**.13.405
Gessner, C., **I**.3.433
Geel, C., **IV**.23.525
Geerts, D., **III**.11.165
Geiken, B., **II**.6.417, **IV**.24.643
Gennis, R., **II**.7.463
Gentle, S., **IV**.26.847
Genty, B., **IV**.24.603
Gerasimenko, T.V., **IV**.26.823
Gerez, C., **II**.5.155
Gest, H., **III**.10.19
Ghanotakis, D.F., **II**.6.337
Ghirardi, M.L., **II**.6.357
Ghiretti-Magaldi, A., **II**.5.13
Giacometti, G.M., **IV**.23.505
Giardi, M.T., **IV**.23.577
Gibbs, P.B., **I**.4.561
Gibson, S., **III**.10.55
Gilchrist, M.L., **II**.6.317
Gillham, N.W., **III**.13.417, **III**.15.567
Gilmore, A.M., **I**.2.255
Gilon, T., **I**.4.505
Gimmler, H., **IV**.21.203
Girard-Bascou, J., **III**.13.359
Glémin, A., **IV**.20.185
Godde, D., **III**.15.563, **IV**.23.467, **IV**.23.501
Golbeck, J.H., **I**.4.487, **I**.4.565, **I**.4.573, **IV**.23.451
Golden, S.S., **III**.13.381
Goldschmidt-Clermont, M., **III**.13.359, **III**.13.393
Golecki, J.R., **I**.1.89
Gombos, Z., **IV**.20.113
Gong, H., **IV**.23.549
Gorgé, J.L., **II**.5.105, **III**.18.927
Gosztola, D., **II**.9.795
Goto, K., **III**.13.441
Gotor, C., **III**.16.593
Gough, S.P., **III**.10.31
Goulas, Y., **IV**.24.603
Gounaris, K., **II**.5.89
Govindjee, **II**.5.29, **II**.5.41, **II**.5.143
Gräber, P., **II**.8.645
Granell, A., **III**.13.445
Grau, D., **IV**.24.687
Gray, H.B., **II**.9.829
Gray, K.A., **II**.8.757
Green, B.R., **I**.2.195, **I**.2.211
Greer, D.H., **IV**.23.561
Greppin, H., **II**.8.741
Gribkov, A.A., **II**.9.841
Griebenow, K., **II**.5.69
Grimes, H.D., **IV**.25.745
Grimm, B., **III**.10.31
Grimme, L.H., **III**.17.717
Grodzitzki, D., **II**.7.471
Gromet-Elhanan, Z., **II**.8.653
Groot, M.L., **I**.2.263, **I**.2.271
Grossman, A.R., **I**.1.157, **IV**.19.3
Groth, G., **II**.8.669
Gu, T.-Q., **III**.10.83
Guiducci, M., **IV**.21.275
Günter, G., **IV**.25.765
Gust, D., **II**.9.801
Guthrie, N., **I**.1.3
Ha, S.-B., **IV**.24.623
Hacker, B., **II**.7.463
Haehnel, W., **II**.7.455, **II**.8.773
Hageman, J., **III**.11.173
Hagman, Å. 8, **IV**.23.435
Hah, Y.-C., **IV**.19.67
Hakala, K., **IV**.26.819
Hála, J., **I**.2.335
Haley, B.E., **III**.16.601
Hallick, R.B., **III**.12.271
Halloren, E., **I**.1.3
Hamid. A., **IV**.24.663
Han, F., **IV**.20.173
Han, K.-C., **II**.6.365
Hanley, J.A., **I**.4.617

Hara, M., I.3.445, I.3.449
Harbinson, J., II.7.527, IV.24.659
Harel, E., III.11.213
Harker, M., III.10.47, IV.23.581
Harn, C., III.17.691
Harnecker, J., II.7.587
Harris, D.A., II.8.645, III.13.385
Harris, E.H., III.15.567
Harrison, M.A., IV.22.345
Hart, H.'t, III.18.943
Hase, T., II.7.535
Hashimoto, A., II.5.215
Hashimoto, M., IV.19.95
Hashimoto, Y., IV.21.271
Hashimoto-Kumpaisal, R., IV.19.91
Hassidim, M., III.13.437
Hastings, G., II.5.243, II.5.247
Hatanaka, H., I.4.601, I.4.605
Hatch, M.D., III.18.747
Haumann, M., II.6.333
Hauska, G., I.4.513, II.7.471, II.7.483
Hausler, R.E., IV.19.27
Havaux, M., IV.20.149
Hayashi, H., IV.20.113, IV.20.137, IV.20.141
Hayashida, N., III.12.307, III.18.923
Hazell, L., III.11.141
He, D.-X., IV.21.291
Heathcote, P., I.4.617
Hebeler, M., III.17.717
Heber, U., II.7.487
Hefer, M., IV.23.467
Heifetz, P.B., III.13.417
Heimann, C., II.6.325, II.6.341
Heineke, D., IV.25.765
Heldt, H.W., IV.25.765, IV.25.773
Hellingwerf, K.-J., II.7.639
Hemelrijk, P.W., II.5.33
Hendrey, G., IV.26.811
Henry, R., III.11.149
Hentrich, S., III.17.717
Hermoso, R., III.18.927
Herrmann, I., II.7.483, III.13.349,
Herrmann, R.G., II.7.455, III.12.219, III.13.377
Hermsmeier, D., III.13.433
Hervás, M., II.8.697
Hibino, T., I.4.597, II.7.519
Hideg, É., III.10.107
Hidema, J., IV.22.365, IV.22.377, IV.24.655
Hienerwadel, R., I.3.437, II.5.49
Higaki, A., IV.19.79, IV.19.83
Higashi, S., IV.20.113
Hikita, M., II.9.809
Hikosaka, K., IV.22.381
Hillier, W., II.5.167
Hillmann, B., II.5.45
Hinrichs, W., I.4.521
Hirano, A., II.5.175
Hirano, M., I.1.73, I.4.601, II.6.413
Hirasawa, T., IV.21.283
Hirata, Y., I.3.445, I.3.449
Hirayama, O., III.17.741
Hirota, M., I.1.17, I.1.81, I.1.113, I.1.137
Hirschberg, J., II.5.223, III.10.11, IV.23.403
Hisabori, T., II.8.725, II.8.729
Hiyama, T., I.4.613, I.4.621
Hladík, J., I.4.585
Ho, L.C., IV.25.729
Hochkoeppler, A., II.7.599
Hod, G.B., III.11.213
Hofbauer, U., I.1.129
Hoff, A.J., I.2.215, I.3.413, I.3.457, I.4.553
Hofstraat, J.W., IV.23.525
Hoganson, C.W., II.6.381
Hohm-Veit, S., II.5.183
Holton, B., II.7.567
Holtum, J.A.M., III.15.571
Holzwarth, A.R., I.2.187, II.5.69
Hong, S., I.2.303, III.16.593
Hong, Y.-N., IV.24.699
Horton, P., I.2.311
Hoshina, S., I.4.581
Hotchkiss, T., III.12.225
Howarth, C., IV.20.121

Huang, D., **II**.7.447, **II**.7.495
Huang, F., **I**.2.275
Huang, H., **IV**.25.753
Huang, Z.H., **II**.8.781
Huber, J.L., **III**.17.675
Huber, R., **I**.1.57
Huber, S.C., **III**.17.675, **IV**.25.737
Huckett, B., **III**.13.449
Hudson, G.S., **IV**.24.595
Hugly, S., **III**.10.55
Hulford, A., **III**.11.141
Humbeck, K., **IV**.22.389
Hundal, T., **IV**.23.455
Huner, N.P.A., **IV**.23.455
Hunt, A., **II**.5.207
Huppe, H.C., **IV**.19.51
Hussey, P., **II**.5.207
Iba, K., **III**.10.55, **III**.10.95, **III**.12.323, **IV**.20.169
Ida, K., **I**.2.223, **IV**.24.635
Ida, S., **IV**.19.83
Iglesias, A., **III**.17.697
Ignatov, N.V., **III**.10.75
Ihara, K., **II**.8.749
Iida, K., **II**.9.809
Iijima,O. **III**.13.397
Ikawa, T., **III**.18.919, **IV**.19.59
Ikegami, I., **I**.4.589
Ikehara, N., **II**.8.701
Ikeuchi, M., **II**.5.175
Il, P.C., **III**.12.299
Ilík, P., **IV**.20.177
Imaizumi, N., **III**.18.875
Imbault, P., **III**.16.641
Inagaki, J., **III**.11.177
Inagaki, N., **III**.12.287, **III**.12.291
Incharoensakdi, A., **III**.10.103
Ingemarsson, B., **IV**.19.63
Inoué, H., **II**.6.405, **II**.7.579, **II**.7.619, **III**.11.205
Inoue, K., **I**.3.389, **I**.3.393, **I**.4.577
Inoue, Y., **II**.5.175, **II**.5.179, **II**.6.293, **II**.6.309, **II**.6.313, **II**.6.369, **II**.6.401, **II**.6.429, **II**.6.429
Inthorn, D., **III**.10.103
Irifune, K., **III**.13.413, **IV**.19.79, **IV**.19.83
Irrgang, K.-D., **II**.5.237, **II**.6.417
Isaacs, N., **I**.1.3
Ishida, K., **III**.18.903
Ishihara, K., **II**.9.833, **III**.18.875, **IV**.21.283, **IV**.24.647, **IV**.25.781, **IV**.25.785
Ishii, R., **IV**.24.683
Ishii, T., **II**.8.729
Ishikawa, H., **I**.4.597
Ishikawa, M., **III**.18.923
Ishikawa, T., **III**.17.741
Ishikawa, Y., **II**.5.187
Ishitani, M., **IV**.21.239
Ishizaki-Nishizawa, O., **IV**.20.113
Ishizuka, M., **II**.7.571
Islam, M.T., **IV**.24.663
Isono, K., **III**.12.311
Issakidis, E., **III**.17.659, **III**.17.701, **III**.17.705
Istokovics, A., **II**.7.631
Itoh, S., **I**.3.385, **I**.3.393, **I**.4.529, **I**.4.541, **I**.4.581, **III**.13.389
Iwadate, H., **II**.7.539
Iwahashi, H., **III**.12.239
Iwaki, H., **IV**.22.373
Iwaki, M., **I**.4.529, **I**.4.541
Iwamoto, K., **III**.18.919
Iwasaki, G., **IV**.19.99
Iwasaki, I., **III**.18.835, **III**.18.899
Iwasaki, N., **IV**.24.723
Iwasaki, T., **IV**.21.227
Iwasaki, Y., **I**.4.625
Iwata, N., **III**.10.59
Izui, K., **III**.18.823, **III**.18.827, **III**.18.831, **III**.18.839
Jackson, J.B., **II**.8.685
Jacquot, J.-P., **III**.17.659, **III**.17.701, **III**.17.705
Jahns, P., **II**.6.333
Jang, J.-C., **IV**.25.753
Jans, W., **IV**.21.287

Jansen, T., II.7.455
Jansson, C., II.5.155, III.13.401, IV.23.419, IV.23.483
Jeannette, E., IV.25.761
Jegerschöld, C., II.6.421
Jennings, R.C., I.2.291
Jensen, R.G., III.16.617
Ji, B. P-735, IV.23.565
Jiang, G.Z., II.5.219
Jiao, D., IV.23.565
Jin, T., II.7.551
Jin, Y., IV.19.83
Jirsakova, V., I.1.33
Jo, J., III.18.871
Jones, T.L., IV.20.145
Joseph, D.M., II.5.243
Joset, F., III.18.771, III.18.819
Joshi, M.K., III.15.551
Joyard, J., III.13.453
Jun, S.-S., I.4.537
Junge, W., II.6.333, II.8.669
Jursinic, P.A., II.5.179
Kaipiainen, E.L., IV.26.823
Kaiser, K., I.1.77
Kakitani, T., I.3.425
Kakutani, S., I.3.385
Kalina, J., IV.20.177
Kallas, T., II.7.567
Kallio, T., II.5.155, IV.23.419, IV.23.483
Kalosaka, K., II.6.349
Kamachi, H., II.6.393
Kamada, M., IV.19.79, IV.19.83
Kamath, B.G., III.18.863
Kamimura, K., III.10.87
Kamo, M., II.7.539
Kanai, R., III.17.737, IV.26.839
Kanai, S., II.6.413
Kanazawa, A., II.5.131
Kaneko, S., III.18.875
Kaneko, Y., I.2.223
Kanemoto, M., II.9.833
Kang, S.-O., IV.19.67
Kanivets, N.P., II.9.837
Kannangara, C.G., III.10.31, III.10.43
Kano-Murakami, Y., II.7.583, III.17.713, III.18.843, III.18.879
Kao, M.Y., II.5.93
Kaphengst, K.J., II.5.93
Kaplan, A., III.13.437
Karapetyan, N.V., I.4.549
Karas, M., II.7.455
Karukstis, K.K., II.5.93
Kasamo, K., IV.21.255
Kashino, Y., II.5.135, II.5.163, II.6.369
Katashiba, K., III.11.157
Katcoff, D., I.2.203
Katoh, S., I.1.73, I.4.601, I.4.605, II.6.365, II.6.377, II.6.413, IV.22.341, IV.22.381
Katoh, T., I.2.227
Katz, E., I.3.441
Kawaguchi, A., III.10.63
Kawamori, A., II.5.57, II.5.61
Kawamoto, K., II.5.115
Kawamukai, M., III.11.157
Kawamura, K., II.5., III.11.181
Kawamura, T., III.18.827
Kawasaki, T., III.18.923
Kazandjian, A., IV.21.279
Kazimirko, Y.V., IV.22.353
Keasar, C., I.4.505, II.5.223
Keegstra, K., III.11.173
Keller, M., III.16.641
Kellner, E., II.7.471
Kemppi, V., IV.26.827
Kerfeld, C., I.1.49
Kernen, P., II.8.741
Kettunen, R., II.5.171, IV.22.309
Keys, A., III.16.609
Khangulov, S.V., II.6.257
Kharkats, Yu.I., I.3.481
Kheilrolomoon, A., IV.19.99
Kim, J.H., IV.22.317, IV.24.709
Kim, J.S., I.4.557
Kim, J.-Y., IV.19.67
Kinoshita, T., IV.24.719
Kishitani, S., IV.21.247

Kita, N., **III**.10.115
Kitao, M., **IV**.24.703
Kitamura, K., **II**.5.127
Kitayama, K., **IV**.23.487
Kitayama, M., **III**.18.935, **III**.18.939
Kittsteiner, U., **III**.15.555
Kiyosue, T., **IV**.21.227
Kiyota, S., **IV**.19.87
Kjær, B., **I**.3.465, **I**.4.497
Kjærulff, S., **I**.4.497, **I**.4.593
Klein, M.P., **II**.5.109, **II**.6.281
Kleinherenbrink, F.A.M., **I**.3.413, **I**.3.453, **II**.6.341
Klimov, V.V., **II**.6.441
Klinkovsky, T., **IV**.20.177
Kloos, R., **III**.15.563
Kloppstech, K., **III**.12.231, **III**.12.331, **III**.12.335, **IV**.23.403
Klösgen, R.B., **II**.7.455, **III**.13.349, **III**.13.377
Klug, D.R., **II**.5.243, **II**.5.247
Knobloch, K., **II**.8.705
Knoetzel, J., **I**.4.645
Ko, K., **III**.13.445
Ko, Y., **I**.2.303
Ko, Z.W., **III**.13.445
Kobayashi, H., **III**.12.311, **III**.13.375, **III**.13.441
Kobayashi, K., **III**.12.311, **III**.13.441
Kobayashi, M., **I**.3.393
Kobayashi, S., **I**.4.621
Kobayashi, Y., **II**.7.579, **III**.10.59, **IV**.22.349
Kodama, M., **II**.6.437
Kodera, Y., **II**.5.57, **II**.5.61
Kohchi, M., **IV**.21.271
Koide, K., **IV**.25.781, **IV**.25.785
Koike, H., **II**.5.135, **II**.5.163, **II**.6.369
Koike, T., **IV**.24.703
Koivuniemi, A., **IV**.23.479
Koizumi, N., **III**.14.531
Koizumi, H., **IV**.22.373
Komatsu-Takaki, M., **II**.8.721
Komenda, J., **I**.2.335
Konami, H., **I**.1.97
Kondoh, A., **II**.7.551
Konev, Y.N., **IV**.22.353
Konishi, T., **III**.11.169
Kono, Y., **III**.18.895
Koo, D., **II**.5.151, **III**.13.421
Koop, H.-U., **III**.13.413
Korstanje, L.J., **III**.10.123
Kosaka, A., **IV**.19.99
Kossmann, J., **III**.17.683
Kothen, G., **II**.8.661
Kotova, E.A., **II**.8.689
Kovács, E., **IV**.20.137
Kowallik, K.V., **III**.14.511
Koyama, H., **I**.2., **IV**.24.635
Kraayenhof, R., **I**.1.101, **II**.8.753
Kraepiel, Y., **IV**.19.11
Kramer, D.M., **II**.5.131, **II**.7.491
Krasnovsky, A.A., **III**.10.127,
Krasnovsky, Jr., A.A., **III**.10.111
Krauss, N., **I**.4.521
Krause, G.H., **IV**.23.423
Krenn, B.E., **II**.8.753
Kreutz, W., **II**.5.49
Krishtalik, L.I., **II**.7.447
Krömer, S., **III**.17.709
Kruip, J., **I**.4.629
Kruk, J., **II**.7.479
Krupinska, K., **III**.12.267
Kuang, T.-Y., **I**.2.247, **I**.2.267, **II**.5.77, **II**.5.219, **II**.8.677, **II**.8.769, **IV**.23.439
Kubota, F., **III**.13.367, **IV**.21.235, **IV**.24.663, **IV**.24.667
Kubota, T., **III**.13.367, **III**.13.371
Kucera, T., **I**.4.585
Kuchitsu, K., **III**.18.931, **IV**.21.255
Kuhn, M.G., **II**.5.231
Kulkarni, R.D., **III**.13.381
Kurawaki, J., **II**.9.817, **II**.9.825
Kuribayashi, K., **IV**.21.251
Kurihara, T., **II**.9.809
Kurita, Y., **IV**.22.365
Kuriyama, A., **II**.5.175
Kuroda, E., **IV**.24.647

Kuroda, H., **III**.12.291
Kuroda, I., **III**.11.177
Kuroiwa, S., **II**.5.123
Kuroiwa, T., **III**.13.453
Kurokawa, T., **II**.7.555
Kuropatwa, R., **IV**.20.177
Kusumi, K., **III**.12.323, **III**.18.835, **III**.18.899
Kusumoto, N., **I**.3.389, **I**.4.577
Kusumoto, Y., **II**.9.817, **II**.9.825
Kusnetsov, V., **III**.13.377
Kusunoki, M., **II**.6.293, **II**.6.297, **II**.6.313
Kuwabara, T., **III**.11.201
Kuznetsov, A., **I**.3.481
Kuznetsov, N.Yu., **I**.5.65
Kwa, S.L.S., **I**.2.263, **I**.2.271
Kwon, Y.W., **III**.13.461
Labates, C., **III**.13.445
Labbe, P., **III**.15.543
Lagarias, J.C., **IV**.22.357
Laing, W.A., **III**.10.39, **IV**.23.561
Lajkó, F., **II**.7.631
Lales, J.S., **IV**.23.569
Lange, B., **II**.6.417
Lapitan, M.A., **IV**.23.569
Larkum, A.W.D., **III**.14.475, **IV**.26.847
Latimer, M.J., **II**.6.281
Lattová, J., **IV**.20.177
Laussermair, E., **I**.3.373, **I**.3.397
Laudenbach, D.E., **IV**.19.3
Lauterwasser, C., **I**.3.429
Lavergne, J., **II**.6.273
Lawlor, D.W., **IV**.26.827, **IV**.26.835
Lázaro, J.J., **III**.18.927
Lea, P.J., **III**.18.891, **IV**.19.27
Lebedev, N.N., **III**.10.127
Lebedeva, N.V., **III**.13.457
Leblanc, R.M., **I**.1.145, **II**.7.479, **IV**.23.459
Lechno, S., **IV**.23.537
Lechowicz, M.J., **IV**.24.703
LeCoutre, J., **II**.7.471
Lee, B., **II**.7.519
Lee, C.B., **IV**.24.623
Lee, C.-H., **I**.2.303, **IV**.24.623
Lee, H.S., **III**.15.579
Lee, K.M., **III**.15.579
Leegood, R.C., **III**.18.891, **IV**.19.27
Leguijt, T., **II**.7.639
Lei, T.T., **IV**.24.703
Lehtonen, E., **IV**.22.309
Leibfritz, D., **III**.17.717
Leibl, W., **I**.4.633
Leidreiter, K., **IV**.25.765
Leitsch, J., **IV**.23.423
Lemaire, M., **III**.17.705
Lemoine, Y., **I**.2.331, **IV**.23.581
Lendzian, F., **I**.3.433
Leon, P., **IV**.25.753
Lers, A., **III**.13.417
Leupold, D., **I**.1.109, **I**.3.421
Levine, Y.K., **III**.10.123
Lewin, K., **IV**.26.811
Li, B., **III**.16.649
Li, C., **IV**.23.565
Li, C.-C., **II**.7.615
Li, C.-J., **III**.11.149
Li, C.Y., **I**.2.267, **I**.5.77
Li, D.Y., **II**.8.733, **II**.8.781
Li, G.Q., **II**.5.219
Li, J.-W., **III**.16.645
Li, L.-B., **I**.2.251
Li, L.R., **III**.16.621
Li, R., **III**.13.381
Li, Y., **III**.12.273
Li, Y.Z., **II**.8.717
Li, Z.-H., **II**.8.733
Liang, W., **II**.5.109
Lichtenthaler, H.K., **IV**.23.517
Liebl, U., **II**.7.471, **II**.7.595, **III**.14.507
Lieman-Hurwitz, J., **III**.13.437
Liker, E., **II**.7.631
Lin, G., **III**.18.859
Lin, S., **I**.3.417
Lin, S.Q., **II**.8.677, **II**.8.769
Lin, X., **I**.3.377
Lin, Z., **III**.18.859

Lindahl, M., I.2.307
Lindberg, K., II.6.301, II.6.353
Linden, H., III.10.51
Lindqvist, Y., I.4.609, III.16.585
Lindsay, J.G, I.1.3
Litvin, F.F., III.10.75
Liu, B., I.1.61, II.9.801
Liu, B.-L., II.9.801
Livne, A., I.2.203
Loach, P.A., I.1.101
LoBrutto, R., II.8.745
Lockhart, P., III.14.499
Loddenkötter, B., III.17.667
Lohaus, G., IV.25.773
Long, J.J., III.12.225
Long, S.P., IV.26.811, IV.26.851, IV.26.855
Loreto, F., IV.26.843
Lorigan, G.-A., II.6.317
Los, D.A., III.12.303
Losada, M., II.8.697
Lotan, O., I.1.65, I.4.505
Lottspeich, F., II.7.511
Lu, C., IV.20.173
Lu, G., III.16.585
Lu, R.Z., I.1.61
Lu, Y.-H., IV.23.439
Lübberstedt, T., III.12.219
Lubitz, W., I.3.433, I.3.461, II.6.289
Lundqvist, T., III.16.585
Lutz, M., I.3.405, I.3.409
Møller, B.L., I.3.465, I.3.473, I.4.497, I.4.609, I.4.637
Ma, G., IV.24.651
Ma, G.-Z., I.2.251
Ma, H., I.2.251
Ma, R.-Y., I.1.165
Mac, M., II.6.381
MacKenzie, R.C., I.1.77
MacLachlan, D.J., II.6.373
Madgwick, P., III.16.601
Mae, T., IV.22.365, IV.22.377, IV.24.655
Maeda, A., II.5.127
Maeda, H., I.4.545, III.10.3
Mäenpää, P., II.5.155, IV.23.419, IV.23.483
Magnin, N., II.5.211
Makino, A., IV.22.365, IV.22.377, IV.24.655
Malakhov, M.P., III.12.303
Malkin, R., I.3.385
Malkin, S., IV.23.557
Malmberg, G., III.17.709
Mamedov, M.D., IV.20.141
Mamyshina, N.S., IV.20.181
Mann, V., III.10.11
Mannan, R.M., III.13.425
Mano, J., II.5.115, IV.19.95, IV.19.99
Mäntele, W., I.1.45, I.3.437, II.5.49
Marano, M.R., III.12.319
Marco, E., III.13.437, III.18.787
Marder, J.B., I.2.327
Markovsky, A.L., II.9.837
Marquardt, J., I.2.287, II.5.13
Marshall, J.S., III.18.757
Martinez, F., III.18.787, III.18.803, III.18.811
Martinez, S.E., II.7.495
Martins, T.C.R., II.7.515
Maruyama, K., II.9.787, II.9.805, II.9.813
Masamoto, K., III.10.35
Maslán, M., IV.20.177
Masson, K., III.15.563
Masuda, T., III.10.43
Masui, H., III.11.161
Masui, Y., IV.21.235
Mataga, N., II.9.787, II.9.805
Mathis, P., I.3.469
Matringe, M., III.15.543
Matsubara, H., I.3.385, III.10.67, III.14.491, IV.19.43
Matsubayashi, T., III.12.263, III.12.343
Matsuda, H., III.11.157
Matsuda, M., III.14.515
Matsumoto, H., III.10.67
Matsumura, T., II.7.535

Matsuno, R., III.11.209
Matsuoka, M., III.17.713, III.18.757, III.18.843, III.18.875, III.18.879
Matsuoka, S., II.9.833
Matsushima, H., I.2.223
Matsushita, T., II.6.293, II.6.313
Matsuura, K., I.1.17, I.1.81, I.1.113, I.3.365, II.7.531
Matsuura, Y., II.7.531
Matthijs, H.C.P., I.2.207
Mattioli, T.A., I.3.405
Mauro, S., II.5.13
Mauzerall, D., III.14.483
Mayer, A., III.17.717
Mayes, S.R., III.13.469
Mazzinghi, P., IV.24.639
McCaffery, S., IV.23.443
McCormack, B., II.5.203
McCracken, J., II.6.381
McDermott, G., I.1.3
McFadden, B.A., III.16.625
McIntosh, L., I.4.573, II.6.381
McKay, S.P., III.15.559
McMichael, Jr., R.W., III.17.675
McNamara, V., II.5.89
McPherson, P.H., I.3.349
Medrano, H., IV.24.691
Mei, R., II.6.321, II.6.345
Mela, T., IV.26.819
Melis, A., IV.22.317
Menachem, A., I.4.505
Meng, B.-Y., III.12.263
Mensink, M.G.J., IV.20.161
Messinger, J., II.5.159, II.6.329
Meyer, S., II.8.709
Mi, H., II.7.603
Miao, Y.-G., III.16.621
Michl, D., III.13.349, III.13.377
Michel, H., I.3.341, I.3.397, II.6.409, II.7.511
Michaeli, D., I.4.505
Michalowski, C.B., IV.21.195
Middleton, K., II.7.567
Miginiac-Maslow, M., III.17.659, III.17.701, III.17.705
Miki, K., II.7.531
Miki, M., II.7.531
Mikkelsen, K.V., II.7.523
Mikota, T., III.10.59
Miller, M., I.3.401
Miller, N., IV.20.157
Mills, W.R., IV.19.55
Mimura, T., III.18.775, IV.25.777
Mimuro, M., I.1.17, I.1.113, I.1.137, I.2.219, I.2.227, I.2.259, I.4.541
Minaka, N., III.12.239
Mino, H., II.5.57, II.5.61
Miranda, T., IV.20.185
Mishra, R.K., IV.23.541
Misra, L.M., I.4.561
Mitchell, R.A.C., IV.26.835
Mitchell, V.J., IV.26.835
Mitsunaga, T., III.17.741
Mittler, R., IV.23.537
Miura, K., II.6.413
Miyachi, S., II.6.437, III.18.799
Miyake, C., II.7.559, II.7.563
Miyake, J., I.3.445, I.3.449
Miyake, M., I.3.477
Miyao-Tokutomi, M., IV.23.509
Mizuno, K., IV.21.247
Mizusawa, N., II.6.425
Möbius, K., I.3.433
Mochizuki, K., II.8.725
Mochensturm-Wislon, M., II.7.595
Mohamed, A., III.13.401
Mohanty, N., III.13.445
Mohanty, P., II.7.591
Monshouwer, R., I.1.37
Monteleone, D., I.3.401
Montoya, G., II.5.73
Moon, B.Y., IV.24.623
Moore, A.L., II.9.801
Moore, T.A., II.9.801
Morand, L.Z., IV.22.357
Mori, H., IV.23.513
Mori, J., III.18.867
Morigasaki, S., II.7.551

Morikawa, H., **III**.13.375, **III**.13.413, **IV**.19.79, **IV**.19.83
Morishige, D.T., **I**.2.319
Morishita, Y., **I**.1.97
Moriyama, T., **I**.1.113
Moskalenko, A.A., **II**.5.65
Mostowska, A., **III**.15.555
Motoki, A., **II**.6.413
Motomura, Y., **IV**.24.711
Moureaux, T., **IV**.19.11
Moya, I., **IV**.24.603
Moyer, M., **IV**.19.95
Mu, M.H., **I**.2.275
Mueller, U.W., **III**.13.381
Mühlenhoff, V., **I**.4.565
Mukerji, I., **II**.6.281
Mukohata, Y., **II**.8.749
Muller, J.M., **III**.10.123
Müller, M.G., **II**.5.69
Mullineaux, C.W., **I**.1.141
Mulo, P., **IV**.23.483
Münzer, S., **IV**.19.91
Mur, L.R., **I**.2.207
Murai, N., **III**.11.209
Murakami, A., **II**.7.503, **IV**.22.301
Murata, N., **IV**.20.113, **IV**.20.137, **IV**.20.141
Murchinson, H.A., **I**.3.377
Murota, K., **IV**.21.231, **IV**.21.259
Muto, S., **IV**.21.263
Myers, J., **III**.18.791
Na, J.-U., **IV**.19.67
Nabedryk, E., **I**.3.437, **II**.5.53
Nada, K., **IV**.24.667
Nadanaciva, S., **III**.13.385
Nagai, A., **IV**.19.95, **IV**.19.99
Nagano, Y., **III**.11.209
Nagashima, K.V.P., **I**.3.365
Nagata, T., **IV**.25.777
Nagy, L., **III**.13.469
Nakagawa, T., **III**.11.157
Nakai, M., **III**.11.181
Nakajima, S., **II**.9.787
Nakamoto, H., **I**.4.613, **I**.4.621
Nakamura, M., **III**.13.367, **III**.13.371
Nakamura, Y., **IV**.19.59
Nakano, M., **III**.13.397
Nakano, T., **III**.12.315
Nakashima, K., **III**.13.389
Nakata, M., **IV**.19.79
Nakatani, H., **IV**.25.781
Nakayama, K., **I**.2.219
Nango, M., **II**.9.809
Naruta, Y., **II**.9.813
Nash, D.P., **II**.5.93
Nasu, J., **IV**.20.177
Nasu, H., **I**.3.389
Nasu, M., **II**.5.101
Nechushtai, R.,, **I**.1.65, **I**.4.505, **III**.11.193
Ne'eman, E., **III**.11.213
Nelson, C.J., **IV**.25.789
Nelson, H., **I**.4.513, **II**.7.471
Nelson, N., **I**.4.513, **II**.7.471
Nie, G.Y., **IV**.26.811, **IV**.26.855
Niederman, R.A., **I**.1.93
Nielsen, V.S., **I**.4.497, **I**.4.637
Niemczyk, M.P., **II**.9.795
Nikkola, M., **III**.16.585
Nilsen, S., **IV**.23.549
Nilsson, F., **IV**.23.435
Nishida, I., **IV**.20.113
Nishida, Y., **I**.5.101
Nishikawa, S., **III**.12.239
Nishikawa, T., **II**.7.543
Nishimoto, E., **III**.10.59, **IV**.22.349
Nishimura, M., **IV**.20.169, **IV**.24.719
Nishimura, Y., **I**.1.17, **I**.1.113, **I**.1.137, **I**.2.219, **II**.9.787, **II**.9.805
Nishio, J.N., **IV**.23.573
Nishiuchi, T., **III**.12.323
Nishiyama, Y., **IV**.20.113, **IV**.20.137
Nitschke, W., **II**.7.471, **III**.14.507
Niwa, Y., **III**.12.311, **III**.13.375, **III**.13.441
Nixon, P.J., **II**.5.175
Noguchi, T., **II**.6.293, **II**.6.309, **II**.6.313
Nohno, M., **IV**.19.79

Nonami, H., **IV**.21.271
Nonomura, A.M., **III**.18.911
Nore, B.F., **IV**.22.345
Nose, A., **IV**.24.679
Nozaki, K., **II**.9.787
Nozawa, T., **I**.1.97
Nugent, J.H.A., **II**.5.191, **II**.6.373
Nukanobu, K., **I**.3.449
Numata, Y., **I**.4.625
Nyhus, K.J., **I**.4.569
Nyrén, P., **II**.8.693
Oba, T., **III**.10.3
Oberhuber, W., **III**.18.907
Obokata, J., **III**.13.367, **III**.13.371
Ocheretina, O., **II**.7.587
Ochiai, H., **III**.11.157, **III**.12.307
Oelmüller, R., **III**.12.219, **III**.13.377
Oelze, J., **I**.1.89
Oesterhelt, D., **I**.3.373, **I**.3.397
Oettmeier, W., **III**.15.563
Ogata, T., **II**.9.833
Ogawa, N., **III**.18.831
Ogawa, T., **II**.7.603, **III**.18.763
Oh-oka, H., **I**.3.385, **I**.3.393, **III**.14.491
Ohad, I., **III**.12.335, **IV**.23.403, **IV**.23.501
Ohad, N., **II**.5.223, **III**.13.437, **IV**.23.403
Ohashi, K., **I**.4.641
Ohki, K., **IV**.19.103
Ohkouchi, M., **II**.9.787
Ohnishi, J., **III**.17.737
Ohno, H., **IV**.26.839
Ohno, T., **II**.9.787
Ohsugi, R., **III**.17.713
Ohta, D., **IV**.19.91, **IV**.19.95, **IV**.19.99
Ohta, M., **III**.12.273
Ohtomo, K., **I**.1.97
Ojima, K., **IV**.22.365, **IV**.22.377, **IV**.24.655
Okada, A., **I**.3.425
Okada, K., **IV**.22.341
Okada, M., **I**.2.219
Okada, T., **II**.9.787, **II**.9.805
Okamura, M.Y., **I**.3.349, **I**.3.437, **II**.5.195
Okamura, Y., **III**.18.783
Okayama, S., **II**.8.701
Okazaki, M., **III**.18.783
Okazaki, Y., **IV**.24.723
Okkels, J.S., **I**.3.465, **I**.3.473, **I**.4.497, **I**.4.593, **I**.4.637
Okochi, M., **II**.9.805
Oku, T., **II**.6.393, **II**.7.579, **IV**.22.349
Okumura, S., **III**.18.827, **III**.18.923
Olson, J.M., **I**.3.401
O'Malley, P.J., **III**.15.559
Omata, T., **III**.18.807, **IV**.19.75
O'Neil, M.P., **II**.5.41
Ono, T., **II**.6.265, **II**.6.293, **II**.6.309, **II**.6.313, **II**.6.401
Ookawa, T., **IV**.24.647
Öquist, G., **IV**.23.455
Orellano, E.G., **III**.12.319
Orsat, B., **III**.12.255
Orsenigo, M., **III**.14.523
Ort, D.R., **IV**.20.145
Ortega, J.M., **I**.3.469, **II**.8.697
Orus, M.I., **III**.18.787, **III**.18.803, **III**.18.811
Osmond, B., **I**.5.37, **IV**.24.655
Osmond, C.B., **III**.13.417
Osteryoung, K.W., **IV**.20.129
Osuka, A., **II**.9.787, **II**.9.805
Ota, K., **III**.18.895
Otma, E.C., **IV**.20.161
Ottander, C., **IV**.23.455
Otte, S.C.M., **I**.3.413
Ougham, H., **IV**.20.121
Owens, T.G., **I**.2.179
Oya, T., **I**.4.621
Oyanagi, H., **II**.6.293, **II**.6.313
Ozaki, Y., **I**.1.85
Padan, E., **II**.7.483
Paddock, M.L., **I**.3.349, **I**.3.437
Padmasree, K., **III**.17.725
Paillotin, G., **I**.4.633
Pakrasi, H.B., **I**.4.569, **II**.5.175, **III**.13.409, **III**.13.425

Palmer, T., **II**.8.685
Palmqvist, K., **III**.18.815
Pancic, P.G., **III**.14.511
Papageorgiou, G.C., **II**.6.349
Papiz, M.Z., **I**.1.3
Park, S.-Y., **II**.8.761
Park, T.S., **IV**.24.707
Park, Y.-I., **IV**.24.699
Park, Y.M., **I**.4.557
Parmar, S., **III**.16.609
Parot, P., **II**.7.639
Parry, M.A., **III**.16.609, **IV**.26.835
Pashchenko, V.Z., **I**.4.549
Patrignani, G., **III**.14.523
Paulsen, H., **III**.11.193
Pavlová, Z., **IV**.20.177
Pecker, I., **III**.10.11
Peeters, J.C.H., **IV**.23.525
Pehu, E., **IV**.26.827
Peloquin, J.M., **I**.3.377
Peltier, G., **IV**.24.603, **IV**.24.695
Peng, D.-C., **I**.2.247, **I**.2.267, **II**.5.77, **IV**.23.439
Pennanen, A., **IV**.26.827
Penner-Hahn, J.E., **II**.6.321
Penny, D., **III**.14.499
Perewoska, I., **III**.15.575
Pesheva-Boneva, I., **II**.6.437
Pessiki, P., **II**.6.257
Peterson, R.B., **IV**.24.619
Petrouleas, V., **II**.5.119
Picaud, M., **III**.15.575
Pichersky, E., **I**.2.195
Pickering, N., **IV**.26.831
Picorel, R., **II**.5.73
Pilon, M., **III**.11.185
Pilon, R., **III**.11.133
Pilon-Smith, E.A.H., **III**.18.943
Pineau, B., **I**.2.287
Pinther, W., **I**.4.513
Pirner, B., **II**.8.705
Piruzian, E., **III**.12.299
Plato, M., **I**.3.433
Pol, A., **IV**.24.691
Polewski, K., **I**.3.401
Pölös, E., **IV**.23.495
Ponquett, R., **III**.13.449
Ponticos, M., **IV**.23.427
Pontoppidan, B., **III**.10.31
Poole, K., **II**.7.611
Porter, G., **II**.5.243, **II**.5.247
Portis, Jr., A.R., **III**.16.653
Post, A., **IV**.26.847
Postl, W.F., **IV**.22.369
Pötter, E., **III**.12.231
Powles, S.B., **III**.15.571
Prásil, O., **IV.23.501**
Preiss, J., **III**.17.697
Preston, C., **III**.15.571
Prioul, J.-L., **IV**.25.761
Psencík, J., **I**.2.335
Purcell, M., **II**.5.139
Qian, M, **II**.5.179
Qiu, Y.-Y., **III**.14.519
Quick, P., **IV**.25.737
Quigley, A., **IV**.20.121
Raghavendra, A.S., **III**.17.725, **III**.18.887
Rajagopalan, K., **III**.16.601
Ramazanov, Z.M., **III**.18.803
Rao, S.R., **III**.18.863
Rappaport, F., **II**.6.273
Raskin, V.I., **I**.2.327
Raschke, K., **IV**.25.765
Redinbaugh, M.G., **III**.17.675
Reeves, M., **IV**.19.55
Reinhold, L., **III**.13.437
Reiss-Husson, F., **I**.1.33
Renger, G., **II**.5.159, **II**.5.183, **II**.6.289, **II**.6.329, **II**.6.417, **IV**.24.643
Rhew, T.H., **I**.2.303
Rich, P., **II**.5.203
Richards, J.H., **II**.9.829
Richter, M., **IV**.23.471
Richter, P., **I**.1.153
Riedel, A., **II**.7.471
Rietveld, A., **III**.11.185
Riggs, P.J., **II**.6.321
Rigoni, F., **IV**.23.505

Rintamäki, E., **IV**.23.431
Robert, B., **I**.3.405, **I**.3.409
Robinson, C., **III**.11.141
Robinson, D.G., **IV**.25.773
Rochaix, J.D., **III**.13.359, **III**.13.393
Rodday, S.M., **I**.4.537
Rodríguez, I., **III**.18.927
Rodriguez, M.L., **III**.18.787
Rögner, M., **I**.4.629
Romanowska, E., **II**.7.507
Ronen-Tarazi, M., **III**.13.437
Rongey, S., **I**.3.349, **I**.3.437
Röll, K., **II**.6.409
Rousseau, B., **IV**.23.581
Roskelley, A., **II**.8.745
Rother, T., **II**.7.587
Rozen, A., **IV**.23.537
Ruban, A.V., **I**.2.311
Rüdiger, W., **III**.15.555
Ruffle, S.V., **II**.5.191
Rutherford, A.W., **II**.5.21, **II**.5.235
Ryals, J., **IV**.19.95
Rybtsov, S.A., **III**.13.465
Sabat, S.C., **II**.7.591
Saeda, M., **II**.7.531
Saeki, K., **III**.14.491, **IV**.19.43
Saenger, W., **I**.4.521
Saitou, K., **IV**.21.235
Sakai, K., **II**.7.543
Sakai-Nore, Y., **II**.8.693
Sakakibara, H., **IV**.19.71
Sakamoto, A., **IV**.23.545
Sakamoto, T., **IV**.20.113
Sakano, K., **IV**.19.87
Sakashita, H., **IV**.24.655
Sakata, Y., **II**.9.841
Sakihama, N., **I**.4.641, **II**.7.543, **II**.7.547
Sakurai, H., **I**.3.389, **I**.4.577, **II**.8.729
Salih, G.F., **II**.5.155, **IV**.23.483
Salnikow, J., **II**.7.499
Salo, R., **IV**.23.431
Salter, A.H., **IV**.23.395
Salvucci, M.E., **III**.16.601, **III**.16.629
Samejima, M., **III**.18.875, **IV**.24.683
Sanada, Y., **IV**.21.251
Sanada, M., **IV**.24.703
Sanakis, Y., **II**.5.119
Sandmann, G., **II**.5.105, **III**.10.11, **III**.10.51
Sanjose, M., **IV**.24.687
Sano, S., **IV**.23.533
Santini, C., **II**.5.13
Santore, U.J., **IV**.23.423
Saradadevi, K., **III**.17.725
Sasaki, H., **IV**.24.683
Sasaki, J., **II**.5.127
Sasaki, Y., **III**.11.209
Sato, A., **I**.3.445, **III**.13.397
Sato, F., **I**.2.223, **III**.12.315, **III**.14.531, **IV**.21.231, **IV**.21.259
Sato, N., **III**.10.63, **III**.13.453
Sato, R., **III**.15.567
Satoh, A., **III**.18.779
Satoh, H., **IV**.20.169
Satoh, K., **II**.5.1, **II**.5.135, **II**.5.163, **II**.6.369, **III**.12.287, **III**.12.291
Satoh, N., **III**.10.63
Satoh, T., **III**.11.161
Sauer, K., **II**.5.239, **II**.6.281
Sawa, Y., **III**.12.307
Sawada, S., **IV**.25.769
Sawasaki, T., **IV**.19.83
Scalla, R., **III**.15.543
Schaefer, M.R., **I**.1.157, **III**.13.381
Schäffner, A.R., **IV**.25.753
Schansker, G., **IV**.23.475
Scheer, H., **I**.1.109, **I**.3.421, **I**.3.429
Scheibe, R., **II**.7.587
Scheidegger, A., **IV**.19.91, **IV**.19.95, **IV**.19.99
Scheller, H.V., **I**.3.465, **I**.3.473, **I**.4.497, **I**.4.593, **I**.4.609, **I**.4.637
Schelvis, H., **I**.3.413
Schelvis, J.P.M., **II**.5.81
Schiappa, T., **IV**.21.275
Schindler, C., **IV**.23.517
Schlodder, E., **II**.5.45
Schluchter, W.M., **I**.4.565

Schmid, G.H., II.6.433
Schmid, R., II.5.227, II.7.587
Schmidt, A., III.12.267
Schneider, G., I.4.609, III.16.585
Schnettger, B., IV.23.423
Schoefs, B., III.10.71
Schönknecht, G., II.8.777
Schreiber, U., II.7.487, II.7.603
Schröder, W.P., I.5.105, II.5.159
Schroth, H., I.1.109
Schürmann, P., II.7.539, IV.20.121
Schouten, S.P., IV.20.161
Schwarz, B., IV.24.611
Schwarz, O., II.8.661
Schwarz, R., III.13.437
Scott, M.P., I.4.593
Scott, P., I.4.497
Seibert, M., II.5.41, II.5.167, II.6.357
Seidler, A., II.6.409
Seki, M., III.13.375, III.13.413, IV.19.83
Sekido, T., II.7.547z
Sekiguchi, K., III.11.209
Semenenko, V.E., III.12.303, III.13.457
Sen, N., III.17.733
Senda, M., I.4.621
Senger, H., III.13.433, IV.22.389
Serra, E.C., III.12.319
Setchell, B.A., IV.24.595
Shahak, Y., II.7.483
Shallan, M.A.-A.M., II.7.499
Sharkey, T.D., IV.26.843
Sharma, R., III.17.721
Sheen, J., IV.25.753
Shen, J.-R., II.5.175, II.5.179, II.6.429
Shen, Y.-K., II.8.781, III.12.243
Shenderova, L.V., IV.22.353
Sherman, L.A., II.5.179
Shi, D.-J., III.10.83, III.14.519
Shi, J.-Z., IV.21.291
Shi, S., IV.20.173
Shibata, H., III.15.567, IV.23.553
Shibata, M., III.13.389
Shibuya, N., IV.21.255
Shigemoto, N., III.13.413
Shigeoka, S., III.12.271, III.17.741
Shiina, T., III.12.259
Shimada, H., III.10.91, III.10.95, III.18.923
Shimada, K., I.1.17, I.1.81, I.1.113, I.1.137, I.3.365, I.4.29
Shimazaki, K., II.8.701, IV.24.715, IV.24.719
Shimazu, T., I.1.73, II.6.413
Shimizu, M., II.7.575
Shimizu, T., I.4.621
Shimmen, T., III.18.775
Shimogawara, K., III.18.883
Shin, M., I.4.641, II.7.543, II.7.547
Shinohara, K., II.6.401, II.8.729
Shinoyama, H., III.18.903
Shinozaki, K., III.18.923, IV.21.227
Shioi, Y., III.10.91, III.10.99, III.10.115
Shiozawa, J.A., I.1.41
Shipton, C.A., IV.23.427
Shirai, M., III.13.397
Shiraishi, T., II.7.627
Shiraiwa, Y., III.18.779
Shirota, M., IV.22.333
Shkuropatov, A., I.3.441
Shochat, S., I.3.413
Shonai, F., III.10.67
Shreve, A.P., I.2.179
Shubin, V.V., I.4.549
Shukla, V.K., III.13.409
Shuvalov, V.A., I.3.357, I.3.441
Sieckmann, I., I.4.533
Sievert, G., III.16.601
Siffel, S., III.10.127
Simidjiev, I., II.7.631
Simonis, W., II.8.777
Simpson, D., I.4.645
Sinclair, J., II.7.611
Singhal, G.S., IV.23.541
Sivaraja, M., II.6.257
Skibinski, A., I.1.145
Smart, L.B., I.4.573
Smith, C.M., III.18.851

Smith, E., III.18.757
Smith, J., II.5.147
Smith, J.L., II.7.495
Snel, J.F.H., II.8.681, IV.23.475, IV.23.525, IV.24.615
Socias, X., IV.24.691
Sockalingum, D., I.3.405
Söderlind, E., III.16.585
Sofrová, D., I.4.585
Soga, M., I.1.73
Sogabe, S., II.7.531
Soh, C.H., III.13.461
Sokolov, M., II.8.653
Solov'ev, A., I.3.441
Somerville, C., III.10.55
Someya, J., III.12.239
Sommer, A., III.11.213
Somsen, O., I.1.9, I.1.133
Son, D., III.18.871
Soncini, F.C., III.16.637
Sone, N., II.7.571
Song, C.P., I.2.275
Sonnewald, U., III.17.683, IV.25.765
Sonoike, K., I.4.545, I.4.601, I.4.605
Sopory, S., III.12.219
Soroka, Y., IV.23.403
Spampinato, C.P., III.18.855
Spreitzer, R.J., III.16.593, III.16.633
Stahl, B., II.7.455
Stefansson, H., I.2.283
Stehlik, D., I.3.461, I.4.533
Stein, M., III.17.659
Steingröver, E., IV.21.287
Stephens, B.W., IV.19.55
Steppuhn, J., III.13.349
Stiel, H., I.3.421
Strasser, R.J., II.5.29, II.8.741, IV.20.149, IV.24.611
Strid, Å., II.8.693, IV.22.361
Strotmann, H., II.8.661, III.14.511
Struck, A., I.3.429
Strzalka, K., II.7.479
Stubbs, J.D., III.18.757
Stutz, E., III.12.255
Styring, S., II.5.147, II.5.251, II.6.421, IV.23.411, IV.23.479, IV.23.491
Su, Q., III.11.197
Sue, S., I.4.581
Sugiharto, B., IV.19.19, IV.19.39
Sugita, M., III.12.273, III.12.279, III.13.405, III.13.413
Sugiura, M., III.12.247, III.12.251, III.12.263, III.12.273, III.12.279, III.12.283, III.12.343, III.13.389, III.13.405, III.13.413
Sugiyama, T., III.18.867, III.18.871, IV.19.19, IV.19.39, IV.19.71, IV.19.75
Sugiyama, Y., II.8.749
Sukenik, A., I.2.203
Sun, G., III.18.859
Sun, J., IV.23.573
Sundby, C., IV.23.443
Surzycki, S.J., III.18.939
Suzuki, E., III.18.795, III.18.799
Suzuki, I., IV.19.19, IV.19.75
Suzuki, K., III.11.201, IV.19.95
Suzuki, M., I.1.97, II.6.293
Suzuki, Y., IV.22.385
Svec, W.A., II.9.795
Svensson, B., II.5.147, II.5.251
Swiezewska, E., IV.23.479
Syme, A.J., IV.22.337
Szczepaniak, A., II.7.447, II.7.495
Tachibana, T., I.1.85
Tada, S., IV.19.95
Tada, Y., III.18.923
Tae, G.-S., II.7.447
Taglicht, D., II.7.483
Taisova, A.S., II.8.689
Tajima, T., II.9.809
Takabe, T., I.4.597, I.4.625, II.7.519
Takahashi, M., I.4.529, II.6.385, II.7.627, IV.22.385
Takahashi, Y., III.10.67, III.13.393, III.14.491
Takaichi, S., I.1.149
Takamiya, K., II.7.575, III.10.43, III.10.91, III.10.95, III.10.99, III.10.115

Takamoto, D.Y., **II**.5.93
Takano, H., **I**.3.389
Takano, A., **III**.11.205
Takeda, M., **IV**.21.251
Takeda, S., **I**.2.223, **IV**.21.231, **IV**.24.635, **IV**.24.635
Takeda, T., **III**.17.741
Takimura, O., **III**.10.87
Takura, K., **II**.5.57
Tal, S., **IV**.23.403
Tamai, N., **IV**.21.251
Tamura, N., **II**.6.393, **II**.6.405, **II**.7.619
Tamura, T., **I**.3.445
Tanaka, A., **I**.2.295, **I**.2.299, **I**.4.641
Tanaka, K., **IV**.23.545
Tanaka, T., **II**.6.405
Tanaka, Y., **I**.2.295, **I**.2.299, **I**.4.625
Tang, C.-Q., **I**.2.247, **I**.2.267, **II**.5.77, II.**5.219,** II.**8.677,** IV.**23.439**
Tang, P.-S., **I**.2.247, **I**.2.267, **II**.5.77, **IV**.23.439
Tang, X.-S., **II**.6.257
Tang, Y., **IV**.22.373
Tano, H., **II**.7.571
Taylor, W.C., **III**.18.757
Tazawa, M., **IV**.24.723, **IV**.25.777
Tel-Or, E., **IV**.23.537
Telfer, A., **IV**.23.463
Tenchov, B., **IV**.20.165
Terada, K., **III**.18.823
Terashima, I., **IV**.22.381
Tessier, L.-H., **III**.16.641
Teuchner, K., **I**.3.421
Thaler, M., **II**.8.777
Thomas, C.M., **II**.8.685
Thomas, J.C., **IV**.21.195
Thornber, J.P., **I**.1.49, **I**.2.319, **I**.2.323, **III**.11.213
Thow, G., **III**.16.593, **III**.16.633
Thunnissen, M., **I**.1.3
Tidu, V., **II**.5.13
Timpmann, J., **II**.5.65
Tiwari, B.S., **IV**.21.267
Tiwari, S., **II**.7.591
Tjus, S.E., **IV**.23.521
Tobin, A.K., **IV**.19.47
Tobin, E.M., **III**.11.213
Togasaki, R.K., **III**.18.935, **III**.18.939, **IV**.23.487
Toh, H., **III**.18.827
Tokai, H., **III**.16.613
Tokuda, K., **IV**.19.43
Tominaga, H., **III**.12.307
Tomizuka, N., **I**.3.477
Tommos, C., **II**.5.251
Tomo, T., **II**.6.377
Tong, H., **IV**.23.565
Toon, S., **II**.5.41
Torazawa, K., **III**.12.263
Torii, H., **III**.11.181
Torres-Ruiz, J.A., **III**.16.625
Toyohara, G., **IV**.19.79, **IV**.19.83
Toyoshima, Y., **II**.5.123, **II**.5.127, **III**.12.259
Trebst, A., **III**.15.537
Tremolieres, A., **II**.5.159
Tripathi, S.N., **IV**.21.267
Trissl, H.-W., **I**.4.633
Trost, J.T., **II**.7.595
Trunk, J.G., **I**.3.401
Tsavalos, A.J., **III**.10.47
Tsionremas, N., **III**.13.381
Tsiotis, G., **II**.7.511
Tsuda, K., **II**.9.809
Tsudzuki, J., **III**.13.389
Tsudzuki, T., **III**.13.389
Tsugeki, R., **III**.11.189
Tsugita, A., **II**.7.539
Tsuji, H., **I**.2.295, **I**.2.299, **I**.4.641
Tsunooka, M., **I**.1.85
Tsunoyama, Y., **III**.12.259
Tsuru, T., **IV**.26.839
Tsuzuki, M., **III**.10.63, **III**.18.931
Tuffery, P., **II**.5.147
Tugulea, L., **II**.9.845
Tuhkanen, E.-M., **IV**.26.819
Turpin, D.H., **III**.13.445, **IV**.19.51
Tusov, V.B., **I**.4.549

Tyagi, A.K., **III**.12.219
Tyystjärvi, E., **II**.5.171, **IV**.22.301, **IV**.23.483
Uehara, A., **II**.6.293
Uehara, K., **I**.1.85
Ulstrup, J., **I**.3.481, **II**.7.523
Uno, A., **II**.7.531
Uodome, N., **IV**.19.99
Urao, S., **IV**.21.227
Usuda, H., **III**.18.883, **IV**.25.769
Utsunomiya, E., **III**.18.931
Vácha, M., **I**.2.335
Vadell, J., **IV**.24.691
Valkunas, L., **I**.1.9, **I**.1.133
Vallon, O., **I**.4.557
Vally, K.J.M., **III**.17.721
van Brederode, J., **III**.18.943
van de Meent, E.J., **I**.3.393, **III**.10.3
van der Beek, J., **IV**.21.287
van der Est, A., **I**.3.461, **I**.4.533
van der Staay, G.W.M., **I**.2.207
van der Vos, R., **I**.2.215, **I**.3.413
van Ginkel, G., **III**.10.123
van Gorkom, H.J., **II**.5.33, **II**.5.81, **II**.6.325, **II**.6.341
van Grondelle, R., **I**.1.9, **I**.1.37, **I**.1.101, **I**.1.133, **I**.2.263, **I**.2.271, **II**.7.639
van Hasselt, P.R., **IV**.23.447
van Kan, P.J.M., **I**.2.263, **I**.2.271
van Kooten, O., **IV**.20.161
van Leeuwen, P.J., **II**.6.325, **II**.6.341
van Mourik, F., **I**.1.9, **I**.1.37, **I**.1.101, **I**.1.133
van Noort, P.I., **I**.1.105, **I**.3.413, **II**.5.81
van Orden, W., **IV**.21.287
van Rensen, J.J.S., **III**.15.551, **IV**.23.475
van Roekel, G., **IV**.21.287
van Stokkum, I.H.M., **I**.1.101, **I**.2.271
van Schaik, A.C.R., **IV**.20.161
van Tegelen, L., **III**.11.165
van't Hof, R., **III**.11.185
van Vliet, P.H., **II**.7.527, **IV**.24.659
van Voorthuysen, T., **II**.8.681
van Wijk, K.J., **IV**.23.447
van Zandvoort, M.A.M.J., **II**.8.853, **III**.10.119
Váradi, Gy., **IV**.23.495
Vasil'ev, I.R., **IV**.22.353
Vasiliev, S.S., **I**.4.549
Vass, I., **III**.10.107, **III**.13.469, **IV**.23.411
Vater, J., **II**.7.499
Veeranjaneyulu, K., **IV**.23.459
Venediktov, P.S., **IV**.22.353
Venturoli, G., **II**.7.599
Vera, A., **III**.12.247, **III**.12.263
Vergara, B.S., **IV**.24.707, **IV**.24.709
Vermaas, W., **I**.2.239, **II**.5.175, **II**.5.199, **II**.5.231, **II**.5.251, **II**.7.595, **III**.13.429
Verméglio, A., **II**.7.639
Vernon, D.M., **IV**.21.195
Vernotte, C., **III**.15.575
Viale, A.M., **III**.16.637
Vidal, D., **IV**.24.687
Vierling, E., **IV**.20.129
Villarejo, A., **III**.18.803, **III**.18.811
Vincentz, M., **IV**.19.11
Visschers, R.W., **I**.1.9, **I**.1.37, **I**.1.101, **II**.7.639
Vivekanandan, M., **II**.8.765
Voigt, B., **I**.1.109
von Caemmerer, S., **IV**.24.595
von Wettstein, D., **III**.10.31
Vredenberg, W.J., **II**.8.681, **IV**.24.615
Vrieze, J., **I**.3.413, **I**.4.553
Wacker, U., **II**.6.329
Wada, H., **IV**.20.113
Wada, K., **I**.4.581, **II**.6.405, **II**.7.551, **IV**.21.251
Wada, T., **III**.12.259
Wada, Y., **II**.9.833
Wadano, A., **III**.17.729
Wakamatsu, K., **II**.6.405
Wakasugi, T., **III**.12.263, **III**.13.389
Wallmeier, H., **III**.17.667
Wallsgrove, R.M., **IV**.19.47
Walmsley, J., **III**.10.79
Walters, R.G., **I**.2.311

Walz, D., **II**.8.713
Wang, J.-L., **III**.12.225
Wang, K.-B., **II**.7.615
Wang, M.-Z., **III**.14.519
Wang, S., **I**.3.381
Wang, T.-D., **IV**.21.291
Wang, W., **IV**.24.671, **IV**.24.675
Wang, Y., **IV**.24.671, **IV**.24.675
Wang, Z.-G., **III**.12.243
Ward, E., **IV**.19.95
Ward, J.B., **I**.4.561
Warren, P.V., **I**.4.573
Washitani, I., **IV**.22.373
Wasielewski, M.R., **II**.5.41, **II**.9.795
Watanabe, A., **III**.11.169
Watanabe, N., **IV**.22.333
Watanabe, T., **I**.3.393, **I**.4.545, **III**.10.3, **IV**.20.137
Watanabe, Y., **I**.1.41
Watling, J., **IV**.20.189
Webber, A.N., **I**.4.561
Weber, A., **III**.17.667
Wedel, N., **III**.13.349
Wei, J.-M., **II**.8.733, **III**.12.243
Weil, J.-H., **III**.16.641
Weisbeek, P.J., **II**.7.519, **III**.11.133, **III**.11.165, **III**.11.173, **III**.11.185
Welty, B.A., **I**.2.323
Wen, X.G., **II**.8.769
Westerhuis, W.H.J., **I**.1.93
Weyhermüller, T., **II**.6.289
Whitelegge, J.P., **II**.5.151, **III**.13.421
Wieber, R., **III**.11.193
Wieghardt, K., **II**.6.289
Wild, A., **IV**.23.471
Wilke, I., **IV**.25.765
Williams, J.C., **I**.1.53, **I**.3.377, **I**.3.381
Williams, R., **II**.8.685
Willmitzer, L., **III**.17.683, **IV**.25.765
Winkler, J.R., **II**.9.829
Winter, H., **IV**.25.773Witt, H.T., **I**.4.521, **II**.7.455
Witt, I., **I**.4.521, **II**.7.455
Wolf, H.C., **I**.1.129
Wolfe, G.R., **I**.2.315
Wong, R., **I**.3.369
Woodbury, N.W., **I**.3.377
Woodrow, I., **IV**.20.189, **IV**.26.795
Wróbel, D., **II**.9.853, **III**.10.119
Wu, G.-Y., **III**.16.649
Wu, P.-C., **III**.14.519
Wu, R., **III**.13.409
Wu, S.L., **II**.8.717
Wu, Y., **IV**.24.651
Wu, Y.-Q., **III**.12.243
Wu, X.-Y., **III**.16.649
Wydrzynski, T., **II**.5.167
Xiao, Z., **I**.1.93
Xie, D.-L., **I**.4.513, **II**.7.471
Xu, C.-H., **II**.7.615
Xu, L., **II**.8.769
Yachandra, V.K., **II**.5.109, **II**.6.281
Yacobi, Y.Z., **I**.2.203
Yalovsky, S., **III**.11.193
Yamada, H., **II**.9.805
Yamada, K., **III**.14.515
Yamada, Y., **I**.2.223, **III**.12.315, **III**.14.531, **IV**.21.231, **IV**.21.259
Yamaguchi-Shinozaki, K., **IV**.21.227
Yamamoto, H.Y., **I**.2.255
Yamamoto, K., **II**.9.833, **IV**.22.349
Yamamoto, M., **III**.15.567
Yamamoto, N., **III**.14.515
Yamamoto, Y., **II**.5.187, **II**.5.215, **III**.11.177, **III**.13.367, **III**.13.371, **IV**.23.513
Yamanaka, T., **II**.7.555
Yamaoka, Y., **III**.10.87
Yamasaki, H., **II**.8.701
Yamashita, K., **II**.9.809
Yamashita, T., **II**.6.389, **II**.6.397, **II**.6.425
Yamazaki, I., **I**.1.17, **I**.1.113, **I**.1.137, **II**.9.787, **II**.9.805
Yanagida, S., **II**.9.833
Yanagisawa, S., **III**.18.839
Yang, J., **III**.16.645
Yang, S.-Y., **II**.9.821

Yano, K., **II**.7.539
Yano, M., **III**.18.823
Yasnikov, A.A., **II**.9.837
Ye, J.-Y., **IV**.24.627
Ye, L., **III**.12.283
Yeates, T., **I**.1.49
Yerkes, C.T., **II**.7.635
Yildiz, F.H., **III**.10.19
Yocum, C.F., **I**.2.263, **II**.6.321, **II**.6.345
Yokoi, F., **III**.12.251
Yokota, A., **III**.16.613, **III**.17.741
Yoshida, S., **III**.10.3
Yoshihira, T., **II**.6.393, **II**.7.579, **II**.7.619, **IV**.22.349
Youn, H., **IV**.19.67
Young, A.J., **III**.10.47, **IV**.23.581
Younis, H.M., **II**.8.737
Yruela, I., **II**.5.73
Yu, J., **II**.5.199
Yu, L., **I**.4.565
Yu, S.-G., **I**.2.283, **III**.14.527
Yu, Y.L., **II**.5.219
Yu, Z.-B., **I**.2.247, **I**.2.267, **II**.5.77, **IV**.23.439
Yuan, J., **III**.11.149
Yuasa, T., **IV**.21.263
Yun, C.-H., **II**.7.463
Yusibov, V., **III**.12.299
Zabulon, G., **I**.2.331
Zák, D., **IV**.20.177
Zannoni, D., **II**.7.599
Zarka, D., **II**.7.567
Zastrizhnaya, O.M., **II**.6.441
Zelent, B., **I**.1.145
Zer, H., **IV**.23.403, **IV**.23.501
Zergers, W., **III**.13.359
Zhai, X.-J., **I**.2.251
Zhang, B., **IV**.24.671, **IV**.24.675
Zhang, D., **III**.16.593
Zhang, H.-M., **III**.10.83
Zhang, Q.D., **II**.8.677, **II**.8.769
Zhang, R., **IV**.24.651
Zhang, Y., **II**.8.781, **III**.12.339
Zhang, Z.-Y., **II**.7.615
Zhao, H.-R., **I**.2.251
Zhao, J., **I**.1.25, **I**.4.565
Zhao, Q., **I**.2.247, **I**.2.267
Zheng, M., **II**.6.305
Zhu, G., **III**.16.593, **III**.16.617
Zhou, J., **I**.1.25
Ziemke, W., **II**.8.713
Zimmermann, J.-L., **II**.5.235
Zinth, W., **I**.3.429
Zirngibl, S., **II**.7.471
Zuber, H., **I**.1.117
Zucchelli, G., **I**.2.291
Zuo, B.Y., **II**.5.219
Zweygart, W., **II**.6.289